Ter— Merry Christmas! I knew
you wanted this book
so I thought I'd surprise
you!
    I love you!
        Love, Anne

Great Disasters

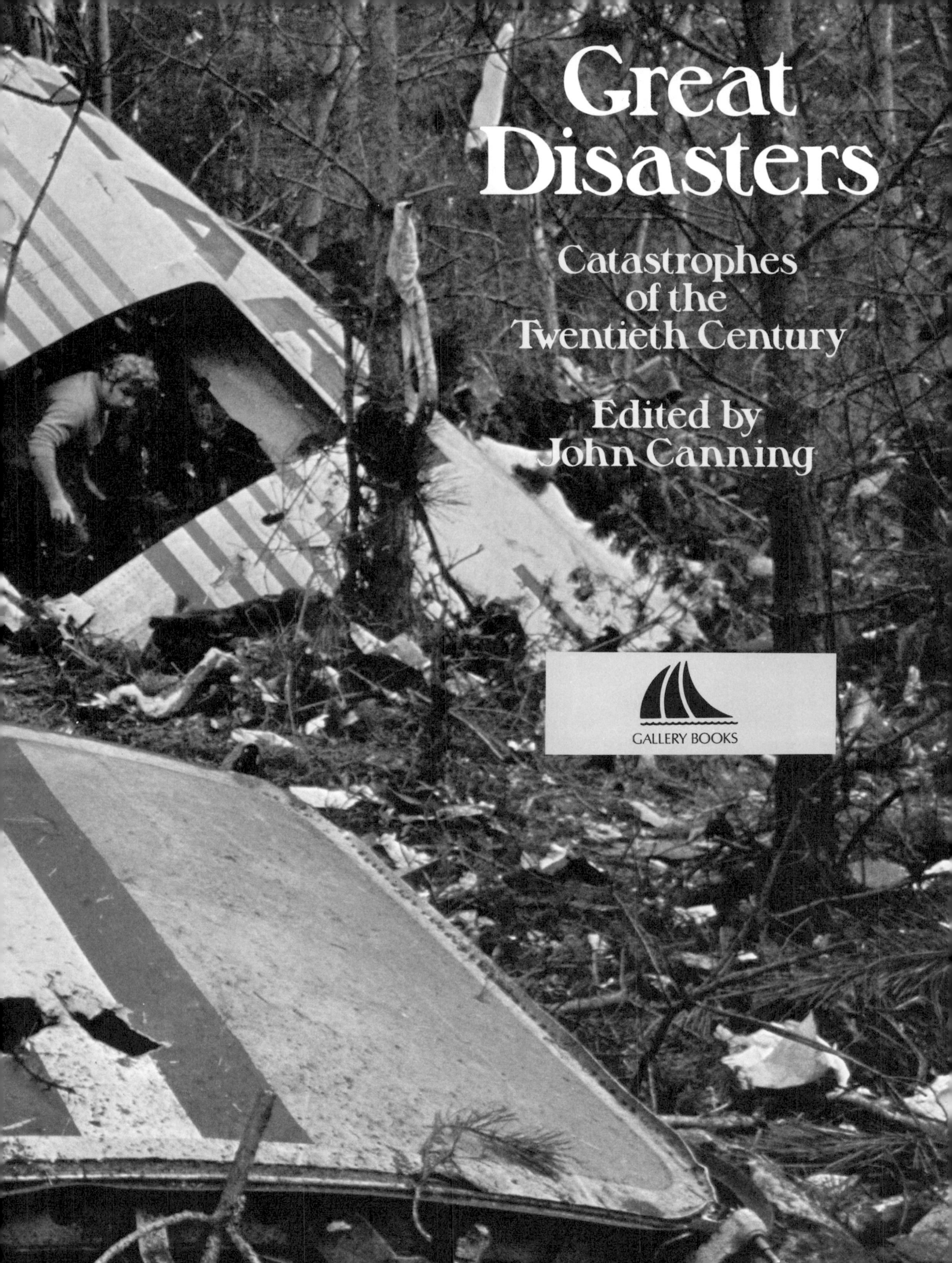

Great Disasters

Catastrophes of the Twentieth Century

Edited by John Canning

GALLERY BOOKS

Contents

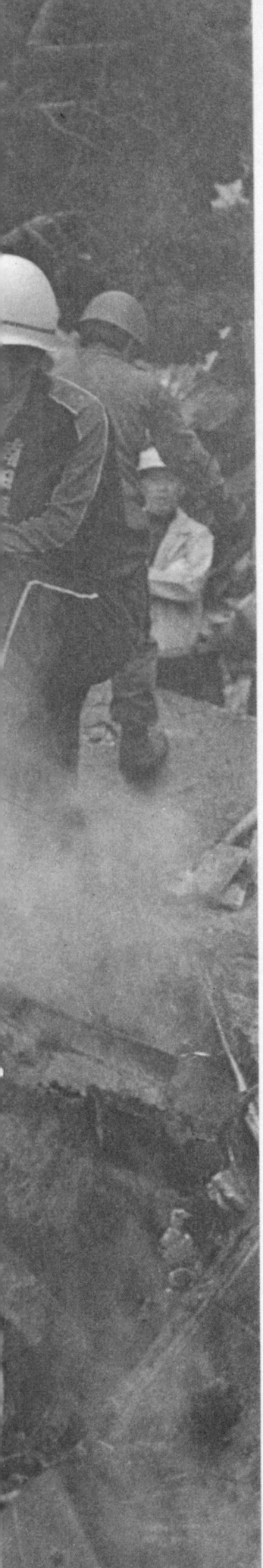

Introduction

The disasters in this book are of two kinds. The first is the gigantic convulsion of nature: earthquake, volcanic eruption, hurricane, tornado, avalanche and flood. The second exemplifies some of the terrible accidents that have resulted from man's interaction with the highly artificial environment he has himself created: disasters on the railway, down the mine and in the factory, in theatre and club, in ship and submarine, on the race-track, in the air.

We have deliberately excluded atrocities, which presuppose intentional wickedness–man's inhumanity to man. Though probably the cause of more suffering in this century than disasters, they lay outside our purview.

Our presentation has been chronological for disasters do not observe neat classifications and groupings; they occur haphazardly and men learn haphazardly from them.

In each case we have sought to describe and illustrate a very dramatic and tragic event. But in addition we have attempted to look at the causes, and to see if a reduction of risk could be numbered among the consequences.

There is, alas, little that men can do to arrest or mitigate the great eruptions of nature. The San Andreas fault still threatens San Francisco; and Tokyo remains similarly vulnerable, perched as she is on the edge of that great seismic hazard, the Tuscarora Deep. Yet even here something can be done. Continuous monitoring can give advance warning of an earthquake's imminence, and research is active on the unlocking of dangerous faults under strain. Also, as was shown in the Peruvian earthquake of 1970, the better siting and construction of buildings can have a profound influence on the effect of a disaster.

Avalanche protection–prevention and warning–is a highly developed science in Switzerland, and an efficient flood-warning system would have done much to help Florence in 1966.

It is horrifying to think that even when an active volcano was giving alarming indications of imminent eruption, as was Mont Pelée in 1902, the Governor should have stationed troops to stop the citizens of St Pierre from leaving their doomed city. This was a case of human intervention actually ensuring that nature would exact the utmost toll. But in the majority of instances in which men are capable significantly of influencing events–and this applies particularly in the environmental area of his own making–it is not intervention but inertia, ineptitude, carelessness and blind stupidity that are the main causes of disaster.

The circumstances of the fire at the Club Cinq-Sept in 1970 are depressingly similar to those at the Cocoanut Grove a generation earlier. And the same mad behaviour in sections of the crowd during the human stampedes at Ibrox and Burnden Park brought about the same sad results, though the events were separated by 25 years.

Carelessness links the railway accidents at Quintins-hill and Lewisham; while structural defects (careless workmanship) probably accounted for the deaths of the submarines *Thresher* and *Thetis*. Massive official inertia was the cause of the Aberfan landslide; and massive official ineptitude the predisposing condition of the Vaiont Dam overflow.

There is a brighter side, however. Slowly and painfully, lessons are learned from bitter experience. Places of entertainment in the United States were made safer as a result of the Iroquois Theatre fire; San Francisco is more earthquake and fire-resistant to-day than it was in 1906; maritime safety was improved as a result of the sinking of the *Titanic*; race-tracks have been redesigned since the Le Mans crash; Quintinshill and Lewisham combined to minimize the element of human vagary in British railway signalling; Aberfan changed the course of tipping policy.

And the brighter side must also include the courage and sublime selflessness with which so many people face or react to the gravest challenge. Even when a disaster seems to be unmitigated, it is perhaps this that saves it from being total.

JOHN CANNING

Half title : Tornado in the American mid-west.

Title spread : Turkish DC10 crash in Ermenonville Forest outside Paris.
Left : Rescue workers amid the rubble of Tokyo after the 1923 earthquake.

First published in Great Britain by Octopus Books Ltd

This edition published by Gallery Books
An Imprint of W. H. Smith Publishers Inc.
112 Madison Avenue
New York City 10016

© 1976 Octopus Books Ltd

ISBN 0 8317 3987 8

Printed in Czechoslovakia
50544

Mont Pelée, 1902

It may not be good for the tourist trade to call some of the Lesser Antilles the Volcanic Caribees, but that is what they are. Stretching in an arc from the Virgin Islands in the north to Grenada in the south, the Windward and the Leeward Islands have been built up from the ocean floor by volcanic action. On some the volcanoes are extinct, on others, still active. Only two have erupted in historic times, Mont Pelée on Martinique and La Soufrière on St Vincent.

Martinique is now a Department of France, so firmly integrated that when someone says '*Je vais en métropole*' he means he is going to Paris, not Fort de France, the island's capital. But in 1902 the most important commercial centre was St Pierre, a town of 26,000 inhabitants, lying in a mile-long, crescent-shaped strip on the north-west coast, below ravines rising steeply towards Mont Pelée ('bald mountain') which reared, 4,430 feet above sea level, five miles away, almost due north.

Sugar, rum and bananas were the basis of the island's prosperity. St Pierre was a gay town – people called it the Paris of the West Indies – with riotous tropical vegetation, a mixed population of whites, mulattos and blacks, and strongly contrasting wealth and poverty.

Mont Pelée steamed and puffed occasionally, rather like an old man smoking his pipe. The main crater had remained dormant for ages, although there had been a minor eruption in the volcano 50 years earlier. For as long as anyone could remember there had been a lake there called *L'Etang des Palmistes*, and it was a favourite picnic spot. The only other eruption recorded had been in 1792 and that, too, had been insignificant.

On the south side of the mountain, facing St Pierre, there was a dry secondary crater, *L'Etang Sec*, with steep flanks unbroken except at one point, where, also on the south side, a gash in the rim led into a ravine called *La Rivière Blanche* which extended right to the coast. In the rainy season flood water flowing down this and other ravines could cause considerable damage.

On 2 April 1902, fresh steaming vent-holes were noticed in the upper part of *La Rivière Blanche*. Three weeks later, a small amount of volcanic ash floated down on to the streets of St Pierre and there were a few earth tremors, just enough to upset crockery. In the following days the situation became more ominous. There were explosions in the secondary crater which hurled up rocks and clouds of ash. Then a lake formed there, 200 yards across, and also a cinder cone as high as a house, with steam spurting from the top. Soon ash was falling more heavily, mantling and muffling the town, seeping into shops and houses, killing birds and animals and bringing with it the nauseating stench of sulphur. Mrs Prentiss, wife of the American consul, wrote: 'The smell is so strong that horses in the street stop and snort, and some of them drop dead in their harness.'

In response to the considerable alarm caused by these events, Louis Mouttet, Governor of Martinique, appointed a commission to assess the situation and he visited the town. It was the last trip he ever made. Incredibly, the commission reported no immediate danger and while Mouttet maintained a studied air of calm the local newspaper, *Les Colonies*, backed him up with soothing editorials. The extraordinary complacency of all three has been ascribed to political collusion: important elections were due to be held on 10 May and Mouttet was anxious not to let his supporters disperse.

As ash continued to fall, St Pierre began to look like a body drained of blood. Deep rumblings could be heard coming from the belly of the mountain. Despite troops brought in by the Governor, law and order became difficult to maintain. Shops and businesses closed. Terrified villagers from the mountain slopes burst into bars and hotels demanding refuge. From the other end of the town, people were pouring southwards, swelling the population of St Pierre to 30,000. On 5 May came a foretaste of what Pelée could do. The cleft in its side becoming blocked with ash, massive quantities of rain water had collected in *L'Etang Sec*, been heated by volcanic action and now burst out in a seething torrent of boiling mud to hurtle down the mountain side. The tide engulfed a sugar-mill on the coast north of St Pierre, killing over 100 people, then plunged into the sea, causing a huge wave which swamped the lower parts of the town. *Les Colonies* reported 'the entire city afoot' and 'a flood of humanity pouring up from the low point of the anchorage, not knowing where to turn.'

Far worse was to come. On 6 May Pelée's rumblings turned to a steady roar interspersed with explosions which threw up masses of red-hot cinders. And the Governor did something unforgivable: he stationed troops on the roads to stop people leaving the town. *Les Colonies* found a disreputable professor to declare: 'Mont Pelée is no more to be feared than Vesuvius is feared by Naples. Where could one be better off than in St Pierre?' In a proclamation the Mayor gave his support: 'Please allow us to advise you to return to your normal occupations.'

All through Wednesday 7 May the roaring and the explosions continued. Heavy rain sent more torrents of mud down the mountain carrying huge boulders many tons in weight. Mingled with water, the ash gave the town a top-coating of hot sticky paste. There was only one slender ray of hope for the 30,000 residents: La Soufrière on St Vincent was reported to be in eruption. Perhaps that would relieve the pressure.

Thursday dawned clear and sunny. The people glanced apprehensively upwards to Pelée, and were relieved to see only a vapour column of unusual height. At 6.30 a.m. a passenger ship, the S.S. *Roraima*, arrived in port and tied up alongside 17 other vessels. By then the scene was dramatically different. 'For hours before we entered the roadstead,' said Assistant Purser

Thompson, 'we could see flames and smoke rising from Mont Pelée. No one on board had any idea of danger. As we approached we could distinguish the rolling and leaping red flames that belched from the mountain in huge volume and gushed high in the sky. Enormous clouds of black smoke hung over the volcano. The flames were then spurting straight up in the air, now and then waving to one side or the other a moment, and again suddenly leaping higher up. There was a constant muffled roar. It was like the biggest oil refinery in the world burning up on the mountain top.'

Thompson thought the spectacle magnificent. Almost everyone on board was watching. There were no premonitions, except perhaps on the part of the Captain, who told a passenger: 'I am not going to stay any longer than I can help'.

But he stayed too long. The mountain-side facing the town was already glowing red-hot and at 7.52 a.m. exactly (the time was recorded on the military hospital clock which somehow escaped destruction) it exploded. 'There was no warning,' wrote Thompson. 'The side of the volcano was ripped out and there hurled towards us a solid wall of flame. It sounded like a thousand cannon. The wave of fire was on us and over us like a lightning flash, a hurricane of fire which rolled in mass straight down on St Pierre and the shipping. The town vanished before our eyes . . .'

In fact there were two explosions, one which shot upwards from the main crater in a dense black cloud pierced with lightning flashes and the other which blew out sideways from *L'Etang Sec*. Expanding sulphurous gases had shattered lava into fragments and now, through the gaping cleft in the secondary crater, a murderous avalanche of white-hot particles mixed with gas and superheated steam tore down *La Rivière Blanche* at hurricane speed heading straight for the town.

From its effect on metals it has been calculated that the temperature of the blast was around 1,000°C. People died almost instantaneously wherever they happened to be, with hardly a struggle or a movement, from the inhalation of the fiery gases or from burns, some stripped of all clothing by the blast. Of the entire population of 30,000 only two men survived. Thompson recalled: 'After the explosion not one living being was seen on land.' The town was reduced to a heap of smoking rubble. Walls were torn down, metal roofs ripped off and crumpled like paper, trees stripped to the bare trunks. Within seconds, as the blast passed over, St Pierre reappeared as an ancient ruin, stripped of every mark that had given it identity, like something from pre-history unearthed by archaeologists, though here no digging was necessary. There was no lava crust as at Pompeii, only ash. Searching the ruins later,

Before the eruption of Mont Pelée, the 'bald mountain', St Pierre, lying in a mile-long, crescent-shaped strip on the north-west coast of Martinique, was a lively place with a mixed population of whites, mulattos and blacks and strongly contrasting wealth and poverty among its inhabitants.

rescue workers could barely recognize even well-known streets.

The situation in the harbour was little better. The *nuée ardente,** or 'glowing cloud' had caused a tidal wave which capsized or badly damaged every ship, and only one managed to escape to St Lucia with 22 of her crew dead or severely burned. 'Wherever the fire struck the sea,' said Thompson, 'the water boiled and sent up great clouds of steam. The blast shrivelled and set fire to everything it touched. Only 25 of those on the *Roraima* out of 68 were left after the first flash. The fire swept off the ship's masts and smoke-stack as if they had been cut by a knife.'

Thompson saved his life by burying himself under bedding in his cabin. The *Roraima* was in no state to put to sea. One passenger who survived, a Barbadian nurse, described how ash poured in through a skylight in 'boiling splashes' as she and their mother were dressing three children for breakfast. The cabin was filling up with the scalding stuff when the first engineer heard their screams and helped them to the forward deck. By then one little boy was dead and a baby was dying. Parts of the ship were on fire and now the whole town was 'one mass of roaring flames'. 'My mistress lay on the deck in a collapsed state. The lady was collected and resigned, handed me some money, told me to take Rita (the surviving child) to her aunt, and sucked a piece of ice before she died.' On other ships the boiling ash stuck to men's clothing, coating them from head to foot and baking them alive. Some were seen crawling about the decks, charred beyond recognition. Many jumped overboard and 'their scorched flesh sizzled as it entered the water'

One of the two survivors in St Pierre was a Negro shoemaker, Léon Compère-Léandre, aged 28. He was sitting on his doorstep when disaster struck. 'All of a sudden I felt a terrible wind blowing, the earth began to tremble and the sky suddenly became dark. I turned to go into the house, made with great difficulty the three or four steps that separated me from my room, and felt my arms and legs burning, also my body. I collapsed over a table'. Others came into the room, 'crying and writhing with pain, although their clothes showed no sign of having been touched by flame'. Very soon all were dead, also an old man that Léandre found in the house. 'He was purple and inflated, but the clothing was intact. . . . Crazed and almost overcome, I threw myself on a bed, inert and awaiting death. My senses returned to me in perhaps an hour, when I saw that the roof was on fire.' Léandre owed his life to an incredible fluke. Out of all those people, for reasons which will never be known, his lungs escaped fatal damage.

The other survivor was Auguste Ciparis, a 25-year-old Negro stevedore, who was due to be hanged for murder. He was lodged in a structure almost certainly unique in the entire town, a condemned cell, reminiscent of the modern Nissen hut, in the shape of a bisected circle, resting against the outer wall of the local prison. At the front was an aperture blocked by a solid door so low that it could only be entered on all-fours. Above it was a small, heavily grated window.

Once known as the Paris of the West Indies, this is all that remained of St Pierre after Mont Pelée exploded into a solid wall of flame which rolled over the city. A searing wave of heat killed thousands instantaneously and within seconds St Pierre reappeared stripped of every landmark, as though it were an ancient ruin that had recently been excavated by archaeologists. When, three days later, rescue workers were able to enter the silent city they could barely recognize even well-known streets.

Massively constructed to prevent prisoners getting out, the cell protected Ciparis from the full blast.

Dressed in shirt, trousers and hat, he was waiting for his breakfast when the window suddenly darkened and he was struck by searing heat. At the same moment there was a resounding crash as the prison wall collapsed on the roof. Then, as ash blocked out the window entirely, Ciparis found himself in total darkness. 'I smelled nothing but my own body burning,' he said later. 'Soon I heard nothing but my own unanswered cries for help.'

Three days later, when the town could be entered by rescuers, Ciparis was released, horribly burnt but coherent. He was reprieved, with a suspended sentence, and lived until 1929, earning a living as a side-show attraction in a circus: the Prisoner of St Pierre, complete with a replica of his cell.

On 20 May 1902, another eruption of Pelée combined with an earthquake drove many people from Martinique for ever: 2,000 were killed and several villages destroyed. More violent eruptions occurred on 26 May, 6 June, 9 July, and 30 August. There was a pause until September 1929, when once again the terrible *nuée ardente* roared down, with its super-heated steam, gases and incandescent particles, and tore up the modest structures of a new town which 1,000 intrepid citizens had struggled to build. This time Pelée was too late to catch a living soul: the inhabitants had read the signs and had gone. And this time no Governor tried to stop them.

---

*Since 1902 volcanologists have used this expression to describe the Pelean type of eruption, which had never been seen before.

The Iroquois Theatre, Chicago, 1903

The charred interior of Chicago's Iroquois Theatre after the fire in 1903; 602 people died in the fire or were crushed to death when scenery burst into flames. The fire brigade acted so rapidly that on many of the seats the plush upholstery was hardly scorched. Nevertheless 200 people were burnt to death or suffocated by smoke, within ten minutes of the outbreak of the fire. The panic, which broke out among the audience of about 2,000, resulted in a further 400 people being trampled to death in their efforts to escape from a theatre which was so inadequately provided with safety exits that it was, literally, a death trap.

Fire is one of the most terrifying elements. It is accompanied or preceded by smoke which kills more quickly than the fire itself, which travels so swiftly that its victims often have very little chance of escape. When, on 30 December 1903, fire broke out in the Iroquois Theatre in Chicago, nearly 200 people died of the smoke and flames *within 10 minutes*. In the ensuing panic some 400 more were crushed and trampled to death.

It was the pantomime season and one of the first big Drury Lane pantomimes to be imported from England was playing at the Iroquois Theatre, a palace of marble and plate-glass, plush and gilt, with a huge promenade foyer, vast grand staircase and commodious dressing-rooms. It had been opened not long before and was regarded as the last word in efficient theatrical design, convenient, elegant – and safe. The pantomime, *Mr Bluebeard*, had drawn a record crowd to the cut-price matinee, and the theatre contained over 1,700 people according to the management, although witnesses said later that there were many more people standing than the regulations allowed, and the total was probably nearer 2,000.

By 3.15 p.m. the performance was in full swing and the 400 performers, stage-hands and other back-stage workers were fully engrossed in their tasks. A double octet was on stage singing 'In the Pale Moonlight'; the moonlight effect was achieved by the use of gauze draperies and drops and by arc-lamps giving out strong blue light.

It was almost certainly one of these lights – overloaded to obtain the desired effect – which overheated and set on fire the gauzy drapery to the right of the stage which suddenly burst into flame. At once a couple of stage-hands tried to extinguish it, but the equipment available to them was woefully inadequate. One tried to beat out the flames, but the burning fabric was just out

of his reach. Then he got a fire-extinguisher which consisted of a small tin tube of powder and tried to throw the contents on to the blaze, with no effect whatsoever. Later, it was said that no kind of proper chemical fire-extinguisher had ever been seen in the stage area.

The flames began to spread among the closely packed drops which were made of canvas, painted with oils. It was ideal fuel and within a minute the fire was out of control; fire hoses were needed and there was not even a fire-alarm located in or near the theatre. A stage-hand had to run several blocks to raise the alarm.

Meanwhile those members of the audience who were seated on the side opposite to the blaze, and especially those near the stage, could see what was happening and began to get frightened. The auditorium was packed with women and children, parties of students and teachers, and girls in their teens. As the alarm grew someone cried 'Fire!' and the audience began to panic; the flames could be seen spreading through all the borders on one side of the stage and up into the flies. The band continued to play and the stage-hands began to lower the asbestos curtain which would cut the fire off from the auditorium.

But two-thirds of the way down it stopped, one end higher than the other, caught on a wire. The stage-hands struggled frantically to free the curtain or cut the wire, but the fire began to billow round the edges of the curtain as a strong draught, coming from a stage-door left open by the fleeing company, bellied the slack of the curtain out into the auditorium.

In the upper tiers the panic was now complete and the audience began to stampede for the exits. The orchestra abandoned its efforts, and when from the stage there came a sudden blast of fire, fed by the draught, which shot an engulfing tongue of flame into the audience, stark terror reigned.

Now every one of the 2,000 people in the building had only one thought – to save themselves. The actors and the stage employees nearly all escaped, saved by the failure of the asbestos curtain, which diverted the fire into the auditorium.

For the hundreds of people in the auditorium there was no such easy route. As the last of the ropes holding up the scenery drops was burned through, a vast mass of blazing material fell to the stage and another great balloon of flame leaped out, and the lights went out.

The scene in the theatre would have defied the imagination of a Dante. People rushed to the obvious exits. There were, in fact, 30, but few of them were marked. Many had heavy curtains over the doors and others were fastened by levers which nobody could work. On the landings, exit-gates were locked and chained to prevent people from the balcony getting down to the circle. On the balconies the aisles were too narrow and the exits too complicated to allow the people to pass easily.

Fire-escapes ran down the wall of the theatre into a side alley-way. When the exit-doors leading to them were finally burst open, the crowd stampeded out on to the ladders, which were totally inadequate for the number of people. Some fell or jumped over the side of the fire-escapes. Most died, and the few survivors owed their lives to the fact that their fall was cushioned by the bodies of those who had gone before. In one angle of the stair dozens died, crushed by the weight of people surging behind them.

One fire-escape from the balcony exit was made impassable by flames leaping from the exit below. Men in a building on the other side of the alley-way pushed planks across the narrow gap, and 12 people managed to crawl to safety. A crowd of women and children awaiting their turn on the iron platform were too late: the flames caught them before they could escape.

The greatest loss of life occurred inside the building, and once again most of the victims had been crushed or suffocated. At turns in the stairs, bodies were piled high. Occasionally someone was found by firemen alive, but terribly injured, among the bodies. On the dead faces were the marks of boots and shoes: flesh had been trodden from the bones and clothes torn from the bodies.

The fire department had arrived promptly upon the scene and – apparently heedless of anybody who might still be inside – pumped in gallons of water which extinguished the flames in the auditorium so quickly that only the plush was burned off the seats.

Within 15 minutes of the start of the fire bodies were being laid out on the pavements and every ambulance in the city had been called to the scene to aid the dying and unconscious. The final death-toll was 602.

The horror was not yet ended. Undertakers made all they could out of the disaster, apparently, commented the Mayor, 'immune to human grief'. Some not only raised their prices but held unidentified bodies to ransom. And as the bereaved tried to bury their dead, the authorities began to look for a scapegoat. The Mayor insisted that he had sent several warnings to the manager of the theatre, who had merely shrugged them off. Inspectors, it appeared, had been bought off with bribes as small as free tickets. No fire drill had ever been held, nobody knew where fire-fighting appliances were kept – nor indeed if any existed. The next day all the theatres in Chicago, and in many other cities, were closed in mourning – and in fear.

There was an inspection of theatres throughout the country, and within a matter of days no less than 50 had been closed as being fire hazards. A series of indictments followed – from which the Mayor did not escape – and all those involved were duly punished, where responsibility could be proven in law.

Soon afterwards statutes were passed on the provision of proper fire precautions in places of public entertainment. Punishment for failure to keep to the regulations was increased.

Officials examine the backstage area where the fire began. Overheated arc lights set fire to flimsy drops, and the failure of the safety curtain allowed great balloons of flame to billow out into the auditorium. Back stage the 400-strong cast of the pantomime Mr Bluebeard *were luckier than their audience. All of them contrived to escape, including a flying ballet awaiting its turn in the flies.*

San Francisco, 1906

The sounds preceding an earthquake can be as terrifying as the event itself, particularly when they come to the ears of people dazed with sleep. Sometimes there is a boom like distant gunfire, or a sharp, snapping sound. There may be a rumbling noise like heavy traffic moving over cobbled streets. As they move forward, shock waves oscillate with a pull-and-push motion while others called 'strike waves' mingle with them, throwing off impulses at right angles. The total effect is like a clod of earth being shaken in a sieve.

The citizens of San Francisco heard a low and ominous rumble at twelve and a half minutes past five o'clock on the morning of Wednesday, 18 April 1906. A few seconds later came the first shock. William James (brother of novelist Henry James), was in a hotel bedroom with his wife. As the furniture began to rock and dance he stayed remarkably calm. 'This is an earthquake', he said to his trembling spouse, 'there is no cause for alarm'– and proceeded to dress with careful deliberation. The whole hotel now seemed to be bumping about.

Most of the 340,000 population were not so detached, though they had experienced lesser earthquakes before, the most recent in 1898 and 1900. This one was much more severe, more ruthless. There were three shocks, separated by only a few seconds and the third was by far the heaviest. One city official later reported watching horror-struck as a massive oak wardrobe in his bedroom tipped sideways, backwards and sideways again before being hurled forward and splintering into pieces. A local businessman wrote: 'I was awakened by a very severe shock. The shaking was so violent that it nearly threw me out of bed.' A bookcase was thrown off the wall, everything on tables and the mantelpiece was

Left : An aftermath of an earthquake is the fire which so increases the death roll. This view shows devastation in Market Street.

Above : Another view of Market Street, San Francisco, from the south. The downtown areas of the city suffered the worst damage.

17

swept off as in a sudden roll at sea and the floor was littered with smashed china and glass.

Another man in a lodging-house bedroom saw chunks of plaster falling from the ceiling. Then through a gap a child's foot appeared. The next moment, the whole building gave a lurch, the gap closed under violent compression and the foot was severed in a gush of blood. At that point the man panicked and jumped through an open window, just in time to escape from the collapsing house.

A few people were out of doors when the earthquake struck. One was the editor of the *San Francisco Examiner*. He had just left his office with some of the staff and was chatting with them on a side-walk when the ground started rocking violently and they were thrown off their feet. All around, buildings were swaying and tipping under the shocks, throwing down showers of glass, bricks and masonry in a cloud of dust. Tram-lines were snapping under the pressure and reared up like thick metal snakes, short-circuiting in blinding sparks as overhead cables fell on them. Ominously the men could smell gas.

Two young men, Fred Walker and his friend Carlos, had arrived in the city that evening for a sight-seeing tour, coming by sea through the Golden Gate, the passage that links the land-locked Bay with the Pacific. (There was no bridge in those days; it was opened in 1937.) They had put up in a good-class hotel in the north-east corner of the oblong peninsula on which the

San Francisco's newly built City Hall, the pride of its citizens, was said to be indestructible. In fact the dome of its steel-framed tower was virtually the only part of the building to survive.

Left: Nature makes no distinction between rich and poor. This view from the south of Nob Hill, over a waste of destruction, indicates that it was the more modern buildings in the city centre which suffered least from the devastation. In other parts of the city, where the fires had got out of control, houses were dynamited in an attempt to stop the advance of the flames. But the explosive charges, laid by inexperienced hands were often too large, and buildings blew outwards, starting new fires.

Of all the great mansions on Nob Hill, home of millionaires, only the walls of the great Flood family house suffered little damage. Like many other mansions, however, its interior was burned out. Outside the house statuary still stands on the pavement.

pile of rubble with no sign of a single survivor.

While the Palace Hotel was rocking Caruso is said to have sung a few notes through an open window to make sure he had not lost his voice. Then he went out and sat on his suitcase in the street until someone took him to another hotel. There, pampered but resolute, he swore never to come back to San Francisco. He never did.

Meanwhile, the shocks had toppled some of the fine mansions and left others leaning at an angle of 15 degrees from the vertical. Most of the buildings in Market Street, bisecting the wealthy north from the poorer south part of the city, had been shaken to pieces as well as, except for its massive domed tower, the huge City Hall, only recently completed and supposed to be shock-proof. Elsewhere in the smart quarter a hotel in Valencia Street had gently subsided like a deflating balloon, ending up with the fourth floor at ground level from which the people emerged unharmed.

The worst damage from earthquake alone was in the downtown area, near the site of the original Spanish settlement, Mission Dolores. But loss of life was comparatively small and within a couple of hours many citizens could be seen with utensils salvaged from their shattered homes cheerfully cooking breakfast in the streets. Things could have been worse, they were saying.

Then came the fire. Throughout the city, fires started in dozens of different places, in abandoned buildings from heaters left burning, from hearths, kitchen-ranges, or sparked by electricity or the ignition of gas escaping from broken mains. One housewife struck a match in what had been her kitchen and caused an explosion which ended in hundreds of houses being burned to the ground.

Months before, Fire Chief Danny Sullivan had warned city officials that his Service might be unable to cope with a serious conflagration. Now his words proved horribly true. For 52 fires there were only 38 horse-drawn fire-engines. Great fissures in the streets had fractured every single water main. Except from artesian wells here and there, or from the sea in fires close to the shore, there was not a drop of water to pour on the blaze.

city stands, not far from the area known as Chinatown, then as now the biggest Chinese settlement outside the Orient.

They were not guidebook tourists and knew practically nothing about the city. Otherwise they might have chosen North Beach, known as the Barbary Coast, notorious for its vice and crime, or the Latin Quarter, one of many foreign settlements which included Japanese, Spaniards, Portuguese, Irish, Italians; or taken a look at Nob Hill, aptly named, where fabulously wealthy tycoons, nourished on the gold of the 1840s, the West Nevada silver strike of the '50s, the railroad bonanza of the 60s, held state in grotesquely opulent mansions, one with a $30,000 fence of solid brass which had to be polished every day. Below, stretching south, were the downtown areas with clusters of small houses, built mostly of wood.

If the next day had not brought a different scene, the young men might have noted the city's breathtakingly beautiful setting on its hilly strip of land bounded on three sides by water, met some of its robust, independent-minded citizens, and seen one thing more which summed up San Francisco's flamboyant optimism: the $7,000,000 Palace Hotel. Enrico Caruso had arrived to sing with the Metropolitan Opera in *Carmen* and was staying there that night.

Fred and Carlos felt drawn to Chinatown. Its opium dens, gaming saloons, twisting alleys, and grubby, vicious, colourful life drew them like a magnet and they explored it for hours, until nearly 5.00 a.m.

Twelve minutes later, as they were walking back to their hotel, came the rumbling sounds, then the first shock. Fred was thrown against a wall, while buildings all around began to heave. As terrified people in their night clothes rushed screaming into the streets the two hurried on and found their hotel had become a

ings failed. The explosive charges, laid by inexperienced men, were mostly too heavy, making buildings blow outwards instead of collapsing, so starting new fires. On the morning of the second day, Brigadier Funston, commanding federal troops, wired Washington: 'San Francisco practically destroyed. You cannot send too many tents and rations. 200,000 homeless.'

The fires were still raging when a tide of frantic people who had lost everything they possessed began looting. Mayor Schmitz issued a proclamation: 'The Federal Troops . . . have been authorized by me to KILL any and all persons found engaged in looting or in the commission of any other crime.' At the same time soup-kitchens were started and hordes of refugees were fed. One thing was certain: San Franciscans might die from a bullet, but once over the initial shock would never succumb to despair. Some of the accompanying photographs illustrate the resilience required of most San Franciscans.

Fringe areas of the city were saved, but by the Saturday, when the fires were at last burning themselves out, four square miles had been annihilated: 514 blocks containing 28,000 buildings. 450 people had been killed. Loss from earthquake was assessed later at £7 million; from fire no less than £140 million.

Recovery was a daunting prospect, but led by their level-headed Mayor the citizens rallied extraordinarily, helped by a flood of assistance from outside and also by their innate ruggedness and optimism. Many of them were descended from those tough individualists who had come halfway across the world to take part in the 1848 gold rush. Since then there had been many fires and several earthquakes, but every challenge had been met. Now this new one, great as it was, found them undaunted, their civic pride profoundly touched. Even while the fires were still raging orders were being placed for new tram-lines and other equipment. Within two days enough rail track had been repaired for trains to start taking out people whose homes were in other states. Electricity was restored in two weeks.

Proudly, or arrogantly, according to the point of view, San Francisco calls itself 'the city that knows how', but at least the title is deserved. Within three years, while thousands of the victims awaited resettlement in tented camps, more than a third of the city was rebuilt, not simply as a repetition of the old but on new plans with many buildings made earthquake- and fire-resistant. In 1911 the seal on total recovery was set when Congress approved San Francisco as the location of a world's fair to commemorate the opening of the Panama Canal. As if recovery from disaster was not enough, a 650-acre site was then reclaimed from tidal land stretching down from the Golden Gate, covered with landscaped gardens, pavilions, miniature palaces, and the Panama Pacific International Exposition was opened in February 1915. By the time it closed in December, 19,000,000 people had been through the gates.

Nine years had passed since that afternoon when the *Evening World Herald* of Omaha, Nebraska, had reported: '3.45 p.m. EXTRA. San Francisco wrecked and helpless.' Now every trace of that disaster had been obliterated, every connection except one: the cause. That crack in the earth's crust known as the San Andreas Fault had been the culprit, when movement occurred in the rocks on either side. The fault runs for

In the wake of destruction came other fears. A tide of frantic people, who had lost everything they possessed, took to looting. In an attempt to maintain law and order the Mayor issued a proclamation ordering that looters should be shot. Equally drastic steps were taken to prevent the spread of epidemics such as cholera—as this official street sign indicates.

Fanned and driven forward by a stiff breeze the fires were beginning to coalesce into a single inferno and a refugee described the sight from one of the city's many hills. 'Looking down we saw the great tide of fire roaring in the hollow, burning so steadily yet so fast that it had the effect of immense deliberation; roaring on towards miles of uninhabited dwellings so lately emptied of life that they appeared consciously to await their immolation.' He saw roofs and hilltops standing out starkly against the glare of the flames and 'sparks belching like the spray of bursting seas'.

By noon on that first day the fire was totally out of control. Federal troops summoned by the one telegraph wire still intact were on the way, as were units of the National Guard and 600 helpers from the University of California at Berkeley on the east side of the harbour. On the spot, amid the inferno, only two things could be attempted: to save as many lives as possible and blast a gap in the path of the flames. All that afternoon and through the red-glowing night, as the whole of Chinatown was being reduced to ashes, as well as the Palace Hotel, every house but one on Nob Hill, and thousands of houses, shacks, sheds and shanties in the rest of the city, the Navy ferried streams of refugees across the Bay to Oakland on the eastern shore while volunteers strove desperately to keep embarkation points clear of fire. For many there could be no rescue; they had been burned to death where they lay trapped beneath the rubble of their homes. Eighty died in this way in one hotel. As the flames came closer, one man, who was trapped, persuaded a policeman to shoot him.

Attempts to create fire-breaks by dynamiting build-

600 miles from Cape Mendocino in the north to the Colorado Desert, under the sea west of the Golden Gate and down the centre of the peninsula on which San Francisco stands. Along that whole length shifts in the land mass occur frequently, though none has been as severe as in 1906. They cannot be controlled; the most to be hoped for is that some day they will be predicted with greater accuracy. Meanwhile, San Francisco, one of the world's greatest seaports and trading centres, lives on, with its 2,000,000 inhabitants, beautiful, tough, cosmopolitan, energetic, disaster-prone – the city that has known how to survive.

Looking down upon the remains of a once-proud city is the Fairmount Hotel, badly scorched but not burnt out.

The Titanic, 1912

Even at the outset, the *Titanic*'s maiden voyage was marked by near-tragedy. As the immense 46,329-ton vessel moved majestically from her berth at Southampton, she came abreast of a moored liner, the *New York*. Suddenly there came a number of loud reports as the other's thick mooring-ropes snapped like string, and then the two ships began to be drawn irresistibly together. The *Titanic* was stopped, just in time, the strange 'suction' ceased, and tugs nosed the *New York* back to her berth. An identical situation arose a few minutes later when the *Teutonic* also strained at her ropes and heeled over several degrees until the *Titanic* had slid past.

Then the liner was lifting to the surge of the open sea and her crew relaxed. High on the liner's bridge Captain Edward Smith relaxed with them. Beneath his feet, the deck trembling almost imperceptibly with the thrust of her massive turbines, was the largest, the finest and the safest ship that had ever been built. To guarantee that safety, 15 transverse bulkheads sub-divided her from stem to stern; a double bottom was a further guarantee against accident. She was, in the mind of everyone ashore and afloat, the ultimate – the unsinkable ship.

After a brief call at Cherbourg, the *Titanic* left Queenstown (now Cobh) in Ireland during the evening of Thursday, 11 April 1912 and headed out into the Atlantic and waters which the veteran Captain Smith knew well. She steamed steadily westwards, without further incident; the sea was calm, the weather clear and brilliantly bright but very cold. Indeed, the temperature dropped dramatically during the morning of Sunday, 14 April and radio messages received by the *Titanic*'s Marconi man warned of the danger of icebergs.

The ship continued to race on at full speed, her lights twinkling on the dark still water, her engines thrusting her forward at a steady 22 knots. Then, just before midnight, a look-out suddenly screamed, 'Iceberg right ahead!'

Frantic orders were given which would have swung the liner's bows to port, but it was too late. As they began the swing an immense iceberg scraped along her starboard side then slipped astern into the night. Captain Smith was on the bridge almost before his First Officer Murdoch could ring 'Stop engines!' He ordered all watertight doors to be closed then turned to Fourth Officer Boxhall to order him to take soundings. Even as the young officer turned to go, however, the ship's carpenter arrived on the bridge to report 'She's making water fast'.

The doomed Titanic *at the start of her maiden voyage almost experienced a disaster which might have saved her from her fatal end. Here she is seen in near-collision with the* New York *(two funnels) as she sailed from Southampton.*

Those of the passengers still awake were unaware that anything had occurred, for the impact had been slight. Lawrence Beesley, one of the survivors, stated that there was 'no sound of a crash or of anything else; no sense of shock, no jar that felt like one heavy body meeting another . . .'

Up on deck, despite the bitter cold, some energetic passengers were actually having a 'snowball' fight, using the ice that the deadly berg had deposited during the brief encounter, while one, obviously a wag and not wishing to leave the comfort of the lounge, held out his glass and asked a friend to 'see if any ice has come aboard; I would like some for this.'

A few passengers asked stewards why the engines had stopped, and were assured that there was nothing

Above : Captain Edward Smith Commander of the Titanic *was a veteran of Atlantic waters. He died with his ship, remaining on the bridge to ensure that all his passengers had followed his order 'Every man for himself!'*

DAILY GRAPHIC
ACCIDENT **£1,000** INSURANCE
TUESDAY, APRIL 16, 1912
TITANIC SUNK:

Above : Having raced through dangerous, icy waters, the liner Carpathia *reached the scene soon after the* Titanic *sank. Within four hours she had rescued every boatload of survivors. Women passengers of the* Carpathia *at once set about providing care and comfort for the survivors, and sewing and distributing clothes.*

Left : The Titanic *was the last word in luxury. This is the Parisian Café, where passengers met for afternoon tea, or to while away the time with card games.*

wrong. The stewards were acting in good faith – at that moment they truly believed that nothing *was* wrong. Down below, however, it was a different story. The men in the foremost boiler-room found themselves swimming as tons of water began to thrust through a great rent in the ship's side. They managed to struggle into the next boiler-room, and then the next, to reach No. 4 which was nearly amidships but still dry.

Realizing that the damage was severe, Captain Smith went to the radio-room where the two Marconi men Jack Phillips and Harold Bride were now on stand-by, to tell them that the ship had struck an iceberg and he wished them to be ready to send out a distress call.

By the time he had regained the bridge it was obvious that the *Titanic* was slowly sinking. The berg had ripped a jagged gash along the liner's starboard bow for one-third of her length, and the ice-cold Atlantic water was pouring in. At 0025, some 25 minutes after the collision, Captain Smith ordered the boats to be uncovered. Ten minutes later he returned to the radio-room to order the operators to start transmitting, adding grimly: 'It may be your last chance.' Immediately the urgent call was crackling into the night, stating what had happened, giving the ship's call-sign MGY and her position, and asking for immediate help.

It was picked up by two liners, the *Frankfort* and the *Carpathia*, although the captain of the latter twice asked his operator if he had read the message correctly, not believing that the unsinkable *Titanic* could be in such trouble. When reassured that it was, he ordered

his operator to reply that he would be coming to the rescue at full speed, and asked his engineers to give him 'everything that they had'.

Meanwhile the *Titanic*'s stewards were going from cabin to cabin, tapping on doors and almost apologetically asking the occupants to put on warm clothing and go to their boat stations, taking their life-belts with them. Still unaware of the seriousness of the situation, most of the passengers did as they were asked although some refused to leave the warmth of their cabins merely for an unexpected and very inconsiderate drill.

The boats were swung out and the order was passed: 'Women and children only'. At first there was great reluctance to leave the ship for she seemed so safe, so permanent, compared to the frail-looking boats. As Beesley was to state later: 'The sea was as calm as an inland lake save for the gentle swell which could impart no motion to a ship the size of the *Titanic:* To stand on the deck many feet above the water lapping idly against her sides, gave one a sense of wonderful security ...'

Everyone was behaving in a calm, almost detached manner. There was none of the panic which was to cause loss of life in other ships under similar circumstances, although a brief and ugly scene among the steerage passengers was quickly quelled by the officers.

At last the boats began to be loaded and then slowly lowered, but not actually dropped into the sea. This was because Captain Smith had been told of the replies to his distress signal, especially that from the *Carpathia* which had stated that she was only 60 miles away and

became wider as her stern lifted, then she tilted to attain an almost vertically upright position and remained thus, motionless. As she swung all her lights were suddenly extinguished and there came a deep rumble as tons of machinery broke loose and fell towards the bows. Then the great liner slid forwards and down, the waters closing over her like a shroud.

Soon after 0400 hours the *Carpathia*, having raced through dangerous waters at (for her) a hitherto unknown speed of 17 knots, arrived on the scene and by 0800 hours had rescued every boatload. With her was the *California*, a liner that had stopped during the night less than 10 miles from the *Titanic* and whose captain was subsequently severely criticized for not observing the stricken vessel's distress rockets.

The whole world was stunned when the final accounting was released. Of the 2,206 people on board, 1,403 were lost, mostly crew and male passengers. Yet out of the greatest sea disaster of all time came good. The inquiry resulted in the formation of the International Ice Patrol and also stricter Board of Trade regulations regarding the provision of sufficient lifeboats to carry everyone on board ships.

Left : A lifeboat rows away from the sinking ship. Ship's musicians played 'Nearer my God to Thee', and male passengers, unable to get into the too-few lifeboats, joined in the singing.

Below : Captain Lord of the SS California with three other officers. The Captain, whose ship had stopped in the night only ten miles from the Titanic, was severely criticized for not noticing her distress rockets.

would be with them within four hours. But the captain soon realized that his ship was sinking lower with every passing minute, and as her bows went deeper and her stern rose from the water it would be more difficult to lower the boats. Some were still only half-filled, many women refusing to leave their husbands. Mrs Isador Strauss was one, saying firmly, 'Where you go, I go.' They stayed together – and died together.

As the boats splashed down, the strains of 'Nearer my God to Thee' drifted into the night from a group of the ship's musicians who had gathered on deck with their instruments. Some of the male passengers joined in the singing, others stared over the ship's side for a last lingering look at the faces of their loved ones before they became indistinguishable in the darkness. The crews of the boats were mainly stewards and stokers, for every officer and nearly every seaman stayed on board to help those who remained.

Two hours after the liner had been struck Captain Smith ordered 'Abandon ship! Every man for himself!' He remained on his bridge and was never seen again. Despite this order, Phillips and Bride were still transmitting, urging the ships that were straining to their rescue to hurry. Then their power failed and they went on deck.

Those in the lifeboats looked back at the sinking liner The ship, nearly a sixth of a mile long with four towering funnels and still brilliant with light that gleamed from portholes and saloons, was now down by the bows and sinking slowly but discernibly. The angle

Warnings of icebergs in the area had been received by the Titanic's *Marconi* man. When the iceberg struck the ship the Captain ordered the two radio operators, Jack Phillips and Harold Bride, to stand by. Ten minutes later he returned to the radio room to instruct them to transmit an SOS. Immediately the two men started to send out the urgent message, which was picked up by the Carpathia and the Frankfort. Bride and Phillips continued to urge ships to their rescue as the great liner sank lower into the water, and even after Captain Smith had given the order to abandon ship. Only when the power failed did they go on deck to take their chance in the icy waters. Harold Bride, second radio operator, paid for his courage: he was picked up by the Carpathia, both feet crushed and frostbitten, and had to be carried ashore when the ship docked.

Senghenydd, 1913 and Gresford, 1934

The middle week of October 1913 was a time of disaster, bringing tragedy by sea, land, beneath the land, and curiously (for this was 1913), by air. This one black week saw an horrific death by fire take hundreds when their ship, the SS *Volturno*, became a beacon blazing in the night; hundreds of miners lost their lives beneath the Welsh soil of Senghenydd; two express trains collided near Liverpool; and Zeppelin L11, the world's largest airship, was destroyed by a fire which caused the deaths of all her crew of 28.

Of these diverse disasters, the worst was that of the Welsh colliery, representing, in terms of loss of life, the most devastating disaster in British mining history. Until that time, the worst had been at the Oaks Colliery, Yorkshire in 1866, which killed 388 men; and the Hulton Colliery, Lancashire, of 1910, in which 344 miners perished. Previously Wales's worst disaster had been at Ebbw Vale, Monmouthshire, in 1878, when 268 men had died. The number of fatalities at the Universal Colliery, Senghenydd near Cardiff, was to top them all.

It occurred on the morning of Tuesday, 14 October 1913 at about 8.20 a.m. At the mine, high above the small town of Senghenydd, the morning shift had been deep down since the change-over at 6.00 a.m., the main shift of the day, with nearly 1,000 men at work. In most of the rows of humble terraced houses, wives were cleaning up after breakfast, their children, scarf-wrapped against the October chill were on their way to school; and other miners, their morning bath and breakfast behind them, were climbing thankfully into bed.

Left and below: In October, 1913, the sound of an explosion sent anxious relatives running to the local pit at Senghenydd. Rescuers found their way barred by fire.

Then came the sound that every miner's wife dreads – a loud, muffled explosion from the pit. Within minutes, white-faced women, with shawls thrown hastily over their heads, were running into the streets; children, wise in the ways of collieries from babyhood, turned from school and ran crying back to their homes. Soon a sizeable crowd began to gather at the colliery entrance, women and children mostly, standing quietly, apparently unemotional yet desperately eager for news of what had happened. In the beginning all that was clear was that an explosion had occurred within the Lancaster pit (there were two, the other one was York pit), that a cage had been blown out, and that a banks-man had been hurled with it to his death. An ominous column of grey smoke was now pouring from the shaft making everyone present deeply concerned for those below. Mr Shaw, the mine manager, went down at the head of a hastily-collected rescue party to the bottom of the shaft. Some hundred yards along the main haulage road they were met by a wall of fire. Further progress was impossible.

During the morning, rescue brigades poured in from Aberdare, Crumlin and the Rhondda and Rhymney valleys, with ambulance men and Red Cross nurses arriving from all parts of Glamorganshire. The silent crowds stood throughout the long day watching men they knew reporting back to the mine from the other two shifts, to help their comrades. Rescue teams from other mines, strangers perhaps but all brothers in such an emergency, arrived, assembled and then disappeared from sight. There was an occasional stir as black-faced men, reeling with fatigue and hawking up the foul air from their tortured lungs, reappeared and, in some cases, brought back survivors with them.

One survivor, Sydney Gregory, later described how, when working in one part of the mine, he heard two heavy thuds soon after 8.00 a.m. and then smoke started to pour from workings further in. He had a small boy with him from Aber who had only begun working the previous day, and although they were close to each

other, the air was suddenly so thick with coal-dust that they lost sight of each other. Gregory groped around until he found the frightened boy's hand and then, speaking encouraging words as he went, led him towards the lift-shaft. As they moved they could hear the crackling of the flames and the sound of falling timber until the foul air and rapidly increasing heat was almost too much for them, but they staggered on until at last they reached the bottom of the shaft. Although they were conscious of rescue teams tramping past them they had to wait for nearly two hours before they were able to gain the fresh air above.

By evening of the following day, bodies were arriving on the surface until 42 had been recovered, a pitifully small proportion of the 400 or so men still trapped below. There were tales of amazing rescues. Some 16 hours after the explosion, a group of 18 men had been brought up. They had been found alive, crouching together in 'a sort of shelter' and had been saved, they said, because they had not received the full force of the blast. A family of three was also saved, George Moore and his two sons, although their horse had been killed.

Crowds had grown even larger by the second day, the black-shawled women standing patiently for hours. Occasionally there was a muffled scream and a rush of other women to comfort someone who had been gently told that her husband, son, brother or father had been brought up, dead.

As the bodies were recovered they were laid in the colliery carpenters' shop which had been turned into a temporary mortuary. One observer said that 'Many of the poor fellows have the appearance of having been overcome by a kind of frozen sleep.' In one part of the mine a rescue team had found a father and his son dead in each other's arms and a figure standing nearby also dead. They had apparently been overcome by the foul air.

By 9 October, six days after the explosion, nearly 400 men were still unaccounted for but all hope for them was abandoned. Senghenydd had the atmosphere of a graveyard; in the part where most of the miners lived, there was hardly one street which did not have houses plunged into sudden mourning. Twenty men were missing from Commercial Street, 31 from Caerphilly

Road. One woman, on the morning of 14 October, had said goodbye to her husband, three brothers and four sons as they set off for the mine together; that night she was alone in a house to which none of them would ever return. Such are the personal tragedies that mere statistics never adequately reveal.

The figures are terribly significant. Of the 940 miners who were underground at the time of the explosion, 439 were killed, a frightening percentage.

*   *   *   *   *

Some 20 years and a World War later, Wales was again stricken by a terrible colliery disaster. It occurred at Gresford Colliery, some three miles from Wrexham, on 23 September 1934 during the Friday/Saturday night shift.

At 3.00 a.m. on the Saturday there was an explosion, and flame-tinted smoke was seen pouring from the shaft. Rescue was impossible, although it did not stop the teams from trying. One of them was led by J. McGurk, who emerged, his face showing white beneath the smudges of smoke and coal-dust to say: 'It is hell let loose and not safe for anyone to be near where the fire is raging. There have been three explosions while I have been down this afternoon. They may become more frequent because of the fire and carbon monoxide which the fire is giving off. That is the risk we cannot run. I have been in 10 explosions and have seen nothing like this. From the road where the fire is raging, for 20 yards the stones are red-hot.'

In addition to the crowd of sad-faced women and children who waited at the pit-head, the disaster brought in reporters from all over North Wales. They were soon involved in a bitter argument, for although some 240 miners' lamps issued earlier from one lamp-room had not been returned, Dyke Dennis, managing director of the company, stated that he understood 102 men were still missing, nine bodies having been recovered. Despite the urgent pleas of the pressmen, no further information was given out until a round robin

Above: Despite desperate attempts made to penetrate the barrier of fire which raged on the main road of the mine, few bodies were recovered.

Below: For 36 hours men strove to save their colleagues, but rescue teams were withdrawn for they too were in danger.

signed by all of them finally forced the colliery officials to admit that the number of dead and missing was around 260, although no names were available.

Desperate attempts were made over the next 36 hours to penetrate the barrier of fire, but all failed. Further explosions made it clear that to proceed would be to risk further loss of life. On the Sunday evening the last of the rescue teams was withdrawn, and at 8.00 p.m. a further statement was handed to the press. It read: 'The attempt to overcome the fire in the main road has gone on ever since yesterday, but in spite of very strenuous efforts, and although some progress has been made in this road, the fire has got further hold on a road to the right, through which it was hoped that access would have been got to any possible survivors ... the management, the representatives of the miners and His Majesty's inspectors have come to the conclusion that no person can possibly be alive in the workings. In these circumstances, and in view of the increasingly grave risk to the men engaged in combating the fire on the main road, it has been decided that it would not be right to continue to expose workers to such a serious risk, and all persons have been withdrawn from the mine.'

Next day, lorries arrived at the pit-head and a grid of stout steel girders was laid across the shaft after which concrete and sand were laid on top, effectively sealing the tomb of some 250 victims (the final number of casualties was 264) over 800 yards below. Thirty hours later, George Brown, a greaser, was working on the seal when a tremendous explosion blew it and Brown high into the air in a welter of broken concrete and twisted beams. He died two hours later in Wrexham Hospital.

The seal was replaced. It was seven months before miners ventured down again: those months were a period of great hardship which represented the loss of employment for the whole complement of the mine – 1,859 persons – both above and below ground.

Quintinshill, 1915

Until 22 May 1915 Quintinshill was an unimportant country signal box near Gretna Junction, just across the Scottish border, 10 miles north of Carlisle. From that date onwards, however, it became famous as the scene of the worst disaster in British railway history.

In those days Gretna Green still held romantic associations with runaway lovers. When the great express trains from London reached Carlisle they were handed over to Caledonian engines for their journey northwards.

On that morning of 22 May the two Scots expresses which had left Euston at 11.45 p.m. and midnight were approaching Carlisle 30 minutes late. Because of this, a north-bound local which normally followed them was dispatched from Carlisle before they arrived – the usual practice when trains from the south were running late, because the local provided a connection for Edinburgh and Glasgow at Beattock for passengers from Moffat. On this occasion it was decided to send the local forward as far as Quintinshill and to shunt it there to allow the expresses to pass. Quintinshill was a 'block post' with lay-by loops on the up and down side.

As the local entered Gretna the signalman's telephone there rang. George Meakin, the signalman on duty at Quintinshill, had been taking the night shift and, although he was due to book off at 6.00 a.m., he was still on duty when the local arrived at 6.30. This was the result of a private arrangement between Meakin and James Tinsley who was working the day shift. Whenever the local was going to stop at Quintinshill, as on this occasion, the Gretna signalman gave Tinsley the tip-off and he then travelled down on it; meanwhile Meakin would write down all the train movements occurring after 6 a.m. so that Tinsley could later copy them into the Train Register, thus making it seem that he had come on duty at the proper time. It was contrary to regulations that Tinsley should ride on the footplate of the local; it was also against regulations that he should, by a private arrangement, report late for duty.

The local made its way to Quintinshill only to find the loop off the north-bound line filled by a waiting goods train. Into the loop on the south-bound side was slowly running a train of Welsh coal empties. Meakin leaned from his signal-box and waved that he was temporarily switching the local on to the south-bound main line until the north-bound expresses had gone through. Nothing wrong with that decision, provided due precautions were taken . . .

When the train had been switched and was at a standstill, Tinsley and the fireman got down and went to the box. The brakemen from the two goods trains decided to join the party: this was against regulations which were explicit; if the guard, brakeman or fireman of any train had to communicate information to a signal-box, he should do so as concisely as possible, sign the Train Register and go.

Tinsley had brought a morning newspaper with him as usual, and Meakin now handed over to Tinsley and settled down to read the paper. He did not notify anybody that the south-bound main line was occupied by the local. Having taken over, Tinsley dutifully set danger signals on the north-bound track and then began 'cooking' the Register.

The telephone rang and Tinsley was told that the second express, due from Carlisle at 6.05 a.m. but now 30 minutes late, had left and was on its way. He went on writing up the Register but was again interrupted, this time by a bell from Kirkpatrick, the next block post, asking 'line clear' for a south-bound troop-train.

Left: In one of the most tragic rail crashes of all time, involving a crowded troop train, an express and a local, hundreds were killed or injured. Bodies of the victims were laid out in neighbouring fields to wait for medical aid.

Below: The devastating fire, which raged through the coaches and killed so many, was fed by the cylinders beneath the coaches which carried gas for the carriage lights.

Meakin had been warned that this train would be coming through and that was why he had shunted the slow coal empties to one side.

Tinsley accepted the troop-train. The men aboard it were soldiers of the 1st/7th Royal Scots – 15 officers and 470 other ranks (and every one of them glad to see the back of their training camp at Larbert, Stirlingshire). On draft to Gallipoli, they would have left days before if the troopship *Aquitania* had not got stuck in the Mersey mud at Liverpool.

The gas-lit train was packed with the soldiers and their equipment. After the first stop, at Carstairs in Lanarkshire, where – though it was only 5 a.m. – the entire population had turned out to cheer them on their way, most of the men settled down to doze or play cards.

When the bell in Quintinshill announced that the troop-train was entering the section, Tinsley sent his own bell signal to Gretna, which agreed to accept the train. The local which had brought Tinsley to the signal-box in the first place was standing there below him, in full view. But he was half-listening to the chatter of the others and half-worrying about filling up the Register. He reached for the signal-lever controlling the south-bound main line and gave the all-clear.

Now another bell demanded his attention. It announced the second express hurtling north from Gretna. Tinsley accepted it and pulled his down signals.

Both the up and down main lines were now signalled as clear.

At any second during these last fateful minutes there might have been a chance of averting disaster, but already the victims were racing to meet one another ... The troop-train with its complement of Royal Scots had a clear view down the gently graduated three-mile straight which then began to curve slowly under the bridge near the signal-box. The troop-train had been gathering speed down the steep gradient from Beattock and was doing a good 70 m.p.h.

The signals were clear and visibility was good.

Except for the curve.

The driver and fireman had no cause for alarm. There was an unusual huddle of trains by the signal-box, but obviously they must be standing on the loops. The goods train in the down siding obscured the main line, but once beyond the bridge there should be a clear view again.

The troop-train raced down the slight gradient and under the bridge. There, immediately ahead, was the engine of the local train facing them on their own line. There was no possibility of escape. The two engines met head-on. The impact was heard miles away. Coaches of the troop-train telescoped and were crushed forward. The local train was hurled backwards 40 yards. The tender of the troop-train twisted around pulling the splintering coaches with it and heaping wreckage over the parallel north-bound line. The force of the collision was such that the troop-train's length of 213 yards was reduced to less than 70 yards.

Tinsley and Meakin looked at the spectacle, petrified. Suddenly Meakin screamed, 'Where's the 6.05?' Tinsley seemed frozen to the spot, but Meakin made a dash at the levers to set the signals to danger. He was too late. The second express was already in section. No power on earth could have stopped the express as it hurtled into the wreckage of the first coach. Only a minute separated the two collisions – the troop-train was already ablaze when the express smashed into it. Instantly the two fires fused into a single flaming mass fed by gas cylinders under the carriages which had been charged to a pressure of 80 pounds to the square inch.

A reporter on the scene wrote later: 'When the awful force of the second collision burst upon the troop-train, engines were heaped on one another, carriages telescoped and overturned. Men were pinned helplessly beneath them. The carriage doors were jammed and scarlet flames belched from the blazing interior. As dawn was breaking the bird chorus mingled ghoulishly with screams of human anguish. It was an unbearable experience.'

One doctor, hearing a soldier cry out 'For God's sake get me out!' crawled beneath a blazing carriage on which hoses were playing and amputated the man's leg. From the flaming ruin of another coach someone screamed: 'Shoot me, mate, for God's sake shoot me!'

Messages began to speed across the country. A rescue team was on its way but, incredibly, nobody alerted the fire-brigade, and it was three hours before one arrived from Carlisle. It took a long time to give even an approximate reckoning of casualties in the triple crash. In the express eight people had been killed and 54 injured; two passengers died in the local; the driver and fireman of the troop-train had been killed instantly.

The roll-call of the Royal Scots was a macabre experience: all records were destroyed in the disaster and it was left to the colonel and one surviving sergeant to round up the few dazed survivors and work things out.

Out of 15 officers and 470 men, 227 were dead, 246 injured, many of them seriously.

A week after the catastrophe James Tinsley and George Meakin were taken quietly away to await trial for manslaughter. Asked by officials after the crashes how it could possibly have happened, Tinsley had said: 'I forgot about the local on the up-line.'

The Board of Trade's Inspecting Officer, Lieutenant Colonel Druitt, came to the conclusion that the tragedy was certainly caused by lack of discipline on the part of the two signalmen, Meakin and Tinsley. He felt that the means then provided by the Caledonian Railway for reminding signalmen of any vehicles standing within their control at a place like Quintinshill should have been sufficient – if the signalmen concerned had only observed the ordinary simple rules of block working and the regulations laid down for the purpose.

Tinsley was given a three-year prison sentence and Meakin got 18 months. Not included in the sentences was a lifetime of remembering.

Witnesses arriving for the inquiry into the rail disaster at Quintinshill included those who had themselves suffered in it. The Board of Trade's inspecting officer concluded that the tragedy had been caused by lack of discipline on the part of two signalmen who were on duty at the time, and who had failed to observe simple rules.

The roll-call which revealed the full story. Only 52 men out of almost 500 answered the roll-call which had to be taken after the crash, for all the records of the Royal Scots Regiment had been destroyed. In all, 227 men were killed and 246 injured, many of them seriously.

Tokyo, 1923

On Sunday, 2 September 1923, a news report came via Shanghai from Osaka, Japan. It read: 'Yesterday, Yokohama and most of Tokyo totally destroyed in devastating earthquake followed by fire. Heavy loss of life.'

For some days, because of shattered communications, news of what had happened reached the outside world only in fragments.

On 3 September, more reports trickled through: '100,000 people reported killed, 200,000 buildings destroyed, including all Tokyo's business quarter and most government offices. A power station collapsed, killing 600. Tokyo arsenal exploded. Water system completely destroyed. Food warehouses burned to the ground. Fires still raging.'

On 4 September: 'Casualties mounting, possibly 150,000 killed. Railway station in ruins; Japan's longest tunnel at Sasako caved in, suffocating a trainload of passengers. Sumida River burst its banks, drowning hundreds. All bridges down. Almost all schools, hospitals, factories wrecked. Summer resorts on Sagami Bay (20 miles south-west of Tokyo) obliterated.'

On 5 September: 'Many passenger and goods trains derailed with heavy loss of life. Tidal waves, 40 feet high, swamped Sagami Bay, causing massive destruction, then receded, baring the ocean floor. Oil-storage tanks at Yokohama exploded. 40,000 people burned to death by fire cyclone in Tokyo park. 1,600 crushed, then burned in subsequent fire when Fuji cotton mill collapsed. American hospital thrown bodily with all its inmates from cliffs above Yokohama. Count Yamamoto, recently appointed Prime Minister, was attempting to form a cabinet at Tokyo Naval Club when the floor gave way, killing 20 of his colleagues. Estimated casualties: 500,000 homeless of whom many injured. Total dead, in population of 3,000,000, unknown. 1,500 prisoners released from the Ichigaya prison, Tokyo, when the building was threatened with collapse and more have broken out from other prisons. There is now widespread robbery with violence, looting of abandoned premises, rape and motiveless murder. This has been blamed, apparently unjustly, on several thousand Korean immigrants living in the city and some hundreds have been lynched. Martial law has been declared.'

By 6 September, the London *Times* correspondent reported that Yokohama had been 'wiped off the map'. In Tokyo there were now one and a half million homeless. 'The difficulty of telling such a vast story is to

*A plain of black ashes
is all that remains of
much of Tokyo after
the earthquake and fire
which destroyed some
334,000 houses.*

know where to begin.'

The horror had begun at 10 minutes before noon on the hot, sunlit morning of Saturday when the first earthquake shock, more powerful than any felt in 70 years, struck Tokyo and the port of Yokohama, eight miles to the south-west of the outer fringe of the city on the shore of Tokyo Bay.

The islands of Japan, lying within the south-east Asian seismic belt and perched on the edge of the great Pacific trench known as the Tuscarora Deep, suffered thousands of shocks every year and building methods had been adapted accordingly. In Tokyo in 1923 there were some western-style ferro-concrete buildings linked by broad roads near the centre, but the rest of the city was still one gigantic village with narrow twisting paths running between small, one-storey homes clustered closely together and made in a traditional style of lightweight timber, paper and thatch. The beams in these houses were not nailed but dove-tailed together so that when earth-tremors became heavy the inhabitants could simply dismantle the structure.

But in 1923 disaster was beyond control. In Tokyo, the first shock, followed by two others equally massive, destroyed even newer buildings and left the terrain like a corrugated roof with the raised parts eight or nine feet above the normal level. Huge chasms opened in the streets swallowing up people, even tram-cars, then closing on them like a giant mouth. Telephone wires and overhead electric cables were snapped like string, people tripping over them in their panic being electrocuted; an entire tram-load died in this way, struck rigid, according to an eye-witness, as they had been in their last moment of life. 'We saw them sitting in their seats, all in natural attitudes. One woman's hand was held out with a coin as though she had been on the point of paying her fare.'

The earthquake was not the deadliest killer. Fire, caused largely by exploding gas-mains, destroyed thousands more. Driven by a strong wind the flames were soon roaring through the city. Hordes of terrified

Above: In a city largely in ruins, survivors searched among the rubble for what few possessions might have survived

Right: Tents were set up for the homeless and the military and rescue services distributed food, which often only consisted of a handful of rice.

people tried to escape into the large grounds surrounding the Imperial Palace, even into canals where they stood for hours, only to be found later dead, their heads charred beyond recognition and the rest of their bodies intact. One woman was lucky: she stood neck-high in water with a baby on her head for a whole day, and both survived. Elsewhere some young girls were found cowering inside a large drain-pipe. Others had thought themselves safe in Tokyo's many parks but freak conditions produced whirling funnels of flame which swept across great distances to snatch hundreds of victims high in the air and fling them incinerated to earth again.

For the first 36 hours, people could do no more than try to survive. Large numbers of troops for clearance work, military engineers and relief supplies were on the way, but help from beyond Japan took time to organize. Meanwhile the fires could not be stopped, even by blowing up buildings in their path, and on the Saturday night, beneath a sky that itself seemed on fire in a dome of scarlet and orange above the stricken city, pathetic groups huddled wherever they could find space to breathe, clutching the few belongings they had managed to salvage. Some wandered about near where their homes had been with the names of missing children, relatives and friends scrawled on bits of paper which they held out to strangers or hung from their necks, because their throats were too parched to be able to speak. On the following night, Sunday, when the fires were dying for lack of fuel, people were seen still searching, groping about with little paper lanterns on poles, their mouths covered against clouds of choking white dust that the wind was whipping across smouldering ruins.

In Yokohama the scene was equally terrifying. Yet the purely physical destruction was not as tragic as in Tokyo which, under its former name of Edo, had been inhabited for 4,000 years and contained many cultural treasures. Seventeen libraries were destroyed in the fire, including that of the Imperial Palace, as well as 151 Shinto shrines, 633 Buddhist temples and many beautiful gardens brought to perfection by that particular

Below : Thousands of people were evacuated from the city or attempted to flee. In an effort to escape the overwhelming fire many stood for hours in canals or pools, but even there the heat of the flames sought them out and killed them.

Left : The remarkable resilience of the population is illustrated in this picture. At tables methodically arranged in one of the least damaged streets survivors gathered to eat their communal meals.

Right : The earthquake was so comprehensive and violent that even when buildings were not reduced to rubble they were left as gutted and crumbling shells fit only for demolition.

Japanese talent for creating a botanical paradise.

Yokohama, a modern, struggling port with hardly anything old or picturesque about it, but economically most important, was also struck by the earthquake and fire which occurred almost simultaneously. The first great shock which sent the American hospital and many luxurious homes toppling from The Bluff also buckled the quays into snake-like convolutions, wrecked a long pier stretching out into the Bay, destroyed the customs house at its head, tore chasms in the streets, shattered bridges, demolished the two big hotels burying 180 guests, and ripped open the oil tanks.

As the second and third shocks quickly followed, crowds of terrified people stampeded to the shore expecting to find safety in small boats, only to see a wall of blazing oil spreading inexorably towards them across the water. Many were burned, others rowed frantically towards the *Empress of Australia*, at that moment being drawn by tugs out of the Bay, and ultimately 12,000 were picked up by the liner. 21,000 died in Yokohama that day.

Final estimates of the total dead in both cities were around 150,000, and of the severely injured, 100,000. Apart from larger buildings, some of which had stood up well, 700,000 small homes had been destroyed. No one even tried to assess the financial and economic loss. The rescue services, principally the army, and the survivors themselves fought back strongly. At first, there was only a handful of rice for each person each day, and one correspondent noted that a man he knew to have been 'worth millions' was grateful to get even that. But supplies from outlying districts built up quickly and until the telephone system was restored the army ran a carrier-pigeon service with other cities to make known the local needs. Thousands of the homeless were evacuated; tents were provided for the remainder. Within days some water mains had been repaired and in the following weeks, helped by a government scheme for compensation, many small businessmen were back, setting up shop again.

Massive aid came from many countries, including Britain and the U.S.A., in money, emergency supplies and medical teams, and within seven years Tokyo and Yokohama had been completely rebuilt. By 1930 they were new cities with barely a scar.

Today, having risen once more phoenix-like from their ashes, the capital city and its port are only part of a continuous urban-industrial belt containing the largest concentration of population in Japan. Experts say that even reasonable safety from earthquakes has not yet been achieved – and perhaps it never will be.

The R101, 1930 and the Hindenburg, 1937

The R101, hope of the embryo airship industry, flying over St Paul's Cathedral in London.

Below: The troubles, both technical and political, that had attended the birth of the R101 ended in this field in northern France, among the twisted heap of metal which had once been a great airship.

The airship industry is probably the only industry to die in modern times because of disasters although it experienced only two, the *R101* and the *Hindenburg*, which had a combined death-toll of less than 100. There have been much worse disasters, on land, at sea and in the air, but none has brought to such an abrupt halt the industry from which it evolved. Perhaps the seeds of disaster lay not in its flying machines, but in the industry itself, with its vulnerable technology resting upon politics.

It was not a young industry: the rigid airship evolved from the non-rigid blimp, and that in turn came from the ordinary balloon. Manned balloons were used by the French more than 200 years ago, and in wartime had obvious reconnaissance functions, but as they were largely at the mercy of the wind it became obvious that an elongated envelope propelled by an engine was essential if such dirigibles were to prove tactically useful.

The first truly successful airship, designed by Frenchman H. Giffard, was steam-powered and could offer a speed of 5 m.p.h. in still air. A more practical electrically-powered machine named *La France* took to the air in 1884. From then on designs improved until, in the period 1910 to World War I, the German Zeppelin pioneered air travel by safely carrying some tens of thousands of passengers over a distance of several million miles.

Although progress was made mainly by Germany and France, Britain had produced a few non-rigid air-ships (the first rigid machine, *The Mayflower*, crashed on its maiden flight). World War I demonstrated the success of the Zeppelin in air raids, but also its weaknesses (in particular the use of hydrogen as a lifting gas as the U.S.A. would not export non-inflammable helium), but it was from a forced-down Zeppelin in 1916 that Britain, copying the basic design, started serious work on its own rigid airships. Meanwhile the much smaller blimp had become fashionable as an observation post, especially for submarine detection. By the end of the war the airship industry had a rather healthy look about it.

By 1919 Britain had built two rigid airships – the *R33* and the *R34*. Defeated Germany was prevented from making any more Zeppelins until 1926, but had nevertheless been studying some of the more sophisticated problems involved.

Then came the two disasters – seven years apart – that virtually put a stop to airship manufacture in every country in the world. In 1930 came the destruction of Britain's *R101* (47 dead) followed, in 1937, by the more dramatically publicized *Hindenburg* disaster (36 dead). Germany kept its *Graf Zeppelin* in passenger service for another year, but World War II was imminent and it was already obvious that the battlefield of the air would in future be dominated by the much faster and more manoeuvrable heavier-than-air machines, and that bombers, as they were made bigger and adapted for troop transport, would form the nucleus of civil aviation to come.

Although the use of airships as a slow-speed form of transportation for heavy freight today has its protagonists, most people regard the 'gasbag' era as dead. The process of dying began with the *R101* and the subsequent breaking-up for scrap of the better-designed *R100*.

In 1924 the British Government decided to stop toying with airships and moved seriously into the industry with the construction of the *R100* and the *R101*. The *R100* would be built by the Airship Guarantee Company, a subsidiary of Vickers at Howden in Yorkshire, while the *R101* was to be manufactured by the Air Ministry itself, at Cardington in Bedfordshire. The *R100*'s builders were short of cash but long on expertise, being able to call on Dr Barnes Wallis of subsequent 'Dam-buster' fame, and many other top-ranking scientists and engineers including Nevile Shute (*No Highway*) Norway, whose first two names became a household word.

The Ministry, however, suffered from lack of designing talent, as many of its experienced men had been killed in the war. It also suffered from over-exposure in the press as, with taxpayers' money involved, every stage in the work at Cardington had to be publicized. Thus, errors which the Airship Guarantee Company was able to rectify in silence had to be retained – for

example, the too-heavy British diesel engines which the A.G.C. quietly swopped for lighter, petrol-driven power units.

Troubles and arguments, both technical and political, ended with the *R101* slower by 10 m.p.h. at 71 m.p.h. and, at 25 tons, with only half the disposable lift of her sister ship. The airship was flown to the Hendon Air Display in the summer of 1930 to let the public admire her, but only experts could have known she was losing gas and that she would only be able to return to Cardington by throwing out huge amounts of ballast. It was there that drastic and, in the event, foolish action was prescribed: instead of taking steps to reduce weight it was decided to increase it by cutting the airship in half, inserting a new metal bay (thus adding to her length) and putting in more bags of hydrogen for lift.

While all this was going on, the privately built *R100* made a very successful flight to Canada. Air Minister Lord Thompson, perhaps somewhat put out, decreed brusquely that *R101* would leave for India via Egypt on 4 October, with himself on board. By then the airship would be 'safe as a house, save for the millionth chance' – and anyway, he had to get back on time for a meeting. This was all very impressive, though it is not known to what extent Thompson's enthusiasm was generally shared.

The largely untested *R101* left its Cardington mast on the ordained date with 54 people aboard, of which only six were passengers. In these days of plastic syn-thetics it is difficult to realize that the dural frame contained 17 hydrogen-filled gasbags made from the membrane of bullocks' intestines, held in position by hundreds of wires. New valves were fitted to control the gas, but they tended to 'over-react' causing them to release gas at an unexpected air turbulence, thus releasing gas prematurely. This was one of many control problems.

Despite efforts to save overall weight, no limit was placed on personal luggage; Lord Thompson's private effects weighed as much as 24 people. The airship's fittings included silver cutlery, potted palms and 600 feet of heavy Axminster carpeting. Supplies of food and drink were lavish, as there was to be an aerial state banquet over Ismailia, with Egyptian notables and other distinguished figures as guests. Because of the inconvenience of refuelling during a banquet (no smoking, etc.) the ship was carrying nine more tons of diesel oil than she needed to reach her destination.

Small wonder that the *R101* shuddered painfully into the sky that evening. A resident of Hitchin later told the *Daily Express* that she had run out of her house to find everything lit by 'a ghastly red and green light . . . there was the *R101* heading straight for the house . . . she cleared the trees of our drive and the house by the smallest margin . . . as the green and red tail-lights moved away up the drive horror descended on us all.'

A few hours later Le Bourget airport in France confirmed that the airship was one kilometre north of

The vast, burnt-out framework of Britain's R101, *in which 47 people died, lies in a field in Beauvais looking like the skeleton of some strange primeval monster.*

Right: Only seven crew members survived the crash of the R101: one of the injured arriving at Croydon.

Far right: Passengers of the Hindenburg were luckier; 61, out of 97, survived.

Below right: The great ship was as vulnerable as had been the R101: a flash of flame suddenly appeared, and the huge airship was totally burnt out.

Below: The dining saloon of the Hindenburg.

800 feet, she was the biggest airship ever built. Power came from four mighty Daimler diesel engines driving propellers in separate gondolas under the great gas-lifted hull. As with all airships, the gas was contained in a quantity of separate bags, or cells. Today, these would be made completely gas-tight, but in 1937 a slow seepage was expected and allowed for.

This brought with it the danger of fire, but designers had perfected the interior passenger quarters, with their 25 two-berth cabins, spacious dining-room, saloon and reading-room, so that there was almost no risk of hydrogen entering. Smoking was confined to one absolutely safe room, with double-doors and an ingenious method of keeping its air pressure higher than elsewhere, so that no gas could possibly enter. Passengers could smoke freely here, though the cigarette-lighters were chained to tables to prevent the absent-minded taking them to their bedrooms. (Matches and lighters were totally forbidden to all passengers and crew.)

Elsewhere, in this ingenious, luxurious, ship was a baby grand piano, made of aluminium. On either side

Beauvais. After 2.07 a.m. the *R101* stopped replying to wireless messages, and by 2.08 horrified villagers had been woken by the noise and then the inferno. Le Bourget's operator tapped out the words, '*G-FAAW a pris feu*'.

G-FAAW – *R101* – had indeed caught fire, as a result of not clearing a low hill at Beauvais. It was all over in minutes. Unlike the more fortunate *Hindenburg*, there was no chance for passengers and most of the crew, for they were sleeping. Seven crew members survived.

No one knows for certain why the *R101* hit the ground at Beauvais. Perhaps she broke up under aerodynamic stress, perhaps a gas bag punctured, perhaps she simply lacked sufficient lift. Whatever the cause, it ended Britain's contribution to the development of the airship. *R100* was immediately grounded, then broken up for scrap.

That was almost the death of the airship industry as a whole, but not quite. The Germans continued, and by 1936 had completed the *Hindenburg* to join its sister ship *Graf Zeppelin*. With a length of rather more than

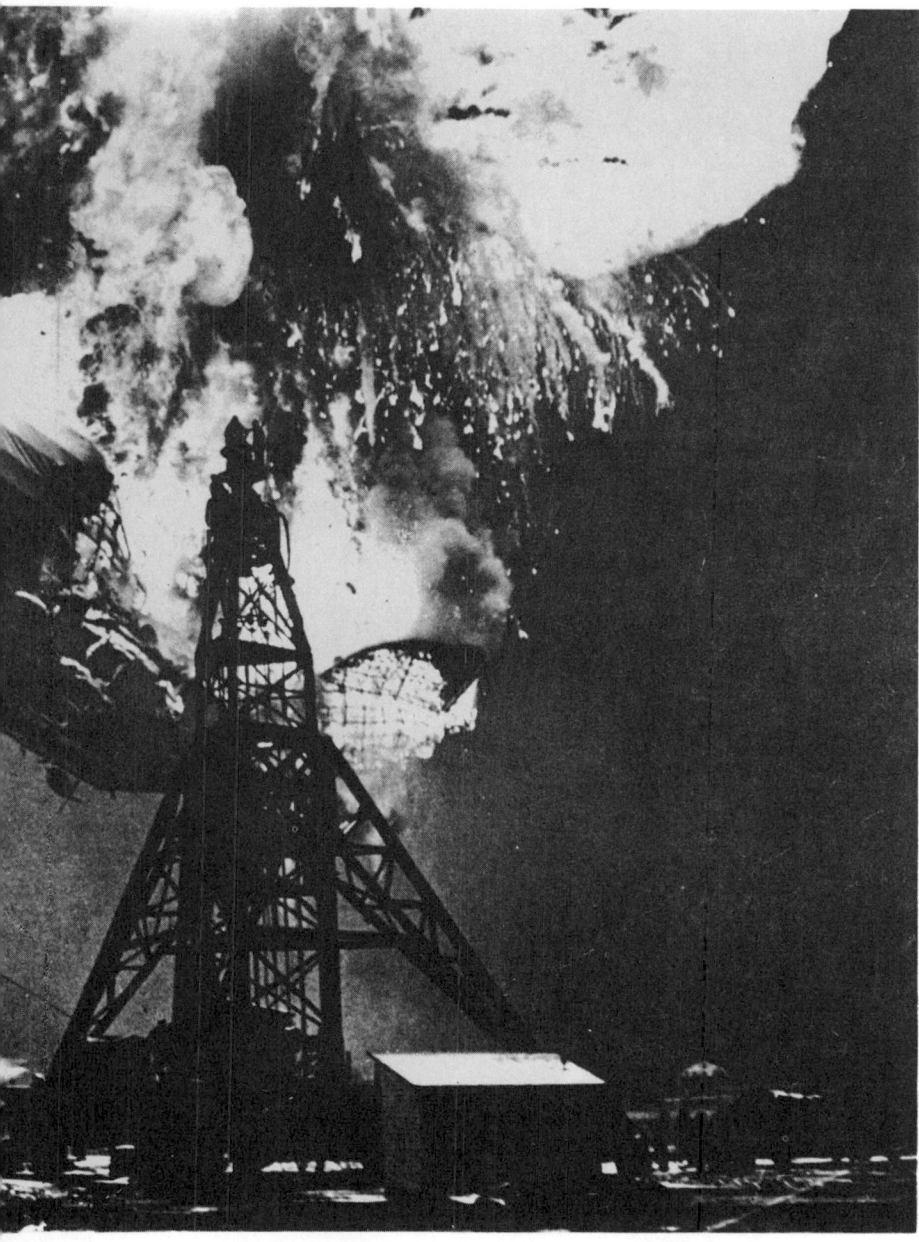

were promenade decks from which passengers could look out and down through big sloping windows.

The *Hindenburg* made a number of flights to the United States and to Brazil during 1936–37, and May 1937 brought yet another scheduled departure from Frankfurt to the American terminus at Lakehurst. Nothing could have been more routine; no German passenger airship or Zeppelin had yet crashed. From those first flights in 1910, many thousands of people had been carried safely to their destinations.

Slowly she rose into Frankfurt's sky on the evening of 3 May. Her passenger accommodation was half empty (though it was almost fully booked for the return trip) and the 36 on board, with a standard crew, totalled 97. Estimated time of arrival at Lakehurst was 8 a.m. on the 6th, but very soon Captain Max Pruss realized that strong headwinds were going to upset the schedule.

It was already 15.30 on the 6th when *Hindenburg* passed over New York's Empire State Building – a regular practice, to advertise Germany and her great airship to the people below, and give passengers an exciting, unfamiliar, look at the city. However, what interest there might have been in the arrival of another airship flight was diminished, rather than heightened, by its lateness. Apart from passengers' friends and relatives, few people were heading for Lakehurst. Hardly any of the press were turning out; one radio company had sent a commentator, Herb Morrison, with a portable recorder.

Bad weather made Pruss delay his arrival still further, and it was not until 7.00 p.m that he began his approach to the Lakehurst mooring-mast.

The first lines were dropped to the ground crew at 7.25 p.m. A slightly bored Herb Morrison began his commentary, unaware that it would become one of the most moving records of human anguish.

There was a flame, and Morrison's voice, abruptly kindling with it to hysteria, sobbed, 'It's broken into flames, it's flashing, flashing, flashing terribly, it's bursting into flames!'

Those inside were the last to know, and to this day no one can be sure what caused that flame. Miraculously, with seven million cubic feet of incandescent hydrogen about them, only 36 died out of *Hindenburg's* airborne total of 97. Much credit for this must go to officers and men at Lakehurst, who risked death to lead shocked, hurt, passengers and crew out of the holocaust.

So ended the day of the passenger airship. The rest of the world, including Britain, which had been watching the Germans with interest, gave up hope that these monsters of the sky would ever be safe and practical. There were undoubtedly other unspoken considerations, for no industry could die with such a small casualty list. The Germans withdrew the perfectly safe *Graf Zeppelin* in 1938, and in retrospect the reason is obvious. Zeppelins were not war machines. Balloons and blimps continued, however, while the real hardware of fighters and bombers took over.

There remains the possible return of the airship for freight transportation. Independent of land or sea it can travel 'as the crow flies', which offers advantages. In the long term, the issue will be decided by sheer economics, for a freight airship must make a profit if it is to survive – or even become a reality.

The Morro Castle, 1934

The *Morro Castle* was a vessel of 11,520 tons, pride of the Ward Line of America, dignified and stately, beautifully furnished and equipped, and only four years old. Although originally designed as a 'ferry' running between New York and Havana, she had become a popular cruising liner for those seeking sun, sea and relaxation and also an escape from the rigours of prohibition of the time. For no illicit speak-easy 'bath-tub' liquor was drunk on board *her*. Everything – spirits, wines and liqueurs – was imported and was the real thing. Consequently the trip to Havana and back was, as many regulars agreed, 'one helluva cruise.'

The final night of each voyage was inevitably the wildest and noisiest of them all with everyone making the most of the last night of riotous freedom before arriving in New York at eight o'clock on the following morning.

Even the repeal of prohibition in the previous year made no difference – the last night in the *Morro Castle* was, by tradition, an abandoned, uninhibited affair and this particular night of Friday 7 September 1934 was no exception. Many of the passengers had been having last-minute parties in their cabins and were arriving in the warm, perfumed and rich-food-scented atmosphere of the main dining-room. Only at the captain's table where a number of the privileged had assembled was there a slight note of discord. The guests were there, but where was their host, Captain Robert Willmott? While they waited, undecided whether to start without him, a page-boy arrived with the captain's apologies – he could not attend for the moment. Actually the popular, English-born captain was already dead from a heart attack and had been found a little earlier by his second-in-command, Chief Officer William Warms, lying slumped, half-dressed, over his bath.

The inevitable rumours began to spread around the room until an officer announced what had happened and that Warms had taken over command of the ship. The sad news effectively ended the evening's festivities. The orchestra left the stand, lights were dimmed and the public rooms slowly emptied, although parties still continued in the cabins. It was said later that several girls had to be carried back, insensible, to their own cabins and that some members of the crew were fired for being drunk.

Up on the bridge, Warms stared into the night, conscious of the responsibility of this, his first command. A strong north-easter was building up, rain was lashing across the decks and vivid lightning was illuminating the dark, churning waves. At 2.00 a.m. the ship altered course for the Ambrose Light and New York harbour and Warms relaxed; another six hours would see the ship at Pier 13 and the present ordeal over.

Then with terrifying suddenness, a report reached the bridge from a night watchman who had seen smoke drifting from a ventilator. An officer sent to investigate returned white-faced and shaken. A fierce fire was already raging in the ship's library and a steward, opening a locker, had staggered back as a great gout of flame leaped from its interior. He had then run to one of the levers which controlled the ship's elaborate fire-control system and pulled, hard. Nothing happened.

From that moment the liner was doomed.

Even as the alarm was being raised, a great mushroom of smoke and flame was rising high above the ship's superstructure, sparks and cinders raining down upon her decks. For the most part the ship's crew was unable to cope with the situation. A good number were stewards – ship-borne waiters – many of whom used the liner as an easy way of life, some even for a little lucrative smuggling on the side, and their first thought was for themselves. It turned out later that in the first six lifeboats, with a total capacity of more than 400, which pulled into Spring Lake, New Jersey, there were only 85 survivors, of whom 80 were members of the crew. Among them was the ship's chief engineer, Eben Abbott, whose immediate responsibility should have been to see that the hoses had ample power to operate. Instead, he was away in the very first boat.

For those experienced officers and seamen who remained, the subsequent hours became an unbelievable nightmare. Panic had spread amongst the passengers who refused, for the most part, to obey orders and

Left: Only six hours out from New York harbour, fire broke out on the popular cruise liner, Morro Castle, carrying 318 passengers and 231 crew. The acting captain and some of the crew members remained in the comparative safety of the bows for many hours.

Below: A view of the Morro Castle's promenade deck indicates the extent and ferocity of the fire which resulted in the death of 90 passengers — many of whom were afraid to take to the boats — and 44 members of the crew.

make for the boats. A crew member said later, 'They wouldn't leave. We pleaded with them. We tried to herd them together. Many tried to fight their way past us and get down the ladder to the lower deck. At last we were forced to leave without them, as sparks and cinders were burning the ropes . . . I told the passengers plainly that they must run the risk of getting singed in going to the boats. They did not seem to understand. We got the boats away in the nick of time, or we should all have been burned.'

But as they rowed away in the near-empty lifeboats they left the confused and panic-stricken passengers to fend for themselves. The scenes were indescribable in their horror. Men, women and children milled about the deck in a bizarre variety of clothing. Some were in pyjamas and nightgowns, others, who a little while before had been enjoying some private party, were in evening attire, the women in elegant gowns and with jewels that sparkled in the glow of the fire. They began to huddle together as the flames drew closer and then, as the pitch between the deck planking began to bubble with the heat, began to perform a grotesque *danse macabre* before finally plunging over the side with cries of utter despair.

Soon the flame-lit, heaving water around the liner seemed filled with passengers, mixed in utter confusion, clinging to wreckage or to the few rafts that had been launched. On one occasion a lifeboat, manned by only eight of the crew, passed through a group of men and women who shouted for help and clutched desperately at the gunwales, but the boat moved relentlessly on to disappear into the darkness. Of the 318 passengers, 90 were to die; of the 231 crew, 44.

George Rogers, the chief radio operator, was seated at his instrument, desperately awaiting the return of his first assistant, George Alagna, whom he had sent to the bridge for permission to start transmitting an SOS. As he sat, a wet towel over his face, he watched as paint began to peel off the walls and as a curtain caught fire and dropped down, setting fire to a settee. Soon he could hardly breathe. Finally, after Alagna had returned with a negative and had been sent back again, he tapped out the CQ (Stand by) then continued his agonizing wait. At last Alagna staggered back into the radio cabin and said, 'Okay chief, start sending.'

This was half-an-hour after the fire had first been reported. Precious time had been lost.

Rogers began to tap out his distress call: SOS. SOS. KGOV. TWENTY MILES SOUTH OF SCOTLAND LIGHT. Halfway through a repeat of this message, an explosion rocked the cabin as the batteries blew out, filling the room with fumes of sulphuric acid. Coughing and spluttering, he managed to turn on his auxiliary generator and then tapped out: SOS TWENTY MILES SOUTH OF SCOTLAND LIGHT. CANNOT WORK MUCH LONGER. FIRE DIRECTLY UNDER RADIO. NEED ASSISTANCE IMMEDIATELY.

Another explosion effectively ended all further transmission but the message had been received by several ships in the vicinity and dawn revealed the great bulk of the *Monarch of Bermuda*, together with the *City of Savannah, Andrea F. Luckenbach* and others, all answering the call. The *Monarch of Bermuda* was the nearest vessel and her captain, Albert Francis 'saw a

lot of men on the poop deck of the *Morro Castle* hanging over the side and yelling for assistance.' He and others on his ship also saw an incredible sight. Many of the *Morro Castle's* passengers, trapped in their cabins, had tried to escape by squeezing through the portholes. These were far too small, however, and most of the desperate people had become helplessly stuck, the expression on their faces revealing the agony of being burnt alive. As a passenger on the *Monarch of Bermuda* said: 'The grimaces made by the people in agony at the portholes was something that I shall never forget. On the deck we saw a young fellow with his wife. She fainted in his arms, and a huge tongue of flame popped out from the wall and sucked them in. We saw a man in pyjamas go up like a torch . . .'

By noon the only signs of life aboard the fiercely burning liner was in her bows where Warms and a few of his men were now stationed. A coastguard cutter, the *Tampa*, nosed as near as it dared and offered to take them off, but Warms refused – his ship was still afloat, he said. This offer was repeated several times but each time Warms replied, 'Not until the *Morro Castle* is in tow.'

The ship was held by an anchor which had been dropped to stop her colliding with rescue ships and this had to be weighed before the ship could be towed away, but there was no power, no winches. Two of Warm's men, however, had small hacksaws in their pockets, and for the next five hours they laboriously sawed through the three-inch anchor-cable, finally freeing the vessel. A hawser was then passed across but snapped as the storm increased.

One by one, the 14 crewmen, including a 14-year-old bell-boy who had elected to stay with them, were finally taken off. At last Warms also agreed to leave his ship and board the *Tampa*, but only after the commander had threatened to use force. Another hawser was passed and the tow began. At first all went well, the cutter towing ahead and a pilot boat acting as a jury rudder astern, but when both ropes parted the liner was abandoned to slowly drift shorewards, still burning furiously, with her paint peeling off in swathes from her once glossy sides, listing at an angle of 30 degrees. Narrowly missing a pier, she came to rest near

the broadwalk at Asbury Park, between New York and Atlantic City, a popular convention and 'fun' town on the Atlantic seaboard.

News of the disaster had already been heard on the radio and by first light a dense crowd of sightseers had assembled to stare seawards as the flame and smoke-blackened liner drifted towards the shore. By noon, owners of ice-cream stalls, hot-dog and frozen-custard stands were eagerly coaxing every cent from this out-of-season show; families stood watching, while bodies were carried up the beach as they were washed ashore. Hawkers also moved amongst the steadily increasing crowds selling pieces of 'genuine' wreckage at a dollar a time.

By early afternoon the crowd had increased to a quarter of a million people and squads of regular soldiers, armed with rifles, were rushed to the scene to drive the mob like sheep before them and establish safety zones around the place where the ship lay beached. Scores of reporters also arrived and the stories they gathered were extremely harrowing.

An inquiry was soon opened before a Federal Grand Jury and proved to be a particularly outspoken one. Warms faced a number of charges, including failure to exercize discipline and control; to arouse the passengers or provide them with lifebelts; to organize the crew to escort the passengers to the boats; to fight the fire; and failure to send out the SOS promptly. He also came in for special criticism when it was disclosed that the liner had been allowed to steam at full speed into a steady head wind which helped fan the flames. Warms, Chief Engineer Abbott and Henry E. Cabaud, executive vice-president of the Ward Line, were arrested, found guilty and sentenced to imprisonment. This sentence, however, was set aside on appeal. The Line itself was fined $10,000 and also had to settle claims amounting to nearly a million dollars.

The inquiry did not establish the cause of the fire. Most experts agreed that a carelessly dropped cigarette had been responsible; others believed that the funnel passing close behind the library walls had overheated them. The loss of life was more simply explained. It was due to naked, uncontrollable panic. On the part of the passengers this was understandable: thrust suddenly into a situation where a horrible death threatened from red fire or black water, their loss of control was excusable.

For Warms, an experienced seaman, there was no such excuse. Faced with sudden responsibility involving his first command and the lives of his passengers and crew, he also cracked, but in a less obvious way. Alagna said at the trial that Warms was 'behaving like a madman'. When the crisis came, he was unable to cope.

That was not the end of the story. The 'hero', Rogers, for a time earned his living recounting the events of that fateful night in vaudeville theatres throughout the U.S.A., but was later convicted of attempted murder and died in gaol. His assistant, Alagna, whose evidence against Warms helped convict that unfortunate officer, later tried to commit suicide.

Not long afterwards the once majestic vessel was towed to Baltimore to be scrapped. She had originally cost five million dollars; she was sold for less than $34,000. Her name passed into history as the principal in one of the ghastliest sea tragedies of all time.

A lucky survivor, Miss Helen Hozanka, is helped down the gangway of a rescue ship on arrival in New York. Several ships were in the vicinity when the fire broke out, and the Monarch of Bermuda *saved many men who were hanging from the poop deck of the* Morro Castle *and yelling for assistance.*

Below : The last hours of the Morro Castle. *Attempts to tow the blazing ship to safety failed, and when the tow ropes parted she was left to drift towards the shore at Asbury Park, New Jersey. There, so many thousands of people came to stare at her that soldiers had to be brought in to clear the crowds.*

HMS Thetis, 1939
and
USS Thresher, 1963

In Birkenhead, Frank Shaw, an engine fitter at Cammell Laird's, lay critically ill. Over and over again he would relive those last hours in H.M.S. *Thetis* in which 99 men died.

Three days previously, on Thursday 1 June 1939, the sleek grey shape of *Thetis* had moved out of Cammell Laird's yard at Birkenhead to undergo simple diving trials. She displaced nearly 1,100 tonnes, one of the latest 'T' class submarines and the first to be built at the Birkenhead yard. Not having been officially handed over to the Admiralty she carried 50 passengers, shipyard men mostly, with a number of extra officers including the senior flotilla officer, Captain H. P. K. Oram. With her five officers and crew of 48 there were 103 men on board and, with the tug *Grebecock* as escort, she left the river and was soon dipping to the surge of the open sea.

At 13.40, some 15 miles west of Great Ormes Head, her captain, Lieutenant-Commander G. H. Bolus, sent a signal to the Flag Officer Submarines (FOSM) at Fort Blockhouse, Gosport, to report that the submarine would be diving for three hours; and almost immediately Lieutenant Coltar, liaison officer on *Grebecock* received the laconic message, 'Diving'. Coltar watched as *Thetis* settled lower in the water, making a perfect dive in 'slow time', then as he was about to turn away he saw her break surface and a sudden splash of air beneath her bows. She then dived horizontally and fairly fast.

Coltar stood watching. The submarine should have dived to periscope depth before descending to 59 feet, firing smoke candles. Nothing happened, so he ordered the tug's captain to stop engines and only use them at intervals to combat a two-knot tide so that she could remain in the vicinity until *Thetis* surfaced once more. Later, Coltar signalled FOSM to ask how long *Thetis* was due to dive. He avoided expressing his personal concern as he did not wish the signal to be picked up by others for, owing to the short range of the tug's radio, the message had to be sent through the Post Office telegraph system. It did not arrive at Gosport until 18.15 due to a series of misfortunes, one of which was the telegraph boy's bicycle having a puncture en route. By then the Duty Officer to FOSM was also worried, having had no direct signal from *Thetis*, and the message from *Grebecock* confirmed his uneasiness.

At 18.50 a call went to the destroyer *Brazen* in the Irish Sea, but as she had only one boiler alight she had to flash up the rest before she could work up to full speed. The Duty Officer at Abbotsfield aerodrome then received a telephone call at 18.50 asking him to organize a search, but as none of the aircraft was in a state of readiness it was nearly an hour before four Ansons

were airborne. By the time they arrived at the disaster area, night had fallen and they had to return. The captain of *Brazen*, seeing the squat outline of the tug against the setting sun was able to ascertain what had happened. Told that *Grebecock* was anchored roughly where *Thetis* had dived, *Brazen* began an ASDIC sweep. In fact, the tug had drifted at least four miles from the actual point of diving and she was making her search *away* from the submarine.

What had caused this urgent, if somewhat delayed, activity?

Bolus had found *Thetis* acting strangely when he first attempted to take her down, and he ordered Lieutenant Frederick Woods to check the forward torpedo tubes. A buoyancy plan showed that tubes 5 and 6, being empty of torpedoes, should be flooded to compensate. Woods checked the valve of No. 5 and no water came out. He was not to know that during construction the outlet hole in the valve had been enamelled over. He decided to open the rear door of the tube to assure himself that there was no water inside. With a rating's help he tugged the door open – and a flood of water cascaded through. By some mischance the tube's bow cap was open to the sea and the tube was completely filled with water. Woods struggled to a telephone and managed to gasp out, 'We're flooding fast through number five tube. Blow main ballast!' then ordered the forward compartment to be evacuated. They then tried to close the watertight door between the forward and the next compartment but one of the bolts had jammed and that also had to be evacuated. Now, with her two forward compartments filling rapidly, *Thetis* dipped and her bows ran into the mud of the sea-bed. Bolus was trying to blow his main ballast and go full astern on his motors but the vessel was too deeply embedded, and remained fast. Finally her stern settled down and the submarine lay in an horizontal position.

The occupants, naval and civilian alike, kept remarkably cool, chatting about sport and joking about a farewell party they would have on their return. There was no panic, but Bolus and Oram, his senior, were concerned about the air supply. The Admiralty had already announced that there was enough for at least 36 hours, quite overlooking the fact that *Thetis* carried double her usual complement which would cut the supply to 18 hours. The two officers then decided to send someone to the surface by means of the after escape chamber to request that a high-pressure hose be connected to the submarine to blow out the flood water.

As there was no indication that rescue craft had arrived overhead, it was probable that anyone being shot to the surface would find himself in an empty sea. Nevertheless, Oram and Woods volunteered to go and after the former had taped messages from the men about his wrist together with details of what had happened should his drowned body be found, both men climbed into their Davis Escape Apparatus and entered the escape chamber. It flooded, they pushed open the escape hatch and within seconds they had shot through 20 feet of sea to arrive, bobbing, on the surface.

Soon after first light *Brazen* had sighted the submarine's stern sticking out of the water and had lowered two whalers to patrol. Oram and Woods were quickly spotted and were soon on board *Brazen* with the first real news of the disaster. Before Oram left the sub-

The tragic Thetis *was salvaged from the seabed on the day that Britain declared war on Germany. She was refitted and, under the name of* Thunderbolt, *went out on her first mission. Before she was finally sunk by an Italian sloop in 1943, she had sunk hundreds of tons of enemy merchant shipping.*

Previous pages: On 3 June 1939 the submarine Thetis *made a trial dive in shallow water off Birkenhead. Despite the fact that, with her bow stuck in the mud, her stern could be clearly seen, rescue work failed and 99 men died.*

marine he had given orders that the remaining men should escape in pairs, a member of the crew and a civilian, but conditions soon deteriorated so much that Bolus, propped against the engine-room door, decided to send four men through the escape chamber at a time. One of the civilians panicked, tore out the mouthpiece of his apparatus and dislodged those of his companions. The chamber was emptied again and when the occupants were dragged out, three were found dead and the survivor managed to gasp that the hatch was jammed before slumping into unconsciousness.

Some indecision followed about who should go next and Frank Shaw found himself pushed forward with Leading Stoker 'Mac' Arnold. Both went into the escape chamber, the rating hurriedly showing Shaw how to fix his apparatus, then signalled for the water to be let in. When, in obedience to the other's signal Shaw helped him push against the hatch, it opened easily. Both men then shot to the surface to be picked up by *Brazen*'s whaler.

Arnold, obviously a man of few words, sent home a telegram reading, 'Am Oke. Mac', while Shaw was taken to his home in Ivydale Road, Birkenhead, and put to bed.

By then a fleet of would-be rescue ships were milling about the spot and divers, oxyacetylene gear and air compressors were demanded; as the stern of the submarine was clearly visible above the surface it was hoped that rescue would soon take place. The first task would be to pump fresh air into her: a diver went down, but he had only half an hour to do the work and was unable to complete the job in time. A wire hawser was placed around *Thetis*'s stern and two tugs took the strain. It was planned to open an aft manhole for fresh air, but at 14.40 *Thetis* suddenly swung around and sank.

Those locked inside the submarine were growing steadily weaker. They had been cheered by the sound of tapping on the hull; at least it seemed a link with the outside world. The divers, too, were gratified when answering taps were received but they grew weaker and then ceased.

Ten minutes after midnight on Saturday, 3 June a hushed crowd clustered about the gates of Cammell Laird's shipyard in Birkenhead to hear a company official say: 'I am sorry but there is no hope for the men remaining in the submarine.' The death-toll was 99 men.

By morning, hundreds of people were thronging the streets demanding a public inquiry, many complaining that the rescue work had been 'bungled'. Others wanted to know why a hole was not cut in the vessel's stern while it was out of the water? Why the stern was not properly secured by hawsers and held above the water as the tide rose? Why *Thetis* had dived in only 130 feet of water? Few of these and other questions were ever satisfactorily answered.

At the inquiry Captain Oram said: 'I would like to make known the excellent behaviour of all the men on board. I saw no sign of panic at any time. I heard men talking and joking until the foul air caused them to keep quiet; and they showed a quiet bravery which is a memory which will live with me for ever.'

* * * *

Postscript. It was decided to salvage *Thetis* as quickly as possible and she was lifted from the seabed on Sunday, 3 September 1939 – the day on which Britain declared war on Germany. She was returned to Cammell Laird's yard and made fighting fit once more. Then, under the name of *Thunderbolt*, she moved out on her first mission which resulted in her torpedoing an Italian submarine. She went on to torpedo another and to sink a considerable amount of enemy merchant shipping until, on 13 March 1943 she was finally sunk by an Italian sloop, *Cigogna*. Her second 'death' was final . . . and honourable.

* * * *

Following the first radio reports that a nuclear submarine was missing, the American nation, and later the world, waited anxiously for more definite news. It came on 11 April 1963 when Admiral George W. Anderson, Chief of Naval Operations, announced grimly: 'Very reluctantly I have come to the conclusion that the *Thresher* has indeed been lost.'

This was the worst submarine disaster in American naval history – 129 deaths including 18 civilians – and the first time that a nuclear submarine had been lost. When launched, *Thresher* was the first of her class, nuclear-powered, 3,750 tons and with a submerged speed of up to 25 knots. She had been launched in July 1960 from the Portsmouth Naval Yard, New Hampshire, representing some $45 million of U.S. taxpayers' money.

Thresher, accompanied by her rescue vessel *Skylark*, began a routine deep dive some 220 miles off Cape Cod in the Gulf of Maine during the morning of Wednesday, 10 April 1963. It was a chill, blustery day with the wind-blown spray showing white around both vessels as the dive began, *Thresher*'s first for some time. Her career had not been a happy one; she had spent nearly half of her two-year life in dock, for repairs and overhauls. She had just slipped from Portsmouth, New Hampshire after a nine-month spell during which she had new equipment installed. That morning was, in effect, part of a shake-down cruise.

At 07.47 *Thresher* signalled that she was preparing to make her deep test dive, and Lieutenant Watson of *Skylark* asked her to give a 'Gertrude check' (navy parlance for underwater telephone communication) every 15 minutes. This was acknowledged, and then her long grey shape slid lower and lower in the water until she had disappeared, contact being maintained by the brief reports at the agreed intervals. At 09.02 she asked for a final confirmation of her course, communication being excellent; then came a call: 'Experiencing minor difficulty. Have positive angle. Am attempting to blow. Will keep you informed.'

To those on board *Skylark* this seemed to imply that the submarine was attempting to close her water vents and to blow air through the manifold system in order to surface, but Watson, listening intently, heard sounds of air under pressure. He summoned his captain, Commander Hecker, to the telephone. Hecker began to call, urgently, 'Are you in control? Are you in control?' but there was no reply. Then, at 19.17 the telephone crackled with a strange garbled message which ended with a word which *could* have been 'exceeding' and then two distinct words . . . 'test depth'.

Then there was silence. It was *Thresher*'s last message.

At 10.58 *Skylark* began dropping hand grenades into the water as a signal to *Thresher* to answer by telephone, but there was no response. The green depths beneath her keel remained as still and silent as the tomb they had so suddenly become.

Rescue ships were rushed to the disaster area and began desperately to search for something – anything – that would give the searchers a lead. The U.S. destroyer *Warrington* reported finding red and yellow gloves and pieces of plastic floating in an oil slick. The gloves were of the kind used by personnel working in the reactor section, the plastic similar to that used to keep the reactor from spreading radiation throughout the craft. The U.S. destroyer *Hazelwood* also came plunging to the scene of the sinking, bringing five civilian scientists and their precision instruments with which, it was hoped, they would be able to locate and fix the position of *Thresher* which by then was resting on the sea bed. But the sea had got up considerably, and winds of 50 m.p.h. screaming from the north-west prevented any accurate or sustained investigation.

It was now debatable whether there was anything to find. *Thresher* had a total depth potential of 1,000 feet, and the ocean bed was more than eight times that depth; no hull yet built could withstand such pressure.

As a submarine descends, its cylindrical-shaped hull, built with heavy steel plates welded to circular 'frames', or ribs, even under normal circumstances becomes compressed by the tremendous weight of the water outside the hull; more than 44 pounds per square inch per 100 feet of depth, and even at 500 feet a submarine creaks and groans as if in protest against such pressure.

Before the inquiry of 4 April 1963, naval technicians and experts alike were endeavouring to determine, on the little evidence to hand, what had actually happened. Some said that the diving planes had jammed during the dive, thrusting her further and further down, a theory dismissed by the more knowledgeable, for had the electro-hydraulic plane control system failed, *Thresher* had two alternative systems that could have been switched on in a matter of seconds. What was more likely was that the pressure had started a major leak, a pipe fitting or intake had failed, or that the pressure hull had suddenly ruptured at a place where a pipe pierced the hull – always a danger point.

Only underwater photographs would reveal the cause of the disaster, and at the depth *Thresher* was lying only one ship in the world was capable of taking them satisfactorily. This was the bathyscaphe, *Trieste II*, an improved version of the original Italian *Trieste* of 1953, which had been bought by the U.S. Office of Naval Research in 1958. At the time of the disaster, *Trieste II* was lying at San Diego on the west coast, and it would be months before the cumbersome craft could be brought to New England. Even so, with closed-circuit television and underwater cameras, and the ability to get close to her subject, she was the obvious – and only – ship which would clearly be suitable for the work ahead.

Until her arrival, a detailed surface and sonar search of the area was carried out and a fleet of vessels, including *Atlantis II*, the world's latest oceanographic ship,

battled 13-feet-high waves and winds. The most sophisticated equipment was used to map the sea-bed at a depth of one and a half miles. The incredibly precise depth-sounders (fathometers) revealed only boulders and rocky ridges, while the surface of the water still ruled out accurate detection by sonar. Nevertheless, something like 100,000 photographs were taken of the calculated area, which was roughly 10 miles square, to make it the most photographed and most charted area in the world.

The inquiry began. The first witness was Commander Dean L. Axene, who had been the commanding officer of *Thresher* from her commissioning in August 1961 until January 1963, when he was relieved by Lt-Commander John W. Harvey, who had gone down with his ship. When asked for his opinion he said he felt sure that the vessel had suffered such sudden flooding that there had been no time for a distress to be transmitted, adding that crew and vessel were of the highest standard.

Lieutenant Watson, when called, referred to hearing 'sounds like a ship breaking up – like a compartment collapsing' soon after the last garbled message had been received. Little else came out of the inquiry, except the reassuring statement that there were no signs of radioactivity at the scene of the disaster, and that *Thresher* had not been armed with Polaris missiles. It was finally agreed that the sinking had probably been caused by some structural or metallurgical defect probably originating in the boat's atomic power plant. For officials of the U.S. naval reactor programme, which until then had achieved a most impressive safety record, this finding was a profound psychological setback.

Outside the court of inquiry, however, other causes were mentioned. Inevitably sabotage was one. People recalled how, at the same naval yard when the original atomic submarine *Nautilus* was being overhauled in 1959, electric cables were found to have been deliberately cut in several places. More dramatic, however, were the comments of some of the unfortunate widows of the crew.

One stated that her husband, on leaving her to join *Thresher* on that last fateful voyage said: 'Honey, I have a feeling that this will be our last trip and that you will be a wealthy widow before the week is out', referring to the generous compensation paid by the U.S. Government under such circumstances. Another woman, widow of one of the submarine's machinist mates recalled bitterly: 'He called it a coffin. He was scared to death to go out in her.'

After a passage of two and a half months, *Trieste II* arrived and began diving operations. She descended to the sea-bed – for her a nominal depth – and eventually squatted alongside the tragic remains of the submarine, photographing the conning-tower, the tail-structure and the débris that had spilled from her interior. The pressure hull was mainly hidden in the sea-bed, having rammed itself into the sand when it had struck. The captain's reports were necessarily of a technical nature, giving no indication of the emotions of the trapped men during those last ghastly seconds, when jets of sea-water were thrusting themselves into the submarine's hull under incredibly high pressure and when the long sleek boat that had been their stable home was dropping down to its inevitable end.

Nearly thirty years after the tragedy of the Thetis, *the American atomic submarine* Thresher *proceeded to make a routine deep test-dive in waters off Cape Cod. Nobody will ever know definitely what went wrong, for the ship continued her death-bringing dive to depths at which the hull could not sustain the pressure, and where it was impossible to reach her. 129 people, including eighteen civilians died in* Thresher.

The Cocoanut Grove, 1942

'Panic' is an ugly word, but the dictionary definition of 'infectious terror' is strictly applicable to events at The Cocoanut Grove, a glittering night-spot in Boston, Massachusetts, on Saturday, 28 November 1942.

From around 7.00 p.m. crowds had been pouring in through the big revolving doors; locals, servicemen with their girl friends, a big party with 'Buck' Jones, the Hollywood Singing Cowboy, and a large posse of fans celebrating the unexpected victory that day of the Holy Cross football team over Boston College.

Over a thousand people jostled to get into a club licensed for 460, but the club's owner Barney Welansky, gangster and racketeer, had never bothered too much about licences, bye-laws and the rest. The club's two main floors had just been rearranged by him to hold more people. The upstairs restaurant, with revolving stage for floor shows, was slightly below the performers' changing-rooms. On the ground floor was 'The Melody Lounge'.

The 40-foot-square, eating, drinking and dancing Lounge was gaudily exotic. Walls and wall-seats were covered with rexine imitation leather. The low ceiling was draped with coloured silks ballooning down like sunset clouds, and palm trees of *papier mâché* were dotted among the tables with lacquered paper foliage stretching up to form a leafy trellis. The big curving bar was made of plywood with walnut veneer and the ceiling lights nestled in cocoanut husks. A Hawaiian dream world!

About 10.00 p.m., in an atmosphere more like Hades than Hawaii, one of the guests took out a ceiling bulb near his table. Minutes later, the manager spotted the dim corner and sent a new bulb with a young waiter, Steve Tomaszewski. He couldn't find the socket and lit a match.

Later, after 492 people had died, Steve swore he had flicked out the match. Some accounts tell of a sudden spurt of flame from a nearby palm tree, so perhaps there had been a short-circuit. No one will ever know the exact cause, only the result was clear.

The place was like a tinder-box and within seconds flames were leaping everywhere. The lacquer, paper and silk flared up, and the Lounge was filled with black, asphyxiating smoke.

One of those present, journalist Martin Sheridan, wrote afterwards: 'We had just been served with an oyster cocktail when, above the babble, I thought I heard cries of "Fight". . . Liquor had been flowing freely for hours . . . I thought to myself it must be just a minor brawl. . . . Suddenly someone at the end of our table screamed "FIRE"! Then I heard the loud crackling of flames. . . . A cloud of black smoke surged across the room. . . . No need to get excited, I thought. Just get up casually and walk to the nearest exit.'

The calm ones fared no better than the rest. Sheridan had not taken three steps before he was on the floor, choking and fainting from fumes, the last sounds in his ears the crash of shattered crockery and the screams of terrified people.

Sheridan survived by a fluke. Everyone believed the nearest exit meant the revolving doors, but the big building had no less than nine exits. As well as the main one there were four smaller doors on the east wall including one gained by some stairs and through an office. To the north were four more and on the west side was a single door with a quick-acting release, though this was temporarily jammed. But no one knew about these other exits: they were neither indicated nor illuminated nor even visible by the time Welansky had finished constructing his Hawaiian scene. All but the front windows were boarded up and all had stout metal frames allowing passage for only the smallest bodies.

People surged straight for the revolving doors. Soon the lights failed and many got out only by the glare of flames. One was Joyce Spector who said later: 'I crawled for what seemed to be miles. Suddenly – I don't know how – I was in the street and could feel the cold night air on my face. Then a heavy weight fell on me'. The weight was the body of a man who had stumbled out after her and dropped dead just as he reached safety.

As the smoke and heat intensified, the rush turned to a stampede and the door became blocked. Some people were trampled underfoot. Others were thrusting to get out of the Lounge when suddenly part of the floor gave way and they were hurled to death in the basement. A naval officer later found dead had his jacket clawed from his back. Firemen who soon arrived saw a wall of contorted faces beyond the door and after breaking it down found corpses, grotesquely splayed and entangled six deep.

Some found different escape routes, like Mr John Gill, from Arlington, who dragged his wife towards the sound of breaking glass at the back of the building. 'One moment I was moving towards that sound. . . . The next few seconds or minutes, I couldn't say which, are blanks in my memory. I don't remember that we were borne through that little door, but we must have been. I don't know whether we were shoved or whether we crawled.'

Others escaped through a basement window, a few through other doors, a few more by shutting themselves in a basement refrigeration room until it was safe to come out. Some floor-show performers climbed on to the flat roof, then down to safety by a ladder. A handful were found later, half-dead, halfway to freedom, their bodies wedged in the broken glass of windows.

Four hundred and thirty-three people, including the Singing Cowboy, died inside The Cocoanut Grove, from asphyxiation, suffocation, burns, heart-failure or fractured skulls. A further 59 died in hospital.

Above: Although there were no less than nine exits from The Cocoanut Grove night-spot in Boston, they were neither indicated nor even visible behind the elaborate décor. People struggled to get through the revolving doors of the main entrance.

Labels on image:
PARKING SPACE
MAIN ENTRANCE
WHERE ROOF FELL IN
USED FOR MORGUE
PIEDMONT ST.
CHURCH ST.

goat, to some extent, for the omissions of the city's administrators: none of the provisions omitted by Welansky was obligatory by law. Boston's building regulations were inadequate and those that did exist could be evaded, if necessary, by political influence.

The summing up by a County Grand Jury was extraordinarily bland. There had been, it was said, a 'shifting of responsibility and a tendency by various officials in different important departments to rely too much on their subordinates without exercising sufficient and proper check'. The Mayor declared that he had repeatedly reminded the citizens that there was a war on, emergencies might be expected and it was their duty at all times to remain 'calm and quiet, cool and collected'.

In America, the Underwriters' Laboratories began an intensive investigation into the problems of highly combustible interior furnishings and finishes. They issued a report in 1962 and research continues.

In Boston the site of the club has long since become a car-park and there is no Cocoanut Grove in the city, possibly in the whole of America. In Britain, the lessons to be drawn from the calamity still feature in fire-prevention courses.

Below: Over a thousand people poured into a building licensed for 460. Such was the panic that broke out in the overcrowded rooms that 433 people died from asphyxiation, suffocation, burns, heart failure and fractured skulls. And although rescue workers were quickly on the spot another 59 people died later in hospital.

The fire was put out within an hour, but rescue work went on all night, helped by the Civil Defence and the Red Cross. Anti-burn drugs were rushed from New York. Local hospitals, where one casualty was being admitted every ten seconds and the corridors were lined with dead bodies awaiting identification, had to open their wartime blood plasma banks. Passing vehicles of every kind were flagged down to provide transport. All night, crowds of sightseers converged on the scene, impeding the work, until martial law was declared in the early hours.

Next day there was a hurried examination of other Boston night-clubs for similar hazards. Then a grand inquiry was held into causes and responsibilities. The immediate cause of the fire was never established. But once started, why did it end in disaster? The answers were clear, and bad for Welansky. No planning permission had been obtained for his 'Melody Lounge', nor permits granted for electrical work carried out by unqualified men. The exits were neither illuminated nor indicated. The club had no emergency lighting or automatic fire-sprinklers and – important for slowly recovering survivors – was not covered by insurance for guests.

Welansky got 12 years in jail, but was released, after three, in 1946, with incurable cancer. He was the scape-

Naples Black Market Express, 1944

Incredibly, a whole train load of 521 people died in one of the eeriest train disasters of all time. Brought to a halt by icy, slippery rails in a narrow two-mile long tunnel, it is assumed that carbon monoxide gas produced by the vainly labouring engine overcame the passengers as they sat in their seats. Only the brakeman and five passengers survived.

World War II provided the most bizarre railway catastrophe of all time. Train No. 8017, which ran between Naples and Lucania every Thursday night, was known as the Black Market Express. It carried 520 passengers, most of them the professional black marketeers of Naples who made this regular journey to fill their bags with meats, grains, vegetables, oils, tobacco and sweets for Naples, then (in March 1944) occupied by the Allied Forces.

Although *la borsa nera* (the black market) was prohibited, the Allied Military Government and the Italian officials realized that if these black marketeers did not use Train 8017 to bring in illegal supplies, there would be hardly enough food available for the million inhabitants of Naples.

On the night of 2 March 1944, the train pulled out of Naples with 521 passengers and six railway workers: the 8017 had 42 box-cars (empty), two steam-engines, four coaches and one caboose. On all its previous trips two engines had been used, as the total weight of the train had never exceeded 500 tons but, on this fateful journey, medical students from Bari were returning from a hospital field exercise. Total weight touched 511 tons – 11 tons over the maximum for a two-engine pull.

The 8017 might have got away with the overloading, but some parts of the Naples-Lucania line had stretches of ice-coated upgrade rails. If it had not attempted to hit top speed on these stretches the chances were that the slippery tracks would prove impassable.

After it pulled out of Balvano-Ricigliano station on the Apennine Mountain chain, the station-master said goodnight to his staff and left some instructions with his assistant, Giuseppe Salonia, for his spell of duty. These done, Salonia curled up with his newspaper for the next hour or so. Just before the next train was scheduled to enter Balvano, he remembered that he had not received any ticker-tape message about the 8017's arrival at Bella-Muro, its next stop nearly four miles further on, thus telling Salonia that the single track would be all clear for use.

Instead, Salonia was told by the Bella-Muro station that the 8017 was running nearly two hours late. He replied that he would hold the 8025 at Balvano and would check the single track himself with a free locomotive. At 2.40 a.m. the 8025 rumbled into the station. Salonia ordered two trackmen, Caponegro and Biondi, to detach the engine from the train so that he could inspect the track leading to Bella-Muro.

The big mystery was the fate of the 8017 from the time it left Balvano station. Moments before it drew out, the train's chief engineer, Gigliani, in the leading engine had ordered his fireman, Rosario Barbato, to shovel a particularly large dosage of coal into the engine's furnace – 'We'll need it for these upgradients later', he had said.

The train had no trouble making the incline within the first tunnel, and puffed through the second reasonably well. Then it emerged on to a snaky viaduct about 25 yards long which fed into a forest-girt S-curve tunnel, the Galleria delle Armi, two miles long. At this disaster-point no-one can be 100 per cent sure what happened. It has been reasoned that the man at the throttle was worried by the high reading on his furnace-pressure gauge which apparently did not correspond with the engine speed, and the train must have been slowing badly in the damp narrow tunnel with its steep incline.

When all the cars, except the caboose, had entered the underground passageway, the 8017 groaned to a standstill under the excess weight on icy rails. Meanwhile, in the caboose brakeman Michele Palo was trying to keep himself warm; the engineer had not pulled the whistle-cord to give warning that anything was amiss so Palo assumed that the train had stopped for a signal of some kind – by no means an unusual event on a railway . . .

Finally he decided to take some action. He forced open a lower window and stuck his head out, but the whole train seemed to be encased in the black hole that bored through the hillside. The brakeman drew on his gloves and swung down from his caboose to find out what was holding things up. He had gone no further than a few yards into the black hole when he realized what had happened.

At once he turned round and ran along the track towards the Balvano depot two miles away downhill. He hoped to arrive in about an hour and get help for some of those aboard 8017. But his nightmare jog-trot took him much, much longer than that – most of the time he found himself forced down on hands and knees.

It was 2.50 a.m. when he came within sight of Balvano – at about the same time as Salonia had boarded the engine and started it up. Palo swung his red lantern from the mouth of the Balvano tunnel and yelled: 'Up the track!' 'Up the track!' When Salonia reached Palo he had collapsed on the line, and was moaning '*Sono tutti morti!*' ('They're all dead!')

Salonia had heard no crash, saw no evidence of an accident. Could the 8017 have left the rails? Not possible, Salonia decided, or some noise would have been heard in that snow-hushed countryside. He concluded that Palo had taken leave of his senses – the man was sobbing bitterly and every now and then buried his face in the station-master's jacket. Salonia picked the distraught railwayman up in his arms and carried him to the station where he was gently coaxed to relate what he could remember.

It was now almost 4.00 a.m. Despite the hour, everyone of importance in the town of Balvano was aroused. Salonia edged the 8025 engine slowly up the track to the tunnel Galleria delle Armi. He stopped the 8025 and, in the early morning mist, he made his way on foot to the last car of the 8017 which was held in the tunnel.

There was no sign of an accident, only an eerie, unnatural silence. Salonia slid open the door of one car and entered, lighting the interior with his lantern. Passengers were seated and sprawled in postures of utter relaxation. They looked as if they were asleep, but they were all dead. In every car Salonia entered, the scene was repeated: not one of the 500 showed the slightest flicker of life. The men in the cab were dead too, the engineer still at his throttle with his head rested on the side of the window-pane.

Salonia broke down, hardly able to bear the evidence of his eyes. He took a grip on himself, undid the brakes and backed the 8017 to the engine of his 8025, hitched the engine to the 8017 caboose, and towed the train of peaceful death back to Balvano. The police took over the macabre duty of carrying out the dead and laying them side by side on the station platform for future identification.

In all, 521 people died in the eeriest railway disaster of the century. The Italian State police had the task of reconstructing what must have happened inside the mountain. The 8017 could not have gone very far into the tunnel before its wheels began to slide. Chief engineer Gigliani could easily have backed the train downhill out of the tunnel and on to the viaduct. Instead he chose to press on in a bid to get over the gradient that impeded the train's forward impetus. The four crewmen in the two locomotive compartments – Gigliani and stoker Barbato in the leading engine, throttler Senatore and foreman Ronga in the second cab – set about scooping coal into the firebox. They worked like men possessed, yet the huge wheels, having lost all grip on the rails, simply spun faster and faster over the slippery track, and the train stayed on the same spot.

As the roaring fires devoured the emergency supply of soft coal, not one of the sweating crewmen realized that the fuel was producing lethal carbon-monoxide gas. The passengers – most of whom were asleep – did not worry because the train had stopped within a mountain. The carbon-monoxide took the lives of the four men in the engines, then worked its deadly way through the lungs of the conductor and 516 passengers.

Police, checking every detail, found that five passengers had not been suffocated by the gas; three were black marketeers who were brought to the station-master's office for medical treatment. Later they disappeared discreetly to avoid the questioning which would certainly have exposed their illegal activities, so they were of no help to the police in tackling the mysteries surrounding the 8017.

One survivor, an olive-oil salesman named Domenico Miele, was to prove of great value. He reported that he had stepped off the train at Balvano to stretch his legs for a few minutes. Finding the cold air too much for him, he took a scarf from his luggage, an action which was to save his life. When the train came to a dead stop inside the tunnel, Miele was one of the few who had not dropped off to sleep.

When the carbon-monoxide gas reached him, it started him coughing. Miele wrapped his scarf round his mouth as a filter, got off the train and made an unsteady way out of the tunnel. He did not guess that there was killer gas about because he climbed into the next, and last, coach to find another seat, but only reached the vestibule where he fainted and remained prostrate until he was picked up by two policemen who presumed him dead and carried him off to the improvised mortuary on the Balvano station platform.

As a result of partial gas poisoning Miele's hair (so says the official police report on the tragedy) turned from a rich black colour to a soapy grey.

The other surviving passenger was found, a small dealer named Luigi Cozzolino, but he suffered such severe brain damage that he did not realize what had happened, not even that his wife and eight-year-old son died on that ill-fated 8017.

Because of wartime censorship only one newspaper was allowed to publish a short official notice about the 'mishap'. All lawsuits were ruled out of order because the Allied Military Government had been technically in charge of Italy's railway system and could not be held accountable in law for a 'wartime accident'.

Rescue services from the neighbouring town of Balvano could do nothing. Their only function was to lay out the bodies along the railway lines and later drive them in lorry loads to the mortuary.

Burnden Park, 1946 and Ibrox Park, 1971

The football fans of Britain, starved of their favourite sport during World War II, were packing the grounds during the first full soccer season since the war's end – and 70,000 of them headed for Burnden Park, Bolton, in Lancashire on 9 March 1946, to watch the local Wanderers at the peak of their success.

Bolton Wanderers had enjoyed a long and glorious history, having won the Football Association Cup outright three times and reached the last four semi-finals nine times. Now they were poised to reach their tenth F.A. Cup semi-final, and they had already defeated their opponents, Stoke City, 2–0 away from home in the first leg of this cup-tie.

Although it was obvious that the Bolton ground would be packed to capacity that afternoon, the Darcy Lever stand, which could seat 2,800 people, stood conspicuously empty; the surrounding terraces were all jammed with a dangerous mass of swaying and singing supporters. Why this apparently ridiculous contradiction? The stand had been used during the war as a storage shed for the Ministry of Supply, and it seems that the Bolton police had refused the club permission to use it during the match because of fire hazards ...

That there was a deadlier hazard – overcrowding – was to become apparent all too soon. Behind one side of the ground the railway ran over an embankment, and in front of that embankment was the enclosed space of the ground's 'railway end'. It was here that the press of teeming banks of supporters was at its worst. The entire length of the road leading to the turnstiles at this end was a solid mass and, with each passing minute, it grew in depth as more and more fans joined it, inexorably increasing the pressure.

One newspaper-man who turned up there just after 2 p.m. – kick-off was due an hour later – reported that he found himself so hemmed in that he could not move forward or backward. 'Before I had a chance to get away', he wrote, 'I was gripped so tightly that I swayed and struggled, sweated and swore for the next hour in a cursing, roaring, mauling crowd of about 15,000 people in that enclosure alone.'

At 2.40 p.m. police ordered the turnstiles at the embankment end to be locked – Burnden Park was now bulging at the seams; every vantage point offering a view of the playing field was occupied and anything that could be climbed inside the ground had been scaled. Spectators were perched precariously on the roofs of refreshment huts and balanced uncomfortably on boundary fences. Men scrambled up the walls of the stands, skidded across sloping roofs, hauled themselves somehow on to huge advertisement hoardings in a desperate attempt to get a bird's-eye view of the game.

The police had to close the turnstiles, but the effect of this decision was to bottle up the embankment end of the ground. As a result this densely packed wedge of humanity became a potential battering-ram. It took some time to realize that a situation of crisis proportions had built up. Then the aged and the children began to collapse and were passed over the sea of bobbing heads to comparative safety.

Suddenly a great and growing roar swelled inside the ground . . . the teams were in position and the game was about to begin: the long build-up of excitement had reached climax-point. When the referee blew his whistle for the kick-off most spectators became so absorbed in the game that they were oblivious of the life-and-death struggle now raging in earnest at the embankment end of the ground. Of the thousands locked out by the police order to close the turnstiles, hundreds now began to force a way past the thin blue line of policemen guarding the railway embankment itself. They smashed their passage through sleeper fencing and some found a grandstand seat on a well-placed shunting engine and its goods wagons in the siding.

But others insisted on hacking and barging their way into the already teeming enclosure, swelling the crowd there to beyond bursting point. Something had to give, the cauldron had to blow its top . . . A running-track circled the ground between the pitch and the terraces and on this track stood a ring of police; their normal duty was to prevent enthusiasts rushing on to the playing area. But this police guard was the first to appreciate that the crowds swaying and yelling on the embankment were convulsed not by football excitement but by stark fear.

Policemen rushed to rip away part of the fencing holding back these spectators from the safety of the running-track, but their action came too late. A low wall on the terracing gave way, two steel crush barriers collapsed and an uncontrollable tidal wave of humanity surged forward and down. Men, women and children were stacked up in piles like broken dolls. Those who could, scrambled over the rails on to the track, and hundreds of others swept to the edge of the playing pitch; all this time the players, the referee and, indeed,

the vast majority of the 70,000 crowd inside the ground were utterly unaware of the disaster in their midst.

At last a police inspector ran across the pitch to implore the referee to stop the game – he did so at once and led the players from the field. Still most of the spectators were ignorant of the tragedy – to them the prostrate bodies looked like fainting cases, a common enough sight at soccer games.

The officials on duty realized only too well that they had a major disaster to deal with. An SOS went out for doctors, ambulances and oxygen cylinders. Gradually the extent of the tragedy began to dawn on the thousands who still milled around in the adjoining streets outside Burnden Park, when they saw the stream of ambulances arrive and the seemingly endless procession of stretchers carrying dead and seriously injured out of the ground.

Behind the scenes police chiefs conferred with the referee, the officials and the captains of both clubs. The police feared further trouble if the game were abandoned and asked that it be re-started. Already sections of the crowd were giving voice to their impatience. The players eventually returned to the field and played out a goalless draw.

Thus Bolton Wanderers reached their tenth F.A. Cup semi-final. The cost in terms of the accompanying

Football frenzy at its peak caused hundreds of people to force their way into an already overcrowded enclosure. The crowds swaying and yelling on the embankment soon became prey to fear as they realized that disaster threatened. Police rushed, too late, to allow people on to the pitch; the sheer weight of a mass of humanity surged forward in an uncontrollable tidal wave in which men, women and children collapsed in piles, like broken dolls.

Left : Reminiscent of a battlefield is the Ibrox football ground where 66 people died when a crush-barrier collapsed. Bodies of some of the victims are laid out on the goal line while doctors, nurses, police and other rescue workers tend some of the hundred people who were injured.

Previous pages : Some of the injured brought out from among the vast crowd which attended a cup final match at Burnden Park, Bolton, Lancashire. Part of the crowd surged forward, trampling those in front of them, and killing 33 people.

human tragedy was 33 killed and 500 injured. It was, until dwarfed by the appalling disaster at Ibrox Park, the worst football tragedy Britain had ever experienced.

*   *   *   *

The worst spectator disaster in the long history of British football killed 66 people and injured 100 in a fearsome stampede down one of the steep stairways leading from the terraces of Ibrox Park, football ground of Glasgow Rangers. It followed the last seconds of the 1971 New Year match between Rangers and Glasgow Celtic, the deadliest rivals in Scottish football. Rangers equalized in the last minute of the game – and police blame that goal for the buckling of a steel barrier under unsupportable pressure.

Thousands of fans were already leaving the ground when a mighty roar stopped them in their tracks. The word flashed round that Rangers had equalized, making the score one all. Many – too many – of the thousands who were leaving the ground tried to turn back, and on the stairway leading to Terrace No. 13 they met a solid mass of spectators coming down. The ensuing build-up of pressure burst the railings of the stairway: some people, children among them, were crushed to death against the iron stanchions; others were suffocated by the weight of bodies falling on top of them.

Fifty-three died inside the stadium and 13 on the way to hospital. Every ambulance in the city of Glasgow was called to Ibrox Park, and police were rushed to the spot – even the mounted police got an SOS; firemen were sent to the ground to light up the huge and now bare stadium.

For many of the 80,000 crowd on 2 January the first hint that something was amiss came when they were walking towards the city centre after the match. Police cars and ambulances by the score flashing blue roof-lights and sounding sirens raced into the streets lined with red-sandstone tenements which border the terracing in Ibrox Park.

Above: The fatal stair-case on which part of the Ibrox crowd attempted to turn as the match ended. They met crowds coming down and the build-up of pressure burst the railings.

Below: A nurse rushes to help the injured.

Inside the high red walls of the ground was a spectacle to turn the strongest stomach . . . corpses lay sprawled at the foot of the stairway which had become a death-trap, and were left unattended while police and firemen tried to revive any who might have a faint chance of life, however slender. Dazed, people were staggering around trying to trace fathers, brothers or friends who had failed to return from the match. They were staring pathetically at the rows of corpses barely concealed under grey sheets on the grassy bank that slopes down behind the wide curve of terraces.

Sir Donald Liddle, the Lord Provost of Glasgow, did his best to hold a Press conference, but broke down at the start and wept. 'The tragedy is enormous', he said in broken tones. 'Words fail me. From seeing the people involved it is obvious that a wide cross-section of the population and all age-groups are affected.'

When the bundles of bodies were disentangled into recognizable human beings it was seen that there were several boys and at least one girl among them. Some were carried down to the pitch and the running-track surrounding it; many were laid out in the gymnasium and offices under the stand.

One witness, shattered by what he saw, said: 'The bodies just kept pouring on top of one another like water over a waterfall.' A policeman remarked: 'I was leaving the match when I heard screaming. I looked back and saw a pile of bodies about 10 feet high all laid the same way with their faces towards me – a wall of faces, some with their tongues lolling out.

'I carried away one little ginger-haired laddie and a colleague tried to give him the kiss of life until a doctor said, "You're wasting your time – the wee boy's dead."

'The injuries of some of those who had been crushed right under the barrier were horrible to see. We came away with our boots, socks and the bottoms of our trousers soaked in blood.'

Tangiwai, 1953

Christmas had a special flavour of delight for the people of New Zealand in 1953. The newly crowned Queen Elizabeth was in their country on a royal visit, and she was to make the traditional Christmas Day broadcast to the Commonwealth from Auckland. Thousands of families travelled from their homes to the places on the Queen's route to catch a glimpse of her. New Zealand was a land of smiles.

One hundred and fifty miles to the south of Auckland, half-way to the city of Wellington, the glowering volcano Ruapehu mumbled and shifted that Christmas Eve. The 9,000-foot mountain is the highest on North Island, and had last stirred eight years earlier. Now it burst into violent wakefulness, erupting in scalding water, mud and rock.

As the volcanic crater split open, the 14-acre lake within it poured down the mountainside and burst out through a cave beneath the Whangaehu Glacier. A large part of the glacier broke up with a roar that was heard at the Waiouru military camp 10 miles away, where soldiers and nurses at the military hospital were enjoying themselves at the Christmas Eve party.

The cascade foaming down the sides of Mount Ruapehu had become what volcanologists call a *lahar*, a type of mud-flow which, as it gains momentum, gathers to itself large quantities of volcanic ash, trees, soil and other débris which together with the water and ice forms a thick slurry. Because of its density this can carry enormous boulders across miles of fairly flat country once the initial momentum has been gained.

The awesome force of this *lahar* burst into the Whangaehu River and joined the current hurtling down the valley carrying great rocks and jagged lumps of ice towards the railway bridge at Tangiwai (a Maori name meaning 'Weeping Waters').

The Tangiwai bridge had been built in 1906 and the rails stood 35 feet over the bed of the river. It was a sturdy construction, 198 feet long, made of steel on concrete piers, but in the path of Nature's unleashed fury it might have been a child's plastic toy. As the *lahar* struck, one of the piers crumpled and joined the onward rush. It was a mortal blow to the bridge.

Cyril Ellis, the local postmaster, heard the roar of the river and went out to investigate. The height of the water was 20 feet above normal, and the railway lines were under its surface. It was 10.21 p.m. and Ellis knew that the main trunk express from Wellington to Auckland was shortly due to pass over the bridge at full speed. He had a powerful electric flash-lamp with him, and he started off down the line in the direction the train would come to stop the Auckland Express from what seemed like certain disaster.

Ellis was already too late. In the distance he saw the light on the powerful locomotive approaching at a good 50 m.p.h. He swung his torch to and fro in the path of the engine, then jumped aside as it passed. He had a

glimpse of the men on the footplate, and screamed at the top of his voice: 'Stop! The bridge has gone!' The driver slammed on the brakes.

With barely 100 yards to the bridge the train squealed along the tracks on locked wheels on to the centre span. The bridge, undermined through the loss of the pier, collapsed in the middle and the 130-ton locomotive dived into the raging torrent and exploded, dragging the first five carriages with it. Ellis watched the lighted carriages slither past him into the river, and heard the screams of the passengers quickly silenced as the water drowned them.

The sixth carriage teetered on the broken edge of the bridge at a 45-degree angle, those behind remaining comparatively steady on the bank. Ellis ran with the guard to the coach on the brink and climbed aboard: 'Everybody out, quick!' he shouted, 'This carriage is going down into the river!'

A moment later the coupling holding it to the seventh carriage snapped and down they went into the water. Three times it rolled over like a log before beaching on the river bank. The carriage was quickly filled with a surge of water, oil and silt, and the passengers were whirled about like corks. Ellis took firm hold of the luggage-rack and managed to keep his head above water. Amazingly his torch still kept alight. He kicked out one of the windows and hoisted himself outside once more. Bracing himself against the coachwork, he hauled people out of the interior. Two other men, John Holman and a man named Hartwell, joined Ellis, and together they crawled along the outside of the carriage, breaking open windows and dragging out the coughing, survivors. Ellis rescued 26 people that night.

To add to the general distress the engine had been towing an oil-tender which had discharged its load into the river, and now everyone was covered with oil as well as silt. The force of the current was so great that the water-sodden clothes were wrenched from their bodies, leaving many of the people naked.

The Christmas Eve express from Wellington to Auckland was carrying a full complement of passengers, on their way to friends and relations for the Christmas holiday, when it roared on to the bridge across the Whangaehu river at Tangiwai. A local resident had tried to stop it, for he knew that a volcanic eruption had brought down a wave of water, mud and rock which had damaged the bridge. He was too late: the 130-ton locomotive, brakes locked, screamed on to the bridge and dived into the raging torrent. Daylight revealed to appalled onlookers the full extent of the disaster.

In mid-stream the depth and speed of the current was carrying everything before it. The five carriages had all their woodwork beaten away and carried downstream, leaving only the mangled iron frames in the vicinity. One carriage and the concrete pier of the bridge were washed along for miles before beaching on an island.

At the road bridge parallel with the rail viaduct, two motorists had drawn up minutes before the catastrophe. Mr Dewar Bell had been driving towards Waiouru with his wife when they came upon the flooded bridge. As Bell stepped out of his car, gazing at the scene with amazement, the ground shook under his feet with the impact of the boulders striking banks and river-bed and the air was vibrating.

Nearby, another motorist had stopped when the caravan he was trailing ran off the road. Together they looked towards the Tangiwai bridge. It was under water. On the far side of the structure the lights of the Auckland Express could be seen, bearing down on the bridge. 'What's going to happen if the bridge isn't there?' yelled Bell to the other motorist. Moments later the doomed train plunged into the river.

While Mrs Bell drove for help, her husband scrambled down to the water's edge. In no more than two feet of water he could barely stand against the force of the current, but he managed to drag several oil-blackened people to the bank. The caravan was used as a makeshift first-aid post. Bell climbed into the carriage lying on the embankment; 20 people, most of them injured, were struggling in three feet of water. Bell began pushing and hauling them out; 16 people owed their salvation to him.

Mrs Bell had found a phone and raised the alarm. At the Waiouru military camp the Christmas dance ended abruptly and nurses piled into lorries with the troops. From the surrounding countryside farmers and clerks and businessmen left their homes to join the volunteers at the scene of suffering.

Along the river bank were many signs that the victims were mostly Christmas holiday-makers returning home with presents; muddy toys, a little girl's doll, a cuddly felt animal, were scattered among the débris.

On the polished dance-floor at Waiouru there soon lay orderly rows of coffins and sheeted corpses. Many had been stripped by the savage water and identification was difficult if not impossible in a number of cases. As a makeshift measure a serial number was chalked on the floor at the feet of each casualty. There were very few injuries for the doctors and nurses to deal with. One of the tragic aspects of Tangiwai was that those who had been injured in the crash almost certainly died in the water, unable to help themselves in the grip of the torrent. For the most part the medical staff had to deal with cases of severe shock.

New Zealand's Prime Minister, Sidney Holland, went immediately to the crash scene. On Christmas Day he spoke to the nation on radio, and read out some of the names of known survivors. The Queen did not go to Tangiwai, having been advised to carry on with her planned programme to avoid disappointing those who were to meet her. At the conclusion of her Christmas Day broadcast she made a moving reference to New Zealand's great sadness.

The Tangiwai tragedy was New Zealand's greatest rail disaster. There had been 285 people on the Auckland Express, of whom 134 were saved. Identified bodies amounted to 123, with a further eight who could not be named; and 20 bodies were not recovered. The unidentified bodies were taken to Wellington for a mass funeral attended by the Duke of Edinburgh.

Before she left New Zealand, the Queen honoured four of the heroes of Tangiwai. Cyril Ellis and John Holman were awarded the George Medal, and Dewar Bell and W. I. Inglis received the British Empire Medal (Civil Division).

The subsequent inquiry concluded that the disaster had been due entirely to capricious Nature.

Such was the depth and speed of the current that the woodwork of five carriages was beaten away. One carriage and the concrete pier of the bridge were carried along for miles before beaching on an island.

Salvage workers in action. Victims and wreckage alike were covered in mud, weeds and oil from the oil tender which the engine had been towing. In all, 135 of the 285 people who had been on the express died.

Le Mans, 1955

Le Mans as we know it is the scene of the world-famous classic motor racing event, the French Grand Prix d'Endurance, a 24-hour non-stop event which has converted this ancient town into a gallic Brands Hatch.

The town-hall is built on the site of a former castle, and the town itself, which lies about 100 miles south-west of Paris, is the seat of a bishopric dating back to the third century A.D. King Henry II of England was born here, and its cathedral houses the tomb of Berengaria of Navarre, wife of England's Richard Coeur de Lion.

Today, Le Mans is synonymous with the best in motor-racing, and it has its own history, of which the most dramatic episode occurred in just a few seconds on Saturday, 11 June 1955. In that instant a Mercedes car, momentarily out of control, rocketed off the track into a part of the crowd of more than a quarter of a million spectators, cut a swathe through them, bounced and then exploded in an incandescent star-burst. In less time than it takes to relate, it killed 82 people and seriously injured more than 100 others.

Shock, frenzy, horror? Certainly, and in full numbing measure – but the officials, with a curious *sang froid*, insisted that the race should continue, complete with its attendant fairground carnival music and amusements, while the police, doctors and ambulancemen gathered the seriously injured, the dead and fragments of the dead, and took them away with speedy efficiency to nearby hospitals and mortuaries.

This particular Le Mans Grand Prix had aroused an enormous amount of international interest. World champion Fangio was competing, and new cars with famous drivers were expected to establish new speed records at, as one newspaper reported, 'a pace never seen here before'. Entrants included Mercedes-Benz of West Germany, the Italian Ferraris and Maseratis, the Gordinis of France, British Jaguars, Aston Martins and so on. It was the days when Fangio, Castelotti and the late Mike Hawthorn were virtually household names, even among the non-aficianados of the sport.

The weather was sunny and hot, and even though some rain was forecast a carnival atmosphere abounded. It was a kind of Royal Ascot of the internal-combustion engine. In the surrounding fairground and bars business boomed as the race got under way in the late afternoon. Bunched together, the leading cars took the bends at 150 m.p.h., and then Fangio and Hawthorn began to break lap records, building up to an average lap speed of 120 m.p.h.– as fast as the fastest of any previous Grand Prix. It was exciting and spellbinding for the first two hours, at which point horror struck like a thunderbolt. One of the Mercedes cars slewed from the track, bounced over the earth safety-bank, rocketed through the massed spectators and finally exploded at a cost of nearly 100 lives, and many injured. Time taken – a matter of two or three seconds.

Precisely how this came about has since been a subject of unending controversy. At the time the contest was running well. The attention of the crowd was centred on Mike Hawthorn in a new D-type Jaguar who was seriously challenging world champion Fangio in his silver Mercedes-Benz. Both had gained a lap on Pierre Levegh, the Frenchman in the Mercedes No. 3 team car. No hazard was evident – the cars were 'all systems go' and the drivers in good trim.

Then Mike Hawthorn began to brake and slow down to pull into his pit on the right so that his co-driver, Londoner Ivor Bueb, could take over. During the subsequent inquiry, and some years later in a letter to *The Times*, Hawthorn was quoted as insisting that he had given the prescribed hand signal in accordance with accepted racing practice. As he slowed and pulled over towards his pit, Levegh's Mercedes came up from behind to pass at around 180 m.p.h. In the resulting swerve the Mercedes touched the rear of a British Austin-Healey driven by Lance Macklin.

All motion is relative. That 'touch' at 180 m.p.h. hurled the Austin-Healey into a frantic broadside skid 100 yards long, but it ended safely enough and few paid much attention. All eyes were on Levegh's Mercedes. The car skewed and ran into the six-foot-thick earth safety-bank designed to function as an exterior brake and divert the driver back on to the track. This time, however, the reverse happened. The earth bank seemed to lift the car into a somersault so that it soared rocket-like into the air, somersaulted again before falling among the spectators, bounced once more and finally exploded into white-hot component parts, like shrapnel from an anti-personnel bomb.

Those few moments brought for many the instant eternity of death, including the driver himself whose body, thrown from the disintegrating car, was found dead near the roadside.

The shock was immediate but localized, and it is quite likely that only a tiny proportion of the crowd realized that anything at all had happened. It was, perhaps, to isolate those near the scene of death and destruction – a relatively small area – that the *gendarmes* moved in to set up a human barrier that could be penetrated only by doctors, firemen and professionally qualified helpers to speed up rescue work. For the same reason, perhaps, the decision was made at a high level to let the show continue – race, music and amusements.

The media were quickly on the spot and the disaster was soon being reported from every angle by international journalists, radio, television and newsreel men. To call it a field-day would be a misnomer; indeed, some film and television reports were so sickening that astonished producers and film editors, despite their love of the sensational, found themselves obliged to make cuts and fades. Even the printed word had to be moderated in many newspapers.

According to one reporter, 'the engine and back axle of the Mercedes sliced like a razor through the packed

Previous pages: The moment of impact. Police rush to the scene as a Mercedes taking part in the famous Le Mans race somersaults the protecting earth bank and explodes among the spectators.

The carnage among the spectators lining the race track was appalling. The scene was described by one reporter as being 'like a bloodstained battlefield. Women's screams rose above the roar of cars as they continued round the course'.

spectators. Some were decapitated, and for 100 yards along the straight the scene was like a bloodstained battlefield. Wailing men and women tried frantically to find out whether their friends or relations were among the victims. Women's screams rose above the roar of the cars as they continued round the course.'

A seasoned cameraman commented: 'I've covered wars and just about every type of horror job you can think of, but the stuff I've got here in the can is so appalling that it would make people sick to see it. There are kiddies with their heads sliced off – and their hands still gripping the ice-cream cornets they'd been sucking only seconds before. There was one father, mad with grief, refusing to believe that his son was dead and trying to carry him away to safety . . .'

Bodies lay everywhere. Many died en route to hospital. Ironically, those already dead were grotesquely covered with torn-down advertisement banners. Many had been charred by the fuel-fed flames of the Mercedes, whose engine contained a high proportion of weight-saving magnesium – an element well known for its explosive inflammability. Like an incendiary bomb, it defied the firemen and simply burned itself out.

Two English doctors worked alongside their French colleagues at the death site, although they had gone to Le Mans merely to see the race. With the approach of night came rain and a new crisis. The local hospital at Le Mans, after carrying out more than 80 transfusions, was rapidly running out of blood supplies. More was needed – much more – and urgently.

For the first time since the tragedy, the fairground music was silenced while doctors used the loudspeaker system to make urgent appeals for blood donors. There was no lack of response. Donors queued at waiting ambulances, then, having given blood, went back to watch the race which was still in progress, or to the funfair stalls which were still open for business.

Overcynical? Who can say? Perhaps it was the emotive reaction of the time, but on the other side of the coin the deliberate continuation of the race and funfair avoided possible chaos and obstruction to the essential rescue work in progress. The effect of a quarter of a million visitors trying to leave the ground at the same time can well be imagined.

The competitors themselves were obliged to drive lap after lap around the floodlit track when all of them wished to withdraw from what had become a fiasco. It was now a race in which there could be no true winner, but the sponsors were divided in their reactions. Mercedes, taking a very firm line, desperately tried to contact the firm's directors at Stuttgart for permission to pull out their cars, but the telephone lines were frantically busy and communication was subjected to long delays. In the end the West German Federal Government at Bonn intervened. Although the Le Mans organizers wanted the Germans to continue, at 1.45 a.m. on the Sunday the German team manager, Alfred Neubauer, received authority to flag in his two remaining cars which were running first and third, with Britain's Mike Hawthorn lying between.

The head of Jaguar, Mr William Lyons, also debated the abandonment of the race, but circumstances were rather different; his own son had been killed while driving a Jaguar to watch the race. He said, 'I can imagine nothing further from my son's wishes,' adding,

Wreaths mark the spot where the victims died, while the curious or the sympathetic come to gaze at the scene of the tragedy.

Among the debris of wreckage from the crashed car and the belongings of the victims, a priest helps in the rescue of the dead and injured. In a matter of seconds 82 people were killed and a hundred more seriously hurt.

without reference to the Mercedes withdrawal, 'racing in that respect is like flying. The risks are acknowledged and respected. But how can we be other than very grieved when a tragedy of this magnitude shadows the sport?'

The 1955 Le Mans Grand Prix was won, if the word has any meaning in retrospect, by Britain's Mike Hawthorn at an average speed of just over 107 m.p.h. He commented after the event: 'It was the one time in my career I'd have been equally glad to lose.'

Hawthorn was naturally the target for criticism, especially in France, for it was his move into the pit that had triggered the subsequent horror. In press correspondence it was alleged that he had failed to give the requisite hand signal to warn the following drivers of his intended move, and that he had misjudged the distance to his pit, overshooting it by some 80 yards. Both Macklin and Fangio echoed these criticisms some years later, although Hawthorn had been exonerated in the official inquiry following the disaster. Perhaps only Hawthorn himself knew the full truth, but he was killed a few years later (1959) in an ordinary road accident.

The French Government wasted no time in taking action. First, all motor racing was banned until new safety rules had been agreed and established. Second, after due deliberation, the new proposed safety regulations were put forward for international agreement.

Three main points emerged. The first was a ban on all racing events in which both high- and low-powered cars could compete simultaneously (it had been concluded that the relatively slow speed of Lance Macklin's Austin-Healey, hit by the much faster Mercedes, had been largely responsible for the catastrophe). Secondly, it was recommended that public stands on the course should be moved further away from the track, so reducing, if not totally eliminating, hazards to spectators. Finally, the pits, where cars were fuelled and maintained, should be moved over to a special side track well away from the public stands. These changes were internationally accepted and duly put into effect.

Lewisham, 1957

The cause of the rear-end collision near Lewisham, London, which killed 90 people on 4 December 1957 – the third worst death-toll in British railway history, exceeded only by Quintinshill and Harrow – was extremely simple: the driver ran through signals.

There were, of course, extenuating circumstances. It was a foggy night and, because of late running and delayed movements of stock in the London area, the driver and fireman on the 4.56 p.m. express from Cannon Street to Ramsgate did not have time to take on water during turn-around time, so the engine was being 'nursed' until the first passenger stop at Sevenoaks, Kent.

The engine was a Battle-of-Britain class Pacific No. 34066 Spitfire; and from London Bridge on the down fast line this express was following the 5.18 p.m. suburban electric train from Charing Cross to Hayes (Kent). There were drifting fog-banks over the southeastern suburbs that evening, and the bulging rush-hour trains were groping their way out of London.

These are the most densely packed lines in the world with the possible exception of Tokyo – it was estimated at the period of the accident that a total of 990 trains passed St Johns signal-box at Lewisham every 24 hours. The box also controlled traffic on the Nunhead-Lewisham loop, which crosses over the Kent coast main line on a steel lattice-girder bridge at this point. This traffic increased the total to 1,115 trains a day.

There is no manual block working, traffic being governed by four-aspect automatic or semi-automatic colour-light signals controlled by continuous track-circuiting. The semi-automatic signals are operated from the signal-boxes, but when this control was exercized by the signalmen in acceptance of a train, they would only clear to the aspect dictated by the state of the track circuits: double-yellow, yellow or green as the case may be.

Double-yellow (YY) means that the driver may expect to find the next signal at single-yellow, an indication which means that the signal after that may be at red. Thus adequate braking distance between trains is

On a dark, foggy winter evening an express train, over an hour late, ran through danger signals and crashed into the back of a local electric train, packed with commuters, bringing down a viaduct on to the rear coaches of one of the trains. Ninety people died.

always maintained. There were 19 of these four-aspect signals in the five miles of line from Cannon Street to Parks Bridge Junction where the mid-Kent line diverged from the old South-eastern main line to Dover and Ramsgate. There were only two signal-boxes within this five miles – St Johns and North Kent East Junction.

The relevant signals are to the right of the line, while the Pacific was driven from the left of the foot-plate and had a special narrow cab for the Kent Coast line. It proved difficult, though not impossible, for the driver to see the signals in fog from his side of the foot-plate, with his close-up view being cut off by the streamlined bulk of the boiler-casing.

The fireman read the signals until the train was approaching St Johns outer and intermediate home signals; because these signals are on the outside of a left-hand curve they were normally within the driver's view and, for this reason, the fireman had no further need to look out, but began firing in readiness for the long climb to the summit of the North Downs at Knockholt.

But the driver did not see these two signals, nor did he cross the foot-plate to do so. Asked at the later inquiry why, having missed them, he failed to slow down, he could only reply that he had never experienced a signal check at this point. But this time the signals were showing a double-yellow and a yellow indicator respectively.

The fireman noticed the St Johns home signal and shouted to his driver: 'You've got a Red!', whereupon the driver at once made emergency application of the vacuum brake. Too late – 138 yards beyond the signal the Pacific crashed into the rear of the 5.18 p.m. Charing Cross-Hayes 10-coach electric train which was standing at the Parks Bridge Junction home signal. They telescoped upwards on to a viaduct and brought a 530-ton mass of steel girders roaring down on top of the wreckage – just as a third train was crossing the bridge...

Only by a fluke was a much greater disaster averted – the third train was derailed as the wrecked coaches shattered the viaduct and the driver stopped within inches of the edge. His train hung poised over the lip of the bridge, saved only by its couplings from a headlong plunge to the death and injury of hundreds more passengers. So threatening was the situation that police roused families living next to the line at 2 a.m. next morning and warned them to get ready to evacuate their homes in case the bridge heeled over down the embankment. Meanwhile, a 45-ton crane was ordered to the scene to pull the third train off the damaged bridge, which was canting over at nearly 45 degrees.

The most dramatic interview after the crash was given to reporters by Harry Chadwick, a 45-year-old window cleaner, who rescued 15 people from one carriage and helped to bring out 10 dead. 'I saw the wrecked coaches and heard screaming', he said. 'I climbed a five-foot fence and dashed up the embankment to see what I could do. I didn't bother watching out for the live lines. One carriage was tilted at an angle so I went underneath it as I heard screams coming from there.

'The first person I saw must be the bravest girl I have ever met. She was about 25 and her legs were smashed

The steel frame of the flyover resting on one of the wrecked coaches in which about 50 people lost their lives. Only by a fluke was a greater disaster averted. A third train crossing the bridge was derailed as the viaduct shattered, and the driver stopped within inches of the edge; the engine poised over the lip of the bridge was saved only by its couplings.

to the bone... Although in obvious pain she was smiling and worrying only about her husband who wouldn't know where she was. The sight of her legs was horrible. I tried to joke with her. She was surrounded by dead and one or two barely alive people who were moaning in the huddle. I had to be careful who I rescued because each time someone moved it hurt someone else as they were so squashed together.

'This girl was weighed down and twisted around other people... Gently and slowly I moved someone's arm and someone's leg, someone's head, someone's shopping-bag to get her free. All this time her face was wincing with pain. Eventually I got her free and it was only then I realized that the force of the crash had pushed her and the rest of the people in her compartment down through the floor on to the sleepers. To comfort her I assured her that her legs would be all right.

'About 10 minutes later I came on a little boy aged about three. He lay dead with his little tin drum lying on his tummy.'

Alongside the dead were strewn handbags, gloves, shoes, coats – and gaily wrapped Christmas parcels. There was an almost continuous procession of stretchers along the track to the assembly point for ambulances at St Johns station. The dead were laid alongside the track. So heavy was the casualty roll that there were not enough ambulances. Many victims had to be carried away laid out on wrenched-off compartment doors. Nearly every home in the district helped to treat the injured – blankets and bandages were willingly provided and tea made non-stop.

In the dense fog and ghostly glare of the floodlights the railway line presented a scene of horror. On the stretchers silk-stockinged feet peeped from beneath

coats and blankets. Gashed limbs and bodies added to the ghastly spectacle.

Police loudspeakers kept broadcasting urgent messages for doctors from a number of hospitals to return to the railway track as soon as possible to treat more injured. As rescue workers stumbled along the line in the swirling fog, a cry was heard: 'Watch out – the engine may explode!'

The stunned crew of the engine worked for an hour carrying bucketfuls of damp earth from the embankment side which they poured into the fire-box of the 120-ton locomotive to put out the fire. At 10.30 p.m., more than four hours after the crash, London Fire Brigade still had around 100 men on the spot with 15 appliances helping with the rescue work. By then all the dead and injured had been removed from the electric train and work was concentrated on the viaduct and the steam train. The wrecked engine lay across crushed coaches, its nose almost in the track cinders, its cabin many feet in the air.

Scores of passengers were trapped in the wreckage. All available police in the area were mobilized, vans were commandeered to help in the rescue work, acetylene lighting was brought by the fire brigade in an attempt to penetrate the fog, logs were fired to be used as flares.

The inquiry into the disaster was held on 12 December 1957, and was told that the speed of the Pacific train was estimated at between 35 and 40 m.p.h. Fog had cut visibility down to five yards in some areas, witnesses said. William John Trew, 61-year-old driver of the Pacific, did not attend the official inquiry – he was still at his home in Ramsgate suffering from shock. His fireman, Cyril Hoare, was also too ill to attend; he was in Lewisham hospital suffering from hip injuries and shock.

The casualty list totalled 90 dead, 109 seriously hurt and 67 slightly hurt. There were 770 passengers in the Pacific and 1,480 in the electric train. The bridge over the lines was brought down by the crash and 49 of the dead in the steam train were killed by the bridge collapse. Motorman J. B. Skilton, the driver of the Hayes electric train which was hit, was asked by Lieutenant Colonel G. R. S. Wilson, Transport Ministry Chief Investigation Officer, if he felt much of the crash. He replied: 'No, I felt a jolt. When I saw the scene it was much worse than I first thought.'

Colonel Wilson told the inquiry that he had made three journeys on the foot-plate of a Battle-of-Britain class locomotive – similar to the one Mr Trew was driving – to see line conditions for himself. 'I decided straight away that the speed could not have been less than 30 m.p.h. That was my guess from what I saw.'

How about visibility? The driver of a London Cannon Street–Hastings steam train, which passed through just before the crash, said he had a red and saw

it between 35 and 40 yards away. Could he see the signals from his left-hand-drive cab? The driver replied: 'All signals were on the right-hand side of the engine. There is no difficulty in seeing them in clear weather, but in fog you could lose them with your engine obstructing them.'

And this is as near as we are likely to get to the truth of the matter; if the driver of the ill-fated express had crossed the foot-plate he should have seen the warning signals. It is in such seemingly small actions that so often lies the difference between a routine journey and a tragedy.

In his final word on Lewisham, Brigadier Langley stressed that the lesson of this crash should be borne in mind when new or replacement over-line bridges were designed, but above all he emphasized that the Lewisham disaster, like the previous one at Harrow and Wealdstone on 8 October 1952 (which had cost 122 lives), would have been prevented by some form of the Automatic Warning System (now in general use) at the distant signal point.

Agadir, 1960

To the people of Agadir and to the several thousand tourists enjoying its winter sunshine, 2 March 1960 had been just another day. Now, half an hour to midnight and with a high, bright moon looking down on the drowsy city enveloped in the warm clinging darkness of a Moroccan evening, that day was almost over.

In the big, modern hotels near the sea, the lights were going out one by one. The children, tired from a day's ceaseless activity on the magnificent beaches of golden sand and from the continuous excitement of new sights and sounds, had long been asleep. Many of their elders had followed their example, tired from another day of continual sunshine, of excursions to the four-centuries-old Casbah, and of an orgy of writing 'Having a wonderful time, wish you were here' postcards to less fortunate friends who were combating the chill of winter.

Some, of course, remained very much awake. The popular bar at the huge Saada Hotel, just off the main sea-front, still had its fringe of dedicated drinkers; the card salon of nearby Gauthier's had its nightly collection of bridge players who rarely looked up from their cards or score-sheets to gaze out across the hotel's boasted 'panoramic view of the bay'. Away from the hotel area, some of the tourists were sampling the more dubious pleasures of the mainly Muslim quarter of the Talbordj lying to the north-west, where cabarets with a 'native' flavour, including the commercialized exotic dances of old Morocco, had their admiring semi-circles of European patrons. Otherwise the whole city was still.

A casual talking point had been three earth tremors that had shaken the city during the week, but they had been so slight that they had passed almost unnoticed, although some of those at the Saada bar had wittily suggested that their duty-free drinks had more of a 'kick' than usual.

But those tremors had been a promise of more to come.

At 11.39 p.m. there came a fourth, a shock which lasted for nearly 10 whole seconds – an unusually long time – to become the worst earthquake tremor ever recorded in Morocco. The whole of the city and the surrounding countryside trembled and shook with the immeasurable power of that subterranean movement. That comparatively brief moment of time seemed an eternity to everyone in Agadir that night. To many it seemed like the end of the world. To several thousand it *was* the end of their world.

At 11.40 p.m. the moon illuminated a scene of utter, terrifying chaos. The great ultra-modern hotels that had been built to satisfy the demand of the post-war

A woman's face of anguish reflects the emotions of the people of Agadir after the terrifying earthquake.

tourist boom had suddenly become grotesque heaps of shapeless, dust-covered rubble. Every street was now littered with great piles of stones, masonry and plaster that had spilled across them, to block nearly every road from the shoreline to Talbordj where, a few moments before, many multi-storied blocks of flats had been silhouetted against the night sky. Now they, too, lay in piles of utter ruin. Only one road to this quarter was still open, and that had a huge gaping crack right across it.

As the rumbling and crashing came to an end, a ghastly screaming and shouting arose which developed into hysterical pandemonium as the survivors began to claw their way free of masonry and stones. Agadir had almost ceased to exist; even the ancient Casbah was destroyed, only a few dazed inhabitants, grey with dust and shock, groped their way from the ruins that had been their homes to stagger, shaking and sobbing, across the high pile of masonry that had formerly been the protecting wall to reach the fresh air and comparative quiet of the countryside.

With every line of communication cut, it was some time before news of the extent of the disaster was received in the French naval and air base which was still at Agadir (although France had recognized Morocco as an independent kingdom some four years earlier), but little could be done until dawn except alert other cities throughout the country, asking for urgent aid.

Dawn revealed an almost unbelievable sight. Nearly every hotel had been flattened, while damage in the thickly-populated Talbordj quarter had been as much as 90 per cent and some 80 per cent in the 'new town' nearby. Wherever the rescue teams looked they saw ruins with parked cars now shattered and half-buried with masonry. In some hotels, walls had crumbled away to reveal beds, some still sheltering the bodies of unfortunates who had been crushed in their sleep, hanging precariously and almost obscenely from the parapets of tottering walls, while the terrible screaming and moaning of the trapped or cries for help in a variety of languages rose on all sides.

The airport had escaped damage and was turned into a clearing house for the casualties. Aircraft began to arrive to carry the injured to Marrakesh, Rabat, and other cities which had escaped the effects of the earthquake, although Mogador, 100 miles to the north, had also suffered some damage from the fringes of the earthquake.

A group of sailors was put to work on what had been the imposing Saada Hotel. They struggled desperately against time, their uniforms dusty and torn, but for the most part they only uncovered the crushed bodies of tourists and hotel staff. Even so, they had some success. One group heard the voice of a child calling for its mother, apparently coming from deep below a huge mound of stones that had previously formed part of the

façade of the hotel. They dug down, first with spades and picks and then, more gently, with bare hands, until they came upon the child, miraculously alive, trapped in a slight hollow beneath great stones and beams.

But that was to be one of their few successes, for out of the hotel's guest-list of more than 150, only 20 survived.

There was no electricity to light up darkened holes beneath the rubble that might shield a body and no water to dampen the flames which licked at shattered woodwork. Initially, every effort was devoted to finding and then removing the injured to safety and quickly burying the dead to avoid the risk of infection – always a danger to the living in tropical climates. Three thousand men of the Moroccan army were rushed to Agadir and then sent to patrol the whole area where the earthquake had also caused much damage. In the Moorish town of Inezgane, some seven miles away, damage was estimated at 30 per cent of the buildings.

A French naval squadron including an aircraft-carrier arrived off the coast; Dutch and Spanish warships joined it; Britain sent aircraft from Gibraltar to land at Agadir's airport. Soon a fleet of some 80 aircraft was operating a shuttle service to airlift the injured. More than 2,000 people were thus evacuated.

There was a number of British tourists in Agadir's hotels, and all of those who survived had alarming stories to tell. Alan Birtles of Warwickshire, for example, recalled that he and his wife were asleep in bed when there was a frightful rushing noise and a lot

Top : French troops digging in the rubble to rescue a fifteen-year-old boy who was trapped, with only his head and one arm exposed, for over 30 hours.

Above : A general aerial view of the ruins of Agadir, which was destroyed by an earthquake on 2 March 1960. Ten thousand people are said to have died in the city.

they got to her.'

At the end of that first day the authorities ordered the complete evacuation of Agadir, then sealed off the whole area except for essential services. The Crown Prince of Morocco held a Press Conference to announce that the death-roll had risen to 10,000. That figure included 4,000 dead already found, with an estimated 6,000 still buried beneath the ruins. Some 20,000 people had escaped unhurt, he said, and the 2,000 injured had already been evacuated. Final figures were never accurately established, and other sources quoted widely differing statistics.

The rescue work went on, although by now it had developed into a search for bodies. So much quicklime had been scattered about to prevent infection that one observer said that parts of the city resembled snow-covered fields.

Yet there were miraculous survivals. On 9 March, a week after the earthquake, three Moroccans were rescued quite unscathed. A father and his 10-year-old son had been dug out alive and rescue workers began to search around the same area until, led by weak cries, they found another man. On the following day, eight more were rescued. Rescue workers listening and calling among the débris were answered by feeble cries on 11 March and during that day they dug out a man of 24, three women and a family of three Jewish children, two girls and a boy of six. The following day two more were rescued, one a 28-year-old Muslim, the other, as it happened, the father of the three children rescued the previous day. The two girls, Alice and Jacqueline Kalfon, related how they had told stories and sung to their little brother Armand during their ordeal beneath the débris of their house. All were rushed to hospital, where Armand died a few hours later.

Rescue work was also going on in the remote areas of the Atlas Mountains where nearly 600 were reported dead and more than 2,000 homeless.

Helicopters circling over the devastated areas reported that in some instances the ground had opened like giant jaws and swallowed villagers 'by the dozen'.

The earthquake had a strange effect upon the Atlantic coastline and seabed which made an extensive hydrographic survey essential. At one place where the water had been charted at 1,200 feet, soundings showed that it was now only 45 feet. This was not only inshore; for nine miles from the coastline soundings showed a depth of 1,200 feet instead of the previous 4,500 feet.

of crashing and screaming. It was pitch dark, which made matters worse. He tried the bedside light but the electricity cables had been ruptured. As he and his wife lurched about the room they found that the earthquake had brought all the drawers tumbling from the furniture, and they soon realized that plaster from the ceiling overhead was still falling about them. He managed to find a cigarette-lighter and by its meagre light they struggled into some clothes. Then, going to the door, they found it had jammed and they had to break it down before they could escape. 'We broke down the doors of other rooms in the corridor to help people out', he concluded.

Richard Waddington who had been staying at the Marhaba Hotel, one of the few large buildings that had not collapsed completely, stated that the most awful thing about the disaster was 'the terrible screaming and shouting from people trapped under the rubble; but you could not do anything about it.' He went on: 'I was fortunate, I suppose, because I was under only six feet of rubble and they got me out in six hours. My father was 16 feet down. It took 22 hours to free him. My mother was farther down still. She was dead when

The upper storey of a house in the Arab quarter of Talbordj stands almost intact, despite the fact that most of the ground floor has collapsed.

In this quarter damage was about 90 per cent, and the famous Casbah was destroyed.

Right: There were miraculous survivals, people being dug alive from the ruins as long as ten days after the disaster. This three-year-old girl was believed to be dead until she stirred and cried out for her mother.

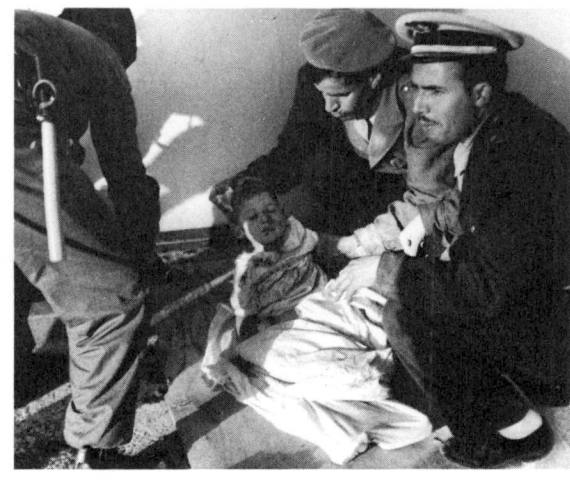

Mid-Air Collision, New York, 1960

It was mid-morning in New York on Friday, 16 December 1960, the last shopping weekend before Christmas. Heavy grey clouds hung over the city and wind-scattered flakes of sleet made shoppers snuggle deeper into their furs and topcoats. Nevertheless, in Manhattan, especially on Park and Fifth Avenues where the dazzling displays of such as Macys and Gimbels were drawing large crowds into their stores, business was brisk.

On the other side of the East River, however, across the Brooklyn Bridge, the streets were almost deserted. In Brooklyn itself, around the Park Slope area, there were as yet few seasonal displays for this was a run-down neighbourhood. Even so, a few Christmas wreaths had already made their appearance on doors and in windows along Sterling Place although, as yet, there were few about to appreciate them. It was just after 10.30 a.m., a time when the men had gone to work and children to school, while housewives and the elderly were mainly indoors, for the dismal weather did not encourage anyone leaving the comparative comfort of their homes.

Soon after 10 o'clock, Jo Colacano and John Opperisano arrived and began to set up some Christmas trees, sticking their sawn butts into a dirty snow-bank opposite a vacant Sterling Place store. Nearby, Charles Cooper, a sanitary worker, was content to lean upon his snow shovel and watch them. For a moment in time the two salesmen and their silent onlooker existed; the next they were completely obliterated.

For out of the morning murk came a blazing airliner which sliced the steeple off the tall, sombre building of the Pillar of Fire Church, then buried itself in the church's foundations, bringing its wall down on top of it and destroying a funeral parlour at the same time, while its tailplane, burning furiously, spun over and over as it bounced along the street. A few moments before, the gutters had been brimming with brown slush. Now they were suddenly filled with blazing rivulets of jet fuel which, racing down the slope of Sterling Place, enveloped parked cars with flame, setting off a chain of smaller explosions as the gasoline tanks were ignited. Within minutes a six-storey tenement building, some shops and offices were blazing furiously. Wreckage was suddenly spread over a square mile, causing a holocaust of fire and ruin that brought brigades dashing to the devastated area from all over Brooklyn and Manhattan.

The crashed aircraft was a United Airlines DC8 jet-liner which had been approaching New York from Chicago, with 77 passengers and a crew of seven. It had been due to touch down at Idlewild (now Kennedy) Airport at 10.45 a.m.

Firemen arrived on the scene of disaster where a series of explosions was igniting roofs and spraying further wreckage in all directions. A few moments after the plane had crashed women, children and elderly persons came pouring from the tenements into the street, dressed in a bizarre variety of sweaters, housecoats and even pyjamas. They were still running in aimless panic beneath a canopy of dense black smoke when the first of the brigades arrived. Any rescue work, so far, had been impossible for as one witness said: 'The heat was terrific and the flames were shooting three

Left: Death fell hideously from the sky to land in Brooklyn. The tailplane and wing of the United Airlines DC8 jet airliner, was involved in a mid-air collision with a Lockheed Super Constellation.

Right: A general view of the devastation. The blazing DC8 sliced the steeple off a church, then buried itself in the church's foundations, bringing a wall down on top of it while the burning tailplane somersaulted down the street.

stories high. We couldn't get near the place, so we helped people out of threatened houses,' significantly adding, 'We heard no screams from the wreckage.'

As the firemen began to move in a miracle happened; a small boy was seen crawling through a hole in the fiercely blazing fuselage. He was Stephen Baltz, an 11-year-old, flying alone to Idlewild to be met by his mother and to spend the Christmas with her. His clothing was on fire, but he was seized and rolled in the snow until the flames were extinguished. Then, as he was carried away, a fireman cradling him gently in his arms, the boy asked, weakly, 'What happened?' before lapsing into unconsciousness.

Although it was a seven-alarm fire, involving 250 firemen and more than 50 pieces of equipment, it took more than two hours to bring the raging fire under control.

At almost the same time as the Brooklyn disaster, another plane crashed at one end of a small army air force strip, known as the Miller Army Air Field, on Staten Island, some 11 miles to the south-west. Unlike the Douglas DC8 which was jet-powered, this machine, a Lockheed Super Constellation, was a four-engined turbo prop aircraft. It was a Trans World airliner bound from Dayton and Columbus, Ohio, to La Guardia airfield with 39 passengers and a crew of five. Its estimated time of arrival was 10.40 a.m. An eye-witness described what happened: 'I saw the engine on the right side blow up. I only saw one plane . . . then the second engine on the right side blew up and when it did it blew the tail section to pieces. I saw a couple of people falling out of the plane. It was on fire from the time it blew up to the time it crashed.'

A 30-foot section of wing and an engine landed about 50 feet from a row of officers' frame quarters at the end of the field, but unlike the other disaster in Brooklyn, no one on the ground was injured. As the rear half of the plane's fuselage swirled out of the heavy overhang to smash into the earth it split open 'like a huge silver lobster shell'.

A Roman Catholic priest had his own version of what had happened. 'I looked up and saw the Constellation coming in towards Miller Field. It seemed under control. Suddenly there was an explosion, one wing fell off and the plane plunged to the ground.'

Above: Bodies of victims lie on the pavement close to the still flaming wreckage of the United Airlines jet which crashed into the street. Miraculously, only six people were killed.

None of the eye-witnesses realized that more than one aircraft was involved, none reported seeing two planes collide in mid-air, and the first editions of the newspapers suggested that the DC8 had crashed while attempting to land and the Constellation had exploded in mid-air and crashed on Staten Island. But the realization that the T.W.A. plane had fallen in three parts on the Island revealed that it could not have broken up after hitting the ground; and then, among its wreckage, an unmistakable jet engine was found.

Within minutes of the crash, fire-engines were at the scene and soon smothered the fiercely burning forward section with foam. One hundred firemen and nearly as many off-duty firemen were on the spot; they quickly quenched the fire and then began to pull the wreckage apart with winches and crowbars. There were no survivors. The firemen lifted out body after body, placing them in long even rows and then covering them with olive drab army blankets brought by servicemen from their quarters at the other end of the field.

The report that bodies had been seen falling from the plane as it plunged earthwards sent a fleet of Coast Guards' boats searching hopefully for survivors in the icy waters of the river and sea. Six were found but none survived the shock of their immersion.

Two off-duty policemen, brothers named Peter and Gerard Paul, were near the crash and immediately rushed to the rear section of the plane. 'We were the

first ones there. I got out a knife and began trying to cut the people free from their safety-belts. We counted nine passengers. It was very quiet.'

Although there was some initial confusion on the ground, the men of both approach control towers at La Guardia and Idlewild were all too horribly aware of what had happened. The United Airlines jet had been ordered by traffic controllers to fly a holding (or stacking) pattern 5,000 feet above Preston, New Jersey, until it was given the clear to proceed to Idlewild. At the same time the T.W.A. plane was directed to fly a similar holding pattern 6,000 feet over La Guardia. Their separate courses from the holding pattern to either airport would be several miles apart. While radar screen operators at both airfields stood almost hypnotized, they saw the images of the two aircraft merge into one and continue for a short distance, until one broke free of the other and fell away out of sight.

A few days after the accident, experts made test flights along the approaches to the New York area and were satisfied that there was nothing wrong with the radio navigation equipment used at both airfields or with their traffic control procedure. They later reported that the disaster was one of human error, for there was a buffer zone of at least three miles between the two holding areas for Idlewild and La Guardia. It was also agreed that the DC8 jet airliner was off-course, it had left its position and, by blundering into the other zone, had collided with the Constellation as it was about to make its approach run for La Guardia.

The only survivor from the New York crash, little Stephen Baltz, recovered consciousness and had given the only first-hand account of the crash. 'I remember looking out of the plane window at the snow below covering the city. It looked like a picture out of a fairy book. It was a beautiful sight. Then, suddenly, there was an explosion. The plane started to fall and people started to scream. I held on to my seat and then the plane crashed. That's all I remember.'

He became unconscious again soon afterwards, and although a team of eight doctors and twelve nurses worked around the clock to save his young life, they were unsuccessful. His lungs had been destroyed by the fumes and flames he had breathed in as he had crawled to safety, and although he fought for life with great bravery, there was no hope. His father spoke his epitaph. 'Stevie tried awfully hard, because he was a wonderful boy.'

The loss of life, 134 persons composed of 128 passengers (including three babies-in-arms) and crews, and six persons on the ground, was the world's worst air disaster up to that time.

There were several strange coincidences in connection with this New York crash. The worst air disaster to date had also involved the same two companies, United Airlines and T.W.A., when two of their planes collided in mid-air over the Grand Canyon, Arizona.

Sir Edmund Hillary, the world-famous conqueror of Everest in 1951, was thought at first to have been on the DC8 from Chicago with two companions, but he had been unable to leave for the airport owing to last-minute pressure of work and the plane left without him: he even had the tickets in his pocket at the time.

The crash sparked off a large number of claims and litigation. One of the passengers carried more than

$500,000 worth of life insurance, six others had more than $450,000 worth between them. There were also suits against the United States Government and both airlines, totalling some $25 million. The inquiry, held in June 1962, put all the blame on the pilot and crew of the DC8, it having been established that at the moment of collision, this aircraft was nine miles off-course. A contributory factor, said the inquiry, was that the pilot had not throttled back when in the holding zone and had allowed his craft to continue at a speed of 346 miles per hour instead of the 200-odd miles per hour that was obligatory at a low level of 5,000 feet.

Yet how much worse the disaster might have been. The T.W.A. Super Constellation ploughed its way along a vacant airfield with no loss of life other than its unfortunate occupants. The DC8, ramming its blazing fuselage into a densely populated area of Brooklyn killed six persons on the ground, whereas the final total could so very easily have been much greater. Indeed, as the forepart of the plane neared the end of its death plunge it narrowly missed the St Augustine's Roman Catholic Church where some 1,700 pupils were at their desks, débris actually landing in the schoolyard. Looking later at the scene and realizing 'what might have been' a bystander exclaimed devoutly, 'God brought that plane in.'

This tragedy at Christmas-time which was to throw a shadow over the whole city, ended on a further tragic and unusual note. Learning of the New York disaster, President Luebke of West Germany sent a cable to America's President Eisenhower to express his country's sympathy. Hardly had his message been received, however, than another disaster occurred in the West German city of Munich. Major-General Ernest Moore, Commanding Officer of the U.S. 3rd Air Force in Britain, had flown to Germany for Christmas leave. Not needing his plane over the weekend, he had allowed it to be used to fly home a dozen American students, sons and daughters of U.S. servicemen in Britain, who had been attending a University of Maryland extension course in Munich.

The plane, with a crew of seven, got out of control and crashed on to a street-car crowded with Christmas shoppers in the centre of Munich. Everyone died in the aircraft and 31 Germans were killed either in the car or in the street where the plane had crashed.

This was a sad ending to 1960, a year which had seen a record number of fatalities in U.S. schedule airlines – 388 persons in all – breaking the previous record of 294 of the previous year.

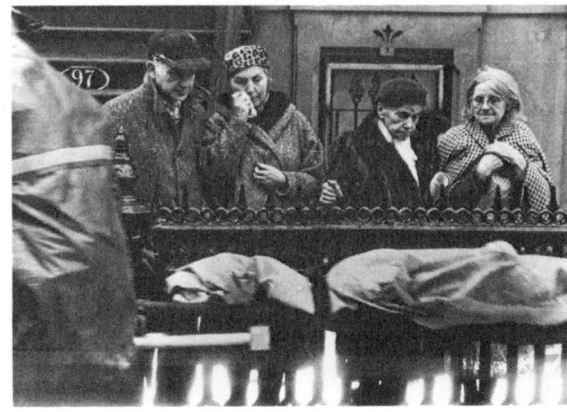

The Vaiont Dam, 1963

In the north-eastern corner of Italy, where the Italian Alps merge with those of Switzerland and Jugoslavia, there are many rivers which are the source of water and hydro-electric power for northern Italy. Across the valleys dams have been built and reservoirs created.

The Vaiont Dam formed part of a complex of five dams, which together made up the north-west-Piave hydro-electric scheme. When it was opened in 1960 it was the third highest concrete dam in the world, its wedge-shaped wall towering 873 feet above the Piave river and the valley below. In this valley, on the banks of the river, lay a number of small villages. Closest to the dam was Longarone, a village of less than 2,000 people, and a number of outlying hamlets.

The autumn of 1963 was unusually wet. Rain had loosened the rocks and earth of the mountain slopes which formed the shores of the reservoir. One of these, Mount Toc, which rises steeply to a height of 6,000 feet, had caused such apprehension that on 8 October a mayor in the district issued a warning to fishermen and others who might venture on the lake shores of the possibility of landslides causing dangerous waves.

Anybody who lives close to a dam is aware of the possibility of a fault and the disaster that could follow. The people in the district of Longarone were no exception, but they had no apprehension of danger on the night of Wednesday, 9 October 1963. At 11.00 p.m. they were all at home, either in bed or watching television. Fifteen minutes later a vast avalanche swept down the slopes of Mount Toc and thousands of tons of rocks, mud, earth and uprooted trees tumbled into the lake. The effect was that of throwing a large stone into a basin of water. Although the reservoir was by no means full it promptly overflowed, spilling over the top of the dam and pouring into the valley below.

The few survivors said later they heard that fearful sound which is so often described as the first intimation of disaster – a noise like thunder. They assumed at once that the dam had given way and, pausing only to gather up those nearest to them, they fled, but only the people whose houses lay close to the high ground at the edge of the valley had any chance. Over the lip of the dam poured a torrent of water, mud, rock and timber, creating a towering wall which swept along the valley below, swirled up the hillside and engulfed villages in a horrifying, overwhelming tide.

The natural assumption that both survivors and the authorities initially made – that the dam had burst – was not corrected until the dawn. The night had been chaos and pandemonium: the sun rose to reveal a macabre scene – a vast, silent desert of rock and mud and rubble, with here and there the remains of a building. Longarone, four-fifths destroyed, was a heap of stones; so were the nearby hamlets of Faè and Pirago, where all the inhabitants died. Two other hamlets, Codissago and Castellavazzo, lost half their population;

the two on the lake were wiped out, with three-quarters of the population missing.

It took time to establish these facts, for communications were destroyed. Telephone and telegraph lines were cut; railway lines turned and twisted in crazy spirals of buckled steel; and roads leading into the devastated villages were unidentifiable swamps. When the Italian Minister of Public Works visited the scene he described it as 'a truly biblical disaster . . . like Pompeii before the excavations began.'

With daylight came the first of the helpers, ploughing through the morass in the valley below the dam, where the river was swollen to twice its natural size by the waters pouring into it. Throughout the day bodies were washed up as workers struggled to reach the stricken villages in a frantic search for survivors. The final approaches to Longarone, now quagmires blocked with rubble and timber and the dead bodies of cattle, became choked with soldiers, ambulances, lorries and people desperately hoping for news of friends or relatives.

There was little hope for those who had not managed to escape to the high ground. The force of the great wave could be seen in the twisted pieces of metal, the total destruction, the bodies found hurled high into trees. The problem of extricating the bodies was immense: the municipal authorities at Belluno immediately ordered 500 coffins but as the days passed it became apparent that these would not be enough. Five days later rescuers were still digging for bodies and the problems of identification grew. Many were disfigured

and denuded of clothing: whole families had died and there was nobody left to identify them. Eventually many were buried, unknown, although occasionally one of the thousands of helpers would find himself facing and able to identify someone he once knew.

The gruesome task was soon well organized. Bodies were extracted, sprayed with disinfectant, put in plastic shrouds and into simple coffins away from the warm sun as quickly as possible. A helicopter service was established and bodies arrived heaped on lorries, or carried, roughly-covered, on stretchers from the helicopters. The final death-toll totalled 1,189, although possibly some were not found. But on the morning of 12 October, two children were discovered, still alive, in the cellar under the débris of their home. While there was still hope of survivors, the rescue work continued at full intensity.

An urgent inquiry was made into the safety of the dam. It was inspected and found to have suffered only some damage to the top of its retaining wall. The vast extent of the landslide could be judged from the fact that little over a third of the original reservoir remained. Instead, a new mountain filled the centre of the dam, some grass and lopsided trees still covering its surface.

Almost immediately the cause of the disaster became a political issue and the subject of exhaustive inquiries. Rock-falls and small earth movements of the mountain were known to have occurred. The crucial question was: should a dam have been built in that situation in the first place? Three years after its completion it came to light that research was still being made into the suitability of its location.

A court of inquiry was set up to consider a number of questions and to establish whether the disaster could have been avoided. It had to consider various aspects: Was the location badly chosen? Was the dam badly designed? Was the area, and in particular the hazard constituted by the mountain, monitored frequently enough? Had the local authorities taken sufficient care in the warnings they issued? A minor earth tremor had

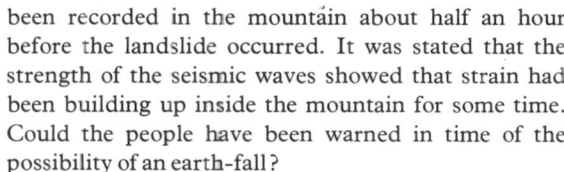

Above : In the morning after the disaster, rescue workers searched among the rubble of houses for the injured and brought them to a makeshift first-aid post.

Below : In Longarone, the village closest to the dam, rescue workers could do little but dig for bodies. The final death roll totalled 1,189.

been recorded in the mountain about half an hour before the landslide occurred. It was stated that the strength of the seismic waves showed that strain had been building up inside the mountain for some time. Could the people have been warned in time of the possibility of an earth-fall?

Although the court had been involved as a result of Communist pressure upon the Government whom they accused of negligence, it soon became apparent that there were grounds for such an inquiry; when its findings were eventually published there seemed little doubt that, with more care and more exhaustive enquiries into its potential dangers, the site would never have been chosen. The nationalized Italian electrical industry, which was responsible for the hydro-electric scheme, was found to be at fault. Builders and civil engineers were also found to carry some of the blame for a construction unsuitable to its particular site. It was common knowledge that there had been concern over the safety of the mountain. When the dam was being built and the reservoir filled, a series of landslides and cracks had appeared in the mountain, which had had to be reinforced with concrete to a depth of several feet on either side of the dam. Instruments recorded stresses and strains on the rock face, and the reservoir was not completely filled until two years after the dam had been completed. At the time of the flood all the men working at the dam were killed, but one who had worked on the original construction claimed that the technicians were waiting for such a disaster from one day to the next.

The local authorities, said the inquiry, must have known of this situation. Why did they do no more than warn the local inhabitants of the dangers on the lake itself? Some communities living around the lake and on Mount Toc had been evacuated. Should not the inhabitants of the valley also have been evacuated? Or at least warned of the possible dangers in strong terms?

As a direct result of the inquiry, the ill-conceived Vaiont Dam was closed down. The devastated villages were rebuilt and new factories sited in the valley.

The Mattmark Dam, 1965

Most people deplore any man-made construction which affects natural beauty and few of them enhance the scenery. Dams, however, are sometimes an exception. If the wall itself is attractive, once the reservoir is filled and its shores covered with grass, trees and undergrowth, the site can be very beautiful.

A dam under construction, however, is a far from beautiful sight. Dirt roads criss-cross the valley and curve round the hillsides; concrete-mixers, silos, stone-crushing plant and huge conveyor-belts are littered – apparently aimlessly – around the site. Where the dam itself is taking shape is an ugly concrete wall, the steel reinforcement rods protruding from its surface. On the valley floor are temporary huts – engineers' and contractors' offices, canteens, engine-sheds and stores; and, often, living quarters for the men, if the site is a long distance from any nearby town. All over the area is a ceaseless movement and a continuous roar from lorries, trucks, bulldozers, earth-moving plant and all the other mechanized equipment involved in a major civil-engineering project. Everywhere two or three hundred men are in constant activity as they go about their work.

In August 1965 the Mattmark Dam presented just such a scene of activity as it neared its final phase of construction. Situated in the Valais Alps in Western Switzerland and overshadowed by the 13,200-foot-high Allalin mountain, the dam was only a few miles from the skiing and mountaineering resort of Saas Fée, a popular place in both summer and winter. On the evening of 30 August a number of tourists and climbers in the area looked down upon 500 men – Italian, Spanish, Austrian and Swiss – at work upon the site while, in the canteen in the construction camp at the foot of the dam, some 60 men who were about to go on night shift were having their evening meal. One of the workers described what happened:

'I heard a roar and looked up towards the mountain and the glacier on its slopes. I saw a section come away from the foot of the glacier. The sound it made was even larger than the engine of my bulldozer. Some of the ice came within 10 feet of me. I saw a truck driven by a friend carry straight on into the course of the slide and disappear.'

Within seconds a part of the Allalin glacier had crashed 1,000 feet, sweeping away a score of trucks and three or four bulldozers and demolishing the camp at the foot of the dam, burying it in ice and rocks to a depth of 80 feet.

For long moments after the terrifying roar ceased and the valley was still again, those who had escaped gazed unbelievingly at the scene. Forty German and Swiss tourists had just been visiting the dam and were waiting to depart. The coach which was on its way to fetch them received a blast of air which rocked the heavy vehicle, while 50 yards in front of it a 30-ton

Above: Scene of the salvage operations which continued throughout the night, but everything hampered the efforts of the rescuers—the weather, the danger of further avalanches, the sheer weight of ice and rock.

Above left: Beneath this waste of ice and rocks 89 people were buried in a matter of seconds when a part of the Allalin glacier roared down the mountain slopes on to the camp of construction workers who were building a dam across the valley below.

Left: Although workers who had themselves escaped death waited patiently for news, it soon became apparent that nobody could still be alive. In fact it was many months before the last of the bodies was retrieved.

bulldozer was flung into the air before being engulfed, with its driver. Two Swiss tourists, a father and son, had, only a few minutes before, been refused a drink at the camp café, which was reserved for workers. They were not far away when the avalanche engulfed it. Now, where the camp had been, there was an incongruous sprawl of white against the grey of the dam and the mountain-slopes scarred with the tracks of bulldozers. The entire area below the dam was piled high with ice and rocks. The débris of a dormitory – beds, clothes, roof and floor – was thrown up on one side of the avalanche; heavy vehicles lay on their sides like toys. On top of one slab of rock stood a small car, its chrome gleaming in the setting sun, apparently undamaged.

Rescue work began at once. Excavators and bulldozers moved in, but the depth and weight of the ice made it impossible for them to do more than hammer at the edges of the avalanche and no more than a handful of bodies was recovered. Experienced rescue teams, police and helpers worked throughout the night and the next day, hoping to find some survivors trapped in a corner of a hut or in a lorry cab. But the evidence of twisted steel girders, which had once formed the frames of the camp huts, and shattered machinery showed that the weight of the ice had crumpled steel plate like tinfoil.

During the days that followed rescue work was continually being suspended for fear of further avalanches. Small landslides that threatened to start a larger one had workers running for cover. It was soon apparent that nobody could be alive under the ice, and relatives waiting at the main camp centre in the nearby village of Saas Amagal were told there was no more hope; and that it might take months to recover all the bodies.

Most of the workers on the dam were Italians, but among them were Swiss, Germans, Hungarians and other nationalities, whose relatives had travelled many miles to wait anxiously for news. The information that their husbands, fathers or brothers were certainly dead was bad enough; to be told that their bodies might remain under tons of ice and rock for many months before they could be decently buried was heartbreaking. They heard the news in stunned silence. For a while some relatives lingered on, in a vain, unreasoning hope. Finally they gave up and returned drearily home.

Everything was against the rescuers. Cloud, a chill wind and driving rain hampered their efforts. Work had to stop when guides reported that the glacier was still in motion. Work was suspended while helicopters dropped small, delayed-action bombs on the glacier in order to dislodge more ice – larger than the first avalanche – which now threatened the site. Rescue work was limited to a small area out of danger, and bodies were recovered slowly. Explosives, mortars and mine-throwers were used to dislodge some menacing icicles; but the unstable, threatening mass of ice remained, and fog and snow made the search even more difficult, while every now and then rescue workers had to run for their lives as rock-falls continued.

Three days after the avalanche only nine bodies had been recovered, although 89 men were missing. Bombs had failed to dislodge the menacing ice above the valley, and Alpine guides climbed the mountain to place high explosives. The weather improved and

recovery work continued – but the better weather brought its own dangers as the ice started to melt and a new collapse was feared.

And so the long, grim story continued. Six weeks later a total of 53 bodies had been found, and it was months before the recovery work ended. Meanwhile the local people were expressing their fears that the glacier had damaged the dam or that a fresh avalanche would occur. The tragedy of the Piave valley was still fresh in everyone's mind. Could the same thing happen here? And why had it ever occurred in the first place?

Scientists inspected the dam itself and pronounced it safe: work continued. As for the avalanche, a small earth tremor the week before was blamed for loosening the vast mass of ice; but there was no real evidence that this was so, and no watch had been put on the glacier which for months had menaced hundreds of men.

Avalanche protection, prevention and warning is a highly developed science in Switzerland, particularly in the resorts popular with skiers and climbers. Most avalanches are caused by special conditions of the snow and may be triggered off by nothing more than a careless, or unlucky, skier. A glacier is normally more stable – although it is, of course, vulnerable through the possible melting of the ice – and has the feature of a landslide rather than a snow avalanche.

It is easy to be wise afterwards, but at any rate it is now clear that a mountain such as the Allalin, which dominated a valley where hundreds of people were working, should have been the subject of continual monitoring to ensure that no danger was threatening. After the avalanche, the glacier and the mountain-side were closely watched, and at one time the valley in the area of the Mattmark Dam was completely closed for fear of further avalanches. In fact none took place, although minor landslides occurred and boulders continued to fall for many days after the disaster. Nobody, however, was hurt, for warnings were given of the instability of the rock and ice-face, and workers were kept out of the path of a possible slide. Such monitoring could have saved the lives of the workers at Mattmark.

The Swiss are also highly skilled and experienced at rescue work. As soon as an avalanche is reported anywhere in Switzerland, a team of scientists from the Davos Institute is mobilized. In addition, rescue teams from the Ski Association, the Alpine Club and the Air-Rescue are called up. The rescue teams of the first two organizations are equipped with long avalanche poles and specially trained avalanche dogs for finding buried victims. In the case of the Mattmark avalanche, ice and rock, not snow, had buried the victims and probing poles were useless. The rescuers used acoustic sounding apparatus to listen – in vain – for any sound of life. Such was the weight of the ice that there was not only little hope of survivors, there was also enormous difficulty in clearing the fall. Earth-moving equipment, bulldozers and other machinery had little effect on the concrete-hard ice, and eventually great pressure hoses were brought in to melt it.

As a result of the demands of the people of the villages below the Mattmark Dam, the dam itself and the neighbouring mountains are now continually surveyed. Warnings will be given if any danger is observed from failure of the dam or movement of the mountain or its glacier.

Turkey, 1966

Every year, throughout the world, there are more than 30,000 recorded earthquakes, but only about 20 per cent of those are felt by people in the affected area. Frequently, only the sensitive seismograph records the fact that there has been a vibration of the earth's crust. These earth tremors occur in all parts of the world, but about 90 per cent of them happen in two great regions. One is the belt surrounding the Pacific Ocean, the other is the mountain chain from the Alps through the Himalayas. Every one of these 30,000-plus tremors is classified, no matter how slight. The worst, judged by loss of life and/or damage to buildings, are termed catastrophic.

An earthquake that easily qualified for this classification devastated part of Turkey in 1966. It was to prove one of the worst earthquakes of all time, certainly since seismology became an exact science.

During Friday, 19 August 1966, the earth suddenly buckled and heaved in a catastrophic series of waves that swept across the Turkish provinces of Erzurum, Mus, Bingol and Bitlis in Eastern Anatolia near the borders of the Soviet Union, Iran and Iraq. The severest damage and the scene of the greatest loss of life was in the vicinity of Varto, west of Lake Van in Mus, about 450 miles east of Ankara, although throughout the four provinces the damage was considerable, some 140 villages being almost totally destroyed.

Varto itself had already had two tremors earlier in the year, one in March which had killed seven persons and another in July which took another 12 lives but now, shaken and riven by the colossal force of this new eruption, the town was left with hardly a building standing and with some 2,000 of its population of 28,000 dead. As is usual with earthquakes, the majority of the deaths were caused by falling buildings and not by the actual disturbance of the earth.

As soon as the news of the disaster was received, men of the Turkish army began to battle towards the disaster area, though for a time were able to make little progress. The roads, poor at the best of times – for the area is remote and primitive – were in many places impassable due to landslides and crevasses and the men had to make many time-consuming diversions. At last they reached Varto and, assisted by police and civilian volunteers, worked throughout the night. The men, digging frantically, had only flares and the cries of the trapped to guide them. They toiled on, extricating families from beneath the ruins of their shattered homes but all too often were met by the still white faces of the dead. Much of the work was done by soldiers from Turkey's 3rd Army Corps based at Erzurum, an ancient hill-top city of mosques and minarets which had also suffered considerably in the earthquake.

Work became easier with the dawn which revealed all

Left : Erzerum, an ancient hill-top city of mosques and minarets, had a population of 70,000 until one of the worst earthquakes of all time reduced it to a mass of rubble, giving it the appearance of a long-since abandoned city.

Far left : Within an hour or two of the earthquake rescuers were digging and probing for bodies in the remains of buildings which were largely constructed of clay and wattle. The Turkish army had a Brigade headquarters well outside the town, and troops were brought to join in the rescue work.

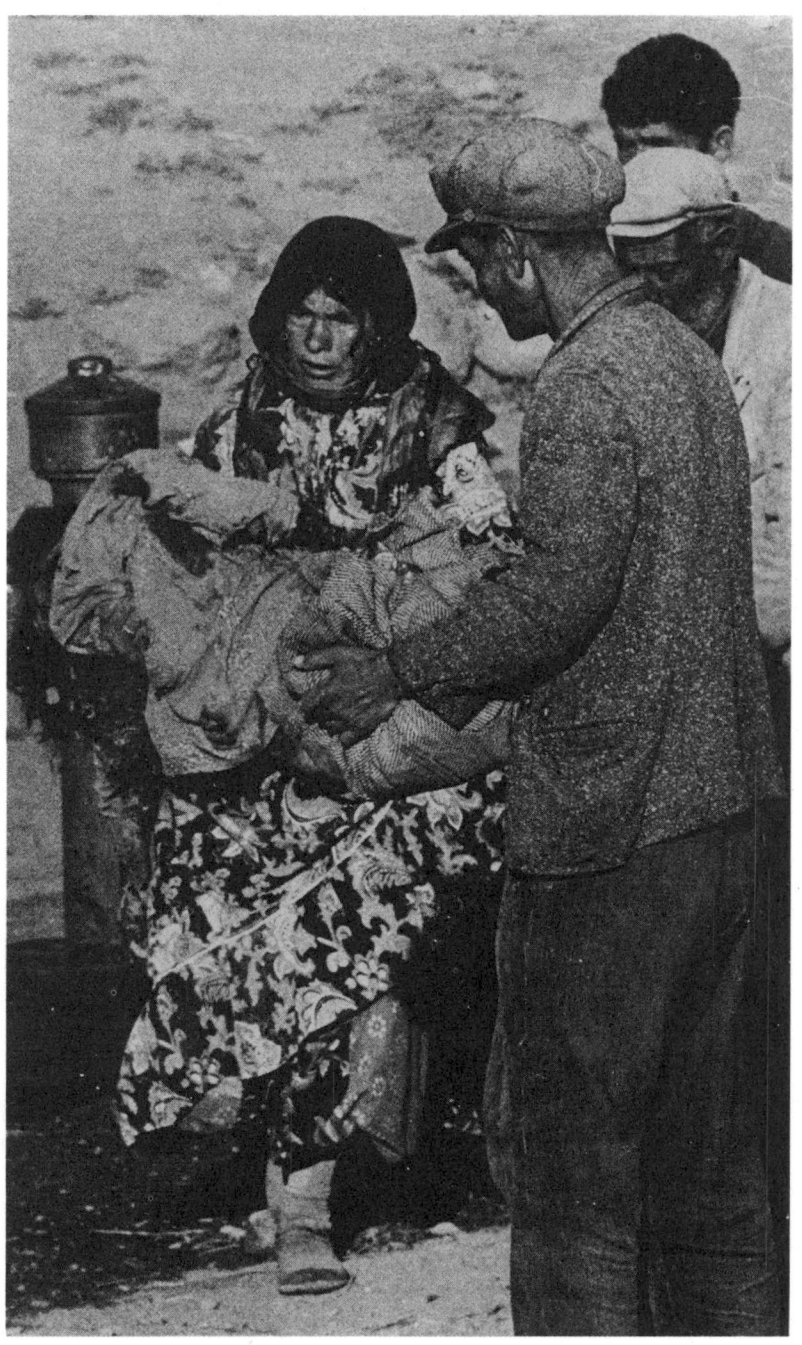

A mother is handed the body of her child, one of the many victims of the town of Varto, which took the full force of the earthquake. She has only a few minutes to wash the body and wrap it in cloth before it is taken to be buried.

Emergency hospitals and field kitchens were soon set up and the starving thousands were more adequately fed. A new threat now emerged: the danger of cholera. Water supplies and sewers had been shattered and wells ruptured or dried up. Great clouds of black flies were settling upon the ruins and the corpses being laid out by the roadside and covered with white bed-linen. A massive anti-cholera campaign was immediately put into operation, more than 200,000 people in the south-eastern provinces being vaccinated in two days – a remarkable achievement. The border with Iraq was closed and patrols on duty had orders to shoot anyone crossing into Turkey from that country who refused to be vaccinated.

National mourning was declared throughout the whole country. All official functions were cancelled, cinemas and night clubs were closed and newspapers printed their titles in black instead of the usual red. Suleiman Demirel, Turkey's Prime Minister, set off on a tour of the devastated areas, going from village to village by helicopter, although tremors were still occurring from time to time. When he arrived in Varto he found that Mustafa Kafanil, mayor of the town, was very angry. 'My people were left to look after themselves for hours when the town collapsed,' he said. 'Please send us picks and shovels so that we may dig for those still buried.'

Demirel promised to do what he could and moved on to the next devastated spot where he narrowly escaped death, for as he moved forward a wall behind him collapsed, crashing on to the spot where he had been standing a moment earlier.

In one village a woman rushed forward and grabbed his arm. 'I have lost three sons,' she sobbed, 'and my fourth child is still buried beneath the school. I could still hear him calling me today . . . please save my last child.' As Demirel turned to comfort her, however, he was cut short by a sudden tremor which made the ground heave and buckle beneath their feet. Most of the crowd which had surrounded him, including the unfortunate woman, ran off and were not seen again.

The vital rescue work went on, men of many nations now working side by side with the Turks. From England came a team of 20 Civil Defence workers, specially trained for such an emergency, who were sponsored by the Oxford Committee for Famine Relief. They were flown out three days after the eruption.

Horrific stories of personal tragedies were soon circulated to the world by eye-witnesses. In one village, a survivor carried the bodies of his wife and four children from his shattered home, washing and then burying them, refusing help offered by sympathetic soldiers. Instead of accepting their aid he pointed to a high mound of rubble which had formerly been a cinema. Following his urging, the troops began to clear the rubble to disclose perhaps the most pathetic incident in the whole terrible disaster. A children's film show had been in progress at the time of the earthquake and some 200 mothers and their children were found dead, many of the latter still cradled in their mothers' arms in a vain attempt to shelter them from the roof that had crashed down upon them. As the troops dug, one young peasant became hysterical with joy for her young daughter was recovered, still alive, after having been buried for 36 hours.

too clearly the terrible nature and extent of the disaster. There were about 2,000,000 people living in the surrounding villages and most of them, dreading new tremors or without homes, were preparing to camp out in the fields. The soldiers began to move into these villages, in some cases finding them virtually ghost towns, lifeless and desolate, with only heaps of rubble to mark where the houses of the peasants had stood. In some villages peasants erected makeshift tents on the pathetic mounds of stones and timbers which had been their homes, as if reluctant to leave the one familiar spot where they had been born and raised.

By Sunday, 21 August, better-equipped rescue teams were getting through, carrying blankets and medical supplies; also a few lorries and trucks arrived with bread and melons for the ravenous people and with 15 Muslim priests who had been sent by the Government to conduct mass burials in the area.

Nearby an old man sat mourning in the rubble of his daughter's home. 'My grandson,' he moaned. 'Dead. And I did not even see him take his first steps.'

There were, of course, other incidents which had happier endings. When troops arrived in one village they found a farmer frantically searching among the ruins of his home. He had already discovered the bodies of his family and had buried them in a makeshift grave nearby, but had still not found his three-year-old son. He begged the soldiers to help him search, saying that he wanted to find the boy to give him a better burial, and several men were detached to help. As they dug, a trunk was unearthed and put to one side until, out of curiosity, one of the soldiers opened it. Curled up inside was the boy, alive, but starving and semi-conscious. The father's joyful shout brought other villagers hastening to the scene and they gathered round, praising Allah for such a deliverance.

When such moving accounts of the disaster reached Britain, the response was immediate. Five British charities joined together under one heading – Disaster Emergency Committee; they were War on Want, Save the Children Fund, Oxfam, Christian Aid and the British Red Cross. Immediate assistance was organized and sent, and an appeal raised more than £250,000 in less than a week. A tremendous amount of supplies were despatched from Britain and other European countries.

As part of its 'Food for Peace' programme, America dispatched $1.1 million in kind to Turkey and its 1966 allocation of aid ($160.2 million) to the country included $15.2 million in straight grants for assistance in emergencies.

A general distribution point for medicines, food and other relief supplies was set up at Varto, the community

which had been hardest hit. It was staffed by nearly 4,000 officers and men, with about 450 vehicles. However, a tremendous argument arose and finally all the relief supplies were taken over, to be handled and distributed by the Turkish Army, following charges in the press that certain civilians were using the supplies for political and personal gain.

The final death-toll was never established. Many bodies had disappeared without trace and so many others had been buried by relatives, that accurate figures were impossible. A conservative estimate was 2,500 dead and 1,500 injured.

Top : In Varto where nearly 2,000 people were crushed by falling buildings, people continued to sleep outside for many days.

Above : Aid was rushed to Turkey from all over the world and temporary camps were set up for the victims.

Aberfan, 1966

On 21 October 1966, the worst disaster of its kind ever to occur in Britain struck the village of Aberfan in South Wales. In a matter of seconds almost an entire generation of children perished under millions of tons of mine waste, rock and sludge, which came pouring down from a nearby tip to engulf the Pontglas Infants' and Junior School, a row of terraced cottages and a farm.

The 'flow slide', as it is called, of relatively dry material came down like an avalanche at 9.30 a.m. just as the children were assembling for roll-call. It had been set in motion by springs building up water pressure in the fissured sandstone underlying the tip and when this pressure was released a second wave of liquid mud and sludge roared down and swamped everything below to a depth of 45 feet, including the school playground; 147 people died, mostly from suffocation, 116 of them children.

Men working on the top of the rubbish-mountain, 800 feet high and over 30 years old, saw the waste below them suddenly fall away with a thunderous noise like a black torrential river before it disappeared from view in thick morning fog. Below, a schoolboy saw it uproot a great tree, then swallow up two other boys trying to escape. 'It hit the school like a big wave, spattering all over the place and crushing the buildings. It was like a dream and I was very scared.'

The first rescuers to arrive were miners from two local collieries who had heard the heavy rumble and abandoned their shifts to help. Faint cries were coming from the fringe of the wreckage which was strewn over half a mile and from parts of the school not completely demolished. One of them, knowing his daughter to be there, ran three miles non-stop to reach the building and was seen still digging in the sludge nine hours later. Other men soon joined them, civil defence workers, police, soldiers and a naval detachment of 200 from the cruiser H.M.S. *Tiger* then visiting Cardiff. All day, and by arc-lights on through the night, 2,500 people or more, including mothers and old women scrabbling at the rubbish with their bare hands, toiled frenziedly to reach the victims. The work was slowed at first for lack of heavy earth-moving machinery and until this arrived human chains were formed to carry buckets of sludge. Meanwhile, in the narrow valley traffic problems intensified as more helpers arrived with their equipment impeded by crowds of idle spectators.

An obscene waste of rock, sludge and shale covers the spot where 147 people, most of them children, died in the Pontglas schoolhouse and its neighbouring cottages and farm-house, when they were engulfed by a 'flow slide' from a nearby coal-tip.

This was small consolation for the bereaved, whose grief was mingled with a strong conviction that the disaster could have been averted. The British National Coal Board stated within hours that the cause was recent heavy rainfall. How could that possibly be known? (In fact, the underlying spring was later found to be discharging at the rate of 100,000 gallons an hour.) What about the warnings that many people were said to have uttered over the years? Why had no action been taken? When the official inquest was held to record the cause of the deaths, one distracted father shouted: 'Murdered by the National Coal Board!'

It was in this mood of grief and anger that 10,000 people assembled on 27 October when 81 children were buried in two long communal graves in the hillside cemetery of Aberfan. Above them was laid an immense cross made up of wreaths sent from all over the world, while throughout Britain flags were flown at half-mast on public buildings at the request of Queen Elizabeth. Two days later, on a completely informal visit to the village with Prince Philip, she was visibly moved on being presented with a small posy by a three-year-old girl 'from the surviving children of Aberfan'.

Not only the villagers, but the nation and Parliament were determined that the truth behind this disaster should be uncovered and a Tribunal of Inquiry was set up immediately under Lord Justice Edmund Davies, himself born two miles from Aberfan and with long experience of mining problems. He was given the widest powers to subpoena attendance and call for documents. Meanwhile, pending its conclusions, an immediate check was ordered on 500 other tips in South Wales, and upwards of 200 were found to be in a dangerous condition.

The Tribunal sat in public for 76 days, heard 136 witnesses and published a Report in August 1967, which prompted Lord Robens, Chairman of the Coal Board, to tender his resignation. It was refused.

A key sentence in the Report read: 'Our strong and unanimous view is that the Aberfan disaster could and should have been prevented.' It went on to record 'ignorance on the part of those charged at all levels with

The *Guardian* said: 'It was a day of the most stark and bitter horror . . . The first two bodies found were little girls. They had just entered the rear playground and their hands were still clasped. A teacher was found dead, her body hunched in a corner by a classroom radiator, protecting a group of children huddled under her. But they, too, were dead'. The bodies of 14 more children were found in another classroom and in yet another those of the deputy headmaster, Mr D. Beynon, and five children clasped in his arms.

Terrible as it was, the death-roll affecting 99 families in the village might have been even higher. Many children in the infant classes were saved with their teachers. Mrs Pauline Evans, one of the mothers, rescued children from a classroom facing away from the tip by climbing in through a window. 'When I got inside there were about a dozen children screaming in a room which had only half collapsed. With the help of a nurse I handed them through the window to safety.' Some lucky ones coming by bus from a nearby village had been delayed by the fog and arrived 10 minutes after the tragedy had occurred.

the siting, control and daily management of tips; bungling ineptitude on the part of those who had the duty of supervising and directing them; and failure on the part of those having knowledge of the factors which affect tip safety to communicate that knowledge and see that it was applied.' Many witnesses, even intelligent ones, 'had been oblivious of what lay before their eyes. They were like moles being asked about the habits of birds.'

Blame rested squarely on the National Coal Board and its local officials. Their failure to devise and implement a tipping policy was the basic cause of the disaster. Sound advice and warnings had been ignored. As early as 1927 Professor Knox had drawn attention in a widely publicized paper to the menace to tip stability from uncontrolled water pressure. In 1939, after the partial subsidence of a tip five miles from Aberfan, the then owners, the Powell Duffryn Company, had issued a document underlining the danger and illustrating it with a description of sub-soil conditions exactly applicable to tip 7 (the disaster tip). In 1944, another tip had partially subsided down the mountainside towards Aberfan, providing 'to all who had eyes to see a constant and vivid reminder that tips built on slopes can and do slip and, having once started, can and do travel long distances.'

Late in 1963, there had been a substantial slide of tip 7 itself, strikingly like the final disaster – and still there were no regular inspections or concern shown by the National Coal Board. The slide was not even recorded in its files. 'For nearly three years', said the Report, that event 'presented a vivid warning of the terrible danger which loomed ahead. But it was a warning which no one in authority ever heeded.'

The Tribunal was at pains to refute charges of outright villainy against officials. 'There are no villains in this harrowing story,' said the Report, and a striking simile made this clear. 'Miners devote certainly no more attention to rubbish tips than householders do to dustbins.'

Now all that was to be changed. The Tribunal considered whether mining waste could be disposed of underground, as in some European countries, but this was considered impracticble. Tips would have to continue and were to be left in charge of the Coal Board. In future they were to be treated as potentially dangerous structures subject to regular inspection under the supervision of the Inspectorate of Mines and Quarries. An Advisory Committee on Tip Safety was set up in 1968 with direct responsibility to the Minister for Power and close links with the Secretary for Trade and Industry. Never again were tips to be treated as mere convenient dumps for rubbish.

Certainly this was consoling and every effort was made to help the inhabitants of Aberfan to surmount the tragedy. A disaster fund amounting, when it closed on 31 January 1967, to over £1,600,000 (with donations from 88,000 people) gave a total of £810,000 to 712 villagers, including £5,000 to each of the bereaved families, and further sums for the needs of injured children and the relief of distress in the village. £250,000 and £200,000 were earmarked for the construction and endowment of a magnificent community centre, with a concert hall, swimming pool and play facilities for children, which was opened by the Queen in 1973. Although the remains of tip 7 were declared safe after the fall, in 1968 the Government deferred to the insistence of the inhabitants and its removal was ordered.

Today there is a new school in Aberfan and the children enjoy a safe life. Only the adults are left with their memories, what might have been if, for instance, the warning of Councillor Mrs Gwynneth Williams had been heeded when she spoke, as recorded in the minutes of the Merthyr District Council Planning Committee in January 1964: 'We have had a lot of trouble from slurry causing flooding at Merthyr Vale. If the tip moves it could threaten the whole school.'

Far left : An aerial view of the village of Aberfan shows the ruined school in the centre with rescue workers labouring around it, while in the background the track made by the sludge as it plunged down the hillside can be clearly seen.

Left above : Miners from two neighbouring collieries were among the first of the hundreds of people who came to help. Throughout the day and night rescue workers, including frantic mothers, scrabbled at the sludge. In the narrow valley traffic bringing help was often impeded by idle onlookers.

Far left below : Among the toiling crowds of rescuers, a policeman raises the blanket which covers the pathetic remains of a child.

Left : In the flower bedecked hillside cemetery of Aberfan one of the surviving children mourns beside the simply marked grave of a friend.

Florence, 1966

In the late autumn of 1966 exceptionally severe weather with gales and frequent cloud-bursts struck almost the whole of Europe, raging for several days from Poland across Germany to the shores of the North Sea, down the coast into Holland and across France and Switzerland. In these areas the storms led to some loss of life, considerable damage and great inconvenience. But in Italy they spawned a disaster.

Because of its physical features many parts of Italy have always been subject to heavy flooding. As distinct from Britain, for instance, where the source of most rivers is only slightly above downstream areas, in Italy they rise in many cases thousands of feet above the plains, in the Western Alps, in the Dolomites to the north-east, and in the Apennines, the central ridge which runs like a backbone down the peninsula. In times of heavy rainfall these rivers, reinforced from innumerable mountain streams, pour down at tremendous speed, bringing with them masses of rock and other débris, particularly in the Dolomites where the higher slopes are very unstable. Certain precautions can be taken, of course, dredging river beds, building up banks, but there are times when Nature mocks these efforts.

Such was the case in 1966. Winds rising sometimes to hurricane force swept through the whole length of Italy and brought with them rains of an enormous intensity. It was as though, after weeks of intermittent rain, the sky had suddenly become an ocean which was now falling in a solid mass on the land.

The deluge lasted for two days and in some places, notably the Dolomites, six months' average rainfall came down in 24 hours. This alone would have flooded the northern plains to a depth of several feet, but at least the water would have been fairly stagnant. However, a swirling, destructive tide was created by the rivers swollen yet further by snow melted by warm mountain winds, which burst their banks and roared down at terrifying speed, sweeping aside great stretches of forest that lay in their path and carrying with them an ever-increasing load of rock and débris.

In Friuli-Venezia-Giulia, the north-eastern province at the head of the Adriatic, scores of farms with all their livestock were overwhelmed by floods, avalanches, mud-slides and giant boulders, while in many villages and towns, Trento, for instance, Merano and Bressanone, the streets were submerged in mud to a depth which swallowed up cars and buses. Long sections of road surfaces were completely carried away, railway lines were cut, bridges demolished and so much wreckage was deposited in river-beds that their level in some places rose many feet above roads running alongside.

For a while the north-east provinces were completely cut off except by radio, and an exhausted messenger who reached Venice over mountain tracks from the Dolomites was regarded as a curiosity. He said: 'For days we have been fighting against the fury of rivers without ceasing.'

One third of Italy was stricken by floods which Interior Minister Taviani described as the worst in history. The Po valley was flooded from both ends, by the overflowing river and by salt water when raging seas broke through dykes protecting the delta. Here one third of the population had to be evacuated, including 12,000 from the island of Donzella lying between two branches of the river.

In Venice sea and sky together produced the worst floods in a thousand years, the main danger coming from the sea. The fate of the city still depended on a system of dykes more than 400 years old which linked the islands separating the Lagoon from the Adriatic. Their upkeep had been neglected, especially during World War II, and early in November exceptionally rough seas combined with gales broke through a section of dyke at the island of Pellestrina. Immediately a wall of water poured into the city, rising to a height of seven

Right: The most extensive floods in Italy for more than 25 years raged throughout the north and central parts of the country in November 1966. In Florence, the Arno broke its banks.

Left: Damage done to the shops on the famous Ponte Vecchio shows chaos caused by the flood waters.

feet in some streets and five feet in St Mark's Square, including the cathedral. For 48 hours, until repairs could be carried out and the flood began to subside, life was completely paralyzed.

The London *Times* correspondent reported that Venice was like a gigantic, half-sunken boat. He should have said 'a torpedoed tanker'. Oil storage tanks used for central heating had burst spreading slicks over the flood, and it was this oil-scummed water that ruined the stocks of 4,000 shops, an immense amount of private property and the ground-floor contents of half the city's hotels. Fortunately there was little damage to art treasures. If the gale had continued for only a few more hours, however, the city centre with its magnificent heritage would have been destroyed. Even so, the damage caused was astronomical.

The shops could be restocked, but it would not be so easy to restore agriculture. Before the war, the fertile area of Tuscany known as the Maremma had been largely marshland ridden by malaria. Much of it had been reclaimed and the malaria eradicated, and a thriving industry started based on dairy farming and the production of fruit and vegetables for export. All this was ruined by the floods which submerged four-fifths of the town of Grosetto lying at the centre of the area, 80 per cent of the livestock was destroyed and damage caused exceeded that in the entire province of Venezia.

The heaviest cultural blow was struck at Florence and this aspect of Italy's disaster above all others caught the horrified imagination of the world. Cradle of the Italian Renaissance, a major shrine of western civilization, with its palaces, magnificent Romanesque buildings, and 40 museums housing many of the world's greatest art treasures, Florence was to suffer the fate of Venice – and worse.

On 4 November, the River Arno traversing the oldest part of the city burst its banks. Normally a man running can keep pace with the fastest flowing river, but on this day the Arno in a huge ungovernable flood surged forward at 40 miles an hour (a film made on the spot shows a car being hurled down the Via Formabuoni at just this speed). For several hours the torrent poured through the city spreading ever wider, flooding buildings and rising in places, including the Cathedral Square and the famous eleventh-century Baptistry, to over 15 feet. The best that anyone could do was to save a few possessions and escape drowning. Twenty-four hours later the deluge began to abate, leaving behind a massive residue of glutinous yellow mud, and in the following days it was possible to start surveying the damage. Final estimates showed 17 people dead, 45,000 homeless (a tenth of the population), 40,000 cars wrecked as well as 18,000 shops, including the workshops of some of the goldsmiths and leather-workers for which Florence was famous.

The loss and damage were enormous. Again, oil from burst tanks, and in some places naphtha, mixed with the flood and added to its destructiveness. Many

Above : Cars lie stranded in the waters as soldiers and other rescue workers use a rubber dinghy to paddle stranded Florentines to safety. More than 100,000 people throughout northern Italy were rendered homeless and the final death roll was 112.

Above right : Renaissance palaces and churches suffered severely. The population took to planks to cross the waterlogged streets.

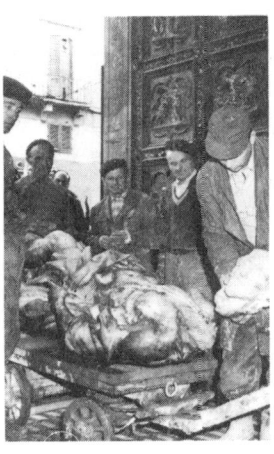

Every job of restoration had to be done as soon as possible to avoid rapid deterioration and speed was achieved by giving crash courses to teams of students and then putting them under the supervision of a single expert. All this caught the attention of the outside world, but naturally the people involved in the 36,000 square miles of Italy that had been devastated were more interested in obtaining credit to get on their feet again. There had been damage in 800 municipalities; 22,000 farms and private homes had suffered; 50,000 animals had been lost, thousands of tractors made useless. Total damage was estimated at £575 million ($1,090 million). The death-roll in all Italy was 112.

In Florence, a fortnight after the disaster, the people were working hard to succour the homeless, start business again and clean up their beautiful city. They were not relying much on government help; they knew official red tape too well. Enthusiasm bursting through his sober prose, the London *Times* correspondent noted: 'Tuscan sturdiness has risen above the ruin of the city's delicate grace.' He noticed an interesting point: it was the 'beatniks', so criticized by their elders as useless drop-outs, who were flinging themselves into relief work with the most astonishing energy. 'Beatniks', he added, 'are better than bureaucrats.'

A year later the people were back in their homes and at work again. Museums, galleries and libraries had re-opened and it was said that: 'The golden city of the Renaissance glitters again.' But despite intensive work on the river-bed and its banks, and the organization of a flood early-warning system, anxiety must remain. Asked what would happen if it rained like *that* again, a city official replied: 'We must just hope that it won't.'

Above : Workers carry the statue of St John the Baptist, by seventeenth-century artist Piemontini, out of the cathedral. It was washed away from its base and decapitated.

Below : The cleaning-up was a massive task, as the mud-strewn square in front of the Church of the Holy Cross indicates.

famous buildings were swamped, among them the Medici Chapel, the San Firenzi Palace, the Casa di Dante, the Capella del Pazzi at Santa Croce and the church of Santa Maria Novella. Six hundred paintings by well-known masters were under water for hours when the basement of the famous Uffizi Gallery was flooded. Totally destroyed at the same time were 130,000 photographic negatives of Florentine art, many of them irreplaceable.

Elsewhere in the city there were other heavy casualties: the entire State Records of Tuscany from the fourteenth century to 1860, nineteenth-century newspaper files – a loss now making a detailed history of the Risorgimento impossible, Etruscan collections in the Archaeological Museum, the musical scores of Scarlatti, the private papers of Amerigo Vespucci (the Italian explorer who gave his name to America) and the earliest painting in Western art, the 'Cruxifixion' by Cimabue (1240–1302).

Worst hit of all were the libraries. For days more than 6,000,000 volumes, a great many of them unique, lay submerged under water and murky sludge in the State Archives and the vaults of the Biblioteca Nazionale, the equivalent of the British Museum Library – a potential loss which would have had a shattering effect on every aspect of future study and research. At once, a massive international rescue operation was set in motion, with experts from all over Europe coming to advise and help. Even so, the restoration, wherever possible, of these works and the paintings was to take years. Owing to the melting of glue used in bindings and size in the paper, many books when salvaged were as solid as bricks. Each volume had to be cleaned, dried, treated with chemicals to prevent fungus and the pages cautiously prised apart. Finally each volume had to be rebound.

Farmington, Virginia, 1968 and Kellogg, Idaho, 1972

'Most coal mines in the United States', said the *New York Times* of 23 November 1968 'are in violation of safety regulations of one kind or another'; and, later, 'The two unavoidably salient facts about the history of coal-mining in the United States are that it has taken an appalling toll of men, and that almost no-one has cared enough to prevent the toll.'

These comments were made after a series of explosions on 20 November 1968, had sparked fierce fires deep below the earth in a soft-coal mine operated by a subsidiary of the Consolidation Coal Company of Pittsburgh. Seventy-eight men died in the disaster in the Consol No. 9 mine, within 10 miles of Monongay, West Virginia, where 361 men had been killed in 1907 in the worst mine disaster in U.S. history. That accident brought into being the U.S. Bureau of Mines, but it was not until 1941 that the Bureau was allowed to send its inspectors on to mine-owners' property except by consent, and by that date more than 12,000 U.S. miners had been killed by underground explosions.

Consol No. 9 mine runs eight miles west and east and six miles north and south, occupying a subterranean coal-seam between the tiny villages of Farmington and Mannington in West Virginia. The mine lies over an oil and natural-gas field. It is in an area where the population has lived from mining for generations and is inured to the possibility of tragedy. When, at 5.40 a.m., an underground explosion shattered the miners' lamp-house where precise records of the men below ground were kept, nobody knew exactly how many were involved. Of the 99 men on the midnight to 8.00 a.m. shift, 21 were known to be safe, but a day of telephone checks to miners' homes finally produced a list of 78 men unaccounted for.

Hours after the initial explosion and the three secondary blasts that followed it, dense black smoke from the fire still rose in a column several hundred feet high over the blasted Llewellyn portal, one of the entrances to the mine, near Manningtree, from which the miners had descended to a depth of 600 feet at midnight.

Rescue attempts had to be put off for fear of further explosions, as teams waited by the mine's nine portals. During the day workmen placed brick-and-concrete seals over two of the ventilation shafts, to try to direct the air flow away from the fire and contain it in one area, thus giving the men a chance to escape to another part of the mine; but at 10.00 p.m. on the night after the first explosion, another blast – apparently of methane gas deep in the mine – blew out the seals, and flames again roared from the wrecked portals, causing a glow in the night sky which apparently could be seen for many miles around.

At the rescue headquarters news of the latest explosion was regarded as a bad sign. Officials began speaking of days and even weeks before conditions would allow rescue teams to enter the blazing mine.

The only hope was that the trapped men had been able to escape into an area remote from that of the explosion – the area from which the 21 men who had escaped the disaster had been rescued or had left after feeling the concussion. But the rescuers were pessimistic. Only two ventilation fans were still working to provide air to the sections of the mine not yet touched by the fire, and it was doubtful if the men could have reached them,

Huge clouds of smoke pour from the Llewellyn Portal of the soft coal mine near Farmington, Virginia. Of the 99 men trapped only 21 escaped.

even using the breathing apparatus kept in lockers in the mine, which could keep a man alive for several days.

As the days passed hopes dwindled. The fire still raged and relations, stoically waiting for news, were kept away from the mine for fear of further explosions. They were kept informed of events by loudspeaker as work continued in the attempt to divert the course of the fire. But another explosion indicated that it had turned west and gone back to the area where the men were believed to be trapped, and fire and smoke belched anew from the main shaft.

The rescue work was almost impossible. The trapped miners would have had about an hour to find a sanctuary from the fire and barricade it with rock, but nobody really thought they could have survived the blast, the heat, and the gas. The only way to stop the fire was to starve it of air, but this would also mean the end of all hope for the men. Ventilation holes were drilled from the surface to the mine galleries in which the men were most likely to be, and a measuring device lowered, but no contact was made.

Further explosions and the appearance of smoke at the Mahan portal, south-west of Manningtree, showed that the fire had swept through the mine corridors into one of the two underground areas where last-ditch rescue efforts were being concentrated. Boreholes were drilled to sample the air in these areas, and the test showed that it was high in methane, low in oxygen and showed some signs of carbon-monoxide. Asked if this could support life, Consol's executive vice president said, after a long pause, 'It is possible'.

This reply was the end of hope for the waiting relations, and on 30 November the mine was finally sealed. 'Cumulative evidence,' the court said as it granted permission, 'shows without question that life is not possible where the men would be located'.

At once the recrimination started. The explosion had undoubtedly been caused by the igniting of the methane gas which was liberated from the coal seam at the rate of eight cubic feet every 24 hours. Consol said the mine was only moderately gassy and that the gas was diluted by the ventilation network. The Bureau said it was extremely gassy. But the tragic fact was that the mine proved to be unsafe.

*   *   *   *

A gas – carbon-monoxide in this case – and a 'callous disregard for safety' also caused the deaths of 91 men in a silver mine in the rugged hills of North Idaho in May 1972. The mine, six miles east of Kellogg with its population of 7,000, is one of the richest and deepest silver mines in the United States, and it has rambled through so much ground that it is now like 'a big apartment house with many rooms'.

The fire which broke out on the morning of 2 May in a worked-out portion of the mine, 3,700 feet underground, was probably caused by spontaneous combustion of old timbers supporting the shafts, where temperatures often exceed 100°F. Smoke from the burning timbers entered the mine's main ventilation-shafts and spread quickly. All day the ominous trail of white smoke which billowed from the mine's exhaust stack indicated that the fire still burned underground, and fresh air was pumped in feverishly. Teams wearing oxygen masks groped through tunnels, sealing off

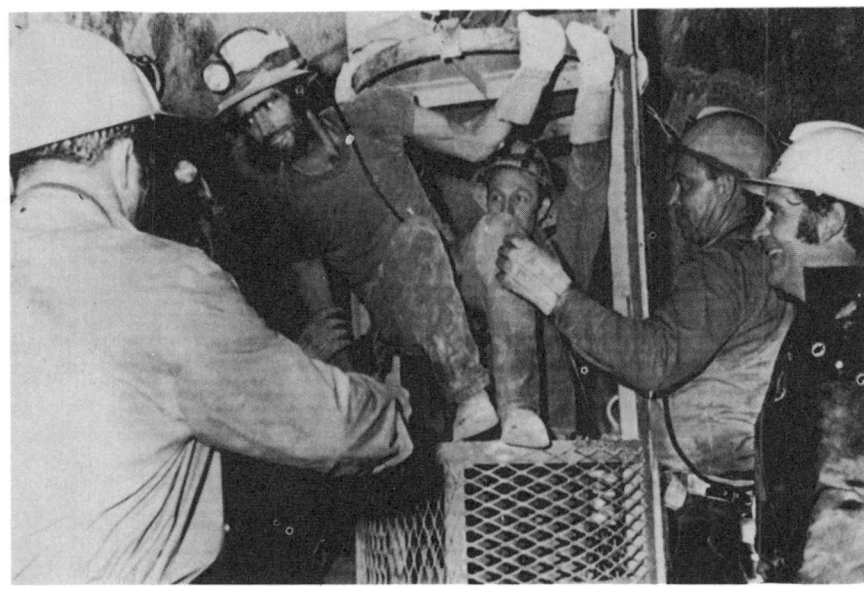

A week after a silver mine in North Idaho caught fire, two young miners were found alive and well, 4,800 feet below ground. Tom Wilkenson, pictured above climbing from the rescue capsule, and Tom Flory were the only two to survive among 93 men trapped in the mine who suffocated when smoke from the burning timbers entered the main ventilation shafts.

empty shafts and searching for men. Although a number of men were brought out, 24 bodies were found and the only hope of reaching further survivors was to penetrate to the lower levels of the mine where men might have fled through some of the hundred miles of tunnels to safety.

While rescuers worked on, now using a capsule, lowered through a narrow shaft at the end of a half-inch steel cable, to take rescue workers down the mine, the inquiry into the disaster had already started. In this area, known as Silver Valley, mining is a way of life. Although the men know the risks of the job – sometimes the mines are so hot that they can only work for half an hour – the rewards are so great that they stay on. Safety training, said some of the men, was non-existent. Survivors did not know how to use the respirators which were provided; and when the elevator operators died through the lack of self-rescue chemical-masks the elevators stopped running, since it was impossible to operate them from above ground.

A week after the fire began searchers found two men 4,800 feet down, and in good health. They said that they and seven others had led the race for safety down the horizontal drift, or shaft, towards a lower level. One of the two men stumbled; the other dragged him into the fresh air of a lower tunnel and went back to look for the others, but all were dead, overcome by smoke and carbon monoxide gas. For a week the two men waited, making their way to the lower levels where they had been told to go in the event of a fire because fresh air would be piped into the shaft. There they had waited. The lights on their hats burnt out, but they were sustained by the food and drink taken from the lunch buckets of the men who had died.

Relatives rushed to the mine with renewed hope, but by now 47 bodies had been found, and hopes for the missing men suffered another blow when a massive cave-in severed lines carrying compressed air. Eventually, on 10 May, the last of the 91 bodies was found and brought out. This had been the largest metal-mine disaster since fire in a mine in 1917 released carbon-monoxide gas which, through lack of breathing apparatus and a shortage of escape aids, killed 163 men in Butte, Montana.

Peru, 1970

In those parts of the world which, through faults in the earth's crust, are particularly susceptible to earthquakes, the people learn to live with the risk and to accept it as part of their lives, in the same way that people who live in the northern hemisphere accept the probability of snow in winter.

Peruvians have been aware of the likelihood of earthquakes throughout the centuries (the recorded history of earthquakes in Peru dates back to the Spanish chroniclers of 1619) and have learned to accept them philosophically. Few, however, imagined such a devastating earthquake as the one which occurred on Sunday, 1 May 1970, affecting 600 miles of the Peruvian coast and a vast hinterland, leaving dozens of towns in ruins or totally obliterated, and killing a staggering total of at least 50,000 people.

Peruvians are ardent football fans, and at 3.00 that afternoon most of them had settled down at home to watch the first match of the World Cup series on television. Twenty-three minutes later, out at sea, 50 miles west of the thriving fishing town of Chimbote with its population of 200,000, the ocean bed cracked and heaved. The earth, tortured by stress, sought to find for itself a more comfortable position, like an old man turning in bed; and all along a 250-mile stretch of coastline, bounded by Trujillo in the north and Lima, the capital, in the south, the ground heaved and shook in a mighty earthquake which achieved an intensity of between seven and eight degrees on the Richter scale. For many hundreds of miles north, south and east across the land, the shock was felt.

At first the magnitude of the disaster was not appreciated. In Lima, people rushed into the streets, but the capital was fortunate and escaped without damage. Not for some hours, for all communications had been cut, was it learned that the full force of this 'act of God' had

Below : Roads winding over the hillsides disappear into the sea of mud and snow, caused by a vast landslide from Mount Huascarán, which has completely engulfed the town of Yungay and most of its 25,000 inhabitants. Only the tips of palm trees can be seen where they once stood in the main square, the Plaza de Armas.

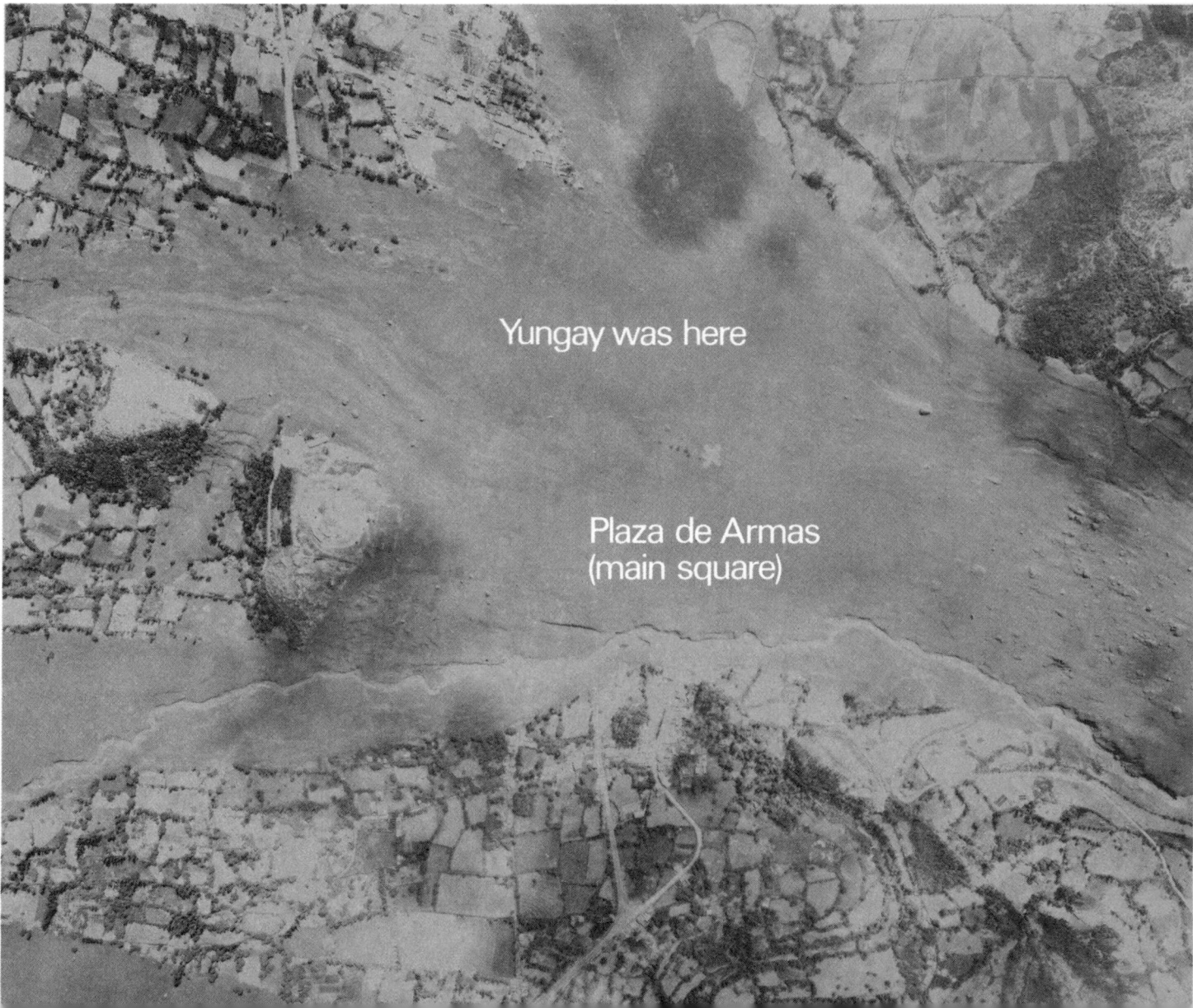

Yungay was here

Plaza de Armas
(main square)

been felt by Chimbote, which lay on the narrow coastal plain, and by the towns and villages inland, in the foothills of the Andean mountain range.

Early reports, even then, seriously underestimated the magnitude of the disaster. They spoke of '250 killed in Chimbote' and '140 in Huaraz'. Slowly the shocking truth emerged: Chimbote lay in ruins and an estimated 2,700 people had died. Casma, Huanmey and all the towns along the coast had suffered to a greater or lesser extent, and unknown thousands of people had been killed. It was quite impossible to discover what had happened inland, in the district of Callejón de Huaylas, a popular tourist area known as the 'Switzerland of Peru', where lay hundreds of mountain towns and small villages.

Radio communication was silenced as a result of damage to the hydro-electric station at Huallanca; roads were impassable through landslides and subsidence; and when, next day, helicopters attempted to reconnoitre, the pilots' view was obscured by mist and huge clouds of dust rising thousands of feet into the air. Nobody knew what had happened in an area the size of Scotland, dominated by the 22,205-foot-high peak of Mount Huascaran.

An hour after the earthquake it was already apparent that the magnitude of the disaster was far greater than the authorities in Lima had originally imagined. The President of Peru, General Velasco, set sail in a naval vessel for Chimbote (for the coastal roads were blocked by landslides, the airfields were unusable and there was always the fear of further tremors) with various senior officials. The next morning he inspected the ruined town and neighbouring Casma and Coishco, and visited the injured at an emergency hospital. Before he returned to Lima – bringing some of the injured on the ship with him – in order to direct rescue operations, he attempted to visit the mountainous Callejón de Huaylas, but it was still impossible.

At Chimbote, General Velasco had found a town in ruins; 60–70 per cent of the buildings were destroyed, the old part of the town, where many buildings were in poor condition, being the worst affected. Almost nothing, whether concrete or adobe, had escaped damage. Despite the efforts of the rescue parties, dozens of people still lay under the rubble, injured and perhaps dying. Many hundreds more camped in the street; some had no roof beneath which to shelter, others were afraid of further earth tremors.

From the Callejón de Huaylas, isolated behind rock-barred roads, confused and unconfirmed reports suggested even worse destruction. Aircraft were still hampered by bad visibility and vast dust-clouds. Eventually an amateur radio operator from within the mountain fastnesses managed to make contact and, with his plea 'Don't forget us!', the world first learned that the town of Yungay and a part of nearby Ranrahirca had completely disappeared under a landslide from Huascaran. Later, the Air Force confirmed this news: a vast wall of mud and snow had swept down the mountainside and, divided by a spur of hills, swallowed the two small towns.

Of Yungay, where the few survivors had managed to flee to the cemetery on the edge of the town, all that could be seen were the tips of the 100-foot-high palm-trees which had stood in the main square. A helicopter

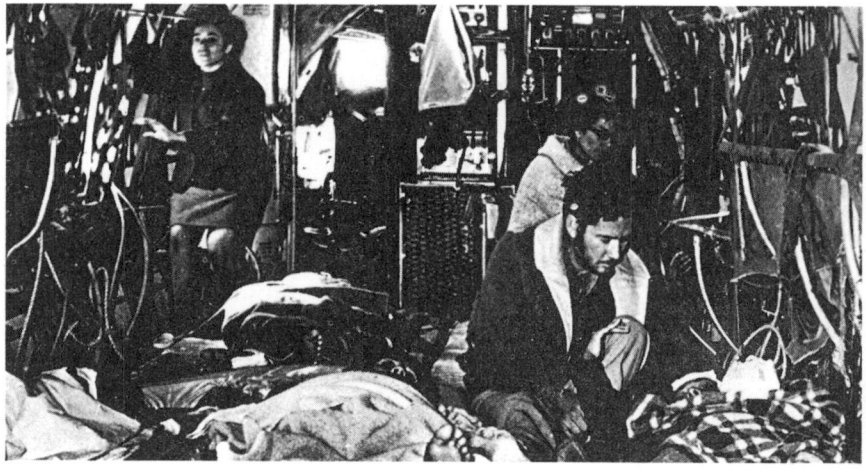

pilot reported that he had counted a dozen more towns, each of between two and three thousand inhabitants, which were now merely heaps of stones.

For two and a half days no helicopter was able to land in the Andes region because of the continuing bad visibility. Until a hundred parachutists managed to land, the only contact with these isolated regions came from the desperate, pleading voice of the radio amateur.

The very size of the area of devastation meant that much of it was inaccessible, and it was many days before relief-workers – their resources stretched to the utmost – managed to reach remoter parts. One of the problems was to know just what supplies were needed. In the mountain villages hundreds of thousands of Indian peasants remained without heating, food or shelter for almost a week. Throughout the area survivors poured on to the passable roads on foot, in carts and lorries, desperately seeking help and refuge. Distracted people made for their nearest towns – often to find, like the two injured village policemen who staggered into Huaraz three days after the earthquake, that the hoped-for sources of assistance were themselves in desperate straits. Without the much-needed help the death-toll mounted steeply.

On the coastal plain rescue operations continued, and relief-workers and aid of all kinds poured in from all over the world. So great was the task in this region, scattered with huge *haciendas* farming sugar or maize, that in Chimbote, despite the all-pervading smell of fish-meal from the damaged factory, five days after the

Above : As rescue workers managed to reach the victims of the villages and towns situated away from the coast, they were taken to the nearest centres for help. This plane-load of victims is being flown from the Huaylas area to the seaside town of Chimbote.

Below : In Lima, some distance from the epicentre of the shock wave, startled and terrified spectators at the Monterrice Hippodrome run out on to the track as they feel the first tremors of the earthquake which was to kill so many of their countrymen.

Disasters create some macabre and bizarre scenes. In Sayan the tremors destroyed a mausoleum, revealing these coffins, which were left hanging precariously in the air.

Previous pages : The will to survive—that remarkable facet of human nature— is clearly illustrated here; inhabitants of a hillside village go about their lives among ruined houses.

earthquake rescue workers could still use their noses to find more and more dead bodies under the rubble. And still the number of dead and dying in the mountain villages in a region some 300 miles long and 120 miles wide could only be guessed at.

The fear continued. From time to time small earth tremors could be felt and when, a couple of days after the earthquake, the ground again trembled, people rushed into the streets in their night-clothes, their hands sheltering their heads. Many preferred to sleep in the open; and the new 'houses', built on the rubble of the old, were made of harmless rushes. Some feared even to sleep, for they had heard that the mountain lakes could break their natural barriers, causing disastrous floods.

This particular horror, however, was spared the luckless population. Although many valley streams turned into torrents, there was comparatively little damage from water; nor did a tidal-wave follow upon the earthquake, the ocean level varying only by a few feet from its normal level.

Rock falls and avalanches, however, had caused major damage. Of these, the greatest and most catastrophic was that which destroyed Yungay and Ranrahirca and killed nearly 30,000 people in these and in neighbouring small towns and villages. On that day, 5,000 feet up in the heights of Huascaran, a party of Japanese mountain climbers visiting this famous mountain resort found themselves the horrified but fascinated spectators of this event. The avalanche began with an almost vertical fall of 10,000 feet of a vast mass of ice and rock, almost a third of a mile wide and nearly two miles long, from the western face of Mount Huascaran. Impelled by the two-mile height of its initial fall, this gigantic mass then poured down the valley at a speed estimated at nearly 250 miles an hour. The million cubic yards of ice that had become detached from the highest point of the glacier then set another 24 million cubic yards in motion.

In the path of this unimaginable terror lay small villages and the towns of Yungay on the west and Ranrahirca on the east of a mountain spur. Above Yungay, a 600-foot hill was swept up in the path of the avalanche and deposited on the other side of the valley. This and the unfortunate mountain towns absorbed the force of the huge landslide. Other rock- and earth-falls blocked roads, particularly in the coastal areas

where the road-side slopes were steep, dammed the River Santa at Recuhat, and destroyed countless houses. Many of these slides took place in stages, giving the threatened population time to flee: but in Yungay and Ranrahirca there was small hope of escaping the roaring death . . . and only eight years after Ranrahirca and seven mountain villages had been the previous victims of the Nevado de Huascaran's monstrous ice-cap, when a part of it broke loose killing 3,000 people.

It took many weeks for the people of the devastated regions to recover from the effects of 'the giant's hand', as one Indian peasant called it, and the villages in the steep Andean valleys, tucked under the towering cliffs, suffered most severely through their sheer inaccessibility. Freezing rain made it even more difficult for troops and parachutists to reach the population, and thus nearly as many died from the aftermath of the earthquake as during the event itself.

In the valleys life came back to normal more quickly. The 'uncomprehending silence', which one observer reported as brooding over shattered towns, turned to the noise and bustle of people trying to rebuild shattered lives. And when, on 2 June, Peru beat Bulgaria in a World Cup match, people even found the heart to cheer, and red-and-white Peruvian flags were planted to wave proudly over pathetic heaps of rubble that had once been homes.

Thousands of people without homes tried to organize new lives – and many realized they would be homeless for a long time. For many, too, there were no more jobs. Young people with knapsacks took to the roads, making for the sugar capital in the north, Trujillo. 'What is the point', one asked 'of rebuilding here?' And indeed with the trade of the towns disrupted and with little, poorly paid, work available on the *haciendas*, their reactions were reasonable. Once again it was the mountain peasants, who knew no other way of life, who suffered most harshly.

It seemed that the whole of Peru and half the world were anxious to help in the vast task of rehabilitation. Peruvian authorities encouraged visits from journalists and notable foreigners who would tell the rest of the world what had happened, and thus recruit much needed aid of all kinds.

Where any disaster is concerned the question that is always asked afterwards is: 'What could have been done to prevent it?' Where natural events are concerned, particularly in the case of one so overwhelming as the Peruvian earthquake, the answer must be 'Very little'. Most of man's protection must lie in warnings which are the result of constant vigilance. Hurricane, flood and avalanche warnings are now commonplace in many parts of the world; and even if they are sometimes too late, they help to save many lives. Predicting an earthquake is more difficult, but the steady series of major disasters to which the world is prone makes it apparent that research into both the prevention and warning of earthquakes is of vital importance.

The imminence of an earthquake can sometimes be detected by continuous monitoring of the fluctuations of the earth's magnetic field, its seismic activities and the strain and tilt of the earth's crust. Just as a threatened ice-fall can be safely triggered off, under controlled conditions, by the use of explosives, so explosives and drilling techniques could be used to provoke land movement and unlock dangerous faults under strain. So far, however, this is a science which has made few practical advances and 'the giant's hand' continues to crush and maim throughout the world.

Many lessons were learned from Peru's disaster. It became apparent that destruction would have been less if buildings had been better sited or better constructed. In the area affected by the worst of the earthquake, the damage was caused mainly to buildings which were of poor quality, unsuited to the type of soil on which they were constructed, and erected on badly laid foundations. The earthquake opened cracks in the saturated sand and clay soils and increased the level of underground water; while rock-sited foundations were not so seriously affected. In Huaraz, for example, the older part of the town, built on the alluvium of the river, suffered the greatest damage; the new part, however, built on rock brought down by a landslide in 1941, was less damaged. Mud-brick buildings proved to be less equal to strain than brick or concrete, but in some cases concrete buildings collapsed because of the poor materials used in their construction.

These lessons are learnt at a fearful cost. In the final analysis, man's puny efforts are all useless when Nature decides to unleash the full fury of her powers.

From all over the world help was rushed to Peru. Although for many days it was impossible to reach some of the mountain villages, made inaccessible by reason of weather or impassable roads, the rescuers struggled on through conditions which were sometimes hazardous in the extreme.

Below: Eventually even the most remote villages were reached, supplies of all kinds were brought in and homeless people were helped to erect tents and provide themselves with temporary shelters.

The Club Cinq-Sept, 1970

Big fires involving heavy loss of life are inevitably followed by official inquiries, accusations of criminal neglect, recriminations, sackings and promises of immediate reforms so that disaster cannot happen again – until it does happen again, somewhere else.

Absolute security against fire is almost impossible to create. Fire-prevention literature outlines three basic factors on which the outbreak of fire depends, known as the 'fire triangle': the presence of fuel, sufficient heat to ignite the fuel and enough oxygen to support combustion. The protection of life and property from fire is said to depend on the limitation as far as possible of combustible fuels, the sub-division of buildings into areas small enough to be controllable and building designs which enable people to be quickly and safely evacuated.

The facts of everyday life are different. The presence of 'combustible fuels' is universal and 'sufficient heat' can be represented by a single cigarette-end or burning match. The mere idea of safe evacuation from some buildings must raise a hollow laugh. The danger of disastrous fire remains widespread especially when coupled with the tendency to neglect possibilities thought to be remote.

It was no more than this which led to the deaths of 146 young people (142 immediately, four later in hospital) in a club near the little town of St Laurent du Pont, France, on Saturday, 1 November 1970. The club was called the Cinq-Sept and had only been open a few months. It was housed inside a large shed cheaply built of breeze-blocks with a corrugated iron roof, an arrangement which positively invited disaster. At ground level there was a dance-floor and beyond it a restaurant with bar. Pillars supporting the roof were wound with flimsy coloured materials and around the floor were simulated grottos with archways, walls and ceilings made of plastic (expanded polyurethane). Above, a gallery reached by a single spiral staircase ran right round the building and this, too, was divided into cosy alcoves constructed in the same manner.

The young people present on that night came from all over the region, from Grenoble, 20 miles away, from Aix-les-Bains and Chambery especially to hear an up-and-coming pop group from Paris called 'Storm'. For a club of its size, French fire regulations stipulated three access doors and two emergency exits. On that night the only way to get in or out was by the main entrance controlled by a spiked turnstile too high to be vaulted. A second entrance had been blocked up during building operations and the third had been locked to prevent gate-crashers. Neither exit was illuminated; one was hidden behind a screen near the bandstand, the other had chairs in front of it. Both were locked and the keys were held separately by two of the three managers.

Around 1.40 a.m., in the hilarity backed by the rhythmic pounding of 'Storm', a careless youth in one of the upper alcoves dropped a lighted match on a cushion stuffed with plastic foam. The cover caught fire and melted the foam which gave off toxic fumes. The youngster and friends tried to beat out the fire, but had to stagger back. Before they could breathe freely again, flames were roaring up out of control. Said one survivor later: 'People in the gallery were enveloped by flames. The whole ceiling seemed to catch light. It all happened so quickly. Everything was just one blazing mass.'

There was a surge for the spiral staircase. Thirty people managed to escape through the turnstile. Among the last to get out was Mlle Joelle Dandry, the cashier. A big fire can create a freak turbulence of extraordinary power. Now, from the gallery, 'a huge flame leaped into the air and suddenly plunged to the main floor like a whirlwind. I tried to save myself,' said the cashier. 'Suddenly I felt my hair burning. Everybody was screaming. Then I could hear nothing except the sirens of the fire-engines arriving. I'm sure I was the last person to leave that unimaginable hell alive.'

M. Gilbert Bas, 25, the only surviving manager, was in his office when a flashing alarm told him there was trouble. 'I thought that, as sometimes happens in an establishment like ours, it was simply a fight.' Then he heard screams of 'Fire!', ran to the dance-floor and saw 'the huge sheet of flame. It burned all of them in a matter of seconds. Those that got out after the big burst were walking torches.'

The whole building was a cauldron of flame and highly toxic smoke from the melting plastic. One

Below : A crowd of young people sit listening as a pop group plays at the Club Cinq-Sept. This picture was taken just a week before the tragic fire which killed 146 boys and girls, who must have been sitting in just such a way listening to the up-and-coming group from Paris called the 'Storm', in what were to be the last few minutes of their lives.

barman wrenched aside the chairs blocking an emergency exit and with a few others battered his way out through the door. A youth with particularly quick reactions who had escaped through the turnstile with his girl friend came back round the outside, heard a girl screaming behind one of the locked doors, broke through it and released her. Behind her he saw a mass of people with groping, outstretched arms, already dead. 'If the emergency exits had not been closed', he told reporters, 'very many people would have got out alive.'

Meanwhile, another serious deficiency had taken its toll. Extraordinary for a club isolated by a mile from all other buildings, there was no telephone at the Cinq-Sept, and Gilbert Bas had to waste precious minutes driving into St Laurent to raise the alarm. When the firemen finally arrived their first sight as they ran to break in was the body of a boy impaled on the spikes of the turnstile. The corrugated roof had melted in the heat and inside were 142 charred corpses. Some couples were found on the floor in each other's arms, some were still sitting along the walls where they had been overwhelmed. According to doctors who examined them later, many had died of asphyxiation before the flames reached them. 'It was a terrible sight', said one fireman. 'They didn't have a chance. The place went up like a matchbox.'

It was some hours before the work of removing the dead could begin. With the daylight, groups of young people, many of them friends of the victims, gathered to watch in stunned silence as ambulances transferred stretchers with anonymous burdens to the town hall, now serving as a mortuary. For them it was an act of respect; not so for those that are always drawn to disasters, who now poured in, jamming the roads from St Laurent until a force of 200 men was brought in to control them.

In the morning all shops were closed and the streets of the town were shuttered as relatives waited with dull foreboding by the town hall to identify personal posses-

Above : The simulated grottoes made of expanded polyurethane, and the flimsy materials twined round pillars were largely blamed for the total destruction caused by the fire. Highly inflammable, they helped to reduce the Club Cinq-Sept to this twisted shell within minutes.

Below : Rows of coffins were laid out in the town hall of St Laurent du Pont. Here a short ecumenical service was held amid terrible scenes of grief.

sions carefully collected in envelopes marked only with the sex of the person concerned – jewellery, key-rings, bits of charred clothing. Most of the bodies had been burned beyond recognition.

Next day, rows of coffins were laid out in the town hall among a mountain of flowers which included wreaths from President Pompidou, M. Chaban Delmas the Prime Minister, and foreign governments. Then, in a room too small to hold all the mourners, a short ecumenical service was held amid terrible scenes of grief.

On Tuesday, 4 November, the Mayor and the Secretary-General of the *Département de L'Isère* were relieved of their duties by the French Cabinet. Eight months later, in June 1971, the Mayor and three building contractors were convicted of causing injury through negligence and given short suspended sentences. Gilbert Bas, manager of the club, received a two-year suspended sentence for manslaughter.

An official inquiry set up in Grenoble revealed a series of omissions and evasions extending to every department of the local administration responsible for enforcing national building and safety regulations, some of which had become law as recently as 1969. Planning permission had been given for the construction of the club, but the finished structure had not been inspected by the Building Safety and Fire Departments, as the law required. Regulations regarding exits, internal firefighting equipment (totally absent at the Cinq-Sept) and the incorrect materials used in decoration had not been noticed, and the club had opened without permission from the Mayor. It was said that the Police Chief of Grenoble and other high officials had been guests at the club only three days before the fire, and nothing amiss had been noticed.

In France, nearly 30 years later, an almost identical chain of cause and effect, official negligence and private indifference had led to the same sickening disaster as at the Cocoanut Grove in Boston – even down to the probable cause, a lighted match.

The Joelma Building, 1974

São Paulo is Brazil's largest city. Every 24 hours, on average, the population of 8,000,000 is swollen by 1,000 new arrivals from all over the country, 60 new buildings are completed and room has to be found for 300 more cars, the property of residents. It has the phenomenal expansion rate of five per cent a year and already produces nearly 60 per cent of Brazil's industrial wealth. With as many skyscrapers as there are quills on a porcupine, São Paulo, it has been said, is constantly dismantling and rebuilding itself. Construction never ceases, road-drills are never silent and there is so much dust that the inhabitants say it is the only city on earth where it is quite possible actually to see the air you breathe.

At the best of times, São Paulo is a noisy and somewhat dangerous place to live in, with high infant mortality, a high rate of crime, bursting with the ruthless and often anti-social energies of first-generation city-dwellers on the make.

But on the morning of 1 February 1974, something else was added. Pandemonium gripped the city when it was realized that one of its newest office blocks, the 25-storey Joelma Building was ablaze. The first six floors of this building were taken up by a car park. Above that were the offices of the Crefisul Bank and on the upper floors were more offices. In all there were about 650 people in the Joelma when fire broke out on the 11th floor (perhaps in an over-heated air-conditioning vent) and spread upwards through the building with terrifying lightning speed.

About 300 who were below the seat of the fire escaped without difficulty into the street, but within minutes the remainder were trapped. In that time 70 or so braved the flames already engulfing them and stampeded down the stairs, but only a few reached safety. A porter on the tenth floor saw them come, before he, too, made a dash for freedom. 'Men were tearing off their ties and shirts', he said later. 'I saw women stripping off their clothing and everybody was shoving like mad to get down. When someone fell, the mob trampled over him; I saw a young girl trampled to death. On the eleventh floor I saw people run through a barrier of fire with their hair and clothing in flames. Others just stood there petrified and did not move until the flames swallowed them up.'

As firemen arrived with ladders too short and hoses not powerful enough to reach the upper storeys, it soon became only too clear that the city authorities had not given proper thought to the intricate problem of fire precautions in tall buildings. As the Fire Chief, Colonel Ribeiro, said later – after being sacked as a scapegoat – they had quite simply shown lack of interest.

The result now was that the fire could not be contained, and those still alive in the building had only two choices: to jump to death from the windows or scramble up on to the flat roof. Even there the heat and smoke were intense and people could be seen running helplessly to and fro with outstretched arms, crying out for rescue, but for a long time rescue was impossible. For two hours a bunch of helicopters hovered overhead, unable to land; when the pilots tried to, the paint peeled off the doors and there was an imminent risk of the petrol tanks exploding. All they could do was to drop cartons of milk, to ease throats and lungs scorched by the fumes, and lower ropes which in desperation some people tried to climb, mostly to fall to their deaths. Eventually, when the fire had abated, the planes were able to touch down and a little band of blackened half-crazed survivors was picked up, perhaps as many as 80 of them in all.

Meanwhile, the flames raged on unchecked. Incredibly, live television coverage had been allowed by the authorities and a densely-packed throng of sightseers had been drawn to the scene from a wide area, blocking approach roads with their abandoned cars and causing serious problems for the rescue services. Hypnotized, they watched as people flung themselves from upper windows to escape the flames or clung to ledges till their strength gave out and they heard one man scream 'Goodbye, goodbye...' as he fell.

Above and right: The Joelma building in São Paulo was one of many skyscrapers in that grandiose modern city. But when the building caught fire, the ladders and hoses of the fire-fighting appliances proved to be woefully inadequate, and 227 people were suffocated or burnt to death, or died in a frantic attempt to leap to safety.

Intrepid rescuers with equipment like harpoon-guns fired ropes from nearby buildings, then crawled across to ferry individuals, pick-a-back, one at a time to safety. One fireman, José Rufino, saved 18 people in this way, then, half across with the nineteenth, collided with a man falling from a higher floor. The passenger was wrenched from his back, but Rufino carried on, and survived.

Outside, at street level, where onlookers jostled for a better view, firemen held up a large placard: 'Courage, we are with you.' But the words were almost meaningless, though no doubt the men were just as horrified at their inability to help as the priest, found later in tears, who said: 'I was not able to get there in time to give the last rites to any of them.'

It took four hours to get the fire under control, by which time the upper floors were a sodden, twisted shambles and the death-toll had mounted to 227, many of the bodies being reduced to ashes in temperatures estimated to have reached 700° Centigrade.

There was an inquiry amid a spate of stories suggesting sabotage. A telephonist at the Crefisul Bank said she had received an anonymous call about a bomb that had been planted (then why had she not reported it?). Firemen found a badly charred drum of paint-thinning fluid on the 11th floor near the spot where the fire had probably started.

More important than such conjectures were lessons for the future in a city cluttered with similar tall buildings. The first and most obvious deficiency was the provision of only 13 fire-stations with a total of 1,300 men to serve a population of 8,000,000. This was a serious matter, especially in the context of safety over the whole city area. Would ten times the number of stations and men have coped any better with the Joelma fire? It seems unlikely. Fires in skyscrapers must be contained from inside rather than extinguished from outside, and in their failure to plan for this possibility it was the city authorities who were to blame.

The Mayor, Miguel Colasuonno, who was an engineer by trade, put his finger on the trouble when he said that the fire had spread rapidly through the upper floors because large amounts of inflammable plastic had been used in interior paintwork and flooring, and that new regulations to deal with the problem of fire in high-rise buildings must come into force as soon as possible. These should have included the compulsory installation of fire-proof floors in skyscrapers, the use of non-combustible materials throughout interiors and the provision of specially-insulated emergency stairways.

*   *   *   *

All this was standard practice in the U.S.A. where what might have been a terrible disaster was averted on Saturday, 28 July 1945, just because of such precautions. On the morning of that day a B-25 Mitchell bomber weighing 10 tons crashed in dense fog into the Empire State Building between the 78th and 79th floors (24 floors below the top), battering a hole 18 feet by 20. One engine went crashing like a thunderbolt through the entire building; the other fell down a lift shaft. Then the petrol tanks exploded with a roar, throwing up a spear of flame 100 feet high and showering the outer walls with blazing petrol. Inside, more petrol set

the 79th floor ablaze. But even there, where the danger was greatest, of 20 women attending a Catholic Welfare Conference 11 were able to escape down the fire-proof emergency stairs. Again, on the 80th and 86th floors, where 60 sightseers were enjoying the view from an observation lounge, the same story was repeated and nearly everyone escaped, panic being avoided because the stairs, spelling safety, were known to exist.

The experience of two men on the 80th floor was typical: 'We were lifted three feet out of our chairs', said one, 'and thrown on to the floor. I thought it was a Japanese bomb.' With a girl lift operator who had been badly burned, they first tried to reach the stairs by a corridor and when they found it full of flames they hacked their way through a thin office wall to another corridor leading to the stair-head.

The fires in the whole building were got under control comparatively quickly and only 14 people lost their lives. Luckily, it was a Saturday and the Empire State, which normally houses 25,000, held only a few hundred. But if it had been like the Joelma with no proper escape system, there is no doubt that the result would have been very different.

In São Paulo fire precautions had been badly neglected with, as emerged after the disaster, almost criminal folly. The neglect was highlighted by the Director of the Police Technical Department when he revealed that his laboratories were not even capable of testing and developing fire-proof materials: help would have to be sought from abroad. The last word was spoken by a highly-placed Brazilian architect who agreed with what the Fire Chief had said about official lack of interest and added that this was due to the character of his countrymen. According to him, they were always happy to draw up grandiose plans, which they did very well, and the proof of this was São Paulo itself with its motorways stacked ingeniously one above the other, and the fantastic conglomerate of skyscrapers. When it came to details such as fire precautions, they were not so interested; these, they tended to think, would look after themselves.

For Brazilians, *The Towering Inferno* is a vivid portrayal of the results of such negligence. The film follows only too closely the tragedy in São Paulo.

Within minutes after the start of the fire the only way out was via the roof where there was a helicopter landing stage. But it was two hours before the heat had abated sufficiently for the machines to land and only 80 people, half-crazed with heat, were rescued.

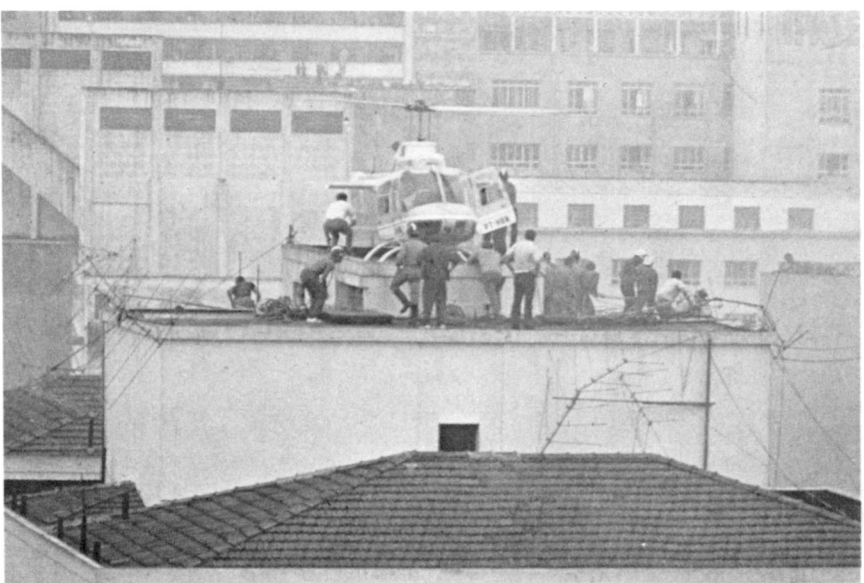

Turkish DC10, Ermenonville Forest, 1974

Flags of 18 nations, topped with black crepe, fluttered over the scene. A thousand people, many still suffering the shock of their bereavement two months earlier, stood in silence. They were only a tiny fraction of those who had wanted to be there, at Thiais, near Orly airport. The others could only mourn in their native lands, hundreds, thousands, of miles away.

Few could understand more than a small part of the ceremony. It was opened in English by the Vicar of the Anglican Church in Paris. After him came Catholics, Jews, priests of the Armenian Christian Church, Mullahs from Turkey, Morocco and Pakistan, Buddhist priests from Japan, and a holy man from India.

Perhaps the words of M. Achille-Fould, French Aviation Minister, were the most moving: 'The world-wide family of all in aviation is in mourning. May the earth of France lie easily on those we commit to it. France, too, looks on them as her own children.' It was France's epitaph on history's greatest air disaster.

Though a few bodies had been identified and handed over to relatives for burial, most of the staggering, tragic, total of 346 instantly killed men, women and children were being committed to a foreign grave on this spring Thursday of 1974 – 9 May. The actual burial would not be public; that would take place in a few days' time, using heavy earth-moving machinery.

The worst air disaster in history had taken almost twice as many lives as any single accident before. At the time of writing, it still holds that unenviable record. It was what every airline had dreaded: an accident to a fully loaded, wide-body jet. As the mystery unfolded, grief gave way to bitterness. It *need* not have happened; it *should* not have happened. Who was to blame?

The DC10 of Turkish Airlines had flown in from Turkey and made a perfect landing at Orly Airport near Paris. Weather conditions were good on that early spring Sunday morning, 3 March, and the pilot taxied briskly up to the terminal buildings; almost immediately passengers started to embark and fill up his lightly-loaded aircraft, while those who had just landed were asked to stay on board. According to airline officials, 216 adult passengers and one infant embarked at Orly.

The need to get more than 200 people on a flight for which they had not booked meant that documentation was hasty. It seemed over the next harrowing hours, that not all of the passengers had been listed; at least one man was travelling on a passport not his own, and some were using other people's tickets.

The plane re-started its three giant General Electric jets, and taxied along to the take-off runway at a few minutes past noon, carrying 335 passengers and 11 crew. In two minutes the DC10 was off, climbing powerfully into the bright sunny sky of France, the three engines – one under each wing, a third in the tail – belching vapour and exhaust. The time: 12.30 p.m.

The plane climbed fast on a wide eastern sweep to skirt Paris. Flight plans ordained that when eventually it turned to its north-west course for London it would be at 16,000 feet. Controllers of France's Northern Air Region watched it on their radar screens as it reached a height of 13,000 feet.

And then, quite simply, the plane vanished from all screens.

At 12.35 it crashed into a shallow depression within the Ermenonville State Forest north-east of Paris.

On that warm Sunday there were many people strolling along the numerous wooded pathways, but although the huge aircraft ploughed a thousand-yard furrow through the trees, shearing them off before kinetic energy was expanded and the wreckage had come to rest, no-one on the ground was hurt.

It had happened without any warning. Some claimed to have seen the aircraft explode in the sky; others had seen it under apparently perfect control, seeming to make an approach towards some not-too-distant airfield. Others, more expert, had seen it in difficulties at a low altitude, trying to drag its nose up from a shallow dive.

Thirty-five minutes after the crash, rescuers arrived by helicopter. One glance showed their journey had been in vain. Little fires, like those of an Indian village, were separated by hundreds of yards, indicating where parts of the engines and fuel system had ended. Bits of fuselage and the débris of human possessions were strewn over the ground; tatters of clothing festooned the branches of trees which had escaped destruction. No one could have survived for an instant.

Meanwhile, at London's Heathrow Airport, there was alarm as the DC10 became first late, then overdue. Anxious relatives awaiting the return of more than two hundred British passengers, demanded news. When it came, an elderly man collapsed, a young woman attacked the press with a stiletto-heel shoe and a man smashed press cameras. Mingled with the horror were elements of desperate hope, total incomprehension.

The worst disaster in air history left a trail of débris of all kinds scattered through the woods of the Ermenonville State Forest. The bric-a-brac of human lives is mingled with the remains of the crashed plane.

Overleaf: The doorway of the crashed DC10 of Turkish Airlines. Decompression resulting from the failure of the rear cargo door was revealed as the probable cause of the accident which killed 346 men, women and children.

Which of the London-bound passengers had transferred to the Turkish airliner? How could a plane, so fast, so safe and foolproof, just plunge to earth on a clear spring day? But it had.

The 'black box', which had automatically recorded all the aircraft's movements, was recovered intact, but it merely stated that the plane had reached 13,000 feet and then dived to a lower altitude before crashing – a fact already well-established. Ground controllers reported having heard a few seconds of excited, unintelligible speech before total silence when the DC10 left their radar screens. This suggested a disaster at 13,000 feet, and not an incomprehensible exercise in hedge-hopping.

The most popular theory was a bomb, but aircraft authorities were adamant that all passengers and luggage had been screened.

A fortnight later: the probable truth. Bodies had been found, still strapped in their seats, a full seven miles from the rest of the wreckage. Then the aircraft's rear cargo door was found, nine miles away, and this seemed to be the missing clue.

Two years before, in Canada, the faulty latch on a DC10 cargo door had nearly caused a similar tragedy. The door had opened suddenly in flight and this, for a reason which was not at first clear to the highly skilled crew, seemed to jam a number of the controls. Somehow they nursed it back to base.

The United States Federal Aviation Administration gave instructions for doors to be modified so that it was impossible for them to open in flight. Further recommendations were made to the manufacturer, McDonnell-Douglas of California, that the floor of the passenger compartment, immediately above the hold, should be strengthened and air vents made in it. This expensive modification would have to be for subsequent aircraft: meanwhile, the doors must be corrected; and McDonnell-Douglas passed on these comparatively simple instructions to all its customers.

Comparison with the near-disaster over Canada proved that the Turkish plane's cargo door had opened at 13,000 feet. This, as over Canada, had caused instant depressurization of the lower, cargo compartment. As in every section of a modern airliner, the cargo compartment was kept at an air pressure approximating to that on the ground; and when this pressure dropped suddenly the light passenger deck immediately above it collapsed. In the more serious Turkish case it dragged seats down into the hold, sucking a number of them in which occupants were still strapped out of the open doorway.

At this point the pilot might have been able to dive safely to a lower altitude – but the control cables of a DC10, from flight deck to tail, run under the passenger deck, and in the Turkish aircraft these were instantly and completely jammed. Helpless, the aircraft fell into a shallow dive which no pilot could have righted.

The recovered door showed that a vital flange, part of the safety modification, was missing. There was no doubt that it had been fitted but no certainty as to when it had come adrift. A cargo handler at Orly was for a time under suspicion of not having closed the door before take-off and furthermore of having been unable to read the instructions printed on it, but he and the airport authorities were able to dispel this suspicion.

Exactly a year later, a group of English people were taken to the scene by a French friend. The whole area had been enclosed by a high fence, and they had to be let in by the *Garde Forestiere*. They looked around them in horror at the wreckage, the minutiae of human tragedy, the bits of clothing, luggage and the rest. It would take years to retrieve all this, and the French government had decided the job should not be done by souvenir hunters, hence the enclosure.

'Yes', said the *Garde Forestière*, 'he might have made it, you know, that pilot from Turkey, he might have saved many lives because the place where he came down was fairly clear. But, *hélas*, he hit this rocky eminence here. And the plane simply broke up, wings, everything, going everywhere. That is why the felled bit of Ermonenville Forest is so large, why the fence has to be so long . . .'

Almost two years after the tragedy the first of many claims from dependents and relatives of those who died was settled in an American court. Others, of course, would follow. The sum awarded was large; as much punitive, some said, as compensatory – in order, perhaps, to impress upon all concerned that something of this sort should never, could never, happen again.

The huge aircraft ploughed a thousand-yard furrow through the trees of the woods in which it crashed, shearing them off short and starting a number of fires. The woods are a popular place for weekend strollers, but on that Sunday afternoon nobody on the ground was killed.

American Mid-West, 1974

For the people of the Gulf and Mid-western states of the U.S.A. the words 'Twister' holds terror. Even the sound of an approaching tornado is awesome; anyone unlucky enough to be in the direct path of a tornado without any shelter available has little chance of surviving it.

In April 1974, in the worst tornado disaster since 1925 (when nearly 700 people were killed), a total of 324 people became victims of tornadoes in the space of eight hours, and hundreds more were injured, while damage ran into many millions of dollars. Although warnings had been given, a part of the area which was struck in 1974 was unfamiliar with tornadoes, and this contributed to the high death-toll.

Nothing can be done to prevent tornadoes and little is known about them, although no storm is more violent. Unlike hurricanes, which can be observed from within, tornadoes are so small that their study has not been practical. The conditions which give rise to them, however, are well-known and are present when warm moist air-masses meet cold dry air-masses.

Precipitating the events of 2 and 3 April 1974 was the swift eastward movement of an egg-shaped mass of cool dry air about one thousand miles across, while at the centre of the air-mass was a region of low pressure similar to that found in the calm eye of a hurricane.

This low pressure region moved very fast from central Kansas to Iowa and then on to the northern tip

of Michigan. In the northern hemisphere air circulates counter-clockwise, round a centre of high or low pressure. Winds to the east of the cool air-mass were moving north, and by 2 April this northward flow was carrying moist air from the Gulf of Mexico which was rapidly warming up with the coming of spring and evaporating large masses of water.

Meanwhile about 200 miles to the landward, west-ward edge of the air-mass a cold front, flowing off the Rocky Mountains, developed, and a series of squall-lanes (instability lines) were formed. There the moist air welled upwards rapidly, spurring a compensating downward flow of cooler air from above and the series of squall-lines brought tornadoes over Alabama, like 'jabs from a boxer' as a meteorologist described it.

Research shows that tornadoes arise within small cyclones, a few miles across, which in turn arise within large thunderstorms. In the funnel of a tornado winds may swirl at 300 miles an hour or more – four times as fast as those in a hurricane. The movement of a tornado has been likened to a dancer, pirouetting on a rotating platform which is itself mounted on a truck, and this accounts for the terrifyingly erratic and unpredictable route many tornadoes take. At the edge of the tornado-funnel trees are uprooted; in the centre, buildings explode and railway carriages are blown over. The twister may be only 100 feet across, but it can leave a trail of damage half a mile wide.

On these two days in April 100 twisters struck in the space of eight hours in an area from Alabama to Windsor, Ontario, across the Canadian border. Two of the worst hit towns were Xenia, Ohio, and Branden-burg, Kentucky, and neither town had much experience of the killing twisters; there had been only seven tornadoes in the Xenia area in the last 24 years, and no deaths, and Brandenburg had never experienced a tornado before.

Since tornadoes strike more than a thousand times a year in the United States, people living in the affected regions have learnt to take shelter when warnings are given; to leave their cars if they cannot drive clear of the twister's path and find some hollow, if they can, in which to hide; to keep away from windows which can shatter; to take cover under large pieces of furniture. In the worst areas the houses are built with storm cellars in which the occupants can take refuge.

In the late afternoon, against a sky filled with black-ness and flying débris, one particular twister roared its way through Xenia from the south-west, slashing a path of destruction three or four miles long and several hundred yards wide. New housing developments, old neighbourhoods, schools, churches, downtown busi-nesses and shopping centre, suffered equally. Within five minutes of sudden, shattering destruction 30 people died, nearly a hundred were injured, and thou-sands made homeless.

Left: This remarkable picture of a tornado shows its peculiar funnel-like form, and the huge dust cloud created by its erratic and terrifyingly destructive route. In the funnel of a tornado winds may swirl at 300 miles an hour.

Above: The damage of a tornado is devastating. In eight hours a series of 'twisters' rampaging through the American middle west killed 324 people, injured hundreds and caused damage such as that pictured here, which ran into many millions of dollars.

been left before the twister had reduced everything round them to chaos.

At least half of Xenia had been destroyed and all the services disrupted. But by the next day the immense task of clearing up had already begun. Electricity was partly restored, and hundreds of volunteers came to help the population search for what remained of their possessions and to find some kind of shelter. A state of emergency was declared and national guardsmen – much of whose time was later spent in keeping sight-seers away – were ordered out in Xenia, in Louisville, Kentucky, and in similarly stricken towns throughout the states of Alabama, Ohio, Indiana and Tennessee. In these states people sifted through the splinters that had been their homes, scraped the débris from the streets and sawed up fallen trees. There was a strange calm as with 'serene faces and certain hands' – as one reporter described it – the volunteers cleared up the rubbish against a background of persistent siren wails.

Throughout the affected areas stories abounded of individual incidents such as that at Windsor, where the roof was ripped off the local curling rink, killing and injuring those in its path, while the bodies of those who had been inside were found scattered over the neighbouring fields; and the metal frame warehouse of a construction company in Fountaintown, Indiana, which was lifted off the ground and carried a mile.

Perhaps one of the saddest results of the tornado's vicious attack was the effect it had upon the 1,600 people living in Brandenburg, Kentucky, 32 miles west of Louisville. This small farming community sat on the banks of the Ohio River, and most of its inhabitants had lived there all their lives. It was a small society, intimate, chatty and with an air of permanence. Its local paper was small and gossipy, and everybody knew everybody and all about each other. Modest houses, mostly of nineteenth-century architecture, stood on top a pair of hills; the pace of life of Brandenburg was slow and restrained – it was 'a Mark Twain town'.

A few minutes of unleashed fury changed all this. Twenty-nine people died and scores were injured. Hundreds of people were made homeless as three-quarters of the buildings were damaged beyond repair. One 21-year-old girl and her 9-year-old brother were in a flat in an old two-storey house, clutching each other in terror as the tornado swept eastwards along the river's edge. Thirty seconds later they were trapped by wreckage while the neighbours in the flat downstairs – a woman and three young children – lay dead. The neighbour's infant daughter was found, in a field at the bottom of a hill 200 yards away, alive.

Later the river was dragged for bodies, as eye-witnesses spoke of houses, cars and bodies flying through the air. Such was the extent and importance of the destruction in this small community that many people decided to leave. It seemed pointless, they said, to try to rebuild: too much had gone for ever; the river town of Brandenburg had all but disappeared.

Months passed before the damage caused throughout the country could be repaired – it was estimated that damage to personal property alone had cost the country £1,000,000,000, and low-interest personal loans to home-owners and businessmen were immediately announced. Damage to property can be made good, but nothing can replace a way of life.

The people who had managed to take shelter emerged dazed, once the roaring inferno had passed, and took stock. They knew that the windows had shattered, for flying glass had rained upon them as they lay on the floors of the downstairs rooms, but out in the street they discovered that almost every house had lost its roof and many their first floors. Some were virtually heaps of rubble and splinters. Dangling wires, loose signs, branches, traffic-lights – all were strewn higgledy-piggledy across once orderly streets.

Cars had been tossed along the roads; a train passing through the town with a load of new cars was safe, but all the cars were dented and their glass broken. Débris littered the streets blown from miles away and among it, untouched by the wind – such is the caprice of tornadoes – stood bizarre objects; a child's scooter, dressing-table ornaments, a pile of magazines, just as they had

Flixborough, 1974

In any disaster situation it is possible for the outside observer to look on the bright side and say that things might have been worse. Certainly with Britain's greatest industrial accident at Flixborough on 1 June 1974, things could have been a lot worse.

In the awesome explosion at the Nypro Works 29 people died and more than 100 were injured, while 100 homes in the village nearby were destroyed or badly damaged. People living 30 miles away thought there had been a nuclear attack, and one man in the Lincolnshire town of Scunthorpe, six miles away, said: 'It parted the clouds and went up like a mushroom – like an atomic bomb!' A village housewife declared: 'We thought they'd dropped an H-bomb. There was a mushroom-shaped cloud spiralling up with two great thick circles!'

The explosion happened at 4.53 p.m. on a Saturday afternoon when comparatively few people were about. Had it been a weekday the likelihood is that many of the 550 workers would have perished in the inferno which followed the explosion. The fire raged uncontrollably for 24 hours, and the Nypro factory was gutted.

Of the 29 who died there, 27 were employees, one was a sub-contractor, and one, an outside driver, happened to be in the wrong place at the wrong time.

The explosion occurred in the plant's Area One. A worker there, Lawrence Harry, said: 'We heard one bang followed by a huge explosion. Everything went pitch black and I was picked up and hurled 30 yards by the blast. For a while I was wandering about dazed, but then I found one of my mates was missing so I went back inside to try and find him.' In one of the laboratories a chemist technician, Tom McCale, saw the flash of the explosion and flames racing along a trail of leaking liquid gas. 'Let's get out of here quick!' he shouted to his seven companions, making for the door. They turned left, Tom turned right, and was engulfed in the force of the explosion. Seriously concussed, he was rushed to hospital.

A mile and a half to the south-west across the River Trent, in the village of Amcotts, Susan Dye's two children were playing out of doors. Nichola, aged three, and five-year-old Lisa were struck by glass splinters which embedded in their faces even before they heard the roar of the explosion. Mrs Dye gathered the screaming girls into her arms and hurried them to hospital. The doctors told her to hold them down on the operating-table as they removed the splinters and carefully stitched their wounds.

The blast took off slates and whole roofs in the village of Flixborough itself; all the windows were shattered, doors wrenched off and walls cracked. Chimney-pots came tumbling down into the streets and people were hurled about like rag-dolls. Within moments the peaceful scene resembled something out of the wartime blitz.

Of the 29 dead only eight bodies were recovered. The rest had been atomized by the force of the explosion and the savage blaze which followed.

The Flixborough Works was jointly owned by the National Coal Board and Holland's equivalent organization, the Dutch State Mining Company. It was the sole British source of caprolactam, an essential ingredient of nylon. The huge Dutch concern had developed the process for making a fibre they called 'Nylon 6' in the 1960s, and subsequently went into partnership with the British Coal Board. Flixborough supplied Courtaulds with 20,000 tons of caprolactam annually for their nylon goods manufacture, but with refinements in the operation they stepped this up to 70,000 tons by the mid-70s. The fibre went into the manufacture of goods ranging from ladies' tights and underwear to curtains, carpets, car-tyres and safety-belts, and Nypro supplied factories employing upwards of 30,000 workers. As a result of the explosion all these jobs were immediately threatened; with a temporary world shortage of caprolactam there was little chance of manufacturers being able to transfer their orders elsewhere.

If the surrounding villages thought they had witnessed an atomic explosion, the Courtauld company took the secondary shock-wave. As Nypro's biggest customer, £20 million was wiped off Courtaulds's stock-market value the following Monday.

Until Flixborough, modern industrial thinking had been to have a giant-scale operation to serve all the most useful purposes, rather than having many smaller plants dispersed about the country. The saving in transport and handling costs between subsidiary factories was a powerful argument; raw materials were cheaper to buy in bulk, and the hyper-factory located on one site often provided employment for virtually the entire local working population (although, curiously enough, not one of the 300 people in quiet, rural Flixborough worked at Nypro). After the explosion this view was called into question, for apart from the matter of having such an awesome explosive-packed complex within blast-distance of inhabited areas, the economic consequence of losing the entire basic raw material was self-evident.

British Employment Secretary Michael Foot set up a Court of Inquiry to establish the cause of the disaster. The government's Chief Inspector of Factories had warned in his 1972 report on modern high-technology factories: 'We are faced increasingly with the risk of failure which could result in multiple deaths and injuries of near-disaster proportions.' Many specialists in industrial safety methods had appreciated that in the event of such a failure it was vital that the right lessons should be learnt; that after any major disaster it should be possible to see where the shortcomings were in the chain of checks, tests, expertise and managerial control which determine the level of industrial safety in any British factory.

The year before the accident the Flixborough plant had begun using a speedier process of manufacture, a short-cut using benzene rather than cyclohexane to start the process. Benzene is cheaper, but also highly toxic, inflammable and explosive. After the benzene has been used to produce cyclohexane (a colourless liquid similar to petrol) this chemical is mixed with

ammonia in an oxidizing plant. At this critical stage of the process the cyclohexane is under tremendous pressure and the oxygen supply must be precisely controlled. The result is cyclohexanone oxide, which is then treated with concentrated sulphuric acid or phosphoric acid at an isomerizing plant. This produces caprolactam, which in turn produces the fibre Nylon 6.

More than 1,000 tons of cyclohexane were stored at Flixborough in 1974, and the company stuck steadfastly to the safety and fire regulations. Workers were searched for lighters, matches and cigarettes, and in high-risk areas of the plant everyone had to wear special footwear; although, as it was pointed out at the inquiry, in certain circumstances if there was a gas leak on a warm day a man in a nylon shirt could create sufficient static electricity to cause a spark.

The inquiry delivered its findings in May 1975, nearly a year after the explosion, which it described as 'of warlike dimensions'.

On 27 March 1974, more than two months before the explosion, cyclohexane was found leaking from a six-foot crack in Reactor No. 5 in a linked series of six reactors. All six were closed down and company officials decided to remove Reactor No. 5 for inspection, and

Previous pages : Flixborough on fire.

Left : People were cut by flying glass seven miles away and the Nypro Works was reduced to a mass of twisted metal.

link Reactors 4 and 6 with a temporary bypass pipe. *This link was badly designed. Nobody consulted the relevant British Standards or the manufacturer's handbook which would have shown the link was unsafe.* The design staff were under pressure to complete their work so that production should be resumed. The emphasis was directed to getting the oxidation process on stream again with the minimum possible delay, though the inquiry accepted that the officials did not knowingly embark on a hazardous course.

The engineering staff at Flixborough was under strength. Both the managing director and the general works manager were qualified and experienced chemical engineers, but the position of works engineer was vacant. Said the report: 'There was no mechanical engineer on site with sufficient qualification, status or authority to deal with complex or novel engineering problems and insist on necessary precautions being taken.'

Before resuming production the five reactors and bypass pipe were pressurized with *nitrogen* to check that the system did not leak: the standard pressure test uses *water*, which is incompressible. If there is a leak, a rapid release of compressed nitrogen is itself dangerous. Had the correct tests been carried out they would almost certainly have shown the bypass pipe to be defective and the disaster would have been averted. From the end of March there had been no thorough inspection of the by-pass pipe.

In the early hours of 1 June pressure in the reactors built up unusually quickly. The increase in pressure was observed but its cause – almost certainly a high-pressure nitrogen leak into the system – was not. Production continued.

At 4.50 p.m. the bypass pipe burst, causing a cloud of cyclohexane to gather outside the reactor system. At 4.53 p.m. the cyclohexane exploded, and Nypro's £18 million Flixborough plant was quickly reduced to rubble. Blame had to be shared by many individuals both at board level and below, the report decided. Experts criticized the inquiry findings, claiming they were a whitewash of the chemical-process industry. Four independent witnesses supported a 'two-event' theory of the Flixborough disaster; that the rupture in the 20-inch temporary pipe was caused by a prior explosion in a permanent 8-inch pipe seconds before the big bang.

This was not merely a technical bicker. By blaming the 20-inch pipe, which everybody accepted was a slipshod piece of engineering, the report in effect gave hundreds of other chemical plants a clean bill of health. The implications of the 'two-event' theory are much more serious, for if the 8-inch permanent pipe *did* fail first it calls into question the design of other plants throughout the world.

Dr Tudor Jones of the University of Leicester supports the 'two-event' theory. In what must be one of the most extraordinary pieces of evidence ever presented to an inquiry, he said that the explosion was recorded in his laboratory on equipment plotting disturbances in the ionosphere, 100 miles up. Forty seconds before the main Flixborough shock his instruments had recorded another explosion, the equivalent of one ton of T.N.T. 'The two events are there, quite plain for everyone to see', he said. 'I think it is highly unlikely to be anything but a small "pre-explosion".'

Left : Flames continued to belch from the plant for hours.

Top : A victim surveys the damage. A hundred houses were wrecked in Flixborough.

Above : Eighteen hours later, firemen were still tackling the blaze. Twenty-nine people in the works died in the explosion on a Saturday afternoon, when most of the work force was absent.

Honduras, 1974

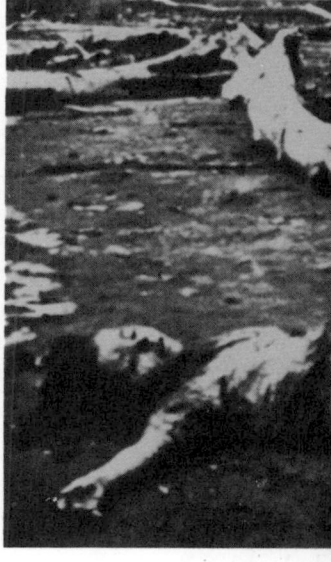

Until September 1974 Honduras was to most people only the name of a country, somewhere in Central America. An unparalleled disaster was to change all that, for by press, radio and television, the almost unknown became suddenly and dramatically familiar.

Honduras lies on the Caribbean in the north and the Pacific in the south and south-west, with Nicaragua to the east, Guatemala to the west and Salvador to the south. In extent it is slightly smaller than England, a country of mountains, deep valleys and fast-flowing rivers which flood down from the mountains to the coastal lowlands and thence to the sea. Essentially it is a very poor country. In 1870 vast sums of money were borrowed from London in order to build railways, but through incompetence and corruption most of the capital was dissipated and the country was left bankrupt and in a state of unrest. From 1883 until 1944 revolutions became a matter of course. No sooner had the Hondurans become familiar with one president than he was toppled from power and another, often very briefly, took his place.

Not that the majority of the country's some three million people have ever been interested in politics. For the most part they are of Indian stock, live in primitive conditions and are far too poor (£100 – or $250 – a year is considered a good wage) and far too busy trying to wring a meagre living from their small farms or farmholdings to worry about what goes on in the Honduran capital of Tegucigalpa. Some breed cattle in the lowland pastures, but the country's chief product is bananas grown in large American-run plantations on the northern coastal plain and which, together with coffee, represents 50 per cent of the country's exports, the rest being made up of coconuts, timber and tobacco. It is a difficult country in which to travel because of a lack of good roads and railways and the deep valleys which cut through it like the troughs of waves (the Spanish word *honduras* may be translated as 'wavelike').

The country has two, or rather three, seasons – the wet from May to November, the dry from November to May, and September, the hurricane season. The terrible toll taken by hurricanes in the area nearly 8,000 people lost their lives in Haiti when Hurricane Flora struck in 1963) has led countries on the Atlantic and Pacific seaboards – especially the U.S.A. – to develop meteorological services with a multiplicity of weather stations, fleets of aircraft, banks of computers and all the other trappings of modern technology to monitor the atmospheric conditions which give rise to the violent disturbances from which hurricanes are created. When one such build-up was spotted in 1974, an urgent warning went to Tegucigalpa informing the government of Honduras that it was likely to be assaulted by a hurricane within the next 48 hours. Following the obscure system that bestows girls' names on hurricanes, this was given the somewhat frivolous name of 'Fifi'.

This house was washed up on top of a bridge in the Agwan Valley, near Tocoa by the severe floods which followed Hurricane Fifi.

The body of a child, one of 8,000 victims of Hurricane Fifi, lies at the edge of the Choloma River, four miles north of Choloma in northern Honduras.

Unfortunately, communications being what they were, little could be done in the outlying districts of Honduras. Those who were informed of the danger could only wait; those who were not – and that was the bulk of the population – went about their back-breaking task of scratching a miserable living from the soil, quite oblivious to the approaching menace.

Hurricane Fifi arrived at dead of night on Wednesday, 18 September, with winds of 140 miles an hour, and torrential rain. Two feet of rain fell in 36 hours. Although the hurricane winds caused the initial

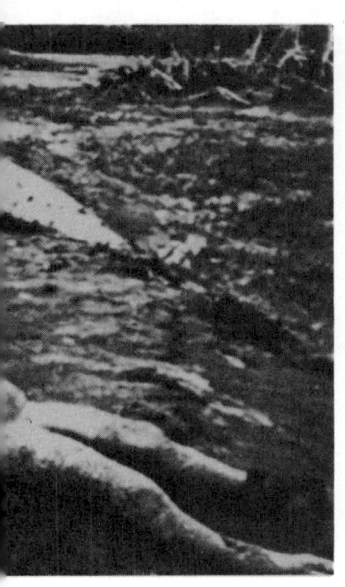

damage, they soon passed and the subsequent fatalities were mainly the result of the flooding. The heavy rainfall caused the many rivers of Honduras to overflow from their sources high in the mountains right down to the plains. Dykes and banks disappeared into a maelström of swirling brown water, and almost everything that stood in the path of the floods as they roared down to the sea was swept away.

The poorly-built homes of the farmers and peasants – stone, wattle and clay for the most part – just disappeared. Even some of the sturdier houses were picked up and carried for several miles, and in some cases, when meeting an obstruction that even the roaring waters could not move, would be piled one on top of another.

Worst hit was the district around the town of Choloma, standing on the banks of the river which gave it its name. Flood water poured through the town bearing trees, rocks and pathetic jumbles of wreckage that had once been homes, carrying away every standing thing along the river's bank. During the first two terrible days more than 3,000 died in the town, many of the bodies never being recovered. Those inhabitants who were left were faced with another great hazard – cholera. Bodies lay everywhere, many half-buried in the nine-feet layer of mud that the floods had left. Soon, under the hot, tropical sun, decay began to set in. Soldiers were rushed to the area and were soon collecting the bodies, piling them into heaps for mass cremation, contrary to the Roman Catholic practice of burial. Nothing, not even the deep religious beliefs of four centuries, could stand in the way of priorities.

As they worked, scarves and handkerchiefs about their mouths to allay the dreadful odour of putrefaction, the pitiful survivors – about half the town's original population – stood and watched, helpless. Many, of course, had tragic stories to tell. 'People were very afraid to leave their homes,' said one survivor. 'I saw nine people from one family embrace each other; they were afraid to move. They died, holding each other in their arms.'

One old man who had lost his entire family in the flood went back to search the pile of wreckage that had been his home, and found the bodies of two dead people. He did not know them; they were not even people of Choloma. They were, as he remarked, 'just poor innocents who were swept down from the mountain and ended up here'. Another added that two separate floods had chased each other through the town early on the morning of Thursday, 19 September. 'The water poured across the street and between my home and my neighbour's like rapids.'

The second city of Honduras, San Pedro Sula, also took the full brunt of Hurricane Fifi and the floods which followed in her wake. With their homes wrecked or completely gone, some 400,000 people were suddenly homeless, without food and with the prospect of an epidemic very near.

The final death toll throughout the country was set at least at 8,000.

The first aircraft from neighbouring countries and the U.S.A. began to drone over the devastated areas, spotting thousands of terrified and desperately hungry survivors clinging to anything that protruded above the vast wastes of frothy, surging water. Some were soon saved, but the rescuers were unable to reach many of the rural areas of northern Honduras where thousands of peasants were marooned without food, fresh water or medical aid of any kind. To add to the difficulties, the only petrol refinery in the country had been isolated by the flooding of roads and the railway tracks, depriving the authorities of the fuel so vital for rescue work.

By 23 September helicopters from the U.S. base at the Panama Canal Zone were hovering wherever they could see signs of life, doubling their usual carrying capacity as they plucked wet, hungry and miserable survivors from roof-tops and trees. At first they were the only means of rescue, for bridges and railway tracks had been swept away and roads had disappeared beneath several feet of black, glutinous mud; electricity supplies were cut and telegraph-poles were down everywhere, while those that remained upright bore their pathetic bundles of squatting humanity whose upturned faces showed their mute appeal as the heavily-laden helicopters droned overhead.

As lines of communication were slowly restored, food and medical supplies began to arrive, Tocoa and San Pedro Sula becoming the main relief centres. Soon the stacks of supplies were beginning to grow, but the teams arriving from other countries ran into trouble. Corruption, always a major problem in any poor and under-developed country, became flagrant. Part of the Honduran army had been mustered to collect and distribute the food and other supplies; the rest was on guard along the Honduras/Salvador border and the government refused to bring them back and leave the border undefended. At the two main centres it was obvious that a large quantity of supplies was being diverted to a black market that had sprung into life within hours of the disaster.

Britain managed to bring some order out of the tension and even rioting at the centres. She had already sent in helicopters and troops with power-boats and medical teams from Belize in the then British Honduras, but realizing the problem was one of administration, co-ordinated all the endeavours of every assisting country through the newly-formed Whitehall Disaster Unit. This stamped out the corruption at source and helped the flow of rescue units, getting them with their supplies to the devastated areas where they were so urgently needed.

It was a prodigious task, for everywhere, it seemed, were thousands of starving people who had lost everything – corn, rice, beans and other subsistence crops having completely gone. For the country as a whole, things were even worse. With her economy utterly reliant on exports of bananas and coffee, and the plantations of these devastated, fresh crops had to be sown at once, with the prospect of at least two years wait before any return from the new plantings could be expected. Livestock had also perished in their thousands and these, too, would have to be replenished – although the country had no foreign currency available.

Only the generosity of other nations can enable Honduras to survive until she is able to return even to the near-starvation level that existed before Hurricane Fifi. Many peasants believe that the calamity was a punishment from God, but for what no-one is quite sure.

Darwin, 1974

Throughout Christmas Eve, 1974 local television and radio stations broadcast warnings of a cyclone, nicknamed Tracy, that was rapidly approaching Darwin, capital of Australia's Northern Territory.

The people of the city did not pay their usual heed to the continual warnings; they had Christmas preparations on their minds. This, surely, was no time to be unduly concerned about a cyclone which might easily miss the city entirely.

In the harbour the warning was acted upon almost immediately, perhaps because those on board the ships and boats had fewer distractions than people ashore, or perhaps they were inclined to be more weather-wise. The harbour began to empty during the early evening, 27 ships putting out to sea in order to ride out the cyclone. They, at any rate, were taking no chances. Three naval vessels, with their crews ashore, elected to stay.

As the evening wore on, the warnings became more insistent, and stated that the cyclone would pass right across the city some time around dawn, at 5.30 a.m. or so. But families, exhausted from last-minute shopping in the unusually humid weather and Christmas preparations, were in bed well before midnight. Soon the city was still.

At 1.30 a.m. on Christmas morning, the nightmare began; Tracy had arrived—four hours earlier than forecast. It arrived with a screeching, unbelievable wind that swept away everything that stood before it, accompanied by a full-throated roar that many later compared with a railway train emerging from a tunnel, but much, much louder.

The subsequent general impression was that the cyclone had 'struck like a bomb', and within minutes screaming residents ran into dark streets that suddenly had lost their comfortable, familiar look. Houses were torn from their foundations, and tall office buildings swayed and crumbled, cascading in utter ruins to lie in piles of masonry and timber. Parked cars were blown over; engines, carriages and trucks at the railway station were hurled about like toy trains; rails were torn from their sleepers and twisted into grotesque tangles of ironware. Telegraph-poles were swept away, wrapped around with strange bundles of twisted wires.

Tracy, its work done, passed over the city and, screaming and moaning as it went, faded away. There came a strange, sudden stillness, broken only by the occasional roar as a weakened building collapsed. A Qantas pilot flying over the city soon afterwards said: 'It was absolutely incredible. There was mile after mile of nothing but wreckage.'

All that remained of the once attractive city was a graveyard of devastation in which dazed inhabitants wandered as if stunned, or frenziedly scrabbled for relatives and friends beneath tons of rubble. Australia's deputy Prime Minister, Jim Cairns, was soon on the

scene and his first comment was that the destruction 'was quite unbelievable'. He went on to say: 'I had heard that Darwin was devastated, but I never imagined it could be as bad as this', stating that the damage was comparable to that caused by an atom bomb, for something like 90 per cent of the buildings in the city were shattered.

Announcing the news to a wider public Cairns stated: 'What happened to Darwin on Christmas Day has never happened in Australia before. Darwin is devastated. Darwin is destroyed. There is virtually no building in Darwin that is not severely damaged. Darwin looks like a battlefield or Hiroshima.'

Above : Tracy, the cyclone which was nature's Christmas gift to the citizens of Darwin, left this trail of destruction on either side of one of the city's main highways.

Above right : Tossed by the fierce vagaries of the 62 mile-an-

... hour wind, a child's toy (above, right) lies beside overturned cars and damaged buildings. The destruction was 'unbelievable'.

Right: Fifty bodies were found in the ruins. Others may have died in boats which vanished from the harbour.

Of the small fleet of 27 ships that had moved out of the harbour into open water, only six returned under their own power. The rest had been hurled on to the rocks or had disappeared in a maelström of white, tortured water. Of the three naval vessels in the harbour, one had run aground, the other two had sunk. The harbour itself, as one observer said, looked like a 'junkyard'. One ship had been picked up and blown 200 yards inland.

A graphic description of his personal ordeal came from skipper Bob Hedditch of the 73-foot prawn-trawler *Anson*. 'We put to sea on Christmas Eve at 19.30 hours and at midnight it hit us. The wind blew in our windows on the helm and tore off the back door. The waves crashed into the wheelhouse and I had to lie on the floor to steer. We had no steering by 0200 hours, no lights and only the main engine to keep us heading into the 162 mile an hour gale. We lost both our anchors and I didn't have a clue where we were. We saw two boats send up distress signals, but there was nothing we could do. We limped back at 1140 hours on the morning of Christmas Day.'

'It was our engineer's first trip to sea. He disappeared when we docked. I think it was his last trip, too!' Hedditch concluded wryly.

At Darwin airport, 50 planes were destroyed on the ground. Some were blown an incredible distance from where they had been standing. After doing his best to cope with the situation at the airport, John Auld, movement controller for Qantas, hastened to his car to drive home, concerned about his family who lived in one of the worst-devastated areas. He threaded his way past piles of rubble and wrecked cars, then decided to call briefly on his manager to give him an up to the minute report. When he arrived he found that his manager's house no longer existed – the site was entirely bare.

Deeply troubled, he drove to his own house. He found it a confusion of dust and débris, and no signs of his wife and child. After some frantic searching he found them in a neighbour's house. They had been discovered huddled together on the floor of the lavatory – the only room in the house which had not been wrecked – crouching there while the building seemed to disintegrate about them. Their escape was typical of the many that had occurred during that fateful night.

The complete death-toll has never been published. Although some 50 bodies were recovered, the actual figure could be much higher; many boats, for example, were not salvaged. The number of injured persons ran into hundreds.

Slowly and painfully the people of Darwin shook themselves free of the nightmare. The next day the Australian and world press reported the disaster, and relatives in other parts of Australia worried about the fate of their families. All telegraph-poles were down, but a temporary communications centre set up in Smith Street provided a free telegram or short telephone service for 'safe and well' messages. Queues for this formed for more than 200 yards.

As the catastrophe had ruptured water-pipes, a further centre was set up to provide water. Water-trucks were towed to a pipeline on Stuart Highway where, all modesty cast aside in the oppressively humid weather, men, women and children stood naked on the highway, revelling in the first shower they had experienced since the cyclone had struck.

Help was on the way. A fleet of seven ships, led by aircraft carrier H.M.A.S. *Melbourne*, was racing to the harbour, bearing emergency supplies. Fresh food and water was flown in daily. Arrangements were also put in hand for a massive airlift to take some 25,000 homeless people to other parts of the territory. By Sunday night, 29 December, more than 10,000 people had been airlifted – mostly the infirm, the ill and the young. As relief teams still toiled in tropic humidity, plans had already been put in hand for a new and even better Darwin.

It was estimated that about $250 million would be needed to replace the 10,000 or so homes that had been destroyed. Cairns had said that the catastrophe represented 'Australia's greatest national challenge for years and, typically, the people of Darwin were ready to meet that challenge.'

Eastern Airlines Boeing 727, Kennedy Airport, 1975

Doris Boehmann, secretary of the Cedarhurst Tennis Club near Brookville Boulevard, New York, had been looking forward to a busy day, with the courts and the club-room filled with members and their friends, playing and gossiping in the pleasant, relaxed atmosphere for which the Cedarhurst was famous. The previous day, however, the weather had changed and this Wednesday, 24 June 1975 was a bad one with constant rain, heavy clouds overhead and sudden gusts of wind.

She watched the airliners coming in to land at Kennedy, for the club-house was near the huge international airport. The great silver shapes roared overhead and then, flattening, each would touch down on the glistening runway. She was about to turn away when she heard the deep roar of another plane overhead. From its blue and white markings she knew that it belonged to Eastern Airlines. It was about 500 yards away from her, moving across the tennis courts and, as she reported later, far too low, 'about 40 or 50 feet off the ground'. As she watched there came a sudden flash of fire and then the aircraft began to break up in the air and fall, a tall pillar of black smoke rising from where it had crashed.

Others saw the disaster too, several claiming with much assurance that it had been struck by lightning just before it struck the ground. Paul Moran, a policeman, said: 'Lightning hit the plane and tilted it to the right. It went about 20 more yards and hit the ground.'

Another, Neal Rairden stated: 'I was about three blocks away when I saw the plane coming in. It was raining very hard at the time – about 4.10. All of a sudden there was lightning. I looked up and all I saw was smoke and flame and no plane. I said "Holy God!" I knew that plane had been hit by lightning.'

The aircraft was an Eastern Airlines Boeing 727 from New Orleans to Kennedy, carrying 116 passengers (including, as it was later discovered, a babe-in-arms not shown on the manifest) and a crew of eight. Among its passengers was a party of 19 Norwegian seamen from several ships in Louisiana port who were en route to their homeland for a holiday. They were among the first later to be identified, and some survived the disaster. One Egon Luftaas explained: 'The pilot seemed to go too much to the left, with one wing down. Then there was an explosion. Everyone was flung around. After that I can only remember the fire . . .'

In fact, the aircraft had not reached the airport but had crashed on the Rockaway Boulevard expressway on its north-eastern fringe in a relatively open section of Rosedale, Queens. It was the beginning of the rush hour, and many drivers had to brake frantically to avoid the burning wreckage that had been spilled out all over the road or to miss the other automobiles pulling up all around them – an especially hazardous procedure for the road was wet with rain and greasy with spilled fuel. The police were soon on the scene to be

Above : Towering monstrously over the bodies of its victims is the fuselage of the Boeing 727. Freak currents of air, lightning or human error—nobody can be sure what caused the crash.

Left : The crushed fuselage and at right the bodies of some of the 110 victims.

met with lurid tales of how the crashing aircraft had smashed a number of cars off the road, but they were later able to report that not a single car had been hit.

The force of the impact as the plane struck the expressway sent a huge fireball into the sky and scattered bodies over a wide area. Fortunately there were few houses at this point, swampy ground being general on both sides of the road. Rescue attempts began almost immediately but they were seriously hampered by the dense traffic caused by the evening rush hour and by the thousands of sightseers who soon converged on the area. Initially rescuers were also delayed by the impossibility of getting into the fiercely burning fuselage to bring out any survivors. Many bodies were scattered on either side of the Rockaway Boulevard, on the boulevard itself and in an old garbage dump just beyond.

The massive emergency efforts that had been called into action by the disaster brought police and firemen, rescue crews and officials from the airport, and ambulances and helicopters racing to the scene, and the Jamaica and South Shore Hospitals in Queens and the Jacobi Hospital in the Bronx were alerted to receive the dead and injured. Kennedy Airport was closed a minute after the crash – at 4.11 p.m., the peak period of the day – and all air traffic was diverted until 4.53 p.m.

Rescue work went on under appalling conditions of darkness, incessant rain, a press of automobiles and gaping sightseers. One of the members of the first rescue team to arrive said, 'We got to the plane just as the first fire trucks were pulling in. Part of the fuselage and tail were on fire. We saw three survivors, two of them lying down and one walking up the road. You couldn't tell if it was a man or a woman. The person was all bloody. Somebody told the person to sit down and the first ambulance that came took the three away. What I was surprised about was that the other two didn't bleed as well.'

The first of the 19 City Fire Departments' equipment arrived and the firemen, wearing asbestos suits, had soon smothered the main fuselage with foam and the flames were quickly dowsed. The pitifully few survivors – 14 in all including two children – were rushed off to Jamaica Hospital where a large team of doctors, many of whom had dashed from their homes when the first news of the disaster came through on their radios, began the delicate task of treating excruciatingly painful burns.

The macabre task of collecting the bodies went on. They were gently laid down at the side of the road and covered with plastic sheets, some of which the rain soon moulded to pathetically small bodies of children. Somehow these shrouded bodies did not seem to be part of an aircraft disaster. There were just the formless mounds beneath the sheets with the scattered, personal objects that marked the whole as a tragedy involving *people* – a handbag, a shoe, a doll, a raincoat. A man's jacket was found lying in the garbage dump. In an inside pocket was more than $4,000, many in $100 bills, but with no indication of its owner. Nearby another jacket was found that had belonged to one of the Norwegian seamen. This also contained money, his pay-off and holiday money – $126.

At dawn the next day officials began to examine the whole disaster area in an endeavour to put forward an early explanation of the tragedy. It became obvious that the flight path of the aircraft had been disturbed by the turbulent weather, and that as it made its approach the plane had been sent out of control by the sudden and dreaded air currents known as 'shears'. It had been thrown to one side and had ploughed into the airport's approach lighting system. This consisted of strings of 20 groups of lights mounted on top of 30-foot metal towers each some 50 yards apart. The plane had obviously come in too low, missed the first two lights, struck the next two and then, missing the next as the pilot tried desperately to pull the plane's nose up, had swept on to demolish the next four, breaking up as it went. It finally plunged sideways and smashed on to the expressway, disintegrating into a thousand pieces that were strewn all over the road. Only two sizeable pieces of the aircraft remained, a large piece of the wing and rear section and part of the underside of the fuselage.

Inevitably, the question of the plane being struck by lightning, so definitely reported by several eyewitnesses, was raised, only to be rejected by the officials. One expert stated that if it was decided that the cause of the crash was due to lightning, it would prove to be a very rare case. 'Lightning strikes on aircraft are common, but seldom result in damage. Unless they are particularly severe they usually go unreported,' he said.

It was finally decided that what the eyewitnesses had thought to be lightning was probably electrical arcing caused when the plane had hit the high-intensity lights that marked the route to the runway.

Yet why had other aircraft which had arrived just before the Boeing 727 not similarly been affected? Three of these were a K.L.M. Boeing 747, a Flying Tiger DC8 and an Eastern Airlines L1011 Jumbo jet. Indeed, the pilot of the Jumbo, worrying about the vicious cross-winds that were throwing even his immense plane about in the air, diverted it to Newark International Airport after reporting such severe shifts that his inertial navigation system was indicating a stream of air moving at a speed of 60–80 knots.

The K.L.M. pilot stated that he found the speed of his aircraft suddenly dropped at 300 feet and he had quickly to boost the power to keep a level approach. He concluded with typically Dutch understatement: 'It was a very unstabilized approach.'

Curiously, the pilots of two other planes, a Finnair jetliner and a small private propellor plane reported that they had experienced no difficulty at all in landing.

The inquiry went on. The flight recorders and the cockpit voice readings were recovered intact, but revealed no indication from the control tower that an emergency was in operation. Kennedy Airport had the standard instrument landing system frequently used to guide aircraft down in bad weather and in any case, according to the control tower, there was only a six-knot wind, a 3,000-foot ceiling and five-mile visibility, conditions that would not normally trouble an experienced pilot.

What had caused the disaster? Was it the sudden air shift, the 'shears'? Had the pilot come too low and misjudged his altitude over the approach lights? Or did the one in several million chance happen, and had a bolt of lightning actually struck the aircraft?

Whatever the cause, the result was terrible – 110 persons killed. It was New York's worst air disaster in a decade and the second worst in the city's history.

Guatemala, 1976

Relations between the Central American republic of Guatemala and the British Government had been tense for some time. The former claimed the neighbouring port of Belize in British Honduras, which had been settled by English buccaneers early in the seventeenth century and formally proclaimed a British possession in 1862. Indeed, during November 1975 the British Government, fearing an invasion, reinforced the garrison at Belize with men and aircraft, but this move appeared to aggravate the situation.

A conference was planned for the first week in February 1976 in an endeavour to arrive at some form of compromise for it was obvious that Guatemala would not readily yield her claim to what she felt was her territory by right, while the British government foresaw the introduction of a form of independence.

Preparations were in hand when, during the night of 4 February, Nature stepped in to postpone the meeting.

A tremendous earthquake struck Guatemala at 3.04 a.m., causing most of its population to pour out into the utter darkness of the night. Within the capital the blackness was lit garishly by sudden tongues of flame flaring upwards from shattered buildings, as in night attire and with blankets hastily draped across their shoulders, the panic-stricken people hurled themselves into the bitterly cold night air. The strident clangour of fire-engines and police vehicles effectively awoke the few who had slept through the initial thirty-second earthquake to the sound of the cries, moans and prayers of the thousands already thronging the streets.

Dawn revealed utter chaos. At least one-third of the buildings of the capital, a city of 1,000,000 people, had been destroyed; there was no water, no electricity and, at first, no organization. It was left to relatives and neighbours to dig frantically among piles of rubble in the hope of finding survivors. Yet even as they scrabbled with spades, broken timber and their bare hands, continual tremors still shook the city, bringing down loosened masonry and starting fresh fires. Altogether some 20 strong tremors were experienced on the first day.

Communication with the outside world was limited to contact by radio. In America, however, the possible extent of the damage was realized even before it was known by the Guatemalan authorities, for at Boulder, Colorado, the seismological station had recorded the earthquake, placing its epicentre at some 120 miles from the capital and measuring an ominous 7.2 on the Richter scale.

Later that day Colonel Manuel Ponce, the military chief of staff of the Guatemalan National Emergency Committee, called a news meeting of officials and pressmen. He announced that at least 2,000 people had been killed throughout the country and insisted that this figure, disturbing as it was, was 'conservative' and that, even as he spoke, alarming reports were coming

in from the interior. Teams of rescue workers were desperately trying to reach towns and villages that had been devastated to the north and east of the city, thousands of survivors were without food, medicine or even drinking water, and thousands of injured – many seriously – awaited the arrival of help of any kind.

As those who had attended this sombre meeting walked out on to the dark streets, crimson flames were thrusting skywards from the Guatemala University's new pharmaceutical school and from an international food institute nearby. The unlit streets were still crowded with people who preferred to face the chill of the night and a near-freezing temperature rather than risk being trapped under masonry, should another serious shock occur. Guests at the expensive tourist hotels in the central area of the capital were preparing to spend the night on the floor near the hotel entrances for fear of being trapped and crushed beneath the débris of already badly shattered buildings.

On the morning of Thursday, 5 February long queues formed outside shuttered shops in the vain hope of buying food, but few opened that day. Most of the city was without drinking water, although electricity had been restored to the central area. One of the hardest hit sections in the city was the slum district where most of the shanty buildings had collapsed at

Above : Destruction and damage to buildings where a disaster has occurred is easily depicted. Human tragedy is not so easy to capture, but it is in this that the real disaster lies. In the village of San Pedro some 300 people died. As the sun rises residents carry their dead from the church in the background towards the cemetery.

Right : In Guatemala City a woman watches anxiously as a doctor treats her injured baby. A total of 23,000 people died in Guatemala.

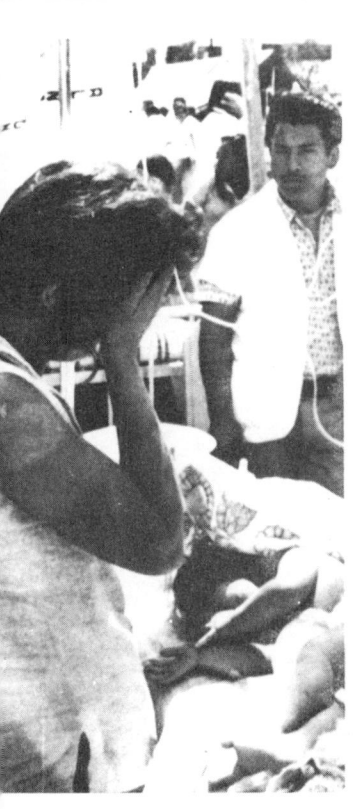

the first shock. The unfortunate inhabitants were now living under improvised shelters of sheets, table-cloths and scavenged pieces of corrugated iron, which offered poor shelter for such cold nights. The city was placed under a state of emergency, with troops patrolling the streets and manning machine-gun posts erected at strategic corners.

On learning of the disaster, the Governor of Belize immediately offered to fly in helicopters to help lift the injured and to provide other assistance. His offer was refused by the Guatemalan authorities. The British Government also offered to send any aid that was needed and British Airways volunteered to provide free cargo space for relief supplies, but the offer was firmly declined, although with consummate tact. A Guatemalan spokesman replied: 'Thank you very much. I am sincerely grateful. It is very thoughtful on the part of the British Government but just now we do not require it.'

By this time the magnitude of the disaster was fully appreciated and alleviation of the situation to meet the urgent needs of the victims came under the direction of the United Nations disaster relief co-ordinator. The League of Red Cross Societies launched a world-wide appeal for funds. In London, the British Red Cross and Help the Aged each announced an immediate donation of £5,000 ($10,000) to the victims of the earthquake. On the day after the earthquake, a team of United States Army disaster relief experts flew in from the Panama Canal Zone and CARE, the American relief organization, began to airlift many tons of food.

The night of 5 February saw most of the population again huddled together in the open. Although many were forced into this because they lacked any shelter, many more were influenced by memories of a similar disaster in their country in 1917, when the first major earthquake had been followed by another and far more fatal shock a week later.

Such forebodings were realized on 6 February when two strong tremors again rocked Guatemala city. They were part of the aftershock, and registered 5.75 on the Richter scale, slightly less than the original earthquake two days earlier. Two hours elapsed between each, the second being followed by a series of smaller tremors. They occurred while firemen were digging among the rubble that had resulted from Wednesday's earthquake. By then the Guatemalan National Emergency Committee had announced provisional figures of 5,000 dead and 15,000 injured.

Hunger, and especially thirst, were causing great suffering in Guatemala City and, indeed, in every town and village in the country. In the capital and larger towns, looting and violence increased and five people were executed in Guatemala City, where army patrols had been brought in to prevent the city from lapsing into chaos. The authorities issued constant appeals for order and calm, but there were frequent fights at emergency food centres and many instances of looting from devastated shops, an understandable crime when families are starving and the sight of easily obtainable food proves more powerful than moral codes.

News soon arrived of the state of the outlying areas, especially to the north-east, the epicentre of the earthquake. In the town of Joyabax, for example, some 55 miles from the capital, hardly a building was left standing and much of the town was under six feet of rubble, from which more than 500 bodies were recovered.

By 8 February, René Baralt, senior relief officer, announced that the death-toll could well rise to 20,000, for the casualty lists had already reported over 12,000 dead and 30,000 injured. Later figures placed the number of dead at 23,000. The Guatemalan earthquake was the worst since 1970, when 50,000 people had died in northern Peru; it was the second worst disaster in the Western hemisphere in modern times.

The donations continued to pour in. In Britain, Christian Aid and Oxfam each subscribed another £5,000 ($9,500) and the Catholic Fund for Overseas Development gave £2,000 ($3,800); Christian Aid later sent a further £20,000 ($40,000). Over £60,000 ($114,000) was spent in Britain on tents, blankets, medical supplies and a sanitation unit. The cost of the transportation of these supplies was taken over by voluntary agencies because of Guatemala's refusal to accept official help from Britain. Even so, permission was withheld for an aircraft flying from Gatwick to land at Guatemala Airport and the plane had to fly on to the neighbouring country of El Salvador, to be unloaded there and the urgently needed relief supplies then transported overland to the disaster areas. Thanks to the response to the call for vaccine, the ever-present fear of a major epidemic was averted.

America sent in 20 Air Force helicopters and their pilots returned with frightening reports of the devastation in the highland areas, where Indian groups lived in hundreds of small, scattered settlements, many of which were not even shown on local maps. First reports estimated that at least 80 per cent of their flimsy dwellings had been destroyed and that the people were in terrible straits, suffering from lack of water and food.

During the evening of Monday, 9 February, James Cameron made an appeal for financial help on British television and on the following day, Jorde Rosales, a Guatemalan doctor working for Save the Children Fund cabled to that organization's London headquarters: 'Desperately in need of vaccines – tetanus, typhoid and polio – and food of high calorific value. Also need refrigerators to keep vaccines fresh.'

On 10 February, Guatemala's President Kjell Eugenio Langerud announced that 17,032 had died, 54,826 had been injured and 221,994 people made homeless. These figures could hardly have been exact because even as he spoke, relief workers were struggling to reach devastated villages in the northern highlands where they pulled corpses from the wreckage of what once had been their homes. Makeshift landing strips were hacked out of scrub and bush to enable doctors and other relief specialists to fly in to the Indian settlements to airlift the wounded. All the hospital beds in Guatemala City were already filled and the injured were placed in the buildings of a trade fair or taken to an American field hospital set up at Chimaltenango, 40 miles north-west of the capital.

Thanks to the response to the call for vaccine the ever-present fear of a major epidemic was averted.

The magnitude of the disaster ruled out proper burial. Instead, communal graves were dug to receive the pitiful remains of thousands of victims, some in properly constructed coffins and then, as supplies ran out, in makeshift enclosures.

Index

The publishers would like to thank the following individuals and organizations for their kind permission to reproduce the photographs in this book:

Associated Press Ltd: 14, 15, 49, 50-51, 50 below, 51, 54-55, 56 above, 70 below, 74 above, 88-89, 91 above right, 101 above, 103 above, 112-113 below, 114-115 above, 114-115 below, 118 below, 121 below; Barnaby's Picture Library: 16-17, 21; Camera Press Ltd: 8, 26 above left, 68-69, 71 below, 76, 84-85, 86 above, 87 above, 95 above, 95 below, 98, 99 above, 110-111; Cine Foto Bucci: 52, 53; Daily Telegraph Colour Library: 87 below; R.A.Gardner: 12, 13; John Hillelson Agency Ltd: 96-97, 101 below, 102, 103 below; Illustrated London News: 18 below, 24 below, 24-25 above, 27, 28-29, 29, 33 below, 34-35, 36 below, 40 above, 42, 44 above, 44 below, 45 above; Keystone Press Agency: 46-47, 57 above, 57 below, 64-65, 66-67 above, 67 left, 77 below left, 77 above right, 82, 83 above, 88, 91 above left, 91 below, 113 below; London Express News and Feature Services: 80-81, 81, 100, 116-117, 117 above, 117 below; Mansell Collection: 19 below; Mirror Group Newspapers Ltd: 22-23; Photri: endpapers, 5, 36-37 above, 37 below, 104, 104-105, Peruvian Embassy: 94; Picturepoint Ltd: 83 below, 99 below; Popperfoto: 40 centre left, 40-41 below, 41 above, 45 below, 67 right, 70 above, 71 above, 72, 72-73, 74-75, 75, 78 above, 78 below, 79, 90, 92, 93, 118-119, 120-121; Press Association: 38 above; Radio Times Hulton Picture Library: 11, 17, 18-19 above, 20, 24 above centre, 24 above left, 25 right, 32 above, 32 below, 33 above, 36 centre, 37 centre, 39, 43; Rapho (Bajande): 106-107, 109, (S. Duboy): 6-7, 108; Sungravure Syndication: 60-61, 62, 63 above, 63 below; Syndication International: 26 below right, 30 above, 30 below, 31 above, 31 below, 38 below, 48, 56 below, 86 below, 112 above, 113 above; Wilson and Horton, New Zealand: 58, 59 above, 59 below.

Back Jacket: Radio Times Hulton Picture Library.

A

B

C

D

E

F

G

H

I

J

K

L

34x (8/21) 10/2

How to Walk Away

How to

Walk Away

KATHERINE CENTER

ST. MARTIN'S PRESS ⊠ NEW YORK

HOW TO WALK AWAY. Copyright © 2018 by Katherine Pannill Center. All rights reserved. Printed in the United States of America. For information, address St. Martin's Press, 175 Fifth Avenue, New York, N.Y. 10010.

www.stmartins.com

Designed by Devan Norman

Library of Congress Cataloging-in-Publication Data

Names: Center, Katherine, author.
Title: How to walk away : a novel / by Katherine Center.
Description: First edition. | New York : St. Martin's Press, 2018.
Identifiers: LCCN 2017060163| ISBN 9781250149060 (hardcover) |
    ISBN 9781250199614 (Canadian) | ISBN 9781466847705 (ebook)
Classification: LCC PS3603.E67 H69 2018 | DDC 813/.6—dc23
LC record available at https://lccn.loc.gov/2017060163

Our books may be purchased in bulk for promotional, educational, or business use. Please contact your local bookseller or the Macmillan Corporate and Premium Sales Department at 1-800-221-7945, extension 5442, or by email at MacmillanSpecialMarkets@macmillan.com

First U.S. Edition: May 2018

First Canadian Edition: May 2018

10 9 8 7 6 5 4 3 2 1

For my mom, Deborah Detering,
who is my personal superhero.

And to the memory of her brother and friend,
my uncle, Herman Detering.
We will always miss you, Bubsie.

Acknowledgments

This story required vast amounts of research, and I'm so grateful to all the people who helped me try to get it right. Hugs to friends who hooked me up with experts to answer my many questions: Vicky and Tony Estrera, Jennifer Hamilton, Eve Lapin, Mark Poag, and J.J. Spedale.

Much gratitude to all the health care professionals who took time to help me research Margaret's treatment. Dr. Darrell Hanson met me for coffee and walked me through exactly the injury Margaret would have had, explained in detail the surgery and recovery, and taught me the world *iliopsoas*. Dr. Forrest Roth walked me through the treatment of burns and skin grafts. Robert Manning, PT, kindly took a morning to show me around the ICU and rehab gym at Houston Methodist hospital. Ross LaBove and all the guys at Project Walk in Houston let me spend a day with them learning about all the creative and inspiring ways they help people work to get better.

Thank you to Jeff Scott and Wesley Branch, who were both gracious enough to share their spinal cord–injury stories with me and to talk at length about the realities of life afterward. Also, I'm glad to have found

two honest and inspiring narratives about life with spinal-cord injuries: Mark Hall's book, *Across the Street from Hell*, and Pamela Henline's book, *Walk, Don't Run*. The Christopher & Dana Reeve Foundation was also helpful.

Many thanks to Mollie Gordon, who connected me with her dad, Alan Gordon—who very kindly took me up in his Cessna, flew me to Galveston and back, even let me "fly" the plane for a little while. Then, once we were safely back on the ground, showed me the best way to crash that plane. Thanks, too, to John Marino, who met me for coffee and told me of his harrowing—and yet somehow very funny—experience of surviving a plane crash.

A quick shout-out to my friend Sam Nichols for the night at the Cherry Blossom in Fishkill, New York, when he just about killed himself eating an entire blob of wasabi on a dare.

I've been inspired for many years by the resilience of my mom's friend Jan Myers, who, with her husband, founded a summer camp for children with health needs after they lost their young son John Marc to cancer. Camp Hope in this novel—its thoughtful and whimsical design and its determination to bring joy into people's struggles—is inspired by Camp John Marc.

I also need to thank friends who've supported me, talked books with me, and gone out of their way to help me either get my writing done or get the word out about it: Brené Brown and Steve Alley, Chris and Connie Seger, Jenny Lawson, Sheryl Rapp, Vicky Wight, Faye Robeson, Andrew and Katherine Weber, Bryn Larsen, Maria Zerr, Tracy Pesikoff, and Dale Andrews. And thanks to my fun family for always being so excited about what I do: Bill Pannill and Molly Hammond, Shelley and Matt Stein (and Yazzie), Lizzie and Scott Fletcher, and Al and Ingrid Center.

My amazing mom, Deborah Detering, and my rock-star husband, Gordon Center, always rack up a million points for helpfulness and self-lessness as I try to get my writing done. (Special thanks to Gordon for mangling the French language so beautifully and inspiring the phrase

"my hams exploded.") My kids, Anna and Thomas, also get a million points. Just for being sweet-hearted and hilarious.

Thanks, also, to all the folks at St. Martin's Press who have supported this book and been so great to work with: Rachel Diebel, Lisa Senz, Jessica Preeg, Erica Martirano, Brant Janeway, Jordan Hanley, Olga Grlic, Elizabeth Catalano, Devan Norman, and Janna Dokos.

Last, but not least: Heartfelt gratitude to my agent, Helen Breitwieser, who's advocated for and stuck by me now for a solid decade. And to my editor, the brilliant Jen Enderlin, who I don't think I can ever thank enough for taking me on. Thank you both beyond words.

You get one life, and it only goes forward.

—Wesley Branch

There are all kinds of happy endings.

—Eve Lapin

How to Walk Away

One

THE BIGGEST IRONY about that night is that I was always scared to fly.

Always. Ever since I was old enough to think about it.

It seemed counterintuitive. Even a little arrogant. Why go up when gravity clearly wanted us to stay down?

Back in high school, my parents took my big sister, Kitty, and me to Hawaii one year. I dreaded the flight from the moment they told us until well after we were home again. The phrase "flying to Hawaii" translated in my head to "drowning in the ocean." The week before the trip, I found myself planning out survival strategies. One night after lights out, I snuck to Kitty's room and climbed into her bed.

I was a freshman, and she was a senior, which gave her a lot of authority.

"What's the plan?" I demanded.

Her face was half buried in the pillow. "The plan for what?"

"For when the plane hits."

She opened an eye. "Hits what?"

"The ocean. On the way to Hawaii."

She held my gaze for a second. "That's not going to happen."

"I have a bad feeling," I said.

"Now you're jinxing us."

"This is serious. We need a survival strategy."

She reached out and patted my bangs. "There is no survival strategy."

"There has to be."

"No." She shook her head. "Because if we don't crash, we won't need one. And if we do crash . . ." She paused so I could catch her drift.

"We won't need one?"

A nod. "We'll just be dead." Then she snapped her fingers.

"You make it sound easy."

"Dying *is* easy. It's *not dying* that's hard."

"Guess you have a point there."

She closed her eyes. "That's why I'm the brains of the family."

"I thought I was the brains," I said, nudging her.

She rolled away. "You know you're the beauty."

Impossibly, we survived that trip.

Just as impossibly, I survived many more trips after that, never hitting anything worse than turbulence. I'd read the statistics about how flying was the safest of all the modes of transportation—from cars to trains to gondolas. I'd even once interned at an office right next to an international airport and watched planes go up and come down all day long with nary a problem. I should have been long over it.

But I never could lose the feeling that "flying" and "crashing" were kind of the same thing.

Now, years later, I was dating—seriously dating—a guy who was just days away from getting his pilot's license. Dating him so seriously, in fact, that on this particular Saturday, as we headed out to celebrate my not-yet-but-almost-official new dream job, I could not shake the feeling that he was also just about to ask me to marry him. Like, any second.

Which is why I was wearing a strapless black sundress.

If I'd thought about it, I might have paused to wonder how my boyfriend, the impossibly fit and charming Charles Philip Dunbar, could be one hundred percent perfect for me in every possible way—and also be such an air travel enthusiast. He never thought twice about flying at all—

or doing anything scary, for that matter, like scuba diving or bungee jumping. He had an inherent faith in the order of the universe and the principles of physics and the right of mankind to bend those principles to its will.

Me, I'd always suspected that chaos was stronger than order. When it was Man against Nature, my money was on Nature every time.

"You just never paid attention in science class," Chip always said, like I was simply under-informed.

True enough. But that didn't make me wrong.

Chip believed that his learning to fly was going to cure my fears. He believed that he'd become so awesome and inspiring that I'd have no choice but to relax and enjoy it.

On this, we had agreed to disagree.

"I will never, ever fly with you," I'd announced before his first lesson.

"You think that now, but one day you'll beg me to take you up."

I shook my head, like, *Nope.* "Not really a beggar."

"Not yet."

Now, he was almost certified. He'd done both his solo and his solo cross-country. He'd completed more than twice his required hours of flight training, just to be thorough. All that remained? His Check Ride, where a seasoned pilot would go up with him and put him in "stressful situations."

"Don't tell me what they are," I'd said.

But he told me anyway.

"Like, they deliberately stall the plane, and you have to cope," he went on, very pleased at the notion of his impressive self-coping. "Or you do a short-field landing, where you don't have enough space. And of course: night flying."

The Check Ride was next week. He'd be fine. Chip was the kind of guy who got calmer when things were going haywire. He'd make a perfect pilot. And I'd be perfectly happy for him to fly all he wanted. By himself.

But first, we were getting engaged—or so I hoped. Possibly tonight. On Valentine's.

I can't tell you how I knew, exactly. I'd just sensed it all day, somehow, the way you can sense it's going to rain. By the time I buckled in beside him in his Jeep, I was certain.

I'd known Chip a long time. We'd been dating for three years. I knew every expression in his repertoire and every angle of his body. I knew when he was faking a laugh, or when he was bullshitting. I could tell in seconds if he liked a person or not. And I certainly knew when he was hiding something—especially something he was excited about. Even though this date seemed exactly like every other date we'd ever had, I just knew something big was about to happen.

I figured he'd take us to the Italian place with the twinkle lights where we'd had our first date. But, instead of heading for downtown, he turned toward the freeway and ramped up.

The top was off his Jeep. I clamped my arms down over my hair. "Where are we going?" I called.

He called back, "It's a surprise!"

My stomach dropped at that. Once again, I knew Chip's intentions without his even hinting. This was kind of a problem with us. I could read him too well. He wasn't taking me to dinner. He was taking me to the airport.

TWENTY MINUTES LATER, we had left the city of Austin far behind. He pulled up the parking brake beside an airplane hangar at a private airfield in the middle of nowhere.

I looked around. "You can't be serious."

He leaned in. "Are you surprised?"

"Yes and no."

"Just pretend. Just once, I'd like to surprise you."

"Fine. I'm shocked. I'm awed."

"Don't pretend that much."

He came around to my side and took me by the hand, and then he pulled me behind him, bent over all sneaky, around to the far side of the hangar.

I followed him in a state of cognitive dissonance—knowing exactly what he was doing while insisting just as clearly that he couldn't possibly be doing it. "Are you sneaking me in here?" I whispered.

"It's fine. My friend Dylan did it with his girlfriend last week."

I tugged back against his hand. "Chip. I can't!"

"Sure you can."

"Is this—illegal?"

"I just want to show you my plane."

"It's not your plane, buddy."

"Close enough."

I had zero interest in seeing his plane. Less than zero. I was interested in wine and appetizers and candlelight. I almost had the job of my dreams! I wanted to be celebrating. I was in the mood to feel good, not bad. "Can't we just go to dinner?"

He peered around, then turned back to me. "*Anybody* can go to dinner."

"I'm cool with being anybody."

"I'm not."

Then, with a coast-is-clear shrug, he pulled me out across the pavement and stopped in front of a little white Cessna. It looked like the kind of plane you'd see in a cartoon—wings up high, body below, and a spinny little propeller nose. Very patriotic, too. Red, white, and blue stripes.

"Cute," I said with a nod, like, *Great. We're done.*

But he took my shoulders and pointed me toward the cockpit.

I took a step back. "What are you doing?"

"Let's go for a ride."

"I'm afraid to fly. Remember?"

"Time to get over that."

"I'll throw up. I'll be motion-sick."

"Not with me, you won't be."

"It's not about you. It's about flying."

"You just need the right pilot."

I was shaking my head—half disbelief, half refusal. "You're not even certified."

"I'm as good as certified. I've done everything there is."

"Except take the test."

"But the test is just to see what you've *already learned*."

"Chip? *No*."

"Margaret? *Yes*. And right now before they catch us."

The force of his insistence was almost physical, like a strong wind you have to brace against. He wanted to do this. He wanted *me* to do this—to show faith in him, to believe in him. It wasn't a test, exactly, but it was still something I could fail.

I wasn't a person who failed things.

I was a person who *aced* things.

It felt like a big moment. It felt draped in metaphorical significance about bravery, and trust, and adventurousness—like it would reveal something essential about who I was and how I'd live the rest of my whole life. Saying no to flying right now suddenly felt like saying no to every possibility forever. Did I want to be a person who let minuscule statistical risks undermine any sense of bravery? Was this a challenge I couldn't rise to? Was I going to let fear make me *small*?

I'm not sure I ever really had a choice. Chip was Chip. He was my perfect man, and I'd thought so ever since his parents moved in next door to my parents, back when we were both in college. Our mothers became best next-door-neighbor friends, drinking wine on the patio and gossiping, but I only saw him on vacations. In the summers, his dad made him mow the lawn, and I'd stand at our window and watch. One time, my mom urged me to take him out a bottle of water, and he glugged the whole thing down in one swoop. I still remember it in slow-mo.

But I really didn't know him at all until we both wound up at business school together back home in Austin by accident. I was team leader of our study group, and he worked under me, which was good for him.

That's how we fell in love.

I'd have married him that first night we kissed, if he'd asked me. He was that kind of guy. Tall, clean-shaven, blond, all-American, high-achieving, confident. And dreamy. People did what he wanted. I felt lucky to be with him, and I'd doodled "Margaret Dunbar" more times

than I'll ever admit. I once Googled dog breeds for our future pet. And one night, when shopping for something else—I swear—on the Home Depot website, I clicked on a little pop-up box for wood fence pickets. Just to see how much they were.

Now we were both out of school with our brand-new MBAs, both about to start our new jobs—Chip as an entry-level financial analyst at an investment bank, a job he found through a friend of his dad, and me as a business development manager for an oil and gas company called Simtex Petroleum. His job was good, but mine was far better, and I thought it was sporting of him, and rather gallant, to be so happy for me.

In truth, I wasn't even qualified for my new job. It required "five years of experience in the sector," "advanced knowledge of bidding for commercial contracts," and actual "international experience," none of which I had—but my B-school mentor had gone out on a limb for me, calling in a favor from a friend and writing a stunning letter of recommendation that called me a "fiercely energetic forward thinker, a problem solver, an excellent communicator, and a team player with strong business and financial acumen."

I'd laughed when he'd showed me the job listing. "I'm not remotely qualified for this."

"People get jobs they're not qualified for all the time."

I stared at the description. "They want 'demonstrated strategic and higher operational level engagement with the logistics environment.'"

"You're a shoo-in."

"I'm a joke."

"Now you're just thinking like a girl."

"I *am* a girl."

"We need to remedy that."

I gave him a look.

"When you go to this interview, I want you to pretend to be a man."

I closed my eyes. "Pretend to be a man."

"A *badass* man," he confirmed. "A man who's not just qualified, but overqualified."

I shook my head at him.

"Qualifications," he said, "pale in the face of confidence."

"If you say so," I said. Though I didn't believe it for a second. I went into the interview that day fully expecting to be laughed out of the room. But I did what he told me to. I pretended like hell—if nothing else, to prove him wrong.

Then they offered me the job. Or, at least, as the HR guy walked me to the lobby, he touched my shoulder and said, "It's not official, but you've got it."

My starting salary was going to be 50K higher than Chip's—but my mother told me not to tell him that. The important thing was: We were beginning our lives. Things were falling into place.

And here, at the airfield, I didn't want to be the only thing that didn't.

Chip squeezed my hands. "You trust me, right?"

"Yes." Sort of.

Then he pulled me into a kiss—a manly, determined, all-this-can-be-yours kiss, digging his tongue into my mouth in a way that he clearly found powerful and erotic, but that I, given how the sheer terror of what I was about to do had iced my blood, was too numb to feel.

Then he swatted me on the butt and said, "Climb in."

What can I say? I did it.

But I'm telling you, my hands were shaking.

As I worked on hooking the shoulder strap, I gave myself a stern talking-to: This was the right thing to do. Wasn't that what love was, after all? Saying *yes*—not just when it was easy, but also when it was hard?

Of course, any analyst worth her degree could have easily made the exact opposite argument: that I should trust my gut, and I shouldn't let Chip push me into doing things I didn't want to do. That his lack of respect for my genuine discomfort in the face of his *Top Gun* fantasies did not bode well for our long-term prospects.

But I wasn't going there.

I was going flying.

Then he was next to me, buckling up and handing me a set of black headphones. I had that feeling you get once you've picked a roller coaster seat and clamped yourself in.

Chip immediately shifted into character as the pilot. He slid his aviator sunglasses on and pressed the headphone mic so close to his mouth that his lips brushed against it, and started speaking a language to the control tower so specialized, it was basically nonsense: "South Austin Clearance Delivery—Cessna Three Two Six Tango Delta Charlie with information Juliet—VFR to Horseshoe Bay cruising three thousand three hundred."

It sounded to me like he was pretending. Who talked like that? But the tower didn't agree. Crackling through the headphones came "Cessna Three Two Six Tango Delta Charlie—South Austin Clearance— squawk two three one four, departure frequency will be one two zero point niner."

Oh, shit. This was happening.

Chip checked instruments and dials, looking them over like a pro. He looked at ease. Capable. Trustworthy. Macho, too. And, dammit, yes: super cool.

"I already went through my safety checklist before I came to get you—twice," he said. His voice was crackly through the headphones, but he took my hand and squeezed. "Didn't want to give you time to change your mind."

Smart.

But I was all in by this point. I'd made my choice. For better or worse, as they say.

So Chip turned his attention to bigger things.

Still in sexy-pilot mode, he spoke into the mic and gave another nonsense message to the tower, confirming that we were waiting for the runway. I'd never been in the cockpit of a plane before, and this plane was all cockpit. Technically, there were two seats behind us, but it felt like we were in a Matchbox car.

Another plane had to land before we could take off, and I studied the dashboard with all its knobs and dials and 'ometers. I pointed at it. "Isn't this kind of tall?" It was higher than my head. I could barely see over.

He nodded. "It's not like driving a car," he explained, "where it's all about what you see. Flying's more instrument based."

"You don't look out the windshield?"

"You do, but you're looking at the instruments and gauges just as much. It's half looking, half math."

The other plane touched down, slowed, and trundled past us. *See?* I said to myself. *They survived.* We revved up, Chip announced us again over the radio, and he started working the pedals to bring us into position. The blades on the propeller spun so fast they disappeared. The plane vibrated and hummed. I sat on my cold hands so I wouldn't squeeze them into fists.

"Please don't do any loop-de-loops or anything," I said then.

He glanced over. "Loop-de-loops?"

"Spins or flips. Or whatever. Show-offy stuff."

"I don't have to show off for you," he said.

"You sure don't."

"You already know how awesome I am."

I gave a nod. "Yes. And also, I might throw up."

We sped up, casting ourselves forward. As we lifted off, I decided it wasn't that different from going up in a regular plane. A little bumpier, maybe. A smidge more front-and-center. A tad more *Out of Africa*.

The ground floated away beneath us. Easy.

Chip was focused and calm, and it was so strange to think he was making it all happen. Once we were airborne, he started narrating everything he was doing, as if he were giving me a lesson. He told me the Cessna 172 was the most popular plane ever built. A classic. We would level off at 3,000 feet. We'd be traveling 125 miles an hour, speeding up as the air thinned out so we didn't stall. He had to scan the sky for other planes, as well as watch the radar on the screen for towers.

Then something disturbing: He mentioned that the fuel was in the wings.

"That seems like bad engineering," I said. "What if the wings break off? You'll get doused in fuel."

"The wings don't break off," Chip said. "That's not a thing."

"But *if they did.*"

"If they did, you've got bigger problems than a fuel spill."

I put my hands in my lap and deliberately arranged them so they would not look clenched.

The plane was loud—hence the headphones—and we vibrated more in the air than we had on the ground, especially when we passed under a cloud. Chip explained that clouds actually sit on columns of rising air, and that turbulence happens when you cut through those columns. I had never thought of clouds as sitting on anything—just floating—but once he said it, it made sense. The more sense he made, the safer I felt.

He grinned over at me. "Awesome, huh?"

Kind of. "Awesome."

"Still scared?"

Yes. "Nope."

"Glad you came?"

"I'll be gladder once we're back on the ground."

"I knew you'd enjoy it. I knew you could be brave if you tried."

Such an odd compliment. As if he'd never seen me be brave before. As if my capacity for bravery had been up for debate.

But I did feel braver now, as we rose above the subdivisions laid out like a mosaic below us.

The hardest part was over, I remember thinking.

Before long, the suburbs beneath us thinned out, and I realized I had no idea where he was taking me.

"Where are we going?" I asked.

"I'm just going to show you one quick thing," Chip said, "and then we'll turn back around and go home."

I could see that up ahead, dark and jagged, was a body of water.

"Is that Horseshoe Bay?" I asked. My grandparents had a house there. I'd been there a million times, but I'd never seen it from this angle.

Chip nodded. "You guessed it."

We were approaching the far shore. "What do you want to show me?"

"Wait and see."

Chip angled us back to circle over the lake, brought our altitude down a bit, and maneuvered us closer to the water. I could see houses and little cars below, but it was hard to recognize anything from this bird's-eye

view. We dipped a little lower, close enough to see little waves breaking against the shore.

"Keep an eye on the beach," he said, taking us lower still.

I peered out my window. A thin strip of sand, and people, and picnic tables on the grass nearby. Now I recognized it. The public beach on the far shore.

After a few minutes, he said, "There!" and pointed.

I looked. "Where?"

"Can you read it?" Chip asked.

"Read what?"

He peered down, out his side window. "Shit. We're too high."

But any lower made the towers on the radar turn red.

Chip turned my way. "There's writing in the sand down there."

I didn't see anything. "What does it say?"

"It says, 'Marry me!'"

My heart gave a little jolt, but I played it cool. "It does?" I couldn't see any writing in the sand.

"I saw it on the news yesterday. A guy proposed by writing the words in giant letters in the sand with rocks, then taking his girlfriend for a picnic by the lake to surprise her."

"Cool," I said, like it was just empirically interesting. What were we talking about?

"I really wanted you to see those words."

"You did?"

"I did." He glanced over again. "Because I've been wanting to ask you the same question."

It's one thing to expect something to happen, or root for it, or hope— and it's another thing entirely to live the actual moment. I put my hand to my mouth and pressed my head to the window one more time for a better look.

"And there's something else. Open the glove box."

Sure enough, there was a little storage compartment in front of me. Inside, I found an emerald-green velvet ring box.

I was so glad I'd forced myself into this plane. Sometimes, terrify-

ing, nausea-inducing risks are worth it. I turned to Chip. "You're asking me to marry you?"

His voice crackled out through the headphones. But I knew the answer was yes.

So I gave my own answer. "Yes!"

"You haven't even opened the box."

"I don't need to. Just: Yes!"

Chip turned toward me with a big smile full of perfect teeth. I could see myself reflected in his sunglasses, and my hair was a mess. I fought the urge to straighten it up. I also fought the urge to climb over and kiss him. It seemed strange not to kiss at a moment like that, but no way was I unbuckling. I couldn't even remember how to unhook the shoulder strap.

Instead, I gave him a thumbs-up.

"It's not official till you put on the ring," he said.

I opened the box to find a very ornate gold-and-diamond engagement ring.

"It was my grandmother's," he said.

I pulled it out and slid it onto my finger. It was a bit big. Big enough, actually, that when I held out my hand to admire it, the diamond slid to the side and hung upside down.

"It's perfect," I said.

"Do you like it?"

"Yes!" I said. Not my style, but who cared?

"Are you surprised?"

Yes and no. I nodded. "Yes."

"Are you glad you came flying with me?"

"Very," I said. And that answer really was one hundred percent true. For a little while longer, at least.

WE NEVER FOUND the letters in the sand. But it was okay. We didn't need them.

It was about twenty minutes back to the airfield, and we filled those minutes by arguing adorably about the wedding.

We agreed we should have the ceremony on that very beach, and then started listing bridesmaids and groomsmen. Most people were shoo-ins, like his brother, and his buddies Woody, Statler, Murphy, and Harris from undergrad—but then, of course, the question of what to do about my sister, Kitty, came up and stumped us for a while.

I hadn't seen or talked to Kitty in three years. Her choice.

"You have to invite her, though," Chip said.

But I wasn't sure I wanted to. When she first went away, she announced she was "taking a breather" from our family. She'd be in touch, she said. Then she never was.

We knew she wasn't dead. Our dad had kept in occasional contact, and he could verify that she was living in New York, alive and well—just unwilling, for some reason she would not share, to come home. Even for a visit.

At first it had been a little heartbreaking, losing her like that—being *rejected* by her like that. But by now, after all this time, I just felt cold. She didn't like me? Fine. I wouldn't like her, either. She wanted to pretend like her family didn't exist? No problem. We could pretend the same thing right back.

Chip thought we needed to invite her to the wedding, at least. If not make her the maid of honor. But I disagreed.

"First of all," I said, "she won't even come. And second, if she does, she'll ruin the whole thing."

"You don't know that for sure."

"Just her being there will ruin things for me. Just feeling weird about seeing her again will suck the joy right out of the day. Instead of looking forward to the most joyful day of my life, I'll dread it. Because of her."

"Maybe you could see each other beforehand and get the weirdness out of the way," Chip said.

I was in no mood for reasonable suggestions. "Even," I went on, "if I manage to get past the weirdness, having her there would still mean *having her there*. Which means a ninety percent chance of her getting drunk and climbing into the punch bowl. Or getting drunk and biting a

groomsman. Or getting drunk and grabbing the microphone for an Ethel Merman impersonation."

Chip nodded. I wasn't hypothesizing. Kitty had actually done each of these things in the past. He shrugged. "But she's your only sister."

"That's not my fault."

"It would seem weird for her not to be there."

I went on. "And it's not my fault we're not close anymore, either."

"No argument there."

"*She* created that situation."

"I agree."

"And now she gets to spoil the only wedding day I'll ever have."

My luck. I'd throw the most exquisite wedding in the history of time, and the only takeaway would be my drunk, black-sheep sister trying to ride the ice sculpture.

If she deigned to come.

Actually, that summed up our dynamic exactly. I was always trying to get things exactly right, and she was always hell-bent on getting them spectacularly wrong.

UP AHEAD, THE airfield came into sight.

Chip was especially good at landings, he mentioned then. He just had a knack for them, kind of the way he had a knack for parallel parking.

That said, the sky up ahead was quite different from the sky we'd seen on the flight down. Darker, stormier. "That's unexpected," Chip said, taking it in.

"Was it supposed to rain?"

"Not last I checked."

"You can fly in the rain, though, right?"

"Not really. You avoid it. Or wait for it to pass."

"I'm fine with either," I said. So agreeable with that ring on.

"The thing is, though," he said then, "we're going to need to land sooner rather than later."

"So we don't miss our fancy dinner reservation?"

"So we don't run out of fuel."

I studied the horizon. The sky behind us was bright blue, but up ahead it was grayer and grayer. And a little purple. With a smidge of charcoal black.

"That's definitely rain—but way past the airport. Right?"

He nodded. "Right."

Off on the horizon, there was a flash of lightning.

Maybe the storm was affecting our air. The ride back had become quite a bit bumpier, and soon I was motion-sick.

As we approached, Chip called in our coordinates in that official pilot's voice, which was a little deeper than his regular one, and then he maneuvered us into the flight pattern for landing. We pulled around to the left, then turned to run along the length of the runway, then U-turned to descend to the ground. Chip was all concentration. I felt, more than saw, the ground getting closer. A welcome idea.

And then a funny thing happened. As we were nearing the runway, the wings did a thing I can only describe as a waggle—dipping sideways a little and then popping back up—that gave me a physical sting of fear in my chest.

It was over in a second, but that second changed everything. Something was wrong.

I looked over at Chip. His face was stone still.

"Chip?" I said.

"The wind's shifted," he said.

"What?" I asked. "Is that bad?"

"It's a crosswind now" was all he answered.

A crosswind? What was a crosswind? It didn't sound good. Chip was checking dials, and working the pedals with his feet. His face was expressionless.

He seemed to be holding us fairly steady. I kept quiet, concentrating on willing us some good luck.

We were maybe twenty feet above the runway now, coming in straight. And then, suddenly, the tarmac just slid off to the side. It was

below us, and then it shifted away, like someone had tried to do a table-cloth trick—and failed—putting a grove of trees in front of us instead.

"Shit!" Chip said, and he hunched closer to the yoke.

He maneuvered us back into position, lined up over the runway again. "Chip?"

But he was talking to the radio tower. "Cessna Three Two Six Tango Delta Charlie. Failed approach, strong crosswind." Then his pilot-speak seemed to fail him, and he fell back into plain English. "Pulling up to try the approach again."

A blast of static on the headphones. "Roger that, Cessna Three Two Six Tango Delta Charlie, proceed on course."

And then the earth dropped away from us again. The engine sounded suddenly extra loud, like a lawn mower on steroids. We rose up in the air and repositioned to start the descent pattern over. To the south, blue skies. To the north, purple. Another flash of lightning.

"Is the crosswind because of the storm?" I asked.

Chip didn't answer. A bead of sweat ran down behind his ear and soaked into his T-shirt collar.

For the second try, he started farther down the runway, as if giving himself room to course-correct if he needed to. Which he did. Twice the runway beneath us rotated out to the side, and twice Chip manhandled the plane into lining up over it again.

"Nice!" I said, wanting to encourage him, hoping like hell he didn't pull up again and make us start all over. It was the least of my worries at this point, I guess, but I was right on the edge of throwing up.

I wanted nothing more than to touch down on that concrete.

It felt like the longest descent in the history of flight. Chip made one more course correction, and then we were lowering closer, and closer. I could see the concrete of the runway welcoming us down. I willed us to touch.

Then we came to a section of the runway with an airplane hangar right beside it. The size and width of that hangar seemed to provide a little windbreak. We were maybe ten feet above the runway as we passed the hangar—so close—and I could feel the wind ease off as we moved

into its shadow. Everything seemed calmer somehow. Even the engine sounded quieter. Chip eased off his struggle with the controls. The ground was so close.

We made it, I thought.

And then we passed out of the wind block, past the corner of the hangar, back into open air again, and as we did, a blast of wind hit, so concentrated and fierce that it scooped up under the wing on my side and punched us into a type of spin that folks in aviation call "cartwheeling."

I remember it in slow motion. I remember slamming hard against my seat belt—so hard, it felt like a wooden post—as my wing jerked up and the plane rotated on the tip of the other. I remember that wing scraping the tarmac with an eardrum-ripping, metal-against-concrete shriek. I remember Chip's shocked voice shouting, "Hold on!" though I had no idea what to hold on to. I remember screaming so hard I felt like nothing but the scream—and Chip doing it, too—the two of us holding each other's shocked gazes, like, *This can't be happening.* I remember some tiny tendril of my consciousness veering off to a funny little philosophical moment in the center of it all—marveling at the pointlessness of the screaming since we were so clearly beyond help—before arriving at the bigger, more salient picture:

This was the moment of our death.

There was no arguing with what was happening, and there was certainly nothing either of us could do about it. We were the very definition of helpless, and as I realized that, it also hit me that everything I'd been looking forward to was over before it even began. Chip and me—and the lakeside wedding we'd never have, and the rescue beagle we'd never adopt, and the valedictorian babies we'd never make. They say your life flashes before your eyes, but it wasn't my life as I'd lived it that I saw. It was the life I'd been waiting for. The one I'd never get a chance to live.

My future slid past my fingers as I fumbled for it—and missed.

I felt suddenly coated with anger like I'd been dunked in it. I didn't think about my parents in that moment, or my friends, or how hard my

death would be on anyone else. I thought only of myself—and how I just couldn't fucking believe this was all the time I got.

I couldn't tell you how many full rotations we completed as we blew across that runway like somebody's lost kite, but there's a reason they call it cartwheeling. The wings were the spokes of a giant wheel, and we were the axle in the middle on a spinning carnival ride from hell. At a certain point, I lost all sense of spatial orientation, and it stopped feeling like we were spinning—more like rocking back and forth. I remember focusing all my energy on not barfing because there was nothing else to even hope to control.

I was maybe three seconds from spewing vomit like in *The Exorcist* when the passenger-side wing mercifully broke off with an unearthly, bone-rattling *crack*. A spray of jet fuel hit the windshield with a *clomp* sound like we were at a drive-through car wash, and we collapsed at last in a ditch, with my side—the passenger side—wedged down in it, and Chip's side angled up at the sky.

We stopped.

Everything was still.

Then I vomited onto the window below me.

Two

A THOUSAND YEARS later, I heard Chip, out of breath: "Margaret? Are you okay?"

"I threw up," I said, not quite catching his urgency.

"Margaret—the fuel—we have to get out. Are you hurt?"

"I don't think so."

Chip was moving around unhooking and unbuckling and trying to work his door open like a hatch. His side didn't seem to be crumpled like mine was. It was stuck for a second, so he had to brace against his seat to kick it, but then it popped easily out with a satisfying *ka-chunk* and fell open wide, squeaking at the hinges for a second as it bounced.

He climbed up and out, then reached back down for me. "Come on!"

I hadn't even unbuckled yet. Everything seemed to be moving in slo-mo and time-lapse all at once. My hands didn't seem like they even belonged to me. I watched them reach to unhook the shoulder strap, and that's when I realized that it was already unhooked. Next, I tried for the lap belt, and discovered that, in ironic contrast, it was jammed.

It might not have mattered anyway. My side of the plane was crum-

pled. I was not exactly *sitting* in my seat anymore—more like sandwiched in between it and the dash.

I tried to wriggle out, but I was wedged in. I tried to move my legs, but they were pinned and didn't budge.

Chip was up on the outside now, peering down through his window like a hatch. "Come on! Margaret! Now!"

"I can't!" I said. "I'm stuck!"

He reached his arm down for me to grab. "I'll pull you."

"I can't. My legs are pinned."

Chip was silent for somewhere between one second and one hour—hard to tell. Then he said, "I'm going for help."

For the first time, at the prospect of being alone, I felt afraid. "No! Don't leave me!"

"This thing could blow at any minute!"

"I don't want to die alone!"

"We need the fire department!"

"Call them on your cell phone!"

Chip's voice was high and strange with panic. "I don't know where it is!"

"Don't go, Chip! Don't go! Don't go!" My voice, too, sounded odd—like someone else, someone I might not even like or feel sympathy for. Some screaming, hysterical, pathetic woman.

Chip was still leaving. "I have to get help. Just hold on. I'll be back in two minutes."

And then he was gone.

I WAS ALONE, in a crumpled plane, breathing air thick with jet fuel fumes. The air was so sour, and toxic, and corrosive, it felt like it was melting my lungs.

"Two minutes," I whispered until the words turned into nonsense. "Two minutes. Two minutes. Two minutes."

Next, a crack of real thunder that rattled the instruments in the dash.

Then it started raining.

The drops sounded frantic against the metal shell of the plane. Chip's door was still wide open, so the water sheeted straight in on my bare shoulders, cold and mean.

More than two minutes went by, but I can't tell you how many. Ten? Thirty? A hundred?

I wondered if it the rain was a good thing or a bad thing. Would it prevent a fire—or make it worse? I just wanted the entire world to hold still until I was out and away and safe. It was dark in the ditch, like the rain had put out the lights, too. Soon I was shivering. The raindrops pinged like gravel hitting the metal shell of the plane. I could hear a ticking noise. I could hear my own breathing. I wondered how long before the ditch filled up with water and I died by drowning in a plane crash.

I kept trying to unwedge myself. Nothing.

I've felt alone plenty of times in my life—in both good ways and bad—but I have never felt alone like this. "Come back," I whispered to Chip. "Come back." But the words were lost in the noise of the storm.

Then, over it all, I heard the most beautiful sound I've ever heard—before or since.

First far away, then closer: a siren.

The fire department.

Chip had not come back, but now I had something better. I was so glad I'd bought that firefighter calendar last year. Best twenty bucks I ever spent.

Just like that, almost as if it had heard them coming, too, the rain slowed and thinned out to a sprinkle.

The acoustics in the plane were pretty good. After they cut the siren, I could hear the firemen outside, maybe five or six, talking and calling orders to each other. I heard noises I couldn't decipher: clanking, squeaking, twisting. One guy called another guy a knucklehead. Minutes passed, then more. I wondered why no one had come to get me yet.

Then I heard a new sound—something different: A *whoosh*. Just like when your gas stove burner finally catches and leaps up into flames.

It came half a second before the flames themselves. Just long enough for me to lean a tiny bit closer to the ground and put my arms over my face.

Then: noise, wind, heat. I kept my head down because it was the only thing to do. I felt a flash of white heat sting my neck, but then it went away. Seconds later, the fire was gone. The cockpit was smoky and smelled like barbecue and burned hair.

THE NEXT SOUND was the clanking and gonglike pounding of metal. I heard banging, men's voices, a motor and a buzzing sound. Then, in what seemed like a second, the roof of the plane—which, given how we'd landed, was more like a wall—was peeled away. Kneeling next to me was a firefighter in full gear and a mask. And all behind him was snow. There was snow in the cockpit, too, now that I noticed.

He took off his mask, and he turned out to be a lady.

That struck me as very novel. A lady firefighter! She told me her name, but I have no idea what she said. Sometimes, even still, when I can't sleep, I try to remember what it was. Karen? Laura? Jenny?

"We have a live patient," she announced.

I wondered if I heard surprise in her voice.

She kneeled down beside me, while another two other guys continued cranking off the roof. "Tell me what hurts the most."

"Nothing hurts," I said, as she leaned in to check my pulse.

She looked doubtful. "Nothing at all?"

"I'm fine," I said. "Just stuck." Then I asked, "Why is it snowing?"

"It's not snow," she said. "It's foam. For the fire."

Foam! For the fire! I'd forgotten the fire for a second! Now I realized my neck and arm were stinging. "I might have some burns, actually," I said.

She smiled at me. "You're very lucky. The fire broke out just as we cranked up the hoses. We had it out in under a minute."

"That does sound lucky," I agreed.

"Plus," she went on, waving a tiny flashlight back and forth in front

of my pupils, "facedown in a ditch is the best place to be when the flames roll over."

"So, double luck," I said.

"Are you kidding? Quadruple. I'm amazed you're not a charcoal briquette."

"Me, too," I said.

"We're going to strap you to a short board now," she said, "and then to a long board while we transport you to the hospital."

"I think I'm really fine," I said. "Just wedged."

But now she was pulling out an oxygen mask and cupping it over my face. "We're going to give you some vitamin O. Just to help you breathe easier."

Vitamin O. Cute. "I'm really fine."

"Just to be safe," she said, winking. "Just procedure. You don't want me to get in trouble, do you?"

I didn't. Lady firefighters probably had the deck stacked against them anyway.

And so I held still, breathing in cool vitamin O while she attached me strap by painstaking strap into a state of snug immobilization. She also put me in a C-collar, even though it seemed perfectly clear to me that I didn't need one. The last step, once I was secure, was also the longest: prying apart the crumpled front of the plane to free my legs. This project involved three different firefighters—who took their sweet time.

I was grateful for their care, though. Nobody took shortcuts. Nobody seemed eager to get off shift. They did things right. My nameless lady firefighter stayed right by me the whole time, asking me over and over to wiggle my fingers and toes and making chitchat to keep me calm. She told me if this had been a jet crash, they'd be calling in heavy rescue—but "these little planes are like tin foil."

Before they had me out, I heard a helicopter. "There's your ride," my new friend said.

"I'm really fine," I tried again.

"You'll like it. It's fun."

"Where is Chip?" I asked.

"Is that your boyfriend?"

"Fiancé," I said, for the first time ever.

"He's back by the truck."

"Is he hurt?"

"They're doing an evaluation," she said. "But I'd say there's not a scratch on him."

Once they finally had me out, and had loaded me onto a rolling stretcher, they wheeled me to an ambulance, where they cut off all my clothes with shears ("Life Flight likes 'em naked") and started an IV with morphine.

The storm had blown off in another direction, and now the sky was remarkably cloudless. I could see a million stars up above, and I thanked them all. I thanked them for luck, and firefighters, and sirens, and flame retardant, and ditches, and bolt cutters, and good timing, and vitamin O, and hope, and miracles, and not being burned to a crisp.

The paramedics worked hard. Every time I told them I was fine, they shrugged and said, "Procedure."

Another procedure: I had to ride in the ambulance two hundred feet to the Life Flight chopper. They wouldn't let Chip come with me, either, even though there was plenty of room.

"I need you to stay with me," I told him, as they rolled me away.

"I can't," he said.

"Do it anyway!"

"I'll meet you there," he called after us, arms at his sides.

If we were flying and he was driving, I thought, he was going to have to hurry up. But he didn't hurry up. I grabbed one last glance of him as the team hustled my gurney into the chopper. He was still in the same spot, standing like a statue.

I could not believe all this fuss. Honestly. Over nothing.

Well, maybe not nothing. A brush with death. A worst nightmare come true. The crash, the rain, the fire. I might never stop shaking.

But we'd survived.

By the time I was loaded, I was pretty sleepy, though. I wondered if being afraid could do that. Or maybe it was the morphine. Or maybe

just too much vitamin O. The last thing I remember before conking out was wondering if I'd have to spend the night in the hospital. I hoped not. If I could get out early enough, maybe Chip and I could still make it to a late dinner.

Crash or no crash, we still had a lot to celebrate.

Three

I WOKE UP as all hell was breaking loose in the trauma bay—but that's not the first thing I noticed. The first thing I noticed was my back hurt like fire. And as soon as I noticed it hurting, I realized it had been hurting all along—since back at the crash site, even.

It sounds completely crazy, I know, but it wasn't until I *noticed* the pain that I *remembered* it.

"My back hurts," I said, to no one in particular—and I wouldn't have even known *who to say it to* because there were at least twenty people moving in and out of my peripheral vision in utter chaos, calling to each other in words so fast they just sounded like noise. I recall sounds and sights in little pinpricks of memory from that room—noises and images I can't even put into the right order. People in aqua scrubs moving with purpose, arms and bodies in motion, machines beeping. An unearthly light rained down from the fluorescent fixture above and blurred out the edges of my vision. Someone changed my IV fluids. Someone else asked for a catheter. I heard the words "x-ray" and "CT scan."

My neck was uncomfortable in the collar, and I asked a plump male nurse with a kind face if we could take it off.

"Not until the C-spine is cleared" came a voice across the room.

"A little longer, sweetheart," the nurse said.

Was I allergic to medications? *No.* Did I have any preexisting conditions they should be aware of? *No.* Was I pregnant? *God, I hoped not.*

"Healthy as a horse," I said.

A guy I later came to recognize as the neurosurgeon paused to tell me that they were evaluating me for pressure and sensation with pinprick tests, and they were starting me on a steroid to prevent swelling because the benefits of its use outweighed the complications.

"Okay," I said. But it didn't occur to me until after he'd stepped away to ask, "Swelling of what?"

I said it to the room, but I got no reply.

After the evaluation and CT scan, the neurosurgeon popped into view again and began to talk nonsense. "Your scans reveal a burst fracture to your L1. We're sending you to surgery to clear out debris. Your evaluation shows some deficits, but there appears to be some sacral sparing. The good news is that your iliopsoas seems to be functioning, and we believe at this time it's an incomplete injury. Of course, we'll know a lot more once we get in there."

"Incomplete injury of what?" I asked at last.

He blinked, like he thought I already knew. "Your spinal cord."

I held my breath a second. "Is that why my back hurts?"

But he'd turned away to a nurse with a question. When he turned back, he said, "You're lucky. The L1 was good and crushed, but it didn't sever the cord. Now we just need to get in there to stabilize and clean up."

"Now?" I asked.

He nodded. "We're heading to surgery. And while you're there, we'll have a plastic surgeon evaluate your face and neck and the area above your trapezius—maybe debride what he can. But that'll be a second surgery. After you've stabilized. First things first."

"What will be a second surgery?"

"The skin grafts. For the burns."

The skin grafts. For the burns.

The surgeon was ready to get moving. "Do you have any questions for me?"

I wanted to nod, but I couldn't. Yes, I had questions for him. A thousand, at least. I just couldn't figure out what they were.

Instead, I asked the only question I could come up with. "Could somebody please find my mother?"

NORMALLY, MEMORIES HAVE a chronology to them. Even if you've lost pieces of the story, you usually have a sense of order, at least—*this led to this*. What I recall from the ICU is just a pile of images, sounds, and feelings so jumbled, it's like a game of pick-up sticks.

They say everybody loses time in the ICU. It's basically Vegas in there, minus the showgirls and slot machines. No windows, for one. Bright fluorescents humming at all hours of the day and night—dimmed, sometimes, but not much. Doctors, nurses, techs, residents, physical therapists, occupational therapists, social workers, case managers, administrators, family members, and just about anyone else who feels like it walking through at all hours. Machines beeping and hissing. Rolling carts with computers. Shoes squeaking the floor. Phones ringing.

It annihilates your circadian rhythms, to say the least.

Plus, you. You're asleep, then you're awake. The world is blurred with drugs and pain. You're woken at all hours—to take medicines, to be turned to avoid bedsores, or even just because someone, anyone, has a question for you. You're a passive, drugged-out element of an unearthly ecosystem that churns day and night to keep you alive—but you're about as far from alive as it's possible to be.

Short of being dead.

I know from my mother, who arrived with my dad just after they wheeled me off to surgery (and found Chip in the waiting room looking "devastated—absolutely devastated") that the surgery took about two hours and they screwed rods to either side of my lumbar vertebrae to stabilize my spine.

I was stable enough the next day to go back in for a second surgery

to skin-graft the burns. I heard all about this later from my mom as well. Ever the overachieving student, she took copious notes in her tidy cursive, and used them not only to tell me the story of my life but to teach me many new vocabulary words, as well.

She explained that I was lucky, in a way, that the burns were so bad. Third-degree burns don't hurt because all the nerves have burned away. She explained that the spinal surgeon met the plastic surgeon in the OR to arrange me on the table so they could get at the burns on my neck without more damage to my spine. She explained, too, how he shaved off the black, crispy, burned skin with a "weck blade" (I imagined it like a carrot peeler), and then harvested skin from two donor sites just under my collarbones (the "superclavicular" area) for "full-thickness skin grafts" on my neck. They sewed the new skin down with "Prolene sutures" in crisscrosses, like quilting.

I was in recovery for both surgeries in the ICU for seven days, and the entire time, I had a dressing over my neck attached to a suction tube sucking the moisture from the skin grafts as they waited to see if they would take. My mom took a picture with her iPhone before deciding it was in bad taste. She let me see it many weeks later before erasing it entirely. I looked like I was being attacked by a giant albino lamprey.

Apparently, the first person I asked for after both surgeries was Chip. He came in after the first (though I have no memory of it), but after the second, he'd gone home to sleep, and they sent my mom in instead.

Other things I know but don't remember: I had an "indwelling Foley catheter" draining into a bag, and my bowels apparently had to be "manually evacuated" by some hospital tech with a very unfortunate job. What was left of my hair kept getting caught in my dressing, and so someone had trimmed it, unceremoniously and without asking—possibly while I was asleep. I took more drugs in one week than I'd taken in my whole life put together—massive doses of acetaminophen, Valium, Cipro, nizatidine, OxyContin, Clonis, Maalox, and a blissful little substance that makes you forget everything called Versed. Visitors were only allowed in for ten minutes at a time. Mostly, I was alone, surrounded by machines—and herds of strangers.

One of the painkillers made me throw up a lot. That I do remember.

I also remember flashes of faces. My mother, leaning down, her face puffy from crying. My father, pursing his lips to be tough and holding out a little thumbs-up gesture at me over and over, like he was giving a toast. Chip, still as a statue, right by the bed but seeming miles away. The weirdest memory I have is of various physical therapists in navy-blue scrubs coming by at all hours to move my legs and feet around for me—bending them, stretching them, turning them. I could see what they were doing, but I couldn't feel it.

It was just like a long, strange dream. With vomiting.

Four

IT WASN'T UNTIL I moved out of the ICU that I started to wake up. And it wasn't until I started waking up that I began to realize how bad things really were.

On the day they moved me out of the ICU, it took all morning to get me into the wheelchair, for example. A nurse called Nina arrived to crank the bed up in slow increments to get me sitting. I'd been lying down for so long, my blood pressure was at risk for crashing, which could cause me to faint or even have a heart attack. You lose muscle mass amazingly fast when you are immobilized and unconscious, and I had lost twenty pounds in one week. I was like a tiny, frail old lady.

I remember worrying about how shocked Chip would be to see me—and feeling kind of glad he wasn't there. Like if I had a few days, that might be enough time to pull myself together.

But that didn't stop me from asking where he was. "Where's Chip?" I asked my mother at least three times before she answered.

"He's not feeling well today, honey," she said.

"Not feeling well?" I asked.

"A touch of the Irish flu," my dad said.

"Cliff!" My mother slapped him on the shoulder.

Nina could easily have lifted me and placed me in the chair, but that's not how they roll at inpatient rehab. It's all about getting you to do things—impossible things—by yourself and before you're ready. So there I was, not even out of the ICU, enduring a three-hour teachable moment, one slow inch at a time.

"Can't you just lift me?" I asked.

"I can help you lift yourself," she said, making her "no" sound a little bit like a "yes."

My parents were nearby, standing shoulder to shoulder, tilting in toward me in sympathy. Cliff and Linda. I'd seen them shoulder to shoulder many times, but never perched so anxiously. They were itching to step in and give me a hand, but Nina body-blocked them. She had a board, and I had to edge my way onto it in my gown—still catheterized, by the way. With all the tubes and bandages and light-headedness, it was a miracle I even sat up at all.

And my legs? I still couldn't feel them—or move them. They were like mutant Japanese udon noodles hanging dead from my knees. Nina edged them over the side of the bed. I watched them dangle.

"How long till the feeling in my legs comes back?" I asked.

"That's a question for the doctor," Nina said.

By the time I was in the chair, and Nina had pulled the little foot flaps down and propped my feet up on them, I was as out of breath as if I'd sprinted a mile.

"Attagirl!" my dad shouted, when I made it—the same shout he'd always used when I crossed the line first at track meets.

I didn't look over.

Nina took my chair handles and wheeled me out, trailing after. We traveled miles through the labyrinth of hallways of the building to find my new room two wings over. It was a double room, but both beds were empty, which meant I got to pick—except my mother really wound up picking, which is kind of her signature move. She asks you what you want to do, waits for your answer, tells you why that won't work, and then makes you do what she wanted all along.

I picked the bed nearest the bathroom, but then my mother said she'd read an article in *Reader's Digest* that looking at nature was "very healing" and didn't I think it might be good to stay near the window?

As usual: I chose one and wound up in the other.

At my new bed, we did the whole wheelchair rigmarole in reverse to get me in. It took an hour, and I was panting and nauseated by the end. My parents stood at the foot of the bed the whole time like statues, watching.

"Where's Chip, again?" I asked.

"Sleeping off his hangover," my father said. This time, my mother let it be.

I turned to Nina. "How long until I get this catheter out?" I asked, as she pulled up the sheets at last, and I leaned back against the crackly hospital pillow.

"That's another question for the doctor."

I got the feeling she said that a lot.

As soon as Nina was gone, my father went for coffee downstairs, and my mother started decorating the room. This was part of her job. She and my dad ran a contracting business together, and he generally handled the construction end of things, and she did the design. So it was both her professional and personal responsibility in almost any situation to make things look better.

She'd brought a blue-and-white-checked quilt from home and a fuzzy throw blanket. She'd been collecting get-well cards all week from friends and relatives, and she'd brought some Scotch tape to affix them to the walls. She'd bought magazines, which she arranged in a fan shape on the side table, and she'd found my favorite stuffed animal from childhood in the attic (a fuzzy bunny named Fuzzy Bunny) and brought it with her. When she ran out of things to do, she took a seat on the reclining side chair and criticized the décor.

"I don't know what they're thinking with this God-awful mauve on the walls. It's like the 1980s threw up in here."

I'd just survived a plane crash, so of course this was what we talked about. Nothing pissed Linda Jacobsen off like bad décor.

"Mauve and gray," she went on. "It's toxic. They're poisoning you visually."

"It's not that bad," I said, like, *Come on.* "It's a hospital room."

But she lifted her chin. "The person who decorated this hospital," she announced, like a woman claiming her dignity in the face of unspeakable horror, "should be in jail."

I took a slow breath.

"You could open the curtains," I suggested at last.

She turned toward the window, as if she'd forgotten it. "Of course. Yes." She clicked right over, her heels making the same noise they'd made my entire life, and yanked the curtain back.

I don't know what either of us had expected to see, but the window overlooked the airshaft of the parking garage.

My mother turned to me. "It's worse open."

Indeed it was.

Just then, the heavy door to the room swung in, and a doctor I'd never seen before walked in, straight toward my bed, grabbing the computer cart on the way and pulling it behind him. He said, "How's everything feeling?" as he leaned in to check the dressings over my neck.

I didn't know how to answer. "Weird. Surreal. Bleak."

"Pain?" he specified.

Oh. "I'm not sure."

"That's the drugs. They're disorienting. But we're weaning you off them, so you should get a better read on the pain tomorrow."

"I'm not sure I want a better read on the pain."

It was a weak, embryonic joke. But he gave me a shrug. "Point taken."

He stepped back to the computer, swiped his ID badge, and started checking my charts. "The good news is," he said, "everything we grafted is working. No rejection of tissue."

Oh! He had operated on me. I guess we had met before.

"We took two full skin grafts from just under your collarbones," he pointed at the large dressing that was taped there, and I noticed it, really, for the first time. "You'll keep that dressing on about five more days, and then we'll just let it air dry. It'll scab up and heal. It'll leave a scar, of

course, but once the skin has grown back, there are ointments to help it fade. In ten years, you won't even see it."

Ten years! If I'd been drinking a beverage, I would have spit it right out.

He went on, unperturbed. "We used full skin on the front of the neck, and partial over the back trapezius area, so there will be more scarring there. Partial leaves a more mottled appearance. But you can cover some of that with hair." He smiled. "No more ponytails."

"Why is there no bandage on the graft?" I asked.

"Once it 'takes' we like to let it air, and just keep Silvadene ointment on it. It doesn't need to be covered. But you will have to go sleeveless on that side for a good while. Just buy some cheap T-shirts and cut the neck and left sleeve off." He chuckled. "Kind of Tarzan and Jane."

My mother was not amused. "What about the face?"

My eyes widened. *The face?* I didn't remember anything about 'the face.'

The doctor looked over at my mom like he hadn't noticed she was there. Then, to me: "Bet it's nice to have your mom here."

"Sort of," I said.

She went on, in a stage whisper, "I can't even look at her," and now that she mentioned it, I noticed that was true.

"The face is all second-degree," the doc said. "It's going to blister and scab and itch like hell—but if she doesn't scratch, there should be minimal scarring. Should heal up in about three weeks."

My mom was a stickler for details. "Does 'minimal scarring' mean *no* scarring?"

But she was being too greedy. "I never make promises," the doctor said, finishing up on the computer and rolling the cart away. "We'll do our best, and we'll hope that's enough."

After he left, it was dead quiet. This room had nothing of the mind-vibrating cacophony of the ICU. Just the white noise of the A/C vent, and the uncomfortable echoes of everything my mom had just said. Then, suddenly, the shuddery breaths of her crying.

I looked over. She had turned toward the window, arms clutched tight at her waist.

"Mom, stop it," I said.

"You're going to be just fine," she told me, like the opposite.

"Pull it together, please, Mom." I closed my eyes again. So tired.

"You were *perfect*," she said then. "No wonder Chip is too sick to come."

My mom had a remarkable talent for making things worse. She could always find the downside. And she had no filter, so once she found it, everybody else had to find it, too.

"You know what?" I said then. "I'm pretty exhausted."

But she wasn't done. "You had your whole life ahead of you."

So. The opposite of comforting, really.

"I've read the statistics," she went on, "about what something like this does to a relationship."

"Mom—"

"Guess what? Women don't leave men, but men do leave women."

"Chip is not going to leave me, Mom." Ridiculous wasn't even a big enough word for how ridiculous that was.

"No," she said, turning to face me. "No, he's not. Because we are going to fix you."

I knew that look on her face far too well.

"God did not give me all this strength for nothing," she went on. "You'll recover, darling girl. We will put you back as good as new. I've already got a file folder as fat as a brick with articles on miraculous re-coveries and people who've defied all their grim diagnoses."

Was my diagnosis "grim"? Something told me not to ask.

My mom turned around and fixed her gaze on the blanket at my feet. "You're going to bounce back from this and show them all," she said, going just the tiniest bit Scarlett O'Hara. "We'll find the best cosmetic surgeons in the world. We'll scour the earth. We will not rest. If Daddy and I have to spend every cent we've ever saved—*Cash in our life insurance! Sell the house!*—we'll do it."

I should have just let it go. I should have let us lapse back into silence. But something in me needed to convince her. "Chip is not going any-where," I tried again. "He loves me."

"The old you, maybe," she said. "But now?" She frowned. "But we're not going to let that happen. I've been online every night, researching people who've faced this type of thing and overcome it, and I know that more than anything, it takes determination. One girl I read about dove into a too-shallow swimming pool at her bachelorette party and broke her neck. She should have *died*—but she fought her way back and now she teaches water ballet. Another woman? Crushed by a truck! Broke every bone in her body and then some. Now she's an aerobics instructor in San Bernardino. Another girl was just crossing the street when a drunk driver mowed her down. Now she's an underwear model."

"I get it, Mom."

But there was no stopping her. "What do all these people have in com-mon? Gumption. Grit. Strength. And you've got all that in spades—you always have. And you've literally got extra, too, because you've got me."

It wasn't uninspiring. It was good to know she had my back. Plus, she wasn't wrong—the woman was strong as an ox. But somehow the sensa-tions it was leaving in me—hazy as they were to identify—seemed equal parts worry, inspiration, and panic. As was always true with my mother, you never could get exactly what you wanted. I wanted the strength without the fear-mongering. I wanted the determination without the control. I wanted the pep talk without the underwear model.

Mostly, right now, I just wanted to close my eyes.

Lucky for me, my dad walked in next with a tray of coffees. He knew in an instant just from the vibe what kind of conversation we were hav-ing. "Look at this room," he said, attempting to redirect. "Linda, you've worked your magic."

But Linda wasn't having it. "The doctor came in. He says there's no guarantee that her face will recover."

"I believe he said there should be minimal scarring," I volunteered.

"You know what?" my dad said, reading us perfectly, "I think our girl

needs some rest." He'd been with my mom for thirty years. He was an expert on damage control.

"What about the coffee?" she protested.

"We'll take it in the car."

He came to me, looked me right in my burned face, and crinkled his eyes into a smile while he squeezed my hand. "Get some rest, sweetheart."

"Dad?" I asked.

"Yeah?"

"Where *is* Chip?" Now she kind of had me worried.

My dad just chuckled. "I'm sure he's just sleeping it off, sweetheart. We could all use some rest. This'll be your first quiet night's sleep in ages." Then he noticed me frowning and patted my hand. He knew what I was asking. "Sometimes, when you really need your man to be big and strong for you the most—that's when we go to pieces."

"I've never seen you go to pieces," I said to him.

He gave my mother a sideways glance. "I'm saving it all up for later."

Okay, I thought, after they left. *Okay. A good night's sleep. I can make that happen.* That was something to look forward to, at least, if nothing else. Rest. Recuperation. A restful sleep in a quiet, dark room.

EASIER FANTASIZED THAN done. Nurses were still in and out quite a bit, checking monitors, emptying catheter bags, and turning me over. I was not wearing a brace—surgeon's orders—so I was extra laborious to turn. I had just fallen asleep when I got a visit from the surgeon, checking in, and had just dozed off again when a hospital social worker woke me to see how I was feeling.

"Fine. Good," I said.

"Any depression?"

"Depression?" I wasn't fully awake.

"Depression's pretty common for situations like yours. It's nothing to be afraid of. And there's medication, if you need it."

"Oh. No."

"Suicidal thoughts?"

"Um," I said, like I was thinking. "Not yet."

I did keep wondering where Chip was, though.

In truth, I wasn't feeling anything yet—at least, when my mother wasn't around. It was like my emotions had gone offline. It was like I wasn't fully there. Things were happening around and to me, and there was pain, discomfort, exhaustion, but it was like I was witnessing it rather than experiencing it. I was across the room, watching somebody else's life unfold, and not even fully paying attention. Even if I'd tried, I suspected, I couldn't make sense of the pieces and how they fit together. There was no story of what was happening. I took each moment as separate from the others and did not try to piece together what those moments meant or where they were headed.

This was probably some kind of feature of emotional shock. I'm sure it had a protective quality: my brain just refusing to grasp what it knew it couldn't handle. But as the pieces of my situation came together, I received them all with detached interest. Like, "Oh? My face is burned? Huh." And, "I can't use my legs right now? Okay." And, "My mother is going to town on my hospital room like Shirley MacLaine in *Terms of Endearment*? It *is* actually kind of nicer now."

No understanding at all that my life would never quite be the same.

Until I fell asleep.

The worst thing about sleeping, after something terrible happens, is that sleeping makes you forget. Which is fine, until you wake up. That night, I had my first nightmare about the crash, and in the dream, I was the pilot—in a wedding dress with a veil—and I steered us straight for the ground at full speed, sure to kill us both, as Chip shouted, "Pull up! Pull up!" But the controls were stuck. I woke just before we hit, breathing hard, tears from nowhere all over my face, thinking, *Thank God, thank God. We didn't crash.*

But we *did* crash.

The dream receded and I was left alone in the dark with real life—which was worse, by far—my heart pounding with panic, my eyes wide.

I stared at the ceiling and tried to take deep breaths—but they were great, heaving, scraping ones instead of anything close to calming. I hadn't died, I kept telling myself.

But what if this was worse?

Now I tried to put the pieces together—but I couldn't. My life as I knew it was over, and that was more than enough to keep me awake all night. I didn't know what was left, or what to expect, or what it might be possible to hope for. I lay there in the dark, breathing deep, terrified breaths for endless hours. I thought about calling the nurse, but what could she do? I needed to talk to someone, but who could I even talk to? My brain raced and spun and searched for avenues of comfort—but there were none. And, for several endless, black hours, through the deepest part of that night, I fought to keep from drowning as comprehension breached the hull of my consciousness and filled it to the top.

Five

I WAS STILL awake at 6:00 A.M. when Nina the nurse and a tech came to turn me.

I was so immobile at that point that I still ran the risk of bedsores. They flipped on all the lights and talked to me about the traffic and the weather as if nothing had changed in the world. They gave me pain meds, and changed the bandage on my donor sites, and smeared the burns with Silvadene ointment using a spatula. They were almost aggressively cheerful and jocular with each other and with me. Nina liked to call me "lady"—like, "Hey, lady, how'd you sleep?"

I didn't know how to begin.

"You start OT and PT today," she went on. "In the rehab gym."

"What's the difference?"

She was fussing with my chart on the computer. "OT is like working on day-to-day tasks, and PT is like strength training."

"Oh," I said.

"You've got Priya for OT, and—uh-oh."

That got my attention. "What?"

"There's a mistake here."

"What mistake?"

"They gave you the wrong PT. I'll talk to them."

I started to ask "What's the wrong PT?" but before I could, the door pushed open and Chip stumbled in.

We all stared. His blond hair looked greasy. His face was covered in stubble. His polo shirt had a brown stain—*Soy sauce? Worcestershire? Blood?*—all down the front, and his pants were ripped. One of his shoes was untied.

He made straight for me and shoved his face down on top of mine in a slobbery kiss that tasted like beer. And dirt. And sleep deprivation.

I held my breath until he finished, and as I did, I realized what this moment was: a simple, clear, all-purpose answer to that question I kept asking.

Where was Chip? At a bar.

I pushed him off. "Are you drunk?"

Chip blinked at the question. "I think so. Probably."

"It's six in the morning."

But he was studying my face. "You used to be so beautiful—and now you look like a pizza." He made himself laugh with that one, and Nina and I stared as he doubled over for a second and hung from his waist, his shoulder shaking with chuckles. Then he stood up. "But I just kissed you anyway! Because you"—here, he held up an imaginary glass for a toast—"are the love of my life."

I looked over at Nina, who lifted her eyebrows to see if she needed to stay.

I waved, like, *No big deal.* "I've got it." Whatever he was about to say, I certainly didn't want her hearing it. I didn't even want to hear it myself.

Nina set the nurse buzzer next to my hand before going. "Call if you need me."

I turned back to Chip. "Where have you been, Chip? I've been waiting for you."

I hated the way my voice sounded. I'd learned many boyfriends back that desperation never works. You can't ask someone to love you or be

there for you or do the right thing—and you certainly can't guilt them into it. Either they will or they won't. I'd have sworn that Chip was a guy who *would*—up until the crash, at least.

Suddenly, I wasn't so sure.

"Do you know I escaped that crash without a scratch?" Chip said then. "The plane is totaled. You"—he let out a bitter honk of a laugh—"are totaled. But me? Nothing. I didn't even get a Band-Aid."

"Chip, what are you doing?"

At the question, he crumpled down beside the bed—literally fell to his knees on the hospital floor, his hands in fists around the bedrails—and he broke into sobs.

It was a shocking sight. I'd never seen him—or any guy—cry like that. My father never cried. He got wet eyes at funerals sometimes, but always quietly, stoically—nothing like this. This was shoulder-shaking, full-body sobbing. I poked my hand through the bars and stroked Chip's hair.

"Hey," I said, after a while, as he started to quiet. "Maybe you should go home and get some sleep."

"I can't sleep," he insisted. "I don't sleep anymore."

I made my voice tender. "I bet you could, if you tried."

He broke away—pushed off from the bed and paced to the far wall. "Don't be so nice to me."

"You're overwhelmed. You need some rest."

Now he was mad. "Don't tell me what I need!"

"Chip," I said. "It was an accident."

But that just made him madder. He stared straight at me. "I ruined your life."

"You didn't. It was the weather! It was the wind!"

"You're blaming *the wind*?"

But who else could I blame?

"You're better at self-delusion than I thought. Have you seen yourself? Have you seen your *face*?"

I hadn't, actually. My mother had covered the mirror in the bathroom with a pillowcase. Not that I could have stood up to see into it anyway.

"You're like something out of a horror movie! Because of me! I did that."

Wow. Okay. "The doctor said there'd be minimal scarring."

"Not on your neck. Those are *third-degree* burns. They're never going to heal right. They will look like Silly Putty until your dying day. You've got me to thank for that—me and my ego and my insecurities—" He shoved his hand into his hair. He looked a little green, like the alcohol was catching up with him.

"It was an accident," I insisted.

He looked up—right at me. "I broke your back. You understand that, right? They told you? You didn't want to go up in that plane with me. It was the last thing on earth you wanted to do, but I fucking forced you. You trusted me. And now—because of me—you will *never, ever—*"

Maybe for the first time ever with Chip, I didn't see his next words coming:

"*—walk again.*"

For a second, I thought I'd maybe heard him wrong.

Then, just like that, I knew I hadn't.

It was like the oxygen had been sucked out of the room. My lungs seemed to flatten. I tried to take a breath, but I couldn't make it work. All I could manage was tiny little flutters.

Chip sobered, reading my face, and peered in closer. "They haven't told you yet?"

I felt dizzy, I still couldn't catch my breath, and then I got that salty tingle you get in your mouth right before you throw up.

Chip took a step back. "Oh, my God! They didn't tell you you're paralyzed!"

Didn't see "paralyzed" coming, either.

Next? I threw up. All over the floor, and the bedrail, and my hospital gown, though my mother's nine-patch quilt from home was miraculously spared.

Right then, as if on cue, the door pushed open and my father walked in, carrying a box of French pastries over his head like a waiter's tray

and announcing, "We've got—" But he stopped short when he saw us, and then finished under his breath, "Croissants."

Chip rounded on him. "Nobody's told her?"

My dad shifted into action, leaning back out into the hallway—"Can we get some help in here?"—then tossing the pastry box on the side chair and leaning over the bed to check on me. I stayed draped over the railing in case I puked again. Plus, now I was afraid to move my back. Had leaning over hurt it? Had the heaving made things worse? Could I have accidentally just made myself *more* paralyzed?

My father grabbed a towel and reached around to wipe my face off.

Chip's outrage seemed to exempt him from caretaking duties. He stayed safely across the room. "She's *paralyzed*—and nobody told her?" Chip demanded of my dad again, slurring a little.

"Sounds like you just did," my father said, tucking my hair back behind my ear.

"She has a right to know, doesn't she?"

"Of course," my dad said, his voice tightening, turning to face him. "But not like this. We were waiting for the right moment."

"Like when?" Chip demanded. "Over Thanksgiving turkey? On Christmas morning?"

"You self-righteous little clown—"

My dad was a big, bearlike guy—a former marine—and Chip was more in the "wiry" category. Everyone knew my dad could crush Chip if he wanted to—and I suddenly understood that maybe that was exactly what Chip wanted.

"Dad!" I called. "He's drunk. He's been out all night drinking. Just take him home."

"I can't leave you."

"I'm fine."

"You don't seem fine to me, sweetheart."

"Just get him out of here, Daddy." I hadn't called him "Daddy" in years. "Please."

My dad let out a long sigh, and as he did, Nina bustled in with a fresh

gown and new sheets. An orderly followed her with a mop cart and spray bleach for the floor.

I let Nina fuss over me, and get me changed, and reposition me in the bed. I watched the orderly mop, wondering if he'd notice the far splat in the corner. The room seemed to fill with a wispy, numbing fog. It was like the real world was too much, and so my brain was going to blur it out. There were noises, there was talking—I heard my dad and Chip muttering and hissing at each other—and the door opened and closed and opened and closed, but the moment seemed to break into puzzle pieces scattered across a table.

For a long time after Nina got me settled, I tried to hold very still, afraid to move and make things worse. When I finally lifted my head to look around, the only person still left—still stuck—in the room was me.

THAT FOG LASTED for a good while.

Never walk again. What did that even mean? How did they know? How could they be certain? Who were they to make predictions about the rest of my life? Wasn't the human body full of mysteries and miracles? Could they just announce something like that about me and then leave me to live with it?

Of course they could. I'd broken my back, apparently. That was what happened to people who broke their backs. They spent the rest of their lives in wheelchairs. I'd watched a documentary about it last year—a team of invincible teenage boys who'd crashed their cars or their motorcycles or dived into shallow water only to spend the rest of their lives in wheelchairs. But now they'd formed a championship wheelchair basketball team. Which might have been inspiring to think about, except that I'd always sucked at basketball.

Paralyzed. Trying to work that idea into my brain was like trying to suck a bowling ball up through a drinking straw.

Impossible.

Not possible.

And yet Chip accepted it. My dad hadn't argued with him. It was apparently already an established fact about my life--one everybody knew but me. On some level, of course, I wasn't surprised. I'd been contending with my dead, pendulous legs for more than a week now. But things heal. Things *always* heal. I'd never had any injury—and I'd had plenty—that didn't mend itself eventually. *Paralyzed.* I couldn't fathom it. How would I drive a car? How would I cook dinner? How would I take a shower? Go to the bathroom? Buy groceries? Go out with friends? Have a job? Be the boss of whatever I was supposed to be the boss of? My brain was short-circuiting. I could feel it throwing sparks and smoking.

I tried for calming breaths, but I accidentally hyperventilated instead.

That's when the physical therapist arrived—while I was basically doing self-Lamaze.

He wore pale blue scrubs and sneakers, and he had short, clean-cut hair that spiked up some in the front. He walked in and said, "I'm Ian Moffat. Your physical therapist."

Except it didn't sound like words to me. Just a bunch of syllables.

He swiped his badge in the computer and looked at my chart a second, before he said, "So. You're Margaret."

But again. Just syllables.

When I didn't answer, he waved a little and said, "Hello?"

That I understood.

"It's time for your physical therapy," he said.

"What?" I asked.

"What what?"

"I can't understand you," I said, shaking my head a little, as if to shake water out of my ears.

"Nobody can understand me. I'm Scottish."

Wow. That explained it. Yes, he certainly was. I thought my brain had shut down—but it wasn't me, it was him. He was super Scottish. So Scottish he sounded like he was talking through a mouth full of pretzels.

"You'll get used to it," he said. "Ready to go?"

I wasn't. I wasn't ready to go. I shook my head.

"Not ready to go?" He held that last *o* with his lips, and I was forced to notice his lower teeth were a little crooked, but in a good way.

I shook my head.

"Why not?" he asked, with no *t* on the end.

My drunk fiancé just told me I'll never walk again. "It's been a tough morning."

"Lots of mornings are tough. We still have to do this."

"No."

"No what?" Later, I would decide that it wasn't just the consonants that were exaggerated—it was the vowels, too.

"No," I explained, "I can't do this right now."

"Look," he said, putting his hands on his hips and narrowing his eyes. "Every day—every hour—that you lie in that bed, your muscles are atrophying. Nothing will make you sicker than lying motionless all day. You have to get out. Whether you feel like it or not. You have to come with me to the physical therapy gym every day, always—not because you want to, or because you feel inspired, but because *not going* will put your health in genuine peril."

I had to work to mold all those syllables into meaning. His words seemed to sit on top of each other, stacked in columns instead of laid out properly in sentences. And for a grand finale, he clacked his *r* on "peril." I wondered if an American could pull off a word like that in conversation. But I got his gist.

"Thank you for the inspiring pep talk," I said. Then: "No."

"You're coming."

"I'm not."

"You are."

"I won't."

I don't really know where we would have gone from there. He didn't much seem like the type to give in, and I was—suddenly—just spoiling for a fight.

But that's when Nina walked in—a last check before she went off shift—and I don't know if she'd been listening at the door or what, but

without skipping a beat she said, "Oh, this one's not starting till tomorrow. It was a typo in the chart."

Ian looked back and forth between us.

"Ask Myles, if you want. She's still got one more day."

He eyed us—suspiciously, like we might be in cahoots. Finally, he said, "Tomorrow, then."

He walked out.

"No, no, no, no, no," Nina said then, typing into the computer at the same time. "They are not giving you that guy for PT. I already told them to switch you out."

"What?" I asked. "Is he bad?"

"He's not bad," she said, "but he's not for you."

"Not for me?"

She kept her eyes on the monitor. "He's just not kind. He's relentless. Merciless. Thoughtless. That works for some people. Not you. We'll get you someone else. You've got enough going on."

On a different day, I might have asked more about him. But who cared about that heartless guy, really? Who cared about anything?

"Nina?" I asked then.

She kept typing. "What is it, sweetheart?"

"My drunk fiancé came in here this morning and told me I was never going to walk again."

Nina looked up.

"Is that true?" I asked.

From her face, I could see that it was.

Still, I waited for more—some words of encouragement, or some little crumb of hope to pick up. But she just let out a long sigh, and paused longer than could possibly be good news. "That's—"

And then I knew exactly how she was going to finish, and so I said it with her: "A question for the doctor."

Six

SO BEGAN THE strangest day of my life—one of them, at least. Top five.

What I wanted most all day was exactly what I wanted least.

I desperately needed time alone to process the news that Chip had just given me, and I just as desperately did not ever want to process any-thing—or be alone—again. I needed to take an emotional breath, but I was petrified to do it. So I spent the day mentally panting, light-headed and oxygen deprived, with my soul crying for air but my brain refusing to breathe it—and also dreading the night, when I'd have no distractions from every impossible thought that would rush in without my permission.

My parents startled me by arriving with lunch—Tex-Mex takeout from my favorite spot—before I realized any time had gone by. They had big, anticipatory smiles, as if fajitas might make everything okay for me.

I didn't touch the food—too nauseated from the meds—but I thanked them. Not even the idea of the food was comforting. My dad gave me the report on driving Chip home: He'd thrown up twice on the drive—"kind of a motif today"—once out the window, and once all over the dashboard. His parents were waiting in their driveway, and they steered him inside to sleep it off.

"Poor Chip," my mother said. "I hope they offered to pay for a detail."

Poor Chip? Was Chip the one we felt sorry for?

"He's not handling this well," my dad said.

My mother gave me a pointed look. "Sometimes I think people are more worried about him than about you," she said, as if we were making chitchat.

"I don't need people's worry," I said. I was worried about me. That was enough.

"He shouldn't have said what he said to you today," my father went on.

"He told me I look like a pizza," I said. "Is that true?"

"No, sweetheart," my dad said. But my mother looked away.

"I'd like to get a look," I said then, catching my mother's eye. "Can I borrow your compact mirror?"

But the headshake she gave, I knew from a lifetime of experience, meant *no way in hell*. "You're not ready."

Okay. Maybe she was right. Maybe I'd learned enough today. On to the next question—the one I didn't want to ask. But I paused a long time. I took a low breath. "He also said I was paralyzed," I said at last.

My mother sat up a little straighter.

"Is that true?"

My father gave me a sad little shrug. "Let's just say it's a good thing you're still on our insurance."

My mother had insisted that I stay on the plan they kept for their employees until I was settled in my career, even though the premiums were higher. We had argued about it more than once.

I hated it when she was right.

"What does that mean?" I asked, turning to my mother, who was braver.

She let out a big sigh. "From what the doctors have told us, only time will tell. It takes about six weeks before the bone heals and all the swelling in your spinal column clears out and we can see what kind of damage is left. Right now, the swelling itself could be blocking nerve signals. It's

possible that once everything has healed there will be no blockage at all, and all normal function will come back."

I read both of their stoic faces. "Possible," I said, "but not likely."

"Not very likely, no," my dad said. "The doc is very encouraged by some parts of your nerve responses and less encouraged by others. But he also says there's real mystery involved in these kinds of injuries. He said there are people you think will never take another step who wind up running marathons."

"Or becoming underwear models," I said, my voice like a robot.

"Exactly," my mother nodded, like that would be a good thing.

"So we're waiting," my father explained. "Doing everything the docs tell us, and waiting."

My mother still couldn't look at me for more than two seconds at a time. "The point is," she chimed in, eyes on her taco salad, "it's all about attitude."

I squinted, like, *Really?* "Sounds to me like it's all about swelling and nerve damage."

She pushed on. "You have to believe you can get better. You have to work hard and never give up. I saw Chip's mother in the yard this morning, and I promised you'd be good as new by summer."

My dad and I both stared at her.

"You didn't," he said.

My mother sat up straighter. "I saw a video just this morning about a young BXM racer—"

"BMX racer," my dad and I both corrected.

"—who simply refused to let his spinal cord injury hold him back. He broke his neck, Margaret!" She reached up and tapped at the spot on her own neck, still averting her eyes from my face. "They told him he'd never feed himself again! Now, he's riding his bike from coast to coast raising money for charity—and he's about to record a country album."

"That's very inspiring," my dad said. "But it's not just mind over matter, Linda. If you break your leg, you can't just tell yourself it's not broken."

"But the human body *does* heal," my mom said, pointing at him.

"Yes, but the spinal cord is different," my dad said patiently. "Remember what the doctor said? When those nerves get damaged, they don't grow back."

"Well, I don't see why not."

My dad looked at me. We both imperceptibly shook our heads. "But they might not be damaged," he emphasized to me. "They might just be compressed. Your job is to get lots of rest, take your medicine, and do whatever these folks tell you. For five and a half more weeks."

"Five and a half?" I asked.

"That's what insurance covers," he said. "One week in the ICU, and five and a half weeks in the hospital afterwards."

"That's awfully specific."

"Yep."

"What happens at the end of five and a half weeks?"

My dad shrugged. "They stop paying. You move home and start out-patient therapy at a gym."

"Move home? Which home?"

My dad smiled. "Any home you want."

I took all this in. I was going to be here for five and a half more weeks.

"The point is," my dad went on, "to make the most of your time here while you have it. We'll just see what happens when we see what happens. That's all we can do."

"And have the right attitude!" my mom added, like he'd forgotten the most important thing. "And believe two hundred percent that you can beat this."

My mom had gone to my apartment and picked up my laptop, and the novel I'd been reading, and some fuzzy socks, and my pale blue chevron-print pillowcase, and some ridiculous, strappy high-heeled sandals that she thought might "cheer me up"—but, of course, did the opposite.

I didn't want to use my laptop or read that novel or even look at the sandals. I didn't want to see anything from before.

"Your cell phone was destroyed in the crash," my mom said next,

"along with everything—burned to a crisp—and so I stopped by the store and got you a replacement. They were really very understanding."

She handed it to me and pulled out a charging cord for my dad to plug in. We watched my dad hunt for the plug.

"They never found the ring, either," she added, after a bit.

"What ring?" I asked.

At that, my mother took a good look at me for the first time all day. "Your engagement ring!" she said, like, *Duh!* Then, "Chip gave us the good news while you were in surgery."

The good news. I looked down at my naked hand. I'd forgotten a ring was ever there. "Oh."

"It must have come off in the crash."

I nodded. "It was enormous."

"Too bad," my mom said, bending back over her bag to root out some other things. "It was his grandmother's. Irreplaceable."

She pulled out some framed photos. She'd grabbed two of the three that I kept on my dressing table: one of Chip and me on a hike in the Rockies, and one of me with my parents the day we'd gone zip-lining. The third picture on my dresser was of me and my sister, Kitty, when we were little, dressed up like cowboys with hats and bandanas, back when I used to adore her. That one, my mom left behind.

My mother and my sister did not get along.

Like, really did not get along.

Like, I suspected my mom was the reason Kitty had been ignoring us all for three solid years.

In fact, my mom was the last of us to see Kit before she took off and didn't come back. My parents were hosting a Fourth of July party three summers ago. Kitty had been drinking that night, as she often did, and she'd been loud and boisterous and causing trouble, and at one point, she accidentally-on-purpose pushed my mom into the swimming pool. Kitty laughed so hard at the sight, she collapsed onto one of the chaises and stayed there until my mother climbed up the pool steps, gushing water onto the patio, and dragged Kitty inside and upstairs to have it out.

I took up my mom's hosting duties while they were gone, keeping an

eye out for them all the while, but when my mom came back much later, fully dried off and wearing a whole new outfit, Kitty wasn't with her.

"Where's Kit?" I asked, but she wouldn't tell me.

In fact, she never told me. To this day, I had no idea what they fought about that night. All I knew was, it must have been bad. Kitty sent me an email the next day, to tell me that she was moving to New York. Immediately.

I tried to get her to come home and talk to me about it, but she wouldn't. I tried to get her to tell me where she was, but she wouldn't. I didn't think she'd really leave, but she did.

I didn't think it would last, either, but it did.

She left, and she didn't look back. She stayed away from all of us. My mom never tried to contact her, but I did, and my dad did, even though emails went unanswered and texts and phone messages were ignored.

The whole situation bewildered me at first. My mom and Kit had never really gotten along, I knew. I also knew my mom had always been harder on Kit than she was on me. But just disappearing? Ignoring everybody? No Thanksgivings, no Christmases? No birthdays? It seemed like a bit much.

After a year and a half of trying and trying and getting nowhere, I stopped trying so hard. I stopped wondering what we'd all done to push her away, and I just found myself feeling resentful of the fact that she'd gone. You can only reach out so many times before you stop trying. After a while, just the fact that somebody is mad at you can make you feel mad at them. The longer she stayed away, the more defensive I became, and without even noticing, I drifted into an alliance with my mother—steadily resenting Kitty for disappearing without ever even saying why.

At this point, my sweet dad was the only one of us still hoping she'd decide to get in touch.

"No picture of Kitty?" I asked—not because I was surprised, but as a way of calling attention to our allegiance, a way of reinforcing a little closeness when I could.

My mom gave me an eye-roll that was just as reinforcing. "Please."

But the mention of Kitty did raise a question. "Has anybody called her about this?" I asked.

"No," my mother said definitively, just as my father said, "Yes."

My mother and I both looked at him. "You did?"

My dad nodded. "I sent her an email with the subject URGENT FAMILY EMERGENCY."

My mom looked away. "I'm surprised she replied."

"Well," my dad said, "she did. And then she hopped on a plane and came home."

"She's *here*?" my mom asked.

My dad nodded. "She came to the ICU several times." Then he glanced at my mom. "When you were out."

I shook my head. "I don't remember seeing her."

"You were on a lot of medication."

My mother gave my dad the look she gives him when he's been very bad. "We didn't *pay* for that plane ticket, did we?"

He ignored her. "She'd like to come see you," he said to me, "but she doesn't want to upset you or make any trouble. Can I tell her it's okay?"

From his expression, he clearly expected me to say *fine*. But I found myself shaking my head. The idea of some big, delayed, years-too-late confrontation with her felt like way too much right now. I couldn't face it. I had enough going on. Even just thinking about seeing her again made me exhausted.

"Okay," my dad said, nodding. "I get it. I'll tell her you're not ready."

"Just tell her to go back to New York," I said. "I won't be ready anytime soon."

My mother had that look she gets when she wants to yell at my dad, but she holds it in for the sake of the children. I did not envy his car ride home.

"Thank you for going to all this trouble to grab my stuff," I said to cheer her a bit.

"No trouble," she said, shrugging in a way that let me know *yes*, it had been trouble, but that's the kind of self-sacrificing mother she was.

Also, she was going to make another trip later to bring her folding bridge chairs "so company would have a place to sit."

"No company," I said then. "I don't want any visitors."

My parents looked at each other. My estranged sister was one thing—but *no visitors at all*?

"A few close friends, at least?" my dad asked, in a *be reasonable* tone.

"No friends. No one."

"Sweetheart," my mother said. "The phone's been ringing off the hook. The front hall table is covered in cards. People want to see you."

It was my moment to reflect graciously on how kind it was of people to think of me. But I just said, "I don't really care."

"We can't barricade the hospital," my mother said.

But my dad said, "We might talk to the nurses. Say she's not ready."

My mom frowned. "But all the literature says not to let them get isolated."

Oh, God. She'd been reading "the literature." It was worse than I thought.

"I just need some time," I said, trying to get her on my side.

Truer words were never spoken. If I had to make a list of things I wanted to see right now, old friends who would pity, judge, and gossip about me would be the last things on it. I didn't want anyone else thinking the things I was thinking. I didn't want anyone else privy to the specific horrors of my new situation. I did not want to be the topic of anyone's phone chats, or get-togethers, or status updates. I didn't want to be the reason other people counted their blessings.

I would see them—*might*—when and if I could do it of my own accord.

Which left my mother with nothing but decorating. After capitulating at last to the No Visitors policy, she made us both weigh in on whether or not the hospital might let her bring some floor lamps. Her next stop, she said, was Bed, Bath & Beyond for a tension curtain rod and some better window treatments. Maybe a throw pillow.

This was my mother's method for loving people: through décor. She

glared at the mauve-and-gray-swirled curtains as if they actually might try to harm us. "Doesn't that fabric make you want to cry?"

I tilted my head. "I'm not sure it's the fabric."

"That fabric," she went on, pointing at it now in accusation, "is a crime against humanity."

My dad and I knew better than to argue. If my mother ruled the world, its prisons would be crammed full of nothing but citizens with bad taste.

AFTER THEY LEFT—taking the morning's sad croissants to donate to the nurses' station after I declared I'd never eat them—I decided to close my eyes for just a second, and I fell dead asleep. You wouldn't think being confined to a bed would be so tiring.

I slept until my new occupational therapist, Priya, came in and wanted me to try to wiggle my toes. She also wanted to work on transferring from the bed to the wheelchair, saying the sooner I could get into the chair on my own, the sooner I could wheel myself to the bathroom—and the sooner I could do *that*, the sooner we could remove my catheter to see if, God willing, I could pee on my own.

We practiced an extra transfer, just for good measure.

I kept expecting to see Chip. All day, every time the door swung open, I expected it to be him—carrying flowers, at least, and full of apologies and encouraging words. But he never did show up. Maybe he was still at his parents' house, sleeping it all off. For his sake, I hoped so.

All of this bustling busy-ness seemed oddly cheerful on the surface. Every professional I interacted with had a pleasant, just-another-day-at-the-office demeanor, and yet I strongly suspected they were faking. I know for sure that I was. I kept things calm, I stayed pleasant, I took my medicine—but the truth is, I had woken up in a dystopic world, one so different that even all the colors were in a minor key, more like a sour, washed-out old photograph than anything real.

It looked that way, and it felt that way, too.

I couldn't imagine the future, and I couldn't—wouldn't—even think about the past. And by "the past," I mean ten days earlier. My past hadn't even had time to fade: It had been severed from me—the whole history of who I'd been, what I did, anything I'd ever dared to hope for—gone.

That kind of thing puts quite a spin on your perception.

By that evening, I was so tired, I had hopes I might actually sleep through the night. Exhaustion is a friend to the grieving. I was the kind of tired where sleep just reaches out and tugs you into its gentle sea without you ever making a choice. Just as I was giving in and closing my eyes, the door opened again.

And it was my sister, Kitty. With a suitcase.

Seven

KITTY HESITATED AT the door. "Hey, Mags," she said.

When I didn't respond, she held her hand up in a little wave.

"I know you said you didn't want me to come," she said. "But I came anyway. Obviously."

I just stared.

She didn't step in. She waited for permission that I wasn't prepared to give.

Three years. Three years of unanswered emails and phone messages. Three years of nothing, and now here she was.

She looked utterly different from the sister I'd last seen. She had short, spiky hair now, bleached a bright yellow, instead of the shoulder-length brown I'd always known. She had little hoop earrings going up the sides of both ears. She had no makeup except for bright red lipstick. She had a ring in her nose like a cow.

But of course, I knew her at once. Even after all this time.

"Nice nose ring," I said.

"So—can I come in?" she asked.

"I don't know," I said. I wasn't sure I was up for it.

"Just a quick minute," she promised.

"I'm super tired."

"I just want to say hi." There was a nervous energy to the way she stood, as if she were standing on the edge of some tall building's flat roof rather than just in my doorway.

I felt that same energy—a little bit of that same stomach-dropping feeling. Plus, so many different things all at once—surprised, uncertain, annoyed. She could have *called*, right? She could have let me know she was coming, at least. Did I really need some weird stealth attack from her right now? She'd had three years to get in touch, and she'd waited until I literally couldn't escape. It felt like too much. My instinct was to send her away.

But I couldn't.

Part of me wanted her to stay. A bigger part than I'd realized.

"Fine," I said, and I kept my eyes on her face as she walked closer.

She set down her bag as she stepped to the side of my bed.

"Hi," she said.

"Dad said you were in town."

She nodded.

"Have you seen him?" I asked.

She nodded again.

"Have you seen Mom?"

She shook her head.

"Are you going to? Before you go back?"

She gave a half-smile. "I'm gathering up my resolve."

I didn't know what to say. I really didn't even know where to start. It was exactly as bizarre to see her as it was not bizarre at all. Of course she was here. She was my big sister. And yet it was like seeing an after-image come back to life.

"You look better," she said.

"That's not what Mom says."

"She's kind of a bitch sometimes, though."

She wasn't wrong. "True enough," I said.

"And a liar," Kitty added.

I frowned. "Not sure about *that*."

Kit went for a subject change: "How are you?"

"I'm not sure there are words in the world that can answer that question."

She shrugged, like, *Fair enough*, and tried a new angle. "How do you feel?"

"Physically? Or emotionally?"

"Either. Both."

But I didn't want to share any of that with her. Talking about things that tender required a closeness she had forfeited a long time ago. "What's with the suitcase?" I asked.

"I was thinking I might come stay here in the evenings. With you. You know: when Mom's not around."

I eyed the recliner chair. It was supposed to flatten into a bed, but I couldn't imagine how.

I shook my head. "No."

"No what?"

"No, you shouldn't stay here."

"Don't you want company?"

"Not yours."

She frowned a little. "Are you mad at me?"

I looked away. "It's just weird to see you. My life is weird enough right now."

"I want to help."

"Yeah, but you're not helping. You're making things worse."

She didn't answer. It was clear that hadn't occurred to her.

"Want to know who I've been staying with?" she asked then, brightly, even *chattily*, and before I could say no, she went on, "Fat Benjamin. From high school. Do you remember him?"

This was a classic Kitty trick: pretending things were fine until everybody forgot they weren't. She was trying to lure me in.

I didn't answer.

"Remember how he used to give me rides home in that Jetta with the broken back windows with Hefty bags duct-taped over them?"

"Did you just call this guy 'Fat Benjamin'?"

"Everybody calls him that."

"Seems kind of mean."

"He doesn't mind. He's the cute kind of fat. Anyway, he had a huge thing for me, but I never gave him the time of day because he was so doughy and had that mullet-y haircut? Well, he's not exactly fat anymore—more 'chubby.' He's cute now! He got cuter! Or maybe my standards went down. Anyway, I'm staying at his place, on the sofa bed, but I can tell he still likes me, and I'm sure I'll wind up sleeping with him before long if I don't get out of there."

I didn't meet her gaze. Was this her argument for why she should be here? So she didn't accidentally screw a guy called Fat Benjamin?

She shrugged. "I wish I could stay here instead."

"Don't ask me again."

"I'm not asking! I just said, *I wish.*"

"We can't all get our wishes."

"I just think it would be a bad idea to sleep with him."

"Then *don't.*"

She shrugged. "I'm terrible at saying no."

I met her eyes. "Well," I said. "I'm not."

She was not going to suddenly reappear in my life after three years and make me talk about *boys,* of all things. She could not just show up like this and expect to pick up in the same naïve place we'd left off.

"Anyway," I said. "I'm pretty tired, so . . ."

"That's fine," Kit said, rejecting the hint. "I brought some magazines."

I shook my head. "You need to go."

She stepped a little closer. "I'd really like to stay."

But I just shook my head. And then I turned my face away until she gave up and left.

Eight

THE NEXT MORNING, I learned something new about my hospital room: It had great acoustics.

This was after all the morning rituals: sponge bath, tooth-brushing into a bedpan, medicines, catheter change, bowel evacuation, breakfast of oatmeal and Jell-O, and OT with Priya for three breathless rounds of getting in and out of the chair and two failed toe-wiggling attempts.

My door was right next to the nurse's station. For the first time, I noticed I could hear voices talking about medicine and medical orders. I could hear someone typing on a keyboard. Someone was making a run to Starbucks. An orderly tried to flirt with one of the nurses, but she shut him right down.

Then I heard Nina's voice, a little louder than the others. "I need to talk to you about this schedule."

A man with a slightly nasal voice replied, "Okay, shoot."

"You gave Ian to this patient."

"Yes."

"I've made several notes in the chart that she should have someone else."

"I saw those notes."

"And you just ignored them?"

"Look, Ian's wide open right now."

"Yeah. There's a reason for that."

"Are you saying Ian is incompetent to work with this patient?"

"I'm saying he's not a good match for her. And I think you know it. I'm wondering if you might be kind of hoping it'll blow up in everybody's face."

"What are you saying, Nina?"

"Exactly what you think I'm saying, Myles."

Sheesh. This guy Myles was a wiener.

"You think I'm trying to bring Ian down? You think I'm sacrificing this patient's well-being so we can all watch him self-destruct?"

"Yes."

"Well, I don't have to. The man's a time bomb. He's going to self-destruct all on his own."

Nina wasn't having it. "Not with my patient, he isn't. She's right on the edge. She'd just gotten *engaged*. She just lost everything. You need to pair her with somebody kind and encouraging—April, or even Rob."

"I'm not redoing the entire schedule for one patient."

Nina's voice tightened. "She needs someone else."

"Everyone else is full."

"So switch somebody out."

But Myles—some kind of supervisor, maybe—apparently didn't like being told what to do. In the silence that followed, I could hear him bristle. "It's not your call. It's my call. And if you make trouble for me, I promise I'll make trouble for you. The schedule stays as it is."

He must have walked off then, because after a few seconds of silence, several nurses, including Nina, started talking trash about him, using words like "jealous" and "control freak" and "little Napoleon." I might even have found it funny, if I could find anything funny anymore. If it weren't so clear that the patient she'd been talking about—the one who had just lost *everything that mattered*—was me.

That's when I heard a Scottish voice out at the station. "I tried to switch, if it's any consolation. I talked to Myles yesterday."

"You didn't try hard enough."

"He never gives me anything I want."

"You never used to let him push you around like that."

"He never used to be the boss."

Nina's voice was all business. "You'd better be nice to her, Ian."

Ian's voice was, too. "Nice doesn't make you strong."

Two seconds later, the door to my room pushed open.

"Time for PT, Maggie Jacobsen," Ian said, not meeting my eye. He wheeled my chair close to the bed.

"It's Margaret," I said. When he didn't respond, I said, "I go by Margaret."

"You don't look like a Margaret," he said. He was dead serious.

"That's not really your call, though, is it?"

"Okay, Maggie. Whatever you say."

He grabbed the transfer board and lowered the bed, as well as the chair arm, and then he arranged the board as a little bridge between the two.

Then he turned and walked toward the door.

Wait—*what?* Where was he going? Had I made him mad with the Maggie thing? Was he really a time bomb? Was he about to self-destruct right now? "Aren't you going to help me?"

He paused but didn't turn. "Nope. Press the call button when you're ready."

Then I was alone—just me, a board, and a chair. Oh, and a catheter bag strapped to my thigh.

It was a problem to solve, I'll give it that.

I found the control for the bed and maneuvered it into a sitting position. Then I edged my butt closer to the transfer board. My yoga pants had a bit of a bell-bottom, and one cuff got caught in the bedrail, but I worked it out. Perched at the edge, about to shift myself onto the board where there'd be nothing below me but stone-hard hospital floor, I felt frightened for the first time since the crash. In fact, I felt *something* for the first time since the crash. I paused, out of breath, and wondered why my first feeling couldn't have been laughter. Or joy.

I edged a little closer, putting all my weight on my palms. The muscles in my trunk were atrophied, yes, but still functioning, which helped—but the dead weight of my legs threw me off balance. I wobbled a little, then hunched down until I was steady again. The chair was maybe twelve inches away, but it might as well have been a football field. I eyed the distance, ooched another inch, lost my balance, hunched down. Then again, and again. After a bit, I noticed that the fabric of my pants had two wet blotches on the thighs, and that's when I realized that I thought I'd just been *concentrating*—but instead, I'd been crying. Possibly for some time.

I decided to take a break, halfway across the board.

That's when Ian walked back in. "God, are you not finished yet? I had a cup of coffee and read the paper."

If he'd been someone else, it might have been okay. If we'd been friends, if I'd known he was on my side, if we'd built up a rapport—he might have been teasing me in a fun way. As it was, he was just a mean stranger.

I looked up, and when he saw my face—no doubt puffy and slick with tears—I saw the hardness on his falter, just for a second, before he came gruffly over and steadied my shoulders.

"I've got you," he said. "Keep after it."

With Ian there, it went much faster—and before I knew it, I was trailing along after him as I rolled myself down the hall toward the therapy gym. I tried to think of another time I'd been with another person and felt so alone at the same time. He didn't speak. He didn't look at me. You'd think he was out for a stroll all by himself.

He paused at a door to hold it open, which I thought was a nice gesture until he started speaking. "No," he said, as I rolled past him. "Your technique's all wrong."

He sounded irritated, like we'd been over this a thousand times.

"Well," I said, "I didn't know there *was* a technique, and this is my first time to ever do this, so—"

"Nobody's shown you how to use the chair?"

I shook my head.

"That's OT 101."

"I guess we're still doing prerequisites." Another sad little attempt at a joke.

He didn't smile. Instead, he bent forward to look into my eyes and then squeezed my biceps. Then, in a voice that sounded like he was about to impart vital, deeply insightful information, he said, "Arms are not legs."

I gave him a look, like, *Really?*

"What I mean is," he went on, unamused, "they can't handle the same amount of work as legs. You have to be careful not to strain them with overuse."

"I don't see that I have much choice about that."

"Not in the big picture, no," he conceded. "But in the details. Hence: chair technique." He put his hand over mine—it was warmer than mine was, I noticed—and placed it on the rim of the wheel. "Instead of ten little pushes," he said, "you want to do one strong push and then coast."

He stretched my hand down low along the back of the wheel and pressed it into a grip around the push rim. Then he brought it up and forward to push off, and I went zooming down the hallway fast enough to scare me, so I grabbed the rim to stop, and got a little friction burn.

Ian jogged up behind me. "You're going to need some gloves" was all he said.

Next we covered turning, rotating in place, and popping wheelies—though we didn't actually practice those. "Are wheelies really necessary?" I asked.

"Yes," he said, though he didn't explain why.

"Why?" I decided to demand.

"Because you need to know how to control your wheels."

"Why?"

"Because you need to know how to manage all kinds of terrain."

"Like for when I go off-roading in the Grand Canyon?"

He looked up. "More like for when you encounter steps. Or potholes. Or a curb." He turned away. "If you want to go anywhere, you need to know how to manage."

"I don't want to go anywhere," I said.

"You will," he said as he walked away, all tall and athletic and sturdy. There was something almost mean about how in shape he was, and the way his scrubs draped from his waistband over what any woman with a heartbeat would have to admit was an utterly perfect guy-butt. He was such a supreme physical specimen. I didn't compare myself to him, exactly, but just being near that kind of robustness made me feel extra weak and shriveled. I looked away.

Anyway, that little Wheelchair 101 moment made us a few minutes late arriving at the therapy gym, and so we signed in a little late, too, which seemed to irritate Ian. "Now we're late," he said, noting time on the clock, as if it were my fault.

As if it mattered.

I looked around while he gathered some equipment. If I'd been able to appreciate anything, I would have appreciated the gym. It had all kinds of machines and colors and games. It had a pop-a-shot basketball machine, and a ring toss, and two pinball machines—*Star Wars* and *Guardians of the Galaxy*. It had weights like a gym, and mirrors everywhere, as well as a set of walking bars, a standing frame, and a full-body harness. It had a fine-motor board with locks and latches and screws to work with, and a beanbag-toss game. It had a flight of practice stairs, a minitramp, and a row of recumbent bikes. It even had an entire car, painted a perky aqua, down at one end—I guessed for people to practice getting in and out. Also, up top: quite the speaker system, playing a relentless mix of lite-rock Eagles and Van Morrison tunes.

The old me would have felt tempted to boogie around a little bit, but the new me sat still as a sack of flour.

Ian wrote my name on a big whiteboard that had a slot for every patient on it, with "goals" written out, and smiley faces, and lots of little encouraging sayings. I watched the other trainers while I waited—without exception, an insistently cheerful, optimistic bunch. They laughed loudly, and high-fived, and called their patients things like "champ." They coaxed. They encouraged. They cheered. They sang along to the music.

One guy with a man-bun, who I would come to know as Rob, was

working with an eighty-year-old lady on a walker—and while he wasn't exactly flirting with her, he was certainly paying her enough attention that she positively bloomed. A female trainer, April, was shooting Nerf hoops with her patient, a forty-something guy in a wheelchair, and high-fiving each swoosh. It was like a big fitness-and-recovery party. All around me, people were moving, and talking, and challenging themselves— and while the patients were more somber, the PTs were nothing short of jovial.

Except for my PT.

I looked over at Ian with his gray frown and his stiff jaw. He was so serious, so sour, so much the opposite of jovial that he practically had a little cartoon scribble of grumpiness above his head.

No wonder he has an open schedule, I thought.

"Late again, Ian," I heard then. The nasal voice. The same one I'd heard talking to Nina. I looked over to get my first eyeful of Myles, walking toward us. He turned out to have wavy, tight-cropped red hair— clashing boldly with the red sweatshirt he'd zipped over his scrubs—and tight, hard little brown eyes. He looked exactly like his voice.

Ian didn't respond.

"Hate to have to mark you in the book," Myles went on, almost glaring at Ian. "But rules are rules."

Ian held menacingly still, eyes averted.

"Just gotta watch that clock and stay timely."

Then, I didn't mean to stand up for Ian, but I did. "He was helping me with wheelchair technique in the hallway," I said. It just popped out.

Myles shifted his eyes to me. "That's not PT. That's OT."

"But he was correcting my technique."

"Not his job," Myles said. "Right, champ? Not your job."

Ian just worked his jaw.

Myles went on, "Wouldn't want people thinking you don't know what your job is."

I started to argue again, but Ian gave me a look.

Myles was baiting him. "Wouldn't want people thinking you have no right to be here."

Ian: Silence. Then more silence.

"Good talk," Myles said after another minute, clapping Ian on the shoulder.

Then he turned to me and said, "If you need any more advice, I suggest you come to me. I'm just right there in my corner office."

I saw Ian squeeze his hand into a fist and then stretch it out.

Then Myles pointed at Ian and said, in a pseudo-inspirational tone, "Go work some miracles."

Did that guy *want* to get punched? *I* even wanted to punch him. "Sorry," I said, once we'd made it to the far side of the gym. "I was trying to help you."

"Don't help me," Ian said, shaking his head. "Don't do that again."

Then he walked off.

He stopped across the room at a mat table and looked exasperated to find that I hadn't followed him. He made a "get over here" motion, and I wheeled in his direction.

When I reached him, he handed me a transfer board and said, "You know what to do."

I hadn't let my armrest down on my own before, and it took me a minute to find the latch—during which time Ian kept his eyes focused out the window, breathing impatiently every so often.

"You could help me, if you're in such a rush."

"I'm not here to do it for you. You're here to do it for yourself."

"I didn't ask you to do it for me. I just said you could help."

"At this point, that's the same thing."

I could imagine one of the other trainers saying that in a playful tone, but Ian was about as playful as roadkill. He was silent, and tense, and now—since seeing that guy Myles—radiating hostility. I could sense it wasn't meant for me, but I was still collateral damage. The rancor fumed from his body—you could see it in his face and his gait and the way he held himself as stiff as an action figure—and I was just unfortunate enough to be stuck with him.

Just as I had that thought, Rob, the trainer with the man-bun, let out

a whoop of a cheer over something amazing and inspiring his patient had just done. Then everybody in the room stopped to applaud.

Except Ian.

"Let's move," he said, urging me toward the mat.

I moved, and I got the armrest down, and I eventually dragged myself across the board onto the mat, but Ian's cranky, impatient, irritated nonhelp did not make things easier. Or faster.

By the time I made it, I was panting.

Before I'd caught my breath, Ian leaned over me and laid me back on the mat, careful of my burns, to start a whole series of exercises to take stock of my starting place—what I could and couldn't do right now. He did this without explaining first, and for a second I thought he was picking me up. I leaned forward just as he did and managed to smush my face into the corner between his neck and his collarbones. Just for a second, before I pulled back, I registered his scratchy, unshaven neck, firm with muscles, and the salty, linen-y smell of him.

It could have been a funny, slightly embarrassing moment, one we could laugh about—but Ian decided to make it humiliating instead. When I looked up, he seemed super annoyed. "Down," he said, pointing at the mat, as if he'd already explained this to me a hundred times.

I felt a sting of embarrassment. "Right," I said.

With that, we took stock of me: Could I sit up on my own? (Barely. With a lot of grunting.) Could I roll over? (Yes. Clumsily, but yes.) Could I lie on my back and lift my knees? (Yes, actually. But my thighs were weak and trembled like earthquakes.) Could I sit on the edge and straighten my leg out? (No. Not even close.) Could I lie on my stomach and lift my feet behind me? (About halfway.) Could I point, wiggle, or flex my toes? (No, no, and no.) By the end, we had the general idea. Everything above the knees seemed to work—though not always well. Below the knees was a different story.

The whole process seemed to go on for hours, and it left me breathless and shaky. I had known that my legs were not exactly working, but breaking it down into specifics—and by "specifics," I mean breaking the

function of my legs and feet down by each specific muscle—made it more real. In a way, I didn't really want to know what I could or couldn't do. Observing this new, broken version of my body only seemed to give it a validity it didn't deserve.

But if Ian was aware of my unhappiness, he didn't seem to care much. He drove us on and on, testing everything: ankles, toes, thighs, hip flexors. He did pressure tests all up and down my legs, poking me with a little pin, and I saw him write down the word "spotty" in his chart over and over.

He was keeping a list of all the muscles that didn't work. It was far longer than I'd expected, but, to be fair, just the list of muscles in the legs was far longer than I'd expected. Ian's "not working" list included several leg muscles that had Latin names starting with "biceps," which seemed needlessly confusing, since "biceps" made them sound like arm muscles, and my arms were fine. Ian totally ignored me and made his list anyway, which, in the end, looked like this:

biceps femoris
biceps semitendinosus
biceps semimembranosus
tibialis—anterior and posterior
peroneus longus
gastrocnemius
soleus
flexor digitorum longus

I wondered if I should ask what some of those muscles were, but as the list grew longer, I wasn't sure I wanted to know.

It was physically exhausting, and it was emotionally grueling, but I really think the worst part of the whole experience was, of all things, the *not talking*.

I'm a talker from a long line of talkers. My mom might be talking to you about the curtains and who should be sent to Guantánamo for choosing them, but she's talking to you. My dad might be placating my mom, but he's doing it with words. I don't think I have ever once, in my entire

life, spent that much time one-on-one with another human being and spoken as few words as I did with Ian. Over the entire afternoon, you probably couldn't make one full sentence out of the words we exchanged.

It bothered me. Viscerally.

But I was too tired, demoralized, shell-shocked, discouraged, and numb to do anything about it. It was Ian's job to work the conversation, dammit. All the other trainers—and I had plenty of time to take stock—were doing the vast majority of the conversational grunt work, giving their patients the gift of conversational pleasure without the usual work, and leaving the patients free to concentrate on their tasks.

With Ian, I got the opposite of conversational pleasure. I got the cringe of uncomfortable silence. Plus the comparative disappointment of knowing I had the worst trainer in the room.

Silent, surly, and relentless. We didn't finish our session until all the other perky people were long gone and my entire body felt like Jell-O. I thought for sure Ian would help me back into the chair at the end, but he just slapped the board down and turned his gaze back to the window.

I gave a long sigh as I looked at it.

I didn't ask for help, because I knew I wouldn't get it.

I had to readjust my catheter tube, which had come untaped, and then I started scooting my butt sideways across the board.

But I was more exhausted than I realized, because just before I reached the chair, as I shifted my weight onto my lead arm, my elbow gave way and I went pitching forward.

I should have hit the floor, but almost as soon as I realized I was falling, Ian caught me. I would have bet you a hundred dollars that his entire focus had been out the gym window, but he must have been using his peripheral vision, because I was caught by his steady arms and settled in my chair before I even fully got what was happening.

"Thank you," I said, before I remembered that he was kind of the reason I'd fallen in the first place.

Before he stood back up, he checked my expression, meeting my eyes for the first time. "I've tired you out," he said.

"In more ways than one." I noticed his eyes were blue. Dark blue—almost navy.

"You worked hard today."

As mad as I was, it felt weirdly nice to have that acknowledged. *And you,* I thought, *stared out the window.*

He studied my face another second, and then he stood up and said, "Time to get you back to your room." I'd seen the other PTs pushing their clients' chairs—especially the elderly and the tired—at the ends of their workouts, and I just assumed that Ian would do the same.

Wrong. Of course.

He and his perfect butt just strolled off toward the exit, and I had no choice but to scramble after him in my chair.

At the door, Ian stopped at the patient whiteboard. Under my name was an empty box. Other patients' boxes had stars and smileys and hearts in them, but Ian marked mine with a solemn black X.

Which was about how I felt.

Nine

BACK AT THE room, a nurse I'd never seen before scolded us. "Ian, she was supposed to be back forty-five minutes ago."

I was? I narrowed my eyes at Ian, but he pretended to ignore me.

"She didn't want to quit," he said. "She's a machine."

"I need her now."

"She's all yours."

Just then, the new cell phone my mother had brought me rang. I'd never heard its ringtone—so loud and screechy—and it startled all of us. Ian picked it up off the side table and handed it to me.

"Hello?" I said.

A guy's voice. "Margaret Jacobsen?"

"Yes?"

"Neil Putnam from HR at Simtex."

My new job! Oh, God—I had forgotten all about it. Should I explain what happened? Did they already know? That interview felt like a hundred years ago in somebody else's life.

"I remember," I said, after a pause. Neil Putnam was the guy who'd told me that I unofficially had the job. "How are you?"

"Doing just great." His voice was overly bright, but I didn't notice at first. "Hey," he went on, like he'd just thought of something. "I've been asked to call and let you know that the guys upstairs have made an official decision about the position."

I held my breath. It was an impossible problem. I was twenty-eight and just out of business school, and I'd landed a dream job that nobody with my lack of experience had any right to, and it really was the offer of a lifetime, and at this moment, given that I couldn't even pee without help, it seemed unlikely I could make the most of it. What would I do if they wanted me to start next week?

I'd never in my life faced a challenge and given up. The non-quitter part of me could not imagine doing anything other than wrestling myself into an Ann Taylor suit and hauling my ass out to their corporate campus the minute they said *go*. But a much more vocal part of me— the part, shall we say, with the catheter sticking out—could not imagine ever even leaving this hospital room, much less dedicating my thoughts to "strategic and higher operational level engagement with the logistics environment."

My only hope was to delay. Maybe I could wrangle a start date later in the summer. How long was it going to take me to get myself back to normal? Two months, maybe? Four?

But as I opened my mouth to suggest it, Neil Putnam said, "They're going with another candidate."

"I'm sorry?"

"Someone with more experience."

"But you said I had it!"

"Unofficially. But then a better candidate came along."

I closed my eyes.

"They'll send an official letter, but we wanted to give you a heads-up."

"I see," I said at last. "Of course." Had they somehow heard about the crash? Did they know what I was up against?

"We wish you the best of luck, and hope you are up and around again soon."

Guess they did.

I pressed END and let out a long sigh comprised entirely of the word "Fuuuuuuuuuck."

When I looked up, Ian and the new nurse were watching me.

"I just got fired," I explained. "Though not really. It wasn't official yet. But right before the crash, they told me it was mine. The most amazing dream job ever. And I was going to rock it out."

"They can't do that!" the nurse said, all sympathy, like we'd been pals for years.

"Sure they can," Ian said. "That's how the world works." No sympathy there. Dry as chalk.

"Bad luck," the nurse said, and took my hand to squeeze it. It wasn't until she touched me that I realized how cold my own hands were. "I'm sorry about your bad news."

I shrugged. "It's okay," I said, and in a way, it was. A relief, at least. An impossible challenge that I didn't have to rise to.

I had enough impossible challenges these days.

But in a much larger way, it wasn't okay. I wanted that job, yes—but I also needed it. I had bought a fancy condo on the strength of my bright future. I had student loan payments and car payments and credit card payments. Plus, I had no idea what the medical bills were going to be like for this situation.

A panic about the future swirled inside my body like a dust storm. Another piece of my old life had just crumbled away.

Here's the weird thing, though, about all the emotions swirling through me right then: I felt them intensely—and, at the exact same time, I could barely feel them at all. I have no idea how that works, but I swear it's true. I felt full-out panicked and quietly numb simultaneously. I wondered if I'd ever feel things normally again—and then immediately hoped it would be a long, long time before I did.

Never would've been fine.

Ian was already back to business. "So," he said, rocking back a little, "let's recap. We basically made a map of your entire body today—and in the coming weeks, we'll strengthen what's working and try to wake up what's not." He spoke with his eyes on his clipboard, as if the topic in

general, and me in particular, bored him to tears. "There's a great deal of mystery with spinal cord injuries, and we can't always predict who will see improvement and who won't. Your deficits are all at the patella level and below, and that's the area we'll focus on. Do you have any questions?"

As he waited for my answer, he looked out the window.

I shook my head.

"I'll be back tomorrow, then," he said, turning away. "And next time," he called over his shoulder, "you have to try."

The nurse and I watched him go. I could have been irritated with him, I suppose, but I was too tired to be mad. In fact, I felt all remaining energy whoosh out of my body like a sigh as he left. The day was over. All I had left to do was get myself back into bed. Then I could close my eyes and sink into oblivion.

But just before I turned to look for the transfer board, another figure appeared in doorway.

Kitty.

Again.

"I thought I told you no," I said.

"That was a long time ago," Kitty said.

"That was *yesterday*."

"I thought maybe you'd changed your mind."

"Nope."

"Fat Benjamin confessed to me after I got home last night that he still had a ponytail holder of mine from high school. And then he tried to put his tongue in my ear."

I faced her dead-on. "I have many problems right now," I said then. "But Fat Benjamin's tongue in *your* ear is definitely not one of them."

Kitty looked affronted. "I'm not asking you to solve my problems."

"Yes, you are. Like you always do." But not anymore. I didn't say it, but she'd lost the right to ask that of me.

"Not this time," Kitty insisted. "*I'm* here to help *you*."

"I already told you that you can't."

She blinked.

So I said it again. "All your being here can possibly do is make things worse."

"What if I bring you cupcakes?"

"No."

"What if I bring trashy novels and spring rolls from that Thai place you love?"

"No."

"Don't just send me away," she said. "Let's talk about it. Let's rap it out."

She was being cute, but I had no patience for cute. "I'm serious," I said. "Get out. Go home. Go back to New York, even. You are something I just can't handle right now."

"Can't? Or won't?"

"Both."

KIT LEFT, BUT she came back again the next night, just as I was finishing dinner. With cookies.

I sent her away.

She came after dinner the night after that with macarons, and I sent her away again.

And then, on the night after that, when she didn't show up after dinner, I noticed I was disappointed. I was waiting to see her. More than that: The idea of seeing her didn't seem weird and destabilizing anymore. In fact, it felt like something to look forward to. I was anticipating the sight of her with her crazy hair and tattoos, wearing a tutu or something equally nutty. Not to mention the cake pops she'd bring, or brownies, or doughnuts, or whatever.

I found myself worrying that she might have given up on me, and regretting being so cold.

When she finally did turn up at last, she was carrying one perfect, exquisite chocolate cupcake from my favorite bakery of all time, twenty minutes across town.

"Are you bribing me?" I asked, as she held it out.

"I am demonstrating," she said, "that I am not just here to escape

trading sexual favors with Fat Benjamin in exchange for lodging. I am here to do whatever I can to make your day just a little bit better. Starting with cupcakes."

I looked at the cupcake. I took it.

"I also apologize for ignoring you for three straight years."

"Fine," I said, taking a bite and pressing the smooth icing against the roof of my mouth. Then, after swallowing: "You can stay."

"Really?"

I took another bite and savored it, then spoke louder for more authority. "But if you wind up making things worse for me, you're out."

"I won't," Kit said.

"For example," I said, throwing down the challenge. "It's time for bed now."

Kit glanced at the clock on my wall. "It's not even nine o'clock."

The cupcake was suddenly gone. We were done here.

"Yeah," I said, like, *Duh*, like it was past the whole world's bedtime. "Get your bed ready and let's hit the sack."

I watched her unfold the recliner and make it up with a sheet from the cabinet. She'd brought a pillow and blanket of her own—both plaid, which added a camp-out vibe. As I watched her work, her movements and her silhouette so familiar, my eyes kept trying to close on their own. I remember thinking I was so tired I'd never wake up. I remember wondering if she was going to sleep with that crazy nose ring in.

I WOKE A couple of hours later to Kitty at my bedside, whispering, "Hey. Hey! Wake up!"

I opened my eyes in the pale darkness. Kitty was leaning over me in a sleep shirt with R2D2 on it. I was out of breath.

"What's going on?" I asked.

"You were having a nightmare."

She wasn't wrong. "I was drowning," I said. "I was trapped in the plane—underwater."

"I figured it was something bad."

I squeezed my eyes closed and took a second to catch my breath.

My hair—what remained of it—was damp with sweat, and I was shaking. Kitty got a nubby white washcloth from the bathroom and pressed it to my forehead. Then, without a word, she crawled into my bed beside me—careful not to touch my neck. She was slender enough to fit. She curled on her side and stroked my hair. "Your hair's a mess," she whispered.

"The fire burned it off," I said.

"Well, that's kind of lucky," she said, "because guess what I've been doing since the last time you saw me?"

"Tell me."

"Cutting hair."

I frowned. "You're a barber?"

"A *hairstylist*. I'm famous. I have forty-six thousand followers on Instagram."

"You're famous?"

She nodded. "I also do tattoos. I have a place called the Beauty Parlor in Brooklyn. And we do piercings."

"You do the tattoos yourself?"

"Yep. Tattoos and haircuts. I'm amphibious. Guess what else? I'm sleeping with the manager. Or maybe he's sleeping with me . . . Either way, it's one-stop shopping."

The manager's name was Ethan, but he had a handlebar moustache that he waxed at the tips, so everybody just called him the Moustache. Even Kitty.

She told me all about him in soothing tones while I waited for my body to settle down and stop shaking—his motorcycle, and his cooking skills, and his favorite books.

At last, after letting her talk and talk, I asked, "Do you always use the article? Like, do you say, 'Hey, the Moustache! Come here!' Or, 'What's for dinner, the Moustache?'"

She thought about it. "Actually, to his face, we call him 'Stache, like it's a name. But when we're talking about him, we call him the Moustache, like it's his title."

"What does he call you?"

"I can't repeat it," she said. "It's X rated."

The last time I'd seen her, she'd been temping as a receptionist. She'd been wearing pumps and an ill-fitting gray suit that she'd refused to have altered. "You've really changed a lot," I said.

"For the better."

"Maybe. Except for that nose ring."

"You don't like it?"

"You look like Elsie the cow."

"But sexy."

My sister, the nose-ringed hairstylist. "Can you fix my hair?" I asked.

"Of course. I'll give you an adorable little pixie. It'll be cuter than what you had before."

It wouldn't, of course. But I was too tired to argue.

"Remember that time," Kitty said, "I cut that girl's hair at summer camp and made her cry?"

"That was actually a really cute little bob."

"I took like ten inches off, though."

I remembered. "She called her parents to come and take her home."

"I should send her a gift certificate. Now, I can make anybody look good." She nudged me. "Even you."

I knew she meant it as a joke. But I closed my eyes.

"I was kidding," she said, when I got quiet.

I said, "Mom can't even look at me."

"That's not about you. That's about her."

"My *face* is burned."

Kitty made a *pshaw* sound. "It's a sunburn. It looks exactly like a sunburn. Except for the blisters. Not a big deal. I'll show you tomorrow."

It was strange to listen to our conversation. It was like I was eavesdropping on it somehow. In one way, we sounded very much like we always did—the back-and-forth, the teasing. We'd only ever had one way of talking to each other, and it was playful and jokey. That way of talking didn't fit the situation now, but it was all we knew how to do.

So we did it. But it was in a minor key, just a muffled, gray version of itself.

Of course, that's how everything I said or did or thought felt now. Flat, and colorless, and altered.

"Kitty?" I asked, after a bit.

"What?"

"Stay here tonight, okay? I don't want to be alone."

"I am staying here."

"No, I mean right here. In the bed."

"Okay."

"I don't want to have any more nightmares," I said.

"I'll keep an eye on you."

"Thanks."

We let ourselves get quiet and start to settle, but then I had to say one last thing. "You can't be drinking here, by the way. I'm making that rule."

"Drinking?" she asked.

"'Cause you get crazy when you drink, and I just can't take any more drama—"

"I haven't had a drink in three years," Kit said. "Dad sent me to rehab."

This should have been thrilling news, but my heart was too numb to feel it. "That's great," I said. "I didn't know."

"Yeah, he thought he should keep that under his hat."

"That's why you went away?"

"That's part of it."

"And you stayed away because—*what?*—you were too fragile?"

"That's part of it, too. I'll give you the whole story sometime. But not tonight. Then you really will have nightmares."

Fair enough. "So . . . you quit drinking entirely?"

"Entirely. It was brutal, but I did it."

"I'm sorry."

"It's okay. We all have our struggles. I'm better for it, actually."

"Does Mom know?"

"I have no idea."

"You should tell her."

"Nah."

"It might help the two of you make up."

"Well, that's the thing, right there," Kit said. "I'm not sure if I want to make up."

She was offering up some answers to questions I'd carried around a long time, but somehow they were raising more questions than they were settling. What had happened that night she pushed our mom into the pool? What had they fought about? Who was mad at who, exactly? What on earth could have made Kit—who always longed so much for attention—shut us out for so long? I wanted to know, but I also didn't. It had to be something big, and I wasn't sure at this point I could even handle something small.

Wondering about Kit did offer a small distraction, and in the face of the wasteland my own life had become, there was something about a distraction that felt like relief.

Until Kit turned it all back to me.

"Can I tell you something comforting about your situation?" she asked, after a minute.

"No."

It hadn't been a real question, of course. It was just an intro. "Really? You don't want to be comforted?"

"Nope."

She wasn't buying it. "Everybody wants to be comforted."

How to explain to her that there was absolutely nothing she could say that would comfort me? Even the attempt would make things worse. There was no upside. There was no silver lining. There was no comfort.

But there was no way she could understand that. "Don't comfort me. Don't say a word. Just go to sleep before I kick you out again."

"Okay," Kit said.

So that's how we stayed, two in the bed, all night long: Kit patiently comforting me while I rejected the very notion of the concept.

As long as she was just breathing in and out beside me in that snoozy, wavy, sleepy-Kitty rhythm of hers—it was fine. I didn't believe in comfort anymore, and I knew for a fact that I would never, ever feel better. But having her with me like that? Not being alone? Well, it didn't make me feel *worse*. That counted for something.

Ten

KITTY WAS GONE in the morning when I woke up, and she'd folded the chair-bed back so neatly that it was almost like she was never there. For a second, I wondered if she'd left for good—until I noticed her stuff in a neat pile in the corner. Maybe she'd left early to make herself scarce to avoid running into my mom.

And so I launched into another day, all on my own—everything pretty much exactly the same until the very end, when Ian walked me back from another awkward, silent, antisocial session of physical therapy, and we found a nurse I'd never seen before waiting for me in my room.

She met my eyes with a bright smile. "How do you feel about good news?"

I glanced at Ian, who gave me a tiny shrug.

I hesitated. "I'm . . . for it?"

The nurse's smile got bigger. "Because I have good news for you."

I waited. "Okay." I wasn't sure I could muster the excitement she was clearly expecting. "I guess you'd better tell me, then."

Then she pointed right at my crotch. "We're about to take out that catheter."

*   *   *

THERE WAS NO guarantee the catheter wasn't going back in. The spinal surgeon had noted "sacral sparing" down in the nether regions, and he was optimistic that I had both enough sensation down there to feel when I needed to pee, and enough muscle control to make it happen—but there was no guarantee.

Only trying would tell.

The nurse put an absorbent pad on the bed before helping me get up into it, and then she slid the tube out with no ceremony at all. Then she helped me into an open-back gown for the night, "for easy access."

"When you feel the feeling and need to pee," she said, "move fast. Press the call button. Don't try to transfer on your own."

"Okay."

"And don't wait until you're about to burst!"

"I won't."

She'd be back soon to check on me. The question now was, would I feel that feeling? And if I did feel it, and manage to get to the bathroom without wetting myself first, would my urethra know what to do when I got there?

Safe to say, I had never adequately appreciated the sheer, elegant genius of the urinary system. Now it became a significant character in the story of my life. It was common for patients with injuries like mine to spend the rest of their lives catheterized, facing all the humiliations and discomfort that implied—not to mention chronic infections from the tubes. I found myself rooting for my bladder to impress us all.

After the nurse left, I lay in the silence of my room, eavesdropping on the conversations outside, waiting alertly to feel that delightful old sensation of needing to pee—what did it even feel like? I could barely remember—and rooting for my brave little-urethra-that-could to face this challenge and triumph.

Until I fell asleep.

I slept until Kitty arrived with Chinese takeout.

She poked me, saying, "Hey, are you sleeping?"

I put my hand over my eyes. "Don't wake me when I'm sleeping, Kit!"

"I brought dinner," she said, as if takeout justified anything, and she started unloading containers.

As I came awake, I noticed something. "Oh, my God. I need to pee! I can feel it!"

Kit looked at me like I was a little nuts. "Hooray?"

I pointed at the transfer board. "We have to get me to the bathroom."

Long story short: I did it. *We* did it—my urethra and I—without a hitch.

Except for the moment when I looked up to find Kit trying to take a picture of me on the toilet.

"Kit! What the hell? Don't take a picture of me peeing!"

"For Instagram!" she said, like that made it better. "It's photojournalism!"

Had she always been this crazy? We were barely back on speaking terms. "Shut it down."

"I'm kidding," Kit said. "But my followers *are* all rooting for you."

"That's rule number two," I went on. "No photos—ever."

"Not even selfies?"

"My hospital room, my rules: No comfort. No photos. And no goddamned selfies."

"Fine."

"Fine. Now help me back into the chair."

We worked me back into the bed, and once I was all tucked in, Kit laid out the Chinese food like a feast—fried dumplings and egg rolls and sesame chicken. All my favorites from childhood.

I knew what she was up to. "This isn't *comfort* food, is it?"

Kit narrowed her eyes. "This is just what I happen to like. You can't blame me if you find it comforting."

"I'll blame you if I want to," I said, but I gave her a little smile. Which felt shaky, like those muscles had atrophied, too.

Kit speared a chicken hunk with her chopstick. "Aren't you kind of glad I'm here?"

I was, actually. Far more than I would admit. "When you're not tak-ing pictures of me on the frigging toilet."

I COULDN'T EAT much, but Kit could. She finished off all the egg rolls and every steamed dumpling, slurping dipping sauce and licking her fin-gers. Then, after she'd cleaned up, she said, "Now: the haircut!"

I wrinkled my nose. "I'm too tired."

"You just had a nap!"

"Yeah. My pre-bedtime nap."

"No!" Kit protested. "I planned us a whole girls' night." She started pulling items out of her purse and stacking them up on the tray table: a box of chocolates, a nail-painting kit with emoji decals, a bag of popcorn, Boggle, and a couple of naughty-looking romance novels. Plus a set of long computer cords.

"You've got quite the party planned."

She nodded. "Total debauchery."

"Glad you woke me now."

She nodded, missing the sarcasm. "I can hook my computer up to the TV. I've got *Grease* cued up."

I smiled for a second despite myself. We loved *Grease* as kids. We'd put on the soundtrack and dance around the house, climbing the furni-ture and singing the duets.

She always made me be Danny, though.

Kit stood up and pointed her finger in the air, striking a Travolta-on-the-bleachers pose.

Nothing from me.

"Come on. I'll let you be Sandy."

Too little, too late. "I don't want to be Sandy."

"Yes, you do."

"I don't feel like singing."

"You always feel like singing."

"Not anymore."

She narrowed her eyes at me. "When was the last time you sang?"

"I don't know."

"I read an article that if you have a talent and you don't find a way to use it, your life can collapse in on itself like a black hole."

I gave her a look. "Too late."

"That's the most depressing thing I've ever heard you say."

"Only because it's true." She was pushing, and all I could do was push back.

"No, it's not."

I felt my hackles lift just a little bit. If I said my life was a black hole, then it was an effing black hole. "We'll have to agree to disagree."

I could read her face so clearly. She thought I was being stubborn.

The longer she stared, the more I felt my body tightening in defensiveness. *Really?* She was going to stand there with her working legs and resent my less-than-sunny attitude?

"Looks like we've got kind of a role reversal going here," Kit said at last.

I waited, and lifted my eyebrow a bit, like, *Oh, really?*

"This may be," she went on, in a conversational tone, like we were just chatting about the weather, "the first time ever that I am the one trying to make things better—and you are the one trying to make things worse."

And just like that, I was mad. "I don't have to *try* to make things worse," I said, my throat tight and strangely sandpapery. "Things are already worse."

"Things can always get worse," Kit declared.

My reply was like a reflex—a shouting reflex. "Not for me!"

I'm always amazed at how fast siblings can warp-speed into a state of rage. It's like they keep everything they were ever angry about growing up shoved into an overstuffed emotional closet, and at moments like these, it takes about two seconds to swing open the door and start an avalanche.

"You have to try!" Kit insisted, in a tone like she'd said it a hundred times.

"I *am* trying!"

"You're not!"

This was the trouble with sisters. This was the trouble with family. I had barely cracked open the door to my life, and she'd just barged in and made herself at home—taking photos of me and judging my coping skills. We hadn't even officially made up yet, and she was ordering me around.

Just as I had that thought, she went on. "You," she said, pointing right at me, "need to sing."

With that, the anger lit inside me like a flame—so physical, I felt myself light up. "I don't want to sing!" I shouted.

It was like all the anger I'd been unwilling to feel—at Chip, at my mother, at the folks in this hospital who kept making me do impossible things—had been quietly gathering like some flammable gas. And Kit had just lit a match.

I slammed both my fists down against the bed. "I'm not going to sing!" My voice both too loud in that moment and not loud enough. "You can't make me sing! Do you really think it's that easy? You can't just come in here with Boggle and show tunes and make everything all right! Stop trying to fix things! Give me a fucking break."

Kit blinked. Then blinked some more. I wondered if she might cry, or run out of the room—but she just nodded.

In the long silence that followed, I deflated.

"Okay," Kit said after a while, in a quiet voice. "Okay, that's fair."

I sighed, long and slow.

"You don't have to sing," Kit went on, shrugging, and looking at me with new eyes.

I matched my voice to hers. "Damn right I don't."

"I hear you," she said. "I'll back off." But then she peeked up from under her eyelashes. "Can I at least do the haircut, though?"

AN HOUR LATER, hair was all over the floor. I'd transferred into the chair so that I wouldn't have to sleep in a bed of "hair fuzz," and we'd made a carpet of hair sprinkles all around the wheels.

Kitty fussed and fussed, and it took far longer than it should have, as all her genetic perfectionist tendencies kicked in. At last, she declared victory and handed me a hand mirror. I started to lift it, but then I hesitated.

"Take a look," she urged.

I wrinkled my nose.

"You don't want to see?"

I did want to see the haircut—but I didn't know how to do that without also seeing my face.

"You know what?" I said then, shaking my head. "I'm good. I'm sure it's fine."

"Are you afraid you look terrible? Because you don't."

Yes. I was afraid I looked terrible. Of course. When your own mother can't even look at you, you have to be a monster. But it was more than that. Once I knew what I looked like now, I would always know. There are things you can't unsee.

It would be like the time my aunt walked me up to my grandmother's open casket to "say good-bye" and I looked down to see an embalmed, flattened, just-plain-wrong version of the face I'd known and loved so long. For a long time after that, the only face I saw when I thought of my grandmother was that wrong one. It had erased the face I wanted to hold on to.

I didn't want to look in that mirror to find that I was gone.

Kit seemed to read my thoughts. "You look just like you. A little sunburned, and with a few scabby blister things on the jaw . . ." She touched her jaw. "And with the cutest haircut you've ever had—*you're welcome.* But still the same you."

I tilted the mirror a little.

"Don't be afraid," she urged.

But I was. My hands felt cold. *Don't think,* I told myself. It was time to face the future, whatever it looked like. I held my breath, and lifted the mirror, and tilted it, one centimeter at a time, until my whole face gazed back at me.

My same face. A little roughed up, but familiar as an old friend.

"See?" Kit said. "You're still the beauty."

A ragged sigh escaped my chest. "I don't need to be the beauty. I just want to be recognizable."

"You are," Kit said. "Just way more stylish."

I'd never had bangs, but this cut flopped down over my forehead in the front and was short and spiky in back. Pixie-ish. I'd never had anything but long hair—out of fear, really, that I'd cut it all off and then hate it and have to wait forever to get back to my old self. Also, my mother thought short hair on girls was ugly.

But this haircut wasn't ugly.

Kit was grinning wide now. "How cute are you?" she demanded. "This is the haircut you've been waiting for all your life!"

"I don't hate it," I said.

"You love it. Come on."

Next, I angled the mirror ever so slowly toward my neck. Seeing my face better than expected made me hopeful that the rest might be, too.

But the skin grafts were *worse*.

The side of my neck, from my jaw to my collarbone, was utterly unrecognizable. It was purple and gooseflesh-y and mottled like pepperoni. It was Frankenstein-esque. My face, if I didn't scratch, would heal. But the grafts, even healed, as Chip had so tactfully pointed out, would look like Silly Putty forever. I would forever be a person that other people tried not to stare at in the grocery store. I would forever be someone who made other people uncomfortable.

Now a new feeling cut through my haze: resentment.

I knew what it was like to hate parts of my own body—what woman doesn't? You "hate" that little bump of fat behind your knee, or that pointy little pinkie toe that doesn't match the others, or that one crooked tooth. Anything about you that insists on being flawed despite all your attempts to get yourself perfectly uncriticizable is fair game for hostility.

But this was different. Those grafts didn't even look human.

It was like some alien creature had laid itself down over my neck. Old dissatisfactions with my old self dissolved in the face of what it felt like to look at my shoulder. I'd "hated" my flabby parts before, and I'd

thought things were "gross," but I didn't even know the meaning of those words until now. The sight of the grafts—puckered and gooey and shiny with Silvadene ointment—was so viscerally shocking, I felt a squeeze at the base of my throat like I might throw up.

I had to look away.

This was the feeling I'd been afraid of—but it was so much worse than I'd feared. It was like a part of the old me, sweet and vulnerable and shockingly innocent, had died. It's one thing to think about in a theoretical way—we know we won't last forever—but it's quite another thing to see it happen. Part of me had been *destroyed*. I squeezed my eyes closed and felt a wash of regret. Why hadn't I ever even appreciated that curve of my neck before, or the smoothness of its skin, or the pattern of its pale freckles? What had I been thinking that night, wearing a strapless dress? Why hadn't I been more careful? How could I have been the keeper of such a precious thing—my body!—and taken it so stupidly for granted?

"That could have been your *face*," Kit said then, peeking at my shoulder through squinted eyes. "You're lucky."

Lucky again.

"That's what people keep telling me," I said.

WE DID NOT wind up watching *Grease* that night. The haircut and all that came after was more than enough for me. I did let Kitty set up my computer so I could check email—but then I shut it right back down again when I saw that Chip had posted a photo of me while I was still in the ICU, looking absolutely ghastly, to Facebook, of all places, asking for prayers.

"After a tragic accident," he wrote, "the love of my life is fighting for survival in the ICU."

"A tragic accident?" Kit demanded, when I showed it to her. "*He's* a tragic accident."

He'd posted the photo on his wall and tagged me. He'd also linked to a news clip and an article in the paper.

People were understandably alarmed. With every comment, Facebook sent me an email notification, so my inbox was flooded. People were "praying" and sending emoticons of hearts and kisses and angels. They made comments about how great I was and cheered me on. But the volume—there must have been a hundred—felt overwhelming to me.

I fixated on the photo itself, amazed that Chip had overshared so wildly by posting it. I didn't even want to see pictures of people's *pedicures* in my feed—much less bruised shots of tubes and vacuums and abject suffering. What had he been thinking? What was he trying to prove? In what universe would I want a picture of myself looking like a meatloaf posted for the world to see? I had barely summoned the courage to look in the mirror myself—and apparently, I was the last one to know. An ex-boyfriend had even left me a GIF of puppies and kittens licking each other.

This must have been how Neil Putnam at Simtex knew about my situation. The whole damn city seemed to know.

"I'm never going back to Facebook," I said.

"Of course not," Kit agreed. "Facebook's for grandmas. Just follow me on Instagram."

LATER, AFTER WE'D fallen quiet for a while, and Kit was already starting to make slow, snoozy sleeping breaths, I had to wake her up.

"Kit!" I whispered. Then, with no response, a little louder: "Kit!"

She startled and sat up.

"Great news!" I said, still whispering.

"What?"

"I have to poop."

She leaned a little forward. "That's great news?"

"Help me out of bed."

"Didn't you just go right before bed?"

I snapped my fingers at her, like, *Let's go.* "That was pee."

She got up and shuffled over.

"You know what this means, don't you?" I said, as we worked me across the board into the chair.

Kit only had one eye open. "What does this mean?"

"It means I can pee and poo on my own."

"Does it mean you're getting better?" she asked.

"Well, I'm not getting worse."

"Can I Instagram *this*?" she asked, as we positioned me onto the toilet.

"Say the word 'Instagram' one more time, and you're on the first flight back to Brooklyn."

"Noted," she said.

She waited outside the door for me a long while, Googling random trivia on her phone to pass the time. "Did you know that Ben Franklin invented the catheter in 1752 when his brother John suffered from bladder stones?"

"I can't say that I did."

"Did you know you can use urine to make gunpowder?"

"That might come in handy."

"Did you know that seventy-three percent of people with spinal cord injuries never void normally again?"

"Don't tell me that! That's depressing."

"Not for you."

"Where are you finding all this?"

"PeeTrivia.com."

I took my time. Kit hinted several times that she was ready to go back to bed, but I was not rushing this miracle for anything.

Eleven

AT LUNCH THE next day, we did not linger more than sixty seconds on the triumph of my newly returned toileting skills before my mother declared the topic "unappetizing" and got back to worrying about my relationship with Chip.

"Has he been to visit you?" she wanted to know.

My BLT suddenly lost its flavor. "Can we not talk about this?"

"I did some reading on the computer—" she said next.

I glanced at my dad. "Here we go," he said.

She continued, "—and I think maybe he's afraid of you."

"*Afraid* of me?"

"Of what you represent. Of how you've come to symbolize his weakness and foolishness."

"Have I?"

"Well, what other explanation can there be?"

"I can't psychoanalyze Chip right now." I had my hands full just making it through the day.

"Well, someone has to!"

"Looks like you're doing a pretty good job."

My mom set her sandwich down—a gesture that meant we were getting down to business. She started to speak, but then she caught herself, turned to my dad. "You know what, sweetheart? This sandwich is not very good."

My dad looked at the sandwich.

"I hate to ask, but would you mind going back and getting me a Caesar salad instead?"

My dad had just taken his first bite of his own sandwich. He looked back and forth between it and my mother for a second. "You want me to drive back to the sandwich shop?"

My mother nodded, then gestured at me with her head. "We could use a little just-us-girls time anyway."

My dad looked at me. Then he nodded and stood up with his sandwich in one hand and his keys in the other and left the room.

My mom leaned closer to me once the door closed, and kept her voice low. "I read an article last night called 'Sexual Functioning After a Spinal Cord Injury.'"

"Mom! Don't read that!"

"Because if Chip's enthusiasm is like his father's—or any man, really—that's going to be important to him."

I wrinkled my nose. "Please don't talk to me about Jim Dunbar's 'enthusiasm.'"

"I've been best friends with Evelyn for years, sweetheart. I know *everything*."

I was shaking my head. "Nope. Please. No."

"The great news is," she pushed on, "even though men in your situation often lose sexual abilities, women typically don't. Which means even if you don't walk again—which, of course, you will—you'll still be good to go in that arena."

Was it worse to talk about Chip's father's sexual functioning with my mom—or to talk about mine? Words cannot express how much I did not want to discuss "that arena." But she had momentum now.

She went on. "You can have babies and everything—typically. In fact,

the only trouble most women in your situation have is finding somebody who's willing to—"

She stopped herself.

"Somebody who's willing to what?"

But she turned her attention back to her sandwich, wrapping it up like she might save it for later.

"Willing to *what*?"

She started again, more carefully. "Women's level of sexual activity does typically go down, but it's not that the injury prevents it. It's that nobody . . ."

She paused, like she couldn't say it.

"It's that nobody wants to fuck them anymore?"

She closed her eyes. "You know I hate that language."

If I could have walked out, I would have.

Instead, with no other option, I banged my head back against the pillow. "Is that the inspiring message you came with today?"

She did have enough self-awareness to be a tiny bit cowed. She folded her napkin and smoothed it on her leg. "I just read the article, and it seemed like information you should have."

"Why?" I asked. "What am I supposed to do with that? Root even harder for a miracle? Defy the laws of human physiology?"

"I'm trying to help," she insisted.

"By freaking me the hell out?"

"The point is," my mother said, "we have to be proactive. We have to face this thing head-on. All the healing and recovery you're going to do takes place in the first six to eight weeks after the accident—and you're already two weeks in."

"Are you saying I'm a slacker?"

"I'm saying you need to get your head in the game."

There was always a kind of backward logic to my mom's crazy. I got it now. She hadn't *accidentally* revealed to me that I was facing a possible lifetime of being unfuckable. She was doing it on purpose. She was attempting to motivate me. To get me focused. To rouse some unsinkable

part of my soul that would stand up in outrage and simply refuse to give in.

The worst part was, it was working.

This was how she'd motivated me my whole life: fear of the worst-case scenario. She was trying to scare me into action. She was trying to generate a *Rocky* moment, trying to cue the music and shift me into a training montage.

Did I think that I could beat my spinal cord into submission? Of course not. Could sheer willpower overcome anything? Of course not. Was there a hazy line between determination and denial? Absolutely.

But what choice did I have? Sure, she was playing dirty. Sure, she was acting like a terrorist. But her heart was in the right place—and she wasn't wrong. I didn't want to spend the rest of my life in a wheelchair. I didn't want to give up everything I'd hoped for. I didn't want to lose Chip.

Wait—was that right? The old me didn't want to lose the old Chip. But now, thinking about it, I wasn't totally clear on how the current me felt about the current Chip. Of course, in the face of my mom's hyperbole, how I specifically felt about Chip was not exactly relevant. According to her, if I didn't pull it together I would lose all guys, period.

This was one of her signature moves. If a little teaspoonful of ice-cold terror could burn off the fog and inspire me to try, was that so bad?

My mother sensed me cratering from across the room. For a lady so tone-deaf to others' emotions, she could be remarkably astute. She put her half-eaten lunch back in its sack and came to stand by the bed and take my hand. "Sweetheart, I know you've had a shock."

I waited.

"We all have."

I waited again.

"Even Chip."

There it was.

"I'm worried about him. He seems to be—" She glanced up to find the word. "Faltering."

"Faltering how?" I asked.

"I think he's lost his way. His mother says he's been out drinking, coming in at all hours, not showering."

Chip always showered. He took three showers a day.

My mom squeezed my hand. "What the two of you had was special."

"I agree."

"Don't you want it back?"

"Have I lost it?"

"No," she said, so emphatically she almost sang it. "Of course not. But—has he been to visit you?"

"Some," I said. *Not really.*

"I'm just saying, it's time to get better and put things right."

Why was this all on my shoulders? Why wasn't it Chip's job to get better and start visiting me? "By 'get better,'" I asked, "do you mean 'walk again'?"

She pretended the idea had never occurred to her. "Well, wouldn't that be ideal? Isn't that worth a try?"

Worth a try? I felt like my eyeballs were going to start spinning. What did she think I was doing over here? Playing Xbox and drinking beer? I *was* trying. Every morning that I woke up and remembered the wreckage of my life, I was trying. Every breath I took, I was trying. Every second of being conscious all day long, I was trying.

I took a slow breath and held it. Then I said, "I'm just glad I can shit on the toilet."

My mother's eyes widened, but before she could respond, someone knocked on the door.

"Come in!" my mother and I both said at the same time, not dropping each other's gaze.

The door pushed open, and it was Kitty. Looking mad.

MY MOTHER HADN'T seen Kitty in three years. Hadn't seen the spiky-blond new hair, or the tattoos, or the piercings. I'm not even sure she recognized her at first.

But when she did, she went very still.

Kitty held her gaze and walked straight in, stopping on the other side of my bed. She was a little out of breath. From below, I watched them eyeing each other.

When my mom finally spoke, her voice was low. "I thought you only came here in the evenings."

"I wanted to see you," Kit said.

My mother lifted an eyebrow. "I can't imagine that's true."

"I have something to say."

"I think we've said it all."

"I haven't."

With that, Kitty raised my curiosity—but not my mother's.

"As you can see," my mother said, "I'm pretty busy right now."

"I want you to tell Margaret why I went away."

My mom looked at Kit dead-on. "No."

"She deserves to know."

"I disagree."

"She is angry at me for leaving. At *me!*"

"I can't tell her how to feel."

"But you can tell her why I had to go."

This was how they always were together—Kit pushing until my mother snapped. This time, it didn't take long. My mother leaned closer, her voice like a hiss. "Hasn't she been through enough?"

The tone right there would have shut me right up. But Kit was always the braver one. "I don't think it's her you're worried about. I think it's you."

"That's ridiculous," my mother said, looking away. In that moment, I knew that whatever it was they were talking about, Kit was right.

"Tell her," Kit pressed. "Tell her right now. This has gone on too long."

"I won't."

"Tell her—or I will."

My mother's eyes looked wild. She had not expected this moment to rise up so fast—out of nowhere, really, like a flash flood: Kit showing up and making these sudden demands. One minute, my mother was trying

to manipulate me—solid, comfortable ground for her—and the next, Kitty was manipulating her. I could see my mom's mind spinning, trying to come up with a way to stop her.

Kit turned to me. "On the night I left, it was because Mom and I fought."

"Stop it," my mother said, her whole body tense.

"I remember," I said to Kit. "You pushed her into the pool."

"I pushed her into the pool because she wouldn't answer a question."

"Stop!" my mother said again, eyes on Kit. "What do I have to threaten you with? Never speaking to you again?"

"You already don't speak to me. I'm not sure you ever did."

But my mom was still searching. "Cutting you out of my will! Not giving you Grandma's ruby ring!"

"I don't need to be in your will," Kit said. "I don't need a ring. I need my only sister"—and here her voice rose to a shout—"to understand what the hell is going on here!"

My mother blinked.

Kit turned back to me. "Remember when I was working for that genealogist?"

I shook my head. "Vaguely."

"She had that business helping people find their ancestors and trace their family histories?"

I squinted. "Okay. Sort of." I did not see where this was going.

"She talked me into having my DNA analyzed. She had a bulk discount with a mail-in company. She was sending in several samples, and she had an extra kit, and so I just did it. On a whim."

I frowned. "I have no memory of that."

"I didn't tell you," Kit said. "I didn't tell anybody. Why would I? The results weren't going to be interesting."

True. We could recite our various heritages in that way that lots of Americans can. Our mom had a little bit of lots of places. Irish, English, German, Canadian, French, and even, rumor had it, some Huron. Our dad's family, in contrast, was all Norwegian. His Norwegian ancestors

had immigrated to an all-Norwegian town in Minnesota where Norwegians just married other Norwegians for generations—until one day, my dad's dad moved their family to Texas and broke the trend.

"Huh," I said. "So you, like, sent in your blood?"

"Saliva, actually."

Then there was a pause.

Kit looked at my mother.

My mother looked at Kit.

"Did you learn anything?" I finally asked.

"Yes," Kit said.

My mother shook her head at Kit. "You don't have to do this."

"Yes, I do! Because you won't!"

My mother looked around the room, her eyes stretched and frantic in a way I'd never seen before—searching, it seemed, for some way to stop what was happening. But short of tackling Kit, there wasn't much my mom could do. "Whatever comes of this," my mom said to her then, "it's all on you."

"Oh," Kit said, narrowing her eyes, "I think it's at least a little bit on you."

Everything about my mother's expression and posture was pleading. She shook her head, like, *Don't.*

Kit tilted her head, like, *You leave me no choice.*

At that, my mom sucked in her breath and, without another word, walked out of the room, clacking her heels, and leaving her purse and her sandwich behind.

When she was gone, I looked at Kit. "Maybe you shouldn't tell me," I said. "Maybe we can agree that you had your reasons, and I'll just promise not to be mad anymore."

"You need to know."

I shook my head. "I'm not sure I do."

But she nodded. "It's time."

I sighed.

"When the results came back, they were surprising."

I could not even fathom how something as random as this could have driven such a rift between my mom and Kit. "Surprising how?"

"You know how proud Dad is of his Norwegian-ness?"

"Yes," I said. Anybody who'd known my dad five minutes knew that.

"Well," Kit said, taking a breath. "This lab breaks down the results by particular regions."

"Okay," I said.

Kit went on. "My results came back with everything you'd expect from Mom: England, Ireland, Western Europe—exactly what we already knew. But I also have Italy and Greece." She checked my expression.

I shrugged. "So?"

"Guess what I don't have? *Scandinavian.*"

I puffed out a little laugh at the idea: Kitty Jacobsen didn't have any Scandinavian.

But she just crossed her arms and waited for me to catch up. "I don't have *any* Scandinavian in my ethnic heritage."

Now I frowned. I shook my head. "That can't be right."

"Think about it," Kit said.

I couldn't think about it. My brain refused to think about it.

"If Dad is fully, or at least mostly, Norwegian," Kit said, "and I don't have *any* Norwegian in my genetic profile . . ." She waited.

I shook my head. "That's crazy. That's wrong."

Kit's eyes were very serious. "It's not wrong."

"They must have mixed up the samples!" I said.

"That's what I thought," Kit said. "So we sent another sample. Same results."

"This can't be right. This is insane."

"Next, I confronted Mom about it. At the Fourth of July party three years ago."

The conversation was starting to feel like a rickety old mine cart on a downhill track. "And what did Mom say?" I asked.

"What *didn't* she say? She told me I was crazy and wrong and spoiled and selfish. She told me to back off, and it was none of my business. She told me to drop the whole subject and throw the test results in the trash. She told me I'd ruined her life. Then she plastered a big, false, Stepford

smile on her face and walked out to the backyard to continue hosting her pool party."

I blinked at Kit.

"And that was the moment when I knew for sure. Our dad is not my father."

Twelve

I RUBBED MY eyes. "That can't be right."

"I'm telling you," Kit said. "It is. The minute I knew, I *knew*."

She had a patient look, like she didn't really have to convince me. Like the facts would get me there, and all she had to do was wait.

"But!" I protested. This was impossible. "You have his same smile! And his same sense of humor! And you both love sailing! And *The Matrix*! And popcorn!" *Case closed!*

Kit gave me a look. "Everybody loves popcorn. That's not genetic."

"There has to be a mistake."

"Mom was livid that night. She denied everything, but she did it so viciously, I knew I was right. I, of course, drank the entire margarita machine after that, because that's what I used to do back then, and then I pushed her into the pool—not my finest moment. When she climbed out, sopping wet, I followed her and got in her face until she finally told me the truth."

I waited a long time before I said, "What was the truth?"

Kit looked right into my eyes. "I was a mistake."

I did not look away.

She went on, "I was an 'unfortunate accident.' With someone who was not Dad."

All the air leaked out of my lungs. I felt like a punctured tire.

When my chest started to sting, I sucked in a big breath. "Does Dad know?"

Kit shook her head.

I tried to put the pieces together. Our mom knew, of course. Kit knew, and had for three years. Now I knew. Everybody except our dad.

A long silence. Then at last I said, "That's why you left."

Kit nodded. "I told her she had to choose. Either she told the truth, or I was gone."

"That's a tough choice," I said.

Kit's eyes snapped to mine. "Are you taking her side?"

"I'm just saying that's tough."

"Not for Linda," Kit said. "She kicked me out in five seconds flat." For just a second, I saw Kit's expression sag—before she raised her shoulders, stood up a little taller, and said, "Whatever."

"Just think," I said. "She carried that secret all those years."

Kit nodded.

"It must have terrified her to be confronted with it."

"That's why she wanted me gone," Kit said. "I'm the evidence."

"Who was the guy?" I asked.

Kit shook her head. "She wouldn't say."

"Are you going to tell Dad?"

"Never!"

"But you told me."

"I told you because I needed you to understand."

It was a lot to process. My head was swirling. "Why did you wait so long?"

Kit sighed. "I kept thinking she'd tell you, but she didn't. I kept thinking she'd reach out and apologize to me, but she didn't. At first, I had bigger fish to fry. I had to get through rehab and that whole first year of being sober. Then I was getting the Beauty Parlor going, and the time

kind of flew. But the truth is, I was really, really, really angry. I thought I would never want to see any of you again."

"But I didn't do anything!"

"No," Kit said. "But you got to be Dad's real daughter—and I didn't. I know this sounds crazy, but it felt like you'd stolen him from me."

"But I *didn't!*"

"My brain knew that," Kit said. "But my heart was a different story."

I tried to put myself in Kit's shoes. "You were just mad at everybody."

"Every*body*. Every*thing*. It stirred up a lot for me. Mainly about how I always thought she loved you better. Turns out, I was right."

"She does *not* love me better," I said, but now I wondered—and not, actually, for the first time.

Kit shrugged. "It's okay. It's hopeless with her. But I didn't want to lose you, too."

"So the crash made you miss me?"

"The crash made me want to stop wasting time."

"So you came home to see me."

"But then I just couldn't explain. It didn't feel like my secret to share. I wanted to give her a chance to say something, at least."

"Why today?" I asked. It was a fair question. She'd been here two weeks. Why come storming in now?

"I ran into Piper McAllen at Starbucks this morning. Do you remember her?"

I shook my head.

Kit shrugged. "A mean girl from my grade, now a show-offy mother of two. She told me everybody says I went crazy and was put into a home. She said that to my face! In *Starbucks*! Apparently, the whole world just thinks I lost my marbles. And that was it for me. I was like, *We're done here.* Time to set the record straight. I left my latte on the counter and stormed over."

I was about to suggest maybe Kit should go find our mom—she'd left her purse here, after all, and wouldn't get too far without it—when there was a knock at the door. When it pushed open, it was our dad.

In the instant I saw him I felt a rush of sympathy. He was my mother's

high school sweetheart. They got married the summer after they graduated, and Kit was born a few months later. My dad had been all set to go to college in California, but he joined the marines instead. Of course, my mom gave up college altogether.

Neither of them had gotten quite what they'd hoped for.

These were facts I'd known for a long time, but they were only part of the story. What would my dad think now, if he knew everything? Would it change how he felt about his family? About Kit? About my mom? Would he leave if he knew? I couldn't imagine our family without him. He was the best thing about it.

Right then, I made a mental vow I would never tell him.

"Hey, girls," my dad said then, as he stepped into the room. "Look what I found!"

Out from behind him, of all people, stepped Chip.

CHIP LOOKED LIKE hell, just like my mother had threatened.

Even so, just seeing that face of his gave me jolt of pleasure. It was like some kind of Pavlovian response. See Chip; feel a thrill. Whether I wanted to or not. Whether he looked like hell or not. Whether he deserved it or not. It was quite a realization, and it reminded me of what Kit had just said. My brain knew one thing, but my heart was a different story.

Plus, my mother had spent our lunch hour scaring the hell out of me.

Chip hesitated in the doorway, sensing they had interrupted something.

He looked like he'd slept in his clothes. He hadn't shaved. He was holding a manila bubble envelope in one hand. He gave Kit a little wave, but then got down to business.

He walked a little closer to the bed, his eyes on me, and we all watched him.

"I just got this package from the FAA." He held it up. "They've closed their investigation of the crash. 'Pilot error.'" He put his head down and gave a breathy laugh. "We could've told 'em that."

"I thought it was a 'senseless tragedy,'" I said, and Chip blinked at me.

"What's in the bag, son?" my dad asked then.

Chip looked down at it. Back on track. "They're scrapping the wreckage, and I'll pay for the plane out of pocket. But they found this."

He pulled his grandmother's engagement ring out of the envelope and held it out for us to see. It was, to put it gently, a little charred.

"They found it," I said.

"They knew our story from the interview, so they knew what it was."

I didn't know what to say. It was so strange to see Chip at all—especially like this. He had always, always been perfectly put together, and in control, and groomed like a male model. This disheveled guy was like his antimatter.

As soon as I thought that, I wondered if he thought the same thing about me. Now that I was unfuckable—according to my mom.

"Hey," he said then. "You got a haircut."

I touched the spiky back. "Yeah."

Chip shrugged. "Don't worry. It'll grow back."

"Chip," I said then. "What are you doing here?"

He shrugged. "Bringing you your ring."

I watched in shock as he bent down on one knee, losing his balance for a second before getting situated, and then lifted the ring up to me like a kid playing King Arthur.

"Margaret—" he began in a thespian-like voice, but then interrupted himself: "Oh, shit! What's your middle name?"

"Rosemary," my dad offered from the wings.

Chip began again. "Margaret Rosemary Jacobsen, we've had a rough month. I have let you down in more ways than I can count. But I think this ring can be a symbol of a new beginning for us. I vow to be a better man. I know I can be a better man. So now I ask you, in front of your dad and your crazy sister, despite everything we've been through—will you marry me?"

I knew my line. But I didn't say it.

I took in the sight of this very different Chip for a good while. True,

my mom had succeeded in stoking some of my insecurities and semi-convinced me that I might never get a better offer than this one, right here, from a disappointing, wrinkled, slightly soused version of the man of my dreams. If my mom were here, she'd be hissing at me to say yes and just lock it down right now before he sobered up.

But I couldn't.

Did I want to marry him?

I'd wanted to marry him for years—so long, I almost didn't know how to *not* want to. Part of me still did, as bad as ever—maybe worse. But another part was having massive second thoughts.

He was looking at me. Waiting. *Well?*

The answer could have been easy. But easy didn't exist anymore. If it ever had. "I don't think so, Chip."

His Shakespearean expression fell away, and he stood up. "No?"

"You said yourself it's been a rough month."

"I'm trying to make it better."

"I get that, but I'm not sure this is the way."

Chip's face crumpled. There was no other word for it. "I'm so indescribably sorry about that night. I never meant for this to happen. I would give anything—anything—to change places with you."

"This isn't about the accident," I said.

"What is it about?"

"How many times have you been to visit me here?" I asked. I genuinely didn't know.

He looked fuzzy, too. "I'm not sure."

"Three," my dad offered, "if you count right now."

I looked at Chip. "Three times in two weeks. Do you think that's enough?"

"It's just—" Chip's voice caught. "It's that every time I see you—all burned and messed up—I feel so guilty, knowing it was all because of me, knowing that I ruined your life. It's like I'm suffocating."

Really? I thought.

"Okay," I said. "One: The jury is still out on whether or not my life is ruined. And two: Fuck you. You should have come anyway. I don't care

if you feel guilty. You should have been here every minute of every day. You should have been sleeping here and waking up here and buying me stuffed animals in the gift shop and bringing me Chinese takeout. *Kitty* has been a better friend to me in here than you have."

Kitty shot a glance over at my dad.

Chip looked down. "I'm sorry."

"So you can see why the idea of marrying you, the idea of 'in sickness and in health,' doesn't make a lot of sense to me right now."

Chip looked down and nodded.

"It's not the accident," I said. "It's everything since the accident."

"But it's not off?" he asked then, looking up. "The engagement's not *off*?"

"Well, it's not frigging *on*."

"Can it just be, like, *on hold*, then?"

I felt all six eyes in the room on me. I wanted to punish him. I wanted to tell him it was off—one hundred percent. I wanted to make it clear, to everybody, that insult to injury would not be tolerated.

Instead, I sighed. "It can be on hold."

Chip broke into a smile. "That's something. I can work with that."

He did not deserve to be smiling right now. But I couldn't have said no, and we both knew it. I wasn't ready to give up on Chip. He'd just failed a test of love, yes. But I couldn't—wouldn't—decide it was the only test that would ever matter.

"And will you wear the ring?" Chip pushed.

Did I want to wear that charred, bent ring? Not really. It was a bit too close to forgiveness. But I let him slide it on my finger anyway. I was too tired to be strong about this. And, more than that: Letting go of my past and my future at the same time felt like more than I could bear.

As he nudged the ring into place on my finger, Chip gave a relieved burst of laughing and crying at the same time, and at this range I got a sour whiff of alcohol. "It's a little bent," he said.

"It fits better now, though."

"Can I kiss you?" Chip asked.

I nodded, but I couldn't meet his eyes. I felt, more than saw, him lean

in. I held still and braced for impact. When his lips touched mine, I tried like hell to feel something. And I did, in a way, but it was not something any kiss had ever made me feel before. It felt like a reminder of exactly how life used to be—followed by an ache of sorrow that it might be gone for good.

Thirteen

AT THE KISS, Kitty and my dad took off, assuming, as you might, that Chip and I wanted to be alone.

In truth, what I really wanted was time to talk to Kitty. And to give my dad a little hug for wounds he didn't even know he had. And to figure out where the heck my mom had disappeared to.

But Chip did not remove his face from mine for a good while.

Something about him kissing me made the burns on my face itch. I tucked my hands under my blankets to remind myself not to scratch.

While I was waiting for him to finish, Ian walked in.

"Smooching hour is over, folks," Ian said.

Chip pulled away, and we both turned toward Ian.

Ian always looked annoyed, but now he looked extra annoyed. "Time for your therapy, Maggie Jacobsen. Maybe your man can help with your transfer while I grab a coffee."

I shook my head, like, *Definitely not.* "He hasn't had any practice."

Ian raised his eyebrows. "Well, there's nothing to it."

Chip turned to me. "What did he say?"

"He's Scottish," I said. "He wants you to help me transfer to my chair. He says there's nothing to it."

Chip frowned, like this was another test he was bound to fail. "Maybe you could show me," he said to Ian.

Ian frowned. "You want me to show you?"

Chip nodded, and, as ever, I read his face so well. He thought getting a lesson would get him out of having to do it himself.

Ian shrugged. "It's not rocket science, man, but if you want a lesson, let's go. For Maggie's sake, if nothing else."

Chip looked at me. "Did he just call you Maggie?"

I shrugged. "He can't pronounce Margaret." I turned back to Ian. "I don't need help."

Ian shook his head. "You do."

"That's not what you said before."

"Before, I was teaching you a lesson."

"What?" I said. "That you're kind of an asshole?"

Ian blinked, and I could not read his expression. "A lesson that you *can* do it yourself," he said. He looked over at Chip. "But that doesn't mean you should have to."

Chip looked at me. "I can't understand him at all. It's like a speech impediment."

Ian didn't take his eyes off me. "Watch yourself, little man."

There was a knock at the door, and then my dad's voice. "Is everybody done kissing?"

"Yes," Chip and I called flatly, at the same time.

My dad stepped in—with my mom trailing behind him, looking dazed. "Look who I found! At the candy machine!"

"Where's Kit?" I asked.

"She had to go," my dad said. Then, in a stage whisper, "She's got a date with Fat Benjamin."

My mother, a few feet behind my dad, held an unopened Hershey bar and looked shaken and pale. I made a stab at mental telepathy, trying to promise *I'll never tell him* from my brain to hers. But I don't think it worked.

My dad was as jolly and unaware as could be, and that just made it sadder all around. He put his arm around my mom and gave her a little squeeze. Then he said to Ian, "I'd like to see how to do a transfer, too."

"You heard that conversation?" I asked.

"Sure," my dad said. "You can hear everything out in the hallway. That's how we knew you and Loverboy were done making out."

"Then why did you ask?"

He lifted his eyebrows like, *Duh.* "To embarrass you."

Ian coughed. Then he reached behind me to grab the transfer board and lower the bed.

I regarded Chip for a second. Next to Ian, he suddenly did look like a *little man.* I'd always thought of him as "trim" or "sporty," but standing next to Ian gave him a slightly shrimpy vibe.

"The trick to the transfer," Ian told us all then, "is letting Maggie do as much for herself as she can. But stay close by. There's a temptation," he added, "when someone you love is struggling, to want to help too much. Keep in mind that the struggle makes her stronger."

I gave Ian a look. I might be in danger of many things, but "getting too much help" was not one of them.

Ian wasn't looking at me. He was looking right at Chip. "The most important thing," he said, "is being there."

When he'd finished staring Chip down, he patted the board and crooked his finger at me, like, *Come here.*

I pulled back my covers, and then we all beheld—because I was wearing a gown for the whole using-the-potty project—my bare legs.

Chip had seen those legs a thousand times, and caressed them, and kissed them—even shaved them once, in an exercise in erotic suspense that worked much better in theory than in practice. But these weren't the legs that he knew. They'd atrophied so much even in the short time I'd been here, they were like a newborn calf's legs—spindly and soft and splayed.

The sight of them made me feel deeply ashamed. I hated them. I wanted to beat them with my fists. I wanted to pummel them into bloody bruises on the mattress.

Ian was unfazed. "You're going to need some pants for the therapy gym, lass."

I pointed my mother toward the cabinet, and she found a pair in a gym bag, along with my last clean bra—hot pink with tiger stripes. She also grabbed one of the several T-shirts we'd cut at the shoulder.

Ian gently helped me into the sweatpants, edging them up, and when it was time to pull them under my butt and around my hips, he leaned down so I could circle my arms around his neck. I pulled up just enough that I inhaled the most delicious scent of him. Kind of gingery. Sweet, cookie-ish spices mixed with a microscopic hint of salty manliness.

I can't even put it into words, but you know when they bring the dessert tray around at a restaurant and you immediately just know what you want—like, *That one. Right there!* I had that reaction to the smell of him. That one.

But we were on to the dressing-the-top-half phase, and so my mother asked the men to leave the room.

"Even me?" Chip asked.

"Especially you," I said.

Minutes later, when the men got the all-clear, I was all decked out in my *Flashdance* look with the bra strap on the burned side tucked down under my armpit. On a normal person, this outfit might have been provocative. On me, it was just sad. My mother promised to bring me something normal tomorrow.

Ian began his lesson, but I didn't even listen. I was too busy trying to catch another whiff of him.

LATER, IN THE gym, on the mat, as Ian worked my legs, I said, "I'm sorry I called you an asshole."

Ian didn't meet my eyes. "You called me 'kind of an asshole.' That's different."

"Not really."

With a normal person, that might have been the start of some kind of conversation, but Ian just let it die. As we continued to work, first on

one side, then on the other, then doing some actual sit-ups, I watched the other therapists talking to, encouraging, and playing around with their patients, and I couldn't help it: I felt a little shortchanged.

Every attempt at talking fizzled out like a spark going dark.

"Are you married?" I tried.

"No."

I waited for more.

Nothing.

Uncomfortable pause.

Me again: "Any kids?"

His jaw went tight. "No."

Pause.

Me: "Hobbies? Things you do for fun?"

Another pause so long I thought he wasn't going to even answer at all. About as conversationally agonizing as I could imagine. Finally: "Triathlons."

"You do triathlons. For fun."

"For a challenge."

"Is there anything you do for fun?"

"Challenges *are* fun."

I'd say, on the whole, he seemed about as excited to talk to me as he'd been to talk to Myles. But, dammit, I wasn't Myles. I wasn't taunting him like that. Or provoking him. Or out to get him.

But maybe I was, in a way.

I didn't realize it at the time, but the fact that Ian was so reticent might have been good for me. With some people—not all, but some—when they run away, it makes you want to chase them. That was Ian: so withdrawn, it coaxed me out.

I tried again. "Thanks for the transfer lesson, by the way."

Nothing.

"My family's all a little freaked out right now," I attempted.

Not even a nod for that one. He was working my ankles and just kept his head down.

Finally, I tried this: "Did you know you can drink your own pee?"

His head popped up, and he was all surprise, and he flashed a shocked smile for half a second before dropping his head back down. "I didn't know that, no," he said, getting back to work.

But now I knew that smile existed. I wanted another one.

"Some tweed coats are dyed with it."

Nothing.

"Romans used to brush their teeth with it to whiten them."

When that didn't get a response, I peeked around at the side of his face to see if he was stifling a smile. He was.

He was hooking giant rubber bands around my ankles now, for resistance. Then he rolled me over onto my stomach and told me pull against them until I could touch my heels to my butt. Apparently, it would strengthen my hamstrings, which were still working.

"You want me to touch my heels to my butt?"

"Just try."

"Do I have to actually touch?"

"No."

"Are you saying trying is more important than succeeding?"

"Always."

Another long silence while I tried, and failed, to touch my butt with my feet.

"Not a big talker, are you?" I said.

"Not when I'm working."

"Other people seem to be able to do both."

"I'm not other people."

"Apparently not."

"We're here to get you stronger. Not joke around."

Just then, a group of other PTs burst out laughing at something one of the patients had said.

I met his eyes. "Okay."

But I couldn't leave it alone. I have never, ever, been comfortable with silence. I can't get a massage, or a manicure, or even a pelvic without making constant chitchat the entire time. I cannot be in the presence of another human being, especially one I don't know very well, and not

talk—whether they want to or not. I surveyed the other PTs, chatting away so solicitously with their patients. If I'd had one of them, I might've stayed more passive and let the conversation come and go—but being stuck with the king of quiet stirred up all the compulsive-need-to-talk chemicals in my body, and I just started yammering on like a nut-job.

Anything, I had apparently decided, was better than nothing.

Hence this monologue, delivered on my back, to the ceiling, as Ian made me push against various objects with my legs:

"Did you know I got engaged on the same day this injury happened? You probably do. Everybody seems to. The nurses keep talking about it. I hear them in the hallway. They feel very sorry for me. They can't imagine what it must be like to be me. Which is funny, because I can't either. The best day of your life and the worst day are the same day. How does that bode for a marriage? If it even happens. If your once-charming prince doesn't turn into a seedy alcoholic and die in some gutter somewhere. And now I'm wearing this ring—and I don't even want to. Or maybe I do. I don't know who I am. I used to be a runner. I ran three different marathons. I didn't place or anything, but I knew how to push myself, and I knew how to be dedicated. When things got tough, I went for a run. I ran in the rain. I ran at night sometimes—or at four in the morning. What am I going to do now? Go for *a roll*? I can't move. I can barely breathe. But then I think, who am I to complain? There are girls who've been sold into slavery. There are children being beaten. Half the world is worse off than me—probably more. Half the time I feel petulant and whiny, and the other half, I think I've suffered something beyond human imagining. And I can't find an in-between. All I know is that my life as I knew it is gone. Nothing is the same. Food doesn't even taste the same. Voices don't sound the same. Things I used to love, I hate. Things I used to hate, I hate. I don't want to see anyone, I don't want to talk to anyone. My cell phone has like fifty messages. I hate myself, and I hate everybody else. I think about dying. It seems like it would be easier. But then I don't want to die. I just don't want to live either. My mom says the only way I can get better is to believe I will get better—to be such a determined maniac that even the laws of nature can't stop me—but

then I look at these noodles I have for legs and I can't believe it. It's like asking me to believe the sky is green. The sky is just not green—you know?—and I can't pretend that it is. All I know is, I don't feel anything at all—not even hope."

Somewhere in my soliloquy, I'd closed my eyes. By the time I ran out of words and fell quiet, I noticed Ian had set my legs down and was no longer touching me. Had he walked away? Gone for a coffee? Left for the day? I knew he wasn't listening, but something about the idea that he wasn't even there stung a little bit.

I opened my eyes, and that's when I saw that he'd stood up and was leaning in to take my hands. "Sit up," he said, not looking at me, in a way that gave the distinct impression I was just another annoying obligation in his day.

I took his hands, but he did not pull me up. He just held them while I worked my way to a sitting position.

Once I was steady, he let go.

Then he bent down in front of me and met my eyes for the first time all day. He looked straight into my pupils until he had my full attention. Then he said, "Whether you walk again or not, I'm going to tell you the one thing I know for certain."

I blinked. "What's that?"

He took a deep breath. "It's the *trying* that heals you. That's all you have to do. Just try."

And he did not say another word for the rest of the day.

Fourteen

LATER, I FELT embarrassed about it.

I had *assaulted* him with my talking. He clearly didn't like to talk, and he certainly hadn't asked to be subjected to my whole pathetic story. He was utterly robotic that whole time, and afterward, he was even more determined to stay poker-faced.

That said, "It's the trying that heals you" really stuck in my head.

The next morning, for whatever reason, I woke up ready to try.

That day, after all the morning routines, I spent the "rest hour"—that I'd been using to stare into space—researching spinal cord injuries. My mother wasn't the only person in the world who could read articles. I started at Christopher Reeve's foundation and worked my way down, reading about expectations, therapies, strategies, equipment, clothing, and experimental theories. I learned terms like "axonal sprouting" and "neurogenesis," and I memorized the names and numbers of all the vertebrae. I studied anatomic charts of the spine and the body. I did Google searches for the phrases "spinal cord injury" and "miraculous recovery," and then I read every article my mother had found and then some. I made a choice to get inspired. I

made lists of reasons to feel hopeful. I forced myself to look at the sky and see green.

During those moments, whether they were in the late afternoon when my muscles were twitching from everything Ian had forced me to do, or in the wee hours of the night when I'd woken and couldn't get back to sleep, I felt the tiniest bit like myself again. Because this was how I had conquered every challenge in my life—with impeccable organization and driven focus. I got Kit to buy me index cards and file folders and a new pack of ballpoint pens. I had my dad set up a printer, and I started printing out articles, organizing them into different folders, and color-coding them with highlighters.

My mother had made a good point: There wasn't time to grieve. Everything I read confirmed what she'd said. There was a window of opportunity for recovery, and after that, it would be foolish to hope for more. I'd wasted two of my weeks in a stupor, and insurance would sponsor exactly four and a half more. So I had a month. A month to try every single possible thing I could think of to get my life back.

I read an article that said to talk to your body and tell it what you wanted, so I did. Another said to massage your limbs to wake up the nerve responses, so I did. One article said to make a list of tangible goals, and to check them off as you met them, so I did that, too.

- wiggle toes
- point toes
- flex toes
- rotate feet 360 degrees at ankles
- strengthen calves and arches
- strengthen core
- extend legs from knee out
- take a step
- stand for 5 minutes alone
- walk again—like a boss!

Of all the things on that list, I could sort of do exactly one: I could stand with my knees locked for two minutes—but only if I had a bar, or a person, to hold on to. Still, being able to lock my knees was huge. Lots of people couldn't do that.

But of all the advice I found, and all the mental tricks I tried, my favorite was the article that told me to visualize my ultimate goal over and over. Want to know my ultimate goal? To wheel myself out of the hospital to go home for good on a breezy spring day and run into Chip.

In the visualization, I'm wearing my favorite jeans and a gray-blue collared shirt that covers all my scars, and he's headed in to pick me up—but he stops still when he sees me because I look so much better than he'd expected. Out of the sickening hospital lights and away from the mauve décor, with the sunlight on my skin for the first time in far too long, I have a new radiance. He sees me now, suddenly, not as an invalid that we all feel so sorry for, but as the real me. In that second, as he's struck by the sight, I push myself up and stand—then I take one step toward him, and then another, and he's so astonished, he can barely breathe.

That's it. That's the grand finale. I'm the old me again, but so much better. Because now I've astonished us all. Now I've done the impossible. Now I've returned from hell—wiser and stronger and grateful as shit for all my ordinary blessings.

Chip feels a surge of awe for me, followed quickly by desperate love— and here's the best part: In the fantasy, identifying with Chip, I get to experience those things, too. Which is such a profound relief, because all I can feel for this mangled, malfunctioning body of mine these days is contempt. Wait—no: "Contempt" is too simple. It's more than that. It's disappointment. It's disgust. It's *revulsion*.

But in the visualization? All that's gone. All viciousness is replaced with admiration. I can see it on his face so clearly that I can feel it, too, and it's bliss. It hooks me and makes it irresistibly fun to return to the moment again and again. Chip is amazed at my strength and determination and power. And then I arrive at his arms, and he kisses me, and

I've aced another challenge. Even my hair is restored to just the way it was before—only better—because *why not.*

This wasn't self-indulgence, the article assured me. This was therapy.

I had to see what I wanted. I had to *want* what I wanted. I had to create a vision to move toward. The more time I could spend making that vision real in my head, the stronger its pull would be. So I let myself long for my old life to the point of aching, on the theory that the more I longed for it, the more strength I would conjure to go after it.

Was centering my image around Chip a little bit antifeminist?

Maybe.

You could argue it either way. You could read it as a rescued-by-the-prince fantasy, I suppose—though, in truth, Chip didn't rescue me. He didn't do anything but behold my awesomeness. I did it all myself. Would my women's studies professor from college point out, though, that my accomplishment wasn't significant or meaningful or emotionally resonant until it was appreciated by a man? Sure. Okay. That's fair. Maybe that was something to work on someday in therapy. But I had four and a half weeks left, and that visualization was addictively powerful. I'd take any power I could get.

Getting focused made me feel in control. It cleared my head. It's possible the worst thing about those first two weeks in the hospital was being so directionless, so passive, so lost.

THEN, ONE NIGHT, Kit came in with a stack of articles on the health benefits of singing and slapped them down on the rolling tray.

"I spent the day online," she said, "researching why you should sing."

I eyed her stack. "I'm not going to sing, Kit."

She lifted up the top third of them. "These detail the emotional benefits of singing."

"Not interested."

She lifted up the second third of them. "These are the social benefits."

I shook my head. "Don't care."

"And these"—she held the final third up like the Statue of Liberty—"are the physical benefits."

I sighed.

Kit started counting off on her fingers. "Singing helps release oxytocin and dopamine and endorphins. It decreases anxiety and depression. It reduces stress and helps regulate the endocrine system. It creates better oxygenation in the blood and leads to better sleep. It increases antibodies and strengthens the immune system. And—" She stepped closer for her grand finale.

"Do not say it makes you happy—"

"It makes you happy."

I dropped my head back against the pillow. "I don't want to be happy."

"Fine. Don't be happy. But sing anyway. Because it's good for your health in just about every possible way."

"Does it reduce inflammation in the spinal cord?"

"There's no study showing it doesn't."

I had to hand it to her. She was ready for me. That girl was going to get me singing or die trying. She described study after study. She told inspirational stories. She barraged me with statistics and inspiration. A study in Denmark—or was it Holland?—had tracked three hundred cancer patients, half of whom joined choirs and sang at least three times a week, and half of whom, the control group, did not. The singers were more likely to go into remission, and stay there—and the singers increased their life expectancy by six months over the nonsingers.

When I started to protest, she said, "I know, I know. You don't feel like singing. Well guess what? You seem to believe that you can only sing if you're *already* happy. But I believe that singing *makes* you happy, and science appears to be backing me up. Plus, an endorphin or two wouldn't kill you."

"Look, I just don't think I can be happy anymore."

"Well, I think you can."

"Why do you keep pushing this?"

"Because you love to sing."

I *used to* love to sing. "I love to sing exactly as much as everybody else."

"False. That's Mom talking."

I squinted at her like she was nuts. "Mom doesn't talk about singing."

"That's right. Or encourage it or value it. Or recognize your talent."

"I am not a talented singer. I'm just a normal person."

Kit nodded, and added, "With perfect pitch."

"I don't have perfect pitch."

"You can harmonize to *anything*. Anything at all! Do you think everybody can do that?"

I shrugged.

"No. *Nobody* can do that."

"Big deal."

"It is a big deal. You never should have left it behind. Now, are you going to start singing, or should I?"

But she didn't even wait for an answer. She just moved fast, so I couldn't shut her down, and then when she finally ran out of ammunition, without even pausing, she tapped her phone, where she had "Let It Be" already cued up, and hit PLAY.

She knew I couldn't resist that song.

She started singing along while I watched her, with my mouth clamped closed and my arms crossed over my chest. Then she started deliberately getting the words wrong, singing things like "And when the broke and hardened people . . ."

"Broken-hearted people!" I couldn't help but correct.

She went on, "For though they may be partying—"

"Parted!" I shouted. "They're not *partying*. This is *not* a song about partying."

But she was having fun now. She mutilated the whole rest of the song, changing "whisper" to "whistle," "cloudy" to "crowded," and "light" to "blight," while I shouted out protest after protest. Finally, we neared the end.

"You know I've got it on repeat, right?"

And so, when it started up again, those deep and soulful piano chords we remembered from my dad's old records, I leaned my head back against the pillow, fixed my gaze on the ceiling, and let myself give in. I

did love that song. It was the comfort food of Beatles tunes. Would it really kill me, I decided, to take a little bite?

"Fine," I said, "but sing it right this time."

"You're the boss."

So we did.

And, yes, I harmonized a little bit.

Did it make me happy? It didn't make me miserable, I'll give it that.

When the song ended, we sang it again.

Fifteen

AFTER THAT, WE fell into a schedule.

My official first order of business every morning was to try to wiggle my toes—which I never could. After that, it was: sponge bath, bandage changing, Silvadene application, and OT with Priya, who was very pleased with my progress in the areas of chair transfer, tooth-brushing, toileting, putting on sneakers and tying them, putting on and taking off socks, and wriggling into yoga pants. I was progressing well in the wheel-chair obstacle course next door to the therapy gym. I could navigate both tight turns and cobblestones without tipping, and Priya was start-ing to eyeball the final frontier—curbs and steps. Next, she wanted to take me to the OT kitchen so we could bake a batch of cookies for practice.

Also, she insisted that I take up knitting.

"Knitting?" I asked.

"It's good to have a hobby," she said.

"Can I pick my own hobby?"

She shook her head. "Nope."

Midday was always lunch with my parents, who nodded with bright,

optimistic faces as I recounted inspirational stories I'd found online about people like me.

And then followed PT with Ian, who continued to bring his not-talking-at-all A-game. We worked our way through the therapy gym, using the bike and mat almost every day, and rotating through other things like the parallel bars and the monkey rings. He even put me on the standing frame a couple of times, which meant getting buckled into a body harness and hanging from a metal frame above a treadmill. I would bring my thighs forward, and Ian would help position my feet and move them through the motions of walking.

The idea was that the spinal cord, and even the muscles themselves, had their own sense of memory. Walking, in theory, was such a fundamental human activity that it might not need the brain to direct it. So, like a reflex, the neurological signals for walking could reroute themselves and leave out the brain altogether, if they just had enough inspiration.

There was improvement, for sure. My knee joint was significantly stronger, and I could lock it now. My whole upper body was stronger now, in fact, and muscle mass I'd lost was coming back.

But the truth is, though everything above the knee was making progress, everything below was not.

Even with all my reading, and charts, and highlighting, and goals. Even with dreams almost every night of walking through the woods, or along the beach, or even just across an empty parking lot—dreams so convincing that I sometimes wondered if my dreaming life was actually my real one and vice versa—improvements were slim.

Below the knee, at least.

One day I thought I wiggled a toe, but nobody else could see it. Another day, on the bike, I felt like I'd pushed off with the ball of my foot, but when I tried to repeat it, it just dragged.

My mother brought in some literature that said plateaus were normal as the body adjusted to previous improvements—and so "plateaus are normal" became my internal mantra.

Ian became quite the subject of discussion during my evenings with Kitty. She always wanted the Grouch Report, and I was under strict

instructions to chronicle all hidden smiles, uttered words, and human moments. We spent so many hours trying to psychoanalyze Ian that we finally came up with a broader theory that we must somehow be doing deep psychological work. Maybe, we decided, women talked about men as a coping mechanism. A distraction from the real troubles in their lives.

No doubt, it was more fun to fret over Ian than to fret over myself.

Maybe we should have wanted to talk about Chip instead. But there wasn't much about him that appealed to me right then.

Despite promises to the contrary, since his re-proposal, he'd managed only three short visits in three long days, standing the entire time for them, as if waiting to be dismissed. His timing was uncanny for the worst possible moments: just as an orderly was arriving for my sponge bath, or as Priya was forcing me to practice taking my sweatpants on and off, or as I was wheeling toward the bathroom. He'd stay for an obligatory thirty minutes or so, checking his texts over and over, and then give me a stiff kiss and head out. I half-waited to see him all day, kept my peripheral vision on the door in hopes he'd show up, but then, when he did come, I found myself wishing almost as fast that he'd leave.

I was muddled, to say the least.

Ian was a much juicier topic. He was almost a mysterious fictional character. Chip and his shortcomings were all too real.

After much discussion, Kitty developed a detailed theory about Ian, that there was a fun person trapped inside him, clawing against his ribs to get out. She labeled it her Beauty and the Beast theory and insisted that something terrible had happened to him in the past. But I disagreed. My theory was that he'd been left unattended too long as a baby in some remote Scottish orphanage and had missed a critical window for developing social skills and human empathy.

"Is he an orphan?" Kitty asked.

I shrugged. "No idea."

Whatever Ian's deal was, as strange as it sounds, he turned out to be good for me.

I really didn't talk much during the rest of the day or with many of the other hospital personnel, but when Ian showed up, I unleashed every

thought, theory, observation, dream, or opinion I'd held in since the day before. Partly this was my fear of conversational silence, but partly, I came to notice more and more, it was just fun to mess with him. It was like trying to provoke a guard at Buckingham Palace. The fact that Ian didn't respond made me want to make him. I tried shock. I tried surprise. I tried every joke I knew. His blank face became more and more irresistible. He didn't react, but he listened, and as the days went on, I found myself Googling crazy things in anticipation of seeing him, just so I'd have good material.

"Did you know," I'd say, "that octopuses have three hearts?" And when that got no response, I'd move on to "Did you know there's an underwater postal box in Japan?" And when that got silence, I'd plunge ahead with "Did you hear about the guy who had to be fed intravenously for a year, and he lost all of his taste buds after going so long without using them? They disappeared. His tongue just got all smooth, like a porpoise."

It was the only time all day when I felt anything like my old self. It was the only time when the fog lifted. The game of it was so engaging that I'd forget myself—to the extent anyone ever could when trying, and failing, to walk the parallel bars from one end to the other.

It should have been my worst time of day, as I fell short on challenge after challenge. But somehow it was my best.

That same week, I got my bandages off the donor sites under my collarbones, and now I had two meaty red scabs like fat strips of bacon adding to the horror show that was my body. But my face was better, at least. A few penny-sized blisters on my jaw had scabbed over. Scabs are far more noticeable than blisters, but I was moving in the right direction, certainly, and the rest of my face barely looked burned anymore. It did, as the doc had promised, itch like hell—but I never scratched it.

Kitty continued to show up at night with a wide array of meals from both our favorite restaurants and ones I'd never heard of, leaving no cuisine undigested: Indian, Thai, Tex-Mex, Italian, Cajun, Japanese, Vietnamese. She made it a goal to surprise and delight me.

She'd also jumped on Priya's knitting bandwagon, insisting I knit a

scarf while we watched all her favorite musicals: *South Pacific, Singin' in the Rain, Meet Me in St. Louis.* I didn't even fight her on the singing anymore. I jumped into every song without protest, quietly at first, but going full Judy Garland by the end.

The scarf they were making me knit was terrible. I thought I'd picked a stormy-sky blue, but it turned out to be just plain gray. It looked like a mutant slug with tumors.

"We'll make some pom-poms for it," Kit said. "No problem."

The truth is, some parts of my personality came back to me fairly quickly. I still found human beings—and conversation—to be the best possible distraction. When I had somebody to talk to, I focused on the talking, and compulsively joked around, bantered, and chatted. Those moments felt—if not *good,* at least better than usual.

But there were lots and lots of quiet, lost, nebulous moments when I felt the opposite of good. I don't want to leave them out. Most were like that, in fact. Everything that happened—every PT session, or sponge bath, or viewing of *Auntie Mame*—was set against a background of just trying to keep my head up. The minute I was alone, or the second I saw something on TV that reminded me of the life I'd left behind, or the moment I came awake each morning and remembered where I was, the grayness would rush back in. The rule, not the exception.

ONE AFTERNOON, DURING the lull between PT and dinner that I had come to regard as a sacred napping period, I had an unexpected visitor. Chip's mom, Evelyn.

She arrived while I was sleeping, and noisily scooted the visitor chair around until I opened my eyes.

"Oh," she said, "were you sleeping?"

She knew I was. "Yes."

"You seem surprised to see me."

I was. I hadn't seen anyone outside a very small inner circle since I'd been in here. On purpose. "I have a no-visitors policy."

"I told them I was your mother-in-law. To-be."

"Guess that worked."

She hadn't seen me since the ER. "You look much better." Her words were kind, but her eyes were critical as she took me in. The way she was studying me made my face start itching. She went on, "Except for those scabs on your neck, and—oh, God!" She'd caught a glimpse of my skin grafts. She looked away and tried to regroup.

"Did they have to shave your head?" she asked after a while, like of course the answer would be yes.

"No," I said. "It's just a pixie cut."

"I'm sure it'll grow out again soon."

"I'm going to keep it this way. I like it."

"Oh, don't!" she said. Then, "It's a little masculine."

"I think it's cool."

"I'm sure you'll change your mind once you're back to your old self."

Chip's mother was a lot like my mother. Overly put-together. Overly focused on how things looked instead of how things felt. Overly hard on both herself and others, but too gracious to say it in polite conversation.

Still, sometimes it leaked out in funny ways.

I'd known her long enough to know what she was thinking. She and my mother played tennis together, and got pedicures together, and had a genuine friendship that they each treasured. They'd lived next door to each other for ten years, and in that time I don't think they'd ever had a disagreement. It was a remarkable coincidence that two such women should wind up neighbors. They shared the same thoughts on almost everything, and the principal gist of every conversation was to validate each other's worldview. What are the odds?

Of course they were rooting for Chip and me. Of course they wanted us all to be just one big, happy family.

Which is why I didn't see it coming when she frowned, pulled her chair a little closer, and said, "I want to talk to you about Chip."

It was funny to hear his name. He had started showering again, I noticed at his last visit, which felt like progress. He'd also sent several flower arrangements, and even though I'd left instructions for all flowers to be

sent down to the children's wing, the ones from him managed to make it through.

My mother liked to arrange and rearrange them on the windowsill.

He was making an effort. I had to give him that.

"He seems better," I said to Evelyn. "He's showering again, I think."

"Yes," she agreed. "And he's not out all night at bars anymore."

"Progress," I said.

"But," she said then, taking my hand and squeezing it, "I don't think he's happy."

Happy? Was that an option? I was just shooting for "conscious."

"That's why I'm here," she went on. "I'm worried about him."

"I'm worried about all of us," I said.

But she had something to say, and she was going to say it. "He's been so crushed by what happened. It really has torn him to shreds. He has to force himself to come here every time he visits. Every time he looks at your poor face, the guilt is just overwhelming."

"Are you asking me to feel sorry for Chip?"

Her voice took an indignant turn. "It's been hard on him, too, Margaret."

"I'm sure it has. Hard on his liver, at the very least."

"Not everyone is as strong as you are."

"I'm *not* strong. I'm just trapped. My body keeps breathing against my will."

She wasn't having it. "Don't be dramatic."

I leaned back against my pillow and squeezed my eyes shut. I was giving up my nap for this.

Evelyn took that moment to get herself back on track. "Chip's father and I have talked about it, and we'd like to ask a favor of you."

I opened my eyes. "A favor?"

"You know how loyal Chip is. You know how important it is to him to do the right thing. You know he would never, ever let himself call off your engagement."

"I'm not even sure that we are technically engaged," I said. Had we settled that?

"You're wearing my mother's two-carat diamond. I think that counts."

"If you say so."

"I'm just not sure what your expectations are—given your situation."

Where was this headed? "My situation *that Chip caused*?"

"You wouldn't want him to marry you out of guilt, would you?"

"What are you saying?"

She sat back a bit. "He's in a very strange predicament."

"Aren't we fucking all?"

"Please watch your language."

"Are you kidding me right now?"

She blinked at me for a second. "We're all coping the best we can."

"Some of us better than others." My thoughts started spinning. "Hold on—did he send you here? Did he send *his mother* to break up with me?"

"He doesn't know I'm here."

"So you just decided this was *any* of your business?"

"My child is my business."

"He's *not* a child!"

She sat up a little straighter. "A marriage—starting a lifetime together—needs a strong foundation of . . ." She seemed to cast around for the word. "Desire."

Desire? Were we talking about *sex* now? "Desire?"

"Among other things."

A strange, acid anger started burning in my chest. She did *not* just walk into this room and creepily tell me her son no longer wanted to screw me. "Oh, he's got plenty of desire," I said. She really wanted to get into this? This was where she wanted to go? Fine. We'd go there. I could go there all day.

"He's got desire in the golf house at the club," I said. "And in his childhood bedroom. And on the garden bench beside your weird little cherub statues. And in your master-bath Jacuzzi when you're on vacation. And even in the kitchen pantry during Christmas dinner. Your 'child' is a tenth-degree horn-dog. He's got more than enough desire. I think he'll find a way to manage."

I wanted it to feel good to attack her like that, but it didn't.

Evelyn stayed still as stone. "That was before," she said at last. "Things have changed."

"Yes they fucking have."

She turned her face away at that word—*again*. "Chip's father and I feel that he's looking for something else now. Something he can't find in you."

I crossed my arms over my chest. "Do you?"

Her face was solemn. "He says he wants to be with you, but we can plainly see his actions."

"What actions?"

She closed her mouth as if I'd asked some wildly inappropriate question. As if she wasn't the person who had brought the whole thing up in the first place.

"You're not going to tell me?" I demanded. "What actions are you talking about?"

I could see that she realized she'd said too much.

I leaned forward. "Tell me," I said, my voice menacing.

She turned away.

As she did, we both caught sight of a figure in the doorway.

Chip.

If I could have slapped him across the face right then, I would have. "Did you send your *mother* to break up with me?"

Chip looked at his mother. "What are you doing?"

"I'm trying to help you." Her voice suddenly got wobbly. "Your father and I are very worried." She lifted her hand to her face, and I realized she was wiping away tears. All at once, she looked very fragile—and I regretted, a little, how many times I'd just said "fuck."

A son can't be angry with his crying mother. His voice got tender. "Mom," he said. "You can't help me. Don't help me, okay?"

He came over, helped her stand, and steered her out of the room. As he did, he held up his hand at me to say *five minutes*. I guessed he was going to walk her back to the hospital valet and send her home.

Once they were gone, I noticed my breathing was ragged, and my

chest stung a little, as if the imaginary acid had burned some kind of sad, hollow hole. I spent several minutes trying to tell myself that it was good to feel *something*, at least, before deciding that was bullshit. Why was it that the only emotions that seemed able to penetrate my fog were the worst of the worst?

When Chip made it back, I noticed then that he looked—for the first time since the accident—just exactly like his old self. Here was the Chip I'd fallen in love with. Here was the Chip who had it all together, ready to confidently stand at the helm of anything and everything. He looked picture-perfect. He'd gotten a haircut. He was wearing a crisp polo and pressed khakis. He'd brushed his teeth—and even possibly flossed.

It was a powerful thing to see him again. It was like the real Chip had been gone all this time, but now he'd finally come back, and all that toughness and resistance I felt about the new Chip disintegrated as soon as I saw the old one again.

"Are we engaged?" I asked him then, my voice soft. "Did we ever settle that?"

He gave me his famous Chip Dunbar smile. "You know we are, on my end at least." He was flirting with me! "Your position's a little less clear. But you're still wearing the ring."

"Your mother thinks," I said, making air quotes, "that you don't 'desire' me anymore."

He let out a honk of a laugh and then sat in the chair his mother had just vacated, grabbing my hand in a very similar way. "I do. Oh, my God, I still do—so much—"

I felt myself release a breath I didn't even realize I'd been holding. I felt a pinch of hope that things might turn out okay for us, after all.

Until he went on. "The old you."

What?

"I think about her all the time." Chip pressed his forehead down against my hand, and his shoulders started to shake. "I miss her so much," he said, all muffled.

"You miss her? She's not gone," I said, not even trying to disguise my astonishment. "She's literally right here."

Was Chip crying? Again? "I miss her hair," he went on. "And how she walked in heels. And the way her jeans hugged her hips."

That was just mean. "You realize you're talking about me in the third person," I said.

"I'm sorry," he said.

"Your mother thinks you're going ahead with the engagement out of guilt," I said next. "She thinks you don't want to marry me anymore, but now that you've, you know, *paralyzed me,* you feel like you have to."

"No." He shook his head as he lifted it. "I still want to marry you. I want that more than anything."

"Her? The girl you miss? Or me?" As if we weren't the same person. "The old me or the current me?"

"Any you I can get my hands on."

That made me smile—a little. I wanted that sunshiny feeling back again. "So you do still want to marry me?"

"More than I can possibly say."

It felt good to hear it. I won't lie.

Chip sat up straight then and let go of my hand to wipe his face. He took a deep breath, as if he might be about to shout something, and then he held it a second. When the words came out at last, they just seeped out in a whisper. "I want to marry you, Margaret. But I think I can't."

I held still.

He lowered his eyes. "I think," he went on, "in the end, you're not going to let me."

Then, like a premonition, I knew what he was about to say. I knew exactly what "actions" his mother had been talking about. Yet again, I found myself several mental steps ahead of Chip.

Now I had a decision to make.

I could end this conversation right now, and let him off the hook, and never hear for certain what he was about to say. If I did that, we could continue on. We could keep muddling through, trying to patch things up. I could chalk everything we'd said or done up to "the tragedy" and forgive it all and stay focused on my impossible odds.

I could so easily take that route. It was wildly tempting.

But I didn't. "Chip. What happened?"

He kept his eyes on the bedspread and shook his head.

"Chip," I said, more pressure in my voice. "Tell me."

He held very still.

"Tell me!"

Then he did tell me. But he closed his eyes first. "I slept with someone."

I HADN'T BEEN wrong. I knew that's where he was headed. But the words, once they were spoken, meant the end. They severed us. That was it. He'd made a choice, but I'd made a choice, too. I'm sure I felt many things at that moment, but the only one I remember is loneliness.

"Who?" I said.

"It doesn't matter."

"It does fucking matter."

Chip stood up then—too fast—and knocked his chair over. It clattered to the floor. He didn't pick it up, just paced around the foot of the bed. "Tara," he admitted at last.

"Your old girlfriend, Tara? The one you call the Whiner?"

He nodded.

"You don't even like her!"

"I know."

I didn't even know where to start. "Chip." It was more of a sigh than a word.

"She saw my post about you on Facebook, and she got in touch. She started coming by to check on me. She brought soup."

"She brought *soup*?"

He shrugged. "I wasn't eating. She was concerned. And then one thing led to another."

"Don't tell me." I felt it like a gasp: I didn't want to know.

But now I'd gotten him going. "She came by one night and found me crying—"

"Am I supposed to pity you?"

"—and I just couldn't pull it together. And so she just kind of put her arms around me—"

"Stop."

"—and kind of cradled me—"

"Chip. Shut it down."

"—and the next thing I knew, we were kissing—"

"Stop! I'm fucking serious! Stop!" I didn't realize how loud I was shouting.

Right then, the door to my room pushed open, and Ian walked in.

He eyed Chip for a second before turning to me. "Everything all right?"

"Get the hell out, man," Chip said. "We're talking."

Ian kept his eyes on me. "I wasn't asking you, prick."

I looked up at Ian. He was motionless with suppressed tension. I knew in an instant my dad had been right, that the acoustics between my room and the hallway went both ways. I could hear them out there perfectly— and they could hear me just as well in here.

Ian had just witnessed this whole, humiliating, life-crushing conversation. Enough of it, anyway.

"Can I do anything for you?" Ian asked me then, his voice as tender as I'd ever heard it. "Get you a glass of water? Beat the crap out of this wanker?"

I gave a microscopic smile, but Ian caught it.

I shook my head.

"Can we finish our conversation, please?" Chip asked, though I couldn't tell if he was asking me or Ian.

"Maggie?" Ian said, never shifting his gaze from mine. "Is this a conversation you'd like to continue?"

I shook my head again. "I think we're done."

"That's it, prick. Beat it."

But Chip wasn't ready to go. "Margaret—"

In a flash, Ian was right up next to him, looming a good six inches above. "You heard her. Get out."

Chip put his hands up and backed away. "Okay." He took several steps

back, without turning, seeming to consider his options, and then, because he really didn't have any, he turned to leave.

Just as he did, I called, "Chip! Wait!"

He turned back, and I pulled off his grandmother's engagement ring and threw it at him with all the force I could muster.

He ducked, and I missed.

The ring bounced off the wall and then skittered under the empty bed next to mine—so Chip had to get down on his hands and knees to crawl after it. It was just enough humiliation to give me a twinge of satisfaction.

But only a twinge.

AS SOON AS he was gone, the fog closed back in.

It was like suffocating in plain air.

I started panting, but in deep, swooping breaths, pushing them out and then sucking them back in. For a second, I couldn't see. The room didn't go black—it went white. It blurred out of focus until there was nothing.

Except Ian's voice. Ian was still there. "Slow it down," he said, near my ear. "Take it slow. Count to four going out. That's it. Now four going in. Good."

As my breathing slowed, the world came back, and I felt Ian's hand on my forehead, stroking my hair. I opened my eyes, and there was his face, just a few inches away.

"You're all right," he said. "You're okay."

"Ian," I said next, when it felt safe to speak. "I need you to do me a favor."

"Anything," he said. "Of course."

"I really, really need you," I said, "to get me the hell out of here."

Sixteen

IAN STOOD UP and evaluated me for a minute. Then he reached over to pull back my covers.

"Right," he said. "Scoot to the edge of the bed."

I dangled my legs over, and he bent down in front of me and backed up. "Climb on."

"What? *On* you? Like a piggyback ride?"

He nodded. "Pretend I'm a horse."

"A Clydesdale, maybe."

"Move it, lass. Make it happen. Squeeze with your thighs."

The good news was, I could do that. My thighs worked just fine. It was everything below them that didn't. I leaned forward until my chest fell against his back, and then I wriggled my legs into position around his waist. I wrapped my arms around his neck.

"Not a choke hold, though," he instructed. "Low, on the collarbones." He moved my hands down.

He stood up. "Is this okay?"

A piggyback ride. When was the last time I'd had one of those? "Yes."

"We're not touching your donor sites? Or pulling on your grafts?"

"I'm good. I should travel like this more often."

He pulled the quilt off my bed and grabbed a pillow, and then he walked us out past the nurses' station—where every single person stopped what they were doing to gape at us going by. As we passed, without even slowing down, he grabbed a bag of Milano cookies off the reception desk.

He took long steps and moved fast. He really was a Clydesdale. He didn't walk, he strode. I hadn't moved that quickly through any space in weeks, and despite everything, it gave me a tickle of a thrill in my stomach. I felt an odd urge to laugh, but I held it back.

He walked us to the elevator, and we rode up to the top floor, then got off and strode to the end of a corridor, directly toward a door with a push handle that said NOT AN EXIT—ALARM WILL SOUND.

"Hey—that's not an exit," I said, as we barreled toward it. "Hey! 'Alarm will sound'!"

We burst through the door anyway, though. No alarm sounded.

"It's disabled," he explained, as the door swung closed behind us. "It's where the nurses go to smoke."

Then we were outside. I caught my breath. It was a crisp, clear March evening—with the most stunning orange and purple sunset I'd ever seen. Or so it seemed. It would have been breathtaking in any situation, but I literally had not been outside since the night of the accident. How long had that been? We were ending my second week in the inpatient wing, and I'd spent a week in the ICU before that, so: three solid weeks without seeing the sky, or feeling the breeze, or breathing fresh air. No wonder I was feeling so crazy.

That, and everything else.

Ian took us across the roof to the far edge, which had a view of downtown Austin and the capitol building. With me still on his back, he laid the blanket out flat and dropped the pillow and the cookies. Then he got down on his hands and knees and backed up to the blanket like a dump truck and tilted up so I could slide down onto my knees. The whole thing gave me just a smidge of vertigo, and I rolled onto my side in the middle of the quilt. He brought the pillow around

to prop me correctly so I could lie back to see the sky without damaging my grafts.

The sky. The wind blew across me and fluttered my hair back. I felt a little cold, but it was okay. It made me aware of all my edges—where I stopped and the rest of the world continued. I was still alive, I thought then. It hit me out on that roof for the first time.

I was alive.

In the next second, I felt Ian lay his fleece sweatshirt over me, and then he flopped down beside me and got settled on his back. Then he lifted a cookie up into my field of vision, and I reached up and grabbed it.

Nobody spoke, and for the first time ever—maybe in my entire life— that was okay. We listened to the wind, and the muted traffic ten stories below, and the crunch of cookies as we chewed. We watched the sky darken as the sun sank out of view. So much of life is just grinding through. So many moments just exist to deliver you to the ones that follow. But this moment was a destination in itself.

Did I feel happy right then? Not exactly. When you feel happy, or joyful, it's kind of like a brightness in your chest, and my heart was too numb for brightness.

If you think of human emotions as music, then mine were like an orchestra with no conductor. I felt a lot of different sounds, but I didn't know quite how to read them or combine them in ways I understood. And yet there was no doubt that the instruments of my body were playing—my skin under the wind, my lungs drawing in crisp breaths, my eyes taking in the vast and brilliant sky. There was music—good music—even if it wasn't a melody I recognized.

Given the context, it seems odd that I should have felt such good feelings right then, and I guarantee it didn't last. My brain still knew that my entire future was ruined—that Chip's confession marked more than just the end of our relationship: It meant the end of my life as I'd known it.

But the physical pleasure of being outside for the first time in so achingly long was too real to deny. Later, there would be fallout—moments

of rage, and bleakness, and grief over everything I'd lost—as I tried to understand what Chip had done and why. But not yet. Not tonight. Ian had given me this impossible gift—a little pause from it all. An experience so viscerally alive that nothing else could compete.

It was just us, and the wind—and now, suddenly, the stars starting to appear—for a long, quiet while.

Then I heard Ian's voice, surprisingly close to my ear, say, "Myles'll fire me for this, for sure."

I turned my head. There he was. Starting a conversation. Of all things. "Will he? Seriously?"

He was gazing up, an arm behind his head, and the pose was so casual, so unguarded, so *friendly*, it was shocking. "Maybe not. He didn't see it with his own eyes, after all. The nurses might not rat us out."

"But don't the PTs take patients out all the time?"

"Sure. On educational excursions. In groups. Not up to the roof alone."

"What does he think you're going to do to me?"

A classic Ian-style silence followed that question—but rather than feeling uncomfortable I suddenly started thinking of all the things that Ian could potentially have been doing to me, right that very moment. The longer the silence lasted, the more vivid my thinking became. He was just inches away. He could so easily roll onto his side and put his face down alongside mine. He could so easily take one of those big hands and run it along my side. The thought took hold of my thinking. I could almost feel it happening—the weight of his hands, the roughness of the stubble on his jaw, the warmth of his mouth.

I drifted off into the fantasy of being kissed by Ian, but then his voice pulled me back out. "There are all kinds of ungentlemanly things I could do to you on this roof," he declared at last. "And I'm sure Myles would accuse me of them all."

It's a little odd—and a bit embarrassing—to confess that I had a vivid, unrequited, thirty-second, highly sexy, totally unauthorized fantasy about my physical therapist not an hour after I'd thrown my engagement ring at my ex-fiancé. But it's important to mention. Because in those seconds,

something happened. I felt a swell of some very potent, very enthusiastic, very *physical* feelings in response to that kissing fantasy.

Which meant—and this was big news—I could feel those feelings.

Suffice it to say, my time in the hospital had not been the most erotic
experience of my life. On my scale of worries that month, my future sex
life rated comically low. Probably, if I'd had a choice between a future
with walking and a future with sex, I'd have picked walking. But I wasn't
given that choice. That said, since all my sensation down there was, as
I'd been told over and over, "spotty," I'd known there was a good chance
that I'd lost that part of my life forever. Though, even if I'd been thinking about it enough to check, I likely would have been afraid to check.
Part of me didn't want to know. *Don't go looking for trouble.*

But now, suddenly, thanks to this roof, I knew.

My body could feel things. Enthusiastically.

True, my body had just felt those things about a man who—most
days, anyway—didn't even want to be in the same room with me, but I
wasn't going to quibble over details. This was great news, dammit, no
matter how foolishly I'd come across it! I could *feel the feelings*! One of
life's greatest pleasures was still on my menu!

Did I feel joyful about it? No. "Joy" didn't seem to be an option
anymore. I wasn't really sure I could access "happy," either. The best I
could do right then was "pleasant." I felt *pleasant* about it. And—
maybe more than that: relief. Relief I didn't even know I'd been waiting for.

The sunset was completely gone now, replaced by a deep blue night
sky full of stars. I tried to sit up then, but lost my balance partway, and
Ian lost no time helping. He sat up, too, and cradled me into a sitting
position. "You okay?" he asked.

"Uh-huh."

"You look a little nauseous."

Reading that so wrong. "I'm fine."

"Do you want to go back?"

I turned and met his eyes. "I *never* want to go back."

He gave a little shrug and then said, "Okay."

"Tell me about your nebbishy boss," I said then, as we watched the lights of the city skyline. "What's going on there?"

"Only if you put on my sweatshirt."

"I'm fine," I said.

"Put it on."

"Bossy," I said. But I put it on, and as I did, I got a great waft of that delicious Ian smell. It was so overpowering in that moment, it was all I could do not to press my face into it and gulp down a big breath. But I covered well. I pretended like the zipper was stuck. Then I looked at Ian to prove that I was waiting for him to start talking.

When he didn't, I prompted: "So? You think Myles would fire you for taking me up here."

"Myles would definitely fire me for taking you up here."

"Even though you don't like me like that." It was the kind of statement girls sometimes make in honor of the one percent chance that the guy might contradict it.

Ian did not contradict it. He kept his gaze straight out on the horizon. "No. I don't like you like that."

"So you're safe."

He looked off. "I am far from safe."

"What's Myles's deal with you, anyway?"

"That's a long story."

The wind kept blowing one lock of my hair into my face. I tried to tuck it behind my ear, but it was too short. "I truly have nothing but time."

Ian sighed. "I used to work here before. That's why I moved to Texas, in fact—to take a job at this hospital. I started young and worked my way to manager of the PT gym. Myles came about when I did, but I got promoted over him again and again."

"Why?"

"Because he's a rule-obsessed wanker, and a petty tyrant."

"Sounds about right."

"Anyway, then a female PT got hired to work in the therapy gym. Her name was Kayla. We hit it off right away, and we started seeing each other."

It was pushing, but I couldn't help it: "What was she like?"

He gave a little shrug. "Lovely. Feisty. She had no patience for foolishness. She could be so mean." He said it with great admiration.

I watched him think about her. After a bit, I said, "What does this have to do with Myles?"

Ian let out a long breath. "Myles liked her, too. He would say that he saw her first—and I stole her away."

"Did you?"

"He might have seen her first," Ian said, shrugging. "But she never liked him. I couldn't steal something that was never his."

"Of course not."

"But that fact was not—still is not—relevant to Myles. He liked her, and that was all that mattered."

"That's why he hates you?"

Ian nodded. "That's why he hates me. I ruined his life, and now he is determined to ruin mine."

"But she wasn't into him!"

"He feels, very strongly, that he could have won her over."

"But you're not still with her?" I asked, to confirm.

"No."

"You broke up?"

Ian seemed to hold his breath. "In a way."

"So what's his problem?"

"I've wondered about that a lot. I think Myles is the kind of guy who needs an enemy. He needs an enemy to fight so that he can feel like a hero."

"But he's *not* a hero!"

Ian looked over and gave a little shrug. "I might be a villain, though."

I waited.

"I wasn't very nice to him. I gloated a bit when I won her. I wish I could go back and change that. It wasn't kind of me."

"Okay," I said, "but Myles is totally the kind of person who makes you want to gloat."

"Maybe," Ian said. "But I should have been the bigger man."

I didn't say anything to that. I knew all about regrets.

Ian went on. "Kayla and I had been together about a year when I had this idea to strike out on my own from the hospital. I wanted to start a rehab gym for people who are beyond the critical phase, but who still want to work to get better—people who insurance won't cover. There's all kinds of great research out there about ways to stimulate the nervous system, get the brain and spinal cord to rewire and communicate with the body in new ways. I wanted to make use of that research."

"That's brilliant."

"And so she came with me. We took out loans, found a facility, worked out a business plan, printed up T-shirts, and sank everything we had into it."

He gave me a look. "I poached all the best people from the hospital and talked them into coming with me. I filled their heads with ideas about the fun we could have and the path we could forge. We could change people's lives. We could change the face of recovery."

"And Myles?" I asked.

"He wasn't invited."

"Because he's a wanker."

Ian nodded. "He's toxic, really, in so many ways. Narrow and vindictive and peevish. Not the kind of guy you want around. I didn't want to work with him. I kept the whole plan a secret from him—but he got wind of it somehow, and he started asking to join. I rejected him over and over. I was cocky about it. When he demanded to know why I didn't want him, I laid it all out in no uncertain terms."

"Like, you said he wasn't right for the job?"

"I told him he was an idiot and everybody hated him."

"Okay. That's laying it out."

"After we all quit, there was almost nobody left. So they promoted him."

"And now Myles is the boss."

"Which was fine with me, until—"

I looked over. "Until what?"

"Until the business crashed and burned. And then I found myself

with no savings and no job. Then a spot opened up here. Somehow, in some circle of hell, I wound up working for him."

"The business crashed?"

Ian nodded.

"How? Why? You had all those great people! And such a great idea."

He shook his head, and I could tell we weren't going to travel far on that topic. "Lots of reasons."

I watched him a long time, but he didn't offer anything more.

Finally, he went back to Myles. "He's had it out for me since the day I came back—just a few weeks before you showed up. He's actively looking to get me fired."

"And it's torture for you to work with him."

He gave a nod. "He goes out of his way to make everything harder. If I don't play things exactly by the book, I'm out. But I've never been very good at playing by the book."

"Could you go work somewhere else?"

He shrugged. "Nowhere else is hiring."

"Maybe in some other city?" I suggested, hating the idea even as I said it.

"I haven't wanted to look in other cities. But I might have to start."

Suddenly, I became aware that my shoulder was leaning against his shoulder. I leaned away—but that felt abrupt. Partly to cover, I said, "So you weren't always so grouchy."

A faint smile. "No."

"Did you used to joke around?"

"Of course."

"And listen to oldies rock?"

"That's a job requirement."

"I've decided it's good that you've been mean to me."

"I haven't been nearly as mean as I intended to be."

I looked over. "Why not?"

He looked away. "Something about your eyes, I think."

I had to ask. "What about them?"

"Let's just say being mean to Myles makes me feel better. Being mean to you made me feel worse."

I didn't know what to say to that, so I just let the wind blow.

"Thank you for telling me about your troubles," I said after a while.

"It wasn't very professional of me."

"Professional is overrated."

He turned to take in the sight of me, as if I'd just said something so true, it surprised him. Then he said, "We should get back."

I shook my head.

But he nodded. "It's late. You need rest."

I suddenly felt tears in my eyes. I wiped them on his sweatshirt. "I don't want to go back."

Ian helped me get up on my knees so I could climb onto his back. "I'd offer you a cookie, but we ate them all."

"Promise me we'll come here again," I said, as I climbed on.

"I promise."

"Soon."

"Soon," he said, and as he stood us both up, the view—and the breeze, and the feel of his back against my chest, and the endlessness of the sky above us—made me so dizzy, I had to close my eyes.

Seventeen

I WENT THROUGH a period of—shall we say—disillusionment after Chip's confession. Once I returned from the roof to my inpatient cell, I had nothing to distract me from the realities of my life—every awful one of them—and I kind of lost sight of the meaning of everything.

To sum up: My motivation for physical therapy, and everything else, was rather low.

There was no way to deny, at this point, that everything I cared about was destroyed, or broken, or had self-destructed. Even my own personal goals. Because that one inspiring fantasy of walking to Chip that I'd used to push back the fog had disintegrated the minute I found out about Tara and her soup.

I would never walk to Chip again.

I would never walk again, period.

In some ways, if I'm honest, giving up felt good. It certainly took the pressure off. Staying hopeful was exhausting.

In life, I'd always had tangible goals. I made good grades so I could get into a good college. I worked hard in college so I could get into a good business school. I worked hard in B-school so that I could get a

great job, make great money, be a leader in the business world, break a few glass ceilings, and make my parents proud. Those weren't the only things I wanted, of course. I wasn't totally shallow. I wanted love and friends and babies and laughter. I wanted to be a good person and help take care of the world. But I'd spent my life working toward specific goals.

What was I suffering for now? What was I working toward now? To get a little more movement in my legs? To *not* get an infection in my skin graft? To approach some vague approximation of the person I used to be? To make it through the day without freaking the hell out? I couldn't motivate for goals like that.

Somehow, the presence of Chip in that recovery fantasy had been the lynchpin holding it all together. Without him, the whole thing fell apart.

My mother had fed me false hope, and I'd swallowed it whole like a baby bird with an open beak. I hadn't questioned it enough because I hadn't wanted to—but there was a fine line between determination and delusion.

Some things really were impossible.

My grandfather had been shot in the eye with a BB gun as a kid. He lost the eye and spent the rest of his life with a glass one, taking it out every night and—I swear this is true—putting it in a glass of water on the bedside table. Kitty and I used to sneak in before he was awake sometimes and steal it out of the cup—and then, totally game, he'd stumble down in his robe and PJs at breakfast time, a hand clapped over his face, saying, "Somebody stole my eye!" We'd cackle until he found it—and he never complained. But no amount of wishing or determination or denial could have grown that eye back.

I hadn't let myself think about that until now.

Now, all I did was just keep breathing, and even that felt like a lot. One breath after another. Easier on some days than others. But let's be clear: I had nothing—nothing—to look forward to.

The day after our lovely night on the roof, for example, Ian showed up for PT, and I just refused to move.

He was all business, of course. None of the warmth from the night before. He walked in as brusque and formal as if he had never carried me piggyback through the hallways, never made me wear his sweatshirt, never told me about his mistakes. From the expression on his face, I could have been anybody—one face in a parade of wheelchairs. Which was how I felt about myself, as well.

He got the transfer board ready, but I didn't sit up. I just stared out the window.

"All right. Let's go," he urged.

I didn't say anything. Didn't look over.

He came around to peer at my face and double-check I wasn't sleeping. "Maggie," he said. "It's time."

I wasn't trying to be rude. Responding just seemed like it would take too much energy.

"Let's go," he urged again.

But I just kept breathing.

"Are you not coming, then? Is this what I get for busting you out of jail?"

I was locked in a stare out the window, but I heard my voice. "I just don't see the point."

"You don't have to see the point. You just have to come with me."

"Not today."

"Maggie," he said, lowering his voice. "Can you look at me?"

I couldn't. I was stuck in that stare, and everything else seemed far away.

Ian leaned his face down in front of mine, but my eyes didn't refocus. He was just a blurry head. "You have to take care of yourself. You can't let him win."

"Who?" I asked, still unfocused.

"The prick who broke your heart."

But I wasn't sure I had a heart anymore. It felt like maybe it had burned away in the crash. I just lay limp. One breath in, then out. Then another in, then out.

"Are you refusing physical therapy?"

It hadn't occurred to me that I could refuse. I kept my eyes on the window. "Yes. I guess I am."

The next day, I refused again. The day after that, too.

My family was concerned. Ian reported me to the supervising physician, who passed the reports on to the social worker and psychologist on staff, as well as my parents. The professionals agreed that a "dose of depression" was normal, even healthy, in my situation, but my parents, and even Kitty, disagreed.

It threw our family ecosystem into disarray. I had always been the hardworking, cheery, rule-following achiever, and Kitty had always been the source of all our problems.

Simple.

What did it mean—to any of us—for *me* to be the problem?

It led them to desperate measures. I later found out that despite all the tension between Kitty and my mom—worse now—Kitty and my parents arranged a secret rendezvous within forty-eight hours of Chip's confession to figure out how to fix me.

They were all business—coming together for the greater good, focusing on the task at hand, meeting in the coffee shop of a Barnes & Noble and then scouring the self-help books to find some inspirational reading to get me back on track. Kitty and my mother wordlessly agreed to set aside everything that had gone down between them, and they wound up spending a hundred dollars on titles like *Why Me? A Daily Guide for Getting Back to Normal* and *The Joy of Suffering*.

My dad suggested that Kitty should be the one to bring the books to me because I'd be less likely to view her as a foe.

"I'm not a foe!" my mother protested.

But she was outvoted.

IT WAS NICE for them to have a project, in a way, Kitty admitted later. What purpose would it have served to rehash all their conflict and strife, anyway? They left things unresolved but moved on to the more important pressing problem of me.

"Didn't the two of you at least apologize to each other?" I asked, when Kit confessed what they'd been up to.

"Apologize? What for?"

"Well," I said, "you, for telling me Mom's biggest secret against her wishes. And Mom, for pretty much your whole childhood."

Kitty shook her head. "There was no apologizing. Have you ever heard Mom apologize?"

Fair enough. Apologizing wasn't Mom's thing.

I refused to read the self-help books, of course. They should've seen that coming. When Kitty tried to read some excerpts aloud, I plugged my ears and sang Aretha Franklin. So, late at night—or rather, after 9:00 P.M.—after I'd fallen asleep, Kitty read the books herself with a flashlight.

If I wouldn't help myself, by God, she'd do it for me.

It was the time pressure that got to all of them. I had three and a half weeks left before the window of improvement would slam closed for good, and, in the wake of my depression, my improvement had stalled.

In truth, my improvements had stalled before Chip's confession—the whole week before had been significantly absent of improvements, as well. We all just noticed it after the breakup. Before, when I still believed in my fairy tale, I viewed the stall as a natural plateau—an adjustment period on the way to more inspiring success.

Now, I saw the slowdown as part of a different narrative: the beginning of the end.

I didn't say that to anybody, but I guess it was obvious.

Then my parents decided I needed a "tutor."

My mother brought it up at lunch. We were eating Vietnamese noodle salad from their favorite spot, and my dad was enjoying it so much, he was smacking.

"So," my mother said brightly, holding a forkful of noodles, "you're starting your last three weeks here—"

"And a half," I added.

"After insurance runs out," my dad said, "you'll come home to live with us."

I snorted. "I am *not* coming home to live with you."

My parents looked at each other. My dad asked tenderly, "Where would you live, sweetheart?"

"At my place," I said, like, *Duh*.

My dad proceeded very gingerly. "Your place is three stories high. With stairs."

I closed my eyes. "I'll stay on the ground floor."

He was almost whispering now. "There's no bathroom on the ground floor. Or kitchen."

I knew that, of course. "I'll figure it out."

We all knew I wouldn't. What would I do—climb the stairs on my knees? Actually, maybe that could work.

"Nonsense," my mother said, in her most authoritative voice. "You can't keep that place. I've already spoken with a real estate agent. He says now's a perfect time to sell. You stand to make a good profit." Then she added, "He also loves your décor."

This from the woman who'd told all the neighbors I'd be good as new by summer. "I am not moving in with my parents," I declared. "I am not a child!"

"Just temporarily," my dad said, ever the spoonful of sugar.

But I pointed at my mother. "Do not talk to agents! Do not sell my place! You said I'd be good as new!"

It was such a childish accusation, in one way—to get mad at her for my misfortune, the way little kids sometimes do before they've come to understand that, in so many big ways, parents are just as powerless as they are.

At the same time, it was a declaration of independence. My whole life, I'd turned to my mother for instructions on what to do, and where to go, and how to get it done. My mother had insisted to me, and the doctors, and, apparently, all our neighbors, that I was going to "beat" this paralysis.

She'd always interpreted my life. Though to be fair, I'd always let her.

But maybe that wasn't her job anymore.

In the strangled silence that followed, we all felt the shift in my thinking

like a little, earth-trembling rumble of plate tectonics. Even if we didn't know what it was.

Faced with this Kitty-like behavior from me, my mother dropped it. She put up her hands in surrender. "Fine. We won't sell your condo."

"Of course not. If you don't want to," my dad said.

"I don't want to." How could anybody possibly think that I would? Hadn't I given up enough?

"The point is," my mom said, getting back to business, "you are running out of time here."

"I'm aware of that," I said, stubbornly leaving my lunch untouched.

"And so we're thinking," my dad said brightly, "why not do everything possible right now to promote healing and recovery?"

I looked back and forth between them for a good long minute before I said, in a low voice like a growl, "My whole life is 'doing everything possible.' I don't go five minutes without 'promoting healing and recovery.'"

My mom leaned in. "Did I forget to tell you that I just read the most inspiring story? About a girl—a former ballerina—in just exactly your situation? She tried very hard for weeks, and got nowhere at all—and then one morning, out of the blue, her right big toe wiggled. Then, the next morning, her left big toe wiggled. The morning after that, she could wiggle them all. The morning after that, she could bend her knees. And by the end of the month, she could do a *pas de bourrée*!"

Quietly, then—secretly—I tried to wiggle my toes.

Nothing.

I wasn't even entirely sure I remembered how.

I'd been thinking I hated these inspirational stories, but that wasn't quite right. I *loathed* them. "What is your point?"

My mom blinked. "We think you might need a tutor."

A *tutor*? I frowned at my dad. "What is this?" I said. "The SAT?"

"Someone to give you a little extra practice," my dad said.

"That's not a thing," I said.

My dad shrugged. "A personal trainer, then, if you like."

"Someone to help you—physically—do more than the bare minimum that insurance requires."

Bare minimum struck me as deeply insulting. Spoken like a person who had no idea what it was like for the bare minimum to be your own personal ultimate maximum.

My mom went on, "We just want to be sure you're doing everything—while you still can."

"I *am* doing everything I can!" I said.

My mom gave me a look, like, *Come on.* "I saw you study for finals, and the SAT, and the GMAT. I know you're capable of more than this."

I heard my voice get very quiet. "You have no idea what I'm capable of."

My dad jumped in. "I think your mother's just trying to say that we want to help. However we can."

That wasn't what she was trying to say. I suddenly saw it very clearly. She wanted to help—but only in the ways that she had already chosen. My mother was always very helpful—when you did exactly what she wanted.

A lifetime of following my mother's every piece of advice ticker-taped through my head. A lifetime of never questioning her type-A standards, and working like a dog to meet them, and internalizing them without question. In that moment, possibly for the first time ever, it occurred to me: She didn't know everything. She didn't have it all figured out. I'd followed her instructions for life to the letter, and look where it had gotten me: right here, trapped in this bed, enduring stories about ballerinas. She said take advanced calculus? I took advanced calculus. She said major in business administration? I majored in business administration. She said get an MBA? I got an MBA. Top of the class. Always. Every time. Like a chump.

Sitting there, I tried to scan back for even one time—one tiny time—that I'd rejected her "help" and done my own thing. That's all Kitty had ever done, by the way—reject my mother's advice—and it had made her teen years in our house pretty miserable for everybody. But had it made Kitty's *life* miserable? Sure, she'd been through some rough times, and

she had a crazy hairdo, and way too many piercings, and a defiantly funky lifestyle—but she was always, unapologetically Kitty. She knew who she was. She did what she loved. Who was I? What was I good at, besides keeping my apartment neat, and keeping myself groomed, and acing tests? What did I like? What was I passionate about? What would it feel like to do what I wanted instead of what was expected?

I had no earthly idea.

"No," I heard myself say then.

My mother blinked at me.

"No thanks, I mean. I don't need a tutor."

"I'm not sure you see the time pressure here," my mother said.

"I think I do."

"In exactly three weeks, your window of opportunity will slam closed."

"Maybe not *slam*," my dad amended.

But my mom was irritated now. "Don't you want to get better?"

"I can't believe you would even ask me that."

"Because right now it doesn't seem like you do."

I looked at my dad for help.

He jumped in. "Maybe we just need to redefine 'better.'"

"'Better' doesn't need to be redefined," my mom said. "It is what it is. It's *better*."

"Unless," I said, "it's you applying it to me. Then 'better' means 'fixed.' As you've promised all the neighbors."

She held her position. "Don't you want to be fixed?"

"That's not a relevant question."

But she lifted one eyebrow the way she always did when she was about to win. "It's the only relevant question there is."

Sure, she had a point. There were some real, physical issues here that I needed to address in a timely way, and now might not be the best moment to give up. But I realized then—possibly for the first time ever—that my parents telling me what to do was making it harder, not easier, to figure out what to do. It was just a glimpse of a feeling, but I now grasped that it was my job—and only mine—to try.

"I don't want to talk about this anymore," I heard myself say.

"Fine," my mother said. "We'll take a break."

I shook my head. "At all. Period. I'm not going to discuss any of this with you." My voice, I noticed, sounded just like my mother's when she was declaring the case closed. "If you want to come have lunch every day and see me, great. But the topic of my recovery is off-limits."

My mother looked at my dad.

"If you try to bring it up," I went on, "I will scream until you leave the room." In my old life, I might have left the room myself—but now that wasn't an option. "And if that doesn't work," I said, adding the thing my mother hated the most, "I will burst into show tunes."

I could almost see her shiver. "Fine," she said.

"I have to figure this out," I said, my voice a little softer as I looked over at my dad. "You can't do it for me. I have to do it myself."

I could see a hundred protests forming in my mother's head. Most notably: What if I did it myself—and did it *wrong*? She had a point. Even I wondered if this was really the best moment to thrust myself out of her nest. Weren't the stakes a little high? Shouldn't we start with what to eat for dinner and work our way up? But I let the questions go unanswered. For the first time ever, I didn't care. This was bigger than me.

This was my mangled body and my hopeless soul, stepping up at last.

Eighteen

STANDING UP TO my mother was surprisingly elating. In a life as out of control as mine was at that moment, little things can be big.

When Ian showed up for PT, I went with him willingly. He didn't talk, and neither did I, but as we worked our way through stretches, and the stationary bike, and a machine I called the "Thighmaster," I did everything he asked with a new kind of determination.

Neither one of us talked this time, and the vibe was decidedly different than it had been. Instead of babbling incessantly to fill the silence, I concentrated on my task at hand. Instead of staring out the window, he watched my form and—of all things—helped me.

"Good," he'd say, as the weights on the machine went up. "That's it."

"Are you *encouraging* me?" I said, not looking over.

I felt, rather than saw, him give a little smile. "Nope."

Even Myles couldn't slow us down. He passed by several times to correct my form and then demand to know why Ian wasn't paying better attention. He also pointed out that Ian's scrubs weren't regulation blue—even though they were barely a shade lighter than the ones Myles him-

self was wearing. At one point, Myles came by for no other reason than to let Ian know he had been "missed at the staff meeting this morning."

Ian didn't look at him. "I was not told about that meeting."

Myles gave him a look, like, *Please*. "Pretty sure you were. There was a staff-wide email."

"I didn't get it."

"You're saying every single member of our team got that message but you?"

"Looks that way."

"I think maybe you just don't like meetings."

"I *detest* meetings," Ian said, standing up to full height and looking down at Myles. "Especially bullshit meetings that waste everyone's time. But I never miss them—unless someone deletes my address from the recipients list."

I caught a flash of *busted* cross Myles's face. Then he regrouped. "I've started taking roll," he said then. "So you'll want to be sure to make it to the next one. On time."

"With pleasure," Ian said, turning away.

"Did he delete your name from the email list?" I whispered, after Myles was gone.

"No comment."

"How are you going to make it to the next one if he doesn't tell you about it?"

Ian met my eyes. "I've alerted my network of spies."

AFTER PT, I was so tired I could barely transfer back to the bed.

I took a coma-like nap, and when I woke, around the time Kitty usually arrived for supper, I was ravenously hungry. I was also ready to report on how I'd both stood up to our mom and rocked it out in PT—and then psychoanalyze how those two things might be related.

But when the door opened, it wasn't Kitty.

It was Ian.

My first thought: He was quitting. He couldn't take me—or Myles—anymore.

He walked close to the bed and stood there, a bit uncomfortable.

I decided to jump the gun. "I'm sorry I've been so difficult lately," I said.

"Your situation is difficult," he said then. "Not you."

That was nice of him.

"I think you're coping remarkably well, actually," he said.

"You do?"

He nodded. "You worked hard today."

"I did?"

"Could you feel the difference?"

The question sparked a realization. This might have been the first time in my life that I did something difficult not for how it would matter to somebody else, but for how it would matter to me.

It was a strange, new feeling, but it felt like a little nudge in the right direction.

"It was different," I agreed. "But I'm not sure why."

"You've got a lot of strength, Maggie," Ian said then. Such a serious face. Practically *mournful*. "Much more than you realize."

"I hope so. I'm going to need it."

"And I think we could be doing more."

Where was he going with this? "Okay."

"That's why I'm here."

"Here now, you mean?"

"Your father hired me for extra sessions in the evenings."

My dad hired *Ian* as the tutor? Hadn't I just put my foot down about that? "Well, I told him I didn't need a tutor."

"He told me that."

I shook my head. "The thing is, I just had this really triumphant moment with my parents where I told them to stop running my life, and then I made a grand step toward—you know—being my own person and making my own choices from the inside out, and that extra gumption you saw in the gym today was me claiming my own long-lost power, so

if I just give in now and let them take back over, I'm kind of surrendering after I've already won the battle."

There was no way he'd followed that.

But he nodded. "I understand."

"You do?"

"I absolutely think you should"—here, he slowed down to get the words right—"'claim your own power.'"

He wasn't going to fight me. "Thank you," I said.

"Except," he said then.

"Except what?"

"As good as it feels to win a battle, I want you to win the war."

"What does that mean?"

"It means your parents are right."

I gave him a look, like, *Really?* "That's not exactly helpful."

"You *could* benefit from extra help. There are all sorts of things we could do that are outside the range of typical PT."

"Like?"

"Like anything. Swimming. Yoga. Horseback riding. Massage. Reflexology. Cold and heat. Acupuncture. Anything we can think of. In the gym, we're limited to a specific insurance-approved list. It's not a bad list, but it's certainly not everything."

Why was he here right now? Why had he said yes to my dad? Why on earth would he stay in this hospital one second longer every day than he had to? "Are you saying we're desperate?"

He shook his head. "Not desperate," he said. "*Creative.*"

I stared at him. I was tired and hungry, and ready for the day to be over, and pissed at my dad for siding with my mom. "Why would you do this?" I asked. "I know my dad. The money couldn't be that good."

"This is what we did at my gym," he said. "This is the part I loved—the creativity, the challenge, the thinking outside the box."

Did I want to give Ian a chance to do what he loved? Of course. But, after finally tasting the sweetness of what it felt like to do something for me, I did not want to backslide and agree to extra PT just so Ian could have better job satisfaction.

Until he said these words: "Plus, I could get you out of here."

"What do you mean, out of here?"

He shrugged. "If you're doing therapeutic horseback, we can't exactly do it in this building."

"You mean, you could check me out?"

"For therapy, yes."

"Often?"

"If you had the energy for it."

"You wouldn't get in trouble with Myles?"

"I'm in trouble with Myles either way."

And voilà! An internal motivation! Doing something that would make my parents happy or give Ian job fulfillment might blur my newly drawn lines, but there was nothing blurry about getting the fuck out of here.

"Sold," I said. "I'm in."

Ian stifled a smile. "Great," he said. "Let's go."

"I can't go now," I said. "My sister's bringing dinner."

"Oh," he said. "That's all right. I'll wait."

"Are you hungry? Do you want to eat?"

"That depends on what you're having."

"Italian, I think." Then, as if to confirm, Kitty walked through the door with a bag from Napoli's.

"Who is this?" she asked, breezing past him.

It was so weird to think she'd never met him. But his shifts were during the day—and she was all about the night.

"Kitty, this is Ian, my physical therapist. Ian, this is Kitty, my sister."

"Your black-sheep sister," Kitty corrected, and then she looked Ian over. "You didn't tell me he was gorgeous." She reached out to shake hands. "You can call me Kitty Kat."

"Do not flirt with my physical therapist," I said.

"He looks like he can resist me," Kitty said. Then, to Ian, "Want a soda?" She pulled a can of full-sugar Coke out of her purse. I looked at her, like, *I can't believe you drink that stuff,* and she shrugged at me, like, *You've gotta have some vices.*

"No, but thanks," Ian said.

Kitty turned to me like a kid who'd just spotted a candy bar. Then she whispered, "He really is Scottish."

I nodded.

"Yum."

"Do *not* flirt with my physical therapist!"

"Hello? *He's Scottish.* All rules are off."

"Dad hired him to be my walking tutor. Against my wishes." At the memory, I tried to wiggle my toes. Nothing.

Ian said, "I really do think I can help you."

"Well," I said, "you'd better. My mother wants me to be perfect again, and she won't accept anything less."

"Amen to that," Kitty said.

But Ian was looking at me. "Were you perfect before?"

I shrugged. "I tried like hell," I said, just as Kitty said, "Yes."

"That sounds like a lot of work," Ian said.

"You have no idea," Kitty said.

"What did you do for fun?" Ian said, looking at me.

I looked at him back. "I worked really hard all the time."

"That doesn't sound like fun to me."

"I'm not sure you're qualified to judge, triathlon guy."

"I'm fun," Ian protested.

"You are the opposite of fun," I said.

"You might not say that after tonight." He raised his eyebrows a little, as if to say, *Listen up.*

I squinted with suspicion. "What happens tonight?"

"I'm taking you swimming."

I stared for a second. "There's a pool?"

"A therapy pool." He nodded. "In the basement."

I looked around the room. "I don't have a swimsuit."

"Yes, you do," Kitty sang out. "Mom packed you one."

Ian nodded at me. "Sounds like you do."

"But you could also just skinny-dip," Kitty suggested.

Suddenly I remembered my donor sites. And the third-degree burns on my neck. "Wait! *Can* I swim?" I gestured at my whole collarbone-neck-jaw area. "With these?"

Ian just gave me a little shrug. "Let's go find out."

AN HOUR LATER, I was wearing my least favorite swimsuit—a retro polka-dot two-piece that I hadn't worn in years—and sitting on the edge of the pool with my spaghetti legs dangling in. It was something I'd done thousands of times before, but it was different now. For one thing, my sensation was spotty below the knees, so I could feel the cold water in some places, but not in others. For another, I could not kick my legs, so they just draped like wet towels over the edge.

The therapy pool was deserted at nine-thirty at night, and it reeked of so much chlorine it was like sniffing a straight bottle of bleach. The fluorescent lighting gave it a slight public-bathroom vibe. I had a distinct feeling we were not supposed to be here.

I was waiting for Ian while he changed, wondering if he kept a swim-suit at work for last-minute swims just like these.

No, it turned out. He appeared in just a pair of regular cotton cargo shorts. No shirt. The sight of his naked shoulders and his torso was so shocking, I could only stare.

"You're going to swim like that?" I asked.

"I could skinny-dip, if you prefer."

"Did you just make a joke?"

"I never joke," he said. Then he cannonballed into the far end of the pool. When he surfaced, he shook out his hair like a dog and then free-styled over to me.

I put my hands out as he approached. "Don't get me wet."

"No," he agreed. "It'll be weeks before your donor sites heal up. Check with the doc, but I think it might be up to a year before you can swim after a graft like that."

"A *year*?" I had not gotten that memo.

"But that doesn't mean you can't use the water, if you're careful."

"I'll be careful, Cannonball Run. *You* just be careful."

He frowned like he didn't get my obscure American reference to my dad's favorite Burt Reynolds movie, and then he went on. "The great thing about water is it makes everything easier."

"What are we going to do?"

"We're going to walk," he said, like it was the easiest thing in the world.

I suddenly got the feeling he was about to pull me into the pool. "Be careful!"

He read the nervousness on my face. "Listen. This is the shallow end. It only comes to your waist."

"But I can't stand up."

"You might be able to in the water."

"What if I fall in?"

"I'll catch you."

"But what if you *don't*?"

Ian lifted an eyebrow. "If I suddenly have a heart attack and die while we're in the middle of the pool, I might not catch you. If that happens, float on your back to the edge, and then scream your lungs out until someone comes to help you. Because you are in a hospital, you will get medical care quickly, and because you are on massive antibiotics already, it's unlikely you'll get an infection, but if you do, again, you're already at the hospital."

"What about you?"

"I'm dead already. Just leave me in the pool."

I stifled a smile. "That would traumatize the other patients."

"Toss me in the bin, then. Whatever."

I took a deep breath and geared up for going in. Ian went to put his palms on either side of my ribs, right on the skin, just under my two-piece top—and watching it happen gave me the giddy anticipation you get when someone's coming to tickle you.

I sucked in a breath.

He stopped short of touching me. "What?"

No way was I explaining to him how visceral the anticipation of his

hands on my body was. That was need-to-know information. "I'm ticklish," I said.

He nodded, like, *Noted,* and then continued.

"I've got you," he said—and all of a sudden, out of context, he was different. He was the Ian from the roof. He was not the guy in the PT gym with the cartoon scribble of angst above his head. He was not the guy who answered my questions with one-word nonanswers, and grunts, and total silence. He was a guy who had just cracked a joke—possibly two! He was looking into my eyes, and paying attention, and promising me I could trust him.

"Are *you* ticklish?" I asked.

He gave me a look. "Do I *look* ticklish?"

I felt a strong temptation to find out, but I was scared I might fall into the water. "Who are you?" I said then, peering at him.

He frowned, as if the question made no sense. "I'm the guy who's going to walk you across the pool."

With that, he pulled me toward him in a little nudge, and I popped off the edge—and instead of floating down gracefully, I squealed and grabbed him tight around the neck in what could only be described as a very clingy hug.

I didn't mean to. I was just going to bob into the water, like always.

But this wasn't always. My burns felt extra-naked, and I didn't trust my legs to work any better in the water than out. I didn't entirely trust Ian, either. And so: the chicken version of a leap of faith—one that involved clutching his neck with my face buried into the crook of his wet, post-cannonball shoulder.

"Too fast?" he said.

I nodded into his neck, liking the way the skin felt.

"Push back a little. Otherwise, it's not therapy. It's just hugging."

"Hugging could be a type of therapy."

"Not the type your father's going to pay me for."

"He might if I asked him to."

"You can do this. Take a breath."

So I did. Then I pushed myself back until there was half a foot

between us, and worked my legs into position as if they were foreign objects. He kept his hands at my rib cage, and I braced mine on his shoulders. Then there we were, waist deep in the water, standing. Right then, I felt it for the first time—almost like an electrical pulse: a tiny flicker of joy.

He saw it. He saw me feel it. There was nowhere to look but straight into his face, and he read me in less than a second.

I couldn't help but smile.

He smiled back. A real smile. The first one of his I'd ever seen. And I felt another electrical pulse.

"You're standing," he said.

"You're smiling," I said.

"I'm not," he said. But that just made him smile more. He threw his head back and said, "Focus! Focus!" To himself, as far as I could tell.

For a flash, as I noticed all those muscles and tendons crisscrossing under the stubble on his throat, I forgot all about myself, and why we were here, and the impossible thing we were trying to do. For a second, he was just a guy in a pool in wet cargo shorts—and I was just a girl, being held.

But just for a second.

Then he brought his face down and got serious. "Okay," he said. "When I take a step backward, you take a step forward."

But it had been too long. I shook my head. "I can't remember how."

"Don't overthink it. Your body remembers. You know how to bring the knee up. Then let the water help the foot follow."

When he took a step back, I brought my knee forward. Then my foot followed behind, carried by the current. Then I set it down.

"I did it!" I whispered.

"Good. Do the other one."

So I did.

It was slow, but it felt so good to work that old, familiar pattern. One foot, then the other, side to side, in that ancient human motion. It was bliss, and heartbreak—both. It was *just enough* of what I wanted to remind me of what I wanted—who I'd been, what I'd lost. That must have

been the aspect that made me cry, because by the time we made it to the far side, my face was cold with tears.

But I was smiling. Crying and smiling both. As sad and happy as I'd been in a while. Not numb, that was certain.

"We made it all the way!" I said. Then, because nothing else seemed like it could possibly be more interesting, I said it again. "We made it all the way!"

"Aye. We did."

"I want to high-five you, but I don't want to let go."

"Don't high-five. We're going back across."

I felt like I could go all night, but he said that was just the excitement. He promised I was working much harder than I realized.

"The thing is," I said, as we moved back across. "I don't think my muscles are bringing my foot forward. I think it might just be drifting in the current behind the knee."

"That's okay. The theory is, the more your body does it, the more it will remember what to do. Going through those motions helps spark memories in your body. That's the hope, at least."

"Thank you for not letting me fall."

"We're not out yet."

"Thank you for being so nice to me today."

But Ian didn't have a reply to that, and once again, he got quiet.

Nineteen

ONE NIGHT, A hospital volunteer showed up just after Kitty arrived with Moroccan lamb tagine. She was perky and big-eyed, and she carried a little clipboard. She was recruiting volunteers for a crafts fair that week in the children's wing, and I was just drawing breath to shoo her out when Kitty said, "What kind of crafts?"

"Oh, everything," the volunteer said. "Rock painting, finger knitting, friendship bracelets, balloon rockets, beeswax sculpting, sand candles. Also: anything with googly eyes."

Kitty looked at me. "They are having a lot more fun in the children's wing than we are."

"Would you like to sign up?" the volunteer asked.

"Yes," Kitty said loudly, just as I said, "No."

The volunteer looked at Kitty. "Great."

"Can we sign up for knitting?" Kitty asked. "My sister is knitting a slug."

"Ooo, bring it!" the volunteer said. "The kids will love it."

Kitty wiggled her eyebrows at me. "Maybe we can steal some googly eyes."

After the volunteer left, I said, "I'm not going."

"Yes you are. You just signed up."

"*You* just signed up."

"What else do you have to do?"

"Stop trying to cheer me up. You know it makes me feel worse."

"You feel worse, anyway."

"Yeah. But you make me feel guilty about it."

"Look, I just saw a very inspiring quote on Instagram that said, 'Our struggles lead us to our strengths.'"

"Say the word 'Instagram' one more time and I will burn this building down."

"Fine, but every single article in the entire world says you need to learn to appreciate what you have and not dwell on what you don't."

"Are you *kidding* me right now?"

She hesitated. "Okay, that sounded a little flip."

I rolled my eyes to the ceiling. "It's been four weeks!! Four weeks since I lost everything I cared about. Can I get five minutes to adjust?"

"Yes! Of course! And in the meantime, let's go teach a bunch of hospitalized children how to knit a slug."

"Dammit, stop trying to fix me!"

Ian showed up in the doorway then, but that didn't slow us down. Kitty flung her arm in his direction. "Ian gets to try to fix you!"

I glanced over at him. "It's his job to fix me."

"So?"

"So! A job is different."

"That's better?"

He was right there, listening, but I was hell-bent on making my point. "Yes! Because in less than three weeks, I will never see him again. He won't think about me, he won't worry about me, and he sure as hell won't spend the rest of my life telling me to cheer up. He will feel a wash of relief as I roll out the door to go live my tragic life, and then he'll be done."

I was about to go on, but Ian stepped in closer. "That's not true."

Kitty and I both turned toward him. "What's not true?" I asked.

"I will think about you after you're gone. I expect I'll think about you often."

Was there more? Nope. A man of few words.

But just enough, as we stared at him, to stop the fight in its tracks.

"Want some Moroccan tagine?" Kitty asked after a bit, peeling the lid off a container and holding it out.

Ian said no.

"Maggie's knitting a slug," Kit said then. "Want to see?"

She got him to smile. I loved when he did that. "I'd love to see," he said.

"Hey," I said to Kit, "don't—"

"*Shh.*" Kit held her finger out. "For a scarf, it's terrible. For a knitted slug, it's divine. Just go with 'slug' and be proud." She thrust it at Ian.

He held it for a second, looked back and forth between us, and then said, "That's a fine knitted slug."

Kit turned to me. "Does *everything* sound sexy in Scottish?" Then, back to Ian, "If you were a kid at the craft fair, wouldn't you love to see that?"

He looked up. "The craft fair?"

"Yeah, they're holding one for the kids, but Cranky McCrankypants doesn't want to volunteer."

I gave Kitty a look.

But I did have to give her credit. He seemed to like it when she teased me. His eyes crinkled up at the edges in an expression that was almost warm. And then, like just a normal, friendly, healthcare professional, he shook his head all wryly and said, "Now you make me think of my mother."

Kit and I both frowned. "Your mother?"

"She always said, 'When you don't know what to do for yourself, do something for someone else.'"

WE WENT TO the fair. What choice did we have? Neither of us had the guts to disobey Ian's mother.

The fair turned out to be the most fun I'd had since my incarceration.

There, surrounded by kids of every variety, I felt more relaxed than I had been in all these weeks. In the rehab gym, the focus was on how we could fix what was broken about me. In my room, I was, well, in a hospital room. But in this rec room in the children's wing, it was just bright colors and helium balloons and yarn animals and sing-alongs and face painting. Noisy? Yes. Chaotic? Totally. As I sat at my finger-knitting station with Kit, teaching kids what to do when they came up, and chatting with Kit in between, I felt noticeably peaceful.

"These are your people," Kitty said.

"They do seem to get me," I said.

"You're craftier than I realized," Kit said next, eyeing the long yarn snake I'd been making.

"I'm craftier than *I* realized," I said with a shrug.

It was here, among all this chaos and peace, that Kit decided to give me two pieces of information.

One: She'd booked her flight back to New York. She was leaving on the morning of the same day I was getting discharged.

"You're not going to come home with me?"

She looked at me like I was crazy. "No."

"Not even for a couple of hours? To help me get settled?"

"No. This was the cheapest flight, and I took it."

"I can't believe you're leaving me."

"It's not for two weeks."

"Two and a half," I corrected.

"That's, like, ten years in hospital time."

"Now I have to dread it."

"I did everything I came here for," she said then. "I cleared things up with you. I confronted Mom. I went on an erotic journey with Fat Benjamin."

"Did you come here for that last one?"

She squinted. "I guess Fat Benjamin was a surprise."

"And *did* you clear things up with Mom?" I asked.

"As much as I ever do," she said.

" 'Cause it seems like we haven't talked about"—I didn't know how to describe it—"*your information* since the day it all came out."

Kit shrugged. "Yeah, well. We've all been kind of busy."

True, we'd been busy. But this was also a classic Jacobsen-family technique for responding to big, earth-shattering news: pretending it didn't exist.

There was probably a more delicate way to ask the question, but I said, "Don't you want to know who your real dad is?"

Kit got quiet at the sound of the words out loud.

"Our dad *is* my real dad."

Had I hurt her feelings? "Of course he is," I corrected. "I just I meant your *biological* dad."

She thought about it. "I've thought about it. I am curious. But as long as Dad doesn't know, it feels disloyal to take it any further."

"And Dad will never know."

We agreed.

Two: Kit's other piece of news was she had decided to throw a party on her last night here. In the rehab gym.

"They'll never let you do that," I said.

"It's closed at night. No one has to know."

It was a "Valentine's Day party," even though it would happen on the first of April.

"Details," Kit said, making a *pshaw* motion. "Love can happen anytime."

"Do you know that's April Fools'?"

"Only you would notice that."

"You realize what happened to me the last time it was Valentine's Day," I said.

"Yes," she said.

Of course she knew. We all knew. But I said it anyway. "I was in a *plane crash.*"

"Duh. I'm aware of that. I'm giving you a do-over."

I shook my head. "No."

But she had a fire in her eyes. "I'll do everything. You don't have to do anything. I'll talk to the nurses, hang the decorations. I've got a vision! Little heart-shaped chocolates everywhere, punch that we'll call 'love potion,' and Fat Benjamin's got a chocolate fountain that he stole from a catering gig. Streamers, and karaoke with nothing but love songs, and I've got that old disco ball in my high school bedroom. I love stuff like this! Let me do something for you. Yes?"

Maybe it was because the kids' craft fair was so unexpectedly charming, but I let out a long sigh, and as soon as my shoulders sank, she knew she'd won.

She held up her arms in victory.

"Who would you even invite?" I said. Then I pointed a warning at her: "Nobody from Facebook. No normal people, okay?"

"Just injured people. Just the folks on your floor. And the nurses. And anybody else good. Plus Fat Benjamin, of course."

"Why do you have to do this?" I asked. "Let's just eat tacos and watch TV."

"I need to go out with a bang," she said. "And guess what? So do you."

That's when it hit me. "You've already started planning this, haven't you?"

She wiggled her eyebrows at me. "It was supposed to be a surprise, but you know I can't keep a secret."

"You sneaky weasel!"

"I dare you to be mad," she said, "when you're drinking straight out of the chocolate fountain."

Twenty

THE NEXT NIGHT, Kitty showed up with some astonishing information: I'd been granted a furlough.

She held out a box of spanakopita with a triumphant flourish and said, "Great news!"

I was knitting a new slug. "What?"

"We have an amazing birthday present for you."

I had to think about it. Sure enough, my birthday was coming up on Sunday. "I forgot about my birthday," I said.

"You are not going to believe how great your present is."

"My face is back to normal?"

Kit frowned and then squinted at me. "Not quite," she said. "But close."

"What, then?"

Kit stretched up taller. "We are about to blow your mind."

"Who's 'we'?"

"Mom and me."

"Since when are you and Mom a 'we'?"

Kitty's expression darkened. "It's a fragile, don't-ask-don't-tell truce."

I frowned. How was that possible?

"Never underestimate Linda's ability to compartmentalize," Kit said. "Or mine, either."

"So you're not talking about anything?"

"Nothing but you."

"Okay."

"She hates everything about how I look, though."

"Of course she does."

"Especially the tattoos."

I gave Kit a look. *Of course she does.*

"It was her idea, actually. This whole thing."

"What whole thing?"

Kit pretended to blow a trumpet. "Announcing the greatest birthday news ever!" she announced. "We are giving you a night out."

"A night out?"

Kit dropped her voice back to normal. "Mom thought you might like to have spaghetti and cake at home."

Our traditional birthday dinner. Spaghetti and cake. The thought of it made me sad. "I don't want to go home."

"I know." Kitty looked pleased with herself. "I told her that! And Dad backed me up."

"I don't have to go to Mom's?"

"No. Better."

"Where?"

Kit did a little shimmy. "The lake."

"The lake? Our lake?"

She clapped.

But it was no good. "I can't go to the lake," I said. It was my grandparents' old fishing cabin. Rustic, to say the least. Hardly wheelchair accessible.

"You can! It's all set up!"

"They'll never let me out of here for that."

"Mom got them to okay it. It's all official. I was waiting to tell you until it was certain. We'll spend Saturday night at the lake. Which means you will wake up on your birthday *not* in the hospital."

"But . . ." I wasn't sure what to think. Kit wanted me to be excited, but it just seemed like such a terrible, awful, exhausting idea.

"We figured it all out. Mom's been down there all week, cleaning so it shines. Fresh sheets, dust-free: the works. Plus a ton of groceries to stock the kitchen."

"Is Mom coming, too?"

"No! That's just it! I said, 'Mom, Margaret is a young person! She wants to spend her birthday with young people!' And Dad backed me up."

"So who am I spending it with?"

"Me!"

This sounded worse and worse. "Kit, you can't take care of me. You can barely take care of yourself."

"Rude. And untrue. And I *can* take care of you, because I talked your boyfriend into coming with us—and he's going to do all the hard stuff."

My boyfriend? "Who—*Chip*?" I hadn't seen or heard from him—absolutely nothing—since the night we'd ended it. It was like he never existed.

Kit shook her head. "No. Your *Scottish* boyfriend."

I put my hand over my mouth. "You didn't."

"I did!"

"You asked him?"

She nodded.

"And he said yes?"

"I might've implied I could accidentally kill you."

I leaned back against the pillow. "No."

"Anyway, that's your real present. Now you can have forbidden sex with your secret love." Then she frowned and leaned in to whisper, "Your vagina still works, right?"

I put my hand over my eyes. "No secret love. No forbidden sex. Come on, Kit!"

"You think I'm an amateur? You think I can't read that sexual tension? Sexual tension is my primary language!"

"Kit, look at me. Look at my life."

"So?"

"This is not junior high. I'm a month into a total shit-storm of utter devastation."

"All the more reason to have a little fun."

"I hate fun. I don't even believe in fun anymore."

"You do when you're with Ian."

"We are not doing this."

"It's all arranged. He's taking a personal day and everything."

"So me, you, and my physical therapist are going to the lake for my birthday?"

Kit nodded. "And Fat Benjamin, too. For a little forbidden sex of my own."

"What about the Moustache?"

"We're nonexclusive."

I'd grown up spending long weekends and summers at this little fishing cottage, scampering around the yard, swimming for endless hours, only breaking for lunch and dinner, and exploring the lake in the rowboat. I'd spent my childhood there, never even imagining—of course—that I'd end up like this. The idea of facing any normal thing now, with my life so changed—even the grocery store or a movie theater—seemed heartbreaking. But a place so happy? A place so densely layered with memories of my other life? A place where the future had always been something to look forward to?

It broke my heart to even consider it.

And yet. It was all arranged. I did want to get out of here. I did love that lake. The cottage was only a hundred feet or so back from the shore, and when you woke, the first thing you saw was morning sunlight glittering on the water. I did want to see that. I longed to be someplace beautiful.

Kit went on, "We're going to eat camp food and make s'mores."

My stomach felt like it was filled with pebbles. I wanted to go exactly as much as I wanted *not* to go.

But I didn't know how to refuse. It was happening. Plus, Kit wasn't wrong: I did believe in fun when Ian was around.

❖   ❖   ❖

IAN AND I had become quite the ninja rehab team since he'd become my tutor. I stayed motivated and focused, and Ian finally caught on to the notion that people do better when you encourage them. We worked every day in the gym, and then we worked again after dinner.

In fact, he was the only person I'd told about my morning toe-wiggling attempts, which had become quite a ritual for me. I never started a day without giving my toes a little pep talk and then trying to rev them up.

"What do you say to them?" he asked, when I told him about it.

"To my toes?"

He nodded. "In the pep talks."

In the name of healthcare, I told the truth. "I say, 'Come on, little guys. You're a lot stronger than you think you are.'"

"What do they say back?"

I gave him a look. "They say, 'Right back atcha, lady.'"

Some nights, I was tired, and he just hung out in the room with Kit and me, working my lower legs in a low-key way, with texture therapy, or stretching, or massage, and talking in a far more relaxed way than I ever saw in the gym. In the gym, with Myles never far off, Ian was always all business. He scowled less now, maybe, but he still scowled a lot.

But after-hours Ian was different.

First of all, he was jazzed about our activities. In the rehab gym, he had a going-through-the-motions vibe, but on his own, he was full of energy and surprises. When I wasn't too tired, we went to the pool, where he had a whole array of inflatables to cheer the place up—surfboards and noodles and blow-up unicorns. Other times, he'd show up with an acupuncturist friend, and do acupuncture right there in my room while Kitty ate sesame chicken and looked on. Now and again, he brought a reflexologist who also dabbled in aromatherapy. Once, he had a chiropractor friend in tow—which was a little alarming because I did not want her even *touching*, must less adjusting, my back—but she just used a handheld ultrasound machine to stimulate my calves and feet.

Was it helping? Who knows? It wasn't *hurting*.

The rehab gym was all work, but tutoring became play.

Some nights, we played Pop-A-Shot outside the rehab gym until bedtime. The first time we ever tried it, after I explained in detail how much I sucked at basketball, I beat Ian's score by thirteen points. He wasn't thrilled about that. After that, I beat him every time we played. I'd sit in front of the basket as Ian handed me basketballs, and I'd make swish after swish after swish until the timer went off. Then Ian would take a turn. Sometimes he made baskets, sometimes he didn't. I'm sure he was fine at it. But, to everyone's surprise, I was remarkable. I never missed. And this drove Ian crazy—especially since I had never even seen a Pop-A-Shot game before now.

I liked driving him crazy.

The first night he'd showed up for tutoring, he'd stood the entire time, like an at-ease officer, and waited for Kit and me to eat. Now, he'd long since given in, and he and Kit sat in visitor chairs on either side of me, the bed lowered to table height, dinner spread out all over it, wedging containers between my ankles or up against my knees.

Maybe it was the food, or the easy rapport between me and Kit, or just being far enough from Myles—but sometimes Ian seemed like a different guy entirely. An easygoing, smiley, *likable* guy. The more we saw that guy, the more we wanted to see him. It became a game.

Kit and I ganged up on Ian a lot, trying to make him smile, or blush, or laugh out loud—ideally all three. Embarrassing him worked like a charm. We cursed. We talked about shocking "lady" things. We made him teach us Scottish insults. Turns out, there were plenty, and they were delightful. Both words—"clipe," "dobber," "scrote," "roaster," "numpty," "jakey," "walloper"—and phrases: "Shut ye geggie," "erse like a bag o' washin'," and "yer bum's oot the windae." Not to mention "baw," meaning "testicle," which apparently goes with just about anything: "bawbag," "bawface," "bawjaws." Plus, just words for regular things were awesome: "oxter" for armpit, "cludgie" for toilet, "blootered" for drunk, and "puggled" for out of breath.

Ian gave us the shocking news that the Scottish accent was not as universally adored in the U.K. as in the U.S.

"They're just jealous," Kit said.

"Should we not make fun of your accent, then?" I asked. It was one thing to make fun of an accent that was unassailably cool—and quite another to kick an accent that was down.

"You can make fun of Scottish," he said, "if I can make fun of Texan."

Kit and I looked at each other. "*Can* you make fun of Texan?"

Ian pointed at me. "You say 'tumped' for 'fell over.' You know that's not a word, right?"

"It *is* a word," I said.

Ian shook his head. "Only in Texas."

We loved to try to copy his accent, but we were bad at it. We also gave him American words to try, especially Native American place names that Kit Googled on her phone, like the Caloosahatchee River, Lake Tangipahoa, and Quittapahilla Creek. It cracked her up to hear him try, and it mesmerized me. I'd watch his lips forming those sounds, pulling back, and pouting out, and making that classic Scottish *o*. Sometimes I forgot to laugh. Sometimes I got hypnotized by it.

He turned out to be remarkably game. We got started to bring him out of his stoic shell, but it always got us going, too. We laughed so hard at dinner sometimes that we couldn't even finish our food. It was the kind of goofy, uncontrollable laughing you almost never do in grown-up life: Things weren't just funny, they were *hysterical*—even things that were objectively not even funny: the noise of a scooting chair, a veggie dumpling that got dropped on the floor, a nurse coming into the room to investigate the noise.

It's strange that I could have laughed so hard under those circumstances, during that very dark moment in my life. But I've decided sorrow can make things funnier. Endure enough hardship, and you start really needing a good laugh. I remember my dad and his brother, on the day of their own mother's funeral back when I was a kid, in the car, driving to the cemetery, making fun of all their relatives and cracking each

other up. They were in the front seat, and Kit and I and our mom were in the back, and I watched those two grown men, now motherless, having just lost forever a woman they both truly loved, not just chuckle a bit but *howl* with laughter.

I was maybe ten at the time. "What are you doing?" I demanded of my dad. "How can you be laughing?"

"Sweetheart," my dad said, "if we don't laugh, we're gonna cry."

That's what this laughing was like. It took us over. It made our faces hurt. And it happened not despite all the sadness, but because of it.

Kit was bolder than I was. She begged him to wear a kilt to work one day.

"Wear a kilt to this building," she said, "and I'll give you ten thousand dollars."

"She doesn't have ten thousand dollars," I whispered to Ian.

Ian smiled. "And I don't have a kilt, so we're even."

Mostly, it was Kit and me egging Ian on, but one night, eating sushi, he picked up a teaspoon-sized wad of wasabi with his chopsticks, held it up so we could see it, and then said, "Do you dare me to eat this?"

I looked at him like he was crazy. "The whole thing?" One tenth of that wasabi ball would be enough to send steam out his ears.

Ian nodded.

"No," Kit said. "I won't dare you. Not even I am that crazy."

"I'll dare you," I said—and before I could take it back, Ian had popped the whole thing in his mouth, swallowed, and thrown his arms up in victory.

Kitty and I both gaped at him.

"Not so bad," Ian said, but the words were barely out before tears started running down his cheeks, and his face turned red, and he started panting and hissing like a feral cat.

He grabbed his water and drank the whole bottle in one go. Then he grabbed my water and drank it all. Then Kit's, too.

"Whooo!" he said, pacing around the room. "Fuck—that stings."

"Curse in Scottish!" we called out.

But he was jogging in place now. "Not my best idea."

"Say 'bawjaws'!" Kit suggested.

"Call yourself a 'numpty jobber'!" I jumped in.

"Dobber," he corrected, while bent over at the waist, panting. Then he banged his head against the foot of the bed. Then he realized he was drooling, and took the wad of Kleenex I was waving at him.

In all, it took half an hour for him to recover, and that's when he threw us a bone and gave us a little Scottish. "I *am* a dobber," he said. "What was I thinking?"

"You were thinking," I said, not even bothering to hide the affection in my voice, "that you'd entertain us."

It was like we had all made an unspoken pact to choose to have fun.

"That's backed up by science," Kitty, Queen of Googling, said, when I noticed how much just the idea of dinner with her and Ian was impacting the rest of my sad days. "Anticipating a reward lights up the same region of the brain as actually getting a reward," she said. "That's what a dum-dum the brain is. It doesn't even know the difference."

There was nothing, truly nothing, fun about any other part of my day. But I anticipated the hell out of dinner.

Twenty-one

THE MORNING OF my furlough was a usual morning—bathing, cleaning, failed attempts to wiggle my toes—and my parents came for their usual lunch. But then, instead of heading off to the rehab gym, I transferred to the chair, and my parents wheeled me down with a little overnight bag to where Kit was waiting in my father's sedan.

I felt surprisingly anxious about leaving the hospital.

I would have said I'd be thrilled, elated, ecstatic to leave. Instead, I just felt shaky. I didn't trust Kit to drive my dad's big car. I didn't trust all the idiot drivers texting their way through intersections. I didn't trust the big, bad, chaotic world outside my controlled little hospital biosphere.

Even in the car, I couldn't relax. If I'd been a cat with claws, they would have been impaled in the dashboard. Every turn, every red light, every touch of the brakes made me wince with anxiety.

"You have got to chill," Kit said.

I nodded. "Yes. Good advice. Chill."

But I had no idea how to do that. How do you *make yourself* chill?

By the time we made it to the cabin, the tension in my neck was

migrating to my head. I felt woozy and headachy, and Kit declared I had to take a nap.

Of course, the house was not wheelchair accessible. Why would it be? We got me into the chair and across the gravel drive, but then we had to pause for a while to puzzle out how to get me into the house.

"I knew this was a bad idea," I said.

"Hush," Kit said. "If nothing else, your Scotsman can carry you in when he gets here." She tromped off to examine the back porch to see if it might make a better point of entry, calling back, "Would that be so awful?"

"Just go," I said, closing my eyes.

Being back here was exactly as bad as I'd feared. Everything was the same as it had been since my grandparents had bought the place in the sixties. The screen porch door still squeaked and slapped. The gopher hole by the back steps hadn't moved. The pear trees my grandmother had planted still rustled in the breeze.

The only thing different was me.

It created such a visceral wash of grief through my body, I had to lean over and put my head between my knees. "We never should have come here," I heard myself whisper.

I was going to throw up. I felt that salty feeling under my tongue you get just before it happens.

But then I heard tires on the gravel of the driveway.

I looked up to see a brown vintage Bronco. With Ian in it. And then the door was slamming. And he was walking across the grass toward me with a duffel bag on his shoulder. In jeans, of all things, instead of scrubs. And brown leather shoes instead of sneakers. And a plaid flannel shirt.

I forgot to throw up.

"This place suits you," Ian said, as he got close.

"Really? Because I was just about to throw up."

"Carsick?"

"Heartsick, I think."

"Does it make you sad to come here again?"

I nodded.

"But happy, too, I hope?"

I shook my head. "Not yet. But I'm glad to see you."

"Why are you out here alone?"

"Kitty's trying to figure out how to get me in."

Ian nodded. "I can help with that," and as he said it, he dropped his duffel without a thought, kneeled down, pivoted, and backed up to me all at once. "Let's go," he said, jerking his head for me to climb on.

So I did. He hooked his arms under my knees, and I gripped with my thighs, and held on to his shoulders. Just for a second, I got another intoxicating whiff of him, and then we were off, rounding the side of the house, looking for Kit.

Ian stopped for a second when he caught sight of the lake—blue and bright and bigger than I remembered. The lawn sloped down to it, and from where we stood, we had a perfect, clear view.

"This is your lake?" Ian asked.

"This is our lake," I said, and when I spoke, my cheek brushed his neck.

"Will you take me out on it?" Ian asked.

"Of course."

Just then, Kit rounded the corner. "We're just going to have to wait for—" Then she saw us, and looked Ian over, in his flannel shirt and jeans. "The Brawny paper-towel guy."

I DIDN'T WANT to go back after that. It's not that Ian showing up made everything okay—it didn't. It made everything a little better, though. My heart was still humming a mournful tune, but it was like Ian arriving had introduced a little countermelody. It hadn't stopped the sad song, but it had altered it.

I needed to pee—we all did, after the drive—so after Kit opened the doors, Ian carried me to the bathroom and set me on the toilet with all my clothes still on.

"Do you need help?" he asked.

Even if I had needed it, no way in hell was I asking. "I've got it," I said.

The wheelchair turned out to be fifty percent useless at the lake. The ground was too grassy and gravelly for it to roll well, and the doorways inside the house were too narrow. Upside: Ian carried me a lot.

It was almost my birthday, after all.

It was a crisp, sunny day, and my next order of business was to sit in an Adirondack chair in the sun near the water while Kit and Ian un-packed. I couldn't expose my grafts to sunlight, so Kitty brought me out a pink dotted umbrella. I positioned it carefully to cover my burns but leave the rest of me—toes, legs, right arm—gloriously exposed. How long had it been since I'd felt the sun on my skin? I closed my eyes and drank in the feeling. The breeze was cool, but I felt warm.

Despite everything that had happened, and everything still to bear, this moment right here was pretty nice.

I don't know how much time passed, but my headache had gone by the time I heard footsteps crunching down the gravel path toward me.

It was Ian. "Kit wants me to bring out the boats," he said, not break-ing stride.

I nodded, and went back to sunning, but I didn't close my eyes again.

Ian unlocked the boathouse and dragged boat after boat to the shore: a rowboat, two kayaks, two wakeboards, a clunky old paddle boat for fishing, and a canoe that my grandpa had painted with Cherokee de-signs. Back and forth he went. Mesmerizing.

After a bit, Kitty joined me, and before she'd even sat down, she said, "Now that's a gorgeous hunk of man, right there."

"He's not a man, he's a physical therapist."

Kit did not shift her gaze. "Pretty sure he's both."

"Where's *your* man?" I asked.

"Which one?" she said, looking sly.

"The chubby-but-cute one," I answered.

She looked a little offended on principle. A little protective even. "He's on his way."

We watched Ian line up the last boat and then turn toward us. I guess

boat dragging must be hard work, because he took off his flannel shirt as he walked, wadding it up to wipe the back of his neck, and leaving only his white undershirt.

Kit let out a low whistle.

"Kit!" I said. "Don't objectify him!"

"That's not my fault," she said, gesturing. "I can't be held responsible for that."

When Ian made it to us, he dropped the flannel shirt on the grass. His eyes were on me. "Want to show me the lake?"

"Yes," I said, too quickly.

"Actually, she wants to take a nap," Kit said.

I swatted Kit. "I do not!"

"I thought about the kayak," Ian said, "but I'm worried about it tipping."

I was worried about my neck, too. The water in this lake was certainly not as chlorinated as the therapy pool.

"The canoe's fine," I said.

"Can I come, too?" Kit asked.

"No," we both said.

Ian carried me and my polka-dot parasol down to the water's edge, and then I waited on the grass while he moved the painted canoe into the water. Then he lifted me again and sloshed into the lake, jeans and all, and set me carefully in the boat.

The canoe wobbled as Ian climbed in, and I felt a little jolt of fear. I hadn't worn a life vest in this thing since I was a little kid, and this was the kind that wrapped around your neck like an airplane pillow. Of course, I couldn't put anything around my neck—I was still wearing all my shirts with the shoulder cut out—so I just wrapped it awkwardly under my arms and snapped it tight.

"I look ridiculous," I said.

Ian shook his head. "You look—" He stopped himself for a few attention-grabbing seconds before continuing on. "Resourceful."

"I get that all the time," I said, putting on my sunglasses, wondering what he'd been about to say.

It wasn't the busy season yet at the lake. It felt like we had it all to ourselves.

"Where to?" Ian asked, and I pointed to the far side.

I was totally okay not talking. The paddle lapped the water, the canoe sloshed and slapped, the wind whispered. I remembered this place so well—it was so much a part of the fabric of who I was—that I could almost put myself here without being here.

But actually being here, out on the water, alive like this—just the fact of it was breathtaking.

I directed Ian to paddle past a hundred-year-old house, the first one built here, and I told him every ghost story I'd ever heard about it. Next, we passed the decade-old unfinished mansion that some hedge fund guy had started and then abandoned. "That one's haunted, too," I said. Later, we passed the spot where the sailboat races happened every July, and then the giant floating trampoline all the kids liked to row out to, and the little hamburger joint that had no parking at all for cars—only docks for boats.

I leaned closer to the water and let my fingers dangle in. I'd dangled my fingers in this very water in this very boat in weather just like this a thousand times. The houses were the same, the clouds were the same, and even the beach where I'd been supposed to get married was the same.

Through it all, Ian paddled a steady pace, and I let myself feel just exactly as happy as I was sad.

I marveled at the feeling, because it really wasn't either-or. It was both, equally strong at the exact same time.

If you'd asked me before the crash, I'd have told you that feelings were like blocks of primary colors: You felt blue for a while, then yellow, then red. But now I saw the emotional landscape quite differently—more like the pointillism of a Seurat painting: each color made up of many other colors. Look closely, and it's dots. Stand back, and it's an afternoon on the lake—all the colors relying on each other for texture and meaning.

Maybe that would turn out to be an upside, I found myself thinking. Maybe I'd see the world like an artist now.

I could have just closed my eyes and given in to the drift. But I had a question for Ian that had been nagging me, and now that I had him alone, I had to ask.

"Tell me something," I said, keeping my voice casual.

"Okay," Ian said, still rowing.

"Why did your business fail?"

I could sense him tensing up at the words.

But I was already in, so I kept going, keeping my eyes out on the water. "What happened?"

Ian didn't answer. Just kept rowing.

"I mean, it was such a brilliant idea."

Ian was quiet for so long, I finally turned to look at him.

"I didn't manage things very well," he said at last. "I neglected it too much."

I shrugged, like, *Okay.* Like that was all the answer I'd wanted.

But, of course, his answer just created more questions. Why would a guy with such a great idea go to all the trouble of setting up a business—inventing an entirely new business!—and then neglect it?

I could tell just from the angle of his posture that he didn't want to talk about it.

I let it go.

We weren't here to be unhappy.

We were here to try, at least for a little while, to be the opposite.

BY THE TIME we got back, the sun was going down, and Fat Benjamin, who was far more "tubby" than fat, with a plump body like a dumpling and a bushy hipster beard, had arrived. He and Kit were building the bonfire. Ian piggybacked me over to the fire and got me settled in a chair, and I watched Kit and Benjamin flirt. He couldn't seem to stop his hands from touching her—and she didn't seem to mind.

Kit made us a vegetable stew in a pot on a grate over the fire. ("He's a vegan," she apologized, when the guys went to get more wood.) As the sun went down, the air cooled, and Ian went in for blankets. When

he came back out with a stack, he also had something else under his arm.

A ukulele.

"You *are* musical!" Kit said when she saw it.

Ian shook his head. "I haven't played in years. But I can play 'Happy Birthday.'"

So he did. Serenaded me with it, really. I wrapped my blanket around everything but my burned neck, and after that, we all sat around the fire while Ian played requests and let us sing along. He messed up over and over, but nobody cared but him.

"Don't apologize," I said. "You are the best ukulele player I've ever met."

Ian gave me a half-smile. "Am I the only ukulele player you've ever met?"

"You bet."

He knew a little Bob Dylan, a little James Taylor, one Van Morrison, and a whole lotta Beatles.

That's how my birthday bonfire turned into a nonstop Beatles birthday luau. We sang and sang and sang. And ate vegan stew. And then, for a birthday cake, made cast-iron skillet brownies with melted marshmallows over the fire.

"I thought we were making s'mores," I said.

"We've made a million s'mores," Kit said. "Time for something new."

I'd cooked many meals in this fire pit before, and I'd celebrated many birthdays here, but I confess, as familiar as it all was, I'd never done it quite like this. Everything felt a little bit new.

I found myself wanting to stay and stay—or, at least, not wanting to go inside.

Ian kept checking with me to see if I was ready, and I kept shaking my head. I got cold, in my sundress, but I still didn't want to leave the fire. Kit and Benjamin cleaned up the stew, and took the pots and pans inside to wash, and then disappeared to get up to who-knows-what kind of mischief, but I didn't care. I loved looking at the fire. I loved feeling cold. I loved being out in the world. I loved calling out songs for Ian to

play. He sang, and I sang, and I loved listening to our voices twist and wind around each other.

Tomorrow, it would all be over. We'd wake up and drive back to real life in an ugly hospital with fluorescent lights and mauve curtains. The sooner I fell asleep, the sooner this would all be gone. And I just didn't want to let that happen.

Finally, Ian said, "You've got to be cold. I'm freezing my arse off."

"I don't care."

He peered in. "Your lips look a little blue."

He set down his uke and came closer, and when he took my hands, he said, "Good God, Maggie. You're frozen solid."

In one swoop, he picked me up—this time, not piggyback, but cradling me in his arms. He tucked my good side against his chest, and I did my best to be easy to carry by hooking my arm around his shoulder and resting my head down against the crook of his neck. That intoxicating Ian smell. I let myself breathe it in and savor it. Then I wondered if I could just brush my lips across the nape without him noticing.

He marched us across the yard and then into the warm, bright house, through the kitchen, and up the stairs.

Inside was quiet, like it was empty, and I wondered if Kit and Benjamin had gone for a walk. Ian nudged lights on as he went. At the top of the stairs, he hesitated. I could feel the pulse in his neck beating.

"Which room?" he asked.

"At the end of the hall," I said.

Ian felt around for the hall light with his elbow, but he didn't find it, so he just moved on ahead through the dark. It wasn't impossible to see. There were shadows and outlines. He stepped carefully, but without too much hesitation. The door to my room was open, and the bed was just beyond it. It was lit by blue moonlight reflected off the lake.

He moved toward it, stepped through the doorway—and then he tripped on a little rag rug at the threshold.

He pitched forward, and then dropped to his knees. He clutched me tight to him as it happened, and then, intent on not falling forward and landing on top of me, he managed to fall backward.

Which meant I landed on top of him.

Fully on top. Smack-dab on top, you could even say.

At first, after impact, we were all about figuring out if anyone was injured. Had he hit his head or twisted anything? *No.* Was my graft okay? *Yes.* My back? *All fine.* Was anybody in any pain? Apparently not.

That's when we took stock of our situation: alone, in a moonlit room by a tranquil lake, on the floor, a little breathless.

My face was just inches from his, and we held there, frozen, for a few very long seconds, breaths churning, eyes alert. His were so dark blue, they looked black.

So I did a crazy thing that seemed like, really, the only thing to do: I leaned down, pressed my mouth against his, and kissed him.

Boom. I wasn't cold anymore.

I pulled back then, to check his expression and see what he thought—but he reached his hand up just as quick behind my head to bring me back. Another kiss. This one deeper and warmer and slower. I'd eyed those lips so much in the past weeks—and longed to touch them, even just with my fingers, to see if they were as soft as they looked. To see if they tasted as good as he smelled. And now I knew. Yes.

"You taste like brownies," I said, through the kiss, my mouth still touching his.

"You taste like marshmallows," he said back, and then he dove back in, brushing his tongue past mine.

"I love your accent," I said, a minute later, pulling back a little.

"I love yours," he said, leaning forward to catch my mouth with his.

"I love your ukulele," I said another minute later.

"I love yours."

"I don't have a ukulele."

"I don't care."

I wriggled around to get a better angle, and he wound up solidly on his back, me straddling him, and my palms flat against the floor on either side of his head, bodies pressed together.

"Are you sure you didn't get hurt?" I asked then, still kissing him.

"I got a little hurt."

"Where?"

"Doesn't matter."

"Does it hurt now?"

"Nothing hurts now."

What was my goal here? Was I trying to seduce my physical thera-pist? I wasn't even sure if I had been cleared for that type of thing! All I knew was, I wanted to get closer. I would have climbed inside his rib cage, if I could have. I wanted to devour him and be devoured back. Whatever tangled forest of feelings bloomed in my body every time I saw him—I just wanted to get lost in that forest and never find my way out.

I did get lost. I brought my mouth down to his neck, nuzzling in and biting a little, and he ran both his hands up my back, stopping short, bringing his hand around on my nonburned side to guide my mouth back to his.

For a moment, the two of us, just like that, made up the entire world. Nothing but longing, and closeness, and warmth.

That's why I didn't hear Kit and Fat Benjamin clomping up the stairs. Or trundling down the hall. Or turning the squeaky old door handle.

No. The first I noticed Kit and Fat Benjamin, they were pushing open the door and flipping on the lights and discovering the two of us down on the floor.

"OMG!" Kit said, slapping her hand over her mouth to cover a gig-gle. "This room appears to be taken."

"Get out, Kit!" I said, in a classic annoyed-sister voice.

"Sorry!" Fat Benjamin said, giving us both a little salute of apology.

They stepped back out of the room and slammed the door shut behind them, leaving the overhead light on.

"Wait!" I heard Kit say on the other side of the door. "Were they hooking up?"

With that, all the moonlight disappeared.

Ian blinked at the doorway where they'd just been, like he was wak-ing up from a dream. I still sat astride him, trying to catch my breath, wondering how to get the moonlight back.

But he was up on his elbows now. "Oh, God, Maggie," he said, twisting sideways to move out from under me.

I shifted onto the floor beside him as he stood and turned to scoop me up.

He lifted me to the bed.

I held on to a doomed little hope that maybe we were just moving to a more comfortable location.

But once he had me securely settled, he turned away and walked to the window. He touched the curtain idly for a minute, delivering his signature silence. Finally, when he spoke, he said, "Maggie, I'm sorry."

"What are you sorry for?"

"I shouldn't have done that."

"You didn't do anything. *I* kissed *you*."

"I shouldn't have kissed you back."

"Because," I guessed, "messing around with patients is against your code of ethics?"

Ian was pacing a little bit now.

I tried again. "Because if Myles ever finds out, you'll lose your job?"

"If Myles ever finds out, I'll lose my *license*," Ian said. "But that's not it."

"What, then?"

"It wasn't fair to you."

There was nothing I wanted more than to be back in his arms. "I think it was fair. I think it was very fair."

Ian shoved his hand into his hair. "You're not qualified to judge."

"I'm not *what*?"

He turned to look at me for the first time. The overhead light seemed awfully bright. "You're not in a fit state to judge."

"You're saying I don't know the difference between what's fair and what's unfair?"

"I'm saying—"

"Because my fiancé crashing a plane that I didn't even want to go anywhere near and paralyzing me while he walks away without even a Band-Aid? Obviously: *unfair*. You coming here and playing 'Happy Birthday' on

the ukulele and giving me the best kiss of my entire life? I'm going with *fair* on that one."

"That's just it. It wasn't the best kiss of your entire life."

I raised my eyebrows in disbelief. "It wasn't?"

"You just thought it was."

"Pretty sure that's the same thing."

But he shook his head. "When a person goes through something like what you've just gone through, when your whole world is ripped apart, it takes a long time before you can see things clearly again. Months. Years, even. The trauma leaves you vulnerable in ways you can't even feel. I know all about this. I've been trained on it—read textbooks, taken tests. It's against my code of ethics for a reason, Margaret—a good reason. To protect you."

I was Margaret now? I noticed tears on my face, but I had no patience for them. I smeared them off with my sleeve. "I don't care about any of that."

"But I have to. For your sake."

"But you—" A big, shaky breath interrupted me. I hesitated to go on, because it felt like a big thing to admit. But I had to try. I had to at least speak honestly. I took another breath, and said it: "You are the only thing I look forward to all day long."

He closed his eyes in what looked like a wince. Not the effect I'd hoped for. "That's exactly what I'm trying to tell you," he said.

"I don't understand."

"The things you feel about me mean that you are not safe. I shouldn't have come here. I knew there was a risk this might happen."

So he knew I liked him before he came. I pulled in a ragged breath. "Don't you like me at all?"

Ian shoved his hand into his hair again. Then he walked to the bedroom door, turning those navy-blue eyes to settle them right on me. "I hate everybody," he said. "Except you." He pulled the door open to leave, then added, "And that's another reason you're not safe."

"Are you leaving?" I asked. He was clearly leaving the room. But I meant, "Are you going back to town?"

"No. Of course not. I'll stay the night to look after you."

"I don't need looking after."

"You want me to leave Tweedle Dum and Tweedle Dee in charge?"

Not really, I supposed.

He continued. "I'll make sure you get back safe tomorrow."

"You're not going to switch me to some other PT, are you?"

"That's up to you."

I couldn't even imagine anybody else. "I don't want another PT."

"Then I'll stay."

"Are you still going to come for tutoring?"

"Yes, if you like. But I'll come after supper—just to keep things clear."

"No goofing around?"

He shook his head. "It's best."

What could I say? It's not best, it's *worst*? There was no way to win. He had decided I wasn't qualified to know what was right for me. And from the sound of things, he didn't trust himself too much, either. Was he rejecting me? Was he uninterested? Could you kiss a person like that and not feel something, at least? I knew there was longing there—but maybe it was just a general longing for anyone at all. Maybe he was so lonely, any live girl would do—even a broken one like me.

He was still standing at the door, staring down at his hand on the knob. He looked up. "I brought a present to give you tomorrow," he said then. "But maybe you don't want it now."

I turned my eyes to the window. "Just throw it away," I said.

I heard the door click closed behind him, and then he was gone.

I stayed awake for a good while after that—waiting to hear Kit creep back to her bedroom, because I needed to pee and I'd be damned before I asked Ian to take me. Maybe I'd be better off without him. He certainly seemed to think so. But in all that time of thinking, I could not for one second imagine how.

Twenty-two

THE NEXT DAY—my actual birthday—did not shake down the way I expected.

I expected to wake up and work my way through an awkward breakfast with Kit and Benjamin all lovey-dovey while Ian stared out the window with a face of stone.

But that's not what happened, exactly.

When I opened my eyes and tried to move my toes, as I did every morning—one of them did something utterly shocking.

It moved.

It *wiggled*.

The big toe on my right foot, to be exact.

Part of me thought I might still be asleep.

I tried again, and it moved again.

"Hey!" I shouted. "Hey!"

In seconds, all three of my lake housemates came bursting through the door in a hilarious potpourri of pajamas that made it clear I was definitely the first one up. Kit was in a hot-pink negligée, a sight I'd never seen before, and Fat Benjamin had a remarkable, gravity-

defying bed-beard situation going on. Ian, I did my best not to notice, slept in blue cotton pajama bottoms. Only. Also, his hair was even more unruly than Benjamin's beard—but to be honest, it just made him cuter.

None of that mattered, anyway. "Am I dreaming?" I demanded.

"The sun's not even up," Kit said, in her best big-sister voice.

"I need to know if I'm dreaming right now. Am I?"

Fat Benjamin ventured, "Of course, if you were dreaming, then we wouldn't really be able to give you a straight answer."

Ian stepped closer. "What's going on?"

"Look," I said, pointing at my toe.

Everybody looked.

I pushed it down, then pulled it back.

"No! You! Did! Not!" Kit shrieked, turning around to hug me.

"What?" Benjamin said. "I missed it."

"Do it again," Ian said.

I did it again.

"Does it happen every time you try?" Ian asked.

"So far," I said.

"Can you do the other one?"

I tried. Nothing. I shook my head.

Ian did a little mini-evaluation right then, even though he didn't have any of the right equipment. Or a shirt. We didn't learn much, except to confirm that—one—the toe was, in fact, wiggling on command, and—two—I was not dreaming.

"What does it mean?" I asked Ian.

"It means there's more information getting through than there used to be."

It wasn't an unreasonable answer, but it wasn't what I'd wanted him to say.

Or Kit, either, apparently. "It means she'll walk again!" She started jumping up and down. "Right?"

We all looked at my toe again.

I wiggled it, showing off.

But Ian wasn't jumping. He stared at the toe somberly. "Not necessarily," he said, like a buzzkill.

"But it's not a bad sign," I said.

"It's a hell of a birthday present," he said. "I'll give it that."

DESPITE THE TOE-RELATED excitement, I managed to have several childish and ungenerous thoughts about Ian on the drive home. What a downer he was, for example. How he refused to let himself—or anyone else—be happy. How he squandered opportunities for joy. Maybe I *should* work with a different trainer. Somebody who knew how to motivate and inspire. Maybe Ian's intolerance for hope was holding me back.

Kit was absolutely spazzy with excitement about the whole outing.

"I never knew your toe was such a genius," she said on the drive. "It's, like, the Neil Armstrong of toes. Or maybe Abraham Lincoln."

As far as she knew, the weekend had been better than perfect. She had many topics she wanted to cover, but number one, for sure, just as soon as we finished our discussion of which famous person from history best represented my big toe, was "What the hell was going on between you and Braveheart when we walked in on you last night?"

I wanted to tell her. Badly. I wanted to give her the slow-mo replay of every single significant moment and spend the rest of the car ride and even the next several days analyzing the data into submission. I could see many vastly different, totally contradictory interpretations of Ian's behavior (and choices, and tone of voice, and facial expressions), and I had no clue which one was right.

But I couldn't tell her.

Kit had no real sense of privacy. I tried to chalk it up to exuberance—if she had the goods, she just had to share—but she was a little gossipy, too. She also gabbed on the cell phone all the time with no sense of who might be nearby listening. And do not get me started on her issues with Instagram.

I did not doubt that Myles would try to take away Ian's license if he

ever got wind of what had happened. I'd seen him menacing Ian in the gym every day for weeks. I'd watch him trying to provoke Ian, needling him, pushing his buttons, hoping to goad him into doing something stupid, and I'd think, "That's a lot of anger."

I felt a little sorry for Myles, and the way something in his life compelled him to seek vengeance instead of just moving on. But I felt sorrier for Ian. Myles really was a revenge-driven prick.

Mostly, that was a problem for Ian, but it was a problem for me today, because it meant I couldn't do the one thing I wanted more than anything in the world to do right then: tell Kitty everything.

She was waiting. "Were you hooking up, or what?"

"Sadly," I said, "no."

"No? What were you doing on the floor?"

"He tripped," I said with a shrug, like, *No big deal.*

Kit squinted her eyes like she did not believe me at all.

I had to ramp it up. "You know those little rag rugs Mom has everywhere? He tripped on one at the threshold. And, seriously, then he managed to heroically catch me on the way down."

Kit studied me out of the side of her eye. "Bullshit."

"I swear," I declared then, "on my wiggly big toe."

That did it. "Okay," she said. "So what was going on between you? Because the romantic tension was so thick you could wear it like a sweater."

I told myself it wasn't lying, exactly. It was just mushing up the truth. "At the bonfire, I confessed some feelings to him."

"Yum," Kit said. "I love confessed feelings."

"I told him I had a huge, all-consuming, heart-wrenching crush and that he was basically the only thing I looked forward to all day."

"Besides gourmet takeout with your sister."

"Of course."

"And what did he say?"

Now I was grateful to him. Because this shit was too good to make up. "He said: No, I didn't."

"No, you didn't what?"

"No, I didn't have a crush on him."

Kit looked straight at me. "What the hell?"

"Eyes on the road, please."

"Explain!"

"He said I only *thought* I had a crush on him, and that this kind of thing happens all the time, and my life has been pulverized and so I'm grasping at any straws of happiness I can, but once I get through this, I'll realize that it was all in my head and I never had any real feelings for him at all. Not really."

"He did *not* say that."

"He did. Then he cited a whole bunch of studies from his training and basically told me that I was a teenage girl with Boy Band syndrome— thinking that some kindhearted prince was going to come in and take all my sorrows away."

I was a better liar than I thought. Though that kind of was what he'd said.

"Is he right?" Kit asked.

"No!" I said. "Nobody can take these problems away. Unless this toe thing turns out to be a surprise miracle."

"He didn't return your feelings at all? Nothing?"

"Nothing," I said. "He basically told me that I have all his best wishes as a healthcare professional, but to shut the fuck up and go to bed. Then he tried to make me do just that, tripped on a rag rug, and got crushed under my dead weight. Insult to injury."

"He's lying," Kit said. "I see the way he looks at you."

I couldn't help it. "How does he look at me?"

"Like you're a waterfall in a desert."

Did he? The idea of it made my stomach flip. But I had to keep obfuscating. "Guess what else? He knew how I felt before I even told him because I've been mooning at him for weeks, and he didn't discourage me because he thought it might help my recovery."

"Narcissist!" Kit shouted.

"Yeah," I said. "But the thing is, he wasn't wrong. You know you always work harder for teachers you have crushes on."

Kit nodded, and just from knowing her face almost as many years as I'd known my own, I knew I was in the clear. She'd bought it.

"I guess now," she said, "you'll just have to work hard for yourself."

"I guess I will," I said.

And that was true—whether I was lying or not.

THE BIG-TOE MIRACLE turned me into quite the celebrity. Doctors who had lost interest were suddenly popping by several times a day. Other patients on the floor wanted to get the story firsthand. Kit even drew me a homemade card that read, "Toe-tally excited about your big break-through!!"

It was such a busy flurry that the shenanigans with Ian seemed distant very quickly. I had bigger fish to fry, I let myself think. I'd get walking again, and then I'd grow my hair out, and then I'd pop by the hospital one day, pretending to look for—what? A lost earring? A book I'd lent out?—and he'd behold me in the hallway, tall and fierce and perfect and invincible. He'd say a sad hello because he'd know he'd missed his chance, and I'd give him a little wow-we-really-could-have-been-something smile, and then I'd flip my hair, walk away, and let him choke on the dust of his own regret.

I will never, ever divulge how many times I partook of that particular fantasy. But I will confess that for some reason, in it, I was wearing the exact same shiny hot pants and high-heeled Dr. Scholl's that Olivia Newton-John is wearing in the grand finale of *Grease*. And I had her fantastic butt, too.

All to say, when I saw Ian again in the therapy gym for the first time since our trip to the lake, the sight of him took me by surprise. He was back in his usual blue scrubs, with his hair in its usual slightly spiky configuration, but what caught me off guard was his new demeanor. He wasn't the hostile, sullen Ian I'd first met, but he sure as hell wasn't the warm, goofy Ian I'd allowed myself to swoon over.

This new Ian was *just not there*. I couldn't quite find the word for it,

but he was just gone. His posture was blank. His shoulders were blank. His eyes were blank. He was like a pod person.

He still did everything he was supposed to. He still walked me through all my paces. He showed up on time. He even went the extra mile to bring in experts to consult and make sure we were doing everything possible. But he never smiled. He never relaxed.

And not once after we came back from the lake did he call me Maggie again.

BY THURSDAY, WITH exactly a week to go until my insurance ran out and I had to go back to live with my parents, I couldn't stand it anymore.

We'd all been on Toe Watch for days now, waiting for some new development—that hadn't come. If anything, that one superstar big toe had become less reliable. Was my improvement stalled because Ian was being weird? Either way, it couldn't be helping. Time was running out. I didn't want a robot for a PT.

That night, when Ian came to tutor, I told him I wanted someone new.

I'd hoped for some kind of reaction—a flash of disappointment across his face, some human curiosity about why, even irritation would have sufficed. But nothing.

"Okay," Ian said, with all the emotion of a glass of milk. "If you think that's best."

"I should probably change trainers in the gym, as well," I added.

No reaction there, either. "I understand," Ian said. "If you wouldn't mind letting me arrange the switch, it might give Myles one less reason to fire me."

"That's fine," I said.

"I'll find you someone good." His poker face broke my heart.

"Great."

Ian headed toward the door, but I called his name. He turned back.

This might be the last time I'd see him. I couldn't stand the idea that he'd always remember me as a pathetic, lovesick, delusional girl. I didn't

want to be the only one who cared. If he could be a robot, so could I. "Thanks for your restraint at the lake, by the way. I cannot imagine what I was thinking."

Ian gave a sad smile. "What restraint at what lake?"

And we left it at that.

LATER THAT NIGHT, with a week minus one day until Kit's first-of-April Valentine's Day party, I asked her to call it off.

"I can't," she said. "I've rented a karaoke machine."

I held my hands out, like, *So?* "Unrent it!"

She mirrored the gesture. "Nonrefundable deposit!"

We were eating enormous taco salads in bowls made of taco shells.

Kit went on, "Plus, I've got a batch of kids popping in early to cut construction paper hearts, I've got a guy named Rodrigo bringing his garage mariachi band to play for free, I've bought the decorations and over a hundred heart-shaped cookies, I've invited everybody on the floor and all the nurses, and I frigging love Valentine's Day. And so should you."

"It's *not* Valentine's Day," I said.

"That's a bad attitude, right there."

"Damn right it is."

"You don't have to like it," Kit said. "You just have to come."

"I'm not coming."

She stopped chewing. "You have to!"

I shook my head. "I have one week left. There's no time for parties. I am not screwing around."

"But it will be my last night—and yours!"

"That's why you should cancel the party and spend it with me."

SHE DIDN'T CANCEL the party. I spent the following days meeting my new PT, working with my new PT, and doing tutoring in the evenings with my new PT—and Kit spent them cutting heart decorations out of construction paper.

The new PT was Rob-with-the-Man-Bun—the one I'd wished for early on. Without a doubt, he was the perkiest and flirtiest of everybody. He had huge energy and a laugh like a trumpet blast. I'd heard it a million times in the background in the gym, and I'd always assumed he was laughing like that because something was wildly funny. I had often wondered how he and his patients had managed to generate so much comedy from activities like riding the stationary bike, and I confess I'd mentally criticized Ian for being so serious.

But now, in this final week, working with Man-Bun-Rob, I came to realize something: That laugh was fake.

He was *over*laughing. He was pretending things were a thousand times funnier than they were. I'd crack the tiniest little nonjoke, and he'd throw his head back and absolutely bellow. That was worse—far worse—than not laughing at all.

Within hours of first starting to work with Rob, I grew to hate that laugh so much, it drove me to silence. I didn't want to do anything to provoke it. But even that didn't work. When he couldn't get anything out of me, he'd turn to other patients and other trainers—and pretend to laugh at *their* unfunny jokes.

Out of the frying pan into the fire.

But at least I wasn't tragically, unrequitedly in love with him. At least he had never given me a life-altering kiss and then said, "You know what? Never mind."

At least I knew I didn't like him.

Simple.

I could just concentrate on my recovery. Or lack thereof.

Every time I went to PT now, I worried Ian would be in the gym. Usually, he was, working with someone else—which, no matter if it was an elderly bald man or a postmenopausal lady, made me jealous. I'd steal glances at him over and over, but he never looked at me or even seemed to notice I was there.

I guess that's what happens when you push people away.

Though, to be fair, he pushed me first.

The person in the gym who did notice me was Myles.

He checked on me much more often now that Ian was across the room.

"Doing all right?" he'd say, materializing from behind a post.

"Fine, thanks," I'd say, not making eye contact.

Sometimes he prodded me about Ian. "Didn't work out with you two, huh?"

Was he tricking me when he did that? Was he trying to goad me into getting Ian in trouble?

"It worked out great," I said, thinking fast.

"So well," Myles pressed, "that you requested another PT?"

"It was Ian's idea," I said. Lying.

Myles tilted his head like I was the biggest liar ever. "Really?"

Here's where my obsessive study of medical journals brought its big payoff. "Yes," I said. "Because Rob has more experience with functional electrical stimulation, and Ian thinks I'd be a good candidate."

Suddenly, Myles wasn't so cocky. "You couldn't have wanted to stay with him, though. He was so unfriendly to you. Borderline hostile—"

I started to say, "I wouldn't call him *hostile*—"

But Myles went on, "When he wasn't standing outside your room listening to you sing."

I turned to face him. "What?"

"Oh, you didn't know he did that?"

I shook my head.

"Yeah." Myles lifted both his eyebrows. "Creepy, right? I had to issue him two different warning slips."

I looked around for Ian. He was helping a very elderly lady out of her chair onto the raised mat.

"Anyway," Myles said, pulling my attention back. "If he bothers you anymore, just let me know." He pointed a finger gun at me, gave me a nod, and pulled the trigger.

MAN-BUN-ROB AND I worked like dogs all week, both during scheduled PT and tutoring sessions, but made no progress. Ian had left a

tutoring spreadsheet—even though he detested spreadsheets—detailing exactly what we were supposed to do, in order, in sections, counted to the minute. Rob and I followed it diligently— but nothing changed.

I did everything I could think of—took my vitamins, got plenty of sleep, drank extra water—and I tried to wiggle my toes about a thousand times a day. The hullaballoo over that toe had set up a strong expectation that a breakthrough was inevitable. But the longer that breakthrough refused to happen, the more I accepted the cognitive dissonance: I might get better any minute, or I might never get better at all.

That said, I was improving in lots of other ways. My shoulder was healing "beautifully," the dermatologist had said, and the scabs on my face had left no scars. The stitches on my neck were starting to dissolve, and, if I didn't look in the mirror, parts of my body felt almost normal.

Just not normal enough.

It wasn't that I hadn't made any progress. I could rattle off every muscle in the lower extremities like some kind of med student. My core strength, Rob said, was "phenomenal," and I could do sit-ups all day long. My arms and shoulders were "beasts." I had the gluteus muscles "of a champion," and my adductors, hip flexors, gluteus medius, rectus femoris, sartiorius, and deep gluteal muscles were all in excellent working order. I could even stand pretty well—twelve minutes was my record—but only if I held on to something, or someone.

The problems were all with the muscles responsible for extending the foot forward when taking a step. They were falling down on the job. Aside from that one delightful big toe (thanks to one feisty flexor hallucis longus), everything below my knee, to use the technical term, was "flaccid."

I preferred "floppy," personally.

Either way, it wasn't good. The tibialis anterior, tibialis posterior, popliteus fibularis longus, fibularis brevis, plantaris soleus, and gastrocnemius were all, um, pretty limp. Particularly frustrating were the semimembranosus, semitendinosus, and biceps femoris, which are the muscles that work to extend the leg. I could bring my thigh forward (thanks to a "boss" iliopsoas), but I couldn't straighten it.

Still.

That's why I wasn't going to the Valentine's party. That whole final week was a slow realization that, where walking was concerned, at least, despite the trying, and the determination, and all those hours of tutoring, and the many impressive gains I could claim—I was still going to fail.

I never failed. I'd never failed anything. Not even a spelling quiz.

It kept me from sleeping. Over and over that final week, I'd doze off for a few minutes at bedtime and then startle awake, restlessly shifting under my covers. Several nights I just couldn't take the anxiety, and I wound up transferring to my chair, careful not to wake Kit, and then sneaking to the gym. There, I'd hoist myself up onto the walking bars, brace with both hands, and pace back and forth until I was on the verge of collapse.

It was probably a bad idea, going to the gym at night. I would no doubt have done better to let my body rest. But I couldn't seem to stop myself. I kept thinking if I just pushed a little harder, I could break through. The prospect of failing this challenge—possibly the only one that ever really mattered—left me too panicked to think straight.

The night before Kit's party, I went to the gym again. My arms were sore from all the laps on the bars, and I could hear Ian's Scottish voice saying "arms are not legs," but I didn't care. It wasn't my arms I cared about. I went back and forth, back and forth—ten times, then twenty, willing my lower legs to swing forward, willing the balls of my feet to push off, willing for something, anything, to spark to life.

Then, just short of thirty, my arm just gave out.

It happened fast. I crumpled, smacking down on the mat hard, and lay there, panting. And there, with my face against the mat, smarting like I'd been slapped, it truly hit me: I wasn't going to walk again.

I really wasn't.

I wasn't going to overcome this. I wasn't going to be good as new. I wasn't going to show them all. I wasn't going to be the exception to the rule. I wasn't going to give an inspirational talk that would go viral on the Internet.

Every single thing I'd experienced, or thought about, or hoped for up until this moment seemed cartoonish. This whole experience had been so frantic and dreamlike it was almost like nothing at all had been real. Until now. Alone, on the floor, I finally, really got it. The only thing that was real anymore:

I was going to spend the rest of my life in a wheelchair.

I'D BARELY FINISHED the thought when I heard a voice—a Scottish voice. "What the hell is going on?"

I didn't move. Just lay there and calculated the odds of another Scottish person happening to pass through the rehab gym in the middle of the night.

Unlikely.

Then I heard Ian's sneakers squeak the floor—fast, like he was running—and then he was saying my name, urgently, like I might be in danger:

"Maggie, what happened?"

I couldn't lift my face from the mat. "You don't call me Maggie anymore."

Then he was down on his hands and knees beside me. "What happened? Tell me."

"Why are you even here?"

"Working late. What happened?"

He was perched to call for help. But I didn't need help. I put my hand out to keep him right there, and then I explained everything the only way I could.

"I failed," I said.

"Were you in here using the bars? By yourself? Jesus, Maggie, you're not supposed to come here alone."

But it didn't matter. Nothing mattered.

"Are you hurt?" Ian asked.

"No."

"Can you get up?"

"No."

"Let's get you back to your room." He gathered me into his arms.

"No," I said. "Just give me a minute."

Ian hesitated.

"Please," I said.

Then Ian rocked back, without letting me go, and sat on the mat, still holding me.

Probably, all his medical training told him to get me back to my room, and check my vitals, and attend brusquely to my physical health. But he went against it. He believed me that I was not hurt. He trusted that I didn't need to be hauled back out into the bright hallway. He understood what I'd been doing. He knew as well as anybody that I hadn't made enough progress. He got it.

And so he didn't ask me any more questions. He just held me there, against his chest, on the mat, in the dark gym, stroking my hair.

I MUST HAVE fallen asleep, and Ian must have carried me back to my bed in his arms, because the next morning, I woke up in my room with Kit still snoozing away—but I didn't remember going back.

I went through the motions that day. This was it. This was really it. Everything was exactly the same, except for one crucial thing: There was no hope anymore.

Kit stayed with me the whole day, cutting hearts for the party and making organizational phone calls, but I didn't tell her. I didn't want her to argue with me. There was nothing to argue about. She popped out for a bit in the late afternoon while I had PT with Rob, and when I came back, she was still gone. I fell asleep hard that afternoon, and I didn't wake until supper: hospital food. There'd be nothing delicious tonight. Kit would be at the helm of her epic party, and I would be in here. Alone. Eating Jell-O.

As my meal came into focus, something across the room came into

focus, too. A dress, hanging from the television stand, with a note on it in Kit's writing—big, in Sharpie:

Genuine vintage roller-disco diva dress
off the (right) shoulder!
JUST YOUR SIZE!
$5 at Salvation Army! (I washed it for you!) Come to the party!!!!!!

It was a pink-and-gold, one-shoulder, polyester maxidress with ruffles. It was hilarious, and also strangely lovely.

But I still wasn't going to the party.

I lifted the yellowish plastic cover on the dinner plate. Some kind of gray meat, rehydrated mashed potatoes, and canned green beans.

Nope.

I poked at the Jell-O. I listened to the nurses joke around out at the station. One of them had a little thing for Man-Bun-Rob, and she'd heard he was going to be there.

Guess that meant there would be no tutoring for me tonight, either.

Fine. It was pointless, anyway.

On the tray, dessert was a chocolate chip cookie, which seemed like a stroke of luck—until I bit in and discovered it was oatmeal raisin.

Things seemed quieter than usual. Everybody, I guess, was in the rehab gym.

Then the door pushed open, and it was Kit.

"I need you," she said.

"What?"

"The mariachi band is terrible! The children are crying!"

"It can't be that bad."

"Oh, yes, it can!" she said, pulling back my covers. "Go pee. Brush your teeth. Put on your dress! You're doing a love song medley in ten minutes."

I shook my head. "I don't think so."

She put a hand on one hip. "How many times have I been there for you when you needed me?"

"Are we talking recently, or our entire lives? Because I think you started with a deficit."

Kit pulled on my arm. "I need you. The kids need you. Valentine's Day needs you. Ian's mother needs you!"

What? She got my attention with that last one. "Ian's mother?"

She pointed at me, and repeated the favorite saying of hers Ian had told us once: "When you don't know what to do for yourself, do something for somebody else."

SHE GOT ME with that.

I did go to the party—although, when I showed up, the mariachi band was totally normal, not one kid was crying, and it was clear that Kit had tricked me.

I glared at her. "Not cool."

"Just try to keep that scowl on your face while you eat one of these cookies," she said, handing me a heart-shaped one with sprinkles.

It wasn't oatmeal raisin, I'll give it that.

Kit had gone all out. There was a craft table, a disco ball, the world-famous stolen chocolate fountain, and hearts and streamers everywhere. She had even hung a ball of mistletoe off the end of a stick to dangle over people's heads and force them to kiss. Rob was doing the honors for her, bursting out with that foghorn laugh every time it worked.

Confessions: It *was* a lovely party, I *did* love wearing my diva dress, I *did* sing a love song medley, and everything about being there was better than being in my room alone. It was, in truth, an effective distraction.

As sad as I was, I felt a little happy, too.

I stayed and stayed. We sent the children to bed at eight o'clock, and we all continued eating cookies and singing our hearts out.

My best song of the night by far was my last one: I absolutely belted out "Best of My Love," and halfway through, I looked up and saw Ian across the room, watching like he was spellbound. That, of course, made me sing harder and better, and I poured everything I had into the rest

of it. At the end, I got the cheering equivalent of a standing O, and when I rolled across the room for cookies afterward, Ian followed and met me there.

We both held still for a few seconds too long.

"That was a hell of a song," he said at last, his expression focused and warm and non-robot-like. The sound of the real Ian filled me with longing.

"Thank you."

"I've never met anybody who could sing like you do."

Now I smiled. "Thank you."

"It's good to see you," he said.

"You could have seen me all week in the gym, if you hadn't been ignoring me."

"I wasn't ignoring you," he said, frowning. "I was—" But then he stopped. And he didn't start again.

"Kit said you weren't coming to the party."

"I'm not."

"But you're here."

"I'm just stealing cookies."

"I see."

He gestured back at the hallway to the offices. "I was working late."

"You do that a lot."

"I've been researching your injury, actually," he said, looking a little embarrassed about it. "Trying to think of some way to help."

I had to hand it to him. That was nice. But I said, "It's a waste of time. It's over."

"What's over?"

"My recovery."

He shook his head. "There are all kinds of ways to recover."

I looked away.

It would have been a good time for him to escape, but he didn't. Instead, he attempted to start up some chitchat. He nodded at the room. "Looks like you're all having fun."

"Not on purpose," I said. "Kit forced us."

He glanced over at Kit, who noticed us talking. When he turned back, he let his eyes take me in. "Great dress."

"I think I'm going to become a one-shoulder-dress person," I said. "You know, even when I have the option of two."

"You should."

"It can be my signature thing. Then, when I do something truly amazing that history needs to commemorate with a statue, they'll have no choice but to put me in this." I flipped one of the ruffles.

Ian smiled then—a genuine smile. Hadn't seen that in a long time.

He was about to say something else when Kit showed up next to us and said, "Mistletoe bomb!"

Ian and I looked up. She was holding the mistletoe over our heads.

"Mistletoe is for Christmas," Ian said.

"Ask me if I care," Kit said.

"She's been forcing people to kiss with that thing all night," I explained.

"You're going to force me to kiss your sister?"

Kit gave a shrug. "Kinda looks that way."

"He can't kiss me," I told Kit. "It's against the rules."

"Which rules?" she asked.

"All of them," I answered.

But Ian was considering his options. "What happens if I refuse?"

Kit leveled a don't-mess-around look at him, and then, like it was a challenge, she said, "Then I guess you'll waste a chance for a kiss."

"You don't have to kiss me," I said to Ian, and then to Kit, "Cut it out! You're going to get him fired!"

But Ian squatted down in front of my chair. He flipped up the foot rests as he lifted one foot, then the other, setting them flat on the floor. I was barefoot and I could feel, in places, how cool the surface was. Then Ian leaned close for me to put my hands on his shoulders, like he'd done so often in the pool, and he placed his hands on my hips to steady me, and I leaned forward, and I locked my knees, and I moved toward him— and we stood.

"It's bad luck to ignore mistletoe," Ian said.

Those blue eyes. His face so close. The air tingled in my lungs. Was he going to do this? "Nobody in this room needs any more bad luck," I said.

His gaze was locked on mine. "Very true."

"But you can't kiss me," I said, hoping like hell he wouldn't agree.

"I can't?"

"What if somebody reports you?"

"I don't care."

"You don't?"

"Want to know the only question I care about?"

I nodded.

He looked into my eyes and said, "What do you want?"

I held my breath. What did I want?

What the hell kind of question was that?

I wanted him.

I wanted to drag him up to the rooftop and stay there all night.

I wanted to be the girl I used to be. The one with the hair, and jeans, and hips. The one with at least a chance of being wanted back.

But no way was I saying that.

I might never get the things I wanted. But at least I was the only one who had to know.

I shrugged.

Ian studied me, as if he could tell by looking.

Then he glanced up at the mistletoe one more time and shrugged right back.

He pressed closer, and he tightened his arm around my waist. I stretched my arms up around his neck, and as I did, I ran my eyes over his collarbones at the V of his blue scrubs, then up along his jaw, to let my gaze rest on his mouth.

Then he leaned down toward me. It felt like slow-motion, with Nina crooning "Midnight Train to Georgia" in the background. Inches away, he slowed down and lingered, like he was savoring the moment. Like he was taking it in. I hadn't noticed how much Kit had dimmed the lights until suddenly the disco-ball light seemed to fill the room with stars, and it felt like the only steady thing in the world was Ian.

Everything about him felt solid and sturdy and like something I wanted to cling to. There he was, so close up, then closer—and then, impossibly, he lowered his mouth to mine.

Maybe he shouldn't have done it. But oh, God, I was so unspeakably glad he did.

And there was his mouth again, the same but better, like something lost forever and then found again, and everything suddenly swirled too much for me to see anything at all. I sank into the warmth and comfort and electricity of that moment, knowing it couldn't last long, but wishing it could go on forever.

Until the music suddenly stopped.

And the lights flipped on, bright as searchlights.

The room froze. The karaoke machine even went dead. We turned to figure out what was going on, and we both saw the same thing at the same time: Myles.

Myles had walked in.

He was halfway across the room, staring straight at us. "What the frick is going on here?"

"It's a party," Kit said, no idea who she was dealing with.

But Myles didn't look over. "Did I just walk in here to see one of my PTs *kissing* one of my patients?"

"You sure did," Kit volunteered. "I just Instagrammed it!"

"Congratulations," Myles said to Ian then. "You just got fired."

The crowd gasped.

"Say good-bye to your job," Myles went on, enjoying this moment far too much. "Say good-bye to your PT license. And I'll have to brush up on my immigration law, but I'm pretty sure you can say good-bye to this entire country, as well." Myles took a step closer and waved his fingers tauntingly at Ian. "Bye-bye, work visa."

But Ian had turned away from him. He was looking at me now, running his gaze over my face, studying the details. I could tell from Ian's expression that Myles wasn't wrong. Ian had just lost his job, and possibly much more.

My knees chose that moment to start to quiver—though Ian

anticipated that, somehow, and he was already setting me back down in my chair. As he got me settled and moved to stand back up, he squeezed my hand, and it felt like good-bye.

"Do you think I'm fricking joking, man?" Myles walked closer. "Because I am dead serious. You just lost everything."

Myles's beady little face was red and sweaty, but Ian seemed to go the other way and get calmer and cooler.

Ian turned to face him. "Actually," he said, "I know what it's like to lose everything—and getting sabotaged by a weasel like you doesn't even come close."

"You sabotaged yourself, friend."

Ian seemed to consider that. "Maybe I did." Then he looked up. "But don't call me friend."

"Who is this guy?" Kit asked the room. Then, to Myles, "It's a Valentine's party. Chill the hell out, dude. Have a cookie."

Myles looked over and noticed her for the first time. "It's not even Valentine's Day."

"Why is everybody so fixated on that?"

"Ian—" I started.

But Ian had not even turned his head before Myles barked, "Do not approach the patient!"

Ian gave him a look, like, *Really?* "I'm just going to walk her back to her room."

"You are *not*," Myles declared, crossing over to us. "Take one step toward her and I will throw you out of this building."

Ian turned to face him dead-on, and at this range we could all see that Ian was a good head taller. "You and what army, you bawfaced prick?"

At that, Myles decided to throw a punch. But Ian somehow blocked it, and then he grabbed Myles's two wrists to hold them still in the air. "You don't want to do that," Ian said calmly. "I'd hate to kill you by accident. For my sake more than yours."

If the expression on Myles's face had been a sound, it would have been a whimper. He was in over his head, and he knew it. He knew Ian

could crush him—and he also knew he'd just made certain that Ian had little to lose.

Myles opened his palm in a gesture of defeat. "Okay," he said.

Ian released his grip. They both stepped back.

Then Ian took a few more steps backward, and I realized he was leaving.

He looked around the room, taking it in for the last time.

Then he turned to me, and said, "Maggie!"

Though my eyes, and everybody else's, were already on him.

Don't say good-bye, I found myself thinking. *Don't say good-bye.*

He looked right at me, gave me a nod, and then said, "Happy Valentine's Day."

Twenty-three

THE NEXT DAY brought a few beginnings—but mostly endings.

It was the day Kitty was leaving for New York, and the day I was leaving the hospital. The plan was for my parents to arrive late morning, and for my dad to drive Kit to the airport while my mom stayed with me to help pack up. As we waited, I tried very hard not to mope.

"I can't believe you're leaving me alone with them."

Kit wasn't having it. "Just in the nick of time," she said. "It's a miracle we got through this whole month unscathed."

She wasn't wrong.

Though some of us were less scathed than others.

When her suitcase was zipped and sitting by the door, she said, "Now can I please tell you the comforting thing I've been wanting to tell you?"

"You can tell me," I said. "But I won't promise to find it comforting."

"*I* find it comforting," Kit said. "That's enough."

"Spit it out, then."

"So I saw this TED Talk, and it was this researcher from Harvard—"

She paused. "Or was it Stanford? Actually, I think it was MIT. Anyway, a total brainiac—"

"You've lost me already. Just know that."

She pushed on. "He researches mathematical probabilities or something, and in his talk, he mentioned that people have, like, a set point for happiness."

"How does that relate at all to mathematical probabilities?"

"The point is, he had these great statistics. People who win the lottery, when you check in with them a year later, you'd think they'd be super happy, right?"

She wanted me to say it. "Right," I said.

"But they're not happy. They're just as miserable as they were before."

I tilted my head. "Were they miserable before?"

"And people," she went on, "who have terrible things happen to them—loss of a spouse, bankruptcy, disfiguring accidents—"

"That would be me?"

At that, Kitty nodded. "Exactly!" She pointed at me. "He specifically mentioned paraplegics."

I had not heard myself described that way before, and the word gave me a little start. But I pushed past it. "I still don't see what this has to do with math."

"There was a specific study on people who had lost the use of their lower limbs—people in wheelchairs—and those findings totally hold true. One year after the accident, they're exactly as happy as they were before."

I stared at her.

"Isn't that great?"

"*That's* what you've been waiting to say all this time?"

"Yes! You're going to be okay. Aren't you glad to know that?"

"Undecided."

Then, as she came in for a final hug, she said, "I just need you to remember that, okay?" She squeezed a little tighter. "There are all kinds of happy endings."

✧   ✧   ✧

NEXT, MY PARENTS showed up at the door—with a top-of-the-line wheelchair with a bow on it. Literally: a bow. Like I'd just turned sixteen and they'd bought me a convertible.

I just stared. "This is the worst best present ever."

My dad came over for one of his signature hugs. "The titanium was developed by NASA," he said. "It has razor-thin inverted wheels, like all the basketball players use."

"Dammit," I said. "Now I have to join a basketball team." I thought about Pop-A-Shot with Ian, and wondered if I just might.

My dad wanted to walk me through all its features and do a little demo, but I shut that right down.

"He loves that thing," my mother said. "Spent all day yesterday scooting around in it."

My dad rubbed one of his shoulders and confirmed, "Arms are a little sore."

They were both so *excited*. My mother loved its compactness—how trim it was. "From just the right angle," she said, "you can barely tell there's a chair there at all."

"So I'll just look like I'm weirdly floating down the street with my legs bent?"

But she pooh-poohed me. "You know what I mean."

Everyone was civil. Everyone was elegantly polite. You'd never even know that we'd all just bounced back from being estranged. And then something weird happened: Just before Kit headed to the airport with my dad, she stepped in to hug my mom good-bye.

And my mom just didn't let go.

How long does a normal hug last? Five seconds? This one went on for five minutes. So long that Kit wound up opening her eyes to look at me like, *What the heck?*

Nobody said anything, either. We just stood there, in silence, and let it happen.

It was the first hug my mom and Kit had shared in years.

When my mom finally let go, there were tears on her cheeks. She wiped them away and turned to my dad. "She's going to need something to eat in the airport."

My dad sensed what was coming. He looked at his watch. "You're sending me to the sandwich shop?"

This was becoming her signature thing. Sending him for sandwiches. Especially when she wanted to have girl talks.

My dad shook his head. "We don't have time."

"We do!" my mother said.

Kit nodded then. "Actually, we have plenty of time."

My dad looked at my mother like, *Really?* Then he sighed, set down Kit's suitcase, and headed out—while Kit and I frowned at each other.

My mother watched him go, and only after he'd boarded the elevator at the end of the hall did she turn around to face us. Her expression was solemn. She took a deep breath and swallowed. Then she closed the door and took a step toward Kit.

"His name," she said, "was Derin Buruk."

Kit held her breath. She glanced at me, then back at my mother, who glanced back at the door, as if confirming the coast was clear.

"He was Turkish. An exchange student. Devastatingly handsome. Black hair and green eyes rimmed with black lashes. He showed up on our first day of senior year, and he was all any girl could talk about for months. I didn't talk about him. I ignored him. I was dating your dad— since ninth grade—and I wasn't looking for dates, but I couldn't help but notice him. He had a movie star quality. He was magnetic. And for some reason, he fixated on me. He passed me notes, flirted with me in the hallways, snuck flowers into my locker. I told him over and over to knock it off, but he said he couldn't. He stared at me constantly in the cafeteria and at football games. He called me almost daily. He professed love—obsessive love—and begged me to break up with your dad and go out with him."

I looked at my mother's hands. They were trembling.

"Turkish men are famously persistent," she went on, "did you know that? They are very determined about love. Your dad—your wonderful

dad, the love of my life—he's not really like that. That steadiness, that easygoing nature—they don't lend themselves to mad passion. He was kind, he was good-hearted, but he was also a high school boy. He got a lot wrong. He knew next to nothing about romance, or wooing, or how to make a woman flutter. We were the best of friends. But I had never come up against a force like Derin. I had no defenses. I did my best. I pushed him away and pushed him away, but he just kept coming back—harder and stronger. The truth was, I liked it. I liked that he noticed me. I liked that of all the girls in love with him, I was the one he chose. I never understood why he picked me. I still don't know why."

My mom looked very shaky. I patted the bed down by my knees. "Come sit down."

Absentmindedly, she did. "That year," she went on, "over Christmas vacation, your father went away to visit family. He was gone for a week. Somehow, Derin heard that he was gone, and he started climbing the tree outside my window at night and tapping on the pane. I turned him away two times, but on the third night, he said he was leaving to go home soon, and he had to tell me something before he left." She closed her eyes. "God forgive me. I let him in.

"For the rest of the week, I let him in every time he knocked. He would stay until just before dawn, and then sneak away. The night before your father returned to town, I forbade Derin to ever come back—and he never did."

"What did he need to tell you?" I asked.

My mom frowned. "You know what? I don't remember."

Kit let out a long sigh.

"When school started up again," my mom went on, "Derin had gone back to Istanbul. I never saw him again. By spring break, I had figured out that I was pregnant, and by summer your dad had figured it out, too. He assumed the baby was his, and I didn't correct him. It could have been. He was so happy about it. He proposed, and I accepted, and I pretended that Derin Buruk never existed."

"Until I had my blood tested," Kitty said.

My mom shook her head. "Until the moment I first saw you. Right then, I knew."

"Do you hate him? The guy?" Kit asked then.

"No," my mom said. "I don't hate him. Not anymore."

"Do you hate me?"

"No!" my mother said.

"But when you look at me, do you see him?"

"Sometimes. You got his eyelashes."

"You always said they were Huron."

My mom gave a little *sorry* shrug.

"Does it make you feel guilty?"

"Sometimes. Or afraid."

Kitty nodded. "That Dad might find out and not love me anymore."

My mom shook her head. "That he might find out and not love *me* anymore."

I nodded at Kit. "You never did anything wrong."

My mom agreed. "He's adored you from day one."

"Mom is a little trickier."

My mom let out a nervous laugh.

"Well, he's not going to find out," Kit said then, looking at me.

Was it morally wrong to collude against him? I didn't really care right then. "I'll never tell."

"Neither will I."

My mom looked physically deflated now, as if releasing all those secrets had emptied her out. She kept her eyes on Kit.

"You're kind of his favorite, you know," I said.

"I know," Kit said. "Just barely."

"He always took your side over Mom's."

"I know."

"I'm glad for that," our mom said. "I'm glad you had each other."

Then, in the little pause that followed, we heard a voice out in the hallway, just outside the room.

"Can I help you with something, sir?" a voice asked.

At first, there was no reply, but then a man cleared his throat. "No," he said. "No. I just . . . forgot my keys."

My mom's eyes went wide. Because it was Dad.

The nurse bustled on past him into the room, leaving the door open behind her, and all three of us turned to see my dad, frozen still at the threshold of the door, eyes not quite focused, gazing uncomprehendingly in our direction.

"I'm so sorry," he said after a minute, a little breathless, his face blank with shock. "I came back to get the car keys. But I found myself eavesdropping instead."

Twenty-four

MY MOTHER RAN to him, a sob like I'd never heard escaping her throat, but he blocked her and stepped back.

He didn't meet her eyes.

"Come on, Kitty," he said, not meeting hers, either. "You've got a flight to catch."

"Cliff—" my mom started.

"No!" my dad barked, and she caught her breath.

Then, in slow motion, he reached down for Kitty's suitcase, walked over to slide the car keys out of my mom's purse, and left the room without a word.

My mother's legs collapsed from under her, but Kitty caught her and steered her over to the bedside chair.

"I'm sorry—I'm so sorry," Kit said. "I'll talk to him."

My mom lifted a trembling hand to her mouth.

"It's going to be okay," I said. "We're going to fix this. He loves you."

Kit had a flight to catch. She met my eyes. "You've got this, right?"

I nodded, though I wasn't at all sure that I did. "Don't miss the plane."

Kit came my way and squeezed me tight. "Call me if you need me."

"Not if," I said, "*when*."

"At least you're not bored," Kit said then.

"Maybe we'll all be better for knowing," I said. But as I glanced at my mother, now catatonic in the face of what had just happened, it was hard to imagine how.

MY FATHER DID not come back for us after the airport. In my whole life, he had never ever not been there when I needed him.

But I got it.

He sent a car service instead.

It took my mother twice as long as anyone could have predicted to pack up and dismantle the décor, and the driver waited in the hall in his driving cap.

My mother, it's fair to say, couldn't seem to focus.

I tried to issue suggestions and encouragement from the bed, but she wound up walking around the room, picking things up randomly and setting them back down. She'd pack a few things, only to lose focus and leave others behind in the cabinet.

Meanwhile, nurses and patients popped in and out, saying good-bye.

I didn't expect to see Ian, of course. Myles probably had security set up around the perimeter. But, despite all the pressing drama of the day, I couldn't stop looking for him. I hadn't gone a day and a half without seeing him since we'd met.

The day was a parade of all the faces I'd come to know these past six weeks: farewells from the social worker, and the hospital psychologist, and Priya, and Nina. I saw the spinal surgeon and the dermatologist, and the insurance rep, and two of the orderlies. It was almost like I'd been at summer camp, and now it was time to say good-bye until next summer.

It took forever to go. Then we hit warp speed.

Next, I was rolling over the threshold of my parents' house, over the new ramp my dad had built for me, mentally thanking him and praising his workmanship while trying to staunch the flow of despair in my chest.

But when I rolled my way into the living room—there was my dad.

He froze when he saw us, and dropped his gaze to the floor. We froze, too.

He had an unzipped duffel bag in one hand—his pajama cuffs and part of a toothbrush sticking out, like he'd been trying to get out before we made it home.

"Hi, Cliff," my mother said, almost in a whisper.

But my dad just turned his head away and waited for her to leave.

She did, moving past us back toward their bedroom.

Once she was gone, he met my eyes.

"How ya holding up, kiddo?" my dad asked, squatting down in front of me.

I looked at my dad's duffel bag. "You're heading out?"

He gave a nod. "I hope that's okay."

"I get it," I said. "I do."

"I just need a few days. Clear my head."

Of course. That didn't surprise me.

But pretty much everything else about that day did surprise me. How much I missed Kitty already, how strange it felt to be "on the outside" again, how simultaneously comforting and terrifying it was to hear the front door close behind me.

My childhood bedroom was a surprise, too. After my dad left, my mom wheeled me right to it, as if to move on to brighter topics. She had redecorated. She pushed open the door and voiced a quiet "Surprise!"

She'd replaced truly everything—my trundle bed with the pink dust ruffle, my floral upholstered chair, my curtains, my rug. Everything old was gone—stuffed animals, photo albums, books, clutter, posters.

"Where is everything?" I asked.

"In storage tubs," she answered. "All the keepsakes, anyway. The furniture I set out on the curb—and it was gone in two days."

It was good and bad—both at the same time. She'd taken away the comfort of all those old familiar things, but she'd also taken away their ability to remind me of my old life. This new room was like a hotel. Roman shades in linen, a chaise longue by the window, a hundred pillows

on the bed. A mirrored chandelier. Spare, and done in tones of her favorite color, "greige," a cross between gray and beige. It was tranquil and
sophisticated and utterly unfamiliar. It looked like a magazine.

"A new room for a new start," she said.

I had to hand it to her. She had great taste. "Well, this is definitely a
best-case scenario."

"And Dad can bring all your old junk in for you to sort through whenever you like," my mom said. Then she remembered and took a shaky
breath. "If he comes back."

"He will," I said. "He just needs some time." Then, because it made
it seem like we were almost doing him a kindness, I said, "We can give
him that, right?"

She nodded. "We can give him that."

My mom lingered at my bedroom door for a good while then, un-
sure if she should leave me alone. "Well," she said, after a long silence.
"I guess I'll let you get settled."

I sat very still for a long time. Twenty minutes? An hour? Maybe I
was in shock. All I know is, I couldn't grasp how on earth my life's path
had led me back here. I couldn't think about the past, but I couldn't see
a future, either.

When the doorbell rang, I wondered if it was my dad.

But a few minutes later, my mom clicked down the hallway, swung
open my door (without knocking), and presented—of all people—Ian.

I think she said something prim, like "You have a visitor." I feel like
she might also have offered Ian a wine spritzer, which he declined. All
I remember was the sight of him.

Because as soon as I looked up, I was alive again.

Ian Moffat was in my bedroom. In a blue T-shirt and button-fly jeans.

"Hello," he said, after my mother left, hooking his thumbs in his pockets and looking around. "Nice place."

I didn't know what to say. I had no idea why he was here.

"I've come to apologize," he said then, shifting his weight. "I think I've
made your life harder, not easier—though that was never my intention."

I waited.

"I just wanted to help you get better—as much as you could."

Okay.

"I should never have let myself care for you the way I did."

I looked up. "You let yourself care for me?"

But I suddenly felt like I'd focused on the wrong part of that statement. Ian didn't answer. He studied the rug.

Right then, a foolish little hope lit up somewhere in my heart. Maybe that's why he'd come. Maybe now that I wasn't his patient anymore, we could—*what?* Hang out? Kiss again? Date? Be together?

"I'm also here," Ian added, "to share the news that I'm officially fired. Myles submitted it yesterday."

"Is that a good thing or a bad thing?"

"Both."

I smiled.

He went on, "I will miss it, though."

"Are they going to take away your license?"

"Yes."

If he lost his license, he lost his visa. "Does that mean you have to leave the country?"

He paused a second on this one, walking over to sit down on the bed beside me. "I think so. Yes."

I blinked. "They're making you leave? The government is going after you?"

He shook his head. "Myles is going after me. And he'll win, too."

"You're not going to fight him?"

"There's nothing to fight. It's over. Your sister posted it on Instagram."

"Oh, my God." I put my hand over my eyes. "Kit."

"It's not her fault," he said. "I kissed you in front of a hundred people in that room. It was hardly a private moment."

"But it wasn't your fault! It was the mistletoe!"

Ian shook his head.

"It was a pity kiss!" I went on. "You were just being nice! I'll testify!"

Now he smiled at me like I was deluded—but in a cute way.

"You weren't even technically my PT anymore!"

"Doesn't matter. I worked there. You were a patient."

It seemed insane. "That's it? One kiss, and you're exiled?"

Ian gave a half-smile. "Apparently."

Ian suddenly seemed very close. Just inches away, really. Having him right here—so near—made the idea of his leaving feel excruciating. "You can't go," I said.

He gave a shrug. "I can't stay. My visa was for a particular job that requires a particular license."

"What will you do?"

"Go home. To Edinburgh."

I felt a cramp in my chest.

He went on, "I've got four brothers there. Two of them are doctors. One's already found me an interview at a hospital."

I tried to keep my voice steady, like we were just chatting. "That's good."

But he didn't answer. He just reached out and took my hand. At the touch, I drew in a shaky breath. Then he let it go.

"The interview's on Monday," he said.

I blinked. "*This* Monday?"

He nodded.

"So that means you're going—when?"

"Tomorrow morning."

Panic. I genuinely could not imagine my postcrash life without Ian in it. It was too pathetic to say out loud, but he was just about the only thing in the world that made me anything even close to happy. My whole life was in black-and-white until he walked into the room—and then everything bloomed into color.

Losing Chip? I had barely blinked. Losing Ian right now? I could barely breathe.

"You're going to be all right, you know. You're a lot stronger than you think—"

But before he could finish, I did something that shocked the hell out of both of us.

I said, "Marry me."

His mouth opened, but no words came out.

It was kind of a great idea. "Marry me," I said again, "and then you can stay."

"You want me to marry you?"

I nodded.

"For a green card?"

"You want to stay, don't you?"

"Yes."

"It's sunny here, and the people are friendly, and we have tacos. Do they have tacos in Scotland?"

"They do have tacos in Scotland," he said, "but they're not the same."

Why were we talking about tacos?

I went on. "I had this great idea a few weeks ago about opening a summer camp for kids in wheelchairs." I was thinking fast now. It was all coming together in my head. "Maybe we could do it together—build it and run it, I mean. We could be partners. You could mastermind all the PT stuff and do your thing and get all outside-the-box, and I could do all the fund-raising, and we could create, like, just, a utopia for kids who've seen so much pain—with a garden, and a wheelchair racecourse, and a splash park, and movie nights, and popcorn, and juggling classes, and cookie baking, and Pop-A-Shot, and therapeutic horseback. And a choir!"

I was on fire now. I went on, "We could have classes for adults, too, in the winter, and hold retreats, and sponsor art fairs and teach adults crafty things, like how to knit slugs, and help create a source of light and hope and connection for people who really, really need it. I know you kind of lost interest in your other business, but this would be different."

I had some momentum now. I could see this idea really working.

Plus, and this is not a minor point, I was utterly, breath-stealingly in love with him. It suddenly seemed like I needed to tell him that. Whether I was ready to or not. If he was leaving the country in the morning—if I was truly never going to see him again—how could I let him go without stepping up and speaking the truth?

I'd done a hundred brave things since the crash, but I swear, not one of them was as scary as this.

"Ian," I said then, my breath swirling cold in my lungs like water. "The thing is, I'm in love with you."

Ian held very still.

I watched his face for some kind of response. Was this good news to him or bad? Was it something he'd been hoping to hear—or hoping *not* to hear? Most likely, of course, I was just a sad, shriveled client to him. But those kisses—those heartbreaking kisses of his—had given me a spark of hope I couldn't ignore. I had no idea how he really felt, but there was no time to guess. He was too good at being unreadable.

Without a response, I just pushed on. "Like crazily, swooningly, heart-burstingly in love. Like the kind of in love I didn't even know was possible. The kind of in love that makes every other emotion look tiny and dollhouse sized. The kind that feels like sunshine and fills you up with excitement somehow—even when there's nothing to be excited about. The kind that makes everything better—no matter how bad it is—and even utterly ordinary things like brushing your teeth feel tinged with magic."

It was hard to know how strongly to state my case. I could also have said, *I think about you at night when I can't sleep.* Or, *What I felt for Chip never even came close to what I feel for you.* Or, *You are the best thing in my life.*

The longer he didn't respond, the more I felt like I should push even harder. The more I felt like begging. I came very close to saying, *Please, please marry me. It wouldn't have to be love!* I'd take him for less than that. I'd take him for friendship. I take him for anything—just to keep him close.

But I never said any of that, and later, I was glad. As the expression on his face finally came into focus, I stopped. If any part of me had been hoping for a yes, that was the moment when it disappeared.

He was holding his breath. He let it out, and stood, turned away, and shoved a hand into his hair, all at once.

"I didn't 'kind of lose interest' in my business," he said.

A huge confession of love from me, and that's his talking point?

He went on. "The business was great. It was working out—growing, even. It was one of those impossible moments in life when everybody got to win. I was happy, my employees were happy, our clients were happy. Kayla was happy. We had moved in together. We were talking about getting married." He took a shaky breath. "Then, one night—it was actually the night the Oscars were on—Kayla stopped by the store on her way home to pick up a box of microwave popcorn, because she had this rule that you couldn't watch the Oscars without popcorn." Ian paused. "And a boy—a teenage boy—walked into the grocery store with an assault rifle and opened fire. For no reason. Nobody ever figured out why—why that store, why that day, why that moment. He shot a security guard, two checkers, and two people standing in line. And the last person he shot, before he shot himself, was Kayla."

I knew the rest without his even saying it.

I remembered that shooting. It had dominated the local news for days. I knew that nobody in that store had survived.

But even if I hadn't remembered, I'd have known from the look on Ian's face—so indelible and so undeniable. The woman he loved— wanted to marry—had gone to the store for popcorn, and she had never come home.

There are facial expressions you can fake. You can fake a smile, for instance, or a frown. You can even fake tears. But certain expressions are so true and so directly connected to the heart that they are beyond description. That's what I saw in Ian then. The most desperate, unspeakable, agonizing, indescribable despair.

I held still and quiet. What could I say? How on earth could I respond? It was beyond anything I had words for. At last, grasping for something—some acknowledgment of what he was telling me—I whispered, "I am so sorry."

He nodded, staring at the floor like he was seeing something else.

After a while, quiet as I could, I said, "I remember it. Something like three years ago, right?"

He didn't look up, but he said, "Three years, almost exactly."

I suddenly understood lots of things. "That's why you lost interest in the business," I said.

He nodded, lost in the memory. "She died at the scene. She never had a chance. He got her twice—one bullet through her right breast and lung, and one through her ear and out the back of her head. Only one person survived. The store was closed during the investigation, but then they re-opened. Mopped away all the blood and opened the doors within two weeks. I've never gone back. I can't even drive down that street. It's so strange to me that people shop there now. They don't even know. They buy their Doritos and their beer and stand in line on the very spot where she took her last breath. She died alone on a cold industrial floor. It all ended right there. Everything she'd ever worked toward, or hoped for, or loved."

I watched his chest rise and fall. At last, I understood his silences. How words must truly fail him in the face of it all. My mind skipped backward to all the times he stood at the gym, holding so still, seeming like it took every ounce of his will to tolerate the world and everyone in it. I guess it really had.

I didn't push against the quiet, or try to fix it, or try to fill it with noise. I just let it surround us, and I stayed right there.

After a while, he looked up, seeming to remember I was there.

"I want to thank you," he said then, meeting my eyes. "You are the only good thing that's happened to me since that day."

Context changes everything. My green card idea seemed so foolish now, knowing everything. I had the idea to grab on to that foolishness and make a little joke. "My offer of a sham wedding is still open," I said.

I'd hoped for a smile, and I got one, just for a second. "I can't marry you for a green card."

I watched his profile at the window, and I felt the most acute long-ing. Knowing what he'd been through made my problems seem small in comparison. It forced me to step back and see my own situation in a broader context. It forced me to notice that I was, if nothing else, still alive. Witnessing even a glimpse of what he'd lost made me feel both embarrassed by my declaration of love for him—and a thousand times more committed to it.

He must have sensed what I was feeling. "And you're not actually in love with me, by the way."

With that shift in topic, the light in the room seemed to change— just barely—as if somewhere not too far away the sun had come out from the clouds.

"Um," I said, "I think I would know."

"We talked about this already," he said. "It's not real."

I tilted my head. "Feels pretty real."

"Listen," he said, "you know how kidnapping victims can fall in love with their captors? That's what this is."

"You're saying I have Stockholm syndrome?"

"I'm saying you have a version of something like it."

"Are you saying you *kidnapped* me?"

He turned back. "I didn't kidnap you, but I have been one of your captors. You have been held hostage—robbed of your old life, isolated from your old friends, and at the mercy of others. You have faced adversity that most people never see. In response, you've created an imaginary bond with one of your captors—to feel safe, and to create hope, and to feel less alone. It's a classic form of self-preservation."

"Sounds like you've thought about this."

"Am I wrong?"

Actually, I didn't know. I guess that was one way of reading the situation. "*Is* the bond imaginary?" I asked.

Ian didn't answer.

"Do you feel it, too?" I pressed. "Or did I just make it up?" My brain could list a hundred reasons why a guy like him would not even remotely be interested in someone like me. Of course! It defied all logic to think that he might. And yet—I didn't *think* it. I *felt* it. I felt it over and over.

"I am fond of you," Ian said then.

"How fond?"

Ian didn't answer again.

"Because, honestly," I finally said, cracking the silence, "if you don't also feel what I'm feeling, then it doesn't matter if what I feel is real or imaginary, does it? If you have no interest in me—and I have no idea:

sometimes I feel like you really do, and sometimes I feel like you absolutely don't—then this conversation is pointless. We don't have to talk
about kidnapping, or theories of psychology. You just say you're not interested, and we're done here."

Ian didn't speak.

"Just say you're not interested, and you go home to Scotland, and I
stay here with my mother and eat spaghetti for dinner, and we'll never
see each other again. Easy."

Ian stared at the floor.

"Just say you're not interested," I whispered then, hoping with every
cell in my body that he would say the opposite.

Finally, he turned to me, and something had shifted in his eyes. There
was no softness there anymore. "I'm not interested," he said.

I sat back. I don't know what I was expecting him to say, but it wasn't
that. Not in that way, at least. Not like it was *true*. "You're not?"

His voice was flat. "I am fond of you. You have been a pleasant patient to work with. Your situation is tough, and I've been impressed with
your drive and your strength. But I do not have romantic feelings for
you."

I took a few breaths in slow motion. Did I believe him? "And so that
very passionate, Olympic-level kiss at the lake?"

He shrugged. "I guess I'm just a good kisser."

"How about that other kiss—when you publicly, in front of a whole
room of onlookers, ended your own career?"

He looked up very carefully, straight into my eyes. "I must have let
myself get too lonely."

"So," I said, putting it together, "it wasn't passion—it was desperation?"

He almost looked a little bored. "That's one way to put it."

"So," I tried again, hoping to make him deny it, "what you're saying
is, you knew I'd developed a slightly overwhelming crush on you, but
you didn't dissuade me because you were lonesome and horny?"

"That's another way to put it."

"Okay," I said, and then I felt a wash of shame.

Of course he wasn't in love with me. Why would he be? What had I been thinking? He could do and be and choose anything he wanted. He had the whole world ahead of him. All I had was a tiny little half-life. What was exciting or attractive or lovable about that? I'd forgotten what I'd become. If Chip, who had known me at my best, didn't even want me, how could I hope for anyone else? I was no longer lovable. *Note to self.*

"Okay," I said again. My chest started to ache as it all hit me.

There was no point in being honest anymore. There was no way to save face at this point, either. I just had to get him out of here. Fast, before the universe collapsed.

We were done. I turned away. "Hey—have a great trip back to Scotland."

But he lingered.

"I have something for you," he said, holding up a small box wrapped in kraft paper. "Your birthday present, actually. I brought it to the lake—but . . . I'd still like you to have it."

I turned away. "No, thanks."

He hesitated. "I could just leave it here for you."

"Don't leave it here. I don't want it."

He stood there.

"Time to go, dude," I said then. "Get out."

"I thought we might exchange contact information."

Why the hell would we do that? "Oh," I said, falsely pleasant. "I don't think that'll be necessary."

"I was hoping we could stay friends."

Fuck you. "No, thanks," I said. "I'm good."

"How will I know how you're doing?"

"I'll be fine," I said, still not turning back. "You said yourself I'm a lot stronger than I think."

"Maybe I could just—"

"Get the hell out," I said. "Please." We were so done here.

He got quiet. I heard him walk toward the door then. When he reached it, he turned. "I'm sorry, Margaret. I will always remember you."

"That's so funny," I said, glancing in his direction, but not actually meeting his eyes. "Because I've already forgotten you."

THE NEXT MORNING, lying awake in my new, greige bedroom, I noticed something on the table by the door. My birthday present from Ian. He'd left it, anyway.

It made me angry to see it. Hadn't I told him not to do that? Didn't I get any say in anything?

I resolved to throw it away in the kitchen trash.

I should probably have gotten up and gotten dressed. But I didn't. I found myself thinking about Kit's comforting thought. Kit's expert said to give it a year. Would I be back to normal in a year? It seemed utterly impossible.

But then I had a comforting thought of my own.

I'll give it a year, I thought, *and if I don't feel any better, I'll kill myself.*

It perked me up quite a bit.

All I had to do for one year was make it through the day. I'd ask my mother to get me a big wall calendar, and then, at the end of every day I successfully suffered through, I'd mark a big X. Things would get better, Kit's mathematician had promised. Great. I hoped so.

But if he was wrong, I had a plan B.

One bit of good news: It was not as hard to move back home as I'd feared.

Though my dad did not come home.

The "little time" he was taking turned into a lot of time.

My parents talked on the phone some, going through the details, my dad trying to get a handle on the story. Sometimes my mother cried and begged, which was disturbing because my mother never cried. Or begged.

But he didn't come home.

In fact, within the month, he called to tell her he was going to take a trip for a "personal project." He was going to donate his woodworking

and construction skills to a help restore a historic whaling ship in a museum in Connecticut. He'd rented a little house up there, and he wasn't
sure when he'd be back. If.

"Your father is moving to Mystic, Connecticut," my mother told me,
before bursting into tears. "He's going to volunteer as a woodworker."

I had never seen my mother fall to pieces in the way she did in the
weeks after my father left town. Her jobs died on the vine. She just didn't
show up. She wandered the house crying, or staring into space. She'd
forget to eat. Or she'd make a meal and then sit staring at it until it was
cold. I'd find her sitting in my father's favorite chair, staring at the rug
or rubbing at the chocolate stain he'd smeared on the arm.

"I snapped at him about this once," she said quietly, when she noticed me watching her. "I waited to reupholster that chair for years, and
we hadn't had it back a week before he melted chocolate on the arm."

She didn't seem so mad about it now.

As bad as this time was, it was good, too. It let me see her differently. It let me see her story in a much wider context. It let me feel, for
the first time ever, almost protective toward her. She had always been
so strong, so in control, until now. I'd only ever seen her as invulnerable—
but now she was the opposite.

There was another bonus to this time, too: Worrying about her gave
me something to worry about other than myself.

I took to emailing my dad every few days, just "checking in" casually,
trying to ascertain when, if ever, he planned to come back. I also called
Kit with updates on the home front and—because she went out to visit
him a couple of times in Mystic—gathered intel on his state of mind.

They never officially separated. My dad was just "taking time." Kitty
promised us he wasn't dating anyone. And, she said, he didn't seem particularly out of sorts, either. Just eating way too much canned soup.

My time with my mom turned out to be a surprise. Something shifted
in her after my dad left. At lunch, back in in the hospital, she had
barraged me with advice and opinions and half-baked inspirational
stories. She'd pushed me the way she'd always pushed me. She'd been
relentless, and critical, and judgmental.

But now that the window had closed, and she'd accepted that, she'd become much calmer. If there was nothing I could do, then she didn't have to make me do it. She could relax and give us all a break. Of course, it turns out that the window never truly closes. I found a bunch of articles saying there's always potential for neurological plasticity, long after that initial healing period.

But my mom didn't know that. And I sure as hell wasn't telling her.

Adjusting the curve for how crushingly depressed we both were, life with my mother was surprisingly pleasant.

Once she'd recovered enough to get back to work, she reduced her workload by half. She made sure to be home for lunch, when she made us sandwiches and smoothies. In theory, I was responsible for dinner—but lots of nights we wound up getting takeout from the Italian place down the road. After dinner, almost every night, we worked puzzles and sipped wine, and half-listened to the news.

We were both miserable, and grateful for the company.

Of course, everything I might have expected to be hard was, in fact, hard.

It was hard to be back in that house as a broken version of myself. It was hard to compare the past to the present at every turn. It was hard to see my old clothes, shoes, keepsakes, photo albums, Rollerblades—not to mention a shelf of diaries filled with all my old assumptions about how my life would turn out. It was hard to glimpse ghostly memories at every turn of what it was like to run and skip and hopscotch and bicycle and shoot hoops. I even missed utterly ordinary things, like walking out the front door, or leaning on the kitchen counter, or standing in the shower. It was hard not to regret everything I'd lost. The abilities I'd taken for granted. The time I'd wasted.

I am not going to lie. Everything that happened in the hospital before I moved home? That was the easy part.

My situation didn't truly feel real until I was out of the hospital.

Without Kit, and Priya, and Nina—and, okay, fine, even Ian—it was like I didn't have anyone to keep me from sinking.

So I sank.

I went through a long, deep period of grief that involved bitterness, anger, mourning, judgment, rage, self-pity, fear, longing, and loneliness—usually more than one in combination, and often all together—as well as nightmares, insomnia, fits of temper, anxiety attacks, and dish throwing. In fact, after accidentally dropping (and smashing) one of my mom's favorite saucers, I got so enraged that I hauled a whole stack out into the backyard and smashed about ten more on the driveway.

Then I cried in the backyard until my mom came home and found me.

She should have yelled at me. But guess what she did instead?

She marched back into the kitchen and brought out her own stack of dishes to smash.

That weekend, she made a trip to Goodwill and brought back crates of unwanted dishes that we could smash at will. We didn't even clean them up afterward. Just left the shattered colors all over the driveway like a great mosaic homage to crazy-town.

"It's pretty, actually," my mom said one day.

In a way, it was.

Years before, I'd seen a video taken by a security camera that went viral on the Internet of some kids playing on a beach where they weren't supposed to be. The tide came roaring in, and the three of them got pulled into the waves. The beach was long and flat. Watching it, you just rooted for them to stand up, get balanced, and run back up to higher shore. But the tide was so strong, they couldn't get their footing. They just washed out to sea and then back in, over and over. They started to stand and then tumbled backward, lifted their heads for a good breath and got pummeled by a giant wave, tried to outrun the waves and were overtaken. You thought, "Those kids are going to drown five feet from dry land." In fact, even though you knew they weren't going to drown—because the title of the video was "Miracle of Survival"—you felt certain they were going to drown anyway.

That was me, during those early months after leaving the hospital. I was all three of those kids at the same time. A miracle of survival—but drowning anyway, all the same.

My old friends wanted to see me, for example, but I didn't want to see them. They wanted to "get together" and "grab a bite" or "have coffee."

Why would I want to do that? I dreaded the pity on their faces and the assumptions they'd make. I dreaded how sorry they'd feel for me. I dreaded every single reaction of every single girlfriend when she heard how Chip had ruined my life and disappeared. I wasn't going to feed their schadenfreude.

My mother read an article saying it was important for "people like me" to stay connected. She even tried to convince me to let her organize a girls' day at a spa. "It'll be fun," she tried to declare. "We'll get our hair done. Mani-pedis. You can roll home feeling great."

"I never feel great, Mom," I said. "That's not a feeling in my collection."

"I just read an article that said human connections help prevent Alzheimer's."

"Alzheimer's," I said, "is the least of my worries right now."

I tried not to feel bleak, but I felt bleak anyway. I tried to leave the house, but I always stopped at the door. I tried to count my blessings, but even just trying made me mad. Things went on like this for months— and months. No change in sight. I don't mean to gloss over it, but there just isn't much to report. Wake up. Feel angry. Avoid human contact. Smash dishes. Repeat.

And then, in late summer, Kit came home for a weekend.

Twenty-five

YES, KIT'S BOYFRIEND, the Moustache, had let the Beauty Parlor fall apart. Yes, things were far worse than she'd expected when she got back. Turns out, he had no interest in the boring, day-to-day activities of running a shop, like sweeping or taking out the trash or writing down appointments. Kit returned to angry customers, disgruntled employees, and a cockroach infestation.

We hadn't talked on the phone every day, as she'd promised—though she had found time to talk every day with my mom.

It was fine. My mom needed her more.

"If you'd just follow me on Instagram," Kit said, "we wouldn't *have* to talk on the phone."

"It's really not the same thing."

Kitty had the most contact with our dad of anyone, so she and my mom suddenly had a lot to talk about. They also had years of resentments, misunderstandings, disappointments, and blame to work through. But I had to hand it to them. They didn't just smile big and make nice. They went for it. They argued, they disagreed, they compared notes—on their lives and everybody else's.

When we did talk, though, Kit was very interested in my health, my progress, my daily routine. She asked tons of questions—sometimes so many we never talked about her at all. Specific questions, too, about how I felt and how I was taking care of myself. She started emailing me articles on spinal health, recovery, home rehab, functional electrical stimulation, and neurogenesis. Specific, highly technical articles, too—far different from the pop psychology we'd started with.

"Where are you finding these?" I asked her. "I thought you were repainting the shop."

"I broke up with the Moustache," she confessed.

"Because he drove your business into the ground?"

"Because I think I'm in love with Fat Benjamin."

"We're all in love with Fat Benjamin. He's adorable."

"Anyway, I have insomnia."

"Do *not* worry about me in the middle of the night!" I said. "Go back to sleep!"

"Nobody *chooses* who they worry about in the night," she said. "Just read the articles and shut up."

So I did. Or tried to. Actually, I just printed out most of them and put them in a stack. They were very dry. My guess was Kit herself only read the titles.

All to say, she'd hoped to visit in early summer, but she didn't make it until August. Which was fine. I wouldn't have been much fun before that anyway.

I wasn't much fun in August, either.

But being with Kit seemed to help.

She made me get dressed and put on lipstick and go out to hip new restaurants with her. She made me listen to disco and sing with her—and she filmed everything. One afternoon, she drove me to the ocean.

"I'm worried about you," she said, snapping my photo as we watched the waves. "You're living like an old person."

"I'm fine," I said.

She leaned over and sniffed me. "You're a little mothballish, even."

I swatted at her. "I am not."

"You do remember you're twenty-eight—not seventy-eight?"

"I think I'm doing okay," I said. I was alive, wasn't I? Maybe I wasn't doing yoga at sunrise, but I did get out of bed every morning. Usually.

"Why haven't you learned how to drive?"

"Where would I drive to?"

"Why haven't you investigated braces for your legs?"

"I'm fine with the chair. It's fine."

"I think you need to try harder."

She probably meant well, but I was tired of people meaning well. "I think you need to mind your own business."

But Kit didn't care. "You are my business," she said with a shrug. "You always have been."

She took a million pictures of me for her followers: me eating spaghetti, me getting my toenails painted rainbow colors, me sunbathing in heart-shaped sunglasses. She gave my pixie cut a freshen-up and Instagrammed that. She made me put on her retro 1950s lipstick and Instagrammed that. She even took a picture of the scars on my shoulder and Instagrammed that.

"Kit! Nobody wants to see my gross shoulder!"

"Everybody wants to see it. You're an Instagram star, lady. Just accept it."

But Kit just had to push me. On her last night, at dinner, in front of my mom, of all people, Kit said, "How's your summer camp coming along?"

It felt like an awfully private question to bring up in a place as public as the dinner table. I glanced at my mother.

"Summer camp!" my mom said. "You want to go to summer camp?"

Kit said, "She wants to *build* a summer camp."

My mom sat straight up. *Build something? Yes, please!*

She lobbed fifty questions at me at once, but I shut them all down.

"I haven't even thought about it in months," I said. Which was true.

But that night, as I was falling asleep, I found myself thinking about it again. Under the onslaught of real life in the real world, I'd almost forgotten the idea entirely. It was so like Kit to remind me.

Overnight, my head flooded with ideas, and the next morning, before I'd even had coffee, I wheeled into the kitchen in my pajamas to find some paper, and I made a list off the top of my head:

chair bowling
bonfires
gardening
singing
hand cycling
wheelchair kung fu
bungee jumping
pinball
Pop-A-Shot
racing
canoeing
zip-lining
ping pong
wheelchair obstacle course
horseback

"What is all that?" my mom asked when she came in, peering over my shoulder.

"Ideas for the summer camp," I said.

She nodded. "I've been thinking about it, too."

"You have?"

"If we built it," she said, "maybe the camp sign could be a mosaic. That would give us something to do with all your broken dishes."

That's how Kit got me to try harder. The same way she got me to sing. By tricking me. By playing a tune I couldn't resist. But I do have to give her credit—or maybe I have to give it to Ian's mom. Because the next

thing I doodled on that paper was her famous quote: *When you don't know what to do for yourself, do something for somebody else.*

KIT LEFT THAT morning, but it was okay. I didn't have that same sense of panic I'd felt when she left the hospital.

Now I had a project.

Or maybe the project had me.

In the following weeks, I got consumed. I took over the dining table. I drew plans for buildings and consulted an architect. I made lists of ideas, resources, people to work with. I did real estate searches online— looking for land that was far enough out to be cheap but close enough to be accessible. I looked at other, nonprofit camps online to see how they did things and what they offered. I brainstormed names and investigated graphics. I made plans for a nature trail, a library, a ceramics studio, a yarn café, a bake shop, a butterfly garden. Everything would be wheel- chair accessible—and everything would be architecturally beautiful. I had rolled my eyes so much at my mother decorating my hospital room— but after we'd taken it all down, I'd seen her point. The feeling of the room changed. Without her quilts and curtains and table lamps and splashes of color, it felt like the saddest place in the world.

I wanted this place to feel like sunshine. I wanted it to feel like hope. Warm, but cool. Bright, but shady. Alert, but calm. I wanted it to feel like magic.

"You could call it Hell on Wheels," my mom suggested one night at dinner.

"'Hell' might give the wrong vibe."

"What about Camp Magic?"

I gave a shrug. "Might sound like an academy for young magicians."

"Not a bad idea," she pointed out.

I pointed at her. "Yes. We should offer magic classes." Then back to the name: "It needs to sound fun enough for kids, but serious enough for grown-ups."

My mom grinned. "So the Margaret Jacobsen Center for Spinal Cord Recovery is out."

I gave her a look. "Too cutesy."

"What about Camp Hope?" she asked.

We let that idea simmer while we sketched out ideas for a camp T-shirt with the slogan THAT'S HOW WE ROLL.

It was both a lucky and a slightly unlucky thing that my mom was a contractor.

It meant that she knew a million workmen, plumbers, electricians, surveyors, real estate agents, bricklayers, painters, distributors, suppliers, A/C guys, and demolition experts. They knew the dirt on everybody and knew how to get the best deals. That was all in the "pro" column.

Under "con": If I really did this, I was about to spend a truckload of time with my mom.

And it did look like I was going to do this. I couldn't seem to make myself think about anything else, for one thing. I can't tell you what a pleasure it was to use my brain again—to use all my business training, and skills, and design sense, and creativity. The project brought together almost everything I loved to do.

More than that, it got me out of the house.

At a certain point, I had to start looking for land, and meeting with people, and talking with them about ideas and strategies, having lunches and coffees with potential contributors and partners. Leaving the house just for the sake of leaving the house had never interested me. But leaving the house to get a donation pledge of five thousand dollars? That I could do.

I dusted off my old pantsuits and my pearl earrings, and I gutted up and went to lunch.

Kit even made me set up a Kickstarter campaign, and then she posted about it to her now *sixty*-six thousand followers. Donations flowed in. Money piled up. The whole thing started to look like it might actually happen.

"They love you!" Kit said on the phone. "Send me a picture of you in that pinstripe Ann Taylor suit!"

Was everything suddenly all fixed and perfect? No. Did I get pitying stares in restaurants? Constantly. Did I still have profound moments— hours, days—of hopelessness, anger, bitterness, frustration, despair, self-hatred, and grief? You could say that. And did I one day run into Neil Putnam from Simtex HR, the guy who had hired-me-but-not-officially for my dream job before the accident and then nixed the whole thing afterward? And did he not recognize me at all? And when I finally explained who I was, did he say, "You changed your hair!"?

Yes. That happened.

But the tone of my life was different now. I had a purpose. I had a reason to take a shower every morning. I had a reason to take care of myself. More than that, I was figuring out how doing something for other people could—in fact—be doing something for yourself. Amazing.

It felt good to feel better, and so I started looking for other ways to amp it up. I got addicted to audiobooks. I joined a choir. I kept knitting, even though I never got any better. I taught myself how to make pastries from scratch. I let my mom sell my old condo.

By the time I put the three hundredth *X* on my suicide calendar, I had signed an earnest-money contract on a hundred-acre plot of land outside of town with a two-hundred-year-old oak tree, three hills, and a catfish pond. I used the money from the condo as a down payment. That night, even though my dad still had not come home after all this time, and even though my mom might well have been *X*-ing off her own set of impossibly strange and altered days, we celebrated with champagne.

Despite everything, I decided at last to bet on hope—and I stuffed my suicide calendar in the recycling.

If this is the rest of my life, I found myself thinking one day, *it's okay.*

It really was.

Twenty-six

THEN CHIP DECIDED to get married.

Married.

To that sneaky, soup-making ex-girlfriend, Tara, a.k.a. the Whiner.

In Europe, of all places. In a famously charming town in Belgium called Bruges.

The invitation arrived on Valentine's Day, of all days. Which forced me to notice three things: One, it was Valentine's Day. Two, it had been exactly a year since the crash. And three, I had completely forgotten about Chip.

I also noticed something else: My mom, my dad, and Kit were the only names on the invitation.

My mother knew about the engagement, though. She was still friends with Evelyn. She just couldn't give her up. Although Evelyn never came to the house once I moved home. For a long time, my mother snuck out to meet her, saying she was "running errands," but I knew what they were up to.

"You can be friends with Evelyn," I told her one night after dinner. "It's okay."

"I'm not!"

"It's not disloyal to me. I'm fine."

"He cheated on you! He gave up on you."

"It was a messy time."

She didn't need to be mad for me. She really didn't. Hadn't we all lost enough?

I got it. I did. Best friends are not easy to come by. The two stayed friends, and they avoided talking about either one of us, until one day Evelyn just had to tell her about the upcoming nuptials.

My mom got the scoop: Chip had been promoted not once, but twice, and had risen through the ranks of his investment bank in exactly the way you'd expect a guy as handsome and WASPy and confident as Chip to rise. He was highly promotable. In fact, they'd transferred him to their Brussels office.

"Chip is living in Belgium?"

My mom nodded.

"He doesn't even speak French!"

I felt a flash of resentment—quick but distinct. Chip got promoted? To Europe? The crash sure hadn't slowed him down. Was his life really going to be that easy? I got that sour feeling that comes when you make the mistake of thinking someone else is beating you at life.

But then I took a mental breath.

So what? Chip was in Brussels. But I was genuinely okay in Texas. We had both moved on. We could both be okay at the same time. We weren't on a seesaw, for Pete's sake! There was plenty of okay to go around.

Just because Chip had gotten what he'd wanted so easily, without ever having to question it, without ever having to struggle—that didn't necessarily mean that what he got was *better*.

"I've known about the wedding for a while," my mother confessed. "Evelyn warned me."

"You didn't tell me?"

"I thought it would fall through," my mom said. "Apparently, that girl *followed* him to Brussels. She showed up at the airport with all her bags and announced she was coming along."

I shrugged. You had to give it to her. "Ballsy."

My mother closed her eyes. "Please don't talk about balls at dinner." Then she went on, "The good news is, it's in Europe, so no one could possibly expect us to go."

"Did you know they were going to invite everybody but me?" I asked, showing her the envelope.

From her face, she didn't. "That must be a mistake," she said.

That calligraphy did not look like a mistake to me, but before I could say so, my mom's phone rang.

It was Kit.

My mom put her on speaker.

"Did you hear about the wedding?" Kit demanded.

"We just got the invitation," my mom said.

"And I'm not on it," I added. "They invited everybody but me."

"I think it was an oversight," my mother declared.

"Maybe they're sending you a special one," Kit suggested.

I gave my mom a look. "Unlikely."

"Well," Kit said, in her determined voice, "you have to come anyway. You have to crash."

"Hell, no," I said, just as my mom said, "We're boycotting, like decent people."

"Listen," Kit said. "They invited Dad, too. Evelyn called him, since she knew he was 'on sabbatical.'"

"I hope he is boycotting, too."

"No," Kit said. "He's going."

My mom frowned. "Why would he go? He doesn't even like to travel."

"He's going," Kit announced, "because I talked him into it."

"Kit—"

"And I talked him into it because we're going to *Parent Trap* him."

My mother frowned, totally uncomprehending.

"We won't tell him you're coming," Kit went on, "and you'll show up looking *devastating*—and the shock of it will catapult him into your arms."

"There may be some logic flaws here," my mother said.

"He talks about you all the time," Kit insisted. "He misses you all the time. I think it's pride keeping him away. I think we need to give him a reason to get past it."

"You want to *surprise* him into forgiving me?" my mother asked.

"Shock and awe," I said, nodding. For a terrible idea, it wasn't too bad.

"Exactly," Kit said.

I shrugged. "It might be just dumb enough to work."

But my mom was shaking her head. "No. I can't."

"Yes! You can!" Kit said.

"It's too much," my mom said, and she suddenly looked remarkably old to me. Smaller, too. She'd always been so forceful—so certain and bulldozer-like about her choices. It was strange to see her hesitating and uncertain like this. It was disarming to see her hang back and hesitate. The little frown lines between her brows seemed deeper. As disorienting as it was to see her this way—so timid—I have to confess, it humanized her, too. It made me feel almost protective.

"Mags and I will help you," Kit offered then. "We'll go with you. We'll make it work."

My mother lowered her voice, like I might not hear. "I can't ask Margaret to do that."

"*Hello?*" I said. "I wasn't invited."

"Skip the wedding, then," Kit said, like, *Duh,* "but come to Belgium. Easy."

But would it be easy? Traveling so far might not be easy. Leaving the safe nest I'd built this year might not be easy. Facing a thousand unknowns had definite potential to not be easy. And flying again—something I'd just assumed I'd never do—would be the exact opposite of easy.

But Kit was ready to make this happen. "Family trip to Belgium! End of discussion!" Kit said. "I'll organize everything. Hit the mall and find something heartbreaking to wear."

My mom squinted at me, like, *Is this a good idea?*

I gave her a nod, like, *Hell, yes.*

Was it a good idea? I didn't know. It actually seemed pretty risky—for everybody. I had just barely let go of my suicide calendar, after all. I hardly even had my head above water, and it wouldn't take much to wash me back under. Could I do this?

I suddenly thought maybe I could.

Especially as it hit me that Belgium was really not all that far away from Scotland.

It didn't seem like such a bad idea to help my mother get some closure with my dad—and then maybe just pop over to Scotland for a little closure of my own.

A terrible, heartbreaking, foolish idea—but once I'd thought it, I couldn't seem to unthink it.

The idea even woke me up from a sound sleep that night and gnawed at me until I Googled the distance. A nonstop flight from Brussels to Edinburgh took under two hours. Easy.

I could pop over for a day or two, maybe. Pretend to be in town "on business." Call Ian in a super-casual way, like I'd remembered him as an afterthought. We could meet for coffee. I could be near him again, even for a few hours. But, as I considered the idea, I had to think about what that might look like.

I'd be—as ever—in my wheelchair. It would be gray outside. We'd meet at some café with a door too skinny for my chair, so Ian would have to leave me outside while he ordered us to-go cups, if they even had things like that in Europe. He'd lead us to a bench nearby, and I would be utterly saturated with longing—like a starving person looking at a fresh-baked loaf of bread—and he would be . . . What? Vaguely pleased to see I was still alive? Professionally curious about the state of my spinal cord? Polite? Even—oh, God—falsely friendly? Or worse! Maybe he'd be seeing someone by now, someone tall and able-bodied—a fellow triathlete—and he'd blithely bring her along so we could meet. You know, thinking that would be *fun for me*. I'd sit in asexual agony in my chair, watching the two of them on a bench with their able bodies side by side, smiling and stealing glances, but trying to keep it down for the desiccated, noodle-legged spinster in their midst.

It would be the worst circle of hell. My stomach cringed at the thought.

But I still wanted to do it anyway. Or maybe *needed* to.

Kit loved this idea—but then, terrible ideas were her favorite kind. She wanted details. "What are you going to do—show up outside Ian's flat and surprise him?"

"No," I said. "I'm going to surprise him on the phone, like a normal person."

"You mean, like—once you're already there. Like, around the corner, in one of those little red phone booths?"

I shook my head. "This is not a spy movie. I'll just tell him I'm in town on business or something."

"I love it. A sneak attack."

"I'd just chicken out otherwise."

"How will you even find him?"

"I have no idea." I thought about it. "Maybe I'll ask Man-Bun-Rob to get his address from the hospital."

Kit clarified: "You're going to ask a former PT to help you stalk his former colleague."

"In a manner of speaking."

"Perfect," Kit said. "What could go wrong?"

Twenty-seven

KIT ARRIVED IN Texas three days before the trip to get us focused.

We spent more hours than I can count strategizing over outfits for my mom—and me, too. Kit wanted my mother in green—my dad's favorite color—and she dragged her to four stores before they found the right look. After that, Kit insisted she get her hair and nails done and buy all new makeup.

"I don't need a new lipstick," my mother protested.

"It's crunch time," Kit said. "Go big or go home."

Me? I was trickier. Kit spent more time on me than on my mother, and I wasn't even going to the wedding. I could easily have just worn some clothes I already owned, but Kit wouldn't hear of it. Nothing in my "sad closet" would do. Kit wanted me in something "smart, sophisticated, and with a just a touch of go-fuck-yourself." But subtle. If I really was just going to "pop by" in Scotland to "say hello" to Ian, I'd have to meet the challenge of finding plausible business wear that could also "reduce a man to tears of longing."

"We might be setting our sights a little high here," I said.

"Hush. I'm working."

It took Kit two days to find my perfect look: a gray pantsuit with a crisp white blouse that cost four hundred dollars.

"Worth it," Kit declared.

She also forced me to buy my first lingerie in over a year. "What if you meet a handsome stranger in the airport?" she demanded, pulling a pair out of my dresser. "Are you going have your way with him in a sports bra and sad gray Jockeys?"

I gave her a look. "I'm not spending two hundred more dollars on uncomfortable underwear that no one will ever see."

"Don't be such an old lady," she said, holding the panties out. "I have to room with you. *I'll* see your underpants, if no one else. And this situation right here"—she dropped the pair in the wastebasket—"makes me lose my will to live."

In the end, she gifted me the lingerie. Against my will.

She also Instagrammed photos of our shopping day—but then she refused to post the final outfit. "You're too gorgeous," she declared. "You'd break the Internet."

I ALMOST CHICKENED out. This couldn't possibly be a good idea. But then I'd circle back around to the sad, quiet version of herself that my mom had been this whole long year, and my resolve would come back. I didn't honestly know if she could win my dad back. The plan seemed like a long shot with deep potential for crushing humiliation.

But it didn't really matter. I knew I had to help her try.

Besides, my mom had already spent all of her frequent flyer miles to get us an upgrade to first class.

Kit gaped when she told her.

My mom shrugged. "Go big or go home."

I looked at Kit. "We're going to need that on T-shirts."

The morning-of, I had a few more second thoughts.

"What was I thinking?" I demanded of Kit as we shotgunned our morning coffees. "How am I supposed to lug this wheelchair all around Europe? That place is one hundred percent stone steps! Stone steps

and fashionable people. This is lunacy. They're going to stop me at the gates and send me home."

Kit wasn't having it. "You're not a quitter."

Maybe not—but I wanted to be. "It's going to be the worst thing ever."

My mom was walking by, and she paused to squeeze my shoulders. "No," she said. "You've already survived the worst thing ever."

And there was the crux of it. This would be my first flight since the crash. "I'm not sure I can do this," I said.

Kit drained the dregs of her coffee and clanked her empty mug down in the sink. "Loving the self-doubt," she said. "Let's definitely run with that. But let's get on the plane first."

FIRST CLASS WAS like a VIP party.

Not only had I never flown to Europe before, I'd never flown anything but coach before. Now I was ruined, because I found out what I'd been missing. First class greeted us with champagne and strawberries, and it only got better from there. It practically had a swimming pool and a DJ.

We had to fly direct to London, then hop over to Belgium on a second quick flight, then take a train out to Bruges. It was going to be a long day and a half. But I couldn't complain. They gave us warm blankets and steamed hot towels for our hands, like we were at a spa. We had our own little sleeping pods with seats that reclined into beds. Plus, our seats were in the closest row to the door, so it was easy to wheel right to my spot.

Still, no amount of luxury could change the fact that this was my first flight since the crash. Despite all my attempts to focus my brain on something else—and I was doing a valiant job—my body could not be fooled. My hands felt cold and quivery. My eyes darted left and right like a trapped rodent's. My heart stumbled around in my chest like it was being attacked. There was no point worrying about it, I knew. This was happening. It was out of my hands. I'd made my choice, and now I just had to survive it.

Once we were buckled in, when my mom reached across the aisle to squeeze my hand, it was ice cold.

She met my eyes. "Are you terrified to fly again?"

I wrinkled my nose. "Just a smidge."

Kit leaned over. "Remember that time we went to Hawaii—and you *lived*?"

"We all lived, as I recall," my mother said.

"Would you like me to distract you?" Kit asked, nodding as she said it to let me know that *Yes, I absolutely would*.

My hands were turning kind of a bloodless gray. "I really can't imagine any possible way you could do that."

Kit wiggled her eyebrows at me. "I can."

The engines were whirring into action. Our seats faced each other. I leaned forward. "How?"

She met my mother's eyes and gave her a little nod, like they shared a yummy secret. My mom fished around in her carry-on and pulled out a little wrapped box that I recognized instantly. It was Ian's birthday present to me.

"Hey," I said. "I threw that in the kitchen trash."

"I fished it back out," my mom said.

I stared at it.

"Do you want it?" she finally asked.

The captain was making final announcements over the loudspeaker. I nodded.

She handed it over, and I peeled off the paper and the tape. Then I lifted the lid off the box. Inside was a necklace—a delicate silver chain attached to each end of a small silver bar, and stamped into the bar, in tiny typewriter-like letters, was one word: Courage.

"What is it?" Kit asked.

"A necklace."

"What does it say?" my mom asked.

"Courage."

Kit and my mom looked at each other. "Well," my mom said, "aren't we glad I rescued it?"

As I fastened it behind my neck and felt the cool pressure of the silver bar against my breastbone, the plane started to back away from the gate.

I felt a surge of fear.

"I've got another distraction for you," Kit said, watching me. "A better one."

"What?"

"The address Rob got you for Ian is wrong."

Okay. That was distracting. "Wrong?"

She nodded. "That's his parents' address in Edinburgh, but he doesn't live there."

"How could you possibly know that?"

She gave me a mysterious *I've got so much to tell you* smile. "We're in touch."

I felt an anxious jolt of *Where is this going?* What could she possibly tell me that was that juicy? Without permission, my brain jumped to a worst-case scenario. "Please don't tell me you are dating Ian," I said.

"What? No! Gross! I'm back with Fat Benjamin."

"Why on earth would you be in touch with Ian?"

That smile again. "He found me online. He wanted to know how you were doing."

The plane stopped a second, then started rolling forward. "He did? When was this?"

"A few weeks after I went back. He asked if he could check in with me from time to time."

"Why didn't you tell me?"

"He asked me not to. He didn't want to freak you out."

I tried to absorb the idea. "Did he? Check in?"

She nodded. "He did indeed."

Off her tone, I said, "A lot?"

"About once a week."

"Once a week!" She was enjoying this reveal too much. "He called you?"

"Mostly just email. Also, you know all those articles I sent you?"

The plane sped up on the runway. "The ones I'm pretty sure you never read?"

"They were from him."

He'd sent the articles! That explained a lot. But why? "How did he sound?"

"Like a concerned professional."

"Did you ever talk about anything else?"

She shook her head. "Mostly just your health. Pretty dry."

The nose of the plane lifted. I nodded. "Okay."

"But my personal opinion? He still likes you."

"He never liked me."

"I disagree."

"He told me in no uncertain terms," I said. "He never liked me. It was all just me being delusional, and he let it go on so I'd have, you know, a reason to live. Trust me. If there were any possibility for hope, I'd have found it."

Kit shrugged, like, *Okay. Have it your way.* The plane left the ground now, rattling and shuddering as it rose. I touched my fingers to my necklace. *Courage.*

Kit said, "There is one other thing, though."

I looked up.

"He started following me on Instagram."

I took in a breath. "Is that why you always take a million pictures of me?"

She nodded, looking very pleased with herself. "And guess what else? He's never posted a picture, and he doesn't follow anyone else. He doesn't even have a profile pic. I am the *one* person he follows."

I tried to process the idea of Ian using Instagram. "He saw the picture you took of my scars?"

Kit nodded very slowly.

"And the one this morning in the airport?"

Kit nodded again. "Assuming he checks his phone."

"So he might know we're headed to Europe."

"He might."

"So much for a stealth attack."

"The upside is," Kit went on, "it makes it easier to find out where he lives."

"How so?"

"When we get to Scotland," Kit said, shrugging, "we'll just message him for his address."

I nodded at her. "It's almost too simple."

Kit patted me on the head. "Almost."

EVEN BEYOND THE white terror of flying, I was nervous about the travel in general. At home, I'd developed routines and ways of doing things that had lifted my confidence. In Europe, I had no idea what to expect. We had researched everything online, of course, and I had a folder of print-outs in my carry-on bag. You can call ahead for a ramp to help you board the train from Brussels to Bruges, for example, but you can't just show up and demand one. I'd also made sure to find a hotel with rooms on the ground floor I could get to. Kit had wanted us to take a boat tour around the canals, but we learned in advance that none of the boats in town could accommodate wheelchairs.

We were as prepared as we could be, but nothing could have pre-pared us for the actual experience of being in Bruges. It was like a fairy-tale city. None of the normal twenty-first-century clutter, like neon signs or billboards. Just medieval stone and brick buildings with turrets and gables, a town square with a Gothic church, and chocolate shops, and cobblestone streets. And the canals! Every few blocks, stone bridges arched over the quiet water below.

Not to mention all the swans.

All my prep was worth it. There were tricky moments of travel—like when we boarded the train and found it packed with people, shoulder to shoulder—so full, folks had to move to the next car to make room for us, and Kitty sat on my lap in the chair to make space. But, in general, it wasn't as hard as I'd feared. I'd expected roadblock after roadblock, and humiliation after humiliation, as I tried to navigate a world set up

for able-bodied, French-and-or-Flemish-speaking foreigners. But we got along with surprising ease.

We reached the hotel in the late morning, and our jet-lag guide said we only had to stay awake until 10:00 P.M., so we ordered room service—steak frites—and watched European TV. Before it got too late, Kit and my mom popped out to raid the chocolate shops, and came back with a full shopping bag of dark, milk, white, peppermint, and salted caramel chocolates in every shape under the sun, from hearts to starfish, and filled with creams and nougats, fruit purees, coffee, almonds, macadamias, and peanut butter.

Kit dumped it all out on her bed in a pile.

"You've lost your marbles," I said to them both. "We can't eat all that."

"Sure we can," Kit said.

"We'll get sick," I insisted.

"Not me," Kit said. "I've spent years building up a tolerance."

In the end, we ate it all. The more we ate, the more it felt like a challenge we had to win. We really did make ourselves sick. It was impressive debauchery. Afterward, my mom and I had to lie green-gilled on the bed, and Kit threw up in the bathroom.

"I think I'm just dehydrated," she said, climbing into her rollaway bed by the window.

But in the morning, Kit was sick again.

"Maybe I picked up dysentery in the airport," she said. The nausea got better by midday. By evening, Kit was exhausted—but luckily nothing worse.

When it was time to get dressed, Kit lay on her rollaway like a corpse.

"You're fine now," I tried to insist, as she adjusted the cool rag over her eyes. "You haven't barfed in four hours. You and Mom need to get going."

But Kit, her voice froggy, didn't open her eyes. "I don't think I'm going."

"Um," I said. "You have to go! This was your crazy idea!"

"I do not feel good at all," Kit said.

My mom clutched her purse. "Maybe we should just skip it," she suggested.

"You're not skipping," Kit said.

"Well, I'm not going by myself," my mom said.

"Mags can go with you."

"I wasn't *invited*," I said.

"Go as me," Kit said. "We RSVP'd for three."

"But they don't want me there."

"Nonsense," my mother said. "It was an oversight."

I looked at Kit, who really did look awful, and then I looked at my nervous mother, who also looked awful. Kit clearly wasn't going anywhere. But no way was I making my mom go alone. I sighed to my mom. "Get me Kit's dress."

It was red—a "your-life-is-ruined crimson," Kit called it—and strapless, and kind of fifties-looking, with a crinoline underskirt. I worked my way into it while my mom fussed and tried to help. I also—fuck it— wore the new lingerie. I did my hair. I put on all the new makeup Kit had bought me, including red lipstick. I thought about wearing a scarf to cover my burn scars before deciding that would look worse.

Taking one last look in the mirror, I stopped to wonder if I should leave Ian's not-quite-formal-enough necklace on, before deciding *of course*. I'd be needing the word "courage" tonight.

Then I forced my mom out the door.

We were doing this.

Honestly, in the face of all the other things we'd survived this year, how hard could it be?

THE WEDDING CHAPEL was not far. Just around the corner.

My research had assured me that Bruges's terrain was very flat and that the cobblestones would be more of a nuisance than a barrier —both true. I also knew from my research that the chapel itself was right on ground level, so I could wheel in with no trouble. What I didn't know, until we got there, was how very tiny the chapel would be.

Seriously. It was like a little Christmas ornament.

Standing around outside, in a large crowd, were all the guests who couldn't fit in the building.

Surely, there were other churches that could have held us all. Surely, Evelyn Dunbar had not overlooked a detail like the size of the venue. But the longer we stood there, surrounded by others who couldn't get in, and craning our heads for glimpses of the action, the more it felt like Chip's mom—perhaps in a grand gesture of triumph to the watching world—had overbooked the wedding on purpose.

"Do you think she knew we wouldn't all fit?"

"I suspect she did," my mom said, nodding. "Better an overflowing church than an empty one."

We found a place in the stone churchyard to wait, but there was no place for my mom to sit, and so we were at different altitudes, not even talking, and I spent the next half hour watching her worry her hands at her waist.

"Why are you doing that?" I asked after a while.

She looked down. "Doing what?"

"Twisting your hands around. Are you nervous?"

"I'm not twisting my hands around," she said, stopping.

That's when I looked up to see that she wasn't peering toward the church like everybody else. She was searching the crowd.

That little moment right there made me glad I'd come all this way. She had something important to do, and I was helping her do it.

Ten more minutes went by. Then another ten. Finally, my mom decided to go check in with the usher standing at the door to see what the holdup was.

That's how we got separated. She disappeared in that direction, cutting right and left through the crowd—and she hadn't been gone five minutes before the church bells started ringing. Before she could come back, the chapel doors pushed open, and the bride and groom came striding out.

Of course they did. This was a wedding! Their wedding.

I felt myself hunch down, suddenly realizing in a new way that I was *crashing Chip's wedding.*

I had nowhere to hide, but as the little stone churchyard flooded with strangers in sparkly gowns and tuxes, the photographer called all the important people off for photos.

An usher directed everyone else to follow a little side street to the reception, but I waited for my mom—who never came back.

I was not positioned well, down low in my chair. People I recognized walked straight on past without seeing my face, and all I could really see was belts and handbags.

Finally, I wheeled up to the church doors to ask after my mom.

"I'm looking for a woman in a green dress," I asked the usher.

He shook his head. "There's no one left inside."

I looked around. Did she miss me in the crush? Did she go ahead to the reception, thinking I'd gone ahead, too? Was she waiting for me there, trembling and nervous? An image of my mother, twisting her hands through the reception, alone, appeared in my head.

Time to find her. I wheeled off, following the last of the migrating crowd.

IT DIDN'T TAKE long for me to lose them entirely.

My research swore that ninety-five percent of the streets in Bruges were manageable for wheelchairs, but this one street belonged firmly in the other five percent. These particular cobblestones were smaller and narrower, with deeper grooves between them. The "razor-thin" tires my dad had been so proud of on this chair were not exactly built for this terrain. In fact, I got stuck over and over—the wheel wedged between stones as I rocked back and forth, wrestling it out. Slow going. Frustrating. My hands got dirty. My fingers got pinched. At one point, the wind tangled the hem of the dress in the spokes.

Then the side street opened onto a better, smoother one, where I was able to pick up some speed and coast up over the crest of a stone bridge. That's where I caught up with all the wedding guests. At a taxi stand. Which turned out to be for a *water* taxi. The kind I knew from the Internet couldn't accommodate wheelchairs.

This was how we were all getting to the reception. Boats.

I stopped right there on the bridge and took in the scene. Two boats, filled to the brim with wedding guests, had just motored away from the dock, and a last boat was loading. Men in tuxes and women in gowns waited in a snaking line around wood turnstiles. I scanned the guests for my mom's green dress, but I couldn't find her. Then I eyed the boat. I might manage to board, if somebody would help me. But as I coasted over and arrived at the entrance to the taxi stand, I found a bigger problem: It was about twenty stone steps from the road down to the water.

Twenty steep, uneven, Escher-like stone steps.

I stopped still at the top. The steps were tall and narrow. I could navigate a curb back in the States, and possibly two low steps on a very lucky day, but not this. No way was I making it down this. Not without dying.

I watched couple after couple use their working legs and feet to walk thoughtlessly up to the boat and step in, and I felt a sharp stab of despair. What was I doing here? Kitty had bailed, I'd lost my mother, and now there was no way I could make it to the reception that I wasn't even invited to.

I felt a funny little pressure in my throat, like I might cry.

I took a shuddery breath. I should never have come. Time to give up. Long past time, probably.

That's when the boat driver noticed me.

"Est-ce que vous allez à la soirée?" he asked, in French.

He thought I was Belgian. How flattering! *"Non!"* I shouted back. *"C'est d'accord."* No. It's okay! High school French for the win. It didn't often come in handy in Texas.

But the driver was already gesturing at the two guys on the dock, both of whom looked about seventy, and then they were both clambering toward me, up the steps with determination.

"Non, non," I said, shaking my hands at them like I didn't need help. *"Mes jambons sont eclatés."* I was trying to say, "My legs are broken," but I didn't realize until later that I'd confused the word *jambe,* French for "leg," with *jambon,* French for "ham." I'd also accidentally switched

"broken" for "burst"—and so I'd basically just told them that my hams exploded.

The two men paused to look at each other.

Then they kept coming. I clearly did need help.

Of course I wasn't just a passerby in wedding attire. *Of course* I was a guest at this wedding. Just because I couldn't make it down those steps didn't mean I wasn't going to.

Over my protests, one elderly but surprisingly strong dock worker lifted me and cradled me in his arms as if he carried women like this every day, and then we were off, teetering down the steps. The other guy folded up my chair and followed us, and before I knew it, they were stepping into the boat and depositing me there—in a seat up at the prow that faced backward toward the crowd.

Every other seat, as far as I could tell, faced forward—except the one I was in, and the empty one beside it. In the churchyard, absolutely no one had noticed me. Now, they all stared.

What could I do? There was no getting off. There was no changing seats. I stared back. I didn't recognize anyone. My chair and my wedding-crashing self were stuck alone on a boat full of curious strangers. A boat that wasn't going anywhere.

The taxi crew had switched back to Flemish, but I could tell that the driver wanted to leave, even though the dockworkers thought he should stay. He kept telling them to untie the boat, but they didn't think they were supposed to. Finally, one of them dashed back up those lethal steps again to get a look around, and he called something down and pointed out of view.

Was somebody coming?

And then I saw.

Somebody was coming, all right.

The wedding party.

Twenty-eight

THEY GATHERED BY the bridge at the top of the steps to the taxi stand like a pouty spread in *Vanity Fair*, at the very spot where I had just been. I got my first good gander, and it was so strange to see all the guys who would have been our groomsmen—Woody, Statler, Murphy, and Harris— paired up with a flock of female strangers. Just as I thought that, a breeze rose up and caused all the bridesmaids' gowns to billow in slow motion.

Then the group parted, and I braced myself for the appearance of the bride and groom. But the couple that appeared were not Chip and the Whiner, but instead, Jim and Evelyn Dunbar. Chip's folks.

I had seen Evelyn several times since the day we'd fought in the hospital, of course. She was our next-door neighbor, after all.

But I had not spoken to her. Not once, in all this time.

At first, if she popped by, I hid. I felt like I couldn't face her, and I gave myself permission not to. As time went by, I stopped caring about avoiding her. But by then, she and my mother had begun their secret rendezvous.

We didn't work to avoid each other. It just happened.

After a while, my mother insisted that Evelyn had "entirely forgotten"

our little "tiff" at the hospital. But I suspected that she'd long ago made me the villain of the situation: the desperate, broken girl who'd tried to manipulate her perfect son into giving up his perfect life out of guilt. Evelyn had never been the kind of person to face her son's limitations head-on. She could be very selective about her facts.

Hence, the "omission" of my name on the invitation.

It was fine. I didn't care. Except for one thing: She was coming my way, and I had no escape.

As she walked closer in her pale blue mother-of-the-groom suit and pearls, I wondered how she would react to the sight of me.

Not well, it turned out.

I have a theory that we are at our meanest when we feel threatened. People really seem to do their worst when they think you're out to hurt them, or steal from them, or take something that's rightfully theirs. And I could tell the minute Evelyn Dunbar's eyes met mine that she immediately thought *all of the above.*

She must have thought I was there to ruin the wedding. In her shoes, I might have thought the same thing.

She stepped into the boat, and froze when she saw me. Mr. Dunbar walked on to chat with some guests, but Evelyn bent toward me in my seat and dropped her voice about an octave. "What are you doing here?"

Other guests looked our way. No way was I discussing the *Parent Trap* plan in public. I shrugged instead. "Kit got sick, so I took her place."

She glanced around. She arranged her face into a smile. "You were not invited."

"I noticed that," I said.

"We thought it would be awkward."

"It would have been."

"But here you are."

"My mother thought it was an oversight."

"It wasn't."

"I'm not going to cause any trouble," I said at last, lifting my hands in a gesture of innocence. I meant to deescalate, but that just made her madder.

"How can you do this?" she hissed.

It seemed like an overreaction. "Do what?" I asked.

"Come uninvited and sit there like a goblin staring at everybody. It's creepy."

Was that what I was doing? "Did you just call me *a goblin*?"

"Just what are you trying to achieve?"

"I still can't get past the word 'goblin.'"

"Chip is moving on, and you should do the same."

"I agree."

"But you still had to come here? You still have to make this day, of all days, weird for him?"

I hadn't come here to make anything weird for anybody. But anger is contagious, I guess. Now, I couldn't resist. "Chip has made every day of the rest of my life weird for me, so maybe we're even. Except we'll never really be even. Unless I paralyze him back."

Evelyn's eyelids stretched a bit in surprise, like she suddenly feared that might be why I'd come here: to paralyze the groom. "That's not funny," she said.

I looked at her, like, *Come on*. "It's a little funny."

"It's time for you to go."

Sometimes you have no choice but to fail. But now was not one of those times. I hadn't gone through all this just to give up at the end. I had a mother to rescue.

"I'm not leaving," I said.

But Evelyn leveled a *don't you dare* look at me. "You're leaving," she said. "Now." She snapped at the boat crew to come over and deal with me.

Was that how this night was going to end? Me being tossed back onto the dock by an elderly team of Flemish boatmen? I thought about why I was here. I thought about who I wanted to be, and I decided that I wanted to be stronger for my struggles. Wiser, too, if I could. I wanted to be someone who made things better, not worse.

"I'm sorry I cursed at you," I said to her then.

Evelyn blinked. "What?"

"Back at the hospital. Last year. I used some language that upset you."

Evelyn pursed her lips at the memory. Her expression didn't exactly soften, but I could tell I'd surprised her.

"I was hurting, a lot," I said, "and I lashed out. I guess I thought if other people hurt, too, I might hurt less. But it didn't make me feel better to hurt you. It made me feel worse. I regret it, and I want you know I'm sorry. I should have been kinder."

Now she blinked some more.

When the crewman she'd snapped at made it over to us, he did not look like he was there to do her bidding. Instead, he looked like he wanted her to sit down. He started insisting that Evelyn take her seat, gesturing at the line behind her.

The usual Evelyn wouldn't have stood for it.

But it was like I'd taken the wind out of her self-righteousness. Or maybe I'd just shown her that I came in peace. Whatever it was, she didn't fight them. Instead, she went all docile and let them lead her to her spot.

THE REST OF the wedding party filled the remaining rows, leaving only the two prime center seats—directly across from me—open for Chip and the Whiner, the guests of honor.

Whatever lagniappe of peace had come from my moment with Evelyn, it disappeared at the sight of them cresting the bridge and then descending the steps so glamorously they could have been in slo-mo.

I looked around to check where the boat driver had stashed my chair. As if I might use it to roll away before they could spot me.

Of course, there was no rolling away. Staying right here, trapped in a seat directly across from the two reserved for the bride and groom, was apparently my only option.

I didn't know what to do with my hands—clasped? loose?—or where to turn my head. Should I gaze out at the swans and pretend I didn't notice them? Or maybe I should bend my face into a pleasant smile and look right at them on arrival, like, *Oh, hello! I didn't see you there.*

Instead, I reached up to rest my fingertips on the silver bar of Ian's necklace. *Courage.*

Chip didn't notice me until after he'd sat down. For a second, as he draped an arm around the Whiner, man-spreading his legs wide and taking in the sight of the canal, I sparked a hope he might never notice me at all.

No luck.

When his gaze drifted to a stop at my face, he leaned forward and flat-out stared. "Margaret?"

At the sound of my name, the Whiner sat up and stared, too.

There she was. Chip's new me. With a spray tan and too much eyeliner.

Tara. A girl I'd only ever seen in pictures. A girl Chip had compared me to from time to time—but only to point out my superiorities. I made better coffee. I had a better sense of humor. I had more rhythm. Here she was, in the flesh.

She looked awfully pouty.

I gave a little wave and said, "Hey!" like I was just now noticing them. "Happy wedding!"

"I didn't know you were coming," Chip said, and in that moment I could just tell: He did not know that I'd been left off the list.

What he didn't know wouldn't hurt him. "We all came," I said, and then added, "Everybody." Safety in numbers.

Chip looked around for the rest of the Jacobsens but came up short.

"I've lost them all now," I said, like, *No biggie.*

Then he looked around for my chair but didn't see it. "Where's your chair?" he asked. "Do you still need it?"

If my life were a movie, the answer would have been "That old thing? I haven't seen it in months." It would've been my moment to rise from my seat like a goddess and triumph over Chip and the Whiner and every person who had ever doubted me, including myself: Stand. Triumph. Roll credits.

I had longed for an ending just like that. But that's not the story I wound up with. And this wasn't the ending, either.

I pointed toward a storage compartment. "It's there."

"So you're still . . ."

"Paralyzed," I said with a nod.

He leaned a little closer, cautiously—like I might be feral. Then he put a big, fake smile on his face, leaned in even more, and said, "How are you?"

That's when I knew. *He pitied me.*

The bride was leaning forward, too, now, her arms crossed over her chest, but it wasn't quite pity on her face.

I matched his expression. "I am super great," I said, showing all my teeth. "How are you?"

Before Chip could respond, the Whiner jumped in, pulling his focus. "Chip!" she whined (there it was). "What the hell?"

Chip let go of his smile and got serious with me. "Why are you here, again?"

"It's a long story," I said.

Chip pushed out a sigh. "Because I'm trying to start fresh here."

"That's great," I said. "I cheer you on."

"Is that sarcastic?"

"No!"

"I don't need you to cheer me on, okay?"

I gave another shrug. "Too late."

My read on the situation at this point: Chip was mostly puzzled, and pitying, and jumping to conclusions about my motivations. But his brand-new wife was only one thing: furious.

"Look," I said to them both, "I wish you both well, okay? I am not pathetically stalking you. I've moved on."

But neither of them believed me.

That's when Statler called out from the next row of seats back, "Here to ruin the wedding, huh, Jacobsen?"

It was a joke, of course—meant, no doubt, to deflate the tension—but I suddenly realized that's what they all must have been thinking: that I'd come here with tragic, ridiculous hopes of sabotaging the wedding.

"I'm just here to celebrate," I said, lifting my hands in surrender.

But Statler just laughed. I was clearly a broken ex making one last

desperate attempt to—*what? Roll off with the groom?* There could be no other explanation. Fair enough. Out of context, flying three thousand miles to your ex's wedding might seem a little suspicious.

Before I knew it, I was trying to make them understand.

"It's been a rough year," I found myself announcing then, to Statler, and the happy couple, and the whole damned boat. "It's not the life I would have chosen," I went on, "and parts of it are absolutely brutal. But there are upsides, too. I'm wiser. I'm kinder. I've taken up knitting."

They couldn't possibly get it. Some kinds of wisdom can only be earned. I should have dropped the whole thing right then. But I just needed to stand up for myself.

"I am building a summer camp," I said next, "and I've started my own nonprofit, and I'm as busy and happy and productive as I've ever been. I've found my calling. I've found work that's so satisfying and thrilling, I wish I didn't even have to sleep."

I read their faces. They weren't convinced.

But it was okay.

Needing to find reasons to live had forced me to build a life worth living. I would never say the accident was a good thing. I would never, ever claim that everything happens for a reason. Like all tragedies, it was senseless.

But I knew one thing for sure: The greater our capacity for sorrow becomes, the greater our capacity for joy.

So I went on, "That's the thing you don't know—that you *can't* know until life has genuinely beaten the crap out of you: I am better for it all. I am better for being broken."

The truth of it both steadied me and left me a little shaky.

It felt like a real triumph.

Until Chip's bride gave me a look, like, *Please.*

Chip didn't seem too convinced, either. "You're saying you've moved on?"

Ugh. "Yes."

His eyes were like dares. "Does that mean," he asked, "that you're seeing somebody?"

Seriously? Was this the only definition of moving on? Was there no way to get better or be happy or live a great life that did not involve *dating*? Was being in love the only kind of happiness out there? I took offense at the question on feminist principle. I felt tempted to lecture him all night on the ways that women's lives did not need to be validated romantically by a man. Ridiculous! Narrow-minded! Conventional!

I almost said so. One more second, and I would have.

Twenty-nine

BUT THAT'S WHEN we all heard a person shout, "Wait! Hold the boat!"

At the sound, I noticed that the guys on the dock had already untied the ropes, and we were starting to motor away.

We turned in the direction of the voice, and one of the dockworkers shouted, in Flemish, what I presumed was "Hold up! One more!"

A lone man in a tuxedo was sprinting down the steps toward us.

A man who at first looked weirdly like Ian.

A man who in fact kept on looking like Ian, even as he got closer.

And then turned out to actually be Ian.

My Ian, of all people. Not in Edinburgh. Here. In Bruges. Running to catch the boat to Chip's reception, in a shawl-collared tux.

Ian. Here, apparently, to crash the reception, too.

I saw him, but he didn't see me. Too busy running and looking deadly handsome.

I would have told you my reaction to seeing Chip and Tara was visceral—but I did not know the meaning of that word until I watched Ian sprinting down those steps.

My lungs stopped working.

If I could have turned my eyes away, I would have looked for a place to hide.

But I couldn't turn my eyes away. I took in Ian's new haircut—a little shorter, a little spikier—and the fit of his tux, noting how European men seemed to wear their pants a smidge tighter than Americans, like they'd shrunk them in the wash.

In a really good way.

Then Ian was vaulting over the wooden turnstile, and then he was on the dock, running—no: sprinting, charging, *pumping*—along it, after us.

The boat had already edged away. It was three feet from the dock by now, but Ian didn't even falter.

He just leapt right off the corner of the dock and landed in a crouch on the one open spot of deck—about three inches from my knees.

It was a cool, badass, James Bond move like I'd never seen in real life.

Ian stood up then and faced the crowd. "This is the boat to the reception, I hope," he said to them all.

The *voice*. That accent—again, after all this time. I felt my insides melting like warm butter.

The driver shouted something angry at Ian in Flemish—I assume something like *Not cool, man! You're going to get yourself killed!*—just as the guests all broke into cheers. Ian brushed off his suit, apologized to the driver, and waved an aw-shucks thank-you at the cheering guests before looking around to notice there were no seats left.

That's when the boat driver pointed straight at him, like, *Sit down, pal!* Then pointed straight at the seat next to me.

Ian turned toward the seat, and that's when he saw me.

Our eyes locked.

If there was a moment for me to die of intensity, this was it. But I couldn't even do that. I couldn't breathe, couldn't think. And from the looks of things, Ian wasn't doing any of those things, either.

"Please take your seat, sir," the boat driver said, in English, at last.

But Ian did not take his seat. Instead, he dropped to his knees on the deck. In front of me. Kneeling at my feet.

"You're here," he said, a bit breathless.

All I could think of was nonsense. "I'm not here. *You're* here."

Every single person on the boat was watching us now, but as the driver revved the engine to pick up speed, the white noise of it gave us a little sound barrier.

"I'm sorry I'm late," he said.

Can you be late to a party you weren't invited to? "You're not late," I said.

Next, his eyes dipped down and caught sight of my necklace. "You're wearing my present," he said.

I nodded.

"I thought you might have thrown it away."

"I did," I said. "My mom fished it out of the trash."

"Good woman," he said. "Do you like it?"

Slowly, I nodded.

If it was good to hear the voice after all this time, seeing the face was just short of ecstasy. It made me woozy to be so close. I didn't have even one photo of him, and so I truly hadn't seen that face in almost a year. I drank in the sight—those dark blue eyes that always looked a little sad, the Adam's apple just above his tux tie, the jaw squarer than I'd remembered.

"What are you doing here?" I asked then.

"What are *you* doing here?"

"I'm here," I said, gesturing at the rest of the guests on the boat, "for a wedding."

"Your prick ex-fiancé's wedding."

"It hasn't been that bad," I said. Then I gave him a little grin. "It hasn't been that good, either."

He leaned forward and took my hands. "What could you possibly have been thinking?"

I shrugged. "My parents broke up, and Kit and I were trying to *Parent Trap* them back together."

Ian frowned. "At your ex-fiancé's wedding?"

"It was kind of a make-it-work moment." I met his eyes. "Plus, I'd never been to Europe."

"You should have come to Scotland."

I couldn't read his face. Did he know? "I was thinking about it," I said.

He seemed surprised. "Were you?"

"I thought I might pop over there when I was done here."

He studied my face. "Is that true?"

"Yes. Did you know that already? Did Kit tell you?"

"No. She didn't."

"'Cause I know you've kept in touch."

He looked down. "I had to keep an eye on you."

"I'm pretty sure the last time I saw you, you told me you never cared about me at all, so I'm not sure you *had to*."

"I was lying."

"What?"

"I was lying to you when I said that."

I squinted at him to get a better look. "You *didn't* not care about me?"

He settled his eyes square on mine. "I didn't not care about you." He leaned closer. "I cared about you." Then he added, "Too much."

"Can you care about a person too much?"

"I'm still trying to figure that out."

I studied his face. What was he saying? "Maybe you're lying now."

But he shook his head and picked up one of my hands and pressed it to his heart. It pounded in his chest. "I'm not lying now," he said.

That was a heck of a confession. "Why did you lie before?"

"Because I thought it was better for you."

"Why? Why would it be better for you to break my heart?"

He frowned and leaned closer. "Did I?"

"Pretty much."

"I'm sorry. I didn't think that would happen."

"Because you thought I didn't really like you?"

Ian nodded. "I thought it was just the aftereffects of the trauma."

"Well, guess what? It wasn't."

"I thought I was doing you a favor, really. I thought I was the only one who would suffer."

I had to ask. "Why would you suffer?"

He held my gaze. "Because I didn't want to be without you."

I kept not breathing.

This didn't seem like it could possibly be happening—me in Kit's red dress, talking to Ian, in a tux, on his knees, holding my hand against his beating heart. And yet there was no denying the boat, the water, breeze, the churn of the current.

We motored under a stone bridge, lit underneath by hanging lanterns, but I barely noticed. Until I heard my name, just as the bridge passed overhead.

"Margaret!" The voice sounded very close.

I looked up.

"Margaret!"

Hands waving on top of the bridge. Two sets of hands.

"Margaret!"

It was my parents. Together, side by side, standing on the bridge at the top of the arch.

"Why aren't you at the reception!" I called up to them.

"We decided to ditch!"

"Did anyone think to tell me that?"

"Couldn't find you!"

That's when my dad put an arm around my mom. In that one gesture, I knew something. *She was okay.*

More than that: *They* were okay.

All that worry about her? I could let that go. They'd found each other, and they knew what to do. They'd either work it out or they wouldn't. But my job there was done.

THE BOAT DIDN'T slow. We kept moving ahead. My parents receded into the Bruges night, waving a little longer, then dropping their hands and turning to continue their stroll.

Ian watched them, too, for a minute, before turning back to me.

"Why are you here again?" I asked.

"I came to find you."

"You came all the way from Scotland to find me?"

He nodded.

"Why?"

"Because I miss you." The word sounded like "mess."

"You do?"

Ian nodded. "Every day."

I didn't want to break this easily. I wanted to hold out and be tough and stay mad. Maybe it was the thump of his heart against my hand, or those earnest eyes, or that tuxedo he was not just wearing but *rocking*— but I couldn't hold out. "I miss you, too."

"Even after so long?"

"I think it might be getting worse, actually," I confessed.

"I told myself I had to wait a year to find you again—give you time to settle and find your way. I consulted with my brothers, even, and everyone agreed—a full year at the minimum. Now, it's a year. I had just bought a plane ticket to the States when I saw Kit's post about you coming to Belgium."

"You bought a ticket to the States?"

Ian nodded.

"But then you came to Bruges?"

Ian nodded again.

"Did Kit know you were coming?"

"In a way, I suppose. She texted me your flight schedule, and the hotel, and a photo of the wedding invite. And then she swore that you'd be all alone all evening long while she and your mother went to this crazy wedding. And then she told me she'd rented a room for me down the hall."

I shook my head. Kit. So sneaky. "So you went to the hotel?"

He nodded. "When I found her there instead of you, she sent me running toward the church."

"And they sent you running to the canal boats. And here we are."

"But," Ian said, "she didn't tell me about Scotland."

I met his eyes. "No?"

"Why were you going there?"

"Oh, you know. Just general tourism. Visit Loch Ness. See a few kilts."
Ian smiled a little. There it was.

It was so strange, looking back, to feel on that crowded boat like there was nobody else around. The sound of the motor disappeared, and so did everyone around us, and so did the past and the future.

"Back when we met," Ian said, "I was supposed to be helping you—but it was really you who helped me. The way you teased me—the way you called out my bitterness—the way you surprised me over and over and showed me the world from different angles. It made me better to be around you. You made me laugh—probably more in those weeks we spent together than in my whole life beforehand. You taught me about goofiness. You showed me a different way to be in the world. You brought out some warmer, more hopeful part of my soul. Then, after I left, I had to go cold again."

He went on. "I moved home to the gray skies, and I took a job I didn't like. I didn't even try to look for something better, because all I could do was count the weeks until I could get back to you. I made a pact with myself to give you a year—but I almost broke it a hundred different times. My only exception was if you started seeing somebody else. Then I was allowed to go to Texas and fight for you."

I gave him a look like he was crazy. "Seeing somebody? Like who?"

"I think that carpenter working on the camp lodge has a thing for you."

"He does not."

"It wouldn't surprise me if the architect did, too. He's a bit too enthusiastic."

"That is bananas."

"And of course I keep expecting Chip to crawl back begging any minute."

"Unlikely. Since he's married now."

"Short of that, I had to wait a year."

"For my sake."

Ian nodded. "So you could get back on your feet."

I let out a long breath. "Not literally, though. Because it's not looking like that's going to happen."

Ian nodded. "Maybe not, but you've done great. I've been cheering you from afar."

Something about not just what Ian was saying but the way he was saying it—so intense, so unflinching—had me practically hypnotized.

"Do you understand what I'm saying to you?" he asked then.

Did I? I could barely think. "Are you saying you're glad I'm better?"

He shook his head, like, *Not quite it.*

"Are you saying it's been a tough year for you, too?"

Not it, either.

I shrugged. "You're going to have to tell me."

He'd been resting back on his heels a bit, but now he rose up on his knees and edged forward, leaning in close.

"I think about you all the time, Maggie Jacobsen. I can hardly sleep for missing you. I ache to see you and be near you. I love you with a longing that I can barely contain, and I fear it's going to drown me."

Those eyes again.

Maybe I should have leaned in to kiss him then, but I found I couldn't move. It seemed impossible that I could want something so badly—and also get it. I'd been holding back for so long, I didn't know how to let go.

Until he brought his hand up to the back of my neck and pulled my mouth to his.

Because at the kiss, I came to life again.

The world stood still, but the boat kept going. We drifted past stone houses with stairstepped gables and gardens with foliage so lush, it tumbled down to the water. We floated past boathouses with wooden shutters. We passed cafés with hanging lanterns and candlelit tables by the water. But we didn't notice any of it.

Even as the boat taxi pulled up to the reception site and docked, and even as the bride and groom, and his parents, and the wedding party, and all the guests averted their eyes as they climbed up out of the boat and off toward the reception, we didn't let go. We barely noticed them.

We just stayed lost in that one kiss we'd waited so long to find.

Epilogue

THAT WAS TEN years ago.

We never made it to the reception, by the way. Just rode the taxi back to the stand and made our way to the hotel from there. Ian kindly—and impressively—carried me piggyback to the hotel, my folded-up chair under one strong arm like it was nothing.

We decided we ought to take it slow, but then we didn't.

We went back to Ian's hotel room—just down the hall from mine—and stayed up all night. I spent much of the evening trying to explain to Ian why he couldn't possibly be attracted to me, and he spent just as much of it proving me wrong. Convincingly.

In the morning, at breakfast, we all ran into each other at the hotel buffet—Kitty, my parents, Ian, and me—and found a table together. None of us looked too perky, but Kitty looked the worst of all.

"I think we're going to need to take you to the doctor," my mother said, touching her hand to Kit's forehead. "You look like a wax figure at Madame Tussaud's."

Kitty wiped her hand away. "I'm fine."

"Wrong," my mother declared. "You are pale and sweaty." Then, giving her a look, "I'm pretty sure they have doctors in Belgium."

"I don't need a doctor."

My mom looked at me for help. "Reason with her."

"You do look"—how to say it nicely?—"*not yourself.* Why don't you just—"

But Kitty started talking over me. "I'm fine! I'm fine! I don't need a doctor—"

As I kept going with "—see somebody? Just in case?"

While my dad added, "It's going to be such a long flight home, and the last thing you need is—"

As my mom chimed in with "It could be Ebola, it could be a burst appendix, it could be some kind of *E. coli* situation—"

We all yammered over one another like the most ridiculous bunch of foreigners, right there in our lovely Belgian hotel's breakfast café, until, maybe just needing to put an end to the madness, Kitty shouted, "I'm not sick! I'm just pregnant!"

We all fell quiet.

"I took a test this morning. Actually, I took three."

"Whose is it?" I stage-whispered, after a good long pause. "Fat Benjamin? Or the Moustache?"

"I vote for Fat Benjamin," my mother said, in her normal voice.

"Me, too," my dad said, raising his hand.

Ian and I raised ours for Fat Benjamin, too. "Unanimous," I declared.

Kitty gave us a look like we were *the worst.*

Then she said, "Benjamin, okay? I have to throw up now."

THAT'S OUR STORY. In the decade since the crash, things have moved on for everyone, like they do.

My parents did get back together. My dad just wasn't a grudge holder, or the kind of guy who could stay mad. As he explained it to me once, when I asked, "Your mother has never been perfect. And I've always loved her anyway." I'm not sure what I would have done if I'd been in

his shoes. But I think choosing to go back and work it out suited him. Leaving wasn't his style. He was a for-better-or-for-worse kind of guy.

My dad retired two years later, and about a month after he did, he got the news that he had lung cancer. Of all things. And he didn't even smoke.

"Too much sawdust," he shrugged, when he told us.

He fought it like a champ, and my mom sat right there with him at every appointment and through every treatment. She crocheted fuzzy socks for him and read him articles from *Reader's Digest,* and made steak, spaghetti, and meatloaf for him in a rotation. All his favorites, over and over.

To fill the time, in between treatments, when he felt good, he started volunteering reading books-on-tape for the blind. It wasn't long before he realized he had a knack for reading stories. For a while, he invented a job for himself as the bedtime story guy at camp, reading by the fire every Friday night to rapt groups of kids—doing all the voices and the sound effects. He loved it so much that even after he'd gotten far too sick to read, or even to walk out to the campfire, he still came out to listen to his replacements and offer them pointers. My mom drove him in a golf cart and brought folding chairs.

One night, near the end, when I was visiting him at hospice, he told me that those last years with my mom had been the best of all.

"Why?" I asked.

He smiled, a little sly. "She appreciated me more."

I flared my nostrils at him.

"I appreciated her more, too," he added. "And guess what else?"

"What?"

He gave me a half-smile. "I wouldn't change a thing." Then he squeezed my hand. "Be sure to tell that to your sister."

My dad didn't want to be buried, he wanted to be *planted.* So we dug a hole for his ashes on the bonfire hill and planted an oak tree there. My mother wants us to plant another tree over her ashes right next to it when it's her turn—so the two can grow together with their branches interlocked.

She brings it up a lot.

It's been three years now since he died, and my mom still seems lost. She keeps busy, though. That year without my dad changed her, and humbled her, and freed her in a lot of ways. She's easier on everyone these days—including, I suspect, herself.

She keeps the books for us at camp now, and helps with the kids, and not long after my dad died, she offered to take his storytelling place at the campfire. She also joined a feminist quilting group called Sew Feisty! that meets every week to sew and talk politics. She still worries too much and starts with *death* in every situation—but between me, Ian, and Oprah, we've got her keeping a gratitude journal.

She's trying. And trying always counts for a lot.

ARE YOU WONDERING if I ever managed to walk again?

I didn't.

We tried braces and walkers and electrical muscle stimulation, and one more surgery about two years after the crash, and then we called it quits. New technologies pop up all the time, and maybe science will catch up with me, but I'm not holding my breath. I no longer scour the Web for hope on that front. I've learned to look for hope in other ways.

I'm happy to report that my donor site scars did heal up, and after ten years of applying vitamin E, you can barely see them. That said, the grafts are a different story. Parts are smooth and parts are ropy and mottled, but no amount of vitamin E could make them anything less than tragic.

Which is why, on the five-year anniversary of the crash, I let Kitty tattoo the whole thing. She'd been begging me for ages, and she had a design all made up: a folk art flower garden "growing" from the back of my shoulder forward over my scar. She did the outline all on the first night, and she's been slowly adding colors ever since. Look at me from one side now, and I look like my old self. Look at me from the other, and I'm graced with flowers.

My mom said she was going to get a tattoo that night, too—but then she couldn't decide. She's still working on it.

I won't lie. Losing the use of my legs has been the hardest thing in my life. I don't want to downplay it. I don't want to pretend it has been easy. It's been the opposite of easy.

But there have been good things, too.

Ian wasn't kidding about being in love with me. I never could talk him out of it.

Guess what we did? We got married.

We dated for a while, long-distance at first, and then Ian came back to Texas. Now we run the camp together. Ian runs the PT side—Myles never did go after his license. Turns out, running Ian out of the country was enough revenge to satisfy him, and then Myles himself got a job in Orlando, left town, and—fingers crossed—forgot all about us. I run the business-y stuff and some fun stuff, too: finger-painting, slug knitting, origami, cake decorating, hay rides, *Sound of Music* sing-alongs.

Everything about Camp Hope turned out better than I imagined. We raised almost twice as much money as I'd been shooting for, due in part to all those followers of Kit's—but also due to my hard, tireless, obsessive work.

Yep. I give myself credit. I give us all credit.

Once my parents were back together, it took them about two minutes to get out the plans and start discussing the build, and my dad jumped in like a pro. I got to see my parents through new eyes, working as a team. My mother's relentless perfectionism, when focused on a project instead of on me, was powerful, inspiring stuff, and my dad's good-natured practicality was a nice counterweight. They collaborated, and even disagreed, in inspiring harmony.

I guess the design apple doesn't fall far from the tree, because my mom and I turned out to love all the same things: big windows, stone fireplaces, kitschy Western retro lamps, wagon-wheel fences, deep porches, ceiling fans, clean modern lines with classic farmhouse details, and whimsy.

We really got along okay.

The camp's been up and running for seven years now. It's a real, bustling, thriving place. It's sunny and warm, and the buildings are stone and stucco with tin Texas roofs, and big porches, and shady trees. We've got fields of wildflowers and nature trails. Everything is entirely ramp accessible—even the treehouse. We found all kinds of craftspeople to create magic with murals and sculptures and fountains. We made mosaics on the camp gates using all my broken dishes, and now we have a mosaic class where folks get to smash their own.

We run camps all summer for kids, and classes all winter for grown-ups. We have movie nights and cookie contests and charity projects for the sick. We have resource networks and referral systems. We offer classes for the newly injured as well as projects and support for their loved ones. We help people cope with where they are—but we also show them where they can go.

We don't fix everything, but we sure do make things better.

That's really become my whole guiding philosophy. I would never tell you that the life you wanted couldn't have been exactly as great as you planned. But you have to live the life you have. You have to find inspiration in the struggle, and pull joy out of the hardship. That's what we try to do—counterbalance the suffering with laughter, fuzzy blankets, hugs, sing-alongs, sunny-day picnics, chocolate chip cookies, and wildflowers. Because that's all we can do: carry the sorrow when we have to, and absolutely savor the joy when we can.

Life is always, always both.

And so: chili cook-offs, karaoke concerts, outdoor movie nights, inner-tubing, nature strolls, campfires, s'mores, skits, painted flowerpots, hayrides, and inspiration of all kinds. We chiseled Ian's mother's saying about helping others into a stone lintel above the office doors, and service to others has become a huge part of the program. Kids mentor each other, and teach crafts classes, and work in the garden, and help clean up. They make valentines for other kids who are in the hospital, bake muffins for the elderly, groom the horses, and work with service dogs to help socialize them. They learn through experience—kind of the only way you *can*—that taking care of others is a way of taking care of yourself.

And, of course, everybody gets a T-shirt that says THAT'S HOW WE ROLL.

Are you wondering what happened with Kitty and Fat Benjamin? As soon as we got back from Europe, he and his hipster beard came charging over to our house to beg Kitty to marry him.

Which she refused to do.

Not her style.

But she did allow a lifetime commitment ceremony, which is pretty much exactly the same thing. And she did tattoo his name on her arm, and she did let him follow her to New York and move in, and he did turn out to be the sweetest, most nurturing mate. And Kitty did give birth to the cutest little cupcake of a baby. Tragically, against all advice, they named her Pandora Snapdragon.

But you can't get everything right.

Somewhere along the way we decided "Fat Benjamin" was mean and changed his nickname to Sweet Benjamin, even though he insisted he liked Fat Benjamin better. Eventually, he became just Sweetie, which he likes even less.

Pandora got the nickname Dorie from us, which was the best we could do for her, and now she is ten and taller than her mom. Kitty and Uncle Sweetie turned out to be quite fertile, adding two brothers to the mix before Dorie was even five, and moving back to Texas after they were outnumbered.

Tragically, against all advice, they named their two boys Wolfgang and Socrates. But we do not tease the boys about it. Only their parents, late at night, when all the kids are fast asleep, and the grown-ups are playing board games and drinking wine—and we are begging Uncle Sweetikins to shave off that crazy beard.

OH! I WAS able to get pregnant, too. We were trying for one, but we got surprise boy-girl twins—and while nothing, truly nothing, about that has been easy, they're six now, and we hope we're through the worst of it. We named them Captain and Tennille.

Just kidding.

We named them after our four parents: Andrew Clifford and Elizabeth Linda. They play with their cousins at the camp all summer—swimming in the lake, and feeding the horses, and "helping" tend the garden.

Is everything perfect? Hell, no. Everything's a mess. A crazy, galloping, heartbreaking mess.

You can't fix everything. Not even close.

But you can look for reasons to be grateful.

More than that, you can work to create them.

That's what I've taken from all this. The crash all those years ago shattered the life I had, but the pieces wound up making a pretty good mosaic. That's what art is, I suppose: transforming things from what they were into what they could be. My life now, without question, is transformed. Maybe that makes it a work of art.

All I know is, we have as much fun as we can.

Every year on April Fools' we throw a giant Valentine's Day party, just so we don't forget. *Love happens all the time.* We made a mosaic out of that saying, too.

Do I ever think about the crash? Do I ever wonder what life would have been like if I had married Chip (who's already on Wife Two), or if I hadn't gotten hurt, or if I was still that perfect girl I used to be?

Not really.

I know better than to look backward. I know how to try, and how to fail, and how to try again. I know how to live from the inside out. I know to savor every snuggle, every morning swim, every tickle, every meal, every warm bath, every moment when somebody makes you laugh.

More than anything, I know that you just have to choose to make the best of things. You get one life, and it only goes forward. And there really are all kinds of happy endings.

SOUTH-WESTERN
CENGAGE Learning™

Survey of Accounting, Fifth Edition
Carl S. Warren

Vice President of Editorial, Business: Jack
  W. Calhoun

Editor-in-Chief: Rob Dewey

Executive Editor: Sharon Oblinger

Developmental Editor: Tracy Newman

Sr. Marketing Manager: Kristen Hurd

Marketing Coordinator: Heather Mooney

Sr. Content Project Manager: Martha Conway

Media Editor: Brian England

Sr. MarCom Manager: Libby Shipp

Production Technology Analyst: Emily Gross

Sr. Frontlist Buyer, Manufacturing:
  Doug Wilke

Production Service: MPS Limited,
  A Macmillan Company

Sr. Art Director: Stacy Jenkins Shirley

Internal Designer: Patti Hudepohl

Cover Designer: cmiller design

Cover Image: Corbis

Sr. Text Permissions Manager:
  Mardell Glinski Schultz

For product information and technology assistance, contact us at
Cengage Learning Customer & Sales Support, 1-800-354-9706
For permission to use material from this text or product,
submit all requests online at **www.cengage.com/permissions**
Further permissions questions can be emailed to
permissionrequest@cengage.com

The names of all products mentioned herein are used for identification
purposes only and may be trademarks or registered trademarks of their
respective owners. South-Western disclaims any affiliation, association,
connection with, sponsorship, or endorsement by such owners.

Library of Congress Control Number: 2009939864

ISBN-13: 978-0-538-74909-1

ISBN-10: 0-538-74909-1

South-Western Cengage Learning
5191 Natorp Boulevard
Mason, OH 45040
USA

Cengage Learning products are represented in
Canada by Nelson Education, Ltd.

For your course and learning solutions, visit
www.academic.cengage.com

Purchase any of our products at your local college store or at our
preferred online store **www.CengageBrain.com**

Printed in the United States of America
1 2 3 4 5 6 7 13 12 11 10 09

Survey of Accounting, Fifth Edition, is designed for a one-term introductory accounting course. It provides an overview of the basic topics in financial and managerial accounting, without the extraneous accounting principles topics that must be skipped or otherwise modified to fit into a one-term course. Written for students who have no prior knowledge of accounting, this text emphasizes how managers, investors, and other business stakeholders use accounting reports.

Hallmark Features

The fifth edition of this text continues to emphasize elements designed to help instructors and enhance the learning experience of students. These features include the following:

- **Integrated Financial Statement Framework** shows how transactions impact each of the three primary financial statements and stresses the integrated nature of accounting.

- **Infographic art** examples help students visualize important accounting concepts within the chapter.

The Operating Cycle

The operations of a merchandising business involve the purchase of merchandise for sale (purchasing), the sale of the products to customers (sales), and the receipt of cash from customers (collection). This overall process is referred to as the operating cycle. Thus, the operating cycle begins with spending cash, and it ends with receiving cash from customers. The operating cycle for a merchandising business is shown to the right. Operating cycles for retailers are usually shorter than for manufacturers because retailers purchase goods in a form ready for sale to the customer. Of course, some retailers will have shorter operating

cycles than others because of the nature of their products. For example, a jewelry store or an automobile dealer normally has a longer operating cycle than a consumer electronics store or a grocery store. Businesses with longer operating cycles normally have higher profit margins on their products than businesses with shorter operating cycles. For example, it is not unusual for jewelry stores to price their jewelry at 30%–50% above cost. In contrast, grocery stores operate on very small profit margins, often below 5%. Grocery stores make up the difference by selling their products more quickly.

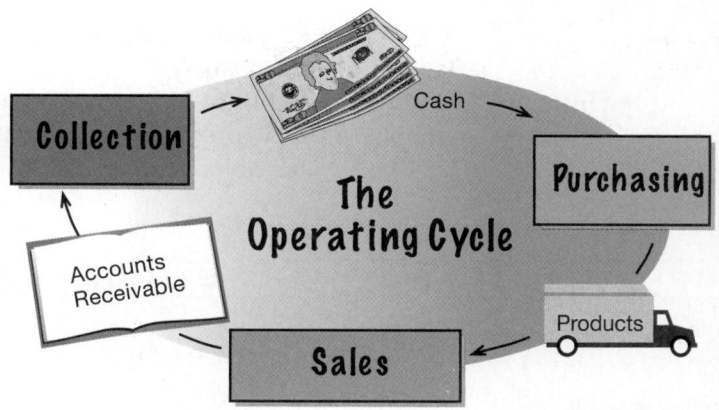

- **Illustrative Problems** help students apply what they learn by walking them through problems that cover the most important concepts addressed within the chapter.

Illustrative Problem

McCollum Company, a furniture wholesaler, acquired new equipment at a cost of $150,000 at the beginning of the fiscal year. The equipment has an estimated life of five years and an estimated residual value of $12,000. Ellen McCollum, the president, has requested information regarding alternative depreciation methods.

Instructions

Determine the annual depreciation for each of the five years of estimated useful life of the equipment, the accumulated depreciation at the end of each year, and the book value of the equipment at the end of each year by (a) the straight-line method and (b) the double-declining-balance method.

Solution

	Year	Depreciation Expense	Accumulated Depreciation, End of Year	Book Value, End of Year
a.	1	$27,600*	$ 27,600	$122,400
	2	27,600	55,200	94,800
	3	27,600	82,800	67,200
	4	27,600	110,400	39,600
	5	27,600	138,000	12,000

*$27,600 = ($150,000 – $12,000) ÷ 5

	Year	Depreciation Expense	Accumulated Depreciation, End of Year	Book Value, End of Year
b.	1	$60,000**	$ 60,000	$ 90,000
	2	36,000	96,000	54,000
	3	21,600	117,600	32,400
	4	12,960	130,560	19,440
	5	7,440***	138,000	12,000

**$60,000 = $150,000 × 40%

***The asset is not depreciated below the estimated residual value of $12,000.

- **"Integrity, Objectivity, and Ethics in Business"** features describe real-world dilemmas, helping students apply accounting concepts within an ethical context, using integrity and objectivity.

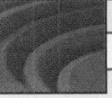

INTEGRITY, OBJECTIVITY, AND ETHICS IN BUSINESS

A History of Ethical Conduct

The **Wrigley Company,** which is now a subsidiary of **Mars Incorporated,** has a long history of integrity, objectivity, and ethical conduct. When pressured to become part of a cartel, known as the Chewing Gum Trust, the company founder, William Wrigley Jr., said, "We prefer to do business by fair and square methods or we prefer not to do business at all." In 1932, Phillip K. Wrigley, called "PK" by his friends, became president of the Wrigley Company after his father, William Wrigley Jr., died. PK also was president of the Chicago Cubs, which played in Wrigley Field. He was financially generous to his players and frequently gave them advice on and off the field. However, as a man of integrity and high ethical standards, PK docked (reduced) his salary as president of the Wrigley Company for the time he spent working on Cubs-related activities and business.

Source: St. Louis Post-Dispatch, "Sports—Backpages," January 26, 2003.

- **"How Businesses Make Money"** vignettes emphasize practical ways in which businesses apply accounting concepts when generating profit strategies.

> ## How Businesses Make Money
>
> ### Not Cutting Corners
>
> Have you ever ordered a hamburger from **Wendy's** and noticed that the meat patty is square? The square meat patty reflects a business emphasis instilled in Wendy's by its founder, Dave Thomas. Mr. Thomas emphasized offering high-quality products at a fair price in a friendly atmosphere, without "cutting corners"; hence, the square meat patty. In the highly competitive fast-food industry, Dave Thomas's approach has enabled Wendy's to become the third largest fast-food restaurant chain in the world, with annual sales of over $7 billion.
>
> *Source:* Douglas Martin, "Dave Thomas, 69, Wendy's Founder, Dies," *New York Times*, January 9, 2002.

- **An attractive design** engages students and clearly presents the material. The Integrated Financial Statement Framework benefits from this pedagogically sound use of color, as each statement within the framework is shaded to reinforce the integrated nature of accounting.

Integrated Financial Statement (IFS) Approach

This framework clearly demonstrates the impact of transactions on the balance sheet, income statement, and the statement of cash flows and the corresponding relationship among these financial statements. The IFS framework moves the student from the simple to the complex and explains the how and why of financial statements.

Chapter 1 introduces students to this integration in the form of actual company financials from **The Hershey Company**, a well-known manufacturer of chocolates.

EXHIBIT 10 Integrated Financial Statements

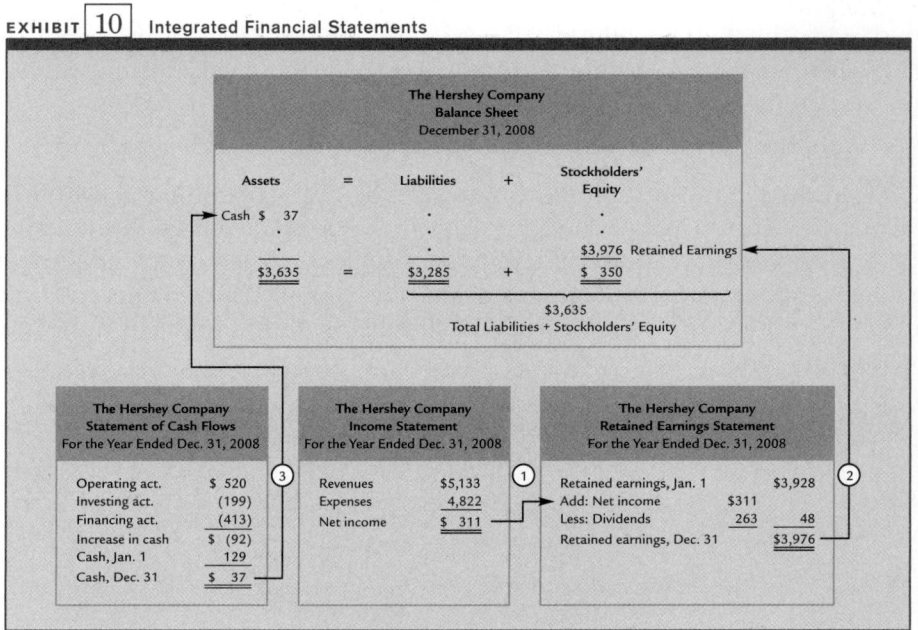

Chapter 2 begins with an example format of the integrated framework used throughout the financial chapters. Early in the course, students will gain a greater understanding of how important trends or events can impact a company's financial statements, which add valuable insight into the financial condition of a business.

EXHIBIT | 1 | Integrated Financial Statement Framework

				Balance Sheet				
Statement of Cash Flows	*Assets*	=	*Liabilities*	+	*Stockholders' Equity*			*Income Statement*
	Assets	=	*Liabilities*	+	*Capital Stock*	+	*Retained Earnings*	
Transactions	XXX		XXX		XXX		XXX	
	XXX		XXX		XXX		XXX	

Statement of Cash Flows				*Income Statement*	
+/− Operating activities	XXX			Revenues	XXX
+/− Investing activities	XXX	**INTEGRATED**		Expenses	XXX
+/− Financing activities	XXX	**FINANCIAL**		Net income or loss	XXX
Increase or decrease in cash	XXX	**STATEMENT**			
Beginning cash	XXX	**FRAMEWORK**			
Ending cash	XXX				

The primary focus in Chapter 2 is on cash transactions, which helps eliminate confusion for students who may have difficulty determining whether an event or transaction should be recorded.

Transaction (d)

During the first month of operations, Family Health Care earned patient fees of $5,500, receiving the fees in cash.

The effects of this transaction on Family Health Care's financial statements are recorded as follows:

1. Under the Statement of Cash Flows column, Cash from Operating activities is increased by $5,500.

2. Under the Balance Sheet column, Cash under Assets is increased by $5,500. To balance the accounting equation, Retained Earnings under Stockholders' Equity is also increased by $5,500.

3. Under the Income Statement column, Fees earned is increased by $5,500.

This transaction illustrates an inflow of cash from operating activities by earning revenues (fees earned) of $5,500. Retained Earnings is increased under Stockholders' Equity by $5,500 because fees earned contribute to net income and net income increases stockholders' equity. Since fees earned are a type of revenue, Fees earned of $5,500 is also entered under the Income Statement column.

The effects of this transaction on Family Health Care's financial statements are shown below.

Statement of Cash Flows	Assets		=	Liabilities	+	Stockholders' Equity		Income Statement
	Cash	+ Land	=	Notes Payable	+	Capital Stock	+ Retained Earnings	
Balances	4,000	12,000		10,000		6,000		
d. Fees earned	5,500						5,500	d.
Balances	9,500	12,000		10,000		6,000	5,500	

Statement of Cash Flows		Income Statement	
d. Operating	5,500	d. Fees earned	5,500

Fifth Edition Changes and Enhancements

- Designed for today's students, the fifth edition has been extensively revised using an innovative, high-impact writing style that emphasizes topics concisely and clearly. Direct sentences, concise paragraphs, numbered lists, and step-by-step calculations provide students with an easy-to-follow structure for learning accounting without sacrificing content or rigor.

- All real-world company data has been updated. This includes *The Hershey Company, Home Depot, Starbucks,* and *Microsoft,* among other real-world examples included in the text.

- Data and solutions to all end-of-chapter exercises and problems have been updated.

- Chapters 1–3 have been revised to incorporate the new high-impact writing style.

- In Chapter 4, "Accounting for Merchandising Businesses," "transportation" terminology has been changed to "freight" for added clarity. For example, instead of "transportation costs," "freight costs" or simply "freight" is used.

- In Chapter 5, "Sarbanes-Oxley, Internal Control, and Cash," "Depositor" terminology has been changed to "Company" in the bank reconciliations. In addition, based on user feedback, check numbers have been added to Exhibit 5, Illustration of a Bank Statement, to reflect that most banks do not return checks but simply list the cleared checks (by check number) on the bank statement. Finally, a stepwise illustration of how to prepare the bank reconciliation has been added.

- In Chapter 6, "Receivables and Inventories," the illustrations for allowance methods have been revised to enhance the ability to compare the percent of sales and aging of receivables methods. In addition, a new Exhibit 3 has been added comparing percent of sales and aging of receivables methods.

- In Chapter 7, "Fixed Assets and Intangible Assets," new Exhibits 5 and 6 have been added that summarize and compare depreciation methods.

- In Chapter 8, "Liabilities and Stockholders' Equity," the contingent liability discussion has been revised, including the addition of Exhibit 2.

- In Chapter 9, "Financial Statement Analysis," a new chapter opener features *Nike, Inc.* Each ratio is highlighted in equation form for easier review. Finally, an appendix on "Unusual Items on the Income Statement" has been added.

- In Chapter 11, "Cost Behavior and Cost-Volume-Profit Analysis," a new opener based on *Netflix* has been added. Also, contribution margin and unit contribution margin equations have been added to the cost-volume-profit discussion, including how to compute the "change in income from operations" equation based on unit contribution margin. An equation for computing the percent change in income from operations using "operating leverage" has been added. Finally, the discussion of margin of safety has been expanded to indicate that margin of safety may be expressed in sales dollars, units, or percent of current sales.

- In Chapter 12, "Differential Analysis and Product Pricing," a new opener based on *RealNetworks* has been added.

- In Chapter 13, "Budgeting and Standard Cost Systems," a new equation format for computing standard cost variances is now utilized so that a positive amount indicates an unfavorable variance while a negative amount indicates a favorable variance.

- In Chapter 14, "Performance Evaluation for Decentralized Operations," equations have been added for computing service department charge rates and determining service department charges. An example format for determining residual income and equations for computing increases and decreases in divisional income using different negotiated transfer prices have also been added.

- Chapter 15, "Capital Investment Analysis," now includes a new opener based on *Carnival Corporation.* New graphics have been added, and the format for using the net present value method was changed to be consistent with the format shown in the solutions manual.

Technology

- **CengageNOW**[TM] **— Just What You Need to Know and Do NOW! CengageNOW for Warren's** *Survey of Accounting* is an online homework solution that delivers better student outcomes—NOW! CengageNOW includes the following:

- Homework, including algorithmic variations

- Integrated e-book

- Personalized Study Plans, which include a variety of multimedia assets (from exercise demonstrations to video to iPod content) for students as they master the chapter materials

- Assessment options, including the full test bank and algorithmic variations

- Reporting capability based on AACSB, AICPA, and IMA competencies and standards

- Course Management tools, including grade book

- WebCT® and Blackboard® integration

WebTUTOR™

- **WebTutor**™ Jumpstart your course with customizable, rich, text-specific content within your Course Management System! Whether you want to Web-enable your class or put an entire course online, WebTutor delivers.
  - Jumpstart—Simply load a WebTutor cartridge into your Course Management System.
  - Customizable—Easily blend, add, edit, reorganize, or delete content.
  - Content—Includes rich, text-specific content, media assets, quizzing, test bank, weblinks, discussion topics, interactive games and exercises, and more.

Supplements for the Instructor

- **Instructor's Resource CD-ROM (IRCD)** This convenient resource includes the PowerPoint® presentations, *Instructor's Manual, Solutions Manual,* Test Bank, ExamView®, an *Instructor's Guide to Online Resources,* and Excel® application solutions.
- **Test Bank** For each chapter, the Test Bank includes true/false questions, multiple-choice questions, and problems. Each question is marked with a difficulty level, chapter objective association, and a tie-in to standard course outcomes. Available on the IRCD.
- **ExamView® Pro Testing Software** A computerized version of the Test Bank allows instructors to quickly and easily customize tests for their students. Instructors can add or edit questions, instructions, and answers and select questions by previewing them on screen. Instructors can also create and administer quizzes and tests online, whether over the Internet, a local area network (LAN), or a wide area network (WAN). Available on the IRCD.
- **PowerPoint® Presentation Slides** Included on the IRCD and on the product support site, each presentation enhances lectures and simplifies class preparation. Available on the IRCD.
- **Instructor Excel® Templates** This resource provides the solutions for the problems and exercises that have enhanced Excel® templates for students. Available on the IRCD.
- **Instructor's Manual** Each chapter contains a number of resources designed to aid instructors as they prepare lectures, assign homework, and teach in the classroom. Available on the IRCD.
- **Solutions Manual** The Solutions Manual contains answers to all exercises, problems, and activities that appear in the text. As always, the solutions are author-written and verified multiple times for numerical accuracy and consistency with the core text. Available on the IRCD.

Acknowledgments

Many people deserve thanks for their contributions to this text over the past several editions. José Hortensi and Jeff Rhinock were outstanding resources

for their careful verification of the end-of-chapter materials. The comments from the following reviewers also influenced recent editions of the text:

Tim Alzheimer, *Montana State University–Bozeman*

Scott R. Berube, *University of New Hampshire, Whittemore School of Business & Economics*

Suzanne Lyn Cercone, *Keystone College*

H. Edward Gallatin, *Indiana State University*

Robert E. Holtfreter, *Central Washington University*

José Luis Hortensi, *Miami Dade College*

Ann E. Martel, *Marquette University*

Craig Pence, *Highland Community College*

Patricia G. Roshto, *University of Louisiana at Monroe*

Geeta Shankar, *University of Dayton*

Alice Sineath, *Forsyth Technical Community College*

Hans Sprohge, *Wright State University*

Your comments and suggestions as you use this text are sincerely appreciated.

Carl S. Warren

Carl S. Warren

Dr. Carl S. Warren is Professor Emeritus of Accounting at the University of Georgia, Athens. For over twenty-five years, Professor Warren has taught all levels of accounting classes. In recent years, Professor Warren has focused his teaching efforts on principles of accounting and auditing courses. Professor Warren has taught classes at the University of Iowa, Michigan State University, and University of Chicago. Professor Warren received his doctorate degree (PhD) from Michigan State University and his undergraduate (BBA) and master's (MA) degrees from the University of Iowa. During his career, Professor Warren published numerous articles in professional journals, including *The Accounting Review, Journal of Accounting Research, Journal of Accountancy, The CPA Journal,* and *Auditing: A Journal of Practice & Theory.* Professor Warren's outside interests include writing short stories and novels, oil painting, handball, golf, skiing, backpacking, and fly-fishing.

Preface iii

About the Author xi

chapter 4   Accounting for Merchandising Businesses 127

chapter 5   Sarbanes-Oxley, Internal Control, and Cash 167

chapter 14 Performance Evaluation for Decentralized Operations 571

chapter 15 Capital Investment Analysis 613

The Role of Accounting in Business

Learning Objectives

After studying this chapter, you should be able to:

Obj 1 Describe the types and forms of businesses, how businesses make money, and business stakeholders.

Obj 2 Describe the three business activities of financing, investing, and operating.

Obj 3 Define accounting and describe its role in business.

Obj 4 Describe and illustrate the basic financial statements and how they interrelate.

Obj 5 Describe eight accounting concepts underlying financial reporting.

*Basic accounting equation:
assets = liabilities + equity*

When two teams pair up for a game of football, there is often a lot of noise. The band plays, the fans cheer, and fireworks light up the scoreboard. Obviously, the fans are committed and care about the outcome of the game. Just like fans at a football game, the owners of a business want their business to "win" against their competitors in the marketplace. While having our football team win can be a source of pride, winning in the marketplace goes beyond pride and has many tangible benefits. Companies that are winners are better able to serve customers, to provide good jobs for employees, and to make more money for the owners.

One such successful company is **Google,** one of the most visible companies on the Internet. Many of us cannot visit the Web without first stopping at Google to power our search. As one writer said, "Google is the closest thing the Web has to an ultimate answer machine." And yet, Google is a free tool—no one asks for your credit card when you use any of Google's search tools. So, do you think Google has been a successful company? Does it make money? How would you know? Accounting helps to answer these questions. Google's accounting information tells us that Google is a very successful company that makes a lot of money, but not from you and me. Google makes its money from advertisers.

In this chapter, the nature, types, and activities of businesses, such as Google, are described and illustrated. In addition, the role of accounting in business, including financial statements, basic accounting concepts, and how to use financial statements to evaluate a business's performance, is also described and illustrated.

Obj 1 Describe the types and forms of businesses, how businesses make money, and business stakeholders.

Nature of Business and Accounting

A **business**[1] is an organization in which basic resources (inputs), such as materials and labor, are assembled and processed to provide goods or services (outputs) to customers. Businesses come in all sizes, from a local coffee house to *Starbucks,* which sells over $9 billion of coffee and related products each year.

The objective of most businesses is to earn a profit. **Profit** is the difference between the amounts received from customers for goods or services and the amounts paid for the inputs used to provide the goods or services. In this text, we focus on businesses operating to earn a profit. However, many of the same concepts and principles also apply to not-for-profit organizations such as hospitals, churches, and government agencies.

Types of Businesses

Three types of businesses operated for profit include service, merchandising, and manufacturing businesses. Each type of business and some examples are described below.

Roughly eight out of every ten workers in the United States are service providers.

Service businesses provide services rather than products to customers.

> *Delta Air Lines* (transportation services)
>
> *The Walt Disney Company* (entertainment services)

Merchandising businesses sell products they purchase from other businesses to customers.

> *Wal-Mart* (general merchandise)
>
> *Amazon.com* (books, music, videos)

Manufacturing businesses change basic inputs into products that are sold to customers.

> *General Motors Corporation* (cars, trucks, vans)
>
> *Dell Inc.* (personal computers)

Forms of Business

A business is normally organized in one of the following four forms:

* proprietorship
* partnership
* corporation
* limited liability company

A **proprietorship** is owned by one individual. More than 70% of the businesses in the United States are organized as proprietorships. The frequency of this form is due to the ease and low cost of organizing. The primary disadvantage of proprietorships is that the financial resources are limited to the individual owner's resources. In addition, the owner has unlimited liability to creditors for the debts of the company.

A **partnership** is owned by two or more individuals. About 10% of the businesses in the United States are organized as partnerships. Like a proprietorship, a partnership may outgrow the financial resources of its

---

[1] A complete glossary of terms appears at the end of the text.

owners. Also, the partners have unlimited liability to creditors for the debts of the company.

A **corporation** is organized under state or federal statutes as a separate legal entity. The ownership of a corporation is divided into shares of stock. A corporation issues the stock to individuals or other companies, who then become owners or **stockholders** of the corporation. About 20 percent of the businesses in the United States are organized as corporations. A primary advantage of the corporate form is the ability to obtain large amounts of resources by issuing shares of stock. In addition, the stockholders' liability to creditors for the debts of the company is limited to their investment in the corporation.

A **limited liability company (LLC)** combines attributes of a partnership and a corporation. The primary advantage of the limited liability company form is that it operates similar to a partnership, but its owners' (or members') liability for the debts of the company is limited to their investment.

In addition to the ease of formation, ability to raise capital, and liability for the debts of the business, other factors such as taxes and legal life of the business form should be considered when forming a business. For example, corporations are taxed as separate legal entities, while the income of sole proprietorships, partnerships, and limited liability companies is passed through to the owners and taxed on the owners' tax returns. As separate legal entities, corporations also continue on, regardless of the lives of the individual owners. In contrast, sole proprietorships, partnerships, and limited liability companies may terminate their existence with the death of an individual owner.

The characteristics of sole proprietorships, partnerships, corporations, and limited liability companies discussed in this section are summarized below.

Many professional practices such as lawyers, doctors, and accountants are organized as limited liability companies.

Organizational Form	Ease of Formation	Legal Liability	Taxation	Limitation on Life of Entity	Access to Capital
Proprietorship	Simple	No limitation	Nontaxable (pass-through) entity	Yes	Limited
Partnership	Simple	No limitation	Nontaxable (pass-through) entity	Yes	Average
Corporation	Complex	Limited liability	Taxable entity	No	Extensive
Limited Liability Company	Moderate	Limited liability	Nontaxable (pass-through) entity by election	Yes	Average

[handwritten annotations: "70% of businesses are", "can take all your personal assets", "hard to get loans"]

The three types of businesses we discussed earlier—manufacturing, merchandising, and service—may be proprietorships, partnerships, corporations, or limited liability companies. However, businesses that require a large amount of resources, such as many manufacturing businesses, are corporations. Likewise, most large retailers such as Wal-Mart, *Sears,* and *JCPenney* are corporations.

Because most large businesses are corporations, they tend to dominate the economic activity in the United States. For this reason, this text focuses on the corporate form of organization. However, many of the concepts and principles discussed also apply to proprietorships, partnerships, and limited liability companies.

How Do Businesses Make Money?

The objective of a business is to earn a profit by providing goods or services to customers. How does a company decide which products or services to

offer its customers? Many factors influence this decision. Ultimately, however, the decision is based on how the company plans to gain an advantage over its competitors and, in doing so, maximize its profits.

Companies try to maximize their profits by generating high revenues while maintaining low costs, which results in high profits. However, a company's competitors are also trying to do the same and thus, a company can only maximize its profits by gaining an advantage over its competitors.

Generally, companies gain an advantage over their competitors by using one of the following two strategies:

- A **low-cost strategy** is one where a company designs and produces products or services at a lower cost than its competitors. Such companies often sell no-frills, standardized products and services.

- A **premium-price strategy** is one where a company tries to design and produce products or services that serve unique market needs, allowing it to charge premium prices. Such companies often design and market their products so that customers perceive their products or services as having a unique quality, reliability, or image.

Wal-Mart and *Southwest Airlines* are examples of companies using a low-cost strategy. *John Deere, Tommy Hilfiger,* and *BMW* are examples of companies using a premium-price strategy.

Since business is highly competitive, it is difficult for a company to sustain a competitive advantage over time. For example, a competitor of a company using a low-cost strategy may copy the company's low-cost methods or develop new methods that achieve even lower costs. Likewise, a competitor of a company using a premium-price strategy may develop products that are perceived as more desirable by customers.

Examples of companies utilizing low-cost and premium-price strategies include:

- Local pharmacies who develop personalized relationships with their customers. By doing so, they are able to charge premium (higher) prices. In contrast, Wal-Mart's pharmacies use the low-cost emphasis and compete on cost.

- Grocery stores such as *Kroger* and *Safeway* develop relationships with their customers by issuing preferred customer cards. These cards allow the stores to track consumer preferences and buying habits for use in purchasing and advertising campaigns.

- *Honda* promotes the reliability and quality ratings of its automobiles and thus, charges premium prices. Similarly, *Volvo* promotes the safety characteristics of its automobiles. In contrast, *Hyundai* and *Kia* use a low-cost strategy.

- *Harley-Davidson* emphasizes that its motorcycles are "Made in America" and promotes its "rebel" image as a means of charging higher prices than competitors Honda, *Yamaha,* or *Suzuki.*

Companies often struggle to find a competitive advantage. For example, JCPenney and Sears have difficulty competing on low costs against Wal-Mart, *Kohl's, T.J. Maxx,* and *Target.* At the same time, JCPenney and Sears have difficulty charging premium prices against competitors such as *The Gap, Eddie Bauer,* and *Talbot's.* Likewise, Delta Air Lines and *United Airlines* have difficulty competing against low-cost airlines such as Southwest and *AirTran.*

At the same time, Delta and United don't offer any unique services for which their passengers are willing to pay a premium price.

Exhibit 1 summarizes the characteristics of the low-cost and premium-price strategies. Common examples of companies that employ each strategy are also listed.

EXHIBIT 1 Business Strategies and Industries

Business Strategy	Industry					
	Airline	Freight	Automotive	Retail	Financial Services	Hotel
Low cost	Southwest	Union Pacific	Saturn	Sam's Club	Ameritrade	Super 8
Premium price	Virgin Atlantic	FedEx	BMW	Talbot's	Morgan Stanley	Ritz-Carlton

Business Stakeholders

A **business stakeholder** is a person or entity with an interest in the economic performance and well-being of a company. For example, owners, suppliers, customers, and employees are all stakeholders in a company.

Business stakeholders can be classified into one of the four categories illustrated in Exhibit 2.

EXHIBIT 2 Business Stakeholders

Business Stakeholder	Interest in the Business	Examples
Capital market stakeholders	Providers of major financing for the business	Banks, owners, stockholders
Product or service market stakeholders	Buyers of products or services and vendors to the business	Customers and suppliers
Government stakeholders	Collect taxes and fees from the business and its employees	Federal, state, and city governments
Internal stakeholders	Individuals employed by the business	Employees and managers

Capital market stakeholders provide the financing for a company to begin and continue its operations. Banks and other long-term creditors have an economic interest in receiving the amount loaned plus interest. Owners want to maximize the economic value of their investments.

Product or service market stakeholders purchase the company's products or services or sell their products or services to the company. Customers have an economic interest in the continued success of the company. For example, customers who purchase advance tickets on Delta Air Lines are depending on Delta continuing in business. Likewise, suppliers depend on continued success of their customers. For example, if a customer fails or cuts back on purchases, the supplier's business will also decline.

Governments stakeholders such as federal, state, county, and city governments collect taxes from companies. The better a company does, the more taxes the government collects. In addition, workers who are laid off by a company can file claims for unemployment compensation, which results in a financial burden for the state and federal governments.

Internal stakeholders such as managers and employees depend upon the continued success of the company for keeping their jobs. Managers of

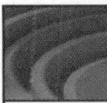

INTEGRITY, OBJECTIVITY, AND ETHICS IN BUSINESS

A Good Corporate Citizen

Many argue that it is good business for a company to be a good corporate citizen and contribute to the welfare of the society and the local community in which it operates. **The Hershey Company** has a long history of such involvement that includes the establishment and operation of the Milton Hershey School for disadvantaged children. The school is funded by an endowment of over $5 billion of The Hershey Company's stock. In addition, Hershey gives nonprofit, charitable organizations cash awards of $200 for each employee who can document 100 hours of volunteer work for the organization. Hershey also donates scholarships for minority students in south-central Pennsylvania.

Sources: Bill Sutton, "Donations to Aid Minority Students," *The Patriot-News*, November 12, 2004, and "Hershey Throws Green-line a Kiss," *The Commercial Appeal*, September 26, 2004.

companies that perform poorly are often fired by the owners. Likewise, during economic downturns companies often lay off workers.

The preceding stakeholders are illustrated in Exhibit 3.

EXHIBIT 3   **Business Stakeholders**

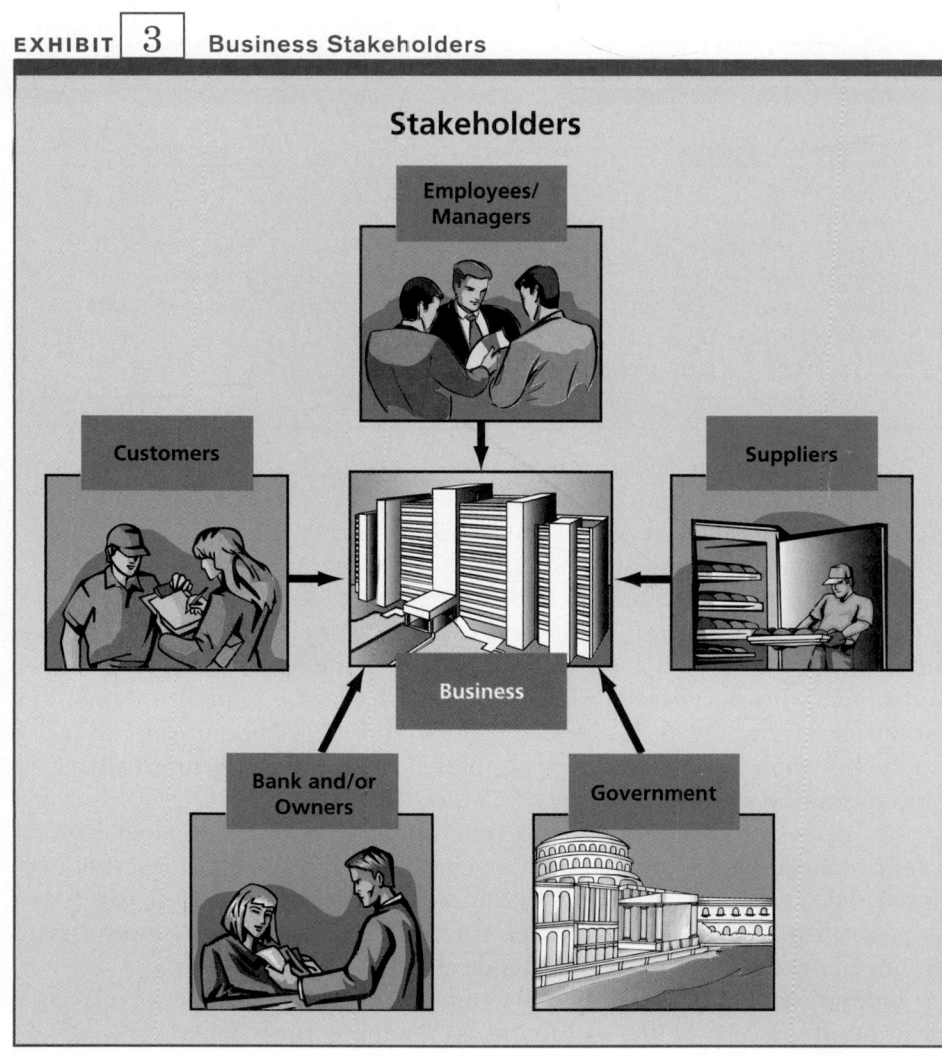

Business Activities

Obj 2 Describe the three business activities of financing, investing, and operating.

All companies engage in the following three business activities:

* **Financing activities** to obtain the necessary funds (monies) to organize and operate the company
* **Investing activities** to obtain assets such as buildings and equipment to begin and operate the company
* **Operating activities** to earn revenues and profits

The preceding business activities are illustrated in Exhibit 4.

EXHIBIT 4 | **Business Activities**

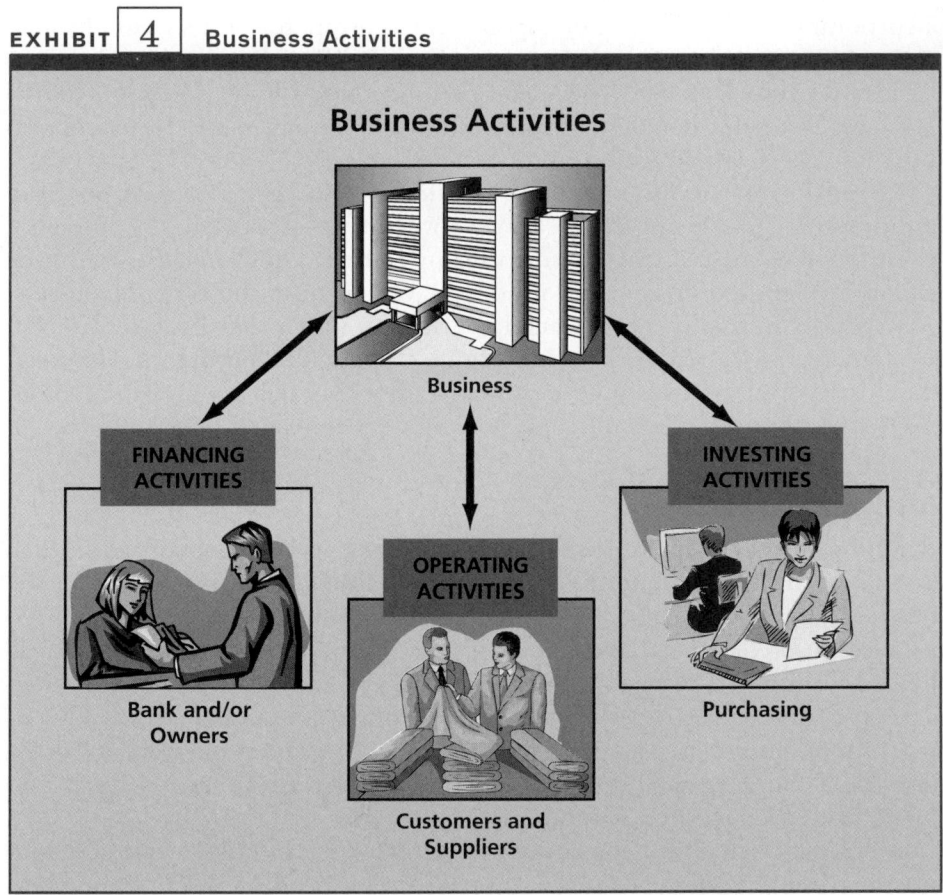

Financing Activities

Financing activities involve obtaining funds to begin and operate a business. Companies obtain financing through the use of capital markets by:

* borrowing
* issuing shares of ownership

When a company borrows money, it incurs a liability. A **liability** is a legal obligation to repay the amount borrowed according to the terms of the borrowing agreement. When a company borrows from a vendor or supplier, the liability is called an **account payable**. In such cases, the company promises to pay according to the terms set by the vendor or supplier. Most

Google reported, as of December 31, 2008, total liabilities of $3,529 million, of which $2,084 million were accounts payable.

vendors and suppliers require payment within a relatively short time, such as 30 days.

A company may also borrow money by issuing bonds. *Bonds* are sold to investors and require repayment normally with interest. The amount of the bonds, called the *face value,* usually requires repayment several years in the future. Thus, bonds are a form of long-term financing. The interest on the bonds, however, is normally paid semiannually. Bond obligations are reported as **bonds payable**, and any interest that is due is reported as **interest payable**.

Many companies borrow by issuing notes payable. A **note payable** requires payment of the amount borrowed plus interest. Notes payable are similar to bonds except that they may be issued on a short-term or long-term basis.

A company may finance its operations by issuing shares of ownership. For a corporation, shares of ownership are issued in the form of shares of stock. Although corporations may issue a variety of different types of stock, the basic type of stock issued to owners is called **common stock**. The term **capital stock** refers to all the types of stock a corporation may issue.[2] Investors who purchase the stock are referred to as **stockholders**.

The claims of creditors and stockholders on the assets of a corporation are different. **Assets** are the resources owned by a corporation (company). Creditors have first claim on the company's assets. Only after the creditors' claims are satisfied do the stockholders have a right to the corporate assets.

Creditors normally receive timely payments, which may include interest. In contrast, stockholders are not entitled to regular payments. However, many corporations distribute earnings to stockholders on a regular basis. These distributions of earnings to stockholders are called **dividends**.

Microsoft is currently paying $.52 per share for dividends on its common stock, which with a market price of $24 yields a return of 2.2% ($.52 /$24.00)

Investing Activities

Investing activities involve using the company's assets to obtain additional assets to start and operate the business. Depending upon the nature of the business, a variety of different assets must be acquired.

Most businesses need assets such as machinery, buildings, computers, office furnishings, trucks, and automobiles. These assets have physical characteristics and as such are **tangible assets**. Long-term tangible assets such as machinery, buildings, and land are normally reported separately as "Property, plant, and equipment." Short-term tangible assets such as cash and inventories are reported separately.

On a recent balance sheet, *Apple* reported goodwill and other intangible assets of $559 million.

A business may also need **intangible assets**. For example, a business may obtain patent rights to use in manufacturing a product. Long-term assets such as patents, goodwill, and copyrights are reported separately as intangible assets. A company may also prepay for items such as insurance or rent. Such items, which are assets until they are consumed, are reported as **prepaid expenses**. In addition, rights to payments from customers who purchase merchandise or services on credit are reported as **accounts receivable**.

Operating Activities

Operating activities involve using the necessary assets to earn revenues and profits. The management of a company does this by implementing one of the business strategies discussed earlier.

---

[2] Types of stock are discussed in Chapter 8, "Liabilities and Stockholders' Equity."

Revenue is the increase in assets from selling products or services. Revenues are normally identified according to their source. For example, revenues received from selling products are called **sales**. Revenues received from providing services are called **fees earned**.

To earn revenue, a business incurs costs, such as wages of employees, salaries of managers, rent, insurance, advertising, freight, and utilities. Costs used to earn revenue are called **expenses,** which may be identified and reported in a variety of ways. For example, the cost of products sold is referred to as the **cost of merchandise sold, cost of sales,** or **cost of goods sold.** Other expenses are normally classified as either selling expenses or administrative expenses. **Selling expenses** include those costs directly related to the selling of a product or service. For example, selling expenses include such costs as sales salaries, sales commissions, freight, and advertising costs. **Administrative expenses** include other costs not directly related to the selling, such as officer salaries and other costs of the corporate office.

By comparing the revenues for a period to the related expenses, it can be determined whether the company has earned net income or incurred a net loss. **Net income** results when revenues exceed expenses. A **net loss** results when expenses exceed revenues.

As discussed next, the major role of accounting is to provide stakeholders with information on the financing, investing, and operating activities of businesses. Financial statements are one source of such information.

On a recent income statement, *Best Buy Inc.* reported revenues of $45 billion, cost of goods sold of $34 billion, and selling and administrative expenses of $9 billion.

What Is Accounting and Its Role in Business?

Obj 3 Define accounting and describe its role in business.

The *role of accounting* is to provide information about the financing, investing, and operating activities of a company to its stakeholders. For example, accounting provides information for managers to use in operating the business. In addition, accounting provides information to other stakeholders, such as creditors, for assessing the economic performance and condition of the company.

In a general sense, **accounting** is defined as an information system that provides reports to stakeholders about the economic activities and condition of a business. This text focuses on accounting and its role in business. However, many of the concepts discussed also apply to individuals, governments, and not-for-profit organizations. For example, individuals must account for their hours worked, checks written, and bills paid. Stakeholders for individuals include creditors, dependents, and the government. A main interest of the government is making sure that individuals pay the proper taxes.

Accounting is often called the "language of business." This is because accounting is a primary means by which business information is communicated to the stakeholders.

A primary purpose of accounting is to summarize the financial performance of the business for external stakeholders, such as banks and governmental agencies. The branch of accounting that is associated with preparing reports for users external to the business is called **financial accounting**. Accounting also can be used to guide management in making financing, investing, and operations decisions for the company. This branch of accounting is called **managerial accounting**. Financial and managerial accounting may overlap. For example, financial reports for external

The chief accountant of a company is called the comptroller or chief financial officer.

stakeholders are often used by managers in assessing the potential impact of their decisions on the company.

This text focuses on financial accounting. The two major objectives of financial accounting are:

- To report the financial condition of a business at a point in time
- To report changes in the financial condition of a business over a period of time

The relationship between these two financial accounting objectives is shown in Exhibit 5.

EXHIBIT 5   Objectives of Financial Accounting

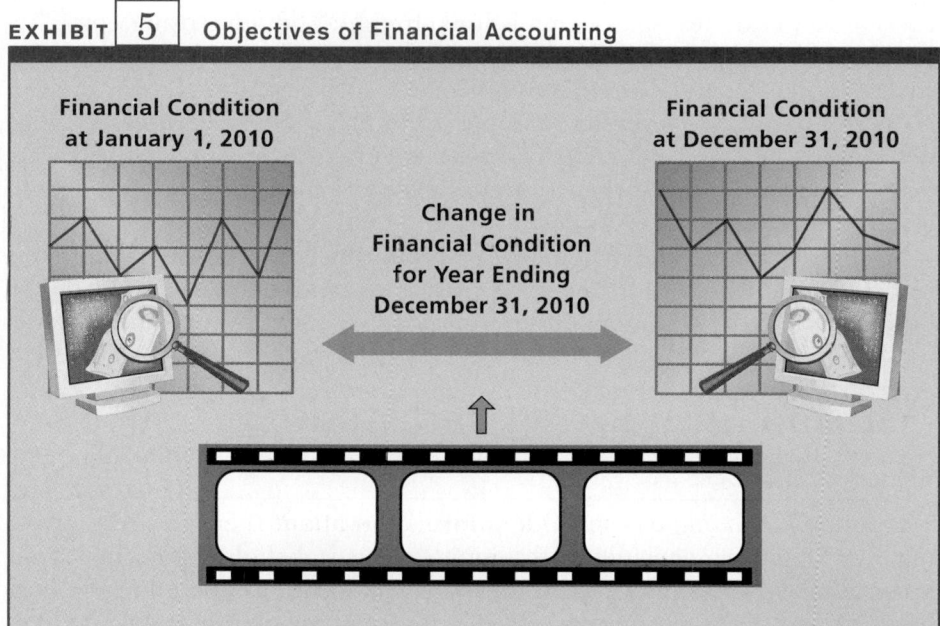

The first objective can be thought of as a still photograph (snapshot) of the company's financial (economic) condition as of a point in time. The second objective can be thought of as a moving picture (video) of the company's financial (economic) performance over time.

The objectives of accounting are achieved by (1) recording the economic events affecting a business and then (2) summarizing the impact of these events on the business in financial reports, called **financial statements**.

Obj 4 Describe and illustrate the basic financial statements and how they interrelate.

Financial Statements

Financial statements report the financial condition of a business at a point in time and changes in the financial condition over a period of time. The four basic financial statements and their relationship to the objectives of financial accounting are listed below.

Financial Statement	Financial Accounting Objective
Income Statement	Reports change in financial condition
Retained Earnings Statement	Reports change in financial condition
Balance Sheet	Reports financial condition
Statement of Cash Flows	Reports change in financial condition

The order in which each financial statement is prepared and the nature of each statement is described below.

Order Prepared	Financial Statement	Description of Statement
1.	Income Statement	A summary of the revenue and expenses for a specific period of time, such as a month or a year.
2.	Retained Earnings Statement	A summary of the changes in the retained earnings in the corporation for a specific period of time, such as a month or a year.
3.	Balance Sheet	A list of the assets, liabilities, and stockholders' equity as of a specific date, usually at the close of the last day of a month or a year.
4.	Statement of Cash Flows	A summary of the cash receipts and cash payments for a specific period of time, such as a month or a year.

The preceding four financial statements are described and illustrated for *The Hershey Company.* These illustrations will introduce you to the financial statements that you will be studying throughout this text.

The four financial statements for The Hershey Company are illustrated in Exhibits 6–9. The data for the statements are adapted from the annual report of The Hershey Company.[3]

Income Statement

The **income statement** reports the change in financial condition due to the operations of the company. The time period covered by the income statement may vary depending upon the needs of stakeholders. Public corporations are required to file quarterly and annual income statements with the Securities and Exchange Commission (SEC). The income statement shown in Exhibit 6 for The Hershey Company is for the year ended December 31, 2008.

EXHIBIT 6 | Income Statement: The Hershey Company

THE HERSHEY COMPANY
Income Statement
For the Year Ended December 31, 2008 (in millions)

Revenues:		
Sales		$5,133
Expenses:		
Cost of sales	$3,375	
Selling and administrative	1,073	
Interest	98	
Income taxes	181	
Other expense	95	4,822
Net income		$ 311

Since the objective of business operations is to generate revenues, the income statement begins by listing the revenues for the period. During 2008, Hershey generated sales of $5,133 million. These sales are listed under

---

[3] The financial statements for The Hershey Company can be found at http://www.hersheys.com through the Investor Relations Link.

"Revenues". The numbers shown in Exhibit 6 are expressed in millions of dollars. It is common for large companies to express their financial statements in thousands or millions of dollars.

Following the revenues, the expenses used in generating the revenues are listed. For Hershey, these expenses include cost of sales, selling and administrative, interest, income taxes, and other expenses. By reporting the expenses and the related revenues for a period, the expenses are said to be matched against the revenues. This is known in accounting as the *matching concept,* which is discussed later in this chapter.

When revenues exceed expenses for a period, the company has *net income.* If expenses exceed revenues, the company has a *net loss.* Net income means that the business increased its net assets through its operations. That is, the assets created by the revenues exceeded the assets used in generating those revenues.

The objective of most companies is to maximize net income or profit. A net loss means that the business decreased its net assets through its operations. While a business might survive in the short run by reporting net losses, in the long run a business must earn net income to survive.

During 2008, Hershey earned net income of $311 million. Is this good or bad? Certainly, net income is better than a net loss. However, the stakeholders must assess net income according to their objectives. For example, a creditor might be satisfied that the net income is sufficient to assure that it will be repaid. In contrast, a stockholder might assess the corporation's profitability as less than its competitors' profits and thus be disappointed. Throughout this text, various methods of assessing corporate performance will be described and illustrated.

Retained Earnings Statement

The **retained earnings statement** reports changes in financial condition due to changes in retained earnings for a period. **Retained earnings** are the portion of a corporation's net income that is retained in the business. A corporation may retain all of its net income for expanding operations, or it may pay a portion or all of its net income as dividends. For example, high-growth companies often do not distribute dividends, but instead retain profits for future expansion. In contrast, more mature corporations normally pay a regular dividend.

Since retained earnings depend upon net income, the time period covered by the retained earnings statement is the same period as the income statement. Thus, the retained earnings statement for Hershey shown in Exhibit 7 is for the year ended December 31, 2008.

EXHIBIT 7   Retained Earnings Statement: The Hershey Company

THE HERSHEY COMPANY Retained Earnings Statement For the Year Ended December 31, 2008 (in millions)		
Retained earnings, January 1, 2008		$3,928
Add net income	$311	
Less dividends	263	
Increase in retained earnings		48
Retained earnings, December 31, 2008		$3,976

Dividends are reported in the retained earnings statement rather than the income statement. This is because dividends are not an expense, but are a distribution of net income to stockholders.

During 2008, Hershey distributed (declared) dividends of $263 million and retained $48 million of its net income in the company. Thus, Hershey's retained earnings increased from $3,928 million to $3,976 million during 2008.

Balance Sheet

The balance sheet reports the financial condition *as of a point in time.* This is in contrast to the income statement, retained earnings statement, and statement of cash flows, which report changes in financial condition *for a period of time.* The financial condition of a business as of a point in time is measured by its total assets and claims or rights to those assets. Thus, the financial condition of a business can be represented as:

Assets = Claims (Rights to the Assets)

The claims on a company's assets consist of rights of creditors and stockholders. The rights of creditors are **liabilities.** The rights of stockholders are referred to as **stockholders' equity** or **owners' equity**. Thus, the assets and the claims on those assets can be expressed in equation form as:

Assets = Liabilities + Stockholders' Equity

This equation is called the **accounting equation**. This equation is the foundation of accounting information systems, which are discussed in later chapters.

The **balance sheet**, sometimes called the **statement of financial condition**, is prepared using the accounting equation. The balance sheet is prepared by listing the accounting equation in vertical rather than horizontal form as follows:

Step 1. Each *asset* is listed and added to arrive at *total assets.*
Step 2. Each *liability* is listed and added to arrive at *total liabilities.*
Step 3. Each *stockholders' equity* item is listed and added to arrive at *total stockholders' equity.*
Step 4. Total liabilities and total stockholders' equity is added to arrive at *total liabilities and stockholders' equity.*
Step 5. *Total assets* must equal *total liabilities and stockholders' equity.*

The accounting equation must balance in Step 5; hence, the name balance sheet. The balance sheet for The Hershey Company as of December 31, 2008, is shown in Exhibit 8.

As of December 31, 2008, Hershey's total assets of $3,635 million equals its total liabilities of $3,285 million plus its total stockholders' equity of $350 million.

Statement of Cash Flows

The **statement of cash flows** reports the change in financial condition due to the changes in cash during a period. The statement of cash flows is organized around the three business activities of financing, investing, and operating. Any changes in cash must be related to one or more of these activities.

EXHIBIT 8   Balance Sheet: The Hershey Company

THE HERSHEY COMPANY
Balance Sheet
December 31, 2008 (in millions)

Assets	
Cash	$ 37
Accounts receivable	455
Inventories	593
Prepaid expenses	189
Property, plant, and equipment	1,459
Intangibles	665
Other assets	237
Total assets	$ 3,635
Liabilities	
Accounts payable	$ 250
Accrued liabilities	504
Notes and other debt	2,512
Income taxes payable	19
Total liabilities	$ 3,285
Stockholders' Equity	
Capital stock	$ 712
Retained earnings	3,976
Repurchased capital stock and other equity items	(4,338)
Total stockholders' equity	$ 350
Total liabilities and stockholders' equity	$ 3,635

The *net cash flows from operating activities* is reported first. This is because cash flows from operating activities is a primary focus of the company's stakeholders. In the short term, creditors use cash flows from operating activities to assess whether the company's operating activities are generating enough cash to repay them. In the long term, a company cannot survive unless it generates positive cash flows from operating activities. Thus, cash flows from operating activities is also a focus of employees, managers, suppliers, customers, and other stakeholders who are interested in the long-term success of the company.

The *net cash flows from investing activities* is reported second. This is because investing activities directly impact the operations of the company. Cash receipts from selling property, plant, and equipment are reported in this section. Likewise, any purchases of property, plant, and equipment are reported as cash payments. Companies that are expanding rapidly, such as start-up companies, normally report negative net cash flows from investing activities. In contrast, companies that are downsizing or selling segments of the business may report positive net cash flows from investing activities.

The *net cash flows from financing activities* is reported third. Any cash receipts from issuing debt or stock are reported in this section as cash receipts. Likewise, cash payments of debt and dividends are reported in this section.

The statement of cash flows is completed by adding the net cash flows from operating, investing, and financing activities to determine the *net increase or decrease in cash* for the period. This net increase or decrease in cash is

then added to the *cash at the beginning of the period* to arrive at the *cash at the end of the period.*

The statement of cash flows for The Hershey Company for the year ended December 31, 2008 is shown in Exhibit 9.

EXHIBIT | **9** | Statement of Cash Flows: The Hershey Company

THE HERSHEY COMPANY
Statement of Cash Flows
For the Year Ended December 31, 2008 (in millions)

Net cash flows from operating activities	$ 520
Cash flows from investing activities:	
Cash received from selling property, plant, and equipment	$ 84
Investments in property, plant, and equipment	(283)
Net cash flows used in investing activities	$ (199)
Cash flows from financing activities:	
Cash receipts from financing activities, including debt	$ 286
Dividends paid to stockholders	(263)
Repurchase of stock	(60)
Other, including repayment of debt	(376)
Net cash flows used in financing activities	$ (413)
Net decrease in cash during 2008	$ (92)
Cash as of January 1, 2008	129
Cash as of December 31, 2008	$ 37

During 2008, Hershey's *operating activities* generated a positive net cash flow of $520 million. Hershey's *investing activities* used $199 million of cash primarily to purchase property, plant, and equipment. Hershey's *financing activities* used $413 million of cash. This cash was used to pay dividends of $263 million, pay debt of $376 million, and purchase $60 million of its own stock. A company may purchase its own capital stock if the corporate management believes its stock is undervalued or for providing stock to employees or managers as part of an incentive (stock option) plan.[4] Hershey received cash of $286 million by borrowing from creditors.

During 2008, Hershey decreased its cash by $92 million. This decrease is added to the cash at the beginning of the period of $129 million to arrive at net cash at the end of the period of $37 million.

Overall, Hershey's statement of cash flows indicates that Hershey generated over $520 million in cash flows from its operations. It used this cash to expand its operations and pay dividends to stockholders. Thus, Hershey appears to be in a strong operating position.

Integrated Financial Statements

The financial statements are prepared in the following order:

1. income statement
2. retained earnings statement
3. balance sheet
4. statement of cash flows

[4] The accounting for a company's purchase of its own stock is discussed in a later chapter.

Preparing the financial statements in the preceding order is important because the financial statements are integrated as follows:[5]

1. The income and retained earnings statements are integrated. The net income or net loss reported on the income statement also appears on the retained earnings statement as either an addition (net income) to or deduction (net loss) from the beginning retained earnings.

2. The retained earnings statement and the balance sheet are integrated. The retained earnings at the end of the period on the retained earnings statement also appears on the balance sheet as a part of stockholders' equity.

3. The balance sheet and statement of cash flows are integrated. The cash on the balance sheet also appears as the end-of-period cash on the statement of cash flows.

To illustrate, The Hershey Company's financial statements in Exhibits 6–9 are integrated as follows:

1. *Net income* of $311 million is also reported on the retained earnings statement as an addition to the beginning retained earnings.

2. *Retained earnings* of $3,976 million as of December 31, 2008, is also reported on the balance sheet.

3. *Cash* of $37 million on the December 31, 2008 balance sheet is also reported as the end-of-period cash on the statement of cash flows.

The preceding integrations are shown in Exhibit 10. These integrations are important in analyzing (1) financial statements and (2) the impact of transactions on the financial statements. In addition, these integrations serve as a check on whether the financial statements have been prepared correctly. For example, if the ending cash on the statement of cash flows doesn't agree with the balance sheet cash, then an error has occurred.

Accounting Concepts

Obj 5 Describe eight accounting concepts underlying financial reporting.

The four corporate financial statements described and illustrated in the preceding section were prepared using accounting "rules," called **generally accepted accounting principles (GAAP)**. Generally accepted accounting principles (GAAP) are necessary so that stakeholders can compare among companies and across time. If the management of a company could prepare financial statements as they saw fit, the comparability between companies and across time would be impossible.

Accounting principles and concepts develop from research, accepted accounting practices, and pronouncements of regulators. Within the United States, the **Financial Accounting Standards Board (FASB)** has the primary responsibility for developing accounting principles. The FASB publishes *Statements of Financial Accounting Standards* as well as interpretations of these *Standards*.

The **Securities and Exchange Commission (SEC)**, an agency of the U.S. government, also has authority over the accounting and financial disclosures

---

[5] Depending upon the method of preparing cash flows from operating activities, net income may also appear on the statement of cash flows. This method of preparing the statement of cash flows is called the *indirect method*. This link and method are illustrated in a later chapter. In addition, Chapter 2 illustrates how cash flows from operating activities may equal net income.

EXHIBIT 10 | **Integrated Financial Statements**

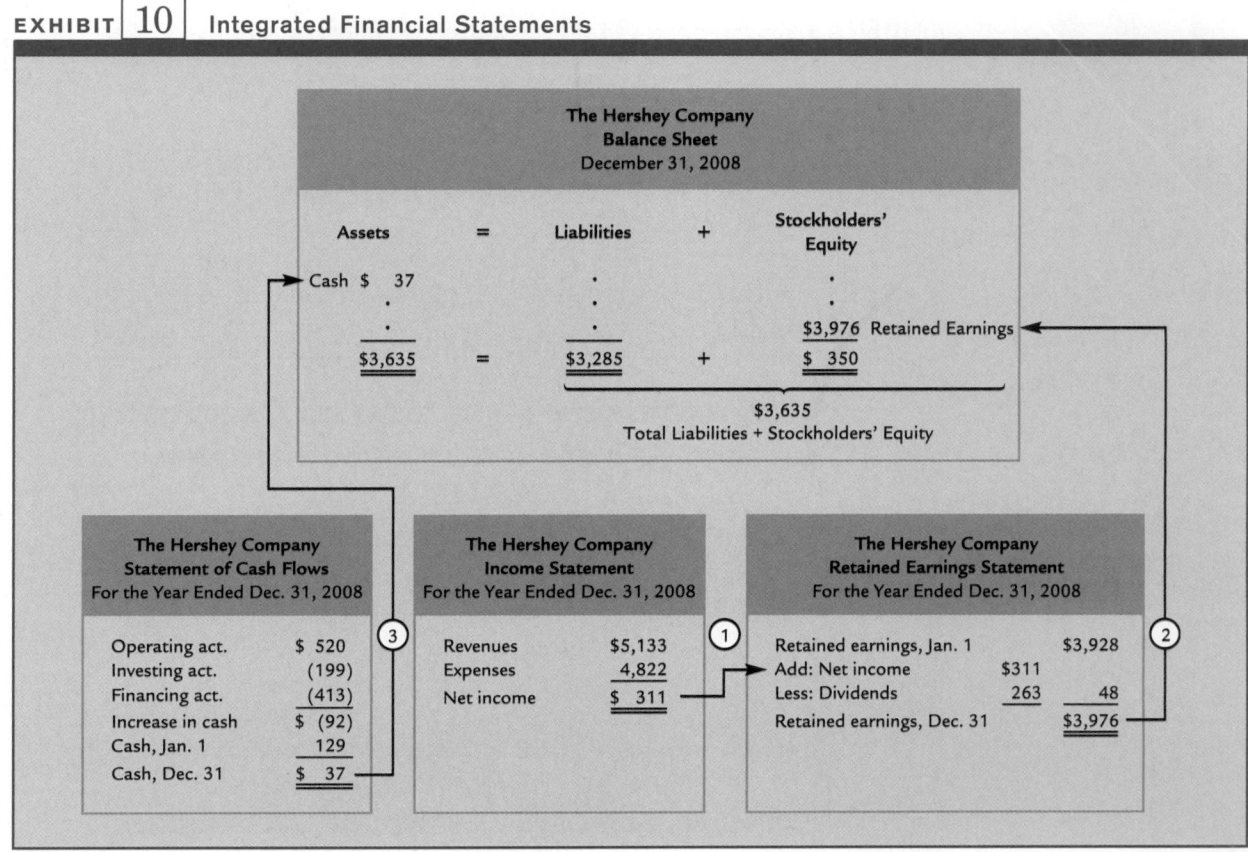

for corporations whose stock is traded and sold to the public. The SEC normally accepts the accounting principles set forth by the FASB. However, the SEC may issue *Staff Accounting Bulletins* on accounting matters that may not have been addressed by the FASB.

Many countries outside the United States use generally accepted accounting principles adopted by the **International Accounting Standards Board (IASB)**. The IASB issues *International Financial Reporting Standards (IFRS)*. Significant differences currently exist between FASB and IASB accounting principles. However, the FASB and IASB are working together to reduce and eliminate these differences into a single set of accounting principles. Such a set of worldwide accounting principles would help facilitate investment and business in an increasingly global economy.

Generally accepted accounting principles (GAAP) rely upon eight supporting accounting concepts as shown in Exhibit 11. Throughout this text, emphasis is on accounting principles and concepts. In this way, you will gain an understanding of "why" as well as "how" accounting is applied in business. Such an understanding is essential for analyzing and interpreting financial statements.

Business Entity Concept   *owners transactions seperate from business transactions*

The **business entity concept** limits the economic data recorded in an accounting system to data related to the activities of that company. In other words, the company is viewed as an entity separate from its owners, creditors, or other companies. For example, a company with one owner records the

EXHIBIT 11   Accounting Principles and Concepts

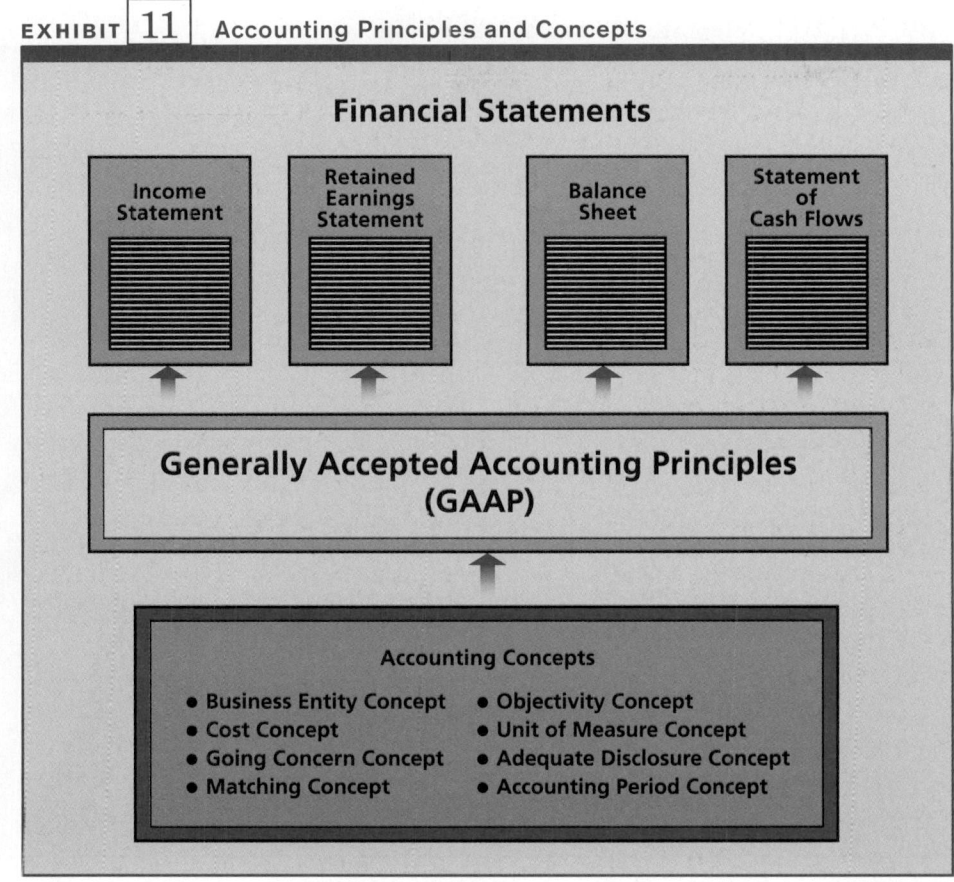

activities of only that company and does not record the personal activities, property, or debts of the owner. A business entity may take the form of a proprietorship, partnership, corporation, or limited liability company (LLC).

To illustrate, the accounting for The Hershey Company, a corporation, is separate from the accounting for other entities. In other words, the accounting for transactions and events of individual stockholders, creditors, or other Hershey stakeholders is not included in The Hershey Company's financial statements. Only the transactions and events of the corporation are included.

Cost Concept

what goes on the books, stays on the books

The **cost** **concept** initially records assets in the accounting records at their cost or purchase price. To illustrate, assume that Aaron Publishers purchased the following land on February 20, 2009 for $150,000:

Price listed by seller on January 1, 2009	$160,000
Aaron Publishers' initial offer to buy on January 31, 2009	140,000
Estimated selling price on December 31, 2012	220,000
Assessed value for property taxes, December 31, 2012	190,000

Under the cost concept, Aaron Publishers records the purchase of the land on February 20, 2009, at the purchase price of $150,000. The other amounts listed above have no effect on the accounting records.

The fact that the land has an estimated selling price of $220,000 on December 31, 2012, indicates that the land has increased in value. However, to use the $220,000 in the accounting records would be to record an illusory or unrealized profit. If Aaron Publishers sells the land on January 9, 2013, for $240,000, a profit of $90,000 ($240,000 − $150,000) is then realized and recorded. The new owner would record $240,000 as its cost of the land.

Going Concern Concept

The **going concern concept** assumes that a company will continue in business indefinitely. This assumption is made because the amount of time that a company will continue in business is not known.

The going concern concept justifies the use of the cost concept for recording purchases, such as land. For example, in the preceding illustration Aaron Publishers plans to build a plant on the land. Since Aaron Publishers does not plan to sell the land, reporting changes in the market value of the land is irrelevant. That is, the amount Aaron Publishers could sell the land for if it went out of business is not important. This is because Aaron Publishers plans to continue its operations.

If, however, there is strong evidence that a company is planning on discontinuing its operations, then the accounting records are revised. To illustrate, the assets and liabilities of businesses in receivership or bankruptcy are valued from a quitting concern or liquidation point of view, rather than from the going concern point of view.

Matching Concept

The **matching concept** reports the revenues earned by a company for a period with the expenses incurred in generating the revenues. That is, expenses are *matched* against the revenues they generated.

Revenues are normally recorded at the time a product is sold or a service is rendered, which is referred to as *revenue recognition*. At the point of sale, the sale price has been agreed upon, the buyer acquires ownership of the product or acquires the service, and the seller has a legal claim against the buyer for payment.

The following excerpt from the notes to Hershey's annual report describes when it records sales:

> *The Corporation records sales when ... a ... customer order with a fixed price has been received, ... the product has been shipped, ... there is no further obligation to assist in the resale of the product, and collectability (of the account receivable) is reasonably assured.*

Objectivity Concept

The **objectivity concept** requires that entries in the accounting records and the data reported on financial statements be based on verifiable or objective evidence. For example, invoices, bank statements, and a physical count of supplies on hand are all objective and verifiable. Thus, they can be used for entering amounts in the accounting system. In some cases, judgments, estimates, and other subjective factors may have to be used in preparing financial statements. In such situations, the most objective evidence available is used.

Unit of Measure Concept

In the United States, the unit of measure concept requires that all economic data be recorded in dollars. Other relevant, nonfinancial information may also be recorded, such as terms of contracts. However, it is only through using dollar amounts that the various transactions and activities of a business can be measured, summarized, reported, and compared. Money is common to all business transactions and thus, it is the unit of measurement for financial reporting.

Adequate Disclosure Concept

the length of time left on debt obligation is shown

The adequate disclosure concept requires that the financial statements, including related footnotes, contain all relevant data a stakeholder needs to understand the financial condition and performance of the company. Nonessential data are excluded to avoid clutter.

Accounting Period Concept

Financial statements are prepared at the end of each year.

The accounting period concept requires that accounting data be recorded and summarized in financial statements for periods of time. For example, transactions are recorded for a period of time such as a month or a year. The accounting records are then summarized and updated before preparing the financial statements.

The financial history of a company may be shown by a series of balance sheets and income statements. If the life of a company is expressed by a line moving from left to right, the financial history of the company may be graphed as shown in Exhibit 12.

EXHIBIT 12 **Financial History of a Company**

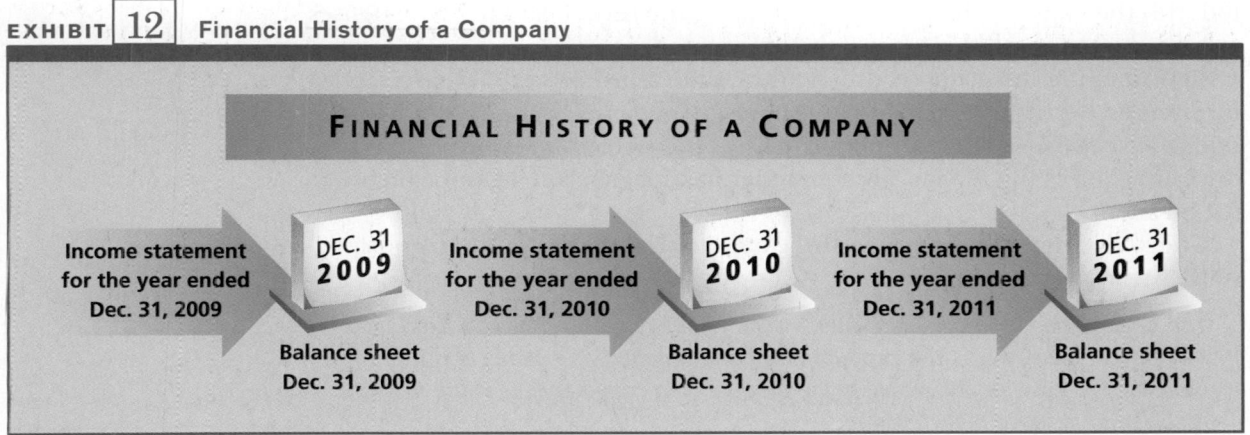

Responsible Reporting

The reliability of the financial reporting system is important to the economy and for the ability of businesses to raise money from investors. That is, stockholders and creditors require accurate financial reporting before they will invest their money. Scandals and financial reporting frauds threaten the confidence of investors. Exhibit 13 is a partial list of financial reporting frauds and abuses.

The companies listed in Exhibit 13 were caught in the midst of ethical lapses that led to fines, firings, and criminal or civil prosecution. The second column of Exhibit 13 identifies the accounting concept that was violated in

EXHIBIT 13 **Accounting Frauds**

Company	Concept Violated	Result
Adelphia	*Business Entity Concept:* Rigas family treated the company assets as their own.	Bankruptcy. Rigas family members convicted of fraud and lost their investment in the company.
AIG	*Business Entity Concept:* Compensation transactions with an off-shore company that should have been disclosed on AIG's books.	CEO (Chief Executive Officer) resigned. AIG paid $126 million in fines.
AOL and PurchasePro	*Matching Concept:* Back-dated contracts to inflate revenues.	Civil charges filed against senior executives of both companies. $500 million fine.
Computer Associates	*Matching Concept:* Fraudulently inflating revenues.	CEO and senior executives indicted. Five executives pled guilty. $225 million fine.
Enron	*Business Entity Concept:* Treated transactions as revenue, when they should have been treated as debt.	Bankruptcy. Criminal charges against senior executives. Over $60 billion in stock market losses.
Fannie Mae	*Accounting Period Concept:* Managing earnings by shifting expenses between periods.	CEO and CFO fired. $9 billion in restated earnings.
HealthSouth	*Matching Concept:* $4 billion in false entries to overstate revenues.	Senior executives face regulatory *and* civil charges.
Quest	*Matching Concept:* Improper recognition of $3 billion in revenue.	CEO and six other executives charged with "massive financial fraud." $250 million SEC fine.
Tyco	*Adequate Disclosure Concept:* Failure to disclose secret loans to executives that were subsequently forgiven.	CEO forced to resign and was convicted in criminal proceedings.
WorldCom	*Matching Concept:* Improperly treated expenses as assets.	Bankruptcy. Criminal conviction of CEO and CFO. Over $100 billion in stock market losses. Directors fined $18 million.
Xerox	*Matching Concept:* Recognized $3 billion in revenue in periods earlier than should have been recognized.	$10 million fine to SEC. Six executives fined $22 million.

committing these unethical business practices. For example, the *WorldCom* fraud involved reporting various expense items as though they were assets. This is a violation of the matching concept and resulted in overstating income and assets. The third column of the exhibit identifies some of the

INTEGRITY, OBJECTIVITY, AND ETHICS IN BUSINESS

Doing the Right Thing

Time magazine named three women as "Persons of the Year 2002." Each of these not-so-ordinary women had the courage, determination, and integrity to do the right thing. Each risked their personal careers to expose shortcomings in their organizations. Sherron Watkins, an *Enron* vice president, wrote a letter to Enron's chairman, Kenneth Lay, warning him of improper accounting that eventually led to Enron's collapse. Cynthia Cooper, an internal accountant, informed *WorldCom's* Board of Directors of phony accounting that allowed WorldCom to cover up over $3 billion in losses and forced WorldCom into bankruptcy. Coleen Rowley, an *FBI* staff attorney, wrote a memo to FBI Director Robert Mueller, exposing how the Bureau brushed off her pleas to investigate Zacarias Moussaoui, who was indicted as a co-conspirator in the September 11 terrorist attacks.

Purchased $1,000 of supplies for cash

assets — increase in assets decrease in cash
liability — NA
equity — NA

results of these events. In most cases, senior and midlevel executives lost their jobs and were sued by upset investors. In some cases, the executives also were criminally prosecuted and are serving prison terms.

What went wrong for the managers and companies listed in Exhibit 13? The answer normally involved one or both of the following factors:

- *Failure of Individual Character.* Ethical managers and accountants are honest and fair. However, managers and accountants often face pressures from supervisors to meet company and investor expectations. In many of the cases in Exhibit 13, managers and accountants justified small ethical violations to avoid such pressures. However, these small violations became big violations as the company's financial problems became worse.

- *Culture of Greed and Ethical Indifference.* By their behavior and attitude, senior managers set the company culture. In most of the companies listed in Exhibit 13, the senior managers created a culture of greed and indifference to the truth.

As a result of accounting and business frauds, the United States Congress passed laws to monitor the behavior of accounting and business. For example, the Sarbanes-Oxley Act of 2002 (SOX) was enacted. SOX established a new oversight body for the accounting profession called the Public Company Accounting Oversight Board (PCAOB). In addition, SOX established standards for independence, corporate responsibility, and disclosure.

How does one behave ethically when faced with financial or other types of pressure? Guidelines for behaving ethically are shown in Exhibit 14.

In 2008, Bernard Madoff admitted of defrauding clients of up to $50 billion in a massive Ponzi scheme that was committed over a number of years.

EXHIBIT 14 **Guidelines for Ethical Conduct**

1. Identify an ethical decision by using your personal ethical standards of honesty and fairness.
2. Identify the consequences of the decision and its effect on others.
3. Consider your obligations and responsibilities to those that will be affected by your decision.
4. Make a decision that is ethical and fair to those affected by it.

Many companies have ethical standards of conduct for managers and employees. In addition, the Institute of Management Accountants and the American Institute of Certified Public Accountants have professional codes of conduct.

Key Points

1. Describe the types and forms of businesses, how businesses make money, and business stakeholders.

The three types of businesses operated for profit include manufacturing, merchandising, and service businesses. Such businesses may be organized as proprietorships, partnerships, corporations, and limited liability companies. A business may make money (profits) by gaining an advantage over its competitors using a low-cost or a premium-price emphasis. Under a *low-cost emphasis*, a business designs and produces products or services at a lower cost than its competitors. Under a *premium-price emphasis*, a business tries to design products or services that possess

unique attributes or characteristics for which customers are willing to pay more. A business's economic performance is of interest to its stakeholders. Business stakeholders include four categories: capital market stakeholders, product or service market stakeholders, government stakeholders, and internal stakeholders.

2. Describe the three business activities of financing, investing, and operating.

All businesses engage in financing, investing, and operating activities. Financing activities involve obtaining funds to begin and operate a business. Investing activities involve obtaining the necessary resources to start and operate the business. Operating activities involve using the business's resources according to its business emphasis.

3. Define accounting and describe its role in business.

Accounting is an information system that provides reports to stakeholders about the economic activities and condition of a business. Accounting is the "language of business."

4. Describe and illustrate the basic financial statements and how they interrelate.

The principal financial statements of a corporation are the income statement, the retained earnings statement, the balance sheet, and the statement of cash flows. The income statement reports a period's net income or net loss, which also appears on the retained earnings statement. The ending retained earnings reported on the retained earnings statement is also reported on the balance sheet. The ending cash balance is reported on the balance sheet and the statement of cash flows.

5. Describe eight accounting concepts underlying financial reporting.

The eight accounting concepts discussed in this chapter include the business entity, cost, going concern, matching, objectivity, unit of measure, adequate disclosure, and accounting period concepts.

Key Terms

Accounting An information system that provides reports to stakeholders about the economic activities and condition of a business.

Accounting equation Assets = Liabilities + Stockholders' Equity

Accounting period concept An accounting concept in which accounting data are recorded and summarized in a period process.

Accounts payable Liabilities for amounts incurred from purchases of products or services in the normal operations of a business.

Accounts receivable Receivables created by selling merchandise or services on credit.

Adequate disclosure concept An accounting concept that requires financial statements to include all relevant data a reader needs to understand the financial condition and performance of a business.

Administrative expenses Costs not directly related to selling, such as officer salaries.

Assets The resources owned by a business.

Balance sheet A list of the assets, liabilities, and owner's equity as of a specific date, usually at the close of the last day of a month or a year.

Bonds payable A type of long-term debt financing with a face amount that is in the future with interest that is normally paid semiannually.

Business An organization in which basic resources (inputs), such as materials and labor, are assembled and processed to provide goods and services (outputs) to customers.

Business entity concept An accounting concept that limits the economic data in the accounting system of a specific business or entity to data related directly to the activities of that business or entity.

Business stakeholder A person or entity that has an interest in the economic performance of a business.

Capital stock Types of stock a corporation may issue.

Common stock The basic type of stock issued to stockholders of a corporation when a corporation has issued only one class of stock.

Corporation A business organized under state or federal statues as a separate legal entity.

Cost concept An accounting concept that determines the amount initially entered into the accounting records for purchases.

Cost of goods sold The cost of products sold may also be referred to as cost of merchandise sold or cost of sales.

Cost of merchandise sold The cost of products sold may also be referred to as cost of sales or cost of goods sold.

Cost of sales The cost of products sold may also be referred to as cost of merchandise sold or cost of goods sold.

Dividends Distributions of the earnings of a corporation to its stockholders.

Expenses Costs used to earn revenues.

Fees earned Revenues received from providing services.

Financial accounting The branch of accounting that is associated with preparing reports for users external to the business.

Financial Accounting Standards Board (FASB) The authoritative body that has the primary responsibility for developing accounting principles.

Financial statements Financial reports that summarize the effects of events on a business.

Financing activities Business activities that involve obtaining funds to begin and operate a business.

Generally accepted accounting principles (GAAP) Rules for the way financial statements should be prepared.

Going concern concept An accounting concept that assumes a business will continue operating for an indefinite period of time.

Income statement A summary of the revenue and expenses for a specific period of time, such as a month or a year.

Intangible assets Long-lived assets that are useful in the operations of a business, are not held for sale, and are without physical qualities.

Interest payable A liability to pay interest on a due date.

International Accounting Standards Board An authoritative body that establishes accounting principles and practices for companies outside of the United States.

Investing activities Business activities that involve obtaining the necessary resources to start and operate the business.

Liabilities The rights of creditors that represent a legal obligation to repay an amount borrowed according to terms of the borrowing agreement.

Limited liability company (LLC) A form of corporation that combines attributes of a partnership and a corporation.

Low-cost strategy A strategy in which a company designs and produces products or services at a lower cost than its competitors.

Managerial accounting The branch of accounting that aids management in making financing, investing, and operating decisions for the company.

Manufacturing businesses A type of business that changes basic inputs into products that are sold to individual customers.

Matching concept An accounting concept that requires expenses of a period to be matched with the revenue generated during that period.

Merchandising businesses Businesses that sell products they purchase from other businesses to customers.

Net income The excess of revenues over expenses.

Net loss The excess of expenses over revenues.

Note payable A type of short- or long-term financing that requires payment of the amount borrowed plus interest.

Objectivity concept An accounting concept that requires accounting records and data reported in financial statements be based on objective evidence.

Operating activities Business activities that involve using the business's resources to implement its business strategy.

Owner's equity The financial rights of the owner.

Partnership A business owned by two or more individuals.

Premium-price strategy A strategy in which a company tries to design and produce products or services that serve unique market needs, allowing it to charge premium prices.

Prepaid expenses Assets resulting from the prepayment of future expenses such as insurance or

rent that are expected to become expenses over time or through the normal operations of the business; often called *deferred expenses*.

Profit The excess of the amounts received from customers for goods or services and the amounts paid for the inputs used to provide the goods or services.

Proprietorship A business owned by one individual.

Retained earnings Net income retained in a corporation.

Retained earnings statement A summary of the changes in the retained earnings of a corporation for a specific period of time, such as a month or a year.

Revenue The increase in assets from selling products or services to customers.

Sales Revenues received from selling products.

Securities and Exchange Commission An agency of the U.S. government that has authority over the accounting and financial disclosures for corporations whose stock is traded and sold to the public.

Selling expenses Costs directly related to the selling of a product or service such as sales salaries and advertising expenses.

Service businesses A type of business that provides services rather than products to customers.

Statement of cash flows A summary of the cash receipts and cash payments for a specific period of time, such as a month or a year.

Statement of financial condition Reports the financial condition as of a point in time; often referred to as the balance sheet.

Stockholders' equity The stockholders' rights to the assets of a business.

Stockholders Investors who purchase stock in a corporation.

Tangible assets Assets such as machinery, buildings, computers, office furnishings, trucks, and automobiles that have physical characteristics.

Unit of measure concept An accounting concept requiring that economic data be recorded in dollars.

Illustrative Problem

The financial statements at the end of Spratlin Consulting's first month of operations follow.

SPRATLIN CONSULTING
Income Statement
For the Month Ended June 30, 2010

Fees earned		$36,000
Operating expenses:		
Wages expense	$12,000	
Rent expense	7,640	
Utilities expense	(a)	
Miscellaneous expense	1,320	
Total operating expenses		23,120
Net income		$(b)

SPRATLIN CONSULTING
Retained Earnings Statement
For the Month Ended June 30, 2010

Net income for June	$ (c)
Less dividends	(d)
Retained earnings, June 30, 2010	$ (e)

SPRATLIN CONSULTING
Balance Sheet
June 30, 2010

Assets

Cash	$ 5,600
Land	50,000
Total assets	$(f)

Liabilities

Accounts payable	$ 1,920

Stockholders' Equity

Capital stock	(g)
Retained earnings	(h)
Total stockholders' equity	$ (i)
Total liabilities and stockholders' equity	$ (j)

SPRATLIN CONSULTING
Statement of Cash Flows
For the Month Ended June 30, 2010

Cash flows from operating activities:		
Cash received from customers	$ 36,000	
Deduct cash payments for operating expenses	(k)	
Net cash flows from operating activities		$14,800
Cash flows from investing activities:		
Cash payments for acquisition of land		(l)
Cash flows from financing activities:		
Cash received from issuing capital stock	$ 48,000	
Deduct dividends	7,200	
Net cash flows from financing activities		(m)
Net cash flow and June 30, 2010 cash balance		$ (n)

Instructions

By analyzing how the four financial statements are integrated, determine the proper amounts for (a) through (n).

Solution

a. Utilities expense, $2,160 ($23,120 – $12,000 – $7,640 – $1,320)

b. Net income, $12,880 ($36,000 – $23,120)

c. Net income, $12,880 (same as b)

d. Dividends, $7,200 (from statement of cash flows)

e. Retained earnings, $5,680 ($12,880 – $7,200)

f. Total assets, $55,600 ($5,600 + $50,000)

g. Capital stock, $48,000 (from the statement of cash flows)

h. Retained earnings, $5,680 (same as e)

i. Total stockholders' equity, $53,680 ($48,000 + $5,680)

j. Total liabilities and stockholders' equity, $55,600 ($1,920 + $53,680) (same as f)

k. Cash payments for operating expenses, $21,200 ($36,000 – $14,800)

l. Cash payments for acquisition of land, $50,000 (from balance sheet)

m. Net cash flows from financing activities, $40,800 ($48,000 – $7,200)

n. Net cash flow and June 30, 2010 cash balance, $5,600 ($14,800 – $50,000 + $40,800)

Self-Examination Questions (Answers appear at the end of chapter.)

1. A profit-making business operating as a separate legal entity and in which ownership is divided into shares of stock is known as a:

   A. proprietorship.

   B. service business.

   C. partnership.

   D. corporation.

2. The resources owned by a business are called:

   A. assets.

   B. liabilities.

   C. the accounting equation.

   D. stockholders' equity.

3. A listing of a business entity's assets, liabilities, and stockholders' equity as of a specific date is:

   A. a balance sheet.

   B. an income statement.

   C. the retained earnings statement.

   D. a statement of cash flows.

4. If total assets are $20,000 and total liabilities are $12,000, the amount of stockholders' equity is:

   A. $32,000.

   B. ($32,000).

   C. ($8,000).

   D. $8,000.

5. If revenue was $45,000, expenses were $37,500, and dividends were $10,000, the amount of net income or net loss would be:

   A. $45,000 net income.

   B. 7,500 net income.

   C. $37,500 net loss.

   D. $2,500 net loss.

Class Discussion Questions

1. What is the objective of most businesses?

2. What is the difference between a manufacturing business and a merchandising business? Give an example of each type of business.

3. What is the difference between a manufacturing business and a service business? Is a restaurant a manufacturing business, a service business, or both?

4. Why are most large companies like *Google, CocaCola, Ford,* and *IBM* organized as corporations?

5. Both *KIA* and *Porsche* produce and sell automobiles. Describe and contrast the business emphasis of KIA and Porsche.

6. Assume that a friend of yours operates a family-owned pharmacy. A *Super Wal-Mart* is scheduled to open in the next several months that will also offer pharmacy services. What business emphasis would your friend use to compete with the Super Wal-Mart pharmacy?

7. What services does *eBay* offer its customers?

8. A business's stakeholders can be classified into capital market, product or service market, government, and internal stakeholders. Will the interests of all the stakeholders within a classification be the same? Use bankers and stockholders of the capital market as an example in answering this question.

9. The three business activities are financing, investing, and operating. Using *Delta Air Lines,* give an example of a financing, investing, and operating activity.

10. What is the role of accounting in business?

11. Briefly describe the nature of the information provided by each of the following financial statements: the income statement, the retained earnings statement, the balance sheet, and the statement of cash flows. In your descriptions, indicate whether each of the financial statements covers a period of time or is for a specific date.

12. For the year ending February 2, 2008, *Gap Inc.* had revenues of $15,763 million and total expenses of $14,930 million. Did Gap Inc. (a) incur a net loss or (b) realize net income?

13. What particular item of financial or operating data appears on both the income statement and the retained earnings statement? What item appears on both the balance sheet and the retained earnings statement? What item appears on both the balance sheet and statement of cash flows?

14. Megan Graft is the owner of Mission Delivery Service. Recently, Megan paid interest of $5,000 on a personal loan of $80,000 that she used to begin the business. Should Mission Delivery Service record the interest payment? Explain.

15. On July 6, Imperial Repair Service extended an offer of $90,000 for land that had been priced for sale at $120,000. On August 17, Imperial Repair Service accepted the seller's counteroffer of $99,000. Describe how Imperial Repair Service should record the land.

16. Land with an assessed value of $300,000 for property tax purposes is acquired by a business for $500,000. Seven years later, the plot of land has an assessed value of $900,000 and the business receives an offer of $1,200,000 for it. Should the monetary amount assigned to the land in the business records now be increased?

Exercises

E1-1

Types of businesses

Obj 1

Indicate whether each of the following companies is primarily a service, merchandise, or manufacturing business. If you are unfamiliar with the company, you may use the Internet to locate the company's home page or use the finance Web site of Yahoo.com.

1. *Alcoa*
2. *AT&T*
3. *Boeing*
4. *Caterpillar*
5. *Citigroup*
6. *CVS*
7. *Dow Chemical*
8. *FedEx*
9. *First Republic Bank*
10. *Ford Motor*
11. *Gap Inc.*
12. *Hilton Hotels*
13. *H&R Block Inc.*
14. *Procter & Gamble*
15. *Sears Roebuck*

E1-2

Business emphasis

Obj 1

Identify the primary business emphasis of each of the following companies as (a) a low-cost emphasis or (b) a premium-price emphasis. If you are unfamiliar with the company, you may use the Internet to locate the company's home page or use the finance Web site of Yahoo.com.

1. *BMW*
2. *Charles Schwab*
3. *Best Buy*
4. *Coca-Cola*
5. *Dollar General*
6. *Goldman Sachs Group*
7. *Home Depot*
8. *Sub-Zero*
9. *Nike*
10. *Office Depot*
11. *Sara Lee*
12. *Southwest Airlines*

E1-3

Accounting equation

Obj 4

✓ Best Buy, $4,484

The total assets and total liabilities of *Best Buy* and *Hewlett-Packard* are shown here.

	Best Buy (in millions)	Hewlett-Packard (in millions)
Assets	$12,758	$113,331
Liabilities	8,274	74,389

Determine the stockholders' equity of each company.

E1-4

Accounting equation

Obj 4

✓ Dell, $4,271

The total assets and total liabilities of *Marathon Oil* and *Dell* are shown here.

	Marathon Oil (in millions)	Dell (in millions)
Assets	$42,686	$26,500
Liabilities	21,277	22,229

Determine the stockholders' equity of each company.

E1-5

Accounting equation

Obj 4

✓ a. $95,000

Determine the missing amount for each of the following:

	Assets	=	Liabilities	+	Stockholders' Equity
a.	X	=	$ 35,000	+	$60,000
b.	$ 80,000	=	X	+	$ 35,000
c.	$675,000	=	$227,000	+	X

✶ E1-6

Accounting equation

Obj 4

✓ a. $30,394

Determine the missing amounts (in millions) for the condensed balance sheets shown below.

	Target	Wal-Mart	Costco
Assets	$ 44,106	$ (b)	$ 20,682
Liabilities	(a)	98,906	11,490
Stockholders' equity	13,712	64,608	(c)

E1-7

Net income and dividends

Obj 4

The income statement of a corporation for the month of June indicates a net income of $150,000. During the same period, $180,000 in cash dividends were paid.

Would it be correct to say that the business incurred a net loss of $30,000 during the month? Discuss.

E1-8

Net income and stockholders' equity for four businesses

Obj 4

✓ Company Alpha: Net income, $110,000

Four different companies, Alpha, Beta, Charlie, and Dawg, show the same balance sheet data at the beginning and end of a year. These data, exclusive of the amount of owners' equity, are summarized as follows:

	Total Assets	Total Liabilities
Beginning of the year	$400,000	$150,000
End of the year	675,000	315,000

On the basis of the preceding data and the following additional information for the year, determine the net income (or loss) of each company for the year. (*Hint:* First determine the amount of increase or decrease in stockholders' equity during the year.)

Company Alpha: No additional capital stock was issued, and no dividends were paid.

Company Beta: No additional capital stock was issued, but dividends of $35,000 were paid.

Company Charlie: Capital stock of $90,000 was issued, but no dividends were paid.

Company Dawg: Capital stock of $90,000 was issued, and dividends of $35,000 were paid.

E1-9

Accounting equation and income statement

Obj 4

✓ 1. $7,441,771

Staples, Inc., is a leading office products distributor, with retail stores in the United States, Canada, Asia, Europe, and South America. The following financial statement data were adopted from Staples' financial statements as of January 31, 2009 and February 2, 2008:

	2009 (in thousands)	2008 (in thousands)
Total assets	$13,005,978	$9,036,344
Total liabilities	(1)	3,318,337
Total stockholders' equity	5,564,207	(2)
Sales	23,083,775	
Cost of goods sold	16,836,839	
Selling and administrative expenses	4,631,219	
Other income and (expense)	(381,590)	
Income tax expense	428,863	

a. Determine the missing data indicated for (1) and (2).
b. Using the income statement data for 2009, determine the amount of net income or loss.

⋆ E1-10

Balance sheet items

Obj 4

From the following list of selected items taken from the records of Metro Appliance Service as of a specific date, identify those that would appear on the balance sheet.

1. Accounts Payable
2. Capital Stock
3. Cash
4. Fees Earned
5. Land
6. Salaries Expense
7. Salaries Payable
8. Supplies
9. Supplies Expense
10. Utilities Expense

⋆ E1-11

Income statement items

Obj 4

Based on the data presented in Exercise 1-10, identify those items that would appear on the income statement.

★ **E1-12**

Financial statement items

Obj 4

Identify each of the following items as (a) an asset, (b) a liability, (c) revenue, (d) an expense, or (e) a dividend:

1. Amounts due from customers
2. Amounts owed vendors
3. Cash on hand
4. Cash paid to stockholders
5. Cash sales
6. Equipment

7. Note payable owed to the bank
8. Rent paid for the month
9. Sales commissions paid to salespersons
10. Wages paid to employees

E1-13

Retained earnings statement

Obj 4

SPREADSHEET

✓ Retained earnings, April 30, 2010: $502,000

Financial information related to In Good Taste Company for the month ended April 30, 2010, is as follows:

Net income for April	$ 125,000
Dividends during April	18,000
Retained earnings, April 1, 2010	395,000

Prepare a retained earnings statement for the month ended April 30, 2010.

E1-14

Income statement

Obj 4

SPREADSHEET

✓ Net income: $352,000

Idyllwild Services was organized on August 1, 2010. A summary of the revenue and expense transactions for August follows:

Fees earned	$800,000
Wages expense	380,000
Miscellaneous expense	17,500
Rent expense	42,200
Supplies expense	8,300

Prepare an income statement for the month ended August 31.

E1-15

Missing amounts from balance sheet and income statement data

Obj 4

✓ (a) $130,000

One item is omitted in each of the following summaries of balance sheet and income statement data for four different corporations, East, North, South, and West.

	East	North	South	West
Beginning of the year:				
Assets	$500,000	$300,000	$160,000	$ (d)
Liabilities	200,000	130,000	121,600	350,000
End of the year:				
Assets	750,000	460,000	144,000	1,200,000
Liabilities	300,000	110,000	128,000	700,000
During the year:				
Additional issue of capital stock	(a)	50,000	16,000	100,000
Dividends	40,000	20,000	(c)	90,000
Revenue	125,000	(b)	184,000	420,000
Expenses	65,000	70,000	196,000	480,000

Determine the missing amounts, identifying them by letter. [*Hint:* First determine the amount of increase or decrease in owners' (stockholders') equity during the year.]

E1-16

Balance sheets, net income

Obj 4

SPREADSHEET

✓ b. $35,000

Financial information related to Joshua Tree Interiors for August and September 2010 is as follows:

	August 31, 2010	**September 30, 2010**
Accounts payable	$ 40,000	$ 55,000
Accounts receivable	75,000	90,000
Capital stock	60,000	60,000
Retained earnings	?	?
Cash	110,000	140,000
Supplies	15,000	20,000

a. Prepare balance sheets for Joshua Tree Interiors as of August 31 and as of September 30, 2010.

b. Determine the amount of net income for September, assuming that no additional capital stock was issued and no dividends were paid during the month.

c. Determine the amount of net income for September, assuming that no additional capital stock was issued but dividends of $17,500 were paid during the month.

E1-17

Financial statements

Obj 4

Each of the following items is shown in the financial statements of *ExxonMobil Corporation.* Identify the financial statement (balance sheet or income statement) in which each item would appear.

a. Accounts payable
b. Cash equivalents
c. Crude oil inventory
d. Equipment
e. Exploration expenses
f. Income taxes payable
g. Investments
h. Long-term debt

i. Marketable securities
j. Notes and loans payable
k. Operating expenses
l. Prepaid taxes
m. Retained earnings
n. Sales
o. Selling expenses

E1-18

Statement of cash flows

Obj 4

Indicate whether each of the following cash activities would be reported on the statement of cash flows as (a) an operating activity, (b) an investing activity, or (c) a financing activity.

1. Issued capital stock
2. Paid rent
3. Paid for office equipment
4. Sold services
5. Issued a note payable

6. Sold excess office equipment
7. Paid officers' salaries
8. Paid for advertising
9. Paid insurance
10. Paid dividends

E1-19

Statement of cash flows

Obj 4

Indicate whether each of the following activities would be reported on the statement of cash flows as (a) an operating activity, (b) an investing activity, or (c) a financing activity.

1. Cash received from investment by stockholders
2. Cash received from fees earned
3. Cash paid for expenses
4. Cash paid for land

E1-20

Statement of cash flows

Obj 4

SPREADSHEET

✓ Net cash flows from
operating activities,
$120,000

Pantera Inc. was organized on May 1, 2011. A summary of cash flows for May follows.

Cash receipts:	
Cash received from customers	$300,000
Cash received for capital stock	275,000
Cash received from note payable	55,000
Cash payments:	
Cash paid out for expenses	$180,000
Cash paid out for purchase of equipment	95,000
Cash paid as dividends	15,000

Prepare a statement of cash flows for the month ended May 31, 2011.

E1-21

Using financial statements

Obj 4

A company's stakeholders often differ in their financial statement focus. For example, some stakeholders focus primarily on the income statement, while others may focus primarily on the statement of cash flows or the balance sheet. For each of the following situations, indicate which financial statement would be the likely focus for the stakeholder. Choose either the income statement, balance sheet, or statement of cash flows and justify your choice.

Situation 1: Assume that you are considering purchasing a personal computer from *Dell*.

Situation 2: Assume that you are considering investing in *eBay* (capital market stakeholder).

Situation 3: Assume that you are employed by *Sara Lee Corporation* (product market stakeholder) and are considering whether to extend credit for a 60-day period to a new grocery store chain that has recently opened throughout the Midwest.

Situation 4: Assume that you are considering taking a job (internal stakeholder) with either *Sears* or *JCPenney*.

Situation 5: Assume that you are a banker for *US Bank* (capital market stakeholder), and you are considering whether to grant a major credit line (loan) to *Target*. The credit line will allow Target to borrow up to $400 million for a 5-year period at the market rate of interest.

E1-22

Financial statement items

Obj 4

Amazon.com, Inc. operates as an online retailer in North America and internationally. Both Amazon and third parties, via the Amazon.com Web site, sell products across various product categories.

The following items were adapted from the annual report of Amazon.com for the period ending December 31, 2008:

	In millions
1. Accounts payable	$ 4,687
2. Accounts receivable	1,031
3. Intangible assets	598
4. Interest expense	71
5. Inventories	1,399
6. Cost of sales	14,896
7. Selling general and administrative expenses	3,428
8. Income tax expense	247
9. Net cash provided by operating activities	1,697
10. Net cash flows used for investing activities	1,199

(Continued)

	In millions
11. Net sales	19,166
12. Other income	121
13. Property, plant, and equipment	854
14. Purchase of capital stock	89
15. Retained earnings (Jan. 1, 2008)	(1,375)

Using the following notations, indicate on which financial statement you would find each of the preceding items. (*Note:* An item may appear on more than one statement.)

IS	Income statement
RE	Retained earnings statement
BS	Balance sheet
SCF	Statement of cash flows

E1-23

Income statement

Obj 4

✓ Net income, $645

Based on the *Amazon.com, Inc.* financial statement data shown in Exercise 1-22, prepare an income statement for the year ending December 31, 2008.

E1-24

Financial statement items

Obj 4

Though the *McDonald's* menu of hamburgers, cheeseburgers, the Big Mac®, Quarter Pounder®, Filet-O-Fish®, and Chicken McNuggets® is easily recognized, McDonald's financial statements may not be as familiar. The following items were adapted from a recent annual report of McDonald's Corporation:

1. Accounts payable
2. Accrued interest payable
3. Capital stock outstanding
4. Cash
5. Cash provided by operations
6. Food and packaging costs used in operations
7. Income tax expense
8. Interest expense
9. Inventories
10. Long-term debt payable
11. Net income
12. Net increase in cash
13. Notes payable
14. Notes receivable
15. Occupancy and rent expense
16. Payroll expense
17. Prepaid expenses not yet used in operations
18. Property and equipment
19. Retained earnings
20. Sales

Identify the financial statement on which each of the preceding items would appear. An item may appear on more than one statement. Use the following notations:

IS	Income statement
RE	Retained earnings statement
BS	Balance sheet
SCF	Statement of cash flows

E1-25

Financial statements

Obj 4

✓ Correct amount of total assets is $195,000

Redwood Realty, organized May 1, 2011, is owned and operated by Lorrimer Fleming. How many errors can you find in the following financial statements for Redwood Realty, prepared after its first month of operations? Assume that the cash balance on May 31, 2011, is $46,600 and that cash flows from operating activities is reported correctly.

REDWOOD REALTY
Income Statement
May 31, 2011

Sales commissions		$308,400
Operating expenses:		
Office salaries expense	$172,600	
Rent expense	31,200	
Miscellaneous expense	2,200	
Automobile expense	7,900	
Total operating expenses		213,900
Net income		$134,500 *94,500*

LORRIMER FLEMING
Retained Earnings Statement
May 31, 2010

Retained earnings, May 1, 2011	$ 17,800	
Less dividends during May	12,000	
	$ 5,800	
Net income for the month	134,500 *94500*	
Retained earnings, May 31, 2011	$140,300 *100300* *82500*	

Balance Sheet
For the Month Ended May 31, 2011

Assets

Cash		$ 46,600
Accounts payable		12,500
Land		60,000
Total assets		$119,100 *195,000*

Liabilities

Accounts receivable		$ 81,200
Prepaid expenses		7,200 *12500*

Stockholders' Equity

Capital stock	$100,000		
Retained earnings	*100300* 140,300	240,300	
Total liabilities and stockholders' equity		$328,700 *195,000*	

Statement of Cash Flows
May 31, 2011

Cash flows from operating activities:		
Cash received from customers	$227,200	
Cash paid for operating expenses	208,600	
Net cash flow from operating activities		$ 18,600
Cash flows from financing activities:		
Cash received from issuance of capital stock	$100,000	
Dividends paid to stockholders	(12,000)	
Net cash flow from financing activities		88,000
Net cash flow and cash balance as of May 31, 2011		$106,600

✶ E1-26

Accounting concepts

Obj 5

Match each of the following statements with the appropriate accounting concept. Some concepts may be used more than once, while others may not be used at all. Use the notations shown to indicate the appropriate accounting concept.

Accounting Concept	Notation
⌣ Accounting period concept	P
⌣ Adequate disclosure concept	D
⌣ Business entity concept	B
⌣ Cost concept	C
⌣ Going concern concept	G
⌣ Matching concept	M
⌣ Objectivity concept	O
⌣ Unit of measure concept	U

Statements

1. Assume that a business will continue forever.
2. Material litigation involving the corporation is described in a footnote.
3. Monthly utilities costs are reported as expenses along with the monthly revenues.
4. Personal transactions of owners are kept separate from the business.
5. This concept supports relying on an independent actuary (statistician), rather than the chief operating officer of the corporation, to estimate a pension liability.
6. Changes in the use of accounting methods from one period to the next are described in the notes to the financial statements.
7. Land worth $800,000 is reported at its original purchase price of $220,000.
8. This concept justifies recording only transactions that are expressed in dollars.
9. If this concept was ignored, the confidence of users in the financial statements could not be maintained.
10. The changes in financial condition are reported at the end of the month.

E1-27

Business entity concept

Obj 5

Chalet Sports sells hunting and fishing equipment and provides guided hunting and fishing trips. Chalet Sports is owned and operated by Cliff Owen, a well-known sports enthusiast and hunter. Cliff's wife, Judy, owns and operates Joliet Boutique, a women's clothing store. Cliff and Judy have established a trust fund to finance their children's college education. The trust fund is maintained by City Bank in the name of the children, John and Morgan.

    For each of the following transactions, identify which of the entities listed should record the transaction in its records.

Entities	
C	Chalet Sports
B	City Bank Trust Fund
J	Joliet Boutique
X	None of the above

1. Cliff paid a local doctor for a physical, which was required by the workmen's compensation insurance policy carried by Chalet Sports.
2. Cliff received a cash advance from customers for a guided hunting trip.
3. Judy paid her dues to the YWCA.
4. Cliff paid a breeder's fee for an English springer spaniel to be used as a hunting guide dog.
5. Judy deposited a $5,000 personal check in the trust fund at City Bank.
6. Cliff paid for an advertisement in a hunters' magazine.

7. Judy authorized the trust fund to purchase mutual fund shares.
8. Judy donated several dresses from the store's inventory to a local charity auction for the benefit of a women's abuse shelter.
9. Cliff paid for dinner and a movie to celebrate Cliff and Judy's fifteenth wedding anniversary.
10. Judy purchased two dozen spring dresses from a Seattle designer for a special spring sale.

Problems

P1-1

Income statement, retained earnings statement, and balance sheet

Obj 4

SPREADSHEET

✓ 1. Net income: $335,000

The amounts of the assets and liabilities of Padre Travel Service as of June 30, 2010, the end of the current year, and its revenue and expenses for the year are listed below. The retained earnings were $210,000, and the capital stock was $90,000 as of July 1, 2009, the beginning of the current year. Dividends of $180,000 were paid during the current year.

Accounts payable	$71,500
Accounts receivable	188,100
Cash	318,300
Fees earned	1,579,200
Miscellaneous expense	16,000
Rent expense	226,800
Supplies	20,100
Supplies expense	42,600
Taxes expense	33,600
Utilities expense	135,000
Wages expense	790,200

Instructions

1. Prepare an income statement for the current year ended June 30, 2010.
2. Prepare a retained earnings statement for the current year ended June 30, 2010.
3. Prepare a balance sheet as of June 30, 2010.

P1-2

Missing amounts from financial statements

Obj 4

SPREADSHEET

✓ j. $303,300

The financial statements at the end of Stone Realty's first month of operations are shown below.

STONE REALTY
Income Statement
For the Month Ended September 30, 2010

Fees earned		$141,000
Operating expenses:		
Wages expense	$ (a)	
Rent expense	14,400	
Supplies expense	12,000	
Utilities expense	8,100	
Miscellaneous expense	4,950	
Total operating expenses		71,700
Net income		$ (b)

STONE REALTY
Retained Earnings Statement
For the Month Ended September 30, 2010

Net income for September	$ (c)
Less dividends	(d)
Retained earnings, September 30, 2010	$ (e)

STONE REALTY
Balance Sheet
September 30, 2010

Assets

Cash	$83,500
Supplies	6,000
Land	(f)
Total assets	$ (g)

Liabilities

Accounts payable	$ 7,200

Stockholders' Equity

Capital stock	$ (h)	
Retained earnings	(i)	(j)
Total liabilities and stockholders' equity		$ (k)

STONE REALTY
Statement of Cash Flows
For the Month Ended September 30, 2010

Cash flows from operating activities:		
Cash received from customers	$ (l)	
Deduct cash payments for expenses and payments to creditors	70,500	
Net cash flows from operating activities		$ (m)
Cash flows from investing activities:		
Cash payments for acquisition of land		216,000
Cash flows from financing activities:		
Cash received from issuing capital stock	$270,000	
Deduct dividends	36,000	
Net cash flows from financing activities		(n)
Net cash flow and September 30, 2010 cash balance		$ (o)

Instructions

1. Would you classify a realty business like Stone Realty as a manufacturing, merchandising, or service business?
2. By analyzing the interrelationships among the financial statements, determine the proper amounts for (a) through (o).

P1-3

Income statement, retained earnings statement, and balance sheet

Obj 4

SPREADSHEET

✓ 1. Net income, $1,003

The following financial data were adapted from the annual report of *Best Buy Inc.* for the period ending February 28, 2009:

	In millions
Accounts payable	$ 4,997
Capital stock	442
Cash	498
Cost of goods sold	34,017
Income tax expense	674

(Continued)

	In millions
Interest expense	$ 94
Inventories	4,573
Investments	406
Goodwill and other intangible assets	2,698
Other assets	1,429
Other expenses	250
Other liabilities	5,673
Other revenue (net)	7
Property, plant, and equipment	4,174
Receivables	1,868
Sales	45,015
Selling, general, and administrative expenses	8,984

Instructions

1. Prepare Best Buy's income statement for the year ending February 28, 2009.
2. Prepare Best Buy's retained earnings statement for the year ending February 28, 2009. (*Note:* The retained earnings at March 1, 2008, was $3,933. During the year, Best Buy paid dividends of $222.)
3. Prepare a balance sheet as of February 28, 2009, for Best Buy.

P1-4

Statement of cash flows

Obj 4

SPREADSHEET

✓ Net increase in cash, $2,575

The following cash data were adapted from the annual report of *Google Inc.* for the period ended December 31, 2008. The cash balance as of January 1, 2008, was $6,082 (in millions).

	In millions
Receipts from capital stock, etc.	$ 41
Purchases of property, plant, and equipment, etc.	21,082
Receipts from sale of investments (net)	15,763
Net cash flows from operating activities	7,853

Instructions

Prepare *Google's* statement of cash flows for the year ended December 31, 2008.

P1-5

Financial statements, including statement of cash flows

Obj 4

SPREADSHEET

✓ 1. Net income, $236,250 NC

eSupplies Corporation began operations on January 1, 2011, as an online retailer of computer software and hardware. The following financial statement data were taken from eSupplies' records at the end of its first year of operations, December 31, 2011.

Accounts payable	$ 20,000
Accounts receivable	60,000
Capital stock	252,000
Cash	?
Cash payments for operating activities	657,000
Cash receipts from operating activities	690,000
Cost of sales	435,000
Dividends	30,000
Income tax expense	53,000
Income taxes payable	8,000
Interest expense	2,000
Inventories	115,000
Note payable (due in 2017)	50,000
Property, plant, and equipment	265,000
Retained earnings	?
Sales	750,000
Selling and administrative expense	80,000

Instructions

1. Prepare an income statement for the year ended December 31, 2011.
2. Prepare a retained earnings statement for the year ended December 31, 2011.
3. Prepare a balance sheet as of December 31, 2011.
4. Prepare a statement of cash flows for the year ended December 31, 2011.

Activities

A1-1

Integrity, objectivity, and ethics at The Hershey Company

ETHICS

The management of *The Hershey Company* has asked union workers in two of its highest cost Pennsylvania plants to accept higher health insurance premiums and take a wage cut. The workers' portion of the insurance cost would double from 6% of the premium to 12%. In addition, workers hired after January 2000 would have their hourly wages cut by $4, which would be partially off set by a 2% annual raise. Management says that the plants need to be more cost competitive. Management has indicated that if the workers accept the proposal, the company would invest $30 million to modernize the plants and move future projects to the plants. Management, however, has refused to guarantee more work at the plants if the workers approve the proposal. If the workers reject the proposal, management implies that it would move future projects to other plants and that layoffs might be forthcoming. Do you consider management's actions ethical?

Source: Susan Govzdas, "Hershey to Cut Jobs or Wages," *Central Penn Business Journal*, September 24, 2004.

A1-2

Ethics and professional conduct in business

GROUP

ETHICS

Beatriz Janke, president and owner of Jaguar Enterprises, applied for a $300,000 loan from First National Bank. The bank requested financial statements from Jaguar Enterprises as a basis for granting the loan. Beatriz has told her accountant to provide the bank with a balance sheet. Beatriz has decided to omit the other financial statements because there was a net loss during the past year.

In groups of three or four, discuss the following questions:

1. Is Beatriz behaving in a professional manner by omitting some of the financial statements?
2. a. What types of information about their businesses would owners be willing to provide bankers? What types of information would owners not be willing to provide?
   b. What types of information about a business would bankers want before extending a loan?
   c. What common interests are shared by bankers and business owners?

A1-3

How businesses make money

GROUP

Assume that you are the chief executive officer for a national poultry producer. The company's operations include hatching chickens through the use of breeder stock and feeding, raising, and processing the mature chicks into finished products. The finished products include breaded chicken nuggets and patties and deboned, skinless, and marinated chicken. The company sells its products to schools, military services, fast-food chains, and grocery stores.

In groups of four or five, discuss the following business emphasis and risk issues:

1. In a commodity business like poultry production, what do you think is the dominant business emphasis? What are the implications in this dominant emphasis for how you would run the company?

2. Identify at least two major business risks for operating the company.

3. How could the company try to differentiate its products?

A1-4
Net income versus cash flow

On January 9, 2011, Dr. Linda Tempkin established M Expert, a medical practice organized as a professional corporation. The following conversation occurred the following September between Dr. Tempkin and a former medical school classmate, Dr. Myron Romo, at an American Medical Association convention in London.

Dr. Romo: Linda, good to see you again. Why didn't you call when you were in Chicago? We could have had dinner together.

Dr. Tempkin: Actually, I never made it to Chicago this year. My husband and kids went to our Wisconsin Dells condo twice, but I got stuck in New York. I opened a new consulting practice this January and haven't had any time for myself since.

Dr. Romo: I heard about it ... Expert ... something ... right?

Dr. Tempkin: Yes, M Expert. My husband chose the name.

Dr. Remo: I've thought about doing something like that. Are you making any money? I mean, is it worth your time?

Dr. Tempkin: You wouldn't believe it. I started by opening a bank account with $60,000, and my August bank statement has a balance of $175,000. Not bad for eight months—all pure profit.

Dr. Romo: Maybe I'll try it in Chicago. Let's have breakfast together tomorrow and you can fill me in on the details.

Comment on Dr. Tempkin's statement that the difference between the opening bank balance ($60,000) and the August statement balance ($175,000) is pure profit.

A1-5
The accounting equation

Obtain the annual reports for three well-known companies, such as *Ford Motor Co., General Motors, IBM, Microsoft,* or *Amazon.com.* These annual reports can be obtained from the library, the company's Web site under "Investor Relations," **http://www.finance.yahoo.com** (type in the company name for Get Quotes), or the company's 10-K filing with the Securities and Exchange Commission at **http://www.sec.gov/.**

To obtain annual report information under Filings & Forms, click on "Search for Company Filings." Next, click on "Companys or funds, ticker symbol...." Key in the company name. The Electronic Data Gathering, Analysis, and Retrieval system (EDGAR) will list the reports available for the company. Click on the 10-K (or 10-K405) report for the year you want to download. If you wish, you can save the whole 10-K report to a file and then open it with your word processor.

Examine the balance sheet for each company and determine the total assets, liabilities, and stockholders' equity. Verify that total assets equal the total of the liabilities plus stockholders' equity.

A1-6
Hershey's annual report

The financial statements of The *Hershey Company* are shown in Exhibits 6 through 9 of this chapter. Based upon these statements, answer the following questions.

1. What are Hershey's sales (in millions)?
2. What is Hershey's cost of sales (in millions)?
3. What is Hershey's net income (in millions)?

4. What is Hershey's percent of the cost of sales to sales? Round to one decimal place.
5. The percent that a company adds to its cost of sales to determine the selling price is called a markup. What is Hershey's markup percent? Round to one decimal place.
6. What is the percentage of net income to sales for Hershey? Round to one decimal place.

A1-7
Income statement analysis

The following data (in millions) were adapted from the December 31, 2008, financial statements of *Tootsie Roll Industries Inc.*:

Sales	$496
Cost of goods sold	334
Net income	39

1. What is Tootsie Roll's percent of the cost of sales to sales? Round to one decimal place.
2. The percent a company adds to its cost of sales to determine selling price is called a markup. What is Tootsie Roll's markup percent? Round to one decimal place.
3. What is the percentage of net income to sales for Tootsie Roll? Round to one decimal place.
4. Compare your answer to (3) with that of *The Hershey Company* in Activity 1-6. What are your conclusions?

A1-8
Financial analysis of Enron Corporation

Enron Corporation, headquartered in Houston, Texas, provided products and services for natural gas, electricity, and communications to wholesale and retail customers. Enron's operations were conducted through a variety of subsidiaries and affiliates that involve transporting gas through pipelines, transmitting electricity, and managing energy commodities. The following data were taken from Enron's December 31, 2000, financial statements:

	In millions
Total revenues	$100,789
Total costs and expenses	98,836
Operating income	1,953
Net income	979
Total assets	65,503
Total liabilities	54,033
Total stockholders' equity	11,470
Net cash flows from operating activities	4,779
Net cash flows from investing activities	(4,264)
Net cash flows from financing activities	571
Net increase in cash	1,086

At the end of 2000, the market price of Enron's stock was approximately $83 per share. Eventually, however, Enron's stock was selling for $0.22 per share.

Review the preceding financial statement data and search the Internet for articles on Enron Corporation. Briefly explain why Enron's stock dropped so dramatically in such a short time.

1. **D** A corporation, organized in accordance with state or federal statutes, is a separate legal entity in which ownership is divided into shares of stock (answer D). A proprietorship (answer A) is an unincorporated business owned by one individual. A service business (answer B) provides services to its customers. It can be organized as a proprietorship, partnership, or corporation. A partnership (answer C) is an unincorporated business owned by two or more individuals.

2. **A** The resources owned by a business are called assets (answer A). The debts of the business are called liabilities (answer B), and the equity of the owners is called stockholders' equity (answer D). The relationship among assets, liabilities, and stockholders' equity is expressed as the accounting equation (answer C).

3. **A** The balance sheet is a listing of the assets, liabilities, and stockholders' equity of a business at a specific date (answer A). The income statement (answer B) is a summary of the revenue and expenses of a business for a specific period of time. The retained earnings statement (answer C) summarizes the changes in retained earnings during a specific period of time. The statement of cash flows (answer D) summarizes the cash receipts and cash payments for a specific period of time.

4. **D** The accounting equation is:

   Assets = Liabilities + Stockholders' Equity

   Therefore, if assets are $20,000 and liabilities are $12,000, stockholders' equity is $8,000 (answer D), as indicated in the following computation:

Assets	= Liabilities + Stockholders' Equity
+$20,000	= $12,000 + Stockholders' Equity
+$20,000 − $12,000	= Stockholders' Equity
+$8,000	= Stockholders' Equity

5. **B** Net income is the excess of revenue over expenses, or $7,500 (answer B). If expenses exceed revenue, the difference is a net loss. Dividends are the opposite of the stockholders investing in the business and do not affect the amount of net income or net loss.

Basic Accounting Concepts

2

Every day it seems like you get an incredible amount of incoming e-mail messages; you get them from your friends, relatives, subscribed e-mail lists, and even spammers! But how do you organize all of these messages? You might create folders to sort messages by sender, topic, or project. Perhaps you use keyword search utilities. You might even use filters/rules to automatically delete spam or send messages from your best friend to a special folder. In any case, you are organizing information so that it is simple to retrieve and allows you to understand, respond, or refer to the messages.

In the same way that you organize your e-mail, companies develop an organized method for processing, recording, and summarizing financial transactions. For example, **Apple, Inc.,** has a huge volume of financial transactions, resulting from sales of its innovative computers, digital media (like iPod^{TM} music and video players), and iPhone^{TM} mobile phones. When Apple sells an iPhone online or at **The Apple Store,** a customer has the option of paying with a credit card, a debit or check card, an Apple gift card, a financing arrangement, or cash (using a cashier's check, a money order, or a wire transfer). In order to analyze only the information related to Apple's cash transactions, the company must record or summarize all these similar sales using a single category or "cash" account. This is comparable to how you summarize cash in the check register of your checkbook. Similarly, Apple will record credit card payments for iPhones and sales from financing arrangements in different accounts (records).

This chapter describes the basic elements of a financial accounting system. Such systems process, record, and summarize financial transactions, allowing for the preparation of financial statements, as discussed in Chapter 1.

The simplest form of an accounting system records and summarizes only transactions involving the receipt and payment of cash. For this reason, this chapter describes and illustrates a cash basis accounting system. This serves as a foundation for later discussions of more complex accounting systems and financial reporting issues.

Elements of an Accounting System

Obj 1 Describe the basic elements of a financial accounting system.

These basic elements are found in all financial accounting systems, including those of **Apple**, **Google**, and **Boeing**.

A financial accounting system is designed to produce financial statements. The financial statements include the income statement, retained earnings statement, balance sheet, and statement of cash flows.

The basic elements of a **financial accounting system** include:

- *Rules* for determining what, when, and the amount that should be recorded
- A *framework* for preparing financial statements
- *Controls* to determine whether errors may have arisen in the recording process

Rules

The rules for determining what, when, and the amount recorded are derived from the eight concepts discussed in Chapter 1. These concepts are the basis of generally accepted accounting principles (GAAP), which require the recording of transactions affecting elements of the financial statements.

A **transaction** is an economic event that under GAAP affects the financial statements. A transaction may affect one, two, or more items within the financial statements. For example, equipment purchased for cash affects only assets. That is, one asset (equipment) increases while another asset (cash) decreases. If, on the other hand, the equipment is purchased on credit, assets (equipment) and liabilities (accounts or notes payable) increase.

Framework

Transactions must be analyzed, recorded, and summarized using a framework. The accounting equation is the basis for all such frameworks. The accounting equation is expressed as follows:

$$\text{Assets} = \text{Liabilities} + \text{Stockholders' Equity}$$

By expanding the accounting equation, as shown in Exhibit 1, an integrated financial statement approach can be designed for analyzing, recording, and summarizing transactions. This is done by including columns for the statement of cash flows, balance sheet, and income statement.

The *left-hand* column in Exhibit 1 shows the effects of transactions on the statement of cash flows. Each cash transaction is recorded and classified into operating, investing, and financing activities. This serves as a basis for preparing the statement of cash flows.

The cash at the beginning of the period plus or minus the cash flows from operating, investing, and financing activities equals the end-of-period cash. This end-of-period cash amount is reported as an asset on the balance sheet. Thus, the statement of cash flows is integrated with the balance sheet in Exhibit 1.

The *right-hand* column in Exhibit 1 shows the effects of transactions on the income statement. Each revenue and expense transaction is recorded and classified as a revenue or expense. This serves as a basis for preparing the income statement.

A net income for the period, revenues less expenses, is added to beginning retained earnings.[1] Thus, revenue and expense transactions are also recorded under the Retained Earnings column of the balance sheet. By doing so, the balance sheet is integrated with the income statement in Exhibit 1.

---

[1] A net loss for the period, which occurs when expenses exceed revenues, is subtracted from beginning retained earnings.

EXHIBIT 1 Integrated Financial Statement Framework

Statement of Cash Flows	Balance Sheet								Income Statement
	Assets	=	Liabilities	+		Stockholders' Equity			
	Assets	=	Liabilities	+	Capital Stock	+	Retained Earnings		
Transactions	XXX		XXX		XXX		XXX		
	XXX		XXX		XXX		XXX		

Statement of Cash Flows			Income Statement	
+/− Operating activities	XXX		Revenues	XXX
+/− Investing activities	XXX		Expenses	XXX
+/− Financing activities	XXX		Net income or loss	XXX
Increase or decrease in cash	XXX			
Beginning cash	XXX			
Ending cash	XXX			

INTEGRATED FINANCIAL STATEMENT FRAMEWORK

Exhibit 1 also illustrates the importance of the balance sheet as the connecting link between the statement of cash flows and the income statement.[2] This integrated financial statement approach for analyzing, recording, and summarizing transactions is illustrated later in this chapter.

The integrated financial statement approach shown in Exhibit 1 is an invaluable tool for analyzing transactions and their effects on the financial statements. It is also an aid for analyzing and interpreting a company's financial statements. This is because, without understanding how a company's financial statements are integrated, important trends or events may be missed or misinterpreted.

To illustrate, assume a company reports net income (profits) on its income statement. As a result, it might be mistakenly concluded that the company's operations are doing well and no major changes are necessary. In fact, the company might be experiencing a continuing negative net cash flow from operations and thus, be headed towards bankruptcy. This is why it is essential to analyze all the financial statements and their integration.

Controls

The integrated financial statement approach shown in Exhibit 1 has built-in controls to ensure that all transactions are correctly analyzed, recorded, and summarized. These controls include the following:[3]

1. The accounting equation must balance.
2. The ending cash on the statement of cash flows must equal the cash on the balance sheet.
3. The net income on the income statement must equal the net effects of revenues and expenses on retained earnings.

[2] In Chapter 3, the use of the balance sheet to reconcile net cash flows from operating activities with net income is described and illustrated.

[3] Additional accounting controls are discussed in Chapter 5.

First, the accounting equation requires that total assets equal total liabilities plus total stockholders' equity. If at the end of the period this equality does not hold, an error has occurred.

To illustrate, assume that a cash purchase of equipment for $10,000 is incorrectly recorded as a $10,000 increase in equipment and a $10,000 increase (instead of decrease) in cash. In this case, the total assets exceed the total liabilities plus stockholders' equity by $20,000. Likewise, assume that the equipment was increased by $10,000, but the $10,000 decrease in cash was omitted. In this case, the total assets exceed total liabilities plus stockholders' equity by $10,000. In both cases, the inequality of the equation indicates that an error has occurred.

The equality of the Equation doesn't necessarily mean that no errors have occurred. To illustrate, assume that a business purchased $10,000 of equipment on credit and recorded the transaction as an increase in equipment of $10,000. However, instead of increasing the liabilities by $10,000, the transaction was recorded as a $10,000 decrease in cash. In this case, the accounting equation still balances, even though cash and liabilities are understated by $10,000.

Second, the ending Cash shown in the Statement of Cash Flows column must equal the ending cash under Assets in the Balance Sheet column. If these two amounts do not agree, an error has occurred.

To illustrate, assume that a $5,000 cash receipt was recorded as an increase in Cash in the Balance Sheet Column under Assets, but was omitted from the Statement of Cash Flows column. In this case, the ending cash shown in the Statement of Cash Flows column would be $5,000 less than the balance of Cash under Assets in the Balance Sheet column.

Third, the net income or loss from the Income Statement column must equal the net effects of revenues and expenses on retained earnings. If these two amounts do not agree, an error has occurred.

To illustrate, assume that a $7,500 payment for rent expense was recorded under Retained Earnings in the Balance Sheet column, but was omitted

How Businesses Make Money

Got the Flu? Why Not Chew Some Gum?

Facing a slumping market for sugared chewing gum—such as Juicy Fruit™ and Doublemint™—**Wm. Wrigley Jr. Company,** a subsidiary of **Mars Incorporated,** is reinventing itself by expanding its product lines and introducing new chewing gum applications. Wrigley's new products include sugarless breath mints and more powerful flavored mint chewing gum, like Extra Polar Ice™. In addition, Wrigley is experimenting with health-care applications of chewing gum. Wrigley's Health Care Division has already developed Surpass™, an antacid chewing gum to compete with Rolaids and Mylanta. Wrigley is also developing a cold-relief chewing gum and a gum that would provide dental benefits, such as whitening teeth and reducing plaque. Given that the U.S. population is aging, the company figures that people might prefer chewing gum to taking pills for sore throats, colds, or the flu. The effects of these new initiatives will ultimately be reflected in Wrigley's financial statements.

Source: Adapted from "A Young Heir Has New Plans at Old Company," by David Barboza, *New York Times,* August 28, 2001.

from the Income Statement column. In this case, the Net income in the Income Statement column would be $7,500 more than the net effects of revenues and expenses on retained earnings.

Recording a Corporation's First Period of Operations

Obj 2 Analyze, record, and summarize transactions for a corporation's first period of operations.

The integrated financial statement framework shown in Exhibit 1 is illustrated using the transactions for a corporation's first period of operations. Assume that on September 1, 2011, Lee Landry, M.D., organizes a professional corporation to practice general medicine. The business is to be known as Family Health Care, P.C., where P.C. refers to a *professional corporation*.

Each of Family Health Care's transactions during September is described and recorded in this section. These transactions are then summarized into financial statements. The transactions begin with Dr. Landry's investment to establish the business.

Transaction (a)

Dr. Landry deposits $6,000 in a bank account in the name of Family Health Care, P.C., in return for shares of stock in the corporation.

Stock issued to owners (stockholders) such as Lee Landry is referred to as **capital stock**. In recording this transaction, increases are recorded as positive numbers, while decreases are recorded as negative numbers.

The effects of this transaction on Family Health Care's financial statements are recorded as follows:

1. Under the Statement of Cash Flows column, Cash from Financing activities is increased by $6,000.
2. Under the Balance Sheet column, Cash under Assets is increased by $6,000. To balance the accounting equation, Capital Stock under Stockholders' Equity is also increased by $6,000.

Since no revenues or expenses are affected, there are no entries under the Income Statement column. The effects of this transaction on Family Health Care's financial statements are shown below.

Statement of Cash Flows	Balance Sheet						Income Statement
	Assets	=	Liabilities	+	Stockholders' Equity		
	Cash	=			Capital Stock		
a. Investment by Dr. Landry	6,000				6,000		
Statement of Cash Flows							
a. Financing	6,000						

Note that the preceding recording of transaction (a) relates only to the business, Family Health Care, P.C. Dr. Landry's personal assets (such as a home or a personal bank account) and personal liabilities are excluded. This is because under the business entity concept, Family Health Care is treated as a separate entity, with cash of $6,000 and stockholders' equity of $6,000.

Transaction (b)

Family Health Care borrows $10,000 from First National Bank to finance its operations.

To borrow the $10,000, Dr. Landry signs a note payable with First National Bank in the name of Family Health Care. The note payable is a liability that Family Health Care must pay in the future. The note payable also requires the payment of interest of $100 per month until the note of $10,000 is paid on September 30, 2016. The interest is to be paid at the end of each month.

The effects of this transaction on Family Health Care's financial statements are recorded as follows:

1. Under the Statement of Cash Flows column, Cash from Financing activities is increased by $10,000.
2. Under the Balance Sheet column, Cash under Assets is increased by $10,000. To balance the accounting equation, Notes Payable under Liabilities is also increased by $10,000.

This transaction changes the mix of assets and liabilities on the balance sheet, but does not change Family Health Care's stockholders' equity of $6,000. Since no revenues or expenses are affected, no entries are made under the Income Statement column.

The effects of this transaction on Family Health Care's financial statements are shown below.

		Balance Sheet						
Statement of Cash Flows		Assets	=	Liabilities	+	Stockholders' Equity		Income Statement
	Cash		=	Notes Payable	+	Capital Stock		
Balances	6,000					6,000		
b. Loan from bank	10,000			10,000				
Balances	16,000			10,000		6,000		

Statement of Cash Flows	
b. Financing	10,000

Transaction (c)

Family Health Care buys land for $12,000 cash.

The land is located near a new suburban hospital that is under construction. Dr. Landry plans to rent office space and equipment for several months. When the hospital is completed, Family Health Care will build on the land.

The effects of this transaction on Family Health Care's financial statements are recorded as follows:

1. Under the Statement of Cash Flows column, Cash from Investing activities is decreased by $12,000.
2. Under the Balance Sheet column, Cash under Assets is decreased by $12,000. To balance the accounting equation, Land under Assets is increased by $12,000.

This transaction illustrates the use of cash for an investing activity. As a result, −$12,000 was entered under the Statement of Cash Flows column. In addition,

the mix of assets changes on the balance sheet. Since no revenues or expenses are affected, no entries are made under the Income Statement column.

The effects of this transaction on Family Health Care's financial statements are shown below.

Statement of Cash Flows	Balance Sheet					Income Statement
	Assets		=	Liabilities +	Stockholders' Equity	
	Cash	+	Land	=	Notes Payable	+	Capital Stock	
Balances	16,000				10,000	6,000	
c. Purchase of land	−12,000	12,000				
Balances	4,000	12,000			10,000	6,000	

Statement of Cash Flows	
c. Investing	−12,000

Transaction (d)

During the first month of operations, Family Health Care earned patient fees of $5,500, receiving the fees in cash.

The effects of this transaction on Family Health Care's financial statements are recorded as follows:

1. Under the Statement of Cash Flows column, Cash from Operating activities is increased by $5,500.
2. Under the Balance Sheet column, Cash under Assets is increased by $5,500. To balance the accounting equation, Retained Earnings under Stockholders' Equity is also increased by $5,500.
3. Under the Income Statement column, Fees earned is increased by $5,500.

This transaction illustrates an inflow of cash from operating activities by earning revenues (fees earned) of $5,500. Retained Earnings is increased under Stockholders' Equity by $5,500 because fees earned contribute to net income and net income increases stockholders' equity. Since fees earned are a type of revenue, Fees earned of $5,500 is also entered under the Income Statement column.

The effects of this transaction on Family Health Care's financial statements are shown below.

Statement of Cash Flows	Balance Sheet						Income Statement
	Assets		=	Liabilities +	Stockholders' Equity		
	Cash	+	Land	=	Notes Payable	+	Capital Stock	+	Retained Earnings	
Balances	4,000	12,000			10,000	6,000		
d. Fees earned	5,500						5,500	d.
Balances	9,500	12,000			10,000	6,000		5,500	

Statement of Cash Flows		Income Statement	
d. Operating	5,500	d. Fees earned	5,500

Transaction (e)

Family Health Care paid expenses during September as follows: wages, $1,125; rent, $950; utilities, $450; interest, $100; and miscellaneous, $275.

Miscellaneous expenses include small amounts paid for such items as postage, newspapers, and magazines. The effects of this transaction on Family Health Care's financial statements are recorded as follows:

1. Under the Statement of Cash Flows column, Cash from Operating activities is decreased by $2,900, which is the sum of the expenses ($1,125 + $950 + $450 + $100 + $275).

2. Under the Balance Sheet column, Cash under Assets is decreased by $2,900. To balance the accounting equation, Retained Earnings under Stockholders' Equity is also decreased by $2,900.

3. Under the Income Statement column, each expense is listed as a negative amount.

This transaction illustrates an outflow of cash of $2,900 for operating activities (paying expenses). Thus, −$2,900 is entered in the Statement of Cash Flows column as an Operating activity. Expenses have the opposite effect from revenues on net income and retained earnings. As a result, −$2,900 is entered for Retained Earnings under Stockholders' Equity. In addition, each expense is listed under the income statement column as a negative amount.

The effects of this transaction on Family Health Care's financial statements are shown below.

	Balance Sheet								
Statement of Cash Flows	Assets		=	Liabilities	+	Stockholders' Equity			Income Statement
	Cash	+ Land	=	Notes Payable	+	Capital Stock	+	Retained Earnings	
Balances	9,500	12,000		10,000		6,000		5,500	
e. Paid expenses	−2,900							−2,900	e.
Balances	6,600	12,000		10,000		6,000		2,600	

Statement of Cash Flows		Income Statement	
e. Operating	−2,900	e. Wages expense	−1,125
		Rent expense	−950
		Utilities expense	−450
		Interest expense	−100
		Misc. expense	−275

Transaction (f)

Family Health Care paid $1,500 to stockholders (Dr. Lee Landry) as dividends.

Dividends are distributions of a company's earnings to stockholders. Dividends should not be confused with expenses. Dividends do not represent assets consumed or services used in earning revenues. Instead, dividends are a distribution of earnings to the stockholders.

The effects of this transaction on Family Health Care's financial statements are recorded as follows:

1. Under the Statement of Cash Flows column, Cash from Financing activities is decreased by $1,500.

2. Under the Balance Sheet column, Cash under Assets is decreased by $1,500. To balance the accounting equation, Retained Earnings under Stockholders' Equity is also decreased by $1,500.

This transaction illustrates an outflow of cash of $1,500 for financing activities (paying dividends). Thus, −$1,500 is entered in the Statement of Cash Flows column as a Financing activity. Dividends decrease retained earnings; thus, −$1,500 is entered for Retained Earnings under Stockholders' Equity. Since dividends are not an expense, no entry is made under the Income Statement column.

The effects of this transaction on Family Health Care's financial statements are shown below.

| Statement of Cash Flows | Balance Sheet | | | | | | Income Statement |
| | Assets | | = | Liabilities | + | Stockholders' Equity | |
	Cash	+	Land	=	Notes Payable	+	Capital Stock	+	Retained Earnings	
Balances	6,600		12,000		10,000		6,000		2,600	
f. Paid dividends	−1,500								−1,500	
Balances	5,100		12,000		10,000		6,000		1,100	

Statement of Cash Flows

f. Financing	−1,500

The September transactions of Family Health Care are summarized in Exhibit 2. Each transaction is identified by letter, and the balances are shown as of the end of September.

Exhibit 2 illustrates the three controls that are built into the integrated financial statement approach. These controls are as follows:

1. The accounting equation under the Balance Sheet column balances. That is, total assets of $17,100 ($5,100 + $12,000) equals total liabilities plus stockholders' equity of $17,100 ($10,000 + $6,000 + $1,100).

2. The ending cash under the Statement of Cash Flows column of $5,100 equals the cash balance under the Balance Sheet column of $5,100.

3. The net income under the Income Statement column of $2,600 equals the net effects of revenues of $5,500 and expenses of $2,900 on retained earnings of $2,600 ($5,500−$2,900).

INTEGRITY, OBJECTIVITY, AND ETHICS IN BUSINESS

A History of Ethical Conduct

The **Wrigley Company,** which is now a subsidiary of **Mars Incorporated,** has a long history of integrity, objectivity, and ethical conduct. When pressured to become part of a cartel, known as the Chewing Gum Trust, the company founder, William Wrigley Jr., said, "We prefer to do business by fair and square methods or we prefer not to do business at all." In 1932, Phillip K. Wrigley, called "PK" by his friends, became president of the Wrigley Company after his father, William Wrigley Jr., died. PK also was president of the Chicago Cubs, which played in Wrigley Field. He was financially generous to his players and frequently gave them advice on and off the field. However, as a man of integrity and high ethical standards, PK docked (reduced) his salary as president of the Wrigley Company for the time he spent working on Cubs-related activities and business.

Source: St. Louis Post-Dispatch, "Sports—Backpages," January 26, 2003.

EXHIBIT 2 | **Family Health Care Summary of Transactions for September**

Statement of Cash Flows	Balance Sheet						Income Statement
	Assets		= Liabilities	+	Stockholders' Equity		
	Cash	+ Land	= Notes Payable	+	Capital Stock	+ Retained Earnings	
a. Investment by Dr. Landry	6,000				6,000		
b. Loan from bank	10,000		10,000				
c. Purchase of land	−12,000	12,000					
d. Fees earned	5,500					5,500	d.
e. Paid expenses	−2,900					−2,900	e.
f. Paid dividends	−1,500					−1,500	
Balances, Sept. 30	5,100	12,000	10,000		6,000	1,100	

Statement of Cash Flows			Income Statement	
a. Financing	6,000		d. Fees earned	5,500
b. Financing	10,000		e. Wages expense	−1,125
c. Investing	−12,000		Rent expense	−950
d. Operating	5,500		Utilities expense	−450
e. Operating	−2,900		Interest expense	−100
f. Financing	−1,500		Misc. expense	−275
Increase in cash and Sept. 30 cash	5,100		Net income	2,600

In reviewing Exhibit 2, you should note that the following apply to all companies:

- The Balance Sheet column reflects the accounting equation (Assets = Liabilities + Stockholders' Equity).

- The two sides of the accounting equation are always equal.

- Every transaction affects (increases or decreases) one or more of the balance sheet elements—assets, liabilities, or stockholders' equity.

- A transaction may or may not affect (increase or decrease) an element of the statement of cash flows or the income statement. Some transactions affect elements of both statements, some transactions affect only one statement and not the other, and some transactions affect neither statement.

- Every cash transaction increases or decreases the asset (cash) on the balance sheet. Every cash transaction also increases or decreases an operating, investing, or financing activity on the statement of cash flows.

- The ending balance of Cash under the Statement of Cash Flows column, ($5,100 in Exhibit 2) agrees with the ending cash balance shown on the balance sheet. Since September was Family Health Care's first period of operations, this ending cash balance equals the net increase in cash for the period. In future periods, the net increase (decrease) in cash is added to (or subtracted from) the beginning cash balance to equal the ending cash balance. This ending cash balance is reported in the statement of cash flows and balance sheet.

On its 2008 balance sheet, **Apple** reported (in millions) assets of $39,572, which equals its liabilities of $18,542 plus its stockholders' equity of $21,030.

- The stockholders' equity is increased by amounts invested by stockholders (capital stock).

- Revenues increase stockholders' equity (retained earnings) and expenses decrease stockholders' equity (retained earnings). The effects of revenue and expense transactions are also shown in the Income Statement column.

- Stockholders' equity (retained earnings) is decreased by dividends paid to stockholders.

- The change in retained earnings for the period is the net income minus dividends. For a net loss, the change in retained earnings is the net loss plus dividends.

- The statement of cash flows is linked to the balance sheet through cash.

- The income statement is linked to the balance sheet through revenues and expenses (net income or loss), which affects retained earnings.

Exhibit 3 summarizes the effects of the various transactions affecting stockholders' equity.

EXHIBIT 3   Effects of Transactions on Stockholders' Equity

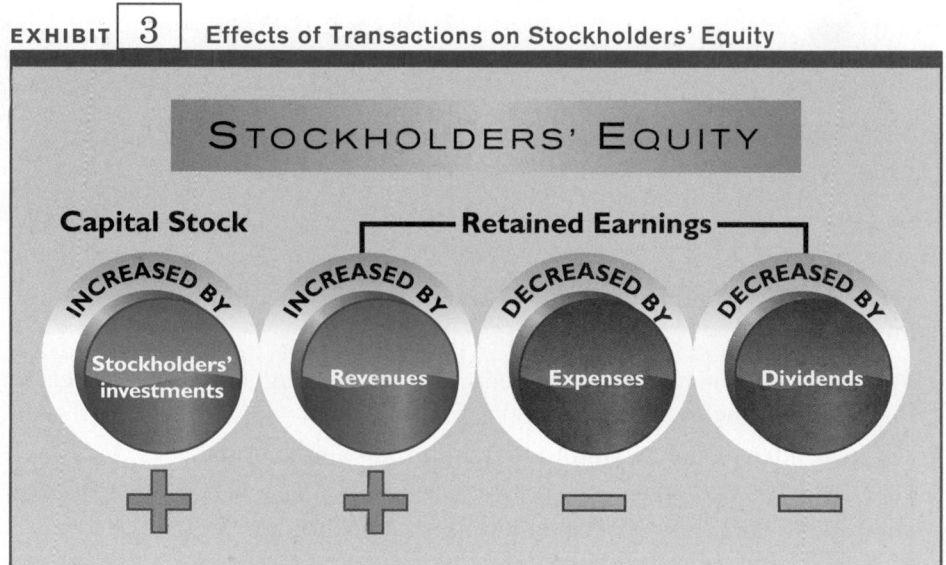

Obj 3 Prepare financial statements for a corporation's first period of operations.

Financial Statements for a Corporation's First Period of Operations

Exhibit 2 lists Family Health Care's September transactions in the order they occurred. Exhibit 2, however, does not group and summarize like transactions together. The accounting reports that provide this summarized information are financial statements.

Family Health Care's September financial statements can be prepared from Exhibit 2. These financial statements are shown in Exhibit 4.

The financial statements shown in Exhibit 4 are prepared from Exhibit 2 as follows:

1. The income statement is prepared using the Income Statement column.

2. The retained earnings statement is prepared next because the ending balance of retained earnings is needed to prepare the balance sheet. The retained earnings statement is prepared using net income from the income statement and the amount recorded for dividends under retained earnings.

3. The balance sheet is prepared next using the balances shown under the Balance Sheet column.

4. The statement of cash flows is normally prepared last using the Statement of Cash Flows column.

Each financial statement is identified by the name of the business, the title of the statement, and the date or period of time.

Income Statement

The income statement for Family Health Care shown in Exhibit 4 reports fees earned of $5,500, total operating expenses of $2,900, and net income of $2,600. The $5,500 of fees earned is taken from the Income Statement column of Exhibit 2. Likewise, the expenses are summarized from the Income Statement column of Exhibit 2. These expenses are reported under the heading "Operating expenses." Operating expenses are normally listed in order of size, beginning with the largest expense. Miscellaneous expense is usually shown as the last item, regardless of amount.

EXHIBIT 4   Family Health Care Financial Statements for September

FAMILY HEALTH CARE, P.C.
Income Statement
For the Month Ended September 30, 2011

Fees earned		$5,500
Operating expenses:		
Wages expense	$1,125	
Rent expense	950	
Utilities expense	450	
Interest expense	100	
Miscellaneous expense	275	
Total operating expenses		2,900
Net income		$2,600

FAMILY HEALTH CARE, P.C.
Retained Earnings Statement
For the Month Ended September 30, 2011

Net income for September	$2,600
Less dividends	1,500
Retained earnings, September 30, 2011	$1,100

(*Continued*)

EXHIBIT 4 Continued

FAMILY HEALTH CARE, P.C.
Balance Sheet
September 30, 2011

Assets

Cash	$ 5,100
Land	12,000
Total assets	$17,100

Liabilities

Notes payable	$10,000

Stockholders' Equity

Capital stock	$6,000	
Retained earnings	1,100	
Total stockholders' equity		7,100
Total liabilities and stockholders' equity		$17,100

FAMILY HEALTH CARE, P.C.
Statement of Cash Flows
For the Month Ended September 30, 2011

Cash flows from operating activities:			
Cash received from customers	$ 5,500		
Deduct cash payments for expenses	2,900		
Net cash flow from operating activities			$ 2,600
Cash flows from investing activities:			
Cash payments for acquisition of land			(12,000)
Cash flows from financing activities:			
Cash received from sale of capital stock	$ 6,000		
Cash received from notes payable	10,000	$16,000	
Deduct cash dividends		1,500	
Net cash flow from financing activities			14,500
Net increase in cash			$ 5,100
September 1, 2011, cash balance			0
September 30, 2011, cash balance			$ 5,100

Retained Earnings Statement

Since Family Health Care has been in operation for only one month, it has no retained earnings at the beginning of September. The ending September balance is the change in retained earnings created by net income and dividends. This change, $1,100, is the beginning retained earnings balance for October.

Balance Sheet

Family Health Care's assets, liabilities, and stockholders' equity as of September 30, 2011 are taken from the last line of the Balance Sheet column of Exhibit 2. The September 30, 2011 balance sheet is shown in Exhibit 4.

In the Assets section of the balance sheet, assets are normally listed in order of liquidity, starting with cash. **Liquidity** refers to the ability to convert an asset to cash. Land is less liquid than cash and thus, would be listed second in Family Health Care's balance sheet.

In the Liabilities section of the Family Health Care's balance sheet, notes payable is the only liability. When there are two or more categories of liabilities, each should be listed and the total amount reported. Liabilities should be presented in the order that they will be paid in cash. Thus, the notes payable due in 2016 will be listed after the liabilities that are due earlier.

The stockholders' equity for Family Health Care as of September 30, 2011, consists of $6,000 of capital stock and retained earnings of $1,100. The retained earnings is the ending retained earnings reported on the retained earnings statement.

Statement of Cash Flows

Family Health Care's statement of cash flows for September is prepared from the Statement of Cash Flows column of Exhibit 2. Cash increased from a zero balance at the beginning of the month to $5,100 at the end of the month.

The $5,100 increase in cash during September was created by:

1. Operating activities that generated $2,600 of cash
2. Investing activities that used $12,000 of cash
3. Financing activities that generated $14,500 of cash

The details of how the operating, investing, and financing activities generated or used cash is reported in the statement of cash flows. For example, financing activities generated $6,000 from the sale of capital stock and $10,000 from borrowing by issuing a note payable. Financing activities used $1,500 for paying dividends.

Integration of Financial Statements

Exhibit 5 shows how Family Health Care's financial statements for September are integrated. As shown in Exhibit 5, these statements are integrated as follows:

1. The ending cash balance of $5,100 on the balance sheet equals the ending cash balance reported on the statement of cash flows.
2. The net income of $2,600 is reported on the income statement and the retained earnings statement.
3. The ending retained earnings of $1,100 is reported in the retained earnings statement and the balance sheet.
4. The cash flows from operating activities of $2,600 reported on the statement of cash flows equals the net income on the income statement. The relationship between cash flows from operating activities and net income is further described and illustrated in Chapter 3.

Recording a Corporation's Second Period of Operations

Obj 4 Analyze, record, and summarize transactions for a corporation's second period of operations.

During October, Family Health Care entered into the following transactions:

a. Received, in cash, fees of $6,400

b. Paid expenses, in cash, as follows: wages, $1,370; rent, $950; utilities, $540; interest, $100; and miscellaneous, $220

c. Paid cash dividends of $1,000

The October transactions are analyzed and entered into the integrated financial statement framework shown in Exhibit 6.

EXHIBIT 5   **Family Health Care Integrated Financial Statements for September**

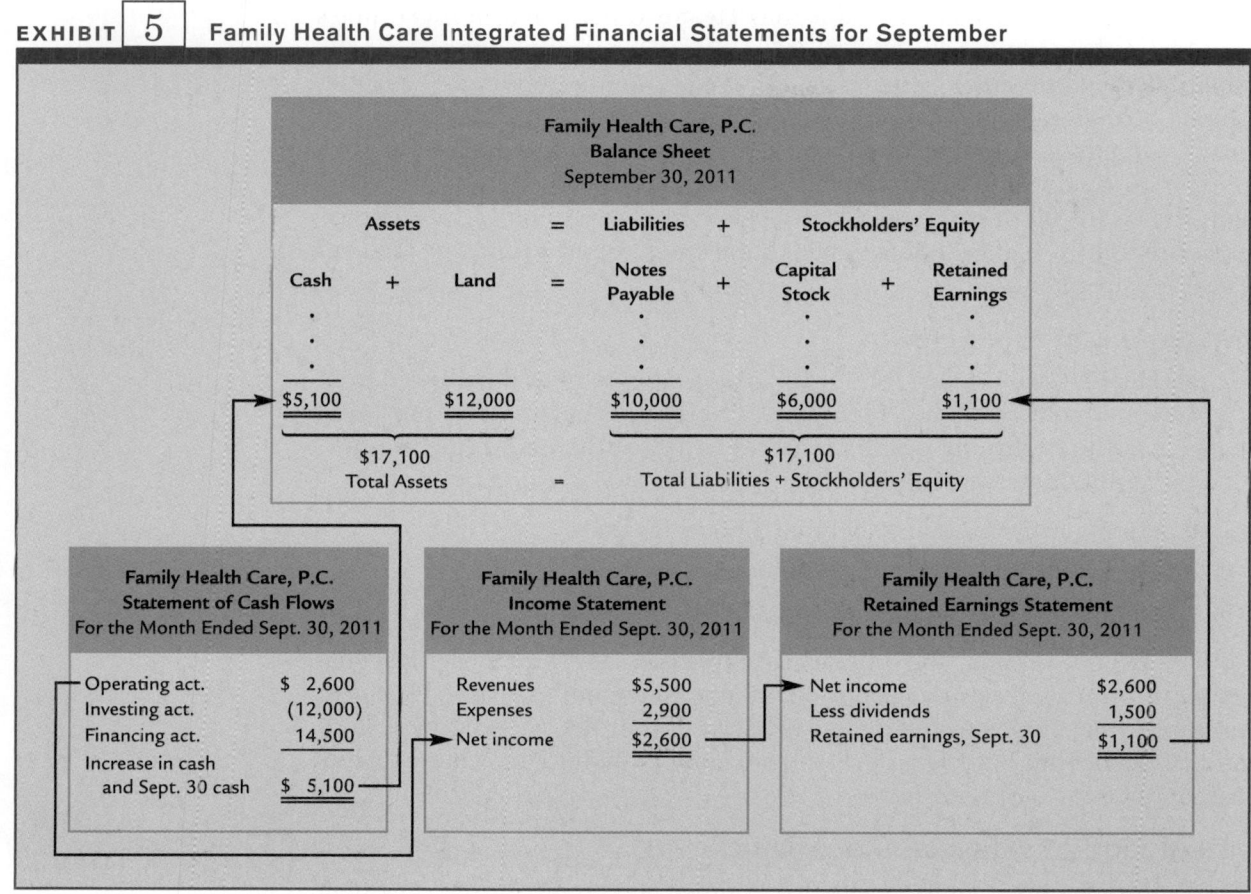

Family Health Care, P.C.
Balance Sheet
September 30, 2011

Assets			=	Liabilities	+	Stockholders' Equity	
Cash	+	Land	=	Notes Payable	+	Capital Stock	+ Retained Earnings
$5,100		$12,000	=	$10,000	+	$6,000	+ $1,100

$17,100
Total Assets   = $17,100
Total Liabilities + Stockholders' Equity

Family Health Care, P.C.
Statement of Cash Flows
For the Month Ended Sept. 30, 2011

Operating act.	$ 2,600
Investing act.	(12,000)
Financing act.	14,500
Increase in cash and Sept. 30 cash	$ 5,100

Family Health Care, P.C.
Income Statement
For the Month Ended Sept. 30, 2011

Revenues	$5,500
Expenses	2,900
Net income	$2,600

Family Health Care, P.C.
Retained Earnings Statement
For the Month Ended Sept. 30, 2011

Net income	$2,600
Less dividends	1,500
Retained earnings, Sept. 30	$1,100

EXHIBIT 6   **Family Health Care Summary of Transactions for October**

Statement of Cash Flows	Balance Sheet						Income Statement
	Assets		=	Liabilities	+	Stockholders' Equity	
	Cash	+ Land	=	Notes Payable	+ Capital Stock	+ Retained Earnings	
Balances, Oct. 1	5,100	12,000		10,000	6,000	1,100	
a. Fees earned	6,400					6,400	a.
b. Paid expenses	−3,180					−3,180	b.
c. Paid dividends	−1,000					−1,000	
Balances, Oct. 31	7,320	12,000		10,000	6,000	3,320	

Statement of Cash Flows

a. Operating	6,400
b. Operating	−3,180
c. Financing	−1,000
Increase in cash	2,220

Income Statement

a. Fees earned	6,400
b. Wages expense	−1,370
Rent expense	−950
Utilities expense	−540
Interest expense	−100
Misc. expense	−220
Net income	3,220

The Balance Sheet column of Exhibit 6 begins with the ending balances as of September 30, 2011 taken from Exhibit 2. This is because the balance sheet is the cumulative total of the entity's assets, liabilities, and stockholders' equity since the company's inception.

As of October 1, 2011, Family Health Care has cash of $5,100, land of $12,000, notes payable of $10,000, capital stock of $6,000, and retained earnings of $1,100. In contrast, the statement of cash flows and the income statement report only transactions for a period and are not cumulative.

Financial Statements for a Corporation's Second Period of Operations

Obj 5 Prepare financial statements for a corporation's second period of operations.

Family Health Care's financial statements for October are shown in Exhibit 7. These statements were prepared from Exhibit 6.

Income Statement

The income statement for October reports net income of $3,220. This is an increase of $620, or 23.8% ($620/$2,600), from September's net income of $2,600. The increase in net income was due to fees increasing from $5,500 to $6,400, a $900, or 16.4% ($900/$5,500), increase from September. At the same time, total operating expenses increased only $280, or 9.7% ($280/$2,900). This suggests that Family Health Care's operations are profitable and expanding.

EXHIBIT | 7 | Family Health Care Financial Statements for October

FAMILY HEALTH CARE, P.C.
Income Statement
For the Month Ended October 31, 2011

Fees earned		$6,400
Operating expenses:		
Wages expense	$1,370	
Rent expense	950	
Utilities expense	540	
Interest expense	100	
Miscellaneous expense	220	
Total operating expenses		3,180
Net income		$3,220

FAMILY HEALTH CARE, P.C.
Retained Earnings Statement
For the Month Ended October 31, 2011

Retained earnings, October 1, 2011		$1,100
Net income for October	$3,220	
Less dividends	1,000	2,220
Retained earnings, October 31, 2011		$3,320

(Continued)

EXHIBIT **7** Continued

FAMILY HEALTH CARE, P.C.
Balance Sheet
October 31, 2011

Assets		
Cash		$ 7,320
Land		12,000
Total assets		$19,320
Liabilities		
Notes payable		$10,000
Stockholders' Equity		
Capital stock	$6,000	
Retained earnings	3,320	
Total stockholders' equity		9,320
Total liabilities and stockholders' equity		$19,320

FAMILY HEALTH CARE, P.C.
Statement of Cash Flows
For the Month Ended October 31, 2011

Cash flows from operating activities:	
Cash received from customers	$ 6,400
Deduct cash payments for expenses	3,180
Net cash flow from operating activities	$ 3,220
Cash flows from investing activities	0
Cash flows from financing activities:	
Deduct cash dividends	(1,000)
Net increase in cash	$ 2,220
October 1, 2011, cash balance	5,100
October 31, 2011, cash balance	$ 7,320

Retained Earnings Statement

The retained earnings statement is prepared by first listing the retained earnings as of the beginning of the period. This is the ending retained earnings balance of the prior period. As shown in Exhibit 4, Family Health Care's retained earnings statement for the month ending September 30, 2011 is $1,100. Thus, retained earnings as of October 1, 2011 is reported as $1,100 in Exhibit 7.

During October, Family Health Care reported an increase in retained earnings of $2,220. This increase is the result of net income ($3,220) less the dividends ($1,000). The ending retained earnings balance as of October 31, 2011 is $3,320.

Balance Sheet

The balance sheet in Exhibit 6 shows that total assets increased from $17,100 on September 30, 2011, to $19,320 on October 31. This increase of $2,220 was due to an increase in cash from $5,100 to $7,320. Total liabilities of $10,000 remained the same.

Since total assets increased by $2,220 and total liabilities remained the same, total stockholders' equity must also have increased by $2,220. This is

because the accounting equation must always balance. Exhibit 7 shows that total stockholders' equity did increase by \$2,220, which is the increase in retained earnings.

Statement of Cash Flows

Family Health Care's statement of cash flows for October indicates that cash increased by \$2,220. This increase is cash generated from operating activities of \$3,220 less cash used by financing activities to pay dividends of \$1,000.

The net increase in cash of \$2,220 is added to the beginning cash balance of \$5,100 to yield the ending cash balance of \$7,320. This ending cash balance of \$7,320 also appears on the October 31, 2011 balance sheet.

Integration of Financial Statements

Exhibit 8 illustrates that Family Health Care's financial statements for October are integrated as follows:

1. The ending cash balance of \$7,320 on the balance sheet equals the ending cash balance reported on the statement of cash flows.

2. The net income of \$3,220 is reported on the income statement and the retained earnings statement.

EXHIBIT 8 | **Family Health Care Integrated Financial Statements for October**

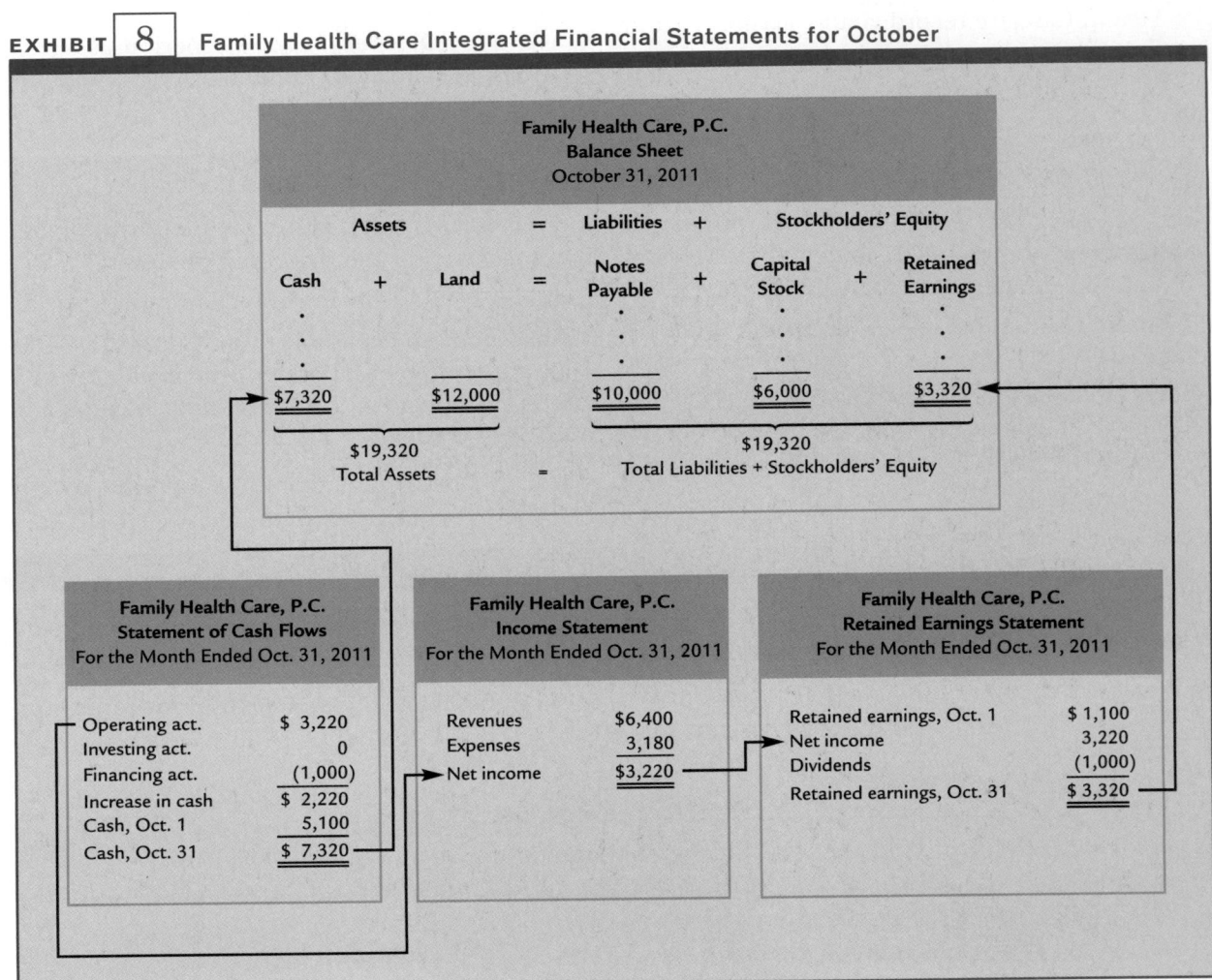

3. The ending retained earnings of $3,320 is reported in the retained earnings statement and the balance sheet.

4. The cash flows from operating activities of $3,220 reported on the statement of cash flows equals the net income on the income statement. The relationship between cash flows from operating activities and net income is further described and illustrated in Chapter 3.

Key Points

1. Describe the basic elements of a financial accounting system.

   The basic elements of a financial accounting system include (1) a set of rules for determining what, when, and the amount that should be recorded; (2) a framework for preparing financial statements; and (3) one or more controls to determine whether errors may have arisen in the recording process.

2. Analyze, record, and summarize transactions for a corporation's first period of operations.

   Using the integrated financial statement framework, September transactions for Family Health Care are recorded and summarized in Exhibit 2.

3. Prepare financial statements for a corporation's first period of operations.

   The financial statements for Family Health Care for September, its first period of operations, are shown in Exhibit 4.

4. Analyze, record, and summarize transactions for a corporation's second period of operations.

   Using the accounting equation as a basic framework, October transactions for Family Health Care are recorded and summarized in Exhibit 6.

5. Prepare financial statements for a corporation's second period of operations.

   The financial statements for Family Health Care for October, its second period of operations, are shown in Exhibit 7.

Key Terms

Capital stock The portion of a corporation's stockholders' equity contributed by investors (owners) in exchange for shares of stock.

Financial accounting system A system that includes (1) a set of rules for determining what, when, and the amount that should be recorded for an economic event; (2) a framework for preparing financial statements; and, (3) one or more controls to determine whether errors could have occurred in the recording process.

Liquidity The ability to convert an asset to cash.

Transaction An economic event that, under generally accepted accounting principles (GAAP), affects an element of the accounting equation and must be recorded.

Illustrative Problem

Beth Sumner established an insurance agency on April 1, 2011, and completed the following transactions during April:

a. Opened a business bank account in the name of Sumner Insurance Inc., with a deposit of $15,000 in exchange for capital stock.

b. Borrowed $8,000 by issuing a note payable.

c. Received cash from fees earned, $11,500.

d. Paid rent on office and equipment for the month, $3,500.

e. Paid automobile expenses for the month, $650, and miscellaneous expenses, $300.

f. Paid office salaries, $1,400.

g. Paid interest on the note payable, $60.

h. Purchased land as a future building site, $20,000.

i. Paid dividends, $1,000.

Instructions

1. Indicate the effect of each transaction and the balances after each transaction, using the integrated financial statement framework.

2. Prepare an income statement and retained earnings statement for April.

3. Prepare a balance sheet as of April 30, 2011.

4. Prepare a statement of cash flows for April.

Solution

(1)

Statement of Cash Flows	Assets			=	Liabilities	+	Stockholders' Equity			Income Statement
	Cash	+	Land	=	Notes Payable	+	Capital Stock	+	Retained Earnings	
a. Investment	15,000						15,000			
b. Issued note payable	8,000				8,000					
Balances	23,000				8,000		15,000			
c. Fees earned	11,500								11,500	c.
Balances	34,500				8,000		15,000		11,500	
d. Rent expense	−3,500								−3,500	d.
Balances	31,000				8,000		15,000		8,000	
e. Paid expenses	−950								−950	e.
Balances	30,050				8,000		15,000		7,050	
f. Paid salary expense	−1,400								−1,400	f.
Balances	28,650				8,000		15,000		5,650	
g. Paid interest expense	−60								−60	g.
Balances	28,590				8,000		15,000		5,590	
h. Purchased land	−20,000		20,000							
Balances	8,590		20,000		8,000		15,000		5,590	
i. Paid dividends	−1,000								−1,000	
Balances, April 30	7,590		20,000		8,000		15,000		4,590	

Balance Sheet

Statement of Cash Flows

a. Financing	15,000
b. Financing	8,000
c. Operating	11,500
d. Operating	−3,500
e. Operating	−950
f. Operating	−1,400
g. Operating	−60
h. Investing	−20,000
i. Financing	−1,000
Increase in cash and April 30 cash	7,590

Income Statement

c. Fees earned	11,500
d. Rent expense	−3,500
e. Auto expense	−650
e. Misc. expense	−300
f. Salary expense	−1,400
g. Interest expense	−60
Net income	5,590

(2)

SUMNER INSURANCE, INC.
Income Statement
For the Month Ended April 30, 2011

Revenues:		
Fees earned		$11,500
Expenses:		
Rent expense	$3,500	
Salaries expense	1,400	
Automotive expense	650	
Interest expense	60	
Miscellaneous expense	300	
Total expenses		5,910
Net income		$ 5,590

SUMNER INSURANCE, INC.
Retained Earnings Statement
For the Month Ended April 30, 2011

Net income	$5,590
Less dividends	1,000
Retained earnings, April 30, 2011	$4,590

(3)

SUMNER INSURANCE, INC.
Balance Sheet
April 30, 2011

Assets		
Cash		$ 7,590
Land		20,000
Total assets		$27,590
Liabilities		
Note payable		$ 8,000
Stockholders' Equity		
Capital stock	$15,000	
Retained earnings	4,590	
Total stockholders' equity		19,590
Total liabilities and stockholders' equity		$27,590

(4)

SUMNER INSURANCE, INC.
Statement of Cash Flows
For the Month Ended April 30, 2011

Cash flows from operating activities:		
Cash receipts from operating activities		$ 11,500
Cash payments for operating activities		5,910
Net cash flows from operating activities		$ 5,590
Cash flows from investing activities:		
Cash payments for land		(20,000)
Cash flows from financing activities:		
Cash receipts from issuing capital stock	$15,000	
Cash receipts from note payable	8,000	
Cash payments for dividends	(1,000)	
Net cash flows used in financing activities		22,000
Net increase in cash during April		$ 7,590
Cash as of April 1, 2011		0
Cash as of April 30, 2011		$ 7,590

Self-Examination Questions (Answers appear at the end of chapter)

1. The purchase of land for $50,000 cash was incorrectly recorded as an increase in land and an increase in notes payable. Which of the following statements is correct?

   A. The accounting equation will not balance because cash is overstated by $50,000.

   B. The accounting equation will not balance because notes payable are overstated by $50,000.

   C. The accounting equation will not balance because assets will exceed liabilities by $50,000.

   D. Even though a recording error has been made, the accounting equation will balance.

2. The receipt of $8,000 cash for fees earned was recorded by Langley Consulting as an increase in cash of $8,000 and a decrease in retained earnings (revenues) of $8,000. What is the effect of this error on the accounting equation?

   A. Total assets will exceed total liabilities and stockholders' equity by $8,000.

   B. Total assets will be less than total liabilities and stockholders' equity by $8,000.

   C. Total assets will exceed total liabilities and stockholders' equity by $16,000.

   D. The error will not affect the accounting equation.

3. If total assets increased $20,000 during a period and total liabilities increased $12,000 during the same period, the amount and direction (increase or decrease) of the change in stockholders' equity for that period is:

   A. a $32,000 increase.

   B. a $32,000 decrease.

   C. an $8,000 increase.

   D. an $8,000 decrease.

4. If revenue was $90,000, expenses were $75,000, and dividends were $20,000, the amount of net income or net loss would be:

   A. $90,000 net income.

   B. $15,000 net income.

   C. $75,000 net loss.

   D. $5,000 net loss.

5. Which of the following transactions changes only the mix of assets and does not affect liabilities or stockholders' equity?

   A. Borrowed $40,000 from First National Bank

   B. Purchased land for cash

   C. Received $3,800 for fees earned

   D. Paid $4,000 for office salaries

Class Discussion Questions

1. What are the basic elements of a financial accounting system? Do these elements apply to all businesses, from a local restaurant to *Apple Inc.*? Explain.

2. Provide an example of a transaction that affects (a) only one element of the accounting equation, (b) two elements of the accounting equation, (c) three elements of the accounting equation.

3. Indicate whether the following error would cause the accounting equation to be out of balance and, if so, indicate how it would be out of balance. The payment of utilities of $3,700 was recorded as a decrease in cash of $3,700 and a decrease in retained earnings (utilities expense) of $7,300.

4. For each of the following errors, indicate whether the error would cause the accounting equation to be out of balance and, if so, indicate how it would be out of balance. (a) The purchase of land for $37,750 cash was recorded as an increase in land of $37,750 and a decrease in cash of $3,775. (b) The receipt of $4,000 for fees earned was recorded as an increase in cash of $4,000 and an increase in liabilities of $4,000.

5. What is a primary control for determining the accuracy of a business's record keeping?

6. Millstone Consulting Services acquired land 8 years ago for $100,000. Millstone recently signed an agreement to sell the land for $375,000. In accordance with the sales agreement, the buyer transferred $375,000 to Millstone's bank account on February 19. How would elements of the accounting equation be affected by the sale?

7. (a) How does the payment of dividends of $40,000 affect the three elements of the accounting equation? (b) Is net income affected by the payment of dividends? Explain.

8. Assume that Esquire Consulting erroneously recorded the payment of $25,000 of dividends as salary expense. (a) How would this error affect the equality of the accounting equation? (b) How would this error affect the income statement, retained earnings statement, balance sheet, and statement of cash flows?

9. Assume that Bell Tower Realty Inc. borrowed $90,000 from First Bank and Trust. In recording the transaction, Bell Tower erroneously recorded the receipt as an increase in cash, $90,000, and an increase in fees earned, $90,000. (a) How would this error affect the equality of the accounting equation? (b) How would this error affect the income statement, retained earnings statement, balance sheet, and statement of cash flows?

10. Assume that as of January 1, 2011, Hamlet Consulting has total assets of $800,000 and total liabilities of $300,000. As of December 31, 2011, Hamlet has total liabilities of $350,000 and total stockholders' equity of $690,000. (a) What was Hamlet's stockholders' equity as of December 31, 2010? (b) Assume that Hamlet did not pay any dividends during 2011. What was the amount of net income for 2011?

11. Using the January 1 and December 31, 2011, data given in Question 10, answer the following question: If Hamlet Consulting paid $45,000 of dividends during 2011, what was the amount of net income for 2011?

Exercises

E2-1

Accounting equation

Obj 1

✓ a. $1,030,000

Determine the missing amount for each of the following:

	Assets	=	Liabilities	+	Stockholders' Equity
a.	X	=	$250,000	+	$780,000
b.	$125,000	=	X	+	$ 39,500
c.	$ 60,000	=	$ 7,500	+	X

E2-2

Accounting equation

Obj 1

✓ a. $30,753

The Walt Disney Company had the following assets and liabilities (in millions) as of September 29, 2007.

Assets	$60,928
Liabilities	30,175

a. Determine the stockholders' equity of Walt Disney as of September 29, 2007.
b. If assets increased by $1,569 and stockholders' equity increased by $1,570, what was the increase or decrease in liabilities for the year ending September 27, 2008?
c. What were the total assets, liabilities, and stockholders' equity as of September 30, 2008?
d. Based upon your answer to (c), does the accounting equation balance?

E2-3

Accounting equation

Obj 1

✓ a. $1,295

Campbell Soup Co. had the following assets and liabilities (in millions) as of July 29, 2007.

Assets	$6,445
Liabilities	5,150

a. Determine the stockholders' equity of Campbell Soup as of July 29, 2007.
b. If assets increased by $29 and liabilities increased by $6, what was the increase or decrease in stockholders' equity for the year ending August 3, 2008?
c. What were the total assets, liabilities, and stockholders' equity as of August 3, 2008?
d. Based upon your answer to (c), does the accounting equation balance?

E2-4

Accounting equation

Obj 1

✓ a. $2,646

One item is omitted in each of the following summaries of balance sheet and income statement data (in millions) for *Google* and *Verizon Communications* as of December 31, 2008 and 2007.

	Google	**Verizon**
December 31, 2007:		
Assets	$25,336	(e)
Liabilities	(a)	(f)
Stockholders' equity	(b)	$ 50,581
Increase (Decrease) in assets, liabilities, and stockholders' equity during 2008:		
Assets	$ 6,432	(g)
Liabilities	883	$ 24,268
Stockholders' equity	5,549	(h)
December 31, 2008:		
Assets	(c)	$202,352
Liabilities	$ 3,529	(i)
Stockholders' equity	(d)	41,706

Determine the amounts of the missing items (a) through (i).

E2-5

Accounting equation

Obj 1

✓ b. $568,000

Bryan Segota is the sole stockholder and operator of Thatch, a motivational consulting business. At the end of its accounting period, December 31, 2010, Thatch has assets of $760,000 and liabilities of $240,000. Using the accounting

equation and considering each case independently, determine the following amounts:

a. Stockholders' equity, as of December 31, 2010.
b. Stockholders' equity, as of December 31, 2011, assuming that assets increased by $120,000 and liabilities increased by $72,000 during 2011.
c. Stockholders' equity, as of December 31, 2011, assuming that assets decreased by $60,000 and liabilities increased by $21,600 during 2011.
d. Stockholders' equity, as of December 31, 2011, assuming that assets increased by $100,000 and liabilities decreased by $38,400 during 2011.
e. Net income (or net loss) during 2011, assuming that as of December 31, 2011, assets were $960,000, liabilities were $156,000, and there were no dividends and no additional capital stock was issued.

E2-6

Effects of transactions on stockholders' equity

Objs 2, 4

For *Target Corporation,* indicate whether the following transactions would (1) increase, (2) decrease, or (3) have no effect on stockholders' equity.

a. Borrowed money from the bank.
b. Paid creditors.
c. Made cash sales to customers.
d. Purchased store equipment.
e. Paid dividends.

f. Paid store rent.
g. Paid interest expense.
h. Sold store equipment at a gain.
i. Received interest revenue.
j. Paid taxes.

E2-7

Effects of transactions on accounting equation

Objs 1, 2, 4

Describe how the following business transactions affect the three elements of the accounting equation.

a. Received cash for services performed.
b. Paid for utilities used in the business.

c. Borrowed cash at local bank.
d. Issued capital stock for cash.
e. Purchased land for cash.

E2-8

Effects of transactions on accounting equation

Objs 1, 2, 4

✓ (1) Assets increased by $60,000

A vacant lot acquired for $150,000, on which there is a balance owed of $80,000, is sold for $290,000 in cash. The seller pays the $80,000 owed. What is the effect of these transactions on the total amount of the seller's (1) assets, (2) liabilities, and (3) stockholders' equity?

E2-9

Effects of transactions on stockholders' equity

Objs 2, 4

Indicate whether each of the following types of transactions will (a) increase stockholders' equity or (b) decrease stockholders' equity.

a. Issued capital stock for cash.
b. Received cash for fees earned.
c. Paid cash for utilities expense.

d. Paid cash for rent expense.
e. Paid cash dividends.

E2-10

Transactions

Objs 1, 2, 4

Lindberg Delivery Service had the following selected transactions during October:

1. Received cash from issuance of capital stock, $75,000.
2. Paid rent for October, $4,200.
3. Paid advertising expense, $4,000.
4. Received cash for providing delivery services, $39,750.
5. Purchased supplies for cash, $2,500.

6. Billed customers for delivery services on account, $81,200. c
7. Paid creditors on account, $9,280. d
8. Received cash from customers on account, $25,600. a
9. Determined that the cost of supplies on hand was $900; therefore, $1,600 of supplies had been used during the month. e
10. Paid dividends, $3,000. e

Indicate the effect of each transaction on the accounting equation by listing the numbers identifying the transactions, (1) through (10), in a vertical column, and inserting at the right of each number the appropriate letter from the following list:

a. Increase in an asset, decrease in another asset.
b. Increase in an asset, increase in a liability.
c. Increase in an asset, increase in stockholders' equity.
d. Decrease in an asset, decrease in a liability.
e. Decrease in an asset, decrease in stockholders' equity.

E2-11

Nature of transactions

Objs 1, 2, 4

✓ b. $16,000 decrease

Sally Fleming operates her own catering service. Summary financial data for February are presented in equation form as follows. Each line designated by a number indicates the effect of a transaction on the balance sheet. Each increase and decrease in stockholders' equity, except transaction (4), affects net income.

	Cash	+	Land	=	Liabilities	+	Capital Stock	+	Retained Earnings
Bal.	30,000		100,000		16,000		24,000		90,000
1.	+25,000								+25,000
2.	–20,000		+20,000						
3.	–18,000								–18,000
4.	–3,000								–3,000
Bal.	14,000		120,000		16,000		24,000		94,000

a. Describe each transaction.
b. What is the amount of net decrease in cash during the month?
c. What is the amount of net increase in retained earnings during the month?
d. What is the amount of the net income for the month?
e. How much of the net income for the month was retained in the business?
f. What is the amount of net cash flows from operating activities?
g. What is the amount of net cash flows from investing activities?
h. What is the amount of net cash flows from financing activities?

E2-12

Net income and dividends

Objs 3, 5

The income statement of a corporation for the month of July indicates a net income of $75,000. During the same period, $100,000 in cash dividends were paid.

Would it be correct to say that the business incurred a net loss of $25,000 during the month? Discuss.

E2-13

Net income and stockholders'
equity for four businesses

Objs 1, 3, 5

✓ Company C: Net
  income, $108,000

Four different companies, A, B, C, and D, show the same balance sheet data at
the beginning and end of a year. These data, exclusive of the amount of stockholders' equity, are summarized as follows:

	Total Assets	Total Liabilities
Beginning of the year	$ 810,000	$324,000
End of the year	1,296,000	540,000

On the basis of the preceding data and the following additional information
for the year, determine the net income (or loss) of each company for the year.
(*Suggestion:* First determine the amount of increase or decrease in stockholders'
equity during the year.)

Company A: No additional capital stock was issued, and no dividends were paid.
Company B: No additional capital stock was issued, but dividends of $72,000 were paid.
Company C: Capital stock of $162,000 was issued, but no dividends were paid.
Company D: Capital stock of $162,000 was issued, and dividends of $72,000 were paid.

E2-14

Missing amounts from balance
sheet and income statement
data

Objs 1, 3, 5

✓ a. $46,890

One item is omitted from each of the following summaries of balance sheet and
income statement data for four different corporations.

	Earth	Mars	Neptune	Pluto
Beginning of the year:				
Assets	$216,000	$250,000	$100,000	(d)
Liabilities	129,600	130,000	76,000	$120,000
End of the year:				
Assets	268,200	350,000	90,000	248,000
Liabilities	117,000	110,000	80,000	136,000
During the year:				
Additional issuance				
of capital stock	(a)	50,000	10,000	40,000
Dividends	14,400	16,000	(c)	60,000
Revenue	71,190	(b)	115,000	112,000
Expenses	38,880	64,000	122,500	128,000

Determine the amounts of the missing items, identifying them by letter.
(*Suggestion:* First determine the amount of increase or decrease in stockholders'
equity during the year.)

E2-15

Net income, retained earnings,
and dividends

Objs 3, 5

✓ a. $96,457

Use the following data (in thousands) for *Barnes & Noble, Inc.* for the year ending February 2, 2008, to answer the questions below:

Retained earnings, February 3, 2007	$ 600,404
Retained earnings, February 2, 2008	696,861
Net cash flows from operating activities	434,680
Net increase in cash	12,280
Net cash flows used for financing activities	(241,837)

a. Determine the amount of earnings retained in Barnes & Noble for the year
   ended February 2, 2008.
b. Determine the net cash flows used for investing activities for the year ended
   February 2, 2008.

E2-16

Balance sheet, net income, and cash flows

Objs 3, 5

SPREADSHEET

✓ b. $120,000

Financial information related to Kate's Interiors for May and June of 2011 is as follows:

	May 31, 2011	June 30, 2011
Notes payable	$200,000	$250,000
Land	500,000	575,000
Capital stock	75,000	90,000
Retained earnings	?	?
Cash	100,000	175,000

a. Prepare balance sheets for Kate's Interiors as of May 31 and June 30, 2011.
b. Determine the amount of net income for June, assuming that dividends of $35,000 were paid.
c. Determine the net cash flows from operating activities.
d. Determine the net cash flows from investing activities.
e. Determine the net cash flows from financing activities.
f. Determine the net increase or decrease in cash.

E2-17

Income statement

Objs 3, 5

SPREADSHEET

✓ Net income, $30,000

After its first month of operation, the following amounts were taken from the accounting records of Polaris Realty Inc. as of November 30, 2011.

Capital stock	$25,000	Notes payable	$ 35,000
Cash	38,000	Rent expense	5,000
Dividends	10,000	Retained earnings	0
Interest expense	2,000	Salaries expense	65,000
Land	42,000	Sales commissions	120,000
Miscellaneous expense	3,000	Utilities expense	15,000

Prepare an income statement for the month ending November 30, 2011.

E2-18

Retained earnings statement

Objs 3, 5

SPREADSHEET

✓ Retained earnings,
November 30, 2011,
$20,000

Using the financial data shown in Exercise 2-17 for Polaris Realty Inc., prepare a retained earnings statement for the month ending November 30, 2011.

E2-19

Balance sheet

Objs 3, 5

SPREADSHEET

✓ Total assets, $80,000

Using the financial data shown in Exercise 2-17 for Polaris Realty Inc., prepare a balance sheet as of November 30, 2011.

E2-20

Statement of cash flows

Objs 3, 5

SPREADSHEET

✓ Net cash flows from operating activities, $30,000

Using the financial data shown in Exercise 2-17 for Polaris Realty Inc., prepare a statement of cash flows for the month ending November 30, 2011.

E2-21

Effects of transactions on accounting equation

Objs 1, 2, 4

Describe how the following transactions of *Sun Microsystems, Inc.* would affect the three elements of the accounting equation.

a. Paid research and development expenses for the current year.
b. Purchased machinery and equipment for cash.
c. Received cash from issuing stock.
d. Received cash from the issuance of long-term debt.
e. Made cash sales.
f. Paid selling expenses.
g. Paid employee pension expenses for the current year.
h. Received proceeds from selling a portion of manufacturing operations for a gain on the sale.
i. Paid officer salaries.
j. Paid taxes.
k. Paid off long-term debt.
l. Paid dividends.

E2-22

Statement of cash flows

Objs 3, 5

Based upon the financial transactions for Sun Microsystems, Inc. shown in Exercise 2-21, indicate whether the transaction would be reported in the cash flows from operating, investing, or financing sections of the statement of cash flows.

Problems

P2-1

Transactions and financial statements

Objs 1, 2, 3

SPREADSHEET

✓ 3. Net income, $18,000

Chris Woods established an insurance agency on July 1, 2011, and completed the following transactions during July:

a. Opened a business bank account in the name of Woods Insurance Inc., with a deposit of $40,000 in exchange for capital stock.
b. Borrowed $30,000 by issuing a note payable.
c. Received cash from fees earned, $28,000.
d. Paid rent on office and equipment for the month, $3,000.
e. Paid automobile expense for the month, $1,800, and miscellaneous expense, $900.
f. Paid office salaries, $4,200.
g. Paid interest on the note payable, $100.
h. Purchased land as a future building site, $55,000.
i. Paid dividends, $2,000.

Instructions

1. Indicate the effect of each transaction and the balances after each transaction, using the integrated financial statement framework.

2. Briefly explain why the stockholders' investments and revenues increased stockholders' equity, while dividends and expenses decreased stockholders' equity.
3. Prepare an income statement and retained earnings statement for July.
4. Prepare a balance sheet as of July 31, 2011.
5. Prepare a statement of cash flows for July.

P2-2

Transactions and financial statements

Objs 1, 2, 3

SPREADSHEET

✓ 1. Net income, $14,000

Wendy Dwyer established Outlaw Computer Services on January 1, 2011. The effect of each transaction and the balances after each transaction for January are shown below in the integrated financial statement framework.

Instructions

1. Prepare an income statement for the month ended January 31, 2011.
2. Prepare a retained earnings statement for the month ended January 31, 2011.
3. Prepare a balance sheet as of January 31, 2011.
4. Prepare a statement of cash flows for the month ended January 31, 2011.

Statement of Cash Flows	Balance Sheet						Income Statement
	Asset		=	Liabilities	+	Stockholders' Equity	
	Cash	+ Land	=	Notes Payable	+	Capital Stock	+ Retained Earnings	
a. Investment	30,000					30,000		
b. Fees earned	22,000						22,000	b.
Balances	52,000					30,000	22,000	
c. Rent expense	−2,500						−2,500	c.
Balances	49,500					30,000	19,500	
d. Issued notes payable	10,000			10,000				
Balances	59,500			10,000		30,000	19,500	
e. Purchased land	−40,000	40,000						
Balances	19,500	40,000		10,000		30,000	19,500	
f. Paid expenses	−1,900						−1,900	f.
Balances	17,600	40,000		10,000		30,000	17,600	
g. Paid salary expense	−3,600						−3,600	g.
Balances	14,000	40,000		10,000		30,000	14,000	
h. Paid dividends	−2,000						−2,000	
Balances, Jan. 31	12,000	40,000		10,000		30,000	12,000	

Statement of Cash Flows			Income Statement	
a. Financing	30,000		b. Fees earned	22,000
b. Operating	22,000		c. Rent expense	−2,500
c. Operating	−2,500		f. Auto expense	−1,200
d. Financing	10,000		f. Misc. expense	−700
e. Investing	−40,000		g. Salary expense	−3,600
f. Operating	−1,900		Net income	14,000
g. Operating	−3,600			
h. Financing	−2,000			
Increase in cash	12,000			

P2-3

Financial statements

Objs 2, 3

SPREADSHEET

✓ 1. Net income,
$110,000

The following amounts were taken from the accounting records of Bontancia Services, Inc., as of August 31, 2011. Bontancia Services began its operations on September 1, 2010.

Capital stock	$ 23,000
Cash	50,000
Dividends	13,000
Fees earned	300,000
Interest expense	2,500
Land	100,000
Miscellaneous expense	7,500
Notes payable	30,000
Rent expense	28,000
Salaries expense	90,000
Taxes expense	22,000
Utilities expense	40,000

Instructions

1. Prepare an income statement for the year ending August 31, 2011.
2. Prepare a retained earnings statement for the year ending August 31, 2011.
3. Prepare a balance sheet as of August 31, 2011.
4. Prepare a statement of cash flows for the year ending August 31, 2011.

P2-4

Financial statements

Obj 5

SPREADSHEET

✓ 1. Net income,
$160,000

After its second year of operations, the following amounts were taken from the accounting records of Bontancia Services, Inc., as of August 31, 2012. Bontancia Services began its operations on September 1, 2010 (see Problem 2-3).

Capital stock	$ 55,000
Cash	?
Dividends	25,000
Fees earned	400,000
Interest expense	3,000
Land	240,000
Miscellaneous expense	11,000
Notes payable	38,000
Rent expense	36,000
Salaries expense	110,000
Taxes expense	28,000
Utilities expense	52,000

Instructions

1. Prepare an income statement for the year ending August 31, 2012.
2. Prepare a retained earnings statement for the year ending August 31, 2012. (*Note:* The retained earnings at September 1, 2011, was $97,000.)
3. Prepare a balance sheet as of August 31, 2012.
4. Prepare a statement of cash flows for the year ending August 31, 2012. (*Hint:* You should compare the asset and liability amounts of August 31, 2012, with those of August 31, 2011, to determine cash used in investing and financing activities. See Problem 2-3 for the August 31, 2011, balance sheet amounts.)

P2-5

Missing amounts from financial statements

Objs 3, 5

SPREADSHEET

✓ a. $117,000

The financial statements at the end of Miramar, Inc.'s first month of operation are shown below. By analyzing the interrelationships among the financial statements, fill in the proper amounts for (a) through (s).

MIRAMAR REALTY, INC.
Income Statement
For the Month Ended July 31, 2011

Fees earned		$ (a)
Operating expenses:		
Wages expense	$33,120	
Rent expense	18,000	
Utilities expense	(b)	
Interest expense	1,800	
Miscellaneous expense	3,960	
Total operating expenses		67,500
Net income		$ (c)

MIRAMAR REALTY, INC.
Retained Earnings Statement
For the Month Ended July 31, 2011

Retained earnings, July 1, 2011		$ (d)
Net income for July	$49,500	
Less dividends	(e)	(f)
Retained earnings, July 31, 2011		$ (g)

MIRAMAR REALTY, INC.
Balance Sheet
July 31, 2011

Assets		
Cash		$ (h)
Land		180,000
Total assets		$ 238,500
Liabilities		
Notes payable		$ 108,000
Stockholders' Equity		
Capital stock	$ (i)	
Retained earnings	(j)	
Total stockholders' equity		(k)
Total liabilities and stockholders' equity		$ (l)

MIRAMAR REALTY, INC.
Statement of Cash Flows
For the Month Ended July 31, 2011

Cash flows from operating activities:			
Cash received from customers		$117,000	
Deduct cash payments for expenses		67,500	
Net cash flows from operating activities			$ (m)
Cash flows from investing activities:			
Cash payment for purchase of land			(180,000)
Cash flows from financing activities:			
Cash received from sale of capital stock	$ 90,000		
Cash received from notes payable	(n)	$ (o)	
Deduct cash dividends		9,000	
Net cash flows from financing activities			(p)
Net increase in cash			$ (q)
July 1, 2011, cash balance			(r)
July 31, 2011, cash balance			$ (s)

P2-6

Financial statements

Objs 3, 5

Bitterroot Realty, Inc., organized October 1, 2011, is operated by Dale Flynn. How many errors can you find in the following financial statements for Bitterroot Realty, Inc., prepared after its first month of operation?

BITTERROOT REALTY, INC.
Income Statement
October 31, 2011

Sales commissions		$92,200
Operating expenses:		
Office salaries expense	$16,300	
Rent expense	7,600	
Automobile expense	3,500	
Dividends	2,000	
Miscellaneous expense	1,550	
Total operating expenses		30,950
Net income		$41,250

DALE FLYNN
Retained Earnings Statement
October 31, 2010

Net income for the month	$41,250
Retained earnings, October 31, 2010	$41,250

Balance Sheet
For the Month Ended October 31, 2010

Assets

Cash	$ 60,850
Notes payable	20,000
Total assets	$ 80,850

Liabilities

Land	$ 40,400

Stockholders' Equity

Capital stock	$20,000	
Retained earnings	41,250	
Total stockholders' equity		61,250
Total liabilities and stockholders' equity		$101,650

BITTERROOT REALTY, INC.
Statement of Cash Flows
October 31, 2011

Cash flows from operating activities:	
Cash receipts from sales commissions	$ 92,200
Cash flows from investing activities:	
Cash payments for land	(40,400)
Cash flows from financing activities:	
Cash receipts from retained earnings	81,250
Net increase in cash during May	$133,050
Cash as of October 1, 2011	0
Cash as of October 31, 2011	$133,050

Activities

A2-1

Business emphasis

GROUP

Assume that you are considering developing a nationwide chain of women's clothing stores. You have contacted a Seattle-based firm that specializes in financing new business ventures and enterprises. Such firms, called venture capital firms, finance new businesses in exchange for a percentage of the ownership.

1. In groups of four or five, discuss the different business emphases that you might use in your venture.
2. For each emphasis you listed in (1), provide an example of a real-world business using the same emphasis.
3. What percentage of the ownership would you be willing to give the venture capital firm in exchange for its financing?

A2-2

Cash accounting

On August 1, 2011, Dr. Dana Hendley established Med, a medical practice organized as a professional corporation. The following conversation occurred the following February between Dr. Hendley and a former medical school classmate, Dr. Elyse Monti, at an American Medical Association convention in New York City.

Dr. Monti: Dana, good to see you again. Why didn't you call when you were in Denver? We could have had dinner together.

Dr. Hendley: Actually, I never made it to Denver this year. My husband and kids went up to our Vail condo twice, but I got stuck in Fort Lauderdale. I opened a new consulting practice this August and haven't had any time for myself since.

Dr. Monti: I heard about it ... Med ... something ... right?

Dr. Hendley: Yes, Med. My husband chose the name.

Dr. Monti: I've thought about doing something like that. Are you making any money? I mean, is it worth your time?

Dr. Hendley: You wouldn't believe it. I started by opening a bank account with $30,000, and my January bank statement has a balance of $75,000. Not bad for six months—all pure profit.

Dr. Monti: Maybe I'll try it in Denver! Let's have breakfast together tomorrow and you can fill me in on the details.

Comment on Dr. Hendley's statement that the difference between the opening bank balance ($30,000) and the January statement balance ($75,000) is pure profit.

A2-3

Business emphasis

Amazon.com, an Internet retailer, was incorporated in the early 1990s and opened its virtual doors on the Web shortly thereafter. On its statement of cash flows, would you expect Amazon.com's net cash flows from operating, investing, and financing activities to be positive or negative for its first three years of operation? Use the following format for your answers, and briefly explain your logic.

	Year 1	Year 2	Year 3
Net cash flows from operating activities	negative		
Net cash flows from investing activities			
Net cash flows from financing activities			

A2-4

Financial information

Yahoo.com's finance Internet site provides summary financial information about public companies, such as stock quotes, recent financial filings with the Securities and Exchange Commission, and recent news stories. Go to Yahoo.com's financial Web site (**http://finance.yahoo.com/**) and enter *Apple, Inc.'s* stock symbol, AAPL. Answer the following questions concerning Apple, Inc. by clicking on the various items under the tab "More Reports for AAPL."

1. At what price did Apple's stock last trade?
2. What is the 52-week range of Apple's stock?
3. When was the last time Apple's stock hit a 52-week high?
4. Over the last six months, has there been any insider selling or buying of Apple's stock?
5. Who is the chief executive officer of Apple Inc., and how old is the president?
6. What was the salary of the president of Apple Inc.?
7. What is the annual dividend of Apple's stock?
8. How many current broker recommendations are strong buy, buy, hold, sell, or strong sell? What is the average of the broker recommendations?
9. What is the net cash flow from operations for this year?
10. What is the operating margin for this year?

A2-5

Analyzing financial information

On February 25, 2009, Gabriel Madway wrote an article titled "Apple Investors Get No Satisfaction on Jobs" which appeared on *Reuters.com.* The article raises concerns about Steve Jobs's health and the possible reoccurrence of his pancreatic cancer. The following excerpt is taken from the article:

> Jobs—who co-founded Apple and is credited with transforming it into a consumer juggernaut after returning as CEO a decade ago—announced in January he would take a five-month leave of absence, handing over the reins of the firm and saying his health problems were "more complex" than originally thought.

Answer the following questions:

1. Is the article favorable, neutral, or unfavorable regarding future prospects for Apple Inc.?

2. Assuming you owned stock in Apple Inc., would you sell your stock based only upon this article? If not, what additional information would you want?

3. Would it be a prudent investment strategy to only rely upon published financial statements in deciding to invest in a company's stock?

4. What sources do you think financial analysts use in making investment decisions and recommendations?

Answers to Self-Examination Questions

1. D Even though a recording error has been made, the accounting equation will balance (answer D). However, assets (cash) will be overstated by $50,000, and liabilities (notes payable) will be overstated by $50,000. Answer A is incorrect because although cash is overstated by $50,000, the accounting equation will balance. Answer B is incorrect because although notes payable are overstated by $50,000, the accounting equation will balance. Answer C is incorrect because the accounting equation will balance and assets will not exceed liabilities.

2. C Total assets will exceed total liabilities and stockholders' equity by $16,000. This is because stockholders' equity (retained earnings) was decreased instead of increased by $8,000. Thus, stockholders' equity will be understated by a total of $16,000.

3. C The accounting equation is:

Assets = Liabilities + Stockholders' Equity

Therefore, if assets increased by $20,000 and liabilities increased by $12,000,

stockholders' equity must have increased by $8,000 (answer C), as indicated in the following computation:

Assets	= Liabilities + Stockholders' Equity
+$20,000	= $12,000 + Stockholders' Equity
+$20,000 − $12,000	= Stockholders' Equity
+$8,000	= Stockholders' Equity

4. B Net income is the excess of revenue over expenses, or $15,000 (answer B). If expenses exceed revenue, the difference is a net loss. Dividends are the opposite of the stockholders investing in the business and do not affect the amount of net income or net loss.

5. B The purchase of land for cash changes the mix of assets and does not affect liabilities or stockholders' equity (answer B). Borrowing cash from a bank (answer A) increases assets and liabilities. Receiving cash for fees earned (answer C) increases cash and stockholders' equity (retained earnings). Paying office salaries (answer D) decreases cash and stockholders' equity (retained earnings).

Accrual Accounting Concepts

3

Do you subscribe to any magazines? Most of us subscribe to one or more magazines such as *Cosmopolitan, Sports Illustrated, Golf Digest, Newsweek,* or *Rolling Stone.* Magazines usually require you to prepay the yearly subscription price before you receive any issues. When should the magazine company record revenue from the subscriptions?

As we discussed in Chapter 2, sometimes revenues are earned and expenses are incurred at the point cash is received or paid. For transactions such as magazine subscriptions, the revenue is earned when the magazine is delivered, not when the cash is received. Most companies are required to account for revenues and expenses when the benefit is substantially provided or consumed, which may not be when cash is received or paid.

One company that records revenue from subscriptions is **Marvel Entertainment, Inc.** Marvel began in 1939 as a comic book publishing company, establishing such popular comic book characters as Spider-Man®, X-Men®, Fantastic Four®, and the Avengers®. From these humble beginnings, Marvel has grown into a full-line, multi-billion-dollar entertainment company that was recently acquired by **The Walt Disney Company.** Marvel not only publishes comic books, but it has also added feature films, such as the *Spider-Man* movies, video games, and toys, to its product offerings.

In this chapter, we continue our discussion of financial statements and financial reporting systems. In doing so, we focus on accrual concepts of accounting that are used by all major businesses, such as Marvel Entertainment. Our discussions will include how to record transactions under accrual accounting concepts, update accounting records, and prepare accrual financial statements. Because all large companies, and many small ones, use accrual concepts of accounting, a thorough understanding of this topic is important for your business studies and future career.

Basic Accrual Accounting Concepts, Including the Matching Concept

Family Health Care's transactions and financial statements for September and October were illustrated in Chapter 2. These illustrations used many of the eight accounting concepts described in Chapter 1. For example, the business entity concept was used to account for Family Health Care as a separate entity, independent of the owner-manager, Dr. Lee Landry. The cost, unit of measure, going concern, accounting period, full disclosure, and objectivity concepts were also used.

The one accounting concept not used in Chapter 2 was the matching concept. This is because all the transactions in Chapter 2 were structured so that cash was either received or paid. This was done to simplify the recording of transactions and preparing of the financial statements. For example, all revenues were received in cash at the time the services were rendered and all expenses were paid in cash at the time they were incurred.

In the real world, cash may be received or paid at a different time from when revenues are earned or expenses are incurred. In fact, companies often earn revenue before or after cash is received and incur expenses before or after cash is paid.

To illustrate, a real estate company might spend months or years developing land for a business complex or subdivision. During this period, the company earns no revenues, but makes payments for materials, wages, insurance, and other construction items. Thus, if revenues were recorded only when cash is received and expenses recorded only when cash is paid, the company would report a series of losses on its income statement while the land is being developed. In such cases, the income statements would not provide a realistic picture of the company's operations. In fact, the development might become highly successful and the early losses misleading.

Accrual accounting is designed to avoid misleading information arising from the timing of cash receipts and payments. Under accrual accounting, transactions are recorded as they occur and thus affect the accounting equation (assets, liabilities, and stockholders' equity). Since the receipt or payment of cash affects assets (cash), all cash receipts and payments are recorded in the accounts under accrual accounting. Conversely, under accrual accounting, transactions are also recorded even though cash is not received or paid until a later point.

How Businesses Make Money

Not Cutting Corners

Have you ever ordered a hamburger from **Wendy's** and noticed that the meat patty is square? The square meat patty reflects a business emphasis instilled in Wendy's by its founder, Dave Thomas. Mr. Thomas emphasized offering high-quality products at a fair price in a friendly atmosphere, without "cutting corners"; hence, the square meat patty. In the highly competitive fast-food industry, Dave Thomas's approach has enabled Wendy's to become the third largest fast-food restaurant chain in the world, with annual sales of over $7 billion.

Source: Douglas Martin, "Dave Thomas, 69, Wendy's Founder, Dies," *New York Times*, January 9, 2002.

Supplies expense are recognized when the supplies are used or consumed.

To illustrate, Family Health Care may provide services to patients who are covered by health insurance. Periodically, Family Health Care files claims with the insurance companies requesting payment. In this case, revenue is recorded, referred to as *recognized,* when the services are provided even though the cash is to be received later. When services are provided with the cash to be received at a later time, the services are said to be provided *on account.* In such cases, an <u>*account receivable*</u> for the amount of the services is recorded as an asset.

Likewise, a company may purchase supplies from a supplier (vendor), with terms that allow the company to pay for the purchase at a later time. In this case, the supplies are said to be purchased *on account* and an *account payable* for the amount to be paid is recorded as a liability.

In accounting, the term *recognized* is often used to refer to when a transaction is recorded. Under accrual accounting, <u>*revenue is recognized when it is earned.*</u> For Family Health Care, revenue is earned when services have been provided to the patient. At this point, the revenue-earning process is complete and the patient is legally obligated to pay for the services.

The matching concept plays an important role in accrual accounting for determining when expenses are recorded. When revenues are earned and recorded, all expenses incurred in generating the revenues are also recorded. In this way, revenues and expenses are *matched* and the net income or net loss for the period is determined.

Accrual accounting also recognizes liabilities at the time the business incurs the obligation to pay for the services or goods purchased. For example, the purchase of supplies on account is recorded when the supplies are received and the business has incurred the obligation to pay for the supplies.

Obj 2 Use accrual concepts of accounting to analyze, record, and summarize transactions.

Unearned revenue is a liability account which appears on a balance sheet.

Using Accrual Concepts of Accounting for Family Health Care's November Transactions

To illustrate accrual accounting, the following November 2011 Family Health Care transactions are used:

a. On November 1, received $1,800 from ILS Company as rent for the use of Family Health Care's land as a temporary parking lot from November 2011 through March 2012.

b. On November 1, paid a premium of $2,400 for a two-year general business insurance policy that covers fire and theft.

c. On November 1, paid $6,000 for an insurance premium on a six-month medical malpractice policy.

d. Dr. Landry invested an additional $5,000 in the business in exchange for capital stock.

e. Purchased supplies for $240 on account.

f. Purchased $8,500 of office equipment. Paid $1,700 cash as a down payment, with the remaining $6,800 ($8,500 − $1,700) due in five monthly installments of $1,360 ($6,800 ÷ 5) beginning January 1.

g. Provided services of $6,100 to patients on account.

h. Received $5,500 for services provided to patients who paid cash.

i. Received $4,200 from insurance companies, which paid on patients' accounts for services that have been provided.

j. Paid $100 on account for supplies that had been purchased.

k. Expenses paid during November were as follows: wages, $2,790; rent, $800; utilities, $580; interest, $100; and miscellaneous, $420.

l. Paid dividends of $1,200 to stockholders (Dr. Landry).

In analyzing and recording the November transactions for Family Health Care, the integrated financial statement framework is used. Transactions that increase or decrease a financial statement element are recorded. These financial statement elements are referred to as **accounts**.

A listing of a company's accounts is called its chart of accounts.

Transaction (a)

On November 1, received $1,800 from ILS Company as rent for the use of Family Health Care's land as a temporary parking lot from November 2011 through March 2012.

In this transaction, Family Health Care entered into a rental agreement for the use of its land. The agreement requires a payment of a rental fee of $1,800, in advance. The rental agreement also gives ILS Company the option of renewing the agreement for an additional four months.

By entering into this rental agreement and accepting the $1,800, Family Health Care has incurred a liability to make the land available for ILS's use. If Family Health Care canceled the agreement on November 1, after accepting the $1,800, it would have to repay the $1,800.

Family Health Care records this transaction as an increase in Cash and an increase in a liability for $1,800. Because the liability relates to rent that has not yet been earned, it is recorded as Unearned Revenue.

The effects of this transaction on Family Health Care's financial statements are recorded as shown below:

Microsoft Corporation reported unearned revenue of $15,297 million as of June 30, 2008.

Statement of Cash Flows	Balance Sheet							Income Statement
	Assets		=	Liabilities		+	Stockholders' Equity	
	Cash	+ Land	=	Notes Payable	+ Unearned Revenue	+	Capital Stock	+ Retained Earnings
Balances, Nov. 1	7,320	12,000		10,000			6,000	3,320
a. Received rent in advance	1,800				1,800			
Balances	9,120	12,000		10,000	1,800		6,000	3,320

Statement of Cash Flows	
a. Operating	1,800

The receipt of the $1,800 of cash increases cash flows from operating activities under the Statement of Cash Flows column. Since no rental revenue has yet been earned, there are no entries under the Income Statement column.

As time passes, Family Health Care will earn the rental revenue. For example, at the end of November, $360 ($1,800 ÷ 5 months) will be earned. Recording the $360 of earned rent revenue at the end of November is described and illustrated later in this chapter.

The November 1 balances shown in the preceding integrated financial statement spreadsheet are the ending balances from October. That is, the cash balance of $7,320 is the ending cash balance as of October 31, 2011. Likewise, the other balances are carried forward from the preceding month.

Tangible assets are assets you can touch.

Copyrights are intangible assets.

In this sense, the Balance Sheet column is a cumulative financial history of Family Health Care.

Transaction (b)

On November 1, paid a premium of $2,400 for a two-year general business insurance policy that covers risks from fire and theft.

By paying the premium, Family Health Care has purchased an asset, insurance coverage, in exchange for cash. The effects of this transaction on Family Health Care's financial statements are recorded as shown below:

Statement of Cash Flows	Balance Sheet							Income Statement
	Assets			= Liabilities		+ Stockholders' Equity		
	Cash +	Prepaid Insurance +	Land =	Notes Payable +	Unearned Revenue +	Capital Stock +	Retained Earnings	
Balances	9,120		12,000	10,000	1,800	6,000	3,320	
b. Paid insurance for 2 yrs.	−2,400	2,400						
Balances	6,720	2,400	12,000	10,000	1,800	6,000	3,320	

Statement of Cash Flows
b. Operating   −2,400

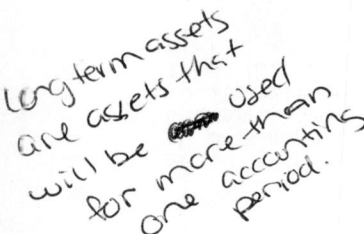

Under the Balance Sheet column the mix of assets has changed, with Cash decreasing by $2,400 and Prepaid Insurance increasing by $2,400. The payment of cash also decreases cash flows from Operating activities under the Statement of Cash Flows column. Since no revenue or expenses are affected, there are no entries under the Income Statement column.

Prepaid insurance is unique in that it expires with the passage of time. For example, $100 ($2,400 ÷ 24 months) of Family Health Care's insurance will expire each month. Such assets are called **prepaid expenses** or **deferred expenses**.

Transaction (c)

On November 1, paid $6,000 for an insurance premium on a six-month medical malpractice policy.

This transaction is similar to transaction (b), except that Family Health Care has purchased medical malpractice insurance that is renewable every 6 months. The effects of this transaction on Family Health Care's financial statements are recorded as shown below:

Statement of Cash Flows	Balance Sheet							Income Statement
	Assets			= Liabilities		+ Stockholders' Equity		
	Cash +	Prepaid Insurance +	Land =	Notes Payable +	Unearned Revenue +	Capital Stock +	Retained Earnings	
Balances	6,720	2,400	12,000	10,000	1,800	6,000	3,320	
c. Paid insurance for 6 mos.	−6,000	6,000						
Balances	720	8,400	12,000	10,000	1,800	6,000	3,320	

Statement of Cash Flows
c. Operating   −6,000

[handwritten: Depreciation is a systematic, rational process to allocate the cost of a long term asset.]

Transaction (d)

Dr. Landry invested an additional $5,000 in the business in exchange for capital stock.

This transaction is similar to the initial transaction in which Dr. Landry established Family Health Care. The effects of these transactions are recorded as shown below:

		Balance Sheet							
Statement of Cash Flows		**Assets**			**=**	**Liabilities**	**+**	**Stockholders' Equity**	**Income Statement**
	Cash +	Prepaid Insurance +	Land =		Notes Payable +	Unearned Revenue +		Capital Stock +	Retained Earnings
Balances	720	8,400	12,000		10,000	1,800		6,000	3,320
d. Issued capital stock	5,000							5,000	
Balances	5,720	8,400	12,000		10,000	1,800		11,000	3,320

Statement of Cash Flows
d. Financing   5,000

Transaction (e)

Purchased supplies for $240 on account.

This transaction is similar to transactions (b) and (c), in that purchased supplies are assets until they are used in the generation of revenue. Family Health Care has purchased and received the supplies, with a promise to pay in the near future. Such liabilities that are incurred in the normal operations are called **accounts payable**. The effects of this transaction on Family Health Care's financial statements are recorded as shown below:

		Balance Sheet									
Statement of Cash Flows		**Assets**			**=**	**Liabilities**		**+**	**Stockholders' Equity**		**Income Statement**
	Cash +	Prepaid Insurance +	Supplies +	Land =	Notes Payable +	Accounts Payable +	Unearned Revenue +		Capital Stock +	Retained Earnings	
Balances	5,720	8,400			12,000	10,000		1,800		11,000	3,320
e. Purchased supplies			240				240					
Balances	5,720	8,400	240		12,000	10,000	240	1,800		11,000	3,320

   Under the Balance Sheet column the asset Supplies increases by $240 and the liability Accounts Payable increases by $240. Since no cash is paid or received, there are no entries under the Statement of Cash Flows column. Likewise, since no revenue or expenses are affected, there are no entries under the Income Statement column.

[handwritten: deduct the accumulated depreciation when looking for the carrying value.]

Transaction (f)

Purchased $8,500 of office equipment. Paid $1,700 cash as a down payment, with the remaining $6,800 (8,500 − $1,700) due in five monthly installments of $1,360 ($6,800 ÷ 5) beginning January 1.

In this transaction, the asset Office Equipment increases by $8,500, Cash decreases by $1,700, and Notes Payable increases by $6,800. Since cash was paid, cash flows from Investing activities is decreased by $1,700 under the Statement of Cash Flows column. No revenues or expenses are affected, so no entries under the Income Statement column are necessary.

The effects of transaction (f) on Family Health Care's financial statements are recorded as shown below:

Statement of Cash Flows	Balance Sheet											Income Statement
	Assets					=	Liabilities			+ Stockholders' Equity		
	Cash +	Prepaid Insur. +	Supp. +	Office Equip. +	Land =	Notes Pay. +	Accts. Pay. +	Unearned Revenue +	Capital Stock +	Retained Earnings	
Balances	5,720	8,400	240			12,000	10,000	240	1,800	11,000	3,320	
f. Purchased office equip.	−1,700			8,500			6,800					
Balances	4,020	8,400	240	8,500		12,000	16,800	240	1,800	11,000	3,320	

Statement of Cash Flows
f. Investing   −1,700

Transaction (g)

Provided services of $6,100 to patients on account.

This transaction is similar to the revenue transactions recorded for Family Health Care in September and October. This transaction is different in that instead of receiving cash the services were provided *on account.*

PepsiCo, Inc. reported net receivables of $4,683 million as of December 28, 2008.

Family Health Care will collect cash from the patients' insurance companies in the future. Such amounts that are to be collected in the future and that arise from the normal operations are called **accounts receivable**. Since a valid claim exists for future collection, accounts receivable are assets. Thus, the asset Accounts Receivable is increased by $6,100 under the Balance Sheet column. In addition, Retained Earnings are increased under the Balance Sheet column and Fees earned is increased under the Income Statement column.

The effects of transaction (g) on Family Health Care's financial statements are recorded as shown below:

Statement of Cash Flows	Balance Sheet												Income Statement
	Assets						=	Liabilities			+ Stockholders' Equity		
	Cash +	Accts. Rec. +	Prepaid Insur. +	Supp. +	Office Equip. +	Land =	Notes Pay. +	Accts. Pay. +	Unearned Revenue +	Capital Stock +	Retained Earnings	
Balances	4,020		8,400	240	8,500	12,000	16,800	240	1,800	11,000	3,320	
g. Fees earned on acct.		6,100									6,100	g.
Balances	4,020	6,100	8,400	240	8,500	12,000	16,800	240	1,800	11,000	9,420	

Income Statement
g. Fees earned   6,100

Transaction (h)

Received $5,500 for services provided to patients who paid cash.

This transaction is similar to the revenue transactions that Family Health Care recorded in September and October. The effects of this transaction on Family Health Care's financial statements are recorded as shown:

[Handwritten margin note: Current assets are cash or other assets that are to be converted to cash, sold or used up within 1 yr.]

Statement of Cash Flows	Cash +	Accts. Rec. +	Prepaid Insur. +	Supp. +	Office Equip. +	Land =	Notes Pay. +	Accts. Pay. +	Unearned Revenue +	Capital Stock +	Retained Earnings	Income Statement
					Balance Sheet			**Liabilities**		**+ Stockholders' Equity**		
		Assets				**=**						
Balances	4,020	6,100	8,400	240	8,500	12,000	16,800	240	1,800	11,000	9,420	
h. Fees earned for cash	5,500										5,500	h.
Balances	9,520	6,100	8,400	240	8,500	12,000	16,800	240	1,800	11,000	14,920	

Statement of Cash Flows
h. Operating   5,500

Income Statement
h. Fees earned   5,500

Transaction (i)

Received $4,200 from insurance companies, which paid on patients' accounts for services that have been provided.

This transaction is similar to transaction (b) in that only the mix of assets changes. Cash is increased and Accounts Receivable is decreased by $4,200 under the Balance Sheet column. The effects of this transaction on Family Health Care's financial statements are recorded as shown below:

Statement of Cash Flows	Cash +	Accts. Rec. +	Prepaid Insur. +	Supp. +	Office Equip. +	Land =	Notes Pay. +	Accts. Pay. +	Unearned Revenue +	Capital Stock +	Retained Earnings	Income Statement
					Balance Sheet			**Liabilities**		**+ Stockholders' Equity**		
		Assets				**=**						
Balances	9,520	6,100	8,400	240	8,500	12,000	16,800	240	1,800	11,000	14,920	
i. Collected cash on acct.	4,200	−4,200										
Balances	13,720	1,900	8,400	240	8,500	12,000	16,800	240	1,800	11,000	14,920	

Statement of Cash Flows
i. Operating   4,200

[Handwritten note: current liabilities are due within 1 year or less.]

Transaction (j)

Paid $100 on account for supplies that had been purchased.

The cash was paid for supplies purchased on account. Thus, this transaction decreases Cash and Accounts Payable by $100 under the Balance Sheet column. Since the supplies are used in the normal operations of Family Health Care, cash flows from Operating activities is also decreased under the Statement of Cash Flows column.

The effects of transaction (j) on Family Health Care's financial statements are recorded as shown below:

[Handwritten note: accounts receivable is amounts due from customers as a result of credit sales.]

Statement of Cash Flows	Cash +	Accts. Rec. +	Prepaid Insur. +	Supp. +	Office Equip. +	Land =	Notes Pay. +	Accts. Pay. +	Unearned Revenue +	Capital Stock +	Retained Earnings	Income Statement
					Balance Sheet			**Liabilities**		**+ Stockholders' Equity**		
		Assets				**=**						
Balances	13,720	1,900	8,400	240	8,500	12,000	16,800	240	1,800	11,000	14,920	
j. Paid on account	−100							−100				
Balances	13,620	1,900	8,400	240	8,500	12,000	16,800	140	1,800	11,000	14,920	

Statement of Cash Flows
j. Operating   −100

Transaction (k)

Expenses paid during November were as follows: wages, $2,790; rent, $800; utilities, $580; interest, $100; and miscellaneous, $420.

This transaction is similar to the September and October expense transactions for Family Health Care. The effects of this transaction on Family Health Care's financial statements are recorded as shown below:

Statement of Cash Flows			Balance Sheet										Income Statement
			Assets					=	Liabilities		+	Stockholders' Equity	
	Cash +	Accts. Rec. +	Prepaid Insur. +	Supp. +	Office Equip. +	Land =	Notes Pay. +	Accts. Pay. +	Unearned Revenue +	Capital Stock +	Retained Earnings	
Balances	13,620	1,900	8,400	240	8,500	12,000	16,800	140	1,800	11,000	14,920	
k. Paid expenses	−4,690										−4,690	k.
Balances	8,930	1,900	8,400	240	8,500	12,000	16,800	140	1,800	11,000	10,230	

Statement of Cash Flows
k. Operating   −4,690

Income Statement
k. Wages expense	−2,790
Rent expense	−800
Utilities expense	−580
Interest expense	−100
Misc. expense	−420

Transaction (l)

Paid dividends of $1,200 to stockholders (Dr. Landry).

This transaction is similar to Family Health Care's dividend transactions of September and October. The effects of this transaction on Family Health Care's financial statements are recorded as shown below:

Statement of Cash Flows			Balance Sheet										Income Statement
			Assets					=	Liabilities		+	Stockholders' Equity	
	Cash +	Accts. Rec. +	Prepaid Insur. +	Supp. +	Office Equip. +	Land =	Notes Pay. +	Accts. Pay. +	Unearned Revenue +	Capital Stock +	Retained Earnings	
Balances	8,930	1,900	8,400	240	8,500	12,000	16,800	140	1,800	11,000	10,230	
l. Paid dividends	−1,200										−1,200	
Balances	7,730	1,900	8,400	240	8,500	12,000	16,800	140	1,800	11,000	9,030	

Statement of Cash Flows
l. Financing   −1,200

Obj 3 Describe and illustrate the end-of-period adjustment process.

The Adjustment Process

Accrual accounting requires the updating of the accounting records prior to preparing financial statements. This updating is called the **adjustment process**. The adjustment process is needed to match revenues and expenses, which is an application of the matching concept.

Adjustments are necessary because, at any point in time, some accounts (elements) of the accounting equation are not up to date. For example, as time passes, prepaid insurance expires and supplies are used. However, it is not efficient to record the daily expiration of prepaid insurance or the daily

use of supplies. Instead, the accounting records are normally updated just prior to preparing financial statements.

Family Health Care's September and October financial statements were prepared in Chapter 2 without recording any adjustments. This is because Family Health Care only entered into cash transactions in September and October. When all of a company's transactions are cash transactions, no adjustments are necessary.

During November, however, Family Health Care entered into several accrual transactions. As a result, Family Health must adjust its accounts before preparing financial statements.

Deferrals and Accruals

Two types of accounts require adjustments as follows:

1. **Deferrals** that are created by recording a transaction in a way that delays or defers the recognition of an expense or revenue.

2. **Accruals** that are created when a revenue or expense has been earned or incurred but has not been recorded.

Common deferrals include prepaid expenses and unearned revenues.

Prepaid expenses or **deferred expenses** are initially recorded as assets, but become expenses over time or through normal operations of the business. For Family Health Care, prepaid insurance is an example of a deferral that requires adjustment. Other examples include supplies, prepaid advertising, and prepaid interest.

Unearned revenues or **deferred revenues** are initially recorded as liabilities, but become revenues over time or through normal operations of the business. For Family Health Care, unearned rent is an example of a deferral that requires adjustment. Other examples include tuition received in advance; an attorney's annual retainer fee; insurance premiums received in advance; and magazine subscriptions received in advance.

McDonald's Corporation reported prepaid and other current assets of $411.5 million as of December 31, 2008.

INTEGRITY, OBJECTIVITY, AND ETHICS IN BUSINESS

Dave's Legacy

When Dave Thomas, founder of **Wendy's,** died in 2002, he left behind a corporate culture of integrity and high ethical conduct. When asked to comment on Dave's death, Jack Schuessler, chairman and chief executive officer of Wendy's, stated:

"People (could) relate to Dave, that he was honest and has integrity and he really cares about people.... There is no replacing Dave Thomas.... So you are left with ... the values that he gave us ... and you take care of the customer every day like Dave would want us to and good things will happen."

"He's [Dave Thomas] taught us so much that when we get stuck, we can always look back and ask ourselves, how would Dave handle it?"

In a recent discussion of corporate earnings with analysts, Kerrii Anderson, chief financial officer of Wendy's, stated: "We're confident about the future because of our unwavering commitment to our core values, such as quality food, superior restaurant operations, continuous improvement, and *integrity to doing the right thing* (emphasis added)."

Sources: Neil Cavuto, "Wendy's CEO—Interview," *Fox News: Your World,* February 11, 2002; "Q1 2003 Wendy's International Earnings Conference Call—Final," *Financial Disclosure Wire,* April 24, 2003.

The Home Depot, Inc. reported accrued salaries and related expenses of $1,094 million as of February 3, 2008.

Common accruals include accrued expenses and accrued revenues.

Accrued expenses or **accrued liabilities** are expenses that have been incurred, but are not recorded in the accounts. For Family Health Care, unpaid wages at the end of November are an example of an accrued expense. Other examples include accrued interest, utility expenses, and taxes.

Accrued revenues or **accrued assets** are revenues that have been earned but are not recorded in the accounts. For Family Health Care, revenue for patient services that have been earned, but not billed at the end of November is an example of accrued revenue. Other examples include accrued interest on notes receivable and accrued rent on property rented to others.

Deferrals are normally the result of cash being received or paid *before* the revenue is earned or the expense is incurred. In contrast, accruals are normally the result of cash being received or paid *after* revenue has been earned or an expense has been incurred. Exhibit 1 summarizes the nature of deferrals and accruals.

EXHIBIT 1   **Deferrals and Accruals**

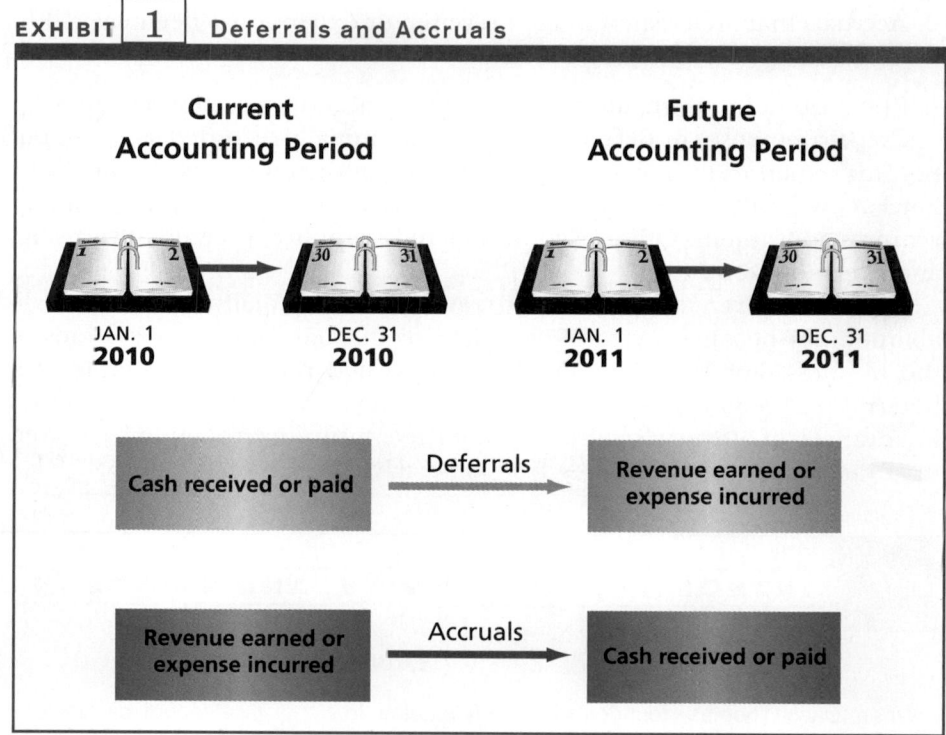

Adjustments for Family Health Care

On November 30, the following adjustment data have been gathered for Family Health Care.

Deferred expenses:

1. Prepaid insurance expired, $1,100.
2. Supplies used, $150.
3. Depreciation on office equipment, $160.

Deferred revenue:

4. Unearned revenue earned, $360.

Accrued expense:

5. Wages owed but not paid to employees, $220.

Accrued revenue:

6. Services provided but not billed to insurance companies, $750.

Adjustment 1

Prepaid insurance expired, $1,100

During November, a portion of the prepaid insurance purchased on November 1 has expired. On November 1, Family Health Care paid for the following two policies:

1. General business policy for $2,400 (transaction b)
2. Malpractice policy for $6,000 (transaction c).

The general business policy is a two-year policy expiring at a rate of $100 ($2,400 ÷ 24) per month. The malpractice policy is a six-month policy that expires at a rate of $1,000 ($6,000 ÷ 6) per month. Thus, a total of $1,100 ($100 + $1,000) of prepaid insurance has expired by the end of November.

Adjustment 1 is recorded by decreasing the asset Prepaid Insurance and decreasing Retained Earnings under the Balance Sheet column. In addition, Insurance expense under the Income Statement column is recorded as −$1,100. Since no cash was received or paid, no entries are necessary in the Statement of Cash Flows column.

The effects of Adjustment 1 on Family Health Care's financial statements are recorded as shown below:

Statement of Cash Flows	Balance Sheet											Income Statement
	Assets					=	Liabilities			+ Stockholders' Equity		
	Cash +	Accts. Rec. +	Prepaid Insur. +	Supp. +	Office Equip. +	Land =	Notes Pay. +	Accts. Pay. +	Unearned Revenue +	Capital Stock +	Retained Earnings	
Balances	7,730	1,900	8,400	240	8,500	12,000	16,800	140	1,800	11,000	9,030	
a1. Insurance expense			−1,100								−1,100	a1.
Balances	7,730	1,900	7,300	240	8,500	12,000	16,800	140	1,800	11,000	7,930	

Income Statement
a1. Insurance exp.   −1,100

All adjustments affect the balance sheet and income statement and thus adjusting entries are recorded in the Balance Sheet and Income Statement columns. In contrast, *no adjustment* affects the statement of cash flows and thus, no adjusting entries are recorded in the Statement of Cash Flows column.

Adjustment 2

Supplies used, $150.

For November, supplies of $150 were used. This leaves $90 ($240 − $150) of supplies on hand as of November 30.

Adjustment 2 is recorded by decreasing the asset Supplies and decreasing Retained Earnings under the Balance Sheet column. In addition, supplies expense under the Income Statement column is recorded as −$150.

The effects of Adjustment 2 on Family Health Care's financial statements are recorded as shown below:

Statement of Cash Flows	Balance Sheet											Income Statement
	Assets						**=**	**Liabilities**		**+ Stockholders' Equity**		
	Cash +	Accts. Rec. +	Prepaid Insur. +	Supp. +	Office Equip. +	Land =	Notes Pay. +	Accts. Pay. +	Unearned Revenue +	Capital Stock +	Retained Earnings	
Balances	7,730	1,900	7,300	240	8,500	12,000	16,800	140	1,800	11,000	7,930	
a2. Supplies expense				−150							−150	a2.
Balances	7,730	1,900	7,300	90	8,500	12,000	16,800	140	1,800	11,000	7,780	

Income Statement
a2. Supplies exp.   −150

Adjustment 3

Depreciation on office equipment, $160.

Fixed assets such as office equipment lose their ability to provide service over time. This reduction in the ability of a fixed asset to provide service is called **depreciation**. However, it is difficult to objectively determine the physical decline in a fixed asset's ability to provide service. For this reason, depreciation is estimated based on the asset's useful life. Methods of estimating depreciation are covered in Chapter 7. In this chapter, the November depreciation for the office equipment is assumed to be $160.

A record of the initial cost of a fixed asset must be maintained for tax and other purposes. For this reason, the fixed asset account is not reduced directly for depreciation. Instead, an offsetting or *contra asset account,* called **accumulated depreciation**, is added to the Balance Sheet column. On the balance sheet, the accumulated depreciation is subtracted from the cost of the fixed asset.

Adjustment 3 is recorded by decreasing the asset Office Equipment by adding Accumulated Depreciation (Acc. Dep.) under Assets in the Balance Sheet column. The accumulated depreciation is then recorded as −$160. Retained Earnings is also decreased under the Balance Sheet column by −$160. In addition, Depreciation expense under the Income Statement column is recorded as −$160.

The effects of Adjustment 3 on Family Health Care's financial statements are recorded as shown below:

Statement of Cash Flows	Balance Sheet												Income Statement
	Assets							**=**	**Liabilities**		**+ Stockholders' Equity**		
	Cash +	Accts. Rec. +	Prepaid Insur. +	Supp. +	Office Equip. −	Acc. Dep. +	Land =	Notes Pay. +	Accts. Pay. +	Unearned Revenue +	Capital Stock +	Retained Earnings	
Balances	7,730	1,900	7,300	90	8,500		12,000	16,800	140	1,800	11,000	7,780	
a3. Depreciation exp.						−160						−160	a3.
Balances	7,730	1,900	7,300	90	8,500	−160	12,000	16,800	140	1,800	11,000	7,620	

Income Statement
a3. Depreciation exp.   −160

Three other points related to depreciation are:

1. Land is not depreciated, because it usually does not lose its ability to provide service.

SOX requires companies & their Incl. accountants to report on the effectiveness of the company's internal controls.

2. The cost of the equipment is a type of deferred expense that is recognized as an expense over the fixed asset's useful life.

3. The cost of the fixed asset less the balance of its accumulated depreciation is called the asset's **book value** or *carrying value*. For example, the book value of Family Health Care's office equipment, after the preceding adjustment, is $8,340 ($8,500 − $160).

Adjustment 4

Unearned revenue earned, $360.

This adjustment recognizes that a portion of the unearned revenue is earned by the end of November. That is, of the $1,800 received for rental of the land for five months (November through March), one-fifth, or $360, would have been earned as of November 30.

Adjustment 4 is recorded by decreasing the liability Unearned Revenue by −$360 under the Balance Sheet column. In addition, Rent revenue is increased by $360 under the Income Statement column.

The effects of Adjustment 4 on Family Health Care's financial statements are recorded as shown below.

Statement of Cash Flows		Balance Sheet											Income Statement
		Assets						= Liabilities		+ Stockholders' Equity			
	Cash +	Accts. Rec. +	Prepaid Insur. +	Supp. +	Office Equip. −	Acc. Dep. +	Land =	Notes Pay. +	Accts. Pay. +	Unearned Revenue +	Capital Stock +	Retained Earnings	
Balances	7,730	1,900	7,300	90	8,500	−160	12,000	16,800	140	1,800	11,000	7,620	
a4. Rent revenue										−360		360	a4.
Balances	7,730	1,900	7,300	90	8,500	−160	12,000	16,800	140	1,440	11,000	7,980	

	Income Statement	
	a4. Rent revenue	360

Adjustment 5

Wages owed but not paid to employees, $220.

It is rare that employees are paid the same day that the accounting period ends. Thus, at the end of an accounting period, it is normal for businesses to owe wages to their employees.

Adjustment 5 recognizes that as of November 30, employees of Family Health Care have not been paid $220 for work they have performed. This adjustment is recorded by increasing the liability Wages Payable by $220 and decreasing Retained Earnings by −$220 under the Balance Sheet column. In addition, Wages expense under the Income Statement column is recorded as −$220.

Statement of Cash Flows		Balance Sheet												Income Statement
		Assets						= Liabilities			+ Stockholders' Equity			
	Cash +	Accts. Rec. +	Prepaid Insur. +	Supp. +	Office Equip. −	Acc. Dep. +	Land =	Notes Pay. +	Accts. Pay. +	Wages Pay. +	Unearned Revenue +	Capital Stock +	Retained Earnings	
Balances	7,730	1,900	7,300	90	8,500	−160	12,000	16,800	140		1,440	11,000	7,980	
a5. Wages exp.										220			−220	a5.
Balances	7,730	1,900	7,300	90	8,500	−160	12,000	16,800	140	220	1,440	11,000	7,760	

	Income Statement	
	a5. Wages expense	−220

Adjustment 6

Services provided but not billed to insurance companies, $750.

This adjustment recognizes that Family Health Care has provided services of $750 to patients who have not yet been billed. Such services are usually provided near the end of the month.

This adjustment is recorded by increasing the asset Accounts Receivable (Accts. Rec.) and increasing Retained Earnings by $750 under the Balance Sheet column. In addition, Fees earned under the Income Statement column is recorded as $750.

The effects of Adjustment 6 on Family Health Care's financial statements are as shown below.

Statement of Cash Flows	Balance Sheet													Income Statement
	Assets							=	Liabilities			+	Stockholders' Equity	
	Cash +	Accts. Rec. +	Prepaid Insur. +	Supp. +	Office Equip. −	Acc. Dep. +	Land =	Notes Pay. +	Accts. Pay. +	Wages Pay. +	Unearned Revenue +	Capital Stock +	Retained Earnings	
Balances	7,730	1,900	7,300	90	8,500	−160	12,000	16,800	140	220	1,440	11,000	7,760	
a6. Fees earned		750											750	a6.
Balances	7,730	2,650	7,300	90	8,500	−160	12,000	16,800	140	220	1,440	11,000	8,510	

	Income Statement	
	a6. Fees earned	750

The November transactions and adjustments for Family Health Care are summarized in Exhibit 2.

Financial Statements

Obj 4 Prepare financial statements using accrual concepts of accounting, including a classified balance sheet.

Based on the summary of transactions and adjustments shown in Exhibit 2, Family Health Care's financial statements for November are described and illustrated in this section. These financial statements are shown in Exhibits 3, 4, 5, and 6.

Income Statement

The income statement is shown in Exhibit 3, on page 96. It is prepared by summarizing the revenue and expense transactions listed under the Income Statement column of Exhibit 2.

Revenues are a result of providing services or selling products to customers. Examples of revenues include fees earned, fares earned, commissions revenue, interest revenue, and rent revenue.

Revenues from the primary operations of the business are reported separately from other revenue. For example, Family Health Care has two types of revenues for November, fees earned and rental revenue. Since the primary operation of the business is providing services to patients, rental revenue is reported under the heading of "Other income."

Expenses are assets used up or services consumed in the process of generating revenues. Expenses are matched against their related revenues to determine the net income or net loss for a period. Examples of typical expenses include wages expense, rent expense, utilities expense, supplies expense, and miscellaneous expense. Expenses are normally listed on the income statement

[handwritten notes: "JOA — A firms internal controls environment is influenced by: management operating style, organizational structure, & personal policies."]

EXHIBIT 2 — Family Health Care Summary of Transactions and Adjustments for November

Statement of Cash Flows	Cash +	Accts. Rec. +	Prepaid Insur. +	Supp. +	Office Equip. −	Acc. Dep. +	Land =	Notes Pay. +	Accts. Pay. +	Wages Pay. +	Unearned Revenue +	Capital Stock +	Retained Earnings	Income Statement
Balances, Nov. 1	7,320						12,000	10,000				6,000	3,320	
a. Rental rev.	1,800										1,800			
b. Paid insurance	−2,400		2,400											
c. Paid insurance	−6,000		6,000											
d. Investment	5,000											5,000		
e. Pur. supplies				240					240					
f. Pur. off. equip.	−1,700				8,500				6,800					
g. Fees earned		6,100											6,100	g.
h. Fees earned	5,500												5,500	h.
i. Collected cash	4,200	−4,200												
j. Paid on acct.	−100								−100					
k. Paid expenses	−4,690												−4,690	k.
l. Dividends	−1,200												−1,200	
a1. Insurance exp.			−1,100										−1,100	a1.
a2. Supplies exp.				−150									−150	a2.
a3. Deprec. exp						−160							−160	a3.
a4. Rental revenue											−360		360	a4.
a5. Wages exp.										220			−220	a5.
a6. Fees earned		750											750	a6.
Balances, Nov. 30	7,730	2,650	7,300	90	8,500	−160	12,000	16,800	140	220	1,440	11,000	8,510	

Statement of Cash Flows

a. Operating	1,800
b. Operating	−2,400
c. Operating	−6,000
d. Financing	5,000
f. Investing	−1,700
h. Operating	5,500
i. Operating	4,200
j. Operating	−100
k. Operating	−4,690
l. Financing	−1,200
Increase in cash	410
Nov. 1 cash bal.	7,320
Nov. 30 cash bal.	7,730

Income Statement

g. Fees earned	6,100
h. Fees earned	5,500
k. Wages exp.	−2,790
Rent exp.	−800
Utilities exp.	−580
Interest exp.	−100
Misc. exp.	−420
a1. Insur. exp.	−1,100
a2. Supplies exp.	−150
a3. Deprec. exp.	−160
a4. Rental rev.	360
a5. Wages exp.	−220
a6. Fees earned	750
Net income	6,390

from largest to the smallest except for miscellaneous expense, which is always listed last.

Expenses not related to the primary operations of the business are reported as "Other expenses." Interest expense is an example of an expense that is often reported as an "Other expense."

Operating income is determined by deducting the operating expenses from the fees earned. Family Health Care has operating income of $6,030 in

EXHIBIT 3   Family Health Care Income Statement for November

FAMILY HEALTH CARE, P.C. Income Statement For the Month Ended November 30, 2011		
Fees earned		$12,350
Operating expenses:		
Wages expense	$3,010	
Insurance expense	1,100	
Rent expense	800	
Utilities expense	580	
Depreciation expense	160	
Supplies expense	150	
Interest expense	100	
Miscellaneous expense	420	
Total operating expenses		6,320
Operating income		$ 6,030
Other income:		
Rental revenue		360
Net income		$ 6,390

November. Other income consisting of $360 in rental revenue is then added to determine the net income for November of $6,390.

Retained Earnings Statement

The retained earnings statement shown in Exhibit 4 is prepared by adding the November net income of $6,390 (from the income statement), less dividends of $1,200, to the beginning amount of retained earnings of $3,320. The result is the ending amount of retained earnings of $8,510, which is included on Family Health Care's November 30, 2011 balance sheet.

EXHIBIT 4   Family Health Care Retained Earnings Statement for November

FAMILY HEALTH CARE, P.C. Retained Earnings Statement For the Month Ended November 30, 2011		
Retained earnings, November 1, 2011		$3,320
Net income for November	$6,390	
Less dividends	1,200	5,190
Retained earnings, November 30, 2011		$8,510

Balance Sheet

The balance sheet shown in Exhibit 5 is prepared from the ending balances shown in the Balance Sheet columns of Exhibit 2. The balance sheet shown in Exhibit 5 is a **classified balance sheet**. As the term implies, a classified balance sheet is prepared with various sections, subsections, and captions.

A classified balance sheet normally reports assets as:

1. Current assets

2. Fixed assets

3. Intangible assets

EXHIBIT | **5** | Family Health Care Balance Sheet for November

FAMILY HEALTH CARE, P.C.
Balance Sheet
November 30, 2011

Assets

Current assets:			
Cash		$ 7,730	
Accounts receivable		2,650	
Prepaid insurance		7,300	
Supplies		90	
Total current assets			$17,770
Fixed assets:			
Office equipment	$8,500		
Less accumulated depreciation	160	$ 8,340	
Land		12,000	
Total fixed assets			20,340
Total assets			$38,110

Liabilities

Current liabilities:			
Accounts payable		$ 140	
Wages payable		220	
Notes payable		6,800	
Unearned revenue		1,440	
Total current liabilities			$ 8,600
Long-term liabilities:			
Notes payable			10,000
Total liabilities			$18,600

Stockholders' Equity

Capital stock		$11,000	
Retained earnings		8,510	
Total stockholders' equity			19,510
Total liabilities and stockholders' equity			$38,110

Current assets are cash and other assets that are expected to be converted to cash or sold or used up within one year or less, through normal operations. In addition to cash, the current assets normally include accounts receivable, notes receivable, supplies, and prepaid expenses.

Accounts receivable and notes receivable are current assets because they are normally converted to cash within one year or less. **Notes receivable** are written claims against debtors who promise to pay the amount of the note plus interest. From the creditor's point of view, a note receivable is a note payable.

Exhibit 5 indicates that Family Health Care has current assets of cash, accounts receivable, prepaid insurance, and supplies as of November 30, 2011. These current assets total $17,770.

Fixed assets are physical assets of a long-term nature. The fixed assets may also be reported on the balance sheet as *property, plant, and equipment,* or *plant assets.* Fixed assets include equipment, machinery, buildings, and land. Except for land, fixed assets depreciate over a period of time. The cost less

accumulated depreciation for each major type of fixed asset is normally reported on the classified balance sheet.

Exhibit 5 indicates that Family Health Care has fixed assets of office equipment and land. The book value, cost less accumulated depreciation, of the office equipment is $8,340. The land is reported at its cost of $12,000, which when added to the book value of the office equipment yields total fixed assets of $20,340.

Intangible assets represent rights of a long-term nature, such as patent rights, copyrights, and goodwill. Goodwill arises from such factors as name recognition, location, product quality, reputation, and managerial skill. Goodwill is recorded and reported on the balance sheet when a company purchases another company at a price above the normal market value of the purchased company's assets. As shown in Exhibit 5, Family Health Care has no intangible assets.

A classified balance sheet normally reports liabilities as:

1. Current liabilities
2. Long-term liabilities

Current liabilities are due within a short time (usually 1 year or less) and are to be paid out of current assets. Common current liabilities include accounts payable and notes payable. Other current liabilities include wages payable, interest payable, taxes payable, and unearned revenue.

Exhibit 5 indicates that Family Health Care has total current liabilities of $8,600 that include accounts payable, wages payable, and notes payable. Unearned revenue (rent) is also reported as a current liability since the revenue has not yet been earned.

Long-term liabilities are not due for a long time (usually more than 1 year). Long-term liabilities are reported following the current liabilities.

As long-term liabilities come due and are to be paid within one year, they are reported as current liabilities. If they are to be renewed rather than paid, they would continue to be classified as long term. When an asset is pledged as security for a long-term liability, the obligation may be called a *mortgage note payable* or a *mortgage payable*.

Exhibit 5 indicates that Family Health Care has total long-term liabilities of $10,000, which consists of notes payable. These notes payable are not due until 2014. However, $6,800 of notes payable are due within the next year and thus, are reported as a current liability.

A classified balance sheet normally reports stockholders' equity as:

1. Capital stock, which has been invested in the company by the stockholders
2. Retained earnings, which is net income that has been retained in the corporation

Exhibit 5 indicates Family Health Care has capital stock of $11,000, which results from $6,000 of capital stock on November 1 plus an additional investment of $5,000 by Dr. Landry during November. The retained earnings of $8,510 is the ending balance of retained earnings as reported on the November retained earnings statement shown in Exhibit 4.

Statement of Cash Flows

The statement of cash flows shown in Exhibit 6 is prepared by summarizing the November cash transactions. These cash transactions are shown in the Statement of Cash Flows column of Exhibit 2.

FedEx Corporation reported goodwill of $2,229 million as of May 31, 2009.

EXHIBIT 6 Family Health Care Statement of Cash Flows for November

FAMILY HEALTH CARE P.C. Statement of Cash Flows For the Month Ended November 30, 2011		
Cash flows from operating activities:		
Cash received from patients	$ 9,700	
Cash received from rental of land	1,800	$ 11,500
Deduct cash payments for expenses		(13,190)
Net cash flow used in operating activities		$ (1,690)
Cash flows from investing activities:		
Purchase of office equipment		(1,700)
Cash flows from financing activities:		
Additional issuance of capital stock	$ 5,000	
Deduct cash dividends	(1,200)	
Net cash flow from financing activities		3,800
Net increase in cash		$ 410
November 1, 2011 cash balance		7,320

The *Cash flows from operating activities* section is prepared from the Statement of Cash Flows column of Exhibit 2 by summarizing the *Operating* activity transactions. The cash receipts from revenue transactions are added and the cash payments for operating transactions are subtracted.

Exhibit 6 indicates that the cash received from revenue transactions consists of $9,700 ($5,500 + $4,200) received from patients and $1,800 received from rental of the land. The cash payments for operating transactions of $13,190 ($2,400 + $6,000 + $100 + $4,690) is determined by adding the negative cash payments for operating activities shown in Exhibit 2.

The *Cash flows from investing activities* is prepared from the Statement of Cash Flows column of Exhibit 2 by summarizing the *Investing* activity transactions. During November, Family Health Care has only one investing transaction for the purchase of office equipment.

The *Cash flows from financing activities* section is prepared from the Statement of Cash Flows column of Exhibit 2 by summarizing the *Financing* activity transactions. During November, Family Health Care received an additional investment from Dr. Landry of $5,000 and paid dividends of $1,200.

Integration of Financial Statements

Exhibit 7 shows the integration of Family Health Care's financial statements for November. The reconciliation of net income and net cash flows from operations is shown in the appendix at the end of this chapter.

Accrual and Cash Bases of Accounting

The financial statements of Family Health Care for November were prepared under accrual accounting concepts. Companies that use accrual accounting concepts for recording transactions and preparing financial statements are said to use the **accrual basis of accounting**. The accrual basis of accounting is used by large companies and is required of corporations whose stock is publicly traded.

Obj 5 Describe how the accrual basis of accounting enhances the interpretation of financial statements.

EXHIBIT | **7** | Integrated Financial Statements—Family Health Care

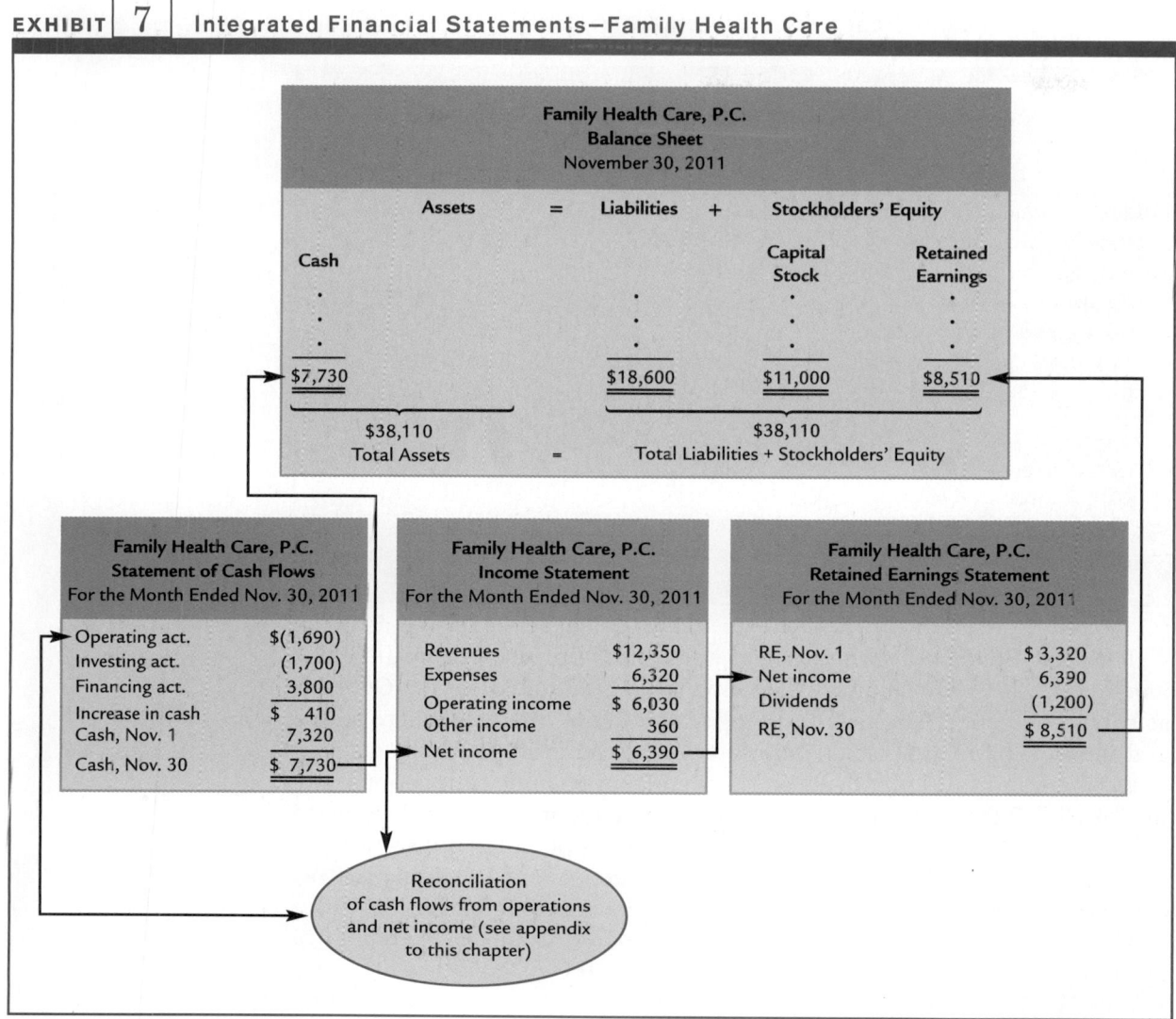

Companies that record transactions only when cash is received or paid are said to use the **cash basis of accounting.**[1] Individuals and small businesses often use the cash basis of accounting.

Using the Cash Basis of Accounting

Under the cash basis of accounting, a company records only transactions involving increases or decreases of cash. Thus, revenue is recorded only when cash is received and expenses are recorded only when cash is paid.

To illustrate, assume that a real estate agency sells a $300,000 piece of property on December 28, 2010, earning a commission of 8% of the selling price. However, the agency did not receive the $24,000 ($300,000 × 8%) commission until January 3, 2011. Under the cash basis, the real estate agency will not record the commission revenue until January 3, 2011. Likewise, a December cellular phone bill paid in January is recorded as a January expense, not a December expense.

[1] Some companies use a modified-cash basis of accounting, which includes some accrual accounting concepts. These bases of accounting are covered in advanced accounting texts.

Under the cash basis, the matching concept is not used. That is, expenses are recorded when paid in cash, not necessarily in the period when the revenue is earned. As a result, adjusting entries to properly match revenues and expenses are not required under the cash basis.

Using the Accrual Basis of Accounting

Under the accrual basis of accounting, a company records transactions using accrual accounting concepts. Thus, revenue is recorded as it is earned, regardless of when cash is received.

To illustrate, the real estate agency in the preceding example would record the $24,000 commission revenue on December 28, 2010. This is because the commission has been earned on December 28, 2010 even though the cash is not received until January 3, 2011.

Once revenue has been earned and recorded, any expenses incurred in generating the revenue are recorded. In this way, the expenses are matched against the revenue they generated. For example, in the preceding example, the December cellular phone bill would be recorded in December even though it was not paid until January.

The accrual basis of accounting was used to record Family Health Care's November transactions. As a result, adjusting entries were used to update the accounting records at the end November.

Exhibit 8 summarizes the basic differences of how revenue and expenses are recorded under the cash and accrual bases of accounting.

EXHIBIT 8   Cash versus Accrual Accounting

	Cash Basis	Accrual Basis
Revenue is recorded	When cash is received	When revenue is earned
Expense is recorded	When cash is paid	When expense is incurred in generating revenue
Adjusting entries	Not required	Required in order to prepare financial statements

Cash and Accrual Bases of Accounting

All the September and October transactions for Family Health Care in Chapter 2 involved the receipt or payment of cash. As a result, the financial statements shown in Exhibit 4 and Exhibit 7 in Chapter 2 are the same as those that would be reported under the cash basis of accounting.

In November, Family Health Care entered into transactions that used accrual accounting concepts. As a result, the November financial statements shown in Exhibits 3 through 6 of this chapter use the accrual basis of accounting.

One of the major differences between accrual and cash basis financial statements is the reporting of net income and net cash flows from operations. Specifically, the following differences exist:

1. Under the cash basis of accounting, net income and net cash flows from operating activities are equal.

2. Under the accrual basis of accounting, net income and net cash flows from operating activities may be significantly different.

The net income and net cash flows from operating activities for Family Health Care are shown below.

	Net Cash Flows from Operating Activities	Net Income
September (Cash basis)	$ 2,600	$2,600
October (Cash basis)	3,220	3,220
November (Accrual basis)	(1,690)	6,390

The difference between the November net cash flows from operating activities and net income is due to the effects of accruals and deferrals.[2]

Importance of Accrual Basis of Accounting

Understanding the accrual basis of accounting is essential for assessing and interpreting the financial performance of a company. To illustrate, Family Health Care's November financial statements are used.

If the *cash basis* of accounting is used, Family Health Care's November financial statements report negative net cash flows from operating activities and net income of $(1,690). This is because under the cash basis, net cash flows from operating activities are equal to net income. When compared to September's net income of $2,600 and October's net income of $3,220, November's operations indicate an unfavorable trend.

If the *accrual basis* of accounting is used, Family Health Care's November financial statements report negative net cash flows from operating activities of $(1,690), but a positive net income of $6,390. When compared to September's net income of $2,600 and October's net income of $3,220, November's operations indicate a favorable trend. For example, since September, revenues have more than doubled, increasing from $5,500 to $12,350. As a result, net income has also more than doubled. Thus, Family Health Care is a profitable, rapidly expanding business.

The preceding Family Health Care illustration shows why generally accepted accounting principles (GAAP) require accrual accounting for all but the very smallest businesses. That is, accrual accounting is generally a better predictor of the profitability of a company than is net cash flows from operating activities and the cash basis of accounting.

Net cash flow from operating activities, however, is useful. For example, in the long run, a business cannot survive if it continually reports negative cash flows from operating activities. This is true even though the company may report net income. In other words, a business *must* generate positive cash flows from operating activities in the long-term in order to survive. For this reason, generally accepted accounting principles (GAAP) require reporting net cash flows from operating activities as well as net income.

Family Health Care's negative cash flows from operations of −$1,690 for November was largely due to prepaying insurance premiums of $8,400. This suggests that Family Health Care's negative cash flows from operations is temporary and not of major concern.

Family Health Care also illustrates why the financial statements must be analyzed and interpreted together rather than individually. This is the primary

---

[2] A reconciliation of net cash flows from operations and the net income is shown in the appendix at the end of this chapter. This reconciliation considers the effects of accruals and deferrals on net income.

reason the integrated financial statements approach is used throughout this text. For example, long-run profitability is best analyzed using accrual accounting and net income. The ability of the company to pay debts as they become due is best analyzed using net cash flows from operating activities.

The Accounting Cycle for the Accrual Basis of Accounting

The **accounting cycle** is the process that begins with analyzing transactions and ends with preparing financial statements. The basic steps in the accounting cycle are as follows:

1. Identifying, analyzing, and recording the effects of transactions on the accounting equation (financial statement elements and accounts)

2. Identifying, analyzing, and recording adjustment data

3. Preparing financial statements

Steps 1–3 have been described and illustrated in this chapter. Using the integrated financial statement framework, the ending balances for the Balance Sheet elements (columns) become the beginning balances for the next accounting period. Steps 1–3 are then repeated for the next accounting period.[3]

Appendix

Reconciliation: Net Cash Flows from Operations and Net Income[4]

Chapter 2 illustrates the financial statements for Family Health Care for September and October 2011. Because all the September and October transactions were cash transactions, the net cash flows from operating activities shown on the statement of cash flows equals the net income shown in the income statements as follows:

	Net Cash Flows from Operating Activities	Net Income
September (Cash basis)	$2,600	$2,600
October (Cash basis)	3,220	3,220

When all of a company's transactions are cash transactions or when a company uses the cash basis of accounting, net cash flows from operating activities always equals net income. This is not true, however, under the accrual basis of accounting.

During November and December, Family Health Care used the accrual basis of accounting. The November financial statements are illustrated in Exhibit 3 through Exhibit 6 of this chapter. The December financial statements for Family Health Care are illustrated in the Illustrative Problem at the end of this chapter. The net cash flows from operating activities and net income for November and December are shown at the top of page 104.

---

[3] In double-entry accounting systems such as described in Appendix A, at the end of the text, another step is necessary to complete the accounting cycle. This fourth step, called the closing process, involves transferring balances of revenues, expenses, and dividends to retained earnings. This step is unnecessary when using the integrated financial statements framework.

[4] This reconciliation is referred to as the indirect method of reporting cash flows from operations.

	Net Cash Flows from Operating Activities	Net Income
September (Cash basis)	$(1,690)	$ 6,390
October (Cash basis)	8,760	10,825

As shown above, net cash flows from operating activities will normally not be the same as net income under accrual accounting. Any difference can be reconciled by considering the effects of accruals and deferrals on the income statement.

Exhibit 9 illustrates the November reconciliation of Family Health Care's net income with operating cash flows from operations.

EXHIBIT 9   November's Reconciliation of Net Income and Cash Flows from Operations

Net income		$ 6,390
Add:		
Depreciation expense	$ 160	
Increase in accounts payable	140	
Increase in wages payable	220	
Increase in unearned revenue	1,440	1,960
Deduct:		
Increase in accounts receivable	$ (2,650)	
Increase in prepaid insurance	(7,300)	
Increase in supplies	(90)	(10,040)
Net cash flows from operating activities		$ (1,690)

Exhibit 9 begins with net income and then adds or deducts the effects of accruals or deferrals that affect net income, but do not result in the receipt or payment of cash. By doing so, Exhibit 9 ends with net cash flows from operating activities.

The effect of an accrual or deferral on net income is a net increase or decrease during the period. For example, during November, depreciation expense of $160 was recorded (a deferred expense) and thus deducted in arriving at net income. Yet, no cash was paid. Thus, to arrive at cash flows from operations, depreciation expense is added back to net income.

Accounts payable also increased during November by $140, and a related expense was recorded. But again, no cash was paid. Similarly, wages payable increased during November by $220, and the related wages expense was deducted in arriving at net income. However, the $220 was not paid until the next month. Thus, for November, the increases of $140 in accounts payable and $220 in wages payable are added back to net income.

Unearned revenue increased by $1,440 during November, which represents land rented to ILS Company. ILS Company initially paid Family Health Care $1,800 in advance. Of the $1,800, one-fifth ($360) was recorded as revenue for November. However, under the cash basis, the entire $1,800 would have been recorded as revenue. Thus, $1,440 (the increase in the unearned revenue) is added back to net income to arrive at cash flows from operating activities.

Accounts receivable increased by $2,650 during November and thus was recorded as part of revenue in arriving at net income. However, no cash was

received. Thus, this increase in accounts receivable is deducted in arriving at cash flows from operations.

Prepaid insurance increased by $7,300 during November. This represents an $8,400 payment of cash for insurance premiums less $1,100 of premiums deducted in arriving at net income. Thus, the remaining $7,300 (the increase in prepaid insurance) is deducted in arriving at cash flows from operations. Similarly, the increase in supplies of $90 is deducted.

The reconciliation of net income to net cash flows from operations is normally prepared as shown in Exhibit 10.

EXHIBIT 10   Reconciling Items

Net income		$XXX
Add:		
Depreciation expense	$XXX	
Increases in current liabilities from operations	XXX	
Decreases in current assets from operations	XXX	XXX
Deduct:		
Increases in current assets from operations	$XXX	
Decreases in current liabilities from operations	XXX	XXX
Net cash flows from operations		$XXX

During November, all the current assets are related to Family Health Care's operations. In addition, current liabilities for accounts payable and wages payable are also related to Family Health Care's operations. However, the increase in the current liability for notes payable, which increased by $6,800, is not included in the reconciliation shown in Exhibit 9. This is because the notes payable is related to the purchase of office equipment, which is an investing activity rather than an operating activity.

During November, Family Health Care did not have any decreases in current assets or current liabilities. Thus, the effects of these items are not shown in Exhibit 9. Normally, however, both increases and decreases in current assets and liabilities are included in reconciling net income and net cash flows from operating activities. For example, Family Health Care's December reconciliation shown on page 111 includes increases and decreases in current assets and current liabilities.

Key Points

1. Describe basic accrual accounting concepts, including the matching concept.

   Under accrual concepts of accounting, revenue is recognized when it is earned. When revenues are earned and recorded, all expenses incurred in generating the revenues are recorded so that revenues and expenses are properly matched in determining the net income or loss for the period. Liabilities are recorded at the time a business incurs the obligation to pay for the services or goods purchased.

2. Use accrual concepts of accounting to analyze, record, and summarize transactions.

   Using the integrated financial statement framework, November transactions for Family Health Care were recorded. Family Health Care's November transactions involved accrual accounting transactions.

3. Describe and illustrate the end-of-period adjustment process.

The accrual concepts of accounting require the accounting records to be updated prior to preparing financial statements. This updating process, called the adjustment process, is necessary to match revenues and expenses. The adjustment process involves two types of adjustments—deferrals and accruals. Adjustments for deferrals may involve deferred expenses or deferred revenues. Adjustments for accruals may involve accrued expenses or accrued revenues.

4. Prepare financial statements using accrual concepts of accounting, including a classified balance sheet.

A classified balance sheet includes sections for current assets; property, plant, and equipment (fixed assets); and intangible assets. Liabilities are classified as current liabilities or long-term liabilities. The income statement normally reports sections for revenues, operating expenses, other income and expense, and net income.

5. Describe how the accrual basis of accounting enhances the interpretation of financial statements.

The net cash flows from operating activities and net income will differ under the accrual basis of accounting. Under the accrual basis, net income is a better indicator of the long-term profitability of a business. For this reason, the accrual basis of accounting is required by generally accepted accounting principles (GAAP), except for very small businesses. The accrual basis reports the effects of operations on cash flows through the reporting of net cash flows from operating activities on the statement of cash flows.

The accounting cycle is the process that begins with analyzing transactions and ends with preparing the accounting records for the next accounting period. The basic steps in the accounting cycle are (1) identifying, analyzing, and recording the effects of transactions on the accounting equation; (2) identifying, analyzing, and recording adjustment data; and (3) preparing financial statements.

Key Terms

Account A record in which increases and decreases in a financial statement element are recorded.

Accounting cycle The process that begins with analyzing transactions and ends with preparing the financial statements.

Accounts payable Liabilities for amounts incurred from purchases of products or services in the normal operations of a business.

Accounts receivable Receivables created by selling merchandise or services on credit.

Accrual basis of accounting A system of accounting in which revenue is recorded as it is earned and expenses are recorded and matched against the revenue they generate.

Accruals Recognition of revenue when earned or expenses when incurred regardless of when cash is received or disbursed.

Accrued assets Revenues that have been earned at the end of an accounting period but have not

been recorded in the accounts; sometimes called *accrued assets.*

Accrued expenses Expenses that have been incurred at the end of an accounting period but have not been recorded in the accounts; sometimes called *accrued liabilities.*

Accrued liabilities Expenses that have been incurred at the end of an accounting period but have not been recorded in the accounts.

Accrued revenues Revenues that have been earned at the end of an accounting period but have not been recorded in the accounts; sometimes called *accrued assets.*

Accumulated depreciation An offsetting or contra asset account used to record depreciation on a fixed asset.

Adjustment process A process required by the accrual basis of accounting in which the accounts are updated prior to preparing financial statements.

Book value The cost of a fixed asset minus accumulated depreciation on the asset.

Cash basis of accounting A system of accounting in which only transactions involving increases or decreases of the entity's cash are recorded.

Classified balance sheet A balance sheet prepared with various sections, subsections, and captions that aid in its interpretation and analysis.

Current assets Cash and other assets that are expected to be converted to cash or sold or used up through the normal operations of the business within 1 year or less.

Current liabilities Liabilities that will be due within a short time (usually 1 year or less) and that are to be paid out of current assets.

Deferrals Delayed recordings of expenses or revenues.

Deferred expenses Items that are initially recorded as assets but are expected to become expenses over time or through the normal operations of the business; sometimes called *prepaid expenses*.

Deferred revenues Items that are initially recorded as liabilities but are expected to become revenues over time or through the normal operations of the business; sometimes called *unearned revenues*.

Depreciation The systematic periodic transfer of the cost of a fixed asset to an expense account during its expected useful life.

Fixed assets Long-lived or relatively permanent tangible assets that are used in the normal business operations; sometimes called *plant assets*.

Intangible assets Long-lived assets that are useful in the operations of a business, are not held for sale, and are without physical qualities.

Long-term liabilities Liabilities that will not be due for a long time (usually more than 1 year).

Notes receivable Written claim against debtors who promise to pay the amount of the note plus interest at an agreed upon rate.

Prepaid expenses Items that are initially recorded as assets but are expected to become expenses over time or through the normal operations of the business.

Unearned revenues Items that are initially recorded as liabilities but are expected to become revenues over time or through the normal operations of the business.

Illustrative Problem

Assume that the December transactions for Family Health Care are as follows:

a. Received cash of $1,900 from patients for services provided on account during November.

b. Provided services of $10,800 on account.

c. Received $6,500 for services provided for patients who paid cash.

d. Purchased supplies on account, $400.

e. Received $6,900 from insurance companies that paid on patients' accounts for services that had been previously billed.

f. Paid $310 on account for supplies that had been purchased.

g. Expenses paid during December were as follows: wages, $4,200, including $220 accrued at the end of November; rent, $800; utilities, $610; interest, $100; and miscellaneous, $520.

h. Paid dividends of $1,200 to stockholders (Dr. Landry).

Instructions

1. Record the December transactions, using the integrated financial statement framework as shown on the following page. The beginning balances of December 1 have already been entered. After each transaction, you should

enter a balance for each item. The transactions are recorded similarly to those for November. You should note that in transaction (g), the $4,200 of wages paid includes wages of $220 that were accrued at the end of November. Thus, only $3,980 ($4,200 − $220) should be recorded as wages expense for December. The remaining $220 reduces the wages payable. You should also note that the balance of retained earnings on December 1, $8,510, is the balance on November 30.

Statement of Cash Flows	Balance Sheet													Income Statement
	Assets						=	Liabilities			+	Stockholders' Equity		
	Cash +	Accts. Rec. +	Prepaid Insur. +	Supp. +	Office Equip. −	Acc. Dep. +	Land =	Notes Pay. +	Accts. Pay. +	Wages Pay. +	Unearned Revenue +	Capital Stock +	Retained Earnings	
Balances, Dec. 1	7,730	2,650	7,300	90	8,500	−160	12,000	16,800	140	220	1,440	11,000	8,510	

2. The adjustment data for December are as follows:

Deferred expenses:

1. Prepaid insurance expired, $1,100.
2. Supplies used, $275.
3. Depreciation on office equipment, $160.

Deferred revenues:

4. Unearned revenue earned, $360.

Accrued expense:

5. Wages owed employees but not paid, $340.

Accrued revenue:

6. Services provided but not billed to insurance companies, $1,050.

Enter the adjustments in the integrated financial statement framework. Identify each adjustment by "a" and the number of the related adjustment item. For example, the adjustment for prepaid insurance should be identified as (a1).

3. Prepare the December financial statements, including the income statement, retained earnings statement, balance sheet, and statement of cash flows.

4. (Appendix) Reconcile the December net income with the net cash flows from operations. (*Note:* In computing increases and decreases in amounts, use adjusted balances.)

Solution

1 and 2. Family Health Care summary of transactions and adjustments for December:

Statement of Cash Flows	Cash +	Accts. Rec. +	Prepaid Insur. +	Supp. +	Office Equip. −	Acc. Dep. +	Land =	Notes Pay. +	Accts. Pay. +	Wages Pay. +	Unearned Revenue +	Capital Stock +	Retained Earnings	Income Statement
Balances, Dec. 1	7,730	2,650	7,300	90	8,500	−160	12,000	16,800	140	220	1,440	11,000	8,510	
a. Collected cash	1,900	−1,900												
Balances	9,630	750	7,300	90	8,500	−160	12,000	16,800	140	220	1,440	11,000	8,510	
b. Fees earned		10,800											10,800	b.
Balances	9,630	11,550	7,300	90	8,500	−160	12,000	16,800	140	220	1,440	11,000	19,310	
c. Fees earned	6,500												6,500	c.
Balances	16,130	11,550	7,300	90	8,500	−160	12,000	16,800	140	220	1,440	11,000	25,810	
d. Pur. supplies				400					400					
Balances	16,130	11,550	7,300	490	8,500	−160	12,000	16,800	540	220	1,440	11,000	25,810	
e. Collected cash	6,900	−6,900												
Balances	23,030	4,650	7,300	490	8,500	−160	12,000	16,800	540	220	1,440	11,000	25,810	
f. Paid accts. pay.	−310								−310					
Balances	22,720	4,650	7,300	490	8,500	−160	12,000	16,800	230	220	1,440	11,000	25,810	
g. Paid expenses	−6,230									−220			−6,010	g.
Balances	16,490	4,650	7,300	490	8,500	−160	12,000	16,800	230	0	1,440	11,000	19,800	
h. Paid dividends	−1,200												−1,200	
Balances	15,290	4,650	7,300	490	8,500	−160	12,000	16,800	230	0	1,440	11,000	18,600	
a1. Insurance exp.			−1,100										−1,100	a1.
Balances	15,290	4,650	6,200	490	8,500	−160	12,000	16,800	230	0	1,440	11,000	17,500	
a2. Supplies exp.				−275									−275	a2.
Balances	15,290	4,650	6,200	215	8,500	−160	12,000	16,800	230	0	1,440	11,000	17,225	
a3. Deprec. exp.						−160							−160	a3.
Balances	15,290	4,650	6,200	215	8,500	−320	12,000	16,800	230	0	1,440	11,000	17,065	
a4. Rental revenue											−360		360	a4.
Balances	15,290	4,650	6,200	215	8,500	−320	12,000	16,800	230	0	1,080	11,000	17,425	
a5. Wages exp.										340			−340	a5.
Balances	15,290	4,650	6,200	215	8,500	−320	12,000	16,800	230	340	1,080	11,000	17,085	
a6. Fees earned		1,050											1,050	a6.
Balances, Dec. 31	15,290	5,700	6,200	215	8,500	−320	12,000	16,800	230	340	1,080	11,000	18,135	

Statement of Cash Flows

a. Operating	1,900	
c. Operating	6,500	
e. Operating	6,900	
f. Operating	−310	
g. Operating	−6,230	
h. Financing	−1,200	
Net increase in cash	7,560	
Beginning cash bal.	7,730	
Ending cash bal.	15,290	

Income Statement

b.	Fees earned	10,800
c.	Fees earned	6,500
g.	Wages exp.	−3,980
	Rent exp.	−800
	Utilities exp.	−610
	Interest exp.	−100
	Misc. exp.	−520
a1.	Insur. exp.	−1,100
a2.	Supplies exp.	−275
a3.	Deprec. exp.	−160
a4.	Rental rev.	360
a5.	Wages exp.	−340
a6.	Fees earned	1,050
	Net income	10,825

3.

FAMILY HEALTH CARE, P.C.
Income Statement
For the Month Ended December 31, 2011

Fees earned		$18,350
Operating expenses:		
Wages expense	$4,320	
Insurance expense	1,100	
Rent expense	800	
Utilities expense	610	
Supplies expense	275	
Depreciation expense	160	
Interest expense	100	
Miscellaneous expense	520	
Total operating expenses		7,885
Operating income		$10,465
Other income:		
Rental revenue		360
Net income		$10,825

FAMILY HEALTH CARE, P.C.
Retained Earnings Statement
For the Month Ended December 31, 2011

Retained earnings, December 1, 2011		$ 8,510
Net income for December	$10,825	
Less dividends	1,200	9,625
Retained earnings, December 31, 2011		$18,135

FAMILY HEALTH CARE, P.C.
Statement of Cash Flows
For the Month Ended December 31, 2011

Cash flows from operating activities:	
Cash received from patients	$15,300
Deduct cash payments for expenses	(6,540)
Net cash flows from operating activities	$ 8,760
Cash flows from financing activities:	
Deduct cash dividends	(1,200)
Net increase in cash	$ 7,560
December 1, 2011 cash balance	7,730
December 31, 2011 cash balance	$15,290

FAMILY HEALTH CARE, P.C.
Balance Sheet
December 31, 2011

Assets

Current assets:			
Cash		$15,290	
Accounts receivable		5,700	
Prepaid insurance		6,200	
Supplies		215	
Total current assets			$27,405
Fixed assets:			
Office equipment	$8,500		
Less accumulated depreciation	320	$ 8,180	
Land		12,000	
Total fixed assets			20,180
Total assets			$47,585

Liabilities

Current liabilities:			
Accounts payable		$ 230	
Wages payable		340	
Notes payable		6,800	
Unearned revenue		1,080	
Total current liabilities			$ 8,450
Long-term liabilities:			
Notes payable			10,000
Total liabilities			$18,450

Stockholders' Equity

Capital stock		$11,000	
Retained earnings		18,135	
Total stockholders' equity			29,135
Total liabilities and stockholders' equity			$47,585

Appendix

4. December's reconciliation of net income with net cash flows from operations:

Net income		$10,825
Add:		
Depreciation expense	$ 160	
Increase in accounts payable	90	
Increase in wages payable	120	
Decrease in prepaid insurance	1,100	1,470
Deduct:		
Increase in accounts receivable	$(3,050)	
Increase in supplies	(125)	
Decrease in unearned revenue	(360)	(3,535)
Net cash flows from operating activities		$ 8,760

Self-Examination Questions *(Answers appear at the end of chapter)*

1. Assume that a lawyer bills her clients $15,000 on June 30, 2011, for services rendered during June. The lawyer collects $8,500 of the billings during July and the remainder in August. Under the accrual basis of accounting, when would the lawyer record the revenue for the fees?

   A. June, $15,000; July, $0; and August, $0
   B. June, $0; July, $6,500; and August, $8,500
   C. June, $8,500; July, $6,500; and August, $0
   D. June, $0; July, $8,500; and August, $6,500

2. On January 24, 2011, Niche Consulting collected $5,700 it had billed its clients for services rendered on December 31, 2010. How would you record the January 24 transaction, using the accrual basis?

   A. Increase Cash, $5,700; decrease Fees Earned, $5,700
   B. Increase Accounts Receivable, $5,700; increase Fees Earned, $5,700
   C. Increase Cash, $5,700; decrease Accounts Receivable, $5,700
   D. Increase Cash, $5,700; increase Fees Earned, $5,700

3. Which of the following items represents a deferral?

   A. Prepaid insurance
   B. Wages payable
   C. Fees earned
   D. Accumulated depreciation

4. If the supplies account indicated a balance of $2,250 before adjustment on May 31 and supplies on hand at May 31 totaled $950, the adjustment would be:

   A. increase Supplies, $950; decrease Supplies Expense, $950.
   B. increase Supplies, $1,300; decrease Supplies Expense, $1,300.
   C. increase Supplies Expense, $950; decrease Supplies, $950.
   D. increase Supplies Expense, $1,300; decrease Supplies, $1,300.

5. The balance in the unearned rent account for Jones Co. as of December 31 is $1,200. If Jones Co. failed to record the adjusting entry for $600 of rent earned during December, the effect on the balance sheet and income statement for December would be:

   A. assets understated by $600; net income overstated by $600
   B. liabilities understated by $600; net income understated by $600
   C. liabilities overstated by $600; net income understated by $600
   D. liabilities overstated by $600; net income overstated by $600

Class Discussion Questions

1. Would *Google* and *Wal-Mart* use the cash basis or the accrual basis of accounting? Explain.

2. How are revenues and expenses reported on the income statement under (a) the cash basis of accounting and (b) the accrual basis of accounting?

3. Fees for services provided are billed to a customer during 2010. The customer remits the amount owed in 2011. During which year would the revenues be reported on the income statement under (a) the cash basis? (b) the accrual basis?

4. Employees performed services in 2010, but the wages were not paid until 2011. During which year would the wages expense be reported on the income statement under (a) the cash basis? (b) the accrual basis?

5. Which of the following accounts would appear only in an accrual basis accounting system, and which could appear in either a cash basis or an accrual basis accounting system? (a) Capital Stock, (b) Fees Earned, (c) Accounts Payable, (d) Land, (e) Utilities Expense, and (f) Accounts Receivable.

6. Is the land balance before the accounts have been adjusted the amount that should normally be reported on the balance sheet? Explain.

7. Is the supplies balance before the accounts have been adjusted the amount that should normally be reported on the balance sheet? Explain.

8. Why are adjustments needed at the end of an accounting period?

9. Identify the four different categories of adjustments frequently required at the end of an accounting period.

10. If the effect of an adjustment is to increase the balance of a liability account, which of the following statements describes the effect of the adjustment on the other account?

 a. Increases the balance of a revenue account

 b. Increases the balance of an expense account

 c. Increases the balance of an asset account

11. If the effect of an adjustment is to increase the balance of an asset account, which of the following statements describes the effect of the adjustment on the other account?

 a. Increases the balance of a revenue account

 b. Increases the balance of a liability account

 c. Increases the balance of an expense account

12. Does every adjustment have an effect on determining the amount of net income for a period? Explain.

13. (a) Explain the purpose of the two accounts: Depreciation Expense and Accumulated Depreciation. (b) Is it customary for the balances of the two accounts to be equal? (c) In what financial statements, if any, will each account appear?

14. Describe the nature of the assets that compose the following sections of a balance sheet: (a) current assets, (b) property, plant, and equipment.

Exercises

E3-1

Transactions using accrual accounting

Obj 2

Luv Care is owned and operated by Debbie Gonalez, the sole stockholder. During May 2011, Luv Care entered into the following transactions:

 a. Debbie Gonalez invested $20,000 in Luv Care in exchange for capital stock.

 b. Paid $7,200 on May 1 for an insurance premium on a 1-year policy.

 c. Purchased supplies on account, $1,200.

 d. Received fees of $32,500 during May.

 e. Paid expenses as follows: wages, $8,000; rent, $2,500; utilities, $1,000; and miscellaneous, $850.

 f. Paid dividends of $3,000.

Record the preceding transactions using the integrated financial statement framework. After each transaction, you should enter a balance for each item.

E3-2

Adjustment process

Obj 3

SPREADSHEET

Using the data from Exercise 3-1, record the adjusting entries at the end of May to record the insurance expense and supplies expense. There were $650 of supplies on hand as of May 31. Identify the adjusting entry for insurance as (a1) and supplies as (a2).

E3-3

Financial statements

Obj 4

SPREADSHEET

✓ Net income, $19,000

Using the data from Exercises 3-1 and 3-2, prepare financial statements for May, including income statement, retained earnings statement, balance sheet, and statement of cash flows.

E3-4

Reconcile net income and net cash flows from operations.

Appendix

Using the income statement and statement of cash flows you prepared in Exercise 3-3, reconcile net income with the net cash flows from operations.

E3-5

Accrual basis of accounting

Obj 2

Merlin Forsyth established Avalon Services, P.C., a professional corporation, on August 1 of the current year. Avalon Services offers financial planning advice to its clients. The effect of each transaction on the balance sheet and the balances after each transaction for August are as follows. Each increase or decrease in stockholders' equity, except transaction (h), affects net income.

Statement of Cash Flows	Balance Sheet							Income Statement
	Assets			=	Liabilities	+	Stockholders' Equity	
	Cash	+ Accounts Receivable	+ Supplies	=	Accounts Payable	+ Capital Stock	+ Retained Earnings	
a.	+20,000					+20,000		
b.			+1,500		+1,500			
Bal.	20,000		1,500		1,500	20,000		
c.	−1,000				−1,000			
Bal.	19,000		1,500		500	20,000		
d.	+22,000						+22,000	d.
Bal.	41,000		1,500		500	20,000	22,000	
e.	−13,000						−13,000	e.
Bal.	28,000		1,500		500	20,000	9,000	
f.			−1,100				−1,100	f.
Bal.	28,000		400		500	20,000	7,900	
g.		+3,100					+3,100	g.
Bal.	28,000	3,100	400		500	20,000	11,000	
h.	−2,000						−2,000	
Bal.	26,000	3,100	400		500	20,000	9,000	

Statement of Cash Flows

a. Financing	20,000	
c. Operating	−1,000	
d. Operating	22,000	
e. Operating	−13,000	
h. Financing	−2,000	
	26,000	

Income Statement

d. Fees earned	22,000	
e. Expenses	−13,000	
f. Expenses	−1,100	
g. Fees earned	3,100	
	11,000	

a. Describe each transaction.

b. What is the amount of the net income for August?

E3-6

Classify accruals and deferrals

Obj 3

Classify the following items as (a) deferred expense (prepaid expense), (b) deferred revenue (unearned revenue), (c) accrued expense (accrued liability), or (d) accrued revenue (accrued asset).

1. Subscriptions received in advance by a magazine publisher.
2. A 2-year premium paid on a fire insurance policy.
3. Fees received but not yet earned.
4. Fees earned but not yet received.
5. Utilities owed but not yet paid.
6. Supplies on hand.
7. Salary owed but not yet paid.
8. Taxes owed but payable in the following period.

E3-7

Classify adjustments

Obj 3

The following accounts were taken from the unadjusted trial balance of Inter Circle Co., a congressional lobbying firm. Indicate whether or not each account would normally require an adjusting entry. If the account normally requires an adjusting entry, use the following notation to indicate the type of adjustment:

AE—Accrued Expense
AR—Accrued Revenue
DR—Deferred Revenue
DE—Deferred Expense

To illustrate, the answer for the first account is as follows.

Account	Answer
Accounts Receivable	Normally requires adjustment (AR).
Accumulated Depreciation	
Capital Stock	
Dividends	
Interest Payable	
Interest Receivable	
Land	
Office Equipment	
Prepaid Rent	
Supplies	
Unearned Fees	
Wages Expense	

E3-8

Adjustment for supplies

Obj 3

✓ a. $2,250

Answer each of the following independent questions concerning supplies and the adjustment for supplies. (a) The balance in the supplies account, before adjustment at the end of the year, is $3,175. What is the amount of the adjustment if the amount of supplies on hand at the end of the year is $925? (b) The supplies account has a balance of $600, and the supplies expense account has a balance of $1,850 at December 31, 2011. If 2011 was the first year of operations, what was the amount of supplies purchased during the year?

E3-9

Adjustment for prepaid insurance

Obj 3

The prepaid insurance account had a balance of $10,800 at the beginning of the year. The account was increased for $7,200 for premiums on policies purchased during the year. What is the adjustment required at the end of the year for each of the following independent situations: (a) the amount of unexpired insurance applicable to future periods is $8,000, (b) the amount of insurance expired during the year is $12,675? For (a) and (b), indicate each account affected, whether the account is increased or decreased, and the amount of the increase or decrease.

E3-10

Adjustment for unearned fees

Obj 3

The balance in the unearned fees account, before adjustment at the end of the year, is $27,300. What is the adjustment if the amount of unearned fees at the end of the year is $14,650? Indicate each account affected, whether the account is increased or decreased, and the amount of the increase or decrease.

E3-11

Adjustment for unearned revenue

Obj 3

For the year ending June 30, 2008, *Microsoft Corporation* reported short-term unearned revenue of $13,397 million. For the year ending June 30, 2008, Microsoft also reported total revenues of $60,420 million. (a) Assuming that

Microsoft recognized $3,000 million of unearned revenue as revenue during the year, what entry for unearned revenue did Microsoft make during the year? Indicate each account affected, whether the account is increased or decreased, and the amount of the increase or decrease. (b) What percentage of total revenues is the short-term unearned revenue as of June 30, 2008? Round to one decimal place.

E3-12

Effect of omitting adjustment

Obj 3

At the end of February, the first month of the business year, the usual adjustment transferring rent earned to a revenue account from the unearned rent account was omitted. Indicate which items will be incorrectly stated, because of the error, on (a) the income statement for February and (b) the balance sheet as of February 28. Also indicate whether the items in error will be overstated or understated.

E3-13

Adjustment for accrued salaries

Obj 3

Oceanside Realty Co. pays weekly salaries of $3,700 on Friday for a five-day week ending on that day. What is the adjustment at the end of the accounting period, assuming that the period ends (a) on Wednesday, (b) on Thursday? Indicate each account affected, whether the account is increased or decreased, and the amount of the increase or decrease.

E3-14

Determine wages paid

Obj 3

The balances of the two wages accounts at December 31, after adjustments at the end of the first year of operations, are Wages Payable, $3,175, and Wages Expense, $93,800. Determine the amount of wages paid during the year.

E3-15

Effect of omitting adjustment

Obj 3

Accrued salaries of $4,950 owed to employees for December 30 and 31 are not considered in preparing the financial statements for the year ended December 31, 2010. Indicate which items will be erroneously stated, because of the error, on (a) the income statement for December 2010 and (b) the balance sheet as of December 31, 2010. Also indicate whether the items in error will be overstated or understated.

E3-16

Effect of omitting adjustment

Obj 3

Assume that the error in Exercise 3-15 was not corrected and that the $4,950 of accrued salaries was included in the first salary payment in January 2011. Indicate which items will be erroneously stated, because of failure to correct the initial error, on (a) the income statement for January 2011 and (b) the balance sheet as of January 31, 2011.

E3-17

Effects of errors on financial statements

Obj 3

For a recent year, the balance sheet for *The Campbell Soup Company* includes accrued expenses of $1,022,000,000. The income before taxes for The Campbell Soup Company for the year was $1,001,000,000.

a. Assume the accruals apply to the current year and were not recorded at the end of the year. By how much would income before taxes have been misstated?

b. What is the percentage of the misstatement in (a) to the reported income of $1,001,000,000? Round to one decimal place.

E3-18

Effects of errors on financial statements

Obj 3

✓ 1. a. Revenue understated, $21,950

The accountant for Mystic Medical Co., a medical services consulting firm, mistakenly omitted adjusting entries for (a) unearned revenue earned during the year ($21,950) and (b) accrued wages ($6,100). Indicate the effect of each error, considered individually, on the income statement for the current year ended July 31. Also indicate the effect of each error on the July 31 balance sheet. Set up a table similar to the following, and record your answers by inserting the dollar amount in the appropriate spaces. Insert a zero if the error does not affect the item.

	Error (a)		Error (b)	
	Over-stated	Under-stated	Over-stated	Under-stated
1. Revenue for the year would be	$__	$__	$__	$__
2. Expenses for the year would be	$__	$__	$__	$__
3. Net income for the year would be	$__	$__	$__	$__
4. Assets at July 31 would be	$__	$__	$__	$__
5. Liabilities at July 31 would be	$__	$__	$__	$__
6. Stockholders' equity at July 31 would be	$__	$__	$__	$__

E3-19

Effects of errors on financial statements

Obj 3

If the net income for the current year had been $424,300 in Exercise 3–18, what would have been the correct net income if the proper adjustments had been made?

E3-20

Adjustment for accrued fees

Obj 3

At the end of the current year, $41,980 of fees have been earned but have not been billed to clients.

a. What is the adjustment to record the accrued fees? Indicate each account affected, whether the account is increased or decreased, and the amount of the increase or decrease.

b. If the cash basis rather than the accrual basis had been used, would an adjustment have been necessary? Explain.

E3-21

Adjustments for unearned and accrued fees

Obj 3

The balance in the unearned fees account, before adjustment at the end of the year, is $110,000. Of these fees, $85,000 have been earned. In addition, $19,200 of fees have been earned but have not been billed. What are the adjustments (a) to adjust the unearned fees account and (b) to record the accrued fees? Indicate each account affected, whether the account is increased or decreased, and the amount of the increase or decrease.

E3-22

Effect on financial statements of omitting adjustment

Obj 3

The adjustment for accrued fees was omitted at March 31, the end of the current year. Indicate which items will be in error, because of the omission, on (a) the income statement for the current year and (b) the balance sheet as of March 31. Also indicate whether the items in error will be overstated or understated.

E3-23

Adjustment for depreciation

Obj 3

The estimated amount of depreciation on equipment for the current year is $12,700. (a) How is the adjustment recorded? Indicate each account affected, whether the account is increased or decreased, and the amount of the increase or decrease. (b) If the adjustment in (a) was omitted, which items would be

erroneously stated on (1) the income statement for the year and (2) the balance sheet as of December 31?

E3-24

Adjustments

Obj 3

Silverado Company is a consulting firm specializing in pollution control. The following adjustments were made for Silverado Company:

Account	Adjustments Increase (Decrease)
Accounts Receivable	$ 8,400
Supplies	(2,100)
Prepaid Insurance	(1,800)
Accumulated Depreciation—Equipment	1,500
Wages Payable	4,500
Unearned Rent	(3,000)
Fees Earned	8,400
Wages Expense	4,500
Supplies Expense	2,100
Rent Revenue	3,000
Insurance Expense	1,800
Depreciation Expense	1,500

Identify each of the six pairs of adjustments. For each adjustment, indicate the account, whether the account is increased or decreased, and the amount of the adjustment. No account is affected by more than one adjustment. Use the following format. The first adjustment is shown as an example.

Adjustment	Account	Increase or Decrease	Amount
1.	Accounts Receivable	Increase	$8,400
	Fees Earned	Increase	8,400

E3-25

Book value of fixed assets

Obj 4

For a recent year, **Barnes & Noble Inc.** reported *Property, Plant, and Equipment* of $2,400,685,000 and *Accumulated Depreciation* of $1,576,052,000.

a. What was the book value of the fixed assets?
b. Would the book values of Barnes & Noble's fixed assets normally approximate their fair market values?

E3-26

Classify assets

Obj 4

Identify each of the following as (a) a current asset or (b) property, plant, and equipment:

1. Accounts Receivable
2. Building
3. Cash
4. Office Equipment
5. Prepaid Insurance
6. Supplies

E3-27

Balance sheet classification

Obj 4

At the balance sheet date, a business owes a mortgage note payable of $350,000, the terms of which provide for monthly payments of $7,000. Explain how the liability should be classified on the balance sheet.

E3-28

Classified balance sheet

Obj 4

✓ Total assets, $182,000

Rehab Health Co. offers personal weight reduction consulting services to individuals. On June 30, 2010, the balances of selected accounts of Rehab Health Co. are as follows:

Accounts Payable	$ 15,200	Prepaid Insurance	$ 11,600
Accounts Receivable	35,000	Prepaid Rent	7,200
Accum. Depreciation—Equipment	33,600	Retained Earnings	112,000
Capital Stock	50,000	Salaries Payable	2,800
Cash	?	Supplies	3,000
Equipment	130,000	Unearned Fees	2,000

Prepare a classified balance sheet that includes the correct balance for Cash.

E3-29

Classified balance sheet

Obj 4

✓ Total assets, $768,870

La-Z-Boy Inc. is one of the world's largest manufacturers of furniture and is best known for its reclining chairs. The following data (in thousands) were adapted from the 2008 annual report of La-Z-Boy Inc.:

Accounts payable	$ 56,421
Accounts receivable	200,422
Accrued expenses	102,700
Accumulated depreciation	267,583
Capital stock	260,816
Cash	14,982
Intangible assets	56,239
Inventories	178,361
Debt due within one year	4,792
Long-term debt	99,578
Other current assets	33,723
Other long-term assets	114,142
Other long-term liabilities	54,783
Property, plant, and equipment	438,584
Retained earnings	189,780

Prepare a classified balance sheet as of April 26, 2008.

E3-30

Balance sheet

Obj 4

List the errors you find in the following balance sheet. Prepare a corrected balance sheet.

VINEYARD SERVICES CO. Balance Sheet For the Year Ended October 31, 2010		
Assets		
Current assets:		
Cash	$ 12,000	
Accounts payable	27,900	
Supplies	4,800	
Prepaid insurance	14,400	
Land	270,000	
Total current assets		$ 329,100
Property, plant, and equipment:		
Building	$ 225,000	
Equipment	90,000	
Total property, plant, and equipment		315,000
Total assets		$ 644,100

(Continued)

Liabilities		
Current liabilities:		
Accounts receivable	$ 40,800	
Accumulated depreciation—building	54,600	
Accumulated depreciation—equipment	32,400	
Net loss	22,500	
Total liabilities		$ 150,300
Stockholders' Equity		
Wages payable	$ 8,100	
Capital stock	90,000	
Retained earnings	444,000	
Total stockholders' equity		542,100
Total liabilities and stockholders' equity		$ 644,100

Problems

P3-1

Accrual basis accounting

Obj 2

SPREADSHEET

Espresso Health Care Inc. is owned and operated by Dr. Merri Eversole, the sole stockholder. During July 2011, Espresso Health Care entered into the following transactions:

July 1 Received $18,000 from Bradshaw Company as rent for the use of a vacant office in Espresso Health Care's building. Bradshaw paid the rent six months in advance.

1 Paid $4,200 for an insurance premium on a general business policy.

6 Purchased supplies of $1,800 on account.

9 Collected $17,500 for services provided to customers on account.

11 Paid creditors $3,000 on account.

18 Invested an additional $50,000 in the business in exchange for capital stock.

20 Billed patients $49,000 for services provided on account.

25 Received $12,900 for services provided to customers who paid cash.

30 Paid expenses as follows: wages, $24,000; utilities, $6,000; rent on medical equipment, $5,000; interest, $200; and miscellaneous, $2,500.

30 Paid dividends of $10,000 to stockholders (Dr. Eversole).

Instructions

Analyze and record the July transactions for Espresso Health Care Inc., using the integrated financial statement framework. Record each transaction by date and show the balance for each item after each transaction. The July 1, 2011, balances for the balance sheet are shown below.

			Assets					=	Liabilities			+	Stockholders' Equity	
	Cash	Accts. Rec.	Pre. Ins.	Supp.	Building	Acc. Dep.	Land	=	Accts. Pay.	Un. Rev.	Wages Pay.	Notes Pay.	Capital Stock	Ret. Earn.
Bal., July 1st	20,000	24,500	700	1,000	150,000	−11,200	120,000		7,500	0	0	30,000	40,000	227,500

P3-2

Adjustment process

Obj 3

SPREADSHEET

Adjustment data for Espresso Health Care Inc. for July are as follows:

1. Insurance expired, $800.
2. Supplies on hand on July 31, $1,100.

3. Depreciation on building, $2,000.
4. Unearned rent revenue earned, $3,000.
5. Wages owed employees but not paid, $1,700.
6. Services provided but not billed to patients, $9,000.

Instructions

Based upon the transactions recorded in July for Problem 3-1, record the adjustments for July using the integrated financial statement framework.

P3-3

Financial statements

Obj 4

SPREADSHEET

✓ 1. Net income, $30,000

Data for Espresso Health Care for July are provided in Problems 3-1 and 3-2.

Instructions

Prepare an income statement, retained earnings statement, and a classified balance sheet for July. The notes payable is due in 2015.

P3-4

Statement of cash flows

Obj 4

SPREADSHEET

✓ Net cash flows from operating activities, 3,500

Data for Espresso Health Care for July are provided in Problems 3-1, 3-2, and 3-3.

Instructions

1. Prepare a statement of cash flows for July.
2. Reconcile the net cash flows from operating activities with the net income for July. (*Hint:* See the appendix to this chapter and use adjusted balances in computing increases and decreases in accounts.)

P3-5

Adjustments and errors

Obj 3

SPREADSHEET

✓ Corrected net income, $135,375

At the end of July, the first month of operations, the following selected data were taken from the financial statements of Monita Forche, Attorney at Law, P.C.:

Net income for July	$135,800
Total assets at July 31	750,000
Total liabilities at July 31	250,000
Total stockholders' equity at July 31	500,000

In preparing the financial statements, adjustments for the following data were overlooked:

a. Unbilled fees earned at July 31, $6,700
b. Depreciation of equipment for July, $3,000
c. Accrued wages at July 31, $2,150
d. Supplies used during July, $1,975

Instructions

Determine the correct amount of net income for July and the total assets, liabilities, and stockholders' equity at July 31. In addition to indicating the corrected amounts, indicate the effect of each omitted adjustment by setting up and completing a columnar table similar to the one shown at the top of the following page. Adjustment (a) is presented as an example.

	Net Income	Total Assets	=	Total Liabilities	+	Total Stockholders' Equity
Reported amounts	$135,800	$750,000		$250,000		$500,000
Corrections:						
Adjustment (a)	+6,700	+6,700		0		+6,700
Adjustment (b)	_____	_____		_____		_____
Adjustment (c)	_____	_____		_____		_____
Adjustment (d)	_____	_____		_____		_____
Corrected amounts	=====	=====		=====		=====

P3-6

Adjustment process and financial statements

Objs 3, 4

SPREADSHEET

✓ 2. Net income, $122,600

Adjustment data for Magnum Therapeutics Inc. for the year ended May 31, 2011, are as follows:

a. Wages accrued but not paid at May 31, $1,800
b. Depreciation of equipment during the year, $12,500
c. Laundry supplies on hand at May 31, $1,900
d. Insurance premiums expired, $5,500

Instructions

1. Using the following integrated financial statement framework, record each adjustment to the appropriate accounts, identifying each adjustment by its letter. After all adjustments are recorded, determine the balances.

Statement of Cash Flows	Balance Sheet									Income Statement
	Assets					= Liabilities	+ Stockholders' Equity			
	Cash +	Laundry Supplies +	Prepaid Insurance +	Laundry Equip. −	Acc. Deprec. =	Accts. Payable +	Wages Payable +	Capital Stock +	Retained Earnings	
Balances, May 31, 2011	48,000	9,000	6,000	250,000	−60,000	7,000	0	50,000	196,000	

Statement of Cash Flows	
Operating (Revenues)	315,000
Financing (Capital Stock)	25,000
Operating (Expenses)	−220,000
Investing (Equipment)	−80,000
Financing (Dividends)	−5,000
Net increase in cash	35,000
Beginning cash balance, June 1, 2010	13,000
Ending cash balance, May 31, 2011	$48,000

Income Statement	
Laundry revenue	315,000
Wages expense	−110,000
Rent expense	−30,000
Utilities expense	−18,000
Misc. expense	−7,500

2. Prepare an income statement and retained earnings statement for the year ended May 31, 2011. The retained earnings balance as of June 1, 2010, was $51,500.

3. Prepare a classified balance sheet as of May 31, 2011.

4. Prepare a statement of cash flows for the year ended May 31, 2011.

Activities

A3-1

Accrued revenue

The following is an excerpt from a conversation between Joel Loomis and Krista Truitt just before they boarded a flight to Paris on *Delta Air Lines.* They are going to Paris to attend their company's annual sales conference.

Joel: Krista, aren't you taking an introductory accounting course at college?

Krista: Yes, I decided it's about time I learned something about accounting. You know, our annual bonuses are based on the sales figures that come from the accounting department.

Joel: I guess I never really thought about it.

Krista: You should think about it! Last year, I placed a $750,000 order on December 28. But when I got my bonus, the $750,000 sale wasn't included. They said it hadn't been shipped until January 3, so it would have to count in next year's bonus.

Joel: A real bummer!

Krista: Right! I was counting on that bonus including the $750,000 sale,

Joel: Did you complain?

Krista: Yes, but it didn't do any good. Ashley, the head accountant, said something about matching revenues and expenses. Also, something about not recording revenues until the sale is final. I figured I'd take the accounting course and find out whether she's just jerking me around.

Joel: I never really thought about it. When do you think Delta Air Lines will record its revenues from this flight?

Krista: Hmmm ... I guess it could record the revenue when it sells the ticket ... or ... when the boarding passes are taken at the door ... or ... when we get off the plane ... or when our company pays for the tickets ... or ... i don't know. I'll ask my accounting instructor.

Discuss when Delta Air Lines should recognize the revenue from ticket sales to properly match revenues and expenses.

A3-2

Adjustments for financial statements

Several years ago, your brother opened Niagara Appliance Repairs. He made a small initial investment and added money from his personal bank account as needed. He withdrew money for living expenses at irregular intervals. As the business grew, he hired an assistant. He is now considering adding more employees, purchasing additional service trucks, and purchasing the building he now rents. To secure funds for the expansion, your brother submitted a loan application to the bank and included the most recent financial statements (shown below) prepared from accounts maintained by a part-time bookkeeper.

NIAGARA APPLIANCE REPAIRS
Income Statement
For the Year Ended October 31, 2010

Service revenue		$112,500
Less: Rent paid	$31,200	
Wages paid	24,750	
Supplies paid	7,000	
Utilities paid	6,500	
Insurance paid	3,600	
Miscellaneous payments	9,100	82,150
Net income		$ 30,350

NIAGARA APPLIANCE REPAIRS
Balance Sheet
October 31, 2010

Assets

Cash	$15,900
Amounts due from customers	18,750
Truck	55,350
Total assets	$90,000

Equities

Owner's equity	$90,000

After reviewing the financial statements, the loan officer at the bank asked your brother if he used the accrual basis of accounting for revenues and expenses. Your brother responded that he did and that is why he included an account for "Amounts Due from Customers." The loan officer then asked whether or not the accounts were adjusted prior to the preparation of the statements. Your brother answered that they had not been adjusted.

a. Why do you think the loan officer suspected that the accounts had not been adjusted prior to the preparation of the statements?
b. Indicate possible accounts that might need to be adjusted before an accurate set of financial statements could be prepared.

A3-3

Business emphasis

GROUP

Assume that you and two friends are debating whether to open an automotive and service retail chain that will be called Auto-Mart. Initially, Auto-Mart will open three stores locally, but the business plan anticipates going nationwide within five years.

Currently, you and your future business partners are debating whether to focus Auto-Mart on a "do-it-yourself" or "do-it-for-me" business. A do-it-yourself business emphasizes the sale of retail auto parts that customers will use themselves to repair and service their cars. A do-it-for me business emphasizes the offering of maintenance and service for customers.

1. In groups of three or four, discuss whether to implement a do-it-yourself or do-it-for-me business emphasis. List the advantages of each emphasis and arrive at a conclusion as to which emphasis to implement.
2. Provide examples of real-world businesses that use do-it-yourself or do-it-for-me business emphases.

A3-4

Cash basis income statement

The following operating data (in thousands) were adapted from the SEC 10-K filings of *Walgreen* and *CVS:*

	CVS		Walgreen	
	2008	**2007**	**2008**	**2007**
Accounts receivable	$5,819,500	$4,909,000	$2,527,000	$2,236,500
Accounts payable	9,792,500	8,634,100	5,487,000	5,100,900

1. Using the preceding data, adjust the operating income for CVS and Walgreen to an adjusted cash basis. For 2008, the operating income for CVS was $6,046,200 and for Walgreen's it was $3,441,000 (in thousands). (*Hint:* To convert to a cash basis, you need to compute the change in each accrual accounting item shown and then either add or subtract the change to determine the operating income.)
2. Compute the net difference between the operating income under the accrual and cash bases.
3. Express the net difference in (2) as a percent of operating income under the accrual basis.
4. Which company's operating income, CVS's or Walgreen's, is closer to the cash basis? Round to one decimal place.
5. Do you think most analysts focus on operating income or net income in assessing the long-term profitability of a company? Explain.

A3-5

Analysis of income and cash flows

The following data (in millions) were taken from http://finance.yahoo.com.

	2008	2007	2006
Company A			
Revenues	$ 19,166	$ 14,835	$10,711
Operating income	842	655	389
Net income	645	476	190
Net cash flows from operating activities	1,697	1,405	702
Net cash flows from investing activities	(1,199)	(42)	(333)
Net cash flows from financing activities	(198)	50	(400)
Total assets	8,314	6,485	4,363
Company B			
Revenues	$ 22,697	$ 19,154	$17,171
Operating income (loss)	(8,314)	1,096	58
Net income (loss)	(8,922)	1,612	(6,203)
Net cash flows from operating activities	(1,707)	1,359	993
Net cash flows from investing activities	1,598	(625)	(361)
Net cash flows from financing activities	1,716	(120)	(606)
Total assets	45,014	32,423	19,622
Company C			
Revenues	$ 31,948	$ 28,857	$24,088
Operating income	8,446	7,252	6,308
Net income	5,807	5,981	5,080
Net cash flows from operating activities	7,571	7,150	5,957
Net cash flows from investing activities	(2,363)	(503)	(1,700)
Net cash flows from financing activities	(3,985)	(6,719)	(6,583)
Total assets	40,519	43,269	29,963
Company D			
Revenues	$ 76,000	$ 70,235	$66,111
Operating income (loss)	2,451	2,301	2,236
Net income (loss)	1,249	1,181	1,115
Net cash flows from operating activities	2,896	2,581	2,351
Net cash flows from investing activities	(2,179)	(2,218)	(1,587)
Net cash flows from financing activities	(769)	(310)	(785)
Total assets	23,211	22,299	21,215

1. Match each of the following companies with the data for Company A, B, C, or D:

   Amazon.com

   Coca-Cola Inc.

   Delta Air Lines

   Kroger

2. Explain the logic underlying your matches.

Answers to Self-Examination Questions

1. **A** Under the accrual basis of accounting, revenues are recorded when the services are rendered. Since the services were rendered during June, all the fees should be recorded on June 30 (answer A). This is an example of accrued revenue. Under the cash basis of accounting, revenues are recorded when the cash is collected, not necessarily when the fees are earned. Thus, no revenue would be recorded in June, $8,500 of revenue would be recorded in July, and $6,500 of revenue would be recorded in August (answer D). Answers B and C are incorrect and are not used under either the accrual or cash bases.

2. **C** The collection of a $5,700 accounts receivable is recorded as an increase in Cash, $5,700, and a decrease in Accounts Receivable, $5,700 (answer C). The initial recording of the fees earned on account is recorded as an increase in Accounts Receivable and an increase in Fees Earned (answer B). Services rendered for cash are recorded as an increase in Cash and an increase in Fees Earned (answer D). Answer A is incorrect and would result in the accounting equation being out of

balance because total assets would exceed total liabilities and stockholders' equity by $11,400.

3. **A** A deferral is the delay in recording an expense already paid, such as prepaid insurance (answer A). Wages payable (answer B) is considered an accrued expense or accrued liability. Fees earned (answer C) is a revenue item. Accumulated depreciation (answer D) is a contra account to a fixed asset.

4. **D** The balance in the supplies account, before adjustment, represents the amount of supplies available during the period. From this amount ($2,250) is subtracted the amount of supplies on hand ($950) to determine the supplies used ($1,300). The used supplies is recorded as an increase in Supplies Expense, $1,300, and a decrease in Supplies, $1,300 (answer D).

5. **C** The failure to record the adjusting entry increasing Rent Revenue, $600, and decreasing Unearned Rent, $600, would have the effect of overstating liabilities by $600 and understating net income by $600 (answer C).

Accounting for Merchandising Businesses

4

Learning Objectives

After studying this chapter, you should be able to:

Obj 1 Distinguish the activities and financial statements of a service business from those of a merchandising business.

Obj 2 Describe and illustrate the financial statements of a merchandising business.

Obj 3 Describe the accounting for the sale of merchandise.

Obj 4 Describe the accounting for the purchase of merchandise.

Obj 5 Describe the accounting for freight and sales taxes.

Obj 6 Illustrate the dual nature of merchandising transactions.

Obj 7 Describe the accounting for merchandise shrinkage.

[handwritten notes:]

net sales = revenue − expenses

Gross profit = Net sales − COGS

T wenty years ago music was purchased at the "record store." No longer. Today, CDs can be purchased at retail stores such as **Best Buy, Borders, Wal-Mart,** and **Disc Exchange;** through online retailers, such as **CD Universe** and **CDNow;** and as individual MP3 downloads from services such as **Apple's** iTunes© and **Real's** Rhapsody©. The way goods (and services) are purchased has undergone significant changes and will continue to change with consumer tastes and technology. For example, an established retailer like **JCPenney** is faced with a rapidly changing competitive landscape with the emergence of (1) discount merchandising, (2) category killers, and (3) Internet retailing.

Wal-Mart, which led the development of discount merchandising, has become the world's largest retailer. Wal-Mart's growth is centered on providing the consumer with everyday discount pricing over a broad array of household products. Category killers include **Toys"R"Us** (toys), Best Buy (electronics), **Home Depot** (home improvement), and **Office Depot** (office supplies), which provide a wide selection of attractively priced goods within a particular product segment. Internet retailers, such as **Amazon.com** and **Lands' End** (now part of **Sears**), allow time-conscious consumers to shop quickly and effortlessly. JCPenney has had to adapt its retailing model in order to respond to all these changes.

Merchandising will undoubtedly continue to evolve as consumer lifestyles and technologies change in the future. In this chapter, the accounting issues unique to merchandisers are introduced. Merchandisers are emphasized because merchandising is significant in its own right, and because even nonmerchandisers have accounting issues similar to those discussed in this chapter.

[handwritten notes:]

Sales discounts = 2/10 or n/30

2% if paid in 10 days   no discount due in 30 days

Balance sheet
assets
liability
equity

Obj 1 Distinguish the activities and financial statements of a service business from those of a merchandising business.

Merchandise Operations

Prior chapters described and illustrated how businesses report their financial condition and changes in financial condition using the cash and accrual bases of accounting. Those chapters focused on service businesses. This chapter describes and illustrates the accounting for merchandise operations.[1]

The activities of a service business differ from those of a merchandising business. These differences are illustrated in the following condensed income statements:

Service Business		Merchandising Business	
Fees earned	$XXX	Sales	$XXX
Operating expenses	–XXX	Cost of merchandise sold	–XXX
Net income	$XXX	Gross profit	$XXX
		Operating expenses	–XXX
		Net income	$XXX

The revenue activities of a service business involve providing services to customers. On the income statement for a service business, the revenues from services are reported as *fees earned*. The operating expenses incurred in providing the services are subtracted from the fees earned to arrive at *net income*.

Revenue is the increase in assets from selling products & services.

The Operating Cycle

The operations of a merchandising business involve the purchase of merchandise for sale (purchasing), the sale of the products to customers (sales), and the receipt of cash from customers (collection). This overall process is referred to as the operating cycle. Thus, the operating cycle begins with spending cash, and it ends with receiving cash from customers. The operating cycle for a merchandising business is shown to the right. Operating cycles for retailers are usually shorter than for manufacturers because retailers purchase goods in a form ready for sale to the customer. Of course, some retailers will have shorter operating

cycles than others because of the nature of their products. For example, a jewelry store or an automobile dealer normally has a longer operating cycle than a consumer electronics store or a grocery store. Businesses with longer operating cycles normally have higher profit margins on their products than businesses with shorter operating cycles. For example, it is not unusual for jewelry stores to price their jewelry at 30%–50% above cost. In contrast, grocery stores operate on very small profit margins, often below 5%. Grocery stores make up the difference by selling their products more quickly.

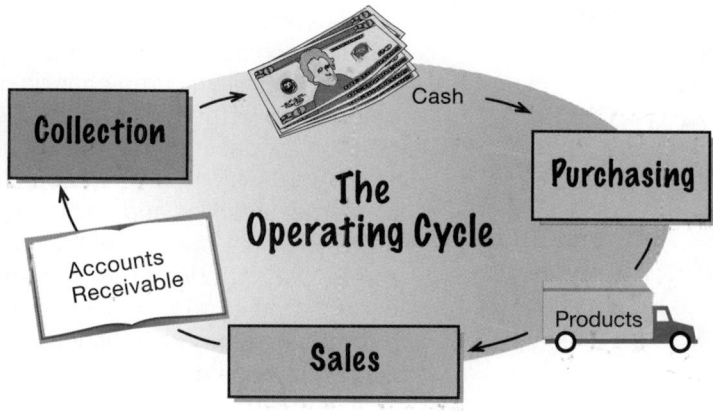

[1] The closing process, which is not illustrated, is similar to that for a service business, which is referenced in Chapter 3 , footnote 3 on page 103.

How Businesses Make Money

Under One Roof at JCPenney

Most businesses cannot be all things to all people. Businesses must seek a position in the marketplace to serve a unique customer need. Companies that are unable to do this can be squeezed out of the marketplace. The mall-based department store has been under pressure from both ends of the retail spectrum. At the discount store end of the market, **Wal-Mart** has been a formidable competitor. At the high end, specialty retailers have established strong presence in identifiable niches, such as electronics and apparel. Over a decade ago, **JCPenney** abandoned its "hard goods," such as electronics and sporting goods, in favor of providing "soft goods" because of the emerging strength of specialty retailers in the hard goods segments. JCPenney is positioning itself against these forces by *"exceeding the fashion, quality, selection, and service components of the discounter, equaling the merchandise intensity of the specialty store, and providing the selection and 'under one roof' shopping convenience of the department store."* JCPenney's merchandise emphasis is focused toward customers it terms the "modern spender" and "starting outs." It views these segments as most likely to value its higher-end merchandise offered under the convenience of "one roof."

In contrast, the revenue activities of a merchandising business involve the buying and selling of merchandise. A merchandising business first purchases merchandise to sell to its customers. When this merchandise is sold, the revenue is reported as sales, and its cost is recognized as an expense. This expense is called the **cost of merchandise sold**. The cost of merchandise sold is subtracted from sales to arrive at gross profit. This amount is called **gross profit** because it is the profit *before* deducting operating expenses.

Merchandise on hand (not sold) at the end of an accounting period is called **merchandise inventory**. Merchandise inventory is reported as a current asset on the balance sheet.

Financial Statements for a Merchandising Business

Obj 2 Describe and illustrate the financial statements of a merchandising business.

In this section, the financial statements for NetSolutions, a retailer of computer hardware and software, are illustrated. During 2010, Chris Clark organized NetSolutions with a business strategy of offering personalized service to individuals and small businesses who are upgrading or purchasing new computer systems. NetSolutions' personal service includes a no-obligation, on-site assessment of the customer's computer needs. By providing personalized service and follow-up, Chris feels that NetSolutions can compete effectively against such retailers as **Best Buy** and **Office Depot, Inc.**

Multiple-Step Income Statement

The 2011 income statement for NetSolutions is shown in Exhibit 1. This form of income statement, called a **multiple-step income statement**, contains several sections, subsections, and subtotals.

EXHIBIT 1 | Multiple-Step Income Statement

NET SOLUTIONS
Income Statement
For the Year Ended December 31, 2011

Revenue from sales:			
Sales		$720,185	
Less: Sales returns and allowances	$ 6,140		
Sales discounts	5,790	11,930	
Net sales			$708,255
Cost of merchandise sold			525,305
Gross profit			$182,950
Operating expenses:			
Selling expenses:			
Sales salaries expense	$53,430		
Advertising expense	10,860		
Depreciation expense--store equipment	3,100		
Delivery expense	2,800		
Miscellaneous selling expense.	630		
Total selling expenses		$ 70,820	
Administrative expenses:			
Office salaries expense	$21,020		
Rent expense	8,100		
Depreciation expense--office equipment	2,490		
Insurance expense	1,910		
Office supplies expense	610		
Misc. administrative expense	760		
Total administrative expenses		34,890	
Total operating expenses			105,710
Income from operations			$ 77,240
Other income and expense:			
Rent revenue		$ 600	
Interest expense		(2,440)	(1,840)
Net income			$ 75,400

[Handwritten margin note: The two sides of the accounting equation are always equal. –True]

Revenue from Sales

This section of the multiple-step income statement consists of sales, sales returns and allowances, sales discounts, and net sales. This section, as shown in Exhibit 1, is as follows:

Revenue from sales:			
Sales		$720,185	
Less: Sales returns and allowances	$6,140		
Sales discounts	5,790	11,930	
Net sales			$708,255

Sales is the total amount charged customers for merchandise sold, including cash sales and sales on account. During 2011, NetSolutions sold merchandise of $720,185 for cash or on account.

Sales returns and allowances are granted by the seller to customers for damaged or defective merchandise. In such cases, the customer may either

return the merchandise or accept an allowance from the seller. NetSolutions reported $6,140 of sales returns and allowances during 2011.

Sales discounts are granted by the seller to customers for early payment of amounts owed. For example, a seller may offer a customer a 2% discount on a sale of $10,000 if the customer pays within 10 days. If the customer pays within the 10-day period, the seller receives cash of $9,800, and the buyer receives a discount of $200 ($10,000 × 2%). NetSolutions reported $5,790 of sales discounts during 2011.

Net sales is determined by subtracting sales returns and allowances and sales discounts from sales. As shown in Exhibit 1, NetSolutions reported $708,255 of net sales during 2011. Some companies report only net sales and report sales, sales returns and allowances, and sales discounts in notes to the financial statements.

Cost of Merchandise Sold

The cost of merchandise sold is the cost of the merchandise sold to customers. NetSolutions reported cost of merchandise sold of $525,305 during 2011. To illustrate how cost of merchandise sold is determined, data when NetSolutions began its merchandising operations on July 1, 2010 is used.

Purchases July 1–December 31, 2010	$340,000
Merchandise inventory on December 31, 2010	59,700

For many merchandising businesses, the cost of merchandise sold is usually the largest expense. For example, the approximate percentage of cost of merchandise sold to sales is 61% for *JCPenney* and 67% for *The Home Depot*.

Since NetSolutions had only $59,700 of merchandise left on December 31, 2010, it must have sold merchandise that cost $280,300 during 2010 as shown below.

Purchases	$340,000
Less merchandise inventory, December 31, 2010	59,700
Cost of merchandise sold	$280,300

To continue, assume the following 2011 data for NetSolutions:

Purchases of merchandise	$521,980
Purchases returns and allowances	9,100
Purchases discounts	2,525
Freight in on merchandise purchased	17,400

Sellers may grant a buyer sales returns and allowances for returned or damaged merchandise. From a buyer's perspective, such allowances are called **purchases returns and allowances**. Likewise, sellers may grant a buyer a sales discount for early payment of the amount owed. From a buyer's perspective, such discounts are called **purchases discounts**. Purchases

returns and allowances and purchases discounts are subtracted from purchases to arrive at **net purchases** as shown below for NetSolutions.

Purchases		$521,980
Less: Purchases returns and allowances	$9,100	
Purchases discounts	2,525	11,625
Net purchases		$510,355

Freight costs incurred in obtaining the merchandise increase the cost of the merchandise purchased. These costs are called **freight in**. Adding freight in to net purchases yields the **cost of merchandise purchased** as shown below for NetSolutions.

Net purchases	$510,355
Add freight in	17,400
Cost of merchandise purchased	$527,755

The beginning inventory is added to the cost of merchandise purchased to determine the **merchandise available for sale** for the period. The ending inventory of NetSolutions on December 31, 2010, $59,700, becomes the beginning (January 1, 2011) inventory for 2011. Thus, the merchandise available for sale for NetSolutions during 2011 is $587,455 as shown below.

Merchandise inventory, January 1, 2011	$ 59,700
Cost of merchandise purchased	527,755
Cost of merchandise available for sale	$587,455

The ending inventory is then subtracted from the merchandise available for sale to yield the cost of merchandise sold. Assuming the ending inventory on December 31, 2011, is $62,150, the cost of merchandise sold for NetSolutions is $525,305 as shown in Exhibit 1 and below.

Cost of merchandise available for sale	$587,455
Less merchandise inventory, December 31, 2011	62,150
Cost of merchandise sold	$525,305

In the preceding computation, merchandise inventory at the end of the period is subtracted from the merchandise available for sale to determine the cost of merchandise sold. The merchandise inventory at the end of the period is determined by taking a physical count of inventory on hand. This method of determining the cost of merchandise sold and the amount of merchandise on hand is called the **periodic inventory system**. Under the periodic inventory system, the inventory records do not show the amount available for sale or the amount sold during the period. Instead, the cost of merchandise sold is computed and reported as shown in Exhibit 2.

For a corporation, stockholders equity consists of: capital stock & Retained earnings.

EXHIBIT 2 | Cost of Merchandise Sold

Merchandise inventory, January 1, 2011			$ 59,700
Purchases		$521,980	
Less: Purchases returns and allowances	$9,100		
Purchases discounts	2,525	11,625	
Net purchases		$510,355	
Add freight in		17,400	
Cost of merchandise purchased			527,755
Merchandise available for sale			$587,455
Less merchandise inventory, December 31, 2011			62,150
Cost of merchandise sold			$525,305

Under the **perpetual inventory system** of accounting, each purchase and sale of merchandise is recorded in the inventory and the cost of merchandise sold accounts. As a result, the amounts of merchandise available for sale and sold are continuously (perpetually) updated in the inventory records. Because many retailers use computerized systems, the perpetual inventory system is widely used. For example, such systems may use bar codes, such as the one on the back of this textbook. An optical scanner reads the bar code to record merchandise purchased and sold.

Businesses using a perpetual inventory system report the cost of merchandise sold as a single line on the income statement. An example of such reporting is illustrated in Exhibit 1 for NetSolutions. Because of its wide use, the perpetual inventory system is used in the remainder of this chapter.

Retailers, such as **Best Buy**, **Sears Holding Corporation**, and **Wal-Mart**, and grocery store chains, such as **Winn-Dixie Stores, Inc.** and **Kroger**, use bar codes and optical scanners as part of their computerized inventory systems.

Gross Profit

Gross profit is computed by subtracting the cost of merchandise sold from net sales, as shown below.

Net sales	$708,255
Cost of merchandise sold	525,305
Gross profit	$182,950

As shown above and in Exhibit 1, NetSolutions has gross profit of $182,950 in 2011.

Income from Operations

Income from operations, sometimes called **operating income**, is determined by subtracting operating expenses from gross profit. Operating expenses are normally classified as either selling expenses or administrative expenses.

Selling expenses are incurred directly in the selling of merchandise. Examples of selling expenses include sales salaries, store supplies used, depreciation of store equipment, delivery expense, and advertising.

Administrative expenses, sometimes called **general expenses**, are incurred in the administration or general operations of the business. Examples of administrative expenses include office salaries, depreciation of office equipment, and office supplies used.

Each selling and administrative expense may be reported separately as shown in Exhibit 1. However, many companies report selling, administrative, and operating expenses as single line items as shown below for NetSolutions.

Gross profit		$182,950
Operating expenses:		
Selling expenses	$70,820	
Administrative expenses	34,890	
Total operating expenses		105,710
Income from operations		$ 77,240

Other Income and Expense

Other income and expense items are not related to the primary operations of the business. **Other income** is revenue from sources other than the primary operating activity of a business. Examples of other income include income from interest, rent, and gains resulting from the sale of fixed assets. **Other expense** is an expense that cannot be traced directly to the normal operations of the business. Examples of other expenses include interest expense and losses from disposing of fixed assets.

Other income and other expense are offset against each other on the income statement. If the total of other income exceeds the total of other expense, the difference is added to income from operations to determine net income. If the reverse is true, the difference is subtracted from income from operations. The other income and expense items of NetSolutions are reported as shown below and in Exhibit 1.

Income from operations		$77,240
Other income and expense:		
Rent revenue	$ 600	
Interest expense	(2,440)	(1,840)
Net income		$75,400

Single-Step Income Statement

An alternate form of income statement is the **single-step income statement**. As shown in Exhibit 3, the income statement for NetSolutions deducts the total of all expenses *in one step* from the total of all revenues.

The single-step form emphasizes total revenues and total expenses in determining net income. A criticism of the single-step form is that gross profit and income from operations are not reported.

Retained Earnings Statement

The retained earnings statement for NetSolutions is shown in Exhibit 4. This statement is prepared in the same manner as for a service business.

Balance Sheet

As discussed and illustrated in Chapters 1–3, the balance sheet may be presented in a downward sequence in three sections. This form of balance sheet is called the **report form.**[2] The report form of balance sheet for

[2] The balance sheet may be presented with assets on the left-hand side and liabilities and stockholders' equity on the right-hand side. This form of the balance sheet is called the **account form.**

EXHIBIT 3   Single-Step Income Statement

NETSOLUTIONS Income Statement For the Year Ended December 31, 2011		
Revenues:		
Net sales		$708,255
Rent revenue		600
Total revenues		$708,855
Expenses:		
Cost of merchandise sold	$525,305	
Selling expenses	70,820	
Administrative expenses	34,890	
Interest expense	2,440	
Total expenses		633,455
Net income		$ 75,400

Expenses are costs incurred in operating a business.

EXHIBIT 4   Retained Earnings Statement for Merchandising Business

NETSOLUTIONS Retained Earnings Statement For the Year Ended December 31, 2011		
Retained earnings, January 1, 2011		$128,800
Net income for the year	$75,400	
Less dividends	18,000	
Increase in retained earnings		57,400
Retained earnings, December 31, 2011		$186,200

a summary of changes in the earnings retained in the corp. for a specific period of time are - r/E statement

NetSolutions is shown in Exhibit 5. In Exhibit 5, merchandise inventory is reported as a current asset and the current portion of the note payable of $5,000 is reported as a current liability.

Statement of Cash Flows

The statement of cash flows for NetSolutions is shown in Exhibit 6 on page 137. It indicates that cash increased during 2011 by $11,450. This increase is generated from a positive cash flow from operating activities of $47,120, which is partially offset by negative cash flows from investing and financing activities of $12,670 and $23,000, respectively.

The net cash flows from operating activities is shown in Exhibit 6 using a method known as the **indirect method**. This method, which reconciles net income with net cash flows from operating activities, is widely used among publicly held corporations.[3] Note that the December 31, 2011 cash balance reported on the statement of cash flows agrees with the amount reported for cash on the December 31, 2011 balance sheet shown in Exhibit 5.

The integration of NetSolutions' financial statements is shown in Exhibit 7 on page 138.

---

[3] The preparation of the statement of cash flows using the indirect method is further discussed and illustrated in the appendix to this chapter.

EXHIBIT 5 Report Form of Balance Sheet

NETSOLUTIONS Balance Sheet December 31, 2011			
Assets			
Current assets:			
Cash		$ 52,950	
Accounts receivable		91,080	
Merchandise inventory		62,150	
Office supplies		480	
Prepaid insurance		2,650	
Total current assets			$209,310
Property, plant, and equipment:			
Land		$ 20,000	
Store equipment	$27,100		
Less accumulated depreciation	5,700	21,400	
Office equipment	$15,570		
Less accumulated depreciation	4,720	10,850	
Total property, plant, and equipment			52,250
Total assets			$261,560
Liabilities			
Current liabilities:			
Accounts payable		$ 22,420	
Note payable (current portion)		5,000	
Salaries payable		1,140	
Unearned rent		1,800	
Total current liabilities			$ 30,360
Long-term liabilities:			
Note payable (final payment due 2021)			20,000
Total liabilities			$ 50,360
Stockholders' Equity			
Capital stock		$ 25,000	
Retained earnings		186,200	
Total stockholders' equity			211,200
Total liabilities and stockholders' equity			$261,560

Obj 3 Describe the accounting for the sale of merchandise.

Sales Transactions

In the remainder of this chapter, transactions that affect the financial statements of a merchandising business are illustrated. These transactions affect the reporting of net sales, cost of merchandise sold, gross profit, and merchandise inventory.

Sales

A business may sell merchandise for cash. Cash sales are normally rung up (entered) on a cash register and recorded in the accounts by increasing cash and sales. Under the perpetual inventory system, the cost of merchandise sold and the reduction in merchandise inventory should also be recorded at the time of sale. In this way, the merchandise inventory account will indicate the amount of merchandise on hand (not sold). To illustrate, assume that on

EXHIBIT 6 Statement of Cash Flows for Merchandising Business

NETSOLUTIONS
Statement of Cash Flows
For the Year Ended December 31, 2011

Cash flows from operating activities:		
Net income		$ 75,400
Add: Depreciation expense—store equipment	$ 3,100	
Depreciation expense—office equipment	2,490	
Decrease in office supplies	120	
Decrease in prepaid insurance	350	
Increase in accounts payable	8,150	14,210
Deduct:		
Increase in accounts receivable	$(39,080)	
Increase in merchandise inventory	(2,450)	
Decrease in salaries payable	(360)	
Decrease in unearned rent	(600)	(42,490)
Net cash flows from operating activities		$ 47,120
Cash flows from investing activities:		
Purchase of store equipment	$ (7,100)	
Purchase of office equipment	(5,570)	
Net cash flows from investing activities		(12,670)
Cash flows from financing activities:		
Payment of note payable	$ (5,000)	
Payment of dividends	(18,000)	
Net cash flows from financing activities		(23,000)
Net increase in cash		$ 11,450
January 1, 2011 cash balance		41,500
December 31, 2011 cash balance		$ 52,950

January 3, NetSolutions sells merchandise for $1,800 that cost $1,200. The effect on the accounts and financial statements of these cash sales is as follows:

Statement of Cash Flows	Balance Sheet						Income Statement
	Assets		=	Liabilities	+	Stockholders' Equity	
	Cash	+	Merchandise Inventory =			Retained Earnings	
Jan. 3.	1,800		−1,200			600	Jan. 3.

Statement of Cash Flows		Income Statement	
Jan. 3. Operating	1,800	Jan. 3. Sales	1,800
		Cost of merch. sold	−1,200
		Net income	600

Sales made to customers using credit cards issued by banks, such as MasterCard or VISA, are treated as *cash sales*. The record of the sale is electronically sent to a clearinghouse for credit card transactions. The clearinghouse processes the sale by contacting the bank that issued the credit card. Within one or two days, the seller's bank account is increased by the amount of the sale.

Retailers are charged service fees for credit card sales. The seller records these service fees as increases to an expense account and decreases to Cash.

EXHIBIT 7   Integrated Financial Statements

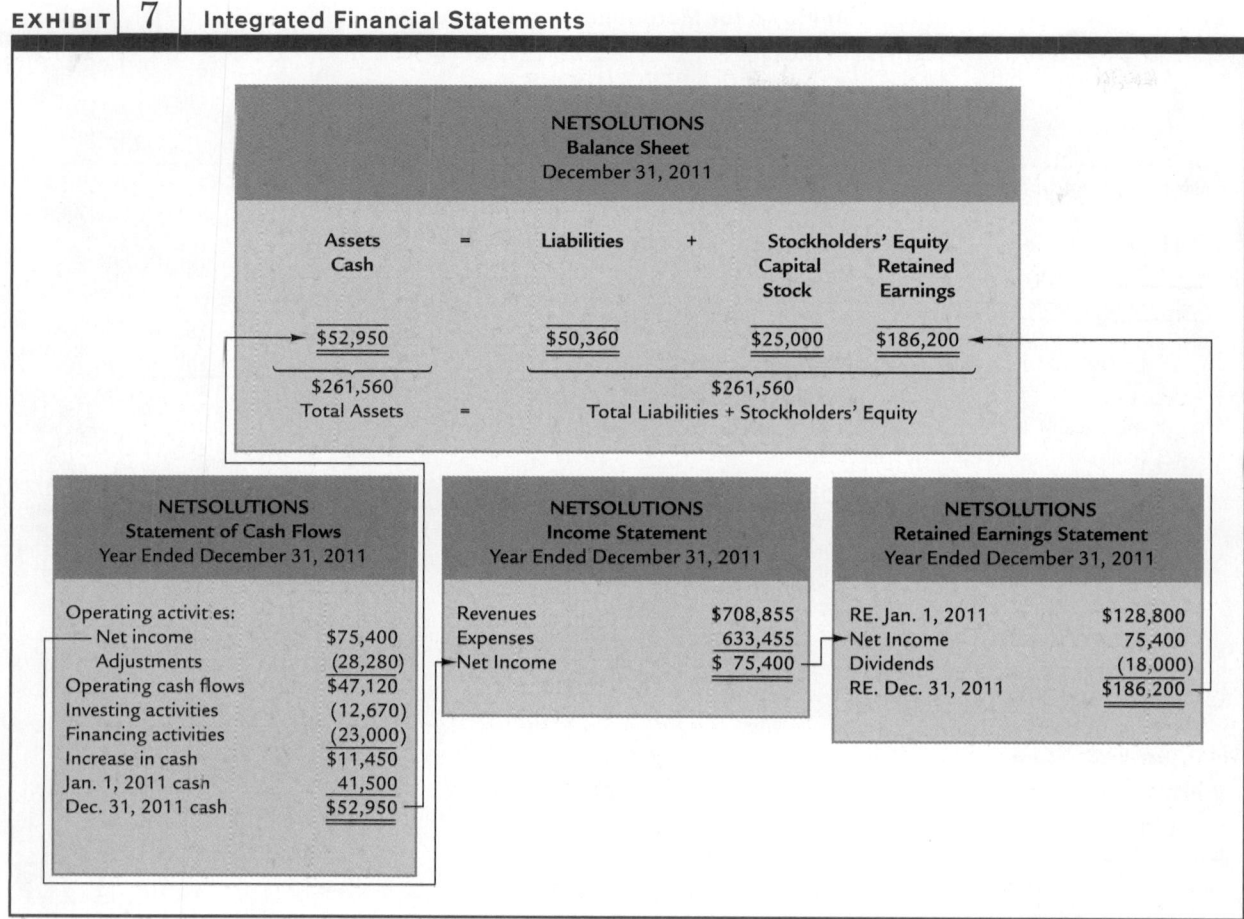

A business can sell merchandise on account. The effect of sales on account is similar to that for cash sales except that Accounts Receivable is increased instead of Cash. When the customer pays the amount, Accounts Receivable is decreased and Cash is increased.

Sales Discounts

The terms of a sale are normally indicated on the **invoice** or bill that the seller sends to the buyer. An example of a sales invoice for NetSolutions is shown in Exhibit 8.

The terms for when payments for merchandise are to be made, agreed on by the buyer and the seller, are called the **credit terms**. If payment is required on delivery, the terms are *cash or net cash*. Otherwise, the buyer is allowed an amount of time, known as the **credit period**, in which to pay.

The credit period usually begins with the date of the sale as shown on the invoice. If payment is due within a stated number of days after the date of the invoice, such as 30 days, the terms are *net 30 days*. These terms may be written as *n/30*.[4] If payment is due by the end of the month in which the sale was made, the terms are written as *n/eom*.

As a means of encouraging the buyer to pay before the end of the credit period, the seller may offer a discount. For example, a seller may offer a 2% discount if the buyer pays within 10 days of the invoice date. If the buyer

---

[4] The word *net* as used here does not have the usual meaning of a number after deductions have been subtracted, as in *net income*.

EXHIBIT | 8 | Invoice

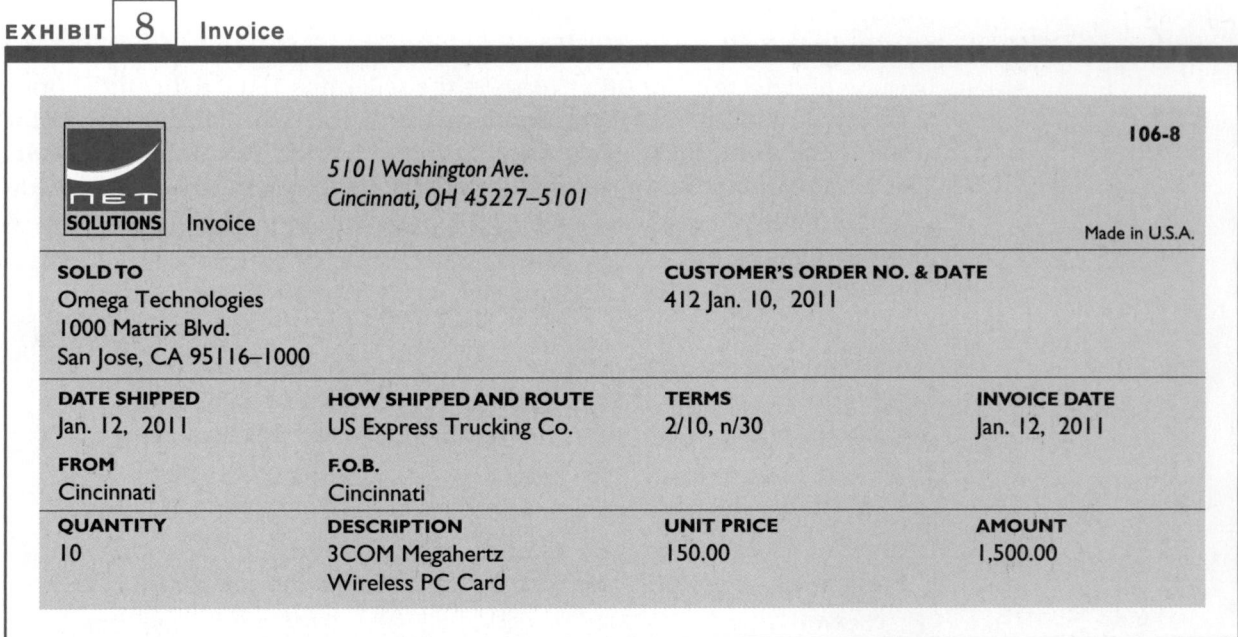

does not take the discount, the total amount is due within 30 days. These terms are expressed as *2/10, n/30* and are read as 2% *discount if paid within 10 days, net amount due within 30 days*. Using the information from the invoice in Exhibit 8, the credit terms of 2/10, n/30 are summarized below.

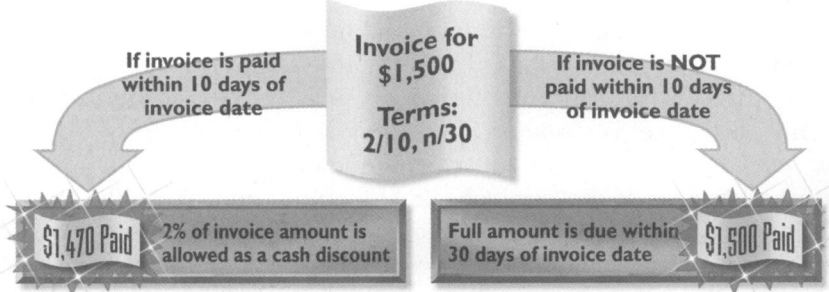

Discounts taken by the buyer for early payment are recorded as sales discounts by the seller. Since managers may want to know the amount of the sales discounts for a period, the seller normally records the sales discounts in a separate account. The sales discounts account is a *contra* (or *offsetting*) account to Sales. To illustrate, assume that cash is received within the discount period (10 days) from the credit sale of $1,500, shown on the invoice in Exhibit 8. The effect on the accounts and financial statements of the receipt of the cash is as follows:

	Balance Sheet							
Statement of Cash Flows	Assets		=	Liabilities	+	Stockholders' Equity		Income Statement
	Cash	+	Accounts Receivable	=			Retained Earnings	
Jan. 22.	1,470		−1,500				−30	Jan. 22.

Statement of Cash Flows		Income Statement	
Jan. 22. Operating	1,470	Jan. 22. Sales discounts	−30

Sales Returns and Allowances

Merchandise sold may be returned to the seller (sales return). In addition, because of defects or for other reasons, the seller may reduce the initial price at which the goods were sold (sales allowance). If the return or allowance is for a sale on account, the seller usually issues the buyer a **credit memorandum**. This memorandum shows the amount of and the reason for the seller's credit to an account receivable. A credit memorandum issued by NetSolutions is illustrated below.

		No. 32
ᴨⴹⴕ SOLUTIONS	5101 Washington Ave. Cincinnati, OH 45227–5101	

CREDIT MEMORANDUM

TO	**DATE**
Krier Company 7608 Melton Avenue Los Angeles, CA 90025–3942	January 13, 2011

WE CREDIT YOUR ACCOUNT AS FOLLOWS

1 Graphic Video Card	225.00

Like sales discounts, sales returns and allowances reduce sales revenue. They also result in additional shipping and other expenses. Since managers often want to know the amount of returns and allowances for a period, the seller records sales returns and allowances in a separate account. Sales Returns and Allowances is a *contra* (or *offsetting*) account to Sales.

The seller increases Sales Returns and Allowances for the amount of the return or allowance. If the original sale was on account, the seller decreases Accounts Receivable. Since the merchandise inventory is kept up to date in a perpetual system, the seller adds the cost of the returned merchandise to the merchandise inventory account. The seller must also decrease the cost of returned merchandise to the cost of merchandise sold account, since this account was increased when the original sale was recorded. To illustrate, assume that the cost of the merchandise returned in the preceding credit memorandum was $140. The effect on the accounts and financial statements of the issuance of the credit memorandum and the receipt of the returned merchandise is as follows:

		Balance Sheet					
Statement of Cash Flows	**Assets**		=	**Liabilities**	+	**Stockholders' Equity**	**Income Statement**
	Accounts Receivable	+ Merchandise Inventory =				Retained Earnings	
Jan. 13.	−225	140				−85	Jan. 13.

Income Statement	
Jan. 13. Sales returns & allowances	−225
Cost of merch. sold	140
Net income	−85

What if the buyer pays for the merchandise and the merchandise is later returned? In this case, the seller may issue a credit and apply it against other accounts receivable owed by the buyer, or the cash may be refunded. If the credit is applied against the buyer's other receivables, the seller records entries similar to those preceding. If cash is refunded for merchandise returned or for an allowance, the seller increases Sales Returns and Allowances and decreases Cash.

Purchase Transactions

Obj 4 Describe the accounting for the purchase of merchandise.

As indicated earlier in this chapter, most large retailers and many small merchandising businesses use computerized perpetual inventory systems. Under the perpetual inventory system, cash purchases of merchandise are recorded as follows:

Statement of Cash Flows	Balance Sheet					Income Statement
	Assets		=	Liabilities	+ Stockholders' Equity	
	Cash	+	Merchandise Inventory			
Jan. 3.	−2,510		2,510			

Statement of Cash Flows		
Jan. 3. Operating	−2,510	

Purchases of merchandise on account are recorded as increases of Merchandise Inventory and Accounts Payable.

Purchase Discounts

Purchase discounts taken by the buyer for early payment of an invoice reduce the cost of the merchandise purchased. Under the perpetual inventory system, the buyer initially increases the merchandise inventory account for the amount of the invoice. When paying the invoice, the buyer decreases the merchandise inventory account for the amount of the discount. In this way, the merchandise inventory shows the *net* cost to the buyer. For example, the effects on the accounts and financial statements of paying the invoice shown in Exhibit 8 at the end of the discount period are as follows:

Statement of Cash Flows	Balance Sheet					Income Statement
	Assets		=	Liabilities	+ Stockholders' Equity	
	Cash	+	Merchandise Inventory	=	Accounts Payable	
Jan. 22.	−1,470		−30		−1,500	

Statement of Cash Flows		
Jan. 22. Operating	−1,470	

If the invoice shown in Exhibit 8 is not paid during the discount period, the payment is recorded as a decrease in Cash and Accounts Payable for $1,500.

Purchase Returns and Allowances

When merchandise is returned (purchase return) or a price adjustment is requested (purchase allowance), the buyer (debtor) usually sends the seller a letter or a debit memorandum. A **debit memorandum**, shown below, informs the seller of the amount the buyer proposes to decrease to the account payable due the seller. It also states the reasons for the return or the request for a price reduction.

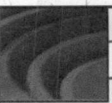

5101 Washington Ave.
Cincinnati, OH 45227–5101

No. 18

DEBIT MEMORANDUM

TO	DATE
Maxim Systems 7519 East Willson Ave. Seattle, WA 98101–7519	March 7, 2011

WE DEBIT (DECREASE) YOUR ACCOUNT AS FOLLOWS

10 Server Network Interface Cards, your Invoice No. 7291, are being returned via parcel post. Our order specified No. 825X.	@ 90.00	900.00

The buyer may use a copy of the debit memorandum as the basis for recording the return or allowance or wait for approval from the seller (creditor). In either case, the buyer must decrease Accounts Payable and increase Merchandise Inventory. To illustrate, the effect on the accounts and financial statements of the return of the merchandise indicated in the preceding debit memorandum is shown below.

	Balance Sheet						
Statement of Cash Flows	**Assets**	=	**Liabilities**	+	**Stockholders' Equity**		**Income Statement**
	Merchandise Inventory	=	Accounts Payable				
Mar. 7.	−900		−900				

When a buyer returns merchandise or has been granted an allowance prior to paying the invoice, the amount of the debit memorandum is deducted from the invoice amount. The amount is deducted before the purchase discount is computed. For example, assume that on May 2, NetSolutions purchases $5,000 of merchandise from Delta Data Link, subject to terms 2/10, n/30. On May 4, NetSolutions returns $3,000 of the merchandise, and on May 12, NetSolutions pays the original invoice less the return. NetSolutions would pay Delta Data Link $1,960 as shown below.

Invoice	$ 5,000
Less return	3,000
Amount due before discount	$ 2,000
Less discount ($2,000 × 2%)	40
Amount due within discount period	$ 1,960

The effect on the accounts and financial statements of paying the invoice on May 12 is as follows:

Statement of Cash Flows			Balance Sheet						Income Statement
	Assets			=	Liabilities	+	Stockholders' Equity		
	Cash	+	Merchandise Inventory	=	Accounts Payable				
May 12.	−1,960		−40		−2,000				

Statement of Cash Flows
May 12. Operating   −1,960

Freight and Sales Taxes

Obj 5 Describe the accounting for freight and sales taxes.

Merchandise businesses incur freight in selling and purchasing merchandise. In addition, a retailer must collect sales taxes in most states. In this section, the unique aspects of accounting for freight costs and sales taxes are discussed.

Freight

The terms of a sale should indicate when the ownership (title) of the merchandise passes to the buyer. This point determines which party, the buyer or the seller, must pay the transportation costs.[5]

The ownership of the merchandise may pass to the buyer when the seller delivers the merchandise to the freight carrier or transportation company. In this case, the terms are said to be **FOB (free on board) shipping point**. This term means that the dealer pays the freight costs from the shipping point (factory) to the final destination. Such costs are part of the dealer's total cost of purchasing inventory and should be added to the cost of the inventory by increasing Merchandise Inventory.

To illustrate, assume that on June 10, NetSolutions buys merchandise from Magna Data on account, $900, terms FOB shipping point, and pays the

[5] The passage of title also determines whether the buyer or seller must pay other costs, such as the cost of insurance, while the merchandise is in transit.

freight cost of $50. The effect on the accounts and financial statements of these transactions is as follows:

Statement of Cash Flows	Balance Sheet						Income Statement
	Assets		=	Liabilities	+	Stockholders' Equity	
	Cash	+	Merchandise Inventory	=	Accounts Payable		
June 10.	−50		950		900		

Statement of Cash Flows		
June 10. Operating	−50	

The ownership of the merchandise may pass to the buyer when the buyer receives the merchandise. In this case, the terms are said to be **FOB (free on board) destination**. This term means that the seller delivers the merchandise to the buyer's final destination, free of freight charges to the buyer. The seller thus pays the freight costs to the final destination. The seller increases Delivery Expense, or Freight Out, which is reported on the seller's income statement as an expense.

Shipping terms, the passage of title, and whether the buyer or seller is to pay the transportation costs are summarized in Exhibit 9.

EXHIBIT 9 **Freight Terms**

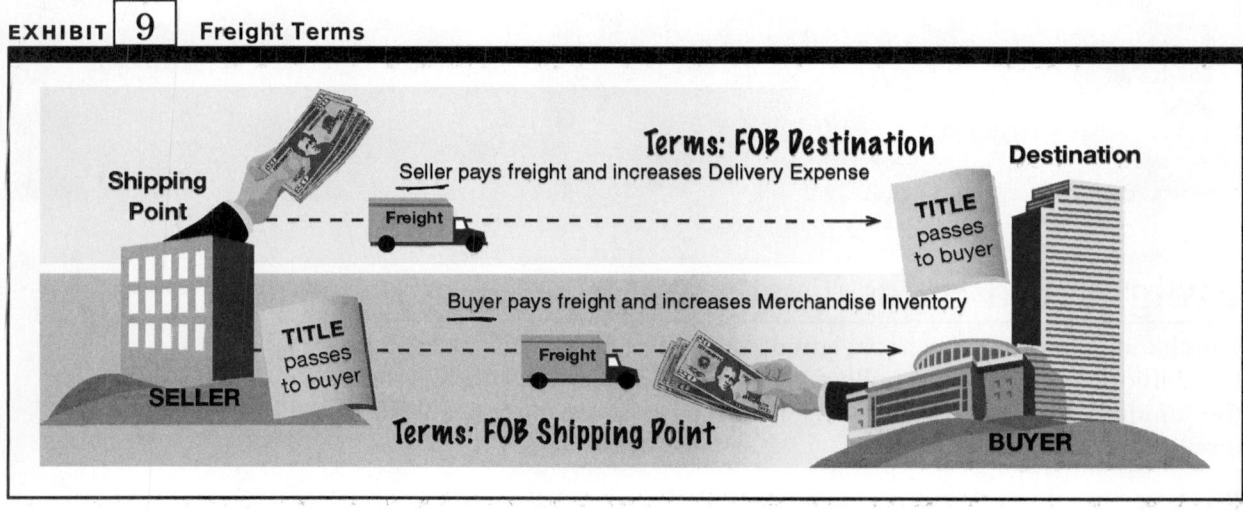

Sales Taxes

Almost all states and many other taxing units levy a tax on sales of merchandise.[6] The liability for the sales tax is incurred when the sale is made.

At the time of a cash sale, the seller collects the sales tax. When a sale is made on account, the seller charges the buyer by increasing Accounts Receivable. The seller increases the sales account for the amount of the sale and increases Sales Tax Payable for the amount of the tax. Normally on a regular basis, the seller pays to the taxing unit the amount of the sales tax collected. The seller records such a payment by decreasing Sales Tax Payable and Cash.

[6] Businesses that purchase merchandise for resale to others are normally exempt from paying sales taxes on their purchases. Only final buyers of merchandise normally pay sales taxes.

Dual Nature of Merchandise Transactions

Each merchandising transaction affects a buyer and a seller. The following illustration shows how the same transactions would be recorded by both the seller and the buyer. In this example, the seller is Scully Company and the buyer is Burton Co.

Obj 6 Illustrate the dual nature of merchandising transactions.

On July 1, Scully Company sold merchandise on account to Burton Co., $7,500, terms FOB destination; 2/10, n/30. The cost of the merchandise sold was $4,500.

Scully Company (Seller)

Statement of Cash Flows	Balance Sheet						Income Statement
	Assets		=	Liabilities	+	Stockholders' Equity	
	Accounts Receivable	+ Merchandise Inventory =				Retained Earnings	
July 1.	7,500	−4,500				3,000	July 1.

Income Statement	
July 1. Sales	7,500
Cost of merch. sold	−4,500
Net income	3,000

Burton Co. (Buyer)

Statement of Cash Flows	Balance Sheet					Income Statement
	Assets	=	Liabilities	+	Stockholders' Equity	
	Merchandise Inventory	=	Accounts Payable			
July 1.	7,500		7,500			

On July 5, Scully Company pays transportation charges of $300 for delivery of the merchandise sold on July1 to Burton Co.

Scully Company (Seller)

Statement of Cash Flows	Balance Sheet					Income Statement
	Assets	=	Liabilities	+	Stockholders' Equity	
	Cash	=			Retained Earnings	
July 5.	−300				−300	July 5.

Statement of Cash Flows		Income Statement	
July 5. Operating	−300	July 5. Delivery exp.	−300

Burton Co. (Buyer)

No effect on the accounts and financial statements.

On July 6, Scully Company issues a credit memorandum for $1,000 for merchandise returned by Burton Co. The cost of the merchandise returned was $600.

Scully Company (Seller)

Statement of Cash Flows	Balance Sheet					Income Statement
	Assets		= Liabilities	+ Stockholders' Equity		
	Accounts Receivable +	Merchandise Inventory =			Retained Earnings	
July 6.	−1,000	600			−400	July 6.

	Income Statement
	July 6. Sales retns. & allow. −1,000
	Cost of merch. sold 600
	Net income −400

Burton Co. (Buyer)

Statement of Cash Flows	Balance Sheet				Income Statement
	Assets	= Liabilities	+ Stockholders' Equity		
	Merchandise Inventory	= Accounts Payable			
July 6.	−1,000	−1,000			

On July 11, Scully Company received payment from Burton Co. less discount.

Scully Company (Seller)

Statement of Cash Flows	Balance Sheet					Income Statement
	Assets		= Liabilities	+ Stockholders' Equity		
	Cash +	Accounts Receivable =			Retained Earnings	
July 11.	6,370	−6,500			−130	July 11.

Statement of Cash Flows		*Income Statement*	
July 11. Operating	6,370	July 11. Sales discounts −130	

Burton Co. (Buyer)

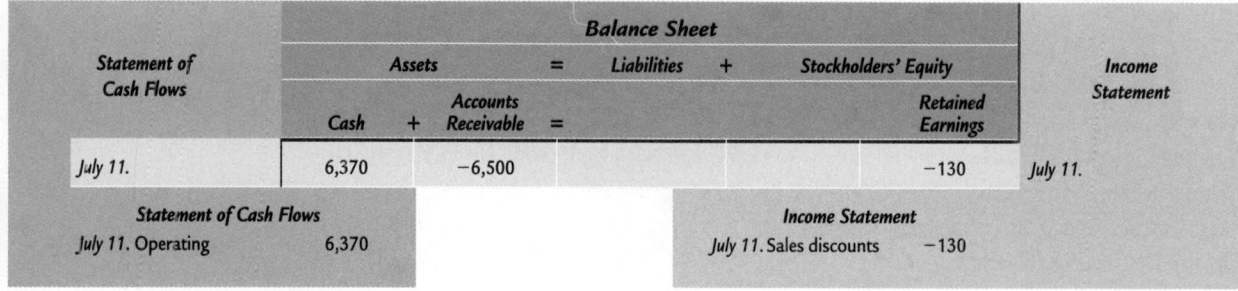

Statement of Cash Flows	Balance Sheet					Income Statement
	Assets		= Liabilities	+ Stockholders' Equity		
	Cash +	Merchandise Inventory =	Accounts Payable			
July 11.	−6,370	−130	−6,500			

Statement of Cash Flows	
July 11. Operating	−6,370

Merchandise Shrinkage

Obj 7 Describe the accounting for merchandise shrinkage.

Under the perpetual inventory system, the merchandise inventory account is continually updated for purchase and sales transactions. As a result, the balance of the merchandise inventory account is the amount of merchandise available for sale at that point in time. However, retailers normally experience some loss of inventory due to shoplifting, employee theft, or errors. Thus, the physical inventory on hand at the end of the accounting period is usually less than the balance of Merchandise Inventory. This difference is called **inventory shrinkage** or **inventory shortage**.

To illustrate, NetSolutions' inventory records indicate the following on December 31, 2011:

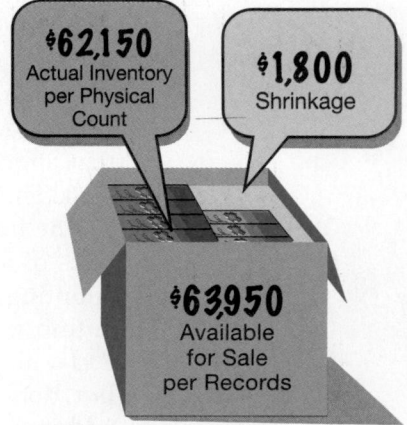

	Dec. 31, 2011
Account balance of Merchandise Inventory	$63,950
Physical merchandise inventory on hand	62,150
Inventory shrinkage	$ 1,800

The effect of the shrinkage on the accounts and financial statements is as follows.

Statement of Cash Flows	Balance Sheet						Income Statement
	Assets	=	Liabilities	+	Stockholders' Equity		
	Merchandise Inventory	=				Retained Earnings	
Dec. 31.	−1,800					−1,800	Dec. 31.

	Income Statement	
Dec. 31.	Cost of merch. sold	−1,800

After the shrinkage is recorded, the balance of Merchandise Inventory agrees with the physical inventory on hand at the end of the period. Since inventory shrinkage cannot be totally eliminated, it is considered a normal cost of operations and is included in the cost of merchandise sold. If, however, the amount of the shrinkage is unusually large, it may be disclosed separately on the income statement. In such cases, the shrinkage may be recorded in a separate account, such as Loss from Merchandise Inventory Shrinkage.

Appendix

Statement of Cash Flows: The Indirect Method

NetSolutions' statement of cash flows for the year ended December 31, 2011, is shown in Exhibit 6 on page 137. The operating activities section of this statement was prepared using a method known as the *indirect method*. This method is used by over 90% of publicly held companies.

The use of the indirect method only affects net cash flows from operating activities. The other method of preparing the net cash flows from operating activities section is called the *direct method*. The direct method analyzes each

transaction and its effect on cash flows. In contrast, the indirect method analyzes only the changes in accounts.

A major reason that the indirect method is so popular is that it is normally less costly to use. However, regardless of whether the indirect or direct method is used, the reporting of net cash flows from investing and financing activities is not affected. In this appendix, the use of the indirect method of preparing the statement of cash flows is illustrated.

The indirect method reconciles net income with net cash flows from operating activities. Net income is adjusted for the effects of accruals and deferrals that affected the net income but did not result in the receipt or payment of cash. The resulting amount is the net cash flows from operating activities.

The indirect method converts net income determined under the accrual basis of accounting to what it would have been under the cash basis of accounting. In other words, net cash flows from operating activities is equivalent to net income using the cash basis of accounting.

To illustrate, depreciation expense is deducted in arriving at net income but does not involve any cash payments. Thus, depreciation expense is added to net income under the indirect method. Likewise, assume that accounts receivable increases during the period by $10,000. This increase is included in the period's revenue and thus increases net income. However, cash was not collected. Thus, an increase in accounts receivable must be deducted from net income under the indirect method.

The typical adjustments to convert net income to net cash flows from operating activities, using the indirect method, are shown in Exhibit 10.

EXHIBIT 10   Indirect Method

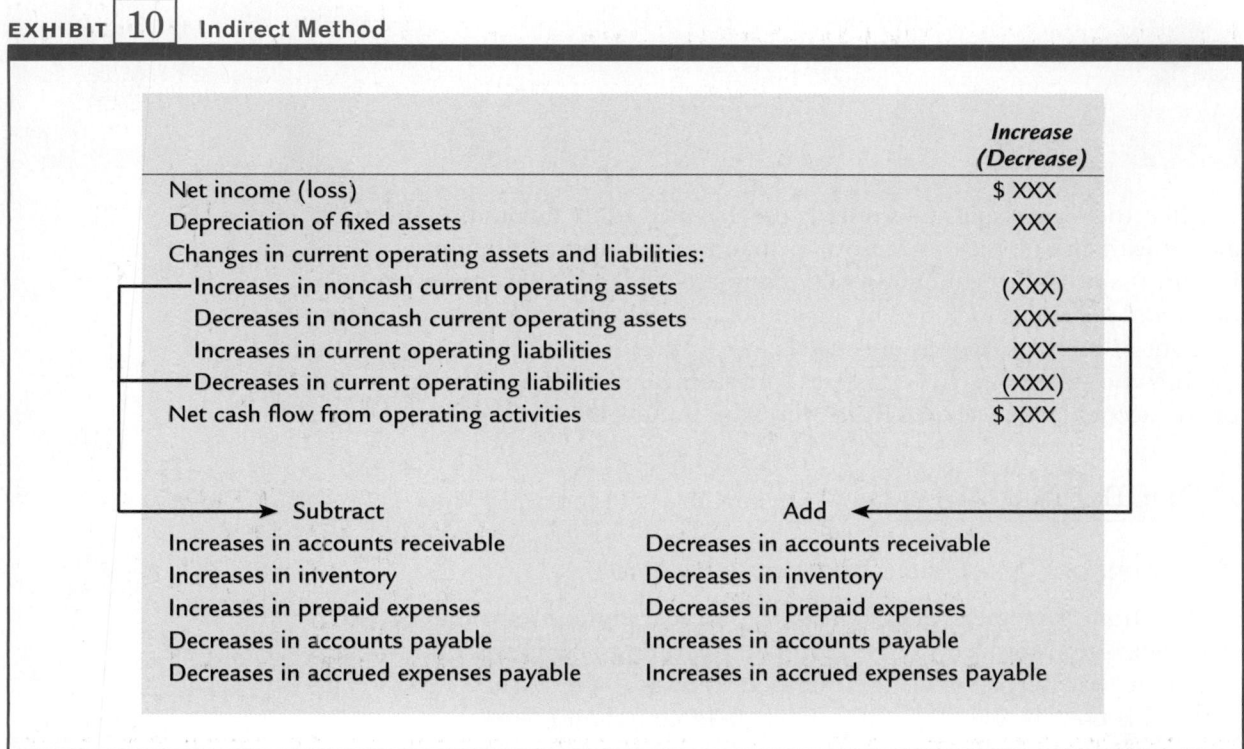

You should note that, except for depreciation, the adjustments in Exhibit 10 are for changes in the current assets and the current liabilities. This is because changes in the current assets and the current liabilities are related to operations

and thus net income. For example, changes in inventories are related to sales, while changes in accounts payable are related to expenses.

Cash Flows from Operating Activities

To prepare the operating activities section for NetSolutions' statement of cash flows, depreciation and the changes in the current assets and the liabilities during the year must be determined. This information is included in Exhibit 11, which shows the comparative balance sheets for NetSolutions as of December 31, 2011 and 2010, and related changes.

EXHIBIT 11 | NetSolutions' Comparative Balance Sheets

NETSOLUTIONS
Balance Sheets

	December 31, 2011	December 31, 2010	Changes Increase (Decrease)
Assets			
Current assets:			
Cash	$ 52,950	$ 41,500	$ 11,450
Accounts receivable	91,080	52,000	39,080
Merchandise inventory	62,150	59,700	2,450
Office supplies	480	600	(120)
Prepaid insurance	2,650	3,000	(350)
Total current assets	$209,310	$ 156,800	$ 52,510
Property, plant, and equipment:			
Land	$ 20,000	$ 20,000	$ 0
Store equipment	27,100	20,000	7,100
Accumulated depreciation—store equipment	(5,700)	(2,600)	(3,100)
Office equipment	15,570	10,000	5,570
Accumulated depreciation—office equipment	(4,720)	(2,230)	(2,490)
Total property, plant, and equipment	$ 52,250	$ 45,170	$ 7,080
Total assets	$261,560	$ 201,970	$ 59,590
Liabilities			
Current liabilities:			
Accounts payable	$ 22,420	$ 14,270	$ 8,150
Notes payable (current portion)	5,000	5,000	0
Salaries payable	1,140	1,500	(360)
Unearned rent	1,800	2,400	(600)
Total current liabilities	$ 30,360	$ 23,170	$ 7,190
Long-term liabilities:			
Notes payable (final payment due 2021)	20,000	25,000	(5,000)
Total liabilities	$ 50,360	$ 48,170	$ 2,190
Stockholders' Equity			
Capital stock	$ 25,000	$ 25,000	$ 0
Retained earnings	186,200	128,800	57,400
Total stockholders' equity	$211,200	$ 153,800	$ 57,400
Total liabilities and stockholders' equity	$261,560	$ 201,970	$ 59,590

Based on Exhibit 11, the net cash flows from operating activities is shown below.

Net income		$ 75,400
Depreciation expense—store equipment	$ 3,100	
Depreciation expense—office equipment	2,490	5,590
Changes in current operating assets and liabilities:		
Increase in accounts receivable	(39,080)	
Increase in merchandise inventory	(2,450)	
Decrease in office supplies	120	
Decrease in prepaid insurance	350	
Increase in accounts payable	8,150	
Decrease in salaries payable	(360)	
Decrease in unearned rent	(600)	(33,870)
Net cash flows from operating activities		$ 47,120

The depreciation expense of $3,100 for store equipment is determined from the increase in the accumulated depreciation for store equipment. Likewise, the depreciation expense of $2,490 for office equipment is determined from the increase in the accumulated depreciation for office equipment. The changes in the current assets and the current liabilities are also taken from Exhibit 11.

Cash Flows Used for Investing Activities

The cash flows for investing activities section can also be prepared by analyzing the changes in the accounts shown in Exhibit 11. For NetSolutions, the cash flows used for investing activities is composed of two items. First, additional store equipment of $7,100 was purchased, as shown by the increase in the store equipment. Likewise, additional office equipment of $5,570 was purchased. Thus, cash of $12,670 was used for investing activities, as shown in Exhibit 6 on page 137.

Cash Flows Used for Financing Activities

The cash flows for financing activities can also be determined from Exhibit 11. For NetSolutions, the cash flows used for financing activities is composed of two items. First, dividends of $18,000 are reported on the retained earnings statement shown in Exhibit 4 on page 135. Since no dividends payable appears on the balance sheets, cash dividends of $18,000 must have been paid during the year. In addition, notes payable decreased by $5,000 during the year, so cash must have been used in paying off $5,000 of the notes. Thus, cash of $23,000 was used for financing activities, as shown in Exhibit 6.

Key Points

1. Distinguish the activities and financial statements of a service business from those of a merchandising business.

The revenue activities of a service enterprise involve providing services to customers. In contrast, the revenue activities of a merchandising business involve the buying and selling of merchandise.

2. Describe and illustrate the financial statements of a merchandising business.

The multiple-step income statement of a merchandiser reports sales, sales returns and allowances, sales discounts, and net sales. The cost of the merchandise sold is subtracted from net sales to determine the gross profit. The cost of merchandise sold is determined

by using either the periodic or perpetual inventory methods. Operating income is determined by subtracting operating expenses from gross profit. Operating expenses are normally classified as selling or administrative expenses. Net income is determined by subtracting income taxes and other expense and adding other income. The income statement may also be reported in a single-step form. The retained earnings statement and the statement of cash flows are similar to those for a service business. The balance sheet reports merchandise inventory at the end of the period as a current asset.

3. Describe the accounting for the sale of merchandise.

Sales of merchandise for cash or on account are recorded by increasing Sales. The cost of merchandise sold and the reduction in merchandise inventory are also recorded for the sale. For sales of merchandise on account, the credit terms can allow sales discounts for early payment. Such discounts are recorded by the seller as an increase in Sales Discounts. Sales discounts are reported as a deduction from the amount initially recorded in Sales. Likewise, when merchandise is returned or a price adjustment is granted, the seller increases Sales Returns and Allowances.

Under the perpetual inventory system, the cost of merchandise sold and the reduction of merchandise inventory on hand are recorded at the time of sale. In this way, the merchandise inventory account indicates the amount of merchandise on hand at all times. Likewise, any returned merchandise is recorded in the merchandise inventory account with a related reduction in the cost of merchandise sold.

4. Describe the accounting for the purchase of merchandise.

Purchases of merchandise for cash or on account are recorded by increasing Merchandise Inventory. For purchases of merchandise on account, the credit terms can allow cash discounts for early payment. Such purchase discounts are viewed as a reduction in the cost of the merchandise purchased. When merchandise is returned or a price adjustment is granted, the buyer decreases Merchandise Inventory.

5. Describe the accounting for freight and sales taxes.

When merchandise is shipped FOB shipping point, the buyer pays the freight and increases Merchandise Inventory. When merchandise is shipped FOB destination, the seller pays the freight and increases Delivery Expense or Freight Out.

The liability for sales tax is incurred when the sale is made and is recorded by the seller as an increase in the sales taxes payable account. When the amount of the sales tax is paid to the taxing unit, Sales Tax Payable and Cash are decreased.

6. Illustrate the dual nature of merchandising transactions.

Each merchandising transaction affects a buyer and a seller. The illustration in this chapter shows how the same transactions would be recorded by both.

7. Describe the accounting for merchandise shrinkage.

The physical inventory taken at the end of the accounting period could differ from the amount of inventory shown in the inventory records. The difference, called *inventory shrinkage*, requires an adjusting entry increasing Cost of Merchandise Sold and decreasing Merchandise Inventory. After this entry has been recorded, the adjusted Merchandise Inventory (book inventory) in the accounting records agrees with the actual physical inventory at the end of the period.

Key Terms

Account form The form of balance sheet presented with assets on the left-hand side and the liabilities and stockholders' equity on the right-hand side.

Administrative expenses Expenses incurred in the administration or general operations of the business, sometimes called general expenses.

Cost of merchandise purchased The cost of merchandise purchased during a period, computed as purchases less purchases returns and allowances, less purchase discounts, plus freight in.

Cost of merchandise sold The cost that is reported as an expense when merchandise or a manufactured product is sold; also called *cost of goods sold*.

Credit memorandum A form used by a seller to inform the buyer of the amount the seller proposes to decrease the account receivable due from the buyer.

Credit period The amount of time the buyer is allowed in which to pay the seller.

Credit terms Terms for payment on account by the buyer to the seller.

Debit memorandum A form used by a buyer to inform the seller of the amount the buyer proposes to decrease the account payable due the seller.

FOB (free on board) destination Freight terms in which the seller pays the transportation costs from the shipping point to the final destination.

FOB (free on board) shipping point Freight terms in which the buyer pays the transportation costs from the shipping point to the final destination.

Freight in Freight costs incurred in obtaining merchandise.

General expenses Expenses incurred in the administration or general operations of the business, sometimes called administrative expenses.

Gross profit Sales minus the cost of merchandise sold.

Income from operations The excess of gross profit over total operating expenses. Sometimes called operating income.

Indirect method A method of preparing the statement of cash flows that reconciles net income with net cash flows from operating activities.

Inventory shortage The amount by which the merchandise for sale, as indicated by the balance of the merchandise inventory account, is larger than the total amount of merchandise counted during the physical inventory. Sometimes called inventory shrinkage.

Inventory shrinkage The amount by which the merchandise for sale, as indicated by the balance of the merchandise inventory account, is larger than the total amount of merchandise counted

during the physical inventory. Sometimes called inventory shortage.

Invoice The bill that the seller sends to the buyer.

Merchandise available for sale The cost of merchandise available for sale to customers.

Merchandise inventory Merchandise on hand (not sold) at the end of an accounting period.

Multiple-step income statement A form of income statement that contains several sections, subsections, and subtotals.

Net sales Gross sales less sales returns and allowances and sales discounts.

Operating income The excess of gross profit over total operating expenses. Sometimes called income from operations.

Other expense Expenses that cannot be traced directly to operations.

Other income Revenue from sources other than the primary operating activities of a business.

Periodic inventory system The inventory method in which the inventory records do not show the amount available for sale or sold during the period.

Perpetual inventory system The inventory system in which each purchase and sale of merchandise is recorded in an inventory account.

Purchases discounts Discounts taken by the buyer for early payment of an invoice.

Purchases returns and allowances From the buyer's perspective, returned merchandise or an adjustment for defective merchandise.

Report form The form of balance sheet in which assets, liabilities, and stockholders' equity are reported in a downward sequence.

Sales The total amount charged to customers for merchandise sold, including cash sales and sales on account.

Sales discounts From the seller's perspective, discounts that a seller can offer the buyer for early payment.

Sales returns and allowances From the seller's perspective, returned merchandise or an adjustment for damaged or defective merchandise.

Selling expenses Expenses that are incurred directly in the selling of merchandise.

Single-step income statement A form of income statement in which the total of all expenses is deducted from the total of all revenues.

6 + 5 x 12

Illustrative Problem

The following selected accounts and their current balances appear in the ledger of Sciatic Co. for the fiscal year ended July 31, 2012:

Cash	$123,000	Sales	$1,028,000
Accounts receivable	96,800	Sales returns and allowances	18,480
Merchandise inventory	140,000	Sales discounts	17,520
Office supplies	4,480	Cost of merchandise sold	620,000
Prepaid insurance	2,720	Sales salaries expense	138,560
Office equipment	68,000	Advertising expense	35,040
Accumulated depreciation—		Depreciation expense—	
office equipment	10,240	store equipment	5,120
Store equipment	122,400	Miscellaneous selling expense	1,280
Accumulated depreciation—		Office salaries expense	67,320
store equipment	27,360	Rent expense	25,080
Accounts payable	44,480	Depreciation expense—	
Salaries payable	1,920	office equipment	10,160
Note payable		Insurance expense	3,120
(final payment due 2018)	44,800	Office supplies expense	1,040
Capital stock	75,000	Miscellaneous administrative	
Retained earnings	301,600	expense	1,280
Dividends	28,000	Interest expense	4,000

Instructions

1. Prepare a single-step income statement.

2. Prepare a retained earnings statement.

3. Prepare a report form of balance sheet, assuming that the current portion of the note payable is $6,000.

4. Prepare a multiple-step income statement.

Solution

1.

SCIATIC CO.
Income Statement
For the Year Ended July 31, 2012

Revenues:		
Net sales		$992,000
Expenses:		
Cost of merchandise sold	$620,000	
Selling expenses	180,000	
Administrative expenses	108,000	
Interest expense	4,000	
Total expenses		912,000
Net income		$ 80,000

2.

SCIATIC CO.
Retained Earnings Statement
For the Year Ended July 31, 2012

Retained earnings, August 1, 2011		$301,600
Net income for the year	$80,000	
Less dividends	28,000	
Increase in retained earnings		52,000
Retained earnings, July 31, 2012		$353,600

3.

SCIATIC CO.
Balance Sheet
July 31, 2012

Assets

Current assets:			
Cash		$ 123,000	
Accounts receivable		96,800	
Merchandise inventory		140,000	
Office supplies		4,480	
Prepaid insurance		2,720	
Total current assets			$367,000
Property, plant, and equipment:			
Office equipment	$ 68,000		
Less accumulated depreciation	10,240	$ 57,760	
Store equipment	$122,400		
Less accumulated depreciation	27,360	95,040	
Total property, plant, and equipment			152,800
Total assets			$519,800

Liabilities

Current liabilities:			
Accounts payable		$ 44,480	
Note payable (current portion)		6,000	
Salaries payable		1,920	
Total current liabilities			$ 52,400
Long-term liabilities:			
Note payable (final payment due 2018)			38,800
Total liabilities			$ 91,200

Stockholders' Equity

Capital stock		$ 75,000	
Retained earnings		353,600	
Total stockholders' equity			428,600
Total liabilities and stockholders' equity			$519,800

4.

SCIATIC CO.
Income Statement
For the Year Ended July 31, 2012

Revenue from sales:			
Sales		$1,028,000	
Less: Sales returns and allowances	$ 18,480		
Sales discounts	17,520	36,000	
Net sales			$992,000
Cost of merchandise sold			620,000
Gross profit			$372,000
Operating expenses:			
Selling expenses:			
Sales salaries expense	$138,560		
Advertising expense	35,040		
Depreciation expense—store equipment	5,120		
Miscellaneous selling expense	1,280		
Total selling expenses		$ 180,000	

(continued)

Administrative expenses:			
Office salaries expense	$ 67,320		
Rent expense	25,080		
Depreciation expense—office equipment	10,160		
Insurance expense	3,120		
Office supplies expense	1,040		
Miscellaneous administrative expense	1,280		
Total administrative expenses		108,000	
Total operating expenses			288,000
Income from operations			$ 84,000
Other expense:			
Interest expense			4,000
Net income			$ 80,000

Self-Examination Questions (Answers appear at the end of chapter)

1. If merchandise purchased on account is returned, the buyer can inform the seller of the details by issuing:

   A. a debit memorandum

   B. a credit memorandum

   C. an invoice

   D. a bill

2. If merchandise is sold on account to a customer for $1,000, terms FOB shipping point, 1/10, n/30, and the seller prepays $50 in freight, the amount of the discount for early payment would be:

   A. $0

   B. $5.00

   C. $10.00

   D. $10.50

3. The income statement in which the total of all expenses is deducted from the total of all revenues is termed:

   A. multiple-step form

   B. single-step form

   C. account form

   D. report form

4. On a multiple-step income statement, the excess of net sales over the cost of merchandise sold is called:

   A. operating income

   B. income from operations

   C. gross profit

   D. net income

5. As of December 31, 2011, Ames Corporation's physical inventory was $275,000 and its book inventory was $290,000. The effect of the inventory shrinkage on the accounts is:

   A. to increase cost of merchandise sold and inventory by $15,000.

   B. to increase cost of merchandise sold and decrease inventory by $15,000.

   C. to decrease cost of merchandise sold and increase inventory by $15,000.

   D. to decrease cost of merchandise sold and inventory by $15,000.

Class Discussion Questions

1. What distinguishes a merchandising business from a service business?

2. Can a business earn a gross profit but incur a net loss? Explain.

3. In computing the cost of merchandise sold, does each of the following items increase or decrease that cost? (a) freight, (b) beginning merchandise inventory, (c) purchase discounts, (d) ending merchandise inventory.

4. Describe how the periodic method differs from the perpetual method of accounting for merchandise inventory.

5. Differentiate between the multiple-step and the single-step forms of the income statement.

6. What are the major advantages and disadvantages of the single-step form of income statement compared to the multiple-step statement?

7. What type of revenue is reported in the "Other income" section of the multiple-step income statement?

8. How are sales to customers using Master-Card and VISA recorded?

9. What is the meaning of (a) 1/10, n/30; (b) n/90; (c) n/eom?

10. What is the nature of (a) a credit memorandum issued by the seller of merchandise, (b) a debit memorandum issued by the buyer of merchandise?

11. Who bears the freight when the terms of sale are (a) FOB shipping point, (b) FOB destination?

12. When you purchase a new car, the "sticker price" includes a "destination" charge. Are you purchasing the car FOB shipping point or FOB destination? Explain.

13. Business Outfitters Inc., which uses a perpetual inventory system, experienced a normal inventory shrinkage of $9,175. What accounts would be increased and decreased to record the adjustment for the inventory shrinkage at the end of the accounting period?

14. Assume that Business Outfitters Inc. in Question 13 experienced an abnormal inventory shrinkage of $80,750. Business Outfitters Inc. has decided to record the abnormal inventory shrinkage so that it would be separately disclosed on the income statement. What account would be increased for the abnormal inventory shrinkage?

Exercises

E4-1

Determining gross profit

Obj 1

During the current year, merchandise is sold for $795,000. The cost of the merchandise sold is $477,000.

   a. What is the amount of the gross profit?
   b. Compute the gross profit percentage (gross profit divided by sales).
   c. Will the income statement necessarily report a net income? Explain.

E4-2

Determining cost of merchandise sold

Obj 1

For a recent year, **Best Buy** reported revenue of $40,023 million. Its gross profit was $9,546 million. What was the amount of Best Buy's cost of merchandise sold?

E4-3

Identify items missing in determining cost of merchandise sold

Obj 2

For (a) through (d), identify the items designated by "X" and "Y."

   a. Purchases – (X + Y) = Net purchases.
   b. Net purchases + X = Cost of merchandise purchased.
   c. Merchandise inventory (beginning) + Cost of merchandise purchased = X.
   d. Merchandise available for sale – X = Cost of merchandise sold.

E4-4

Cost of merchandise sold and related items

Obj 2

✓ a. Cost of merchandise sold, $1,400,600

The following data were extracted from the accounting records of Wedgeforth Company for the year ended November 30, 2010:

Merchandise inventory, December 1, 2009	$ 210,000
Merchandise inventory, November 30, 2010	185,000
Purchases	1,400,000
Purchases returns and allowances	20,000
Purchases discounts	18,500
Sales	2,250,000
Freight in	14,100

a. Prepare the cost of merchandise sold section of the income statement for the year ended November 30, 2010, using the periodic inventory system.

b. Determine the gross profit to be reported on the income statement for the year ended November 30, 2010.

E4-5

Cost of merchandise sold

Obj 2

✓ Correct cost of merchandise sold, $953,500

Identify the errors in the following schedule of cost of merchandise sold for the current year ended July 31, 2010:

Cost of merchandise sold:			
Merchandise inventory, July 31, 2010			$ 140,000
Purchases		$975,000	
Plus: Purchases returns and allowances	$12,000		
Purchases discounts	8,000	20,000	
Gross purchases		$995,000	
Less freight in		13,500	
Cost of merchandise purchased			981,500
Merchandise available for sale			$1,121,500
Less merchandise inventory, August 1, 2009			125,000
Cost of merchandise sold			$ 996,500

E4-6

Income statement for merchandiser

Obj 2

For the fiscal year, sales were $5,280,000, sales discounts were $100,000, sales returns and allowances were $75,000, and the cost of merchandise sold was $3,000,000.

a. What was the amount of net sales?

b. What was the amount of gross profit?

E4-7

Income statement for merchandiser

Obj 2

The following expenses were incurred by a merchandising business during the year. In which expense section of the income statement should each be reported: (a) selling, (b) administrative, or (c) other?

1. Advertising expense
2. Depreciation expense on store equipment
3. Insurance expense on office equipment
4. Interest expense on notes payable
5. Rent expense on office building
6. Salaries of office personnel
7. Salary of sales manager
8. Sales supplies used

E4-8

Single-step income statement

Obj 2

✓ Net income: $1,320,000

Summary operating data for Paper Plus Company during the current year ended June 30, 2010, are as follows: cost of merchandise sold, $4,000,000; administrative expenses, $500,000; interest expense, $30,000; rent revenue, $100,000; net sales, $6,500,000; and selling expenses, $750,000. Prepare a single-step income statement.

E4-9

Multiple-step income
statement

Obj 2

✓ **a. Net income:**
$275,000

On March 31, 2010, the balances of the accounts appearing in the ledger of El Dorado Furnishings Company, a furniture wholesaler, are as follows:

Administrative Expenses	$ 250,000	Office Supplies	$ 21,200
Building	1,025,000	Retained Earnings	937,600
Capital Stock	200,000	Salaries Payable	6,000
Cash	97,000	Sales	2,550,000
Cost of Merchandise Sold	1,400,000	Sales Discounts	40,000
Dividends	50,000	Sales Returns and Allowances	160,000
Interest Expense	15,000	Selling Expenses	410,000
Merchandise Inventory	260,000	Store Supplies	15,400
Notes Payable	59,000		

a. Prepare a multiple-step income statement for the year ended March 31, 2010.
b. Compare the major advantages and disadvantages of the multiple-step and single-step forms of income statements.

E4-10

Determining amounts for
items omitted from income
statement

Obj 2

✓ **a. $15,000**

✓ **h. $520,000**

Two items are omitted in each of the following four lists of income statement data. Determine the amounts of the missing items, identifying them by letter.

Sales	$250,000	$600,000	$1,000,000	$ (g)
Sales returns and allowances	(a)	30,000	(e)	7,500
Sales discounts	10,000	18,000	40,000	11,500
Net sales	225,000	(c) 552,000	910,000	(h) 520,000
Cost of merchandise sold	(b)	330,000	(f)	400,000
Gross profit	90,000	(d)	286,500	120,000

E4-11

Multiple-step income
statement

Obj 2

Identify the errors in the following income statement and prepare a corrected income statement:

ARMORTEC COMPANY
Income Statement
For the Year Ended February 28, 2010

Revenue from sales:			
Sales		$5,345,800	
Add: Sales returns and allowances	$120,000		
Sales discounts	60,000	180,000	
Gross sales			$5,525,800
Cost of merchandise sold			3,100,800
Income from operations			$2,425,000
Expenses:			
Selling expenses		$ 800,000	
Administrative expenses		600,000	
Delivery expense		50,000	
Total expenses			1,450,000
			$ 975,000
Other expense:			
Interest revenue			40,000
Gross profit			$ 935,000

E4-12

Sales-related transactions, including the use of credit cards

Obj 3

Illustrate the effects on the accounts and financial statements of recording the following transactions:

a. Sold merchandise for cash, $18,500. The cost of the merchandise sold was $11,000.

b. Sold merchandise on account, $12,000. The cost of the merchandise sold was $7,200.

c. Sold merchandise to customers who used MasterCard and VISA, $115,200. The cost of the merchandise sold was $70,000.

E4-13

Sales returns and allowances

Obj 3

During the year, sales returns and allowances totaled $65,900. The cost of the merchandise returned was $40,000. The accountant recorded all the returns and allowances by decreasing the sales account and decreasing Cost of Merchandise Sold for $65,900.

Was the accountant's method of recording returns acceptable? Explain. In your explanation, include the advantages of using a sales returns and allowances account.

E4-14

Sales-related transactions

Obj 3

After the amount due on a sale of $25,000, terms 1/10, n/eom, is received from a customer within the discount period, the seller consents to the return of the entire shipment. The cost of the merchandise returned was $15,000. (a) What is the amount of the refund owed to the customer? (b) Illustrate the effects on the accounts and financial statements of the return and the refund.

E4-15

Sales-related transactions

Obj 3

✓ d. $9,654

Merchandise is sold on account to a customer for $12,500, terms FOB shipping point, 1/10, n/30. The seller paid the freight of $400. Determine the following: (a) amount of the sale, (b) amount debited to Accounts Receivable, (c) amount of the discount for early payment, and (d) amount due within the discount period.

E4-16

Purchase-related transaction

Obj 4

Newgen Company purchased merchandise on account from a supplier for $9,000, terms 2/10, n/30. Newgen Company returned $1,200 of the merchandise before payment was made and received full credit.

a. If Newgen Company pays the invoice within the discount period, what is the amount of cash required for the payment?

b. Under a perpetual inventory system, what account is decreased by Newgen Company to record the return?

E4-17

Purchase-related transactions

Obj 4

A retailer is considering the purchase of 100 units of a specific item from either of two suppliers. Their offers are as follows:

A: $200 a unit, total of $20,000, 2/10, n/30, no charge for freight.

B: $195 a unit, total of $19,500, 1/10, n/30, plus freight of $400.

Which of the two offers, A or B, yields the lower price?

E4-18

Purchase-related transactions

Obj 4

✓ (c) Cash, decreased $14,700

Versailles Co., a women's clothing store, purchased $18,000 of merchandise from a supplier on account, terms FOB destination, 2/10, n/30. Versailles Co. returned $3,000 of the merchandise, receiving a credit memorandum, and then paid the amount due within the discount period. Illustrate the effects on the accounts and financial statements of Versailles Co. to record (a) the purchase, (b) the merchandise return, and (c) the payment.

[handwritten notes at top: "a. Inventory 25,000 | accts. payable 25,000 | b. cash -24,500 Inv. -500 accts pay -25,000 (Hodiscant)"]

E4-19

Purchase-related transactions

Obj 4

✓ (e) Cash, increased $900

Illustrate the effects on the accounts and financial statements of the following related transactions of Westcoast Diagnostic Company:

a. Purchased $25,000 of merchandise from Presidio Co. on account, terms 2/10, n/30.
b. Paid the amount owed on the invoice within the discount period.
c. Discovered that $5,000 of the merchandise was defective and returned items receiving credit.
d. Purchased $4,000 of merchandise from Presidio Co. on account, terms n/30.
e. Received a check for the balance owed from the return in (c), after deducting for the purchase in (d).

[handwritten notes in left margin: "C. Inv. -4,900 accts pay -4,900 | acck pay 4,000 | D. Inv. 4,000 | E. cash 900 accts. rec 900"]

E4-20

Determining amounts to be paid on invoices

Obj 5

✓ a. $14,200

Determine the amount to be paid in full settlement of each of the following invoices, assuming that credit for returns and allowances was received prior to payment and that all invoices were paid within the discount period.

	Merchandise	Freight Paid by Seller		Returns and Allowances
a.	$15,000	—	FOB destination, n/30	$ 800
b.	10,000	$400	FOB Shipping point, 2/10, n/30	1,200
c.	8,250	—	FOB shipping point, 1/10, n/30	750
d.	2,900	125	FOB shipping point, 2/10, n/30	400
e.	3,850	—	FOB destination, 2/10, n/30	—

E4-21

Sales tax

Obj 5

✓ c. $14,850

A sale of merchandise on account for $13,750 is subject to an 8% sales tax. (a) Should the sales tax be recorded at the time of sale or when payment is received? (b) What is the amount of the sale? (c) What is the amount of the increase to Accounts Receivable? (d) What is the title of the account to which the $1,100 ($13,750 × 8%) is recorded?

E4-22

Sales tax transactions

Obj 5

Illustrate the effects on the accounts and financial statements of recording the following selected transactions:

a. Sold $3,400 of merchandise on account, subject to a sales tax of 5%. The cost of the merchandise sold was $2,000.
b. Paid $41,950 to the state sales tax department for taxes collected.

E4-23

Sales-related transactions

Obj 3

Summit Co., a furniture wholesaler, sells merchandise to Bitone Co. on account, $23,400, terms 2/10, n/30. The cost of the merchandise sold is $14,000. Summit Co. issues a credit memorandum for $4,400 for merchandise returned and subsequently receives the amount due within the discount period. The cost of the merchandise returned is $2,600. Illustrate the effects on the accounts and financial statements of Summit Co. for (a) the sale, including the cost of the merchandise sold, (b) the credit memorandum, including the cost of the returned merchandise, and (c) the receipt of the check for the amount due from Bitone Co.

E4-24

Purchase-related transactions

Obj 4

Based on the data presented in Exercise 4-22, illustrate the effects on the accounts and financial statements of Bitone Co. for (a) the purchase, (b) the return of the merchandise for credit, and (c) the payment of the invoice within the discount period.

E4-25

Adjusting entry for merchandise inventory shrinkage

Obj 7

Iverson Inc.'s perpetual inventory records indicate that $675,150 of merchandise should be on hand on December 31, 2010. The physical inventory indicates that $649,780 of merchandise is actually on hand. Illustrate the effects on the accounts and financial statements of the inventory shrinkage for Iverson Inc. for the year ended December 31, 2010.

Problems

P4-1

Multiple-step income statement and report form of balance sheet

SPREADSHEET

Obj 2

✓ 1. Net income, $120,000

GROUP

The following selected accounts and their current balances appear in the ledger of Case-It Co. for the fiscal year ended November 30, 2010:

Cash	$ 37,700	Sales	$2,703,600
Accounts Receivable	111,600	Sales Returns and Allowances	37,800
Merchandise Inventory	180,000	Sales Discounts	19,800
Office Supplies	5,000	Cost of Merchandise Sold	1,926,000
Prepaid Insurance	12,000	Sales Salaries Expense	378,000
Office Equipment	115,200	Advertising Expense	50,900
Accumulated Depreciation—		Depreciation Expense—	
Office Equipment	49,500	Store Equipment	8,300
Store Equipment	311,500	Miscellaneous Selling Expense	2,000
Accumulated Depreciation—		Office Salaries Expense	73,800
Store Equipment	87,500	Rent Expense	39,900
Accounts Payable	48,600	Insurance Expense	22,950
Salaries Payable	3,600	Depreciation Expense—	
Note Payable		Office Equipment	16,200
(final payment due 2025)	54,000	Office Supplies Expense	1,650
Capital Stock	50,000	Miscellaneous Administrative	
Retained Earnings	404,800	Expense	1,900
Dividends	45,000	Interest Expense	4,400

Instructions

1. Prepare a multiple-step income statement.
2. Prepare a retained earnings statement.
3. Prepare a report form of balance sheet, assuming that the current portion of the note payable is $8,000.
4. Briefly explain (a) how multiple-step and single-step income statements differ and (b) how report-form and account-form balance sheets differ.

P4-2

Single-step income statement

Obj 2

SPREADSHEET

Selected accounts and related amounts for Case-It Co. for the fiscal year ended November 30, 2010, are presented in Problem 4-1.

Instructions

1. Prepare a single-step income statement in the format shown in Exhibit 3.
2. Prepare a retained earnings statement.

P4-3

Sales-related transactions

Objs 3, 5

The following selected transactions were completed by Tropical Supplies Co., which sells supplies primarily to wholesalers and occasionally to retail customers.

Jan. 2. Sold merchandise on account, $8,000, terms FOB shipping point, n/eom. The cost of merchandise sold was $6,000.

Jan. 8. Sold merchandise on account, $20,000, terms FOB destination, 1/10, n/30. The cost of merchandise sold was $14,000.

16. Sold merchandise on account, $12,000, terms FOB shipping point, 1/10, n/30. The cost of merchandise sold was $7,200.

18. Received check for amount due for sale on January 8.

19. Issued credit memorandum for $3,000 for merchandise returned from sale on January 16. The cost of the merchandise returned was $1,800.

26. Received check for amount due for sale on January 16 less credit memorandum of January 19 and discount.

31. Paid Gallatin Delivery Service $1,500 for merchandise delivered during January to customers under shipping terms of FOB destination.

31. Received check for amount due for sale of January 2.

Instructions

Illustrate the effects of each of the preceding transactions on the accounts and financial statements of Tropical Supplies Co. Identify each transaction by date.

P4-4

Purchase-related transactions

Objs 4, 5

The following selected transactions were completed by Silvergate Co. during May of the current year:

May 3. Purchased merchandise for, $16,000, terms FOB destination, 2/10, n/30.

6. Issued debit memorandum for $4,000 of merchandise returned from purchase on May 3.

10. Purchased merchandise, $25,000, terms FOB shipping point, n/eom.

10. Paid freight of $600 on May 10 purchase.

13. Paid for invoice of May 3, less debit memorandum of May 6 and discount.

31. Paid for invoice of May 10.

Instructions

Illustrate the effects of each of the preceding transactions on the accounts and financial statements of Silvergate Co. Identify each transaction by date.

P4-5

Sales-related and purchase-related transactions for seller and buyer

Obj 6

The following selected transactions were completed during June between Shapiro Company and Bacarti Company:

June 8. Shapiro Company sold merchandise on account to Bacarti Company, $24,000, terms FOB destination, 1/15, n/eom. The cost of the merchandise sold was $17,000.

8. Shapiro Company paid transportation costs of $500 for delivery of merchandise sold to Bacarti Company on June 8.

12. Bacarti Company returned $6,000 of merchandise purchased on account on June 8 from Shapiro Company. The cost of the merchandise returned was $4,000.

23. Bacarti Company paid Shapiro Company for purchase of June 8, less discount and less return of June 12.

24. Shapiro Company sold merchandise on account to Bacarti Company, $15,000, terms FOB shipping point, n/eom. The cost of the merchandise sold was $9,000.

26. Bacarti Company paid transportation charges of $400 on June 24 purchase from Shapiro Company.

30. Bacarti Company paid Shapiro Company on account for purchase of June 24.

4.5

Instructions

Illustrate the effects of each of the preceding transactions on the accounts and financial statements of (1) Shapiro Company and (2) Bacarti Company. Identify each transaction by date.

P4-6

Statement of cash flows using indirect method

Appendix

✓ 1. Net cash flows from operating activities: $70,680

For the year ending August 31, 2011, Gymboree Systems Inc. reported net income of $90,600 and paid dividends of $27,000. Comparative balance sheets as of August 31, 2011 and 2010, are as follows:

GYMBOREE SYSTEMS INC.
Balance Sheets

	August 31, 2011	August 31, 2010	Changes Increase (Decrease)
Assets			
Current assets:			
Cash	$ 79,425	$ 62,250	$17,175
Accounts receivable	114,120	78,000	36,120
Merchandise inventory	93,225	89,550	3,675
Office supplies	720	900	(180)
Prepaid insurance	3,975	4,500	(525)
Total current assets	$ 291,465	$235,200	$56,265
Property, plant, and equipment:			
Land	$ 30,000	$ 30,000	$ 0
Store equipment	40,650	30,000	10,650
Accumulated depreciation—store equipment	(8,550)	(3,900)	(4,650)
Office equipment	23,355	15,000	8,355
Accumulated depreciation—office equipment	(7,080)	(3,345)	(3,735)
Total property, plant, and equipment	$ 78,375	$ 67,755	$10,620
Total assets	$ 369,840	$302,955	$66,885
Liabilities			
Current liabilities:			
Accounts payable	$ 33,630	$ 21,405	$12,225
Notes payable (current portion)	7,500	7,500	0
Salaries payable	1,710	2,250	(540)
Unearned rent	2,700	3,600	(900)
Total current liabilities	$ 45,540	$ 34,755	$10,785
Long-term liabilities:			
Notes payable (final payment due 2015)	30,000	37,500	(7,500)
Total liabilities	$ 75,540	$ 72,255	$ 3,285
Stockholders' Equity			
Capital stock	$ 37,500	$ 37,500	$ 0
Retained earnings	256,800	193,200	63,600
Total stockholders' equity	$ 294,300	$230,700	$63,600
Total liabilities and stockholders' equity	$ 369,840	$302,955	$66,885

Instructions

4.6

1. Prepare a statement of cash flows, using the indirect method.
2. Why is depreciation added to net income in determining net cash flows from operating activities? Explain.

Activities

A4-1

Ethics and professional conduct in business

ETHICS

On February 15, 2010, Tropical Connection Company, a garden retailer, purchased $25,000 of seed, terms 2/10, n/30, from Midwest Seed Co. Even though the discount period had expired, Lydia DeLay subtracted the discount of $500 when she processed the documents for payment on March 16, 2010.

Discuss whether Lydia Delay behaved in a professional manner by subtracting the discount, even though the discount period had expired.

A4-2

Purchases discounts and accounts payable

The Encore Video Store Co. is owned and operated by Sergio Alonzo. The following is an excerpt from a conversation between Sergio Alonzo and Suzie Engel, the chief accountant for The Encore Video Store.

Sergio: Suzie, I've got a question about this recent balance sheet.

Suzie: Sure, what's your question?

Sergio: Well, as you know, I'm applying for a bank loan to finance our new store in Cherokee, and I noticed that the accounts payable are listed as $120,000.

Suzie: That's right. Approximately $100,000 of that represents amounts due our suppliers, and the remainder is miscellaneous payables to creditors for utilities, office equipment, supplies, etc.

Sergio: That's what I thought. But as you know, we normally receive a 2% discount from our suppliers for earlier payment, and we always try to take the discount.

Suzie: That's right. I can't remember the last time we missed a discount.

Sergio: Well, in that case, it seems to me the accounts payable should be listed minus the 2% discount. Let's list the accounts payable due suppliers as $98,000, rather than $100,000. Every little bit helps. You never know. It might make the difference between getting the loan and not.

How would you respond to Sergio Alonzo's request?

A4-3

Determining cost of purchase

The following is an excerpt from a conversation between Ted Mackie and Laurie Van Dorn. Ted is debating whether to buy a stereo system from Classic Audio, a locally owned electronics store, or Sound Unlimited, an online electronics company.

Ted: Laurie, I don't know what to do about buying my new stereo.

Laurie: What's the problem?

Ted: Well, I can buy it locally at Classic Audio for $490.00. However, Sound Unlimited has the same system listed for $499.99.

Laurie: So what's the big deal? Buy it from Classic Audio.

Ted: It's not quite that simple. Sound Unlimited said something about not having to pay sales tax, since I was out of state.

Laurie: Yes, that's a good point. If you buy it at Classic Audio, they'll charge you 6% sales tax.

Ted: But Sound Unlimited charges $13.99 for shipping and handling. If I have them send it next-day air, it'll cost $24.99 for shipping and handling.

Laurie: I guess it is a little confusing.

Ted: That's not all. Classic Audio will give an additional 1% discount if I pay cash. Otherwise, they will let me use my VISA, or I can pay it off in three monthly installments.

Laurie: Anything else???

Ted: Well…Sound Unlimited says I have to charge it on my VISA. They don't accept checks.

Laurie: I am not surprised. Many online stores don't accept checks.

Ted: I give up. What would you do?

1. Assuming that Sound Unlimited doesn't charge sales tax on the sale to Ted, which company is offering the best buy?
2. What might be some considerations other than price that might influence Ted's decision on where to buy the stereo system?

A4-4

Sales discounts

Your sister operates Ennis Parts Company, an online boat parts distributorship that is in its third year of operation. The income statement is shown below and was recently prepared for the year ended March 31, 2010.

ENNIS PARTS COMPANY
Income Statement
For the Year Ended March 31, 2010

Revenues:		
Net sales		$400,000
Interest revenue		5,000
Total revenues		$405,000
Expenses:		
Cost of merchandise sold	$260,000	
Selling expenses	45,000	
Administrative expenses	24,275	
Interest expense	7,500	
Total expenses		336,775
Net income		$ 68,225

Your sister is considering a proposal to increase net income by offering sales discounts of 2/15, n/30, and by shipping all merchandise FOB shipping point. Currently, no sales discounts are allowed and merchandise is shipped FOB destination. It is estimated that these credit terms will increase net sales by 15%. The ratio of the cost of merchandise sold to net sales is expected to be 65%. All selling and administrative expenses are expected to remain unchanged, except for store supplies, miscellaneous selling, office supplies, and miscellaneous administrative expenses, which are expected to increase proportionately with

increased net sales. The amounts of these preceding items for the year ended March 31, 2010, were as follows:

Store supplies expense	$6,000	Office supplies expense	$1,000
Miscellaneous selling expense	1,500	Miscellaneous administrative expense	500

The other income and other expense items will remain unchanged. The shipment of all merchandise FOB shipping point will eliminate all delivery expenses, which for the year ended March 31, 2010, were $9,375.

1. Prepare a projected single-step income statement for the year ending March 31, 2011, based on the proposal. Assume all sales are collected within the discount period.
2. a. Based on the projected income statement in (1), would you recommend implementation of the proposed changes?
   b. Describe any possible concerns you may have related to the proposed changes described in (1).

A4-5

Shopping for a television

GROUP

Assume that you are planning to purchase a 50-inch plasma television. In groups of three or four, determine the lowest cost for the television, considering the available alternatives and the advantages and disadvantages of each alternative. For example, you could purchase locally, through mail order, or through an Internet shopping service. Consider such factors as delivery charges, interest-free financing, discounts, coupons, and availability of warranty services. Prepare a report for presentation to the class.

Answers to Self-Examination Questions

1. **A** A debit memorandum (answer A), issued by the buyer, indicates the amount the buyer proposes to decrease the accounts payable account. A credit memorandum (answer B), issued by the seller, indicates the amount the seller proposes to decrease the accounts receivable account. An invoice (answer C) or a bill (answer D), issued by the seller, indicates the amount and terms of the sale.

2. **C** The amount of discount for early payment is $10 (answer C), or 1% of $1,000. Although the $50 of transportation costs paid by the seller increases the customer's account, the customer is not entitled to a discount on that amount.

3. **B** The single-step form of income statement (answer B) is so named because the total of all expenses is deducted in one step from the total of all revenues. The multiple-step form (answer A) includes numerous sections and subsections with several subtotals. The account form (answer C) and the report form (answer D) are two common forms of the balance sheet.

4. **C** Gross profit (answer C) is the excess of net sales over the cost of merchandise sold. Operating income (answer A) or income from operations (answer B) is the excess of gross profit over operating expenses. Net income (answer D) is the final figure on the income statement after all revenues and expenses have been reported.

5. **B** The inventory shrinkage, $15,000, is the difference between the book inventory, $290,000, and the physical inventory, $275,000. The effect of the inventory shrinkage on the accounts is to increase Cost of Merchandise Sold and decrease Inventory by $15,000.

Sarbanes-Oxley, Internal Control, and Cash

Controls are a part of your everyday life. At one extreme, laws are used to limit your behavior. For example, the speed limit is a control on your driving, designed for traffic safety. In addition, you are also affected by many nonlegal controls. For example, recording checks in your checkbook is a control that you can use at the end of the month to verify the accuracy of your bank statement. In addition, banks give you a personal identification number (PIN) as a control against unauthorized access to your cash if you lose your automated teller machine (ATM) card. As you can see, you use and encounter controls every day.

Just as there are many examples of controls throughout society, businesses must also implement controls to help guide the behavior of their managers, employees, and customers. For example, **eBay Inc.** maintains an Internet-based marketplace for the sale of goods and services. Using eBay's online platform, buyers and sellers can browse, buy, and sell a wide variety of items including antiques and used cars. However, in order to maintain the integrity and trust of its buyers and sellers, eBay must have controls to ensure that buyers pay for their items and sellers don't misrepresent their items or fail to deliver sales. One such control eBay uses is a feedback forum that estabilishes buyer and seller reputations. A prospective buyer or seller can view the member's reputation and feedback comments before completing a transaction. Dishonest or unfair trading can lead to a negative reputation and even suspension or cancellation.

This chapter discusses controls that can be included in accounting systems to provide reasonable assurance that the financial statements are reliable. Controls over cash that you can use to determine whether your bank has made any errors in your account are also discussed. This chapter begins by discussing the Sarbanes-Oxley Act of 2002 and its impact on controls and financial reporting.

Obj 1 Describe the
Sarbanes-Oxley Act of 2002
and its impact on internal
controls and financial
reporting.

The ex-CEO of *WorldCom*,
Bernard Ebbers, was sen-
tenced to 25 years in prison.

Sarbanes-Oxley Act of 2002

During the financial scandals of the early 2000s, stockholders, creditors, and other investors lost billions of dollars.[1] As a result, the United States Congress passed the **Sarbanes-Oxley Act of 2002**. This act, often referred to as *Sarbanes-Oxley*, is one of the most important laws affecting U.S. companies in recent history. The purpose of Sarbanes-Oxley is to restore public confidence and trust in the financial reporting of companies.

Sarbanes-Oxley applies only to companies whose stock is traded on public exchanges, referred to as *publicly held companies*. However, Sarbanes-Oxley highlighted the importance of assessing the financial controls and reporting of all companies. As a result, companies of all sizes have been influenced by Sarbanes-Oxley.

Sarbanes-Oxley emphasizes the importance of effective internal control.[2] **Internal control** is defined as the procedures and processes used by a company to:

1. Safeguard its assets.

2. Process information accurately.

3. Ensure compliance with laws and regulations.

Sarbanes-Oxley requires companies to maintain effective internal controls over the recording of transactions and the preparing of financial statements. Such controls are important because they deter fraud and prevent misleading financial statements as shown below.

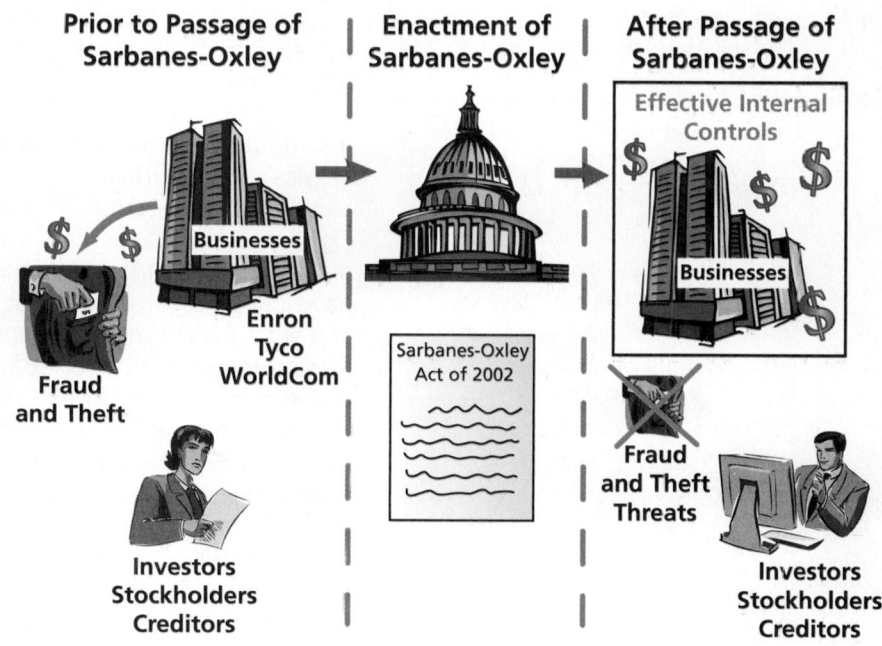

Sarbanes-Oxley also requires companies and their independent accountants to report on the effectiveness of the company's internal controls.[3] These

---

[1] Exhibit 13 in Chapter 1 briefly summarizes these scandals.

[2] Sarbanes-Oxley also has important implications for corporate governance and the regulation of the public accounting profession. This chapter, however, focuses on the internal control implications of Sarbanes-Oxley.

[3] These reporting requirements are required under Section 404 of the act. As a result, these requirements and reports are often referred to as 404 requirements and 404 reports.

reports are required to be filed with the company's annual 10-K report with the Securities and Exchange Commission. Companies are also encouraged to include these reports in their annual reports to stockholders. An example of such a report by the management of *Nike* is shown in Exhibit 1.

It is estimated that companies spend millions each year to comply with the requirements of Sarbanes-Oxley.

EXHIBIT 1   Sarbanes-Oxley Report of Nike

Management's Annual Report on Internal Control Over Financial Reporting

Management is responsible for establishing and maintaining adequate internal control over financial reporting.... Under the supervision and with the participation of our Chief Executive Officer and Chief Financial Officer, our management conducted an evaluation of the effectiveness of our internal control over financial reporting based upon the framework in *Internal Control—Integrated Framework* issued by the Committee of Sponsoring Organizations of the Treadway Commission. Based on that evaluation, our management concluded that our internal control over financial reporting is effective as of May 31, 2009....

PricewaterhouseCoopers LLP, an independent registered public accounting firm, has audited ... management's assessment of the effectiveness of our internal control over financial reporting ... and ... the effectiveness of our internal control over financial reporting ... as stated in their report....

MARK G. PARKER
Chief Executive Officer and President

DONALD W. BLAIR
Chief Financial Officer

Exhibit 1 indicates that Nike based its evaluation of internal controls on *Internal Control—Integrated Framework,* which was issued by the Committee of Sponsoring Organizations (COSO) of the Treadway Commission. This framework is the standard by which companies design, analyze, and evaluate internal controls.

Internal Control

Internal Control—Integrated Framework is used as the basis for discussing internal controls.[4] In this section, the objectives of internal control are described followed by a discussion of how these objectives can be achieved through the *Integrated Framework*'s five elements of internal control.

Obj 2 Describe and illustrate the objectives and elements of internal control.

Information on *Internal Control—Integrated Framework* can be found on COSO's Web site at http://www.coso.org/.

Objectives of Internal Control

The objectives of internal control are to provide reasonable assurance that:

1. Assets are safeguarded and used for business purposes.

2. Business information is accurate.

3. Employees and managers comply with laws and regulations.

---

[4] *Internal Control—Integrated Framework* by the Committee of Sponsoring Organizations of the Treadway Commission, 1992.

These objectives are illustrated below.

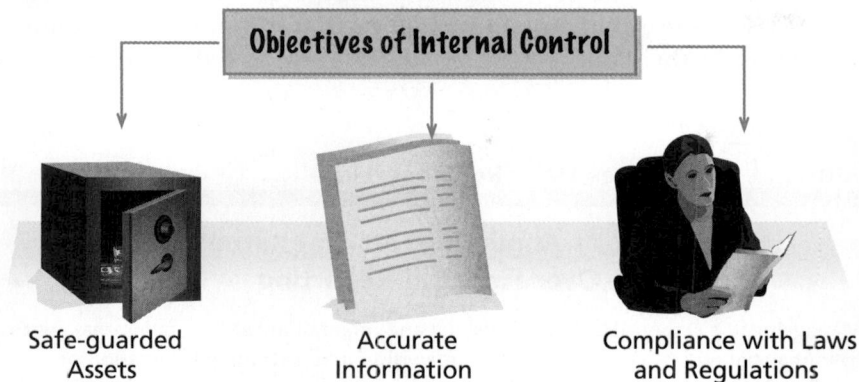

Safe-guarded Assets   Accurate Information   Compliance with Laws and Regulations

The Association of Certified Fraud Examiners has estimated that businesses will lose over $650 billion, or around 5% of revenue, to employee fraud.
Source: *2006 Report to the Nation: Occupational Fraud and Abuse,* Association of Certified Fraud Examiners.

Internal control can safeguard assets by preventing theft, fraud, misuse, or misplacement. A serious concern of internal control is preventing employee fraud. **Employee fraud** is the intentional act of deceiving an employer for personal gain. Such fraud may range from minor overstating of a travel expense report to stealing millions of dollars. Employees stealing from a business often adjust the accounting records in order to hide their fraud. Thus, employee fraud usually affects the accuracy of business information.

Accurate information is necessary to successfully operate a business. Businesses must also comply with laws, regulations, and financial reporting standards. Examples of such standards include environmental regulations, safety regulations, and generally accepted accounting principles (GAAP).

Elements of Internal Control

The three internal control objectives can be achieved by applying the five **elements of internal control** set forth by the *Integrated Framework*.[5] These elements are as follows:

1. Control environment
2. Risk assessment
3. Control procedures
4. Monitoring
5. Information and communication

The elements of internal control are illustrated in Exhibit 2. In this exhibit, the elements of internal control form an umbrella over the business to protect it from control threats. The control environment is the size of the umbrella. Risk assessment, control procedures, and monitoring are the fabric of the umbrella, which keep it from leaking. Information and communication connect the umbrella to management.

Control Environment

The control environment is the overall attitude of management and employees about the importance of controls. Three factors influencing a company's control environment are listed on the next page.

[5] Ibid., 12–14.

EXHIBIT | 2 | Elements of Internal Control

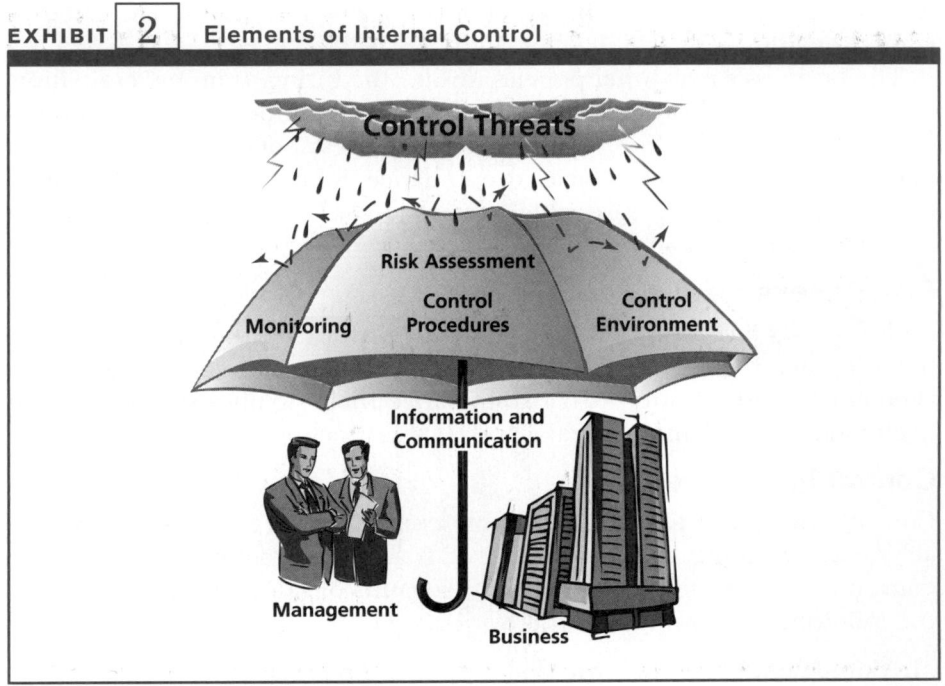

1. Management's philosophy and operating style
2. The company's organizational structure
3. The company's personnel policies

Control Environment

Management's philosophy and operating style relates to whether management emphasizes the importance of internal controls. An emphasis on controls and adherence to control policies creates an effective control environment. In contrast, overemphasizing operating goals and tolerating deviations from control policies creates an ineffective control environment.

The business's organizational structure is the framework for planning and controlling operations. For example, a retail store chain might organize each of its stores as separate business units. Each store manager has full authority over pricing and other operating activities. In such a structure,

each store manager has the responsibility for establishing an effective control environment.

The business's personnel policies involve the hiring, training, evaluation, compensation, and promotion of employees. In addition, job descriptions, employee codes of ethics, and conflict-of-interest policies are part of the personnel policies. Such policies can enhance the internal control environment if they provide reasonable assurance that only competent, honest employees are hired and retained.

Risk Assessment

All businesses face risks such as changes in customer requirements, competitive threats, regulatory changes, and changes in economic factors. Management should identify such risks, analyze their significance, assess their likelihood of occurring, and take any necessary actions to minimize them.

Control Procedures

A bank officer who was not required to take vacations stole almost $5 million by printing fake certificates of deposit. The theft was discovered when the bank began requiring all employees to take vacations.

Control procedures provide reasonable assurance that business goals will be achieved, including the prevention of fraud. Control procedures, which constitute one of the most important elements of internal control, include the following as shown in Exhibit 3.

1. Competent personnel, rotating duties, and mandatory vacations

2. Separating responsibilities for related operations

3. Separating operations, custody of assets, and accounting

4. Proofs and security measures

EXHIBIT 3 | **Internal Control Procedures**

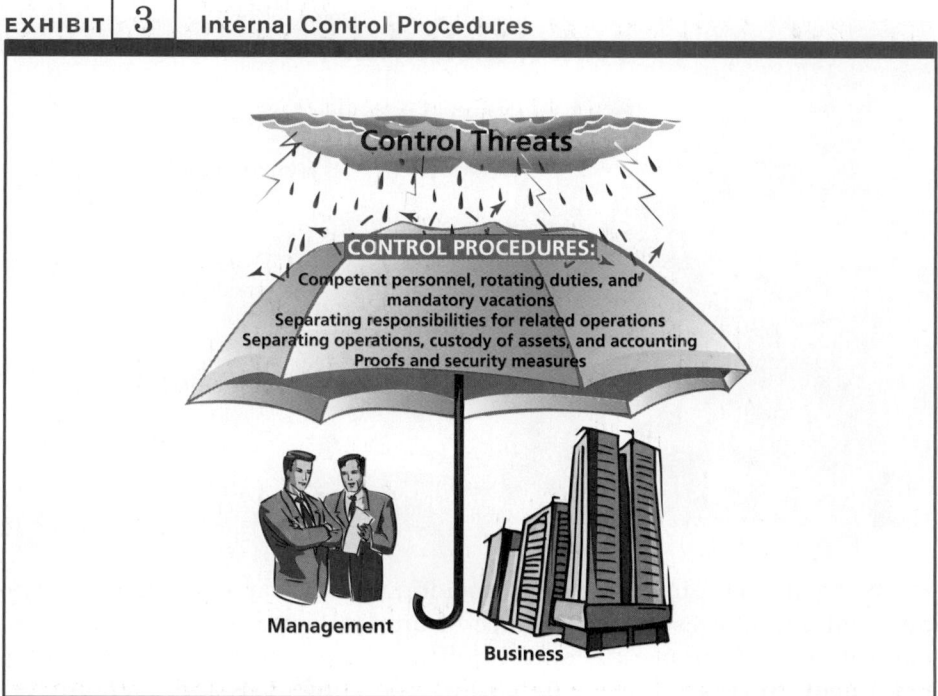

Competent Personnel, Rotating Duties, and Mandatory Vacations

A successful company needs competent employees who are able to perform the duties that they are assigned. Procedures should be established for

properly training and supervising employees. It is also advisable to rotate duties of accounting personnel and mandate vacations for all employees. In this way, employees are encouraged to adhere to procedures. Cases of employee fraud are often discovered when a long-term employee, who never took vacations, missed work because of an illness or another unavoidable reason.

Separating Responsibilities for Related Operations

The responsibility for related operations should be divided among two or more persons. This decreases the possibility of errors and fraud. For example, if the same person orders supplies, verifies the receipt of the supplies, and pays the supplier, the following abuses may occur:

1. Orders may be placed on the basis of friendship with a supplier, rather than on price, quality, and other objective factors.
2. The quantity and quality of supplies received may not be verified; thus, the company may pay for supplies not received or that are of poor quality.
3. Supplies may be stolen by the employee.
4. The validity and accuracy of invoices may not be verified; hence, the company may pay false or inaccurate invoices.

For the preceding reasons, the responsibilities for purchasing, receiving, and paying for supplies should be divided among three persons or departments.

An accounting clerk for the Grant County (Washington) Alcoholism Program was in charge of collecting money, making deposits, and keeping the records. While the clerk was away on maternity leave, the replacement clerk discovered a fraud: $17,800 in fees had been collected but had been hidden for personal gain.

Separating Operations, Custody of Assets, and Accounting

The responsibilities for operations, custody of assets, and accounting should be separated. In this way, the accounting records serve as an independent check on the operating managers and the employees who have custody of assets.

To illustrate, employees who handle cash receipts should not record cash receipts in the accounting records. To do so would allow employees to borrow or steal cash and hide the theft in the accounting records. Likewise, operating managers should not also record the results of operations. To do so would allow the managers to distort the accounting reports to show favorable results, which might allow them to receive larger bonuses.

An accounts payable clerk created false invoices and submitted them for payment. The clerk obtained the checks, cashed them, and stole thousands of dollars.

Proofs and Security Measures

Proofs and security measures are used to safeguard assets and ensure reliable accounting data. Proofs involve procedures such as authorization, approval, and reconciliation. For example, an employee planning to travel on company business may be required to complete a "travel request" form for a manager's authorization and approval.

Documents used for authorization and approval should be prenumbered, accounted for, and safeguarded. Prenumbering of documents helps prevent transactions from being recorded more than once or not at all. In addition, accounting for and safeguarding prenumbered documents helps prevent fraudulent transactions from being recorded. For example, blank checks are prenumbered and safeguarded. Once a payment has been properly authorized and approved, the checks are filled out and issued.

Reconciliations are also an important control. Later in this chapter, the use of bank reconciliations as an aid in controlling cash is described and illustrated.

A 24-hour convenience store could use a security guard, video cameras, and an alarm system to deter robberies.

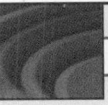

INTEGRITY, OBJECTIVITY, AND ETHICS IN BUSINESS

Tips on Preventing Employee Fraud in Small Companies

- Do not have the same employee write company checks and keep the books. Look for payments to vendors you don't know or payments to vendors whose names appear to be misspelled.

- If your business has a computer system, restrict access to accounting files as much as possible. Also, keep a backup copy of your accounting files and store it at an off-site location.

- Be wary of anybody working in finance that declines to take vacations. They may be afraid that a replacement will uncover fraud.

- Require and monitor supporting documentation (such as vendor invoices) before signing checks.

- Track the number of credit card bills you sign monthly.

- Limit and monitor access to important documents and supplies, such as blank checks and signature stamps.

- Check W-2 forms against your payroll annually to make sure you're not carrying any fictitious employees.

- Rely on yourself, not on your accountant, to spot fraud.

Source: Steve Kaufman, "Embezzlement Common at Small Companies," Knight-Ridder Newspapers, reported in *Athens Daily News/Athens Banner-Herald,* March 10, 1996, p. 4D.

Security measures involve measures to safeguard assets. For example, cash on hand should be kept in a cash register or safe. Inventory not on display should be stored in a locked storeroom or warehouse. Accounting records such as the accounts receivable subsidiary ledger should also be safeguarded to prevent their loss. For example, electronically maintained accounting records should be safeguarded with access codes and backed up so that any lost or damaged files could be recovered if necessary.

Monitoring

Monitoring the internal control system is used to locate weaknesses and improve controls. Monitoring often includes observing employee behavior and the accounting system for indicators of control problems. Some such indicators are shown in Exhibit 4.[6]

Evaluations of controls are often performed when there are major changes in strategy, senior management, business structure, or operations. Internal auditors, who are independent of operations, usually perform such evaluations. Internal auditors are also responsible for day-to-day monitoring of controls. External auditors also evaluate and report on internal control as part of their annual financial statement audit.

Information and Communication

Information and communication is an essential element of internal control. Information about the control environment, risk assessment, control procedures, and monitoring is used by management for guiding operations and ensuring compliance with reporting, legal, and regulatory requirements. Management also uses external information to assess events and conditions that impact decision making and external reporting. For example, management uses pronouncements of the Financial Accounting Standards Board (FASB) to assess the impact of changes in reporting standards on the financial statements.

[6] Edwin C. Bliss, "Employee Theft," *Boardroom Reports,* July 15, 1994, pp. 5–6.

EXHIBIT 4   Warning Signs of Internal Control Problems

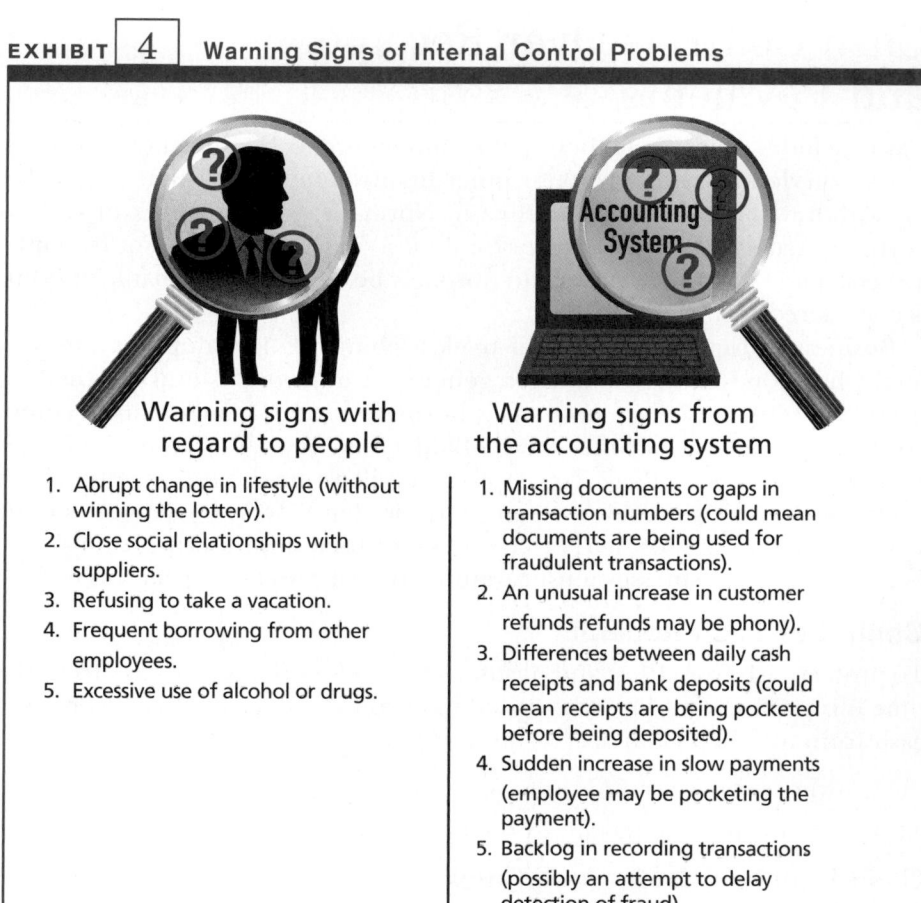

Warning signs with regard to people

1. Abrupt change in lifestyle (without winning the lottery).
2. Close social relationships with suppliers.
3. Refusing to take a vacation.
4. Frequent borrowing from other employees.
5. Excessive use of alcohol or drugs.

Warning signs from the accounting system

1. Missing documents or gaps in transaction numbers (could mean documents are being used for fraudulent transactions).
2. An unusual increase in customer refunds refunds may be phony).
3. Differences between daily cash receipts and bank deposits (could mean receipts are being pocketed before being deposited).
4. Sudden increase in slow payments (employee may be pocketing the payment).
5. Backlog in recording transactions (possibly an attempt to delay detection of fraud).

Limitations of Internal Control

Internal control systems can provide only reasonable assurance for safeguarding assets, processing accurate information, and compliance with laws and regulations. In other words, internal controls are not a guarantee. This is due to the following factors:

1. The human element of controls
2. Cost-benefit considerations

The *human element* recognizes that controls are applied and used by humans. As a result, human errors can occur because of fatigue, carelessness, confusion, or misjudgment. For example, an employee may unintentionally shortchange a customer or miscount the amount of inventory received from a supplier. In addition, two or more employees may collude together to defeat or circumvent internal controls. This latter case often involves fraud and the theft of assets. For example, the cashier and the accounts receivable clerk might collude to steal customer payments on account.

Cost-benefit considerations recognize that costs of internal controls should not exceed their benefits. For example, retail stores could eliminate shoplifting by searching all customers before they leave the store. However, such a control procedure would upset customers and result in lost sales. Instead, retailers use cameras or signs saying *We prosecute all shoplifters.*

Obj 3 Describe and illustrate the application of internal controls to cash.

Cash Controls Over Receipts and Payments

Cash includes coins, currency (paper money), checks, and money orders. Money on deposit with a bank or other financial institution that is available for withdrawal is also considered cash. Normally, you can think of cash as anything that a bank would accept for deposit in your account. For example, a check made payable to you could normally be deposited in a bank and thus is considered cash.

Businesses usually have several bank accounts. For example, a business might have one bank account for general cash payments and another for payroll. A separate ledger account is normally used for each bank account. For example, a bank account at City Bank could be identified in the ledger as *Cash in Bank—City Bank*. To simplify, we will assume in this chapter that a company has only *one* bank account, which is identified in the ledger as *Cash*.

Cash is the asset most likely to be stolen or used improperly in a business. For this reason, businesses must carefully control cash and cash transactions.

Control of Cash Receipts

To protect cash from theft and misuse, a business must control cash from the time it is received until it is deposited in a bank. Businesses normally receive cash from two main sources.

1. Customers purchasing products or services
2. Customers making payments on account

Cash Received from Cash Sales

An important control to protect cash received in over-the-counter sales is a cash register. The use of a cash register to control cash is shown below.

The Internet has given rise to a form of cash called "cybercash," which is used for Internet transactions, such as being used in conjunction with **PayPal**.

Fast-food restaurants, such as **McDonald's**, receive cash primarily from over-the-counter sales. Internet retailers, such **Amazon.com**, receive cash primarily through electronic funds transfers from credit card companies.

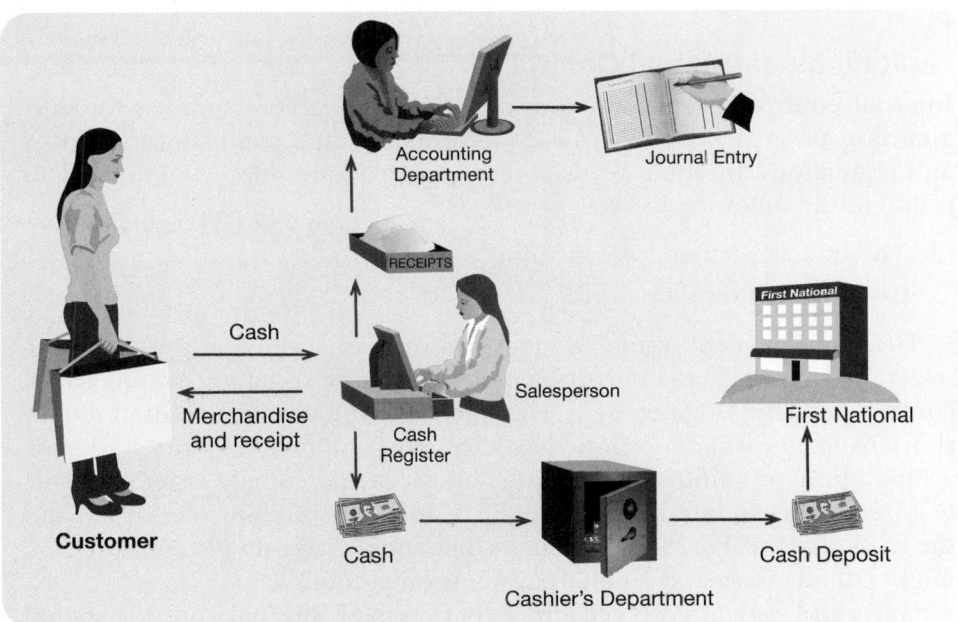

A cash register controls cash as follows:

1. At the beginning of every work shift, each cash register clerk is given a cash drawer containing a predetermined amount of cash. This amount is used for making change for customers and is sometimes called a *change fund*.

2. When a salesperson enters the amount of a sale, the cash register displays the amount to the customer. This allows the customer to verify that the clerk has charged the correct amount. The customer also receives a cash receipt.

3. At the end of the shift, the clerk and the supervisor count the cash in the clerk's cash drawer. The amount of cash in each drawer should equal the beginning amount of cash plus the cash sales for the day.

4. The supervisor takes the cash to the Cashier's Department where it is placed in a safe.

5. The supervisor forwards the clerk's cash register receipts to the Accounting Department.

6. The cashier prepares a bank deposit ticket.

7. The cashier deposits the cash in the bank, or the cash is picked up by an armored car service, such as Wells Fargo.

8. The Accounting Department summarizes the cash receipts and records the day's cash sales.

9. When cash is deposited in the bank, the bank normally stamps a duplicate copy of the deposit ticket with the amount received. This bank receipt is returned to the Accounting Department, where it is compared to the total amount that should have been deposited. This control helps ensure that all the cash is deposited and that no cash is lost or stolen on the way to the bank. Any shortages are thus promptly detected.

Salespersons may make errors in making change for customers or in ringing up cash sales. As a result, the amount of cash on hand may differ from the amount of cash sales. Such differences are recorded in a **cash short and over account**.

To illustrate, assume the following cash register data for May 3:

Cash register total for cash sales	$35,690
Cash receipts from cash sales	35,668

The cash sales are recorded in the normal manner. The cash shortage of $22 ($25,690 − $25,688) is recorded as a normal operating expense. This is done by recording a negative $22 under the account titled Cash Short and Over.

A cash overage is recorded as a positive amount in Cash Short and Over. At the end of the period, a negative balance in the Cash Short and Over is reported as a Miscellaneous operating expense. A positive balance in Cash Short and Over is reported as Other income.

Cash Received in the Mail

Cash is received in the mail when customers pay their bills. This cash is usually in the form of checks and money orders. Most companies design their invoices so that customers return a portion of the invoice, called a *remittance advice,* with their payment. Remittance advices may be used to control cash received in the mail as follows:

1. An employee opens the incoming mail and compares the amount of cash received with the amount shown on the remittance advice. If a customer does not return a remittance advice, the employee prepares one. The remittance advice serves as a record of the cash initially received. It also

helps ensure that the posting to the customer's account is for the amount of cash received.

2. The employee opening the mail stamps checks and money orders "For Deposit Only" in the bank account of the business.

3. The remittance advices and their summary totals are delivered to the Accounting Department.

4. All cash and money orders are delivered to the Cashier's Department.

5. The cashier prepares a bank deposit ticket.

6. The cashier deposits the cash in the bank, or the cash is picked up by an armored car service, such as Wells Fargo.

7. An accounting clerk records the cash received and posts the amounts to the customer accounts.

8. When cash is deposited in the bank, the bank normally stamps a duplicate copy of the deposit ticket with the amount received. This bank receipt is returned to the Accounting Department, where it is compared to the total amount that should have been deposited. This control helps ensure that all cash is deposited and that no cash is lost or stolen on the way to the bank. Any shortages are thus promptly detected.

Separating the duties of the Cashier's Department, which handles cash, and the Accounting Department, which records cash, is a control. If Accounting Department employees both handle and record cash, an employee could steal cash and change the accounting records to hide the theft.

Cash Received by EFT

Cash may also be received from customers through **electronic funds transfer (EFT)**. For example, customers may authorize automatic electronic transfers from their checking accounts to pay monthly bills for such items as cell phone, Internet, and electric services. In such cases, the company sends the customer's bank a signed form from the customer authorizing the monthly electronic transfers. Each month, the company notifies the customer's bank of the amount of the transfer and the date the transfer should take place. On the due date, the company records the electronic transfer as a receipt of cash to its bank account and posts the amount paid to the customer's account.

Companies encourage customers to use EFT for the following reasons:

1. EFTs cost less than receiving cash payments through the mail.

2. EFTs enhance internal controls over cash since the cash is received directly by the bank without any employees handling cash.

3. EFTs reduce late payments from customers and speed up the processing of cash receipts.

Control of Cash Payments

The control of cash payments should provide reasonable assurance that:

1. Payments are made for only authorized transactions.

2. Cash is used effectively and efficiently. For example, controls should ensure that all available purchase discounts are taken.

In a small business, an owner/manager may authorize payments based on personal knowledge. In a large business, however, purchasing goods, inspecting the goods received, and verifying the invoices are usually performed by different employees. These duties must be coordinated to ensure that proper payments are made to creditors. One system used for this purpose is the voucher system.

Voucher System

A **voucher system** is a set of procedures for authorizing and recording liabilities and cash payments. A **voucher** is any document that serves as proof of authority to pay cash or issue an electronic funds transfer. An invoice that has been approved for payment could be considered a voucher. In many businesses, however, a voucher is a special form used to record data about a liability and the details of its payment.

In a manual system, a voucher is normally prepared after all necessary supporting documents have been received. For the purchase of goods, a voucher is supported by the supplier's invoice, a purchase order, and a receiving report. After a voucher is prepared, it is submitted for approval. Once approved, the voucher is recorded in the accounts and filed by due date. Upon payment, the voucher is recorded in the same manner as the payment of an account payable.

In a computerized system, data from the supporting documents (such as purchase orders, receiving reports, and suppliers' invoices) are entered directly into computer files. At the due date, the checks are automatically generated and mailed to creditors. At that time, the voucher is electronically transferred to a paid voucher file.

Cash Paid by EFT

Cash can also be paid by electronic funds transfer systems. For example, many companies pay their employees by EFT. Under such a system, employees authorize the deposit of their payroll checks directly into their checking accounts. Each pay period, the company transfers the employees' net pay to their checking accounts through the use of EFT. Many companies also use EFT systems to pay their suppliers and other vendors.

Bank Accounts

A major reason that companies use bank accounts is for internal control. Some of the control advantages of using bank accounts are as follows:

1. Bank accounts reduce the amount of cash on hand.
2. Bank accounts provide an independent recording of cash transactions. Reconciling the balance of the cash account in the company's records with the cash balance according to the bank is an important control.
3. Use of bank accounts facilitates the transfer of funds using EFT systems.

Bank Statement

Banks usually maintain a record of all checking account transactions. A summary of all transactions, called a **bank statement**, is mailed to the company (depositor) or made available online, usually each month. The bank

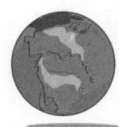

Howard Schultz & Associates (HS&A) specializes in reviewing cash payments for its clients. HS&A searches for errors, such as duplicate payments, failures to take discounts, and inaccurate computations. Amounts recovered for clients range from thousands to millions of dollars.

Many businesses and individuals are now using Internet banking services, which provide for the payment of funds electronically.

Obj 4 Describe the nature of a bank account and its use in controlling cash.

statement shows the beginning balance, additions, deductions, and the ending balance. A typical bank statement is shown in Exhibit 5.

Checks or copies of the checks listed in the order that they were paid by the bank may accompany the bank statement. If paid checks are returned, they are stamped "Paid," together with the date of payment. Many banks no longer return checks or check copies. Instead, the check payment information is available online.

The depositor's checking account balance in the bank records is a liability. A credit memo entry on the bank statement indicates an increase in the depositor's account. Likewise, a debit memo entry on the bank statement indicates a decrease in the depositor's account. This relationship is shown below:

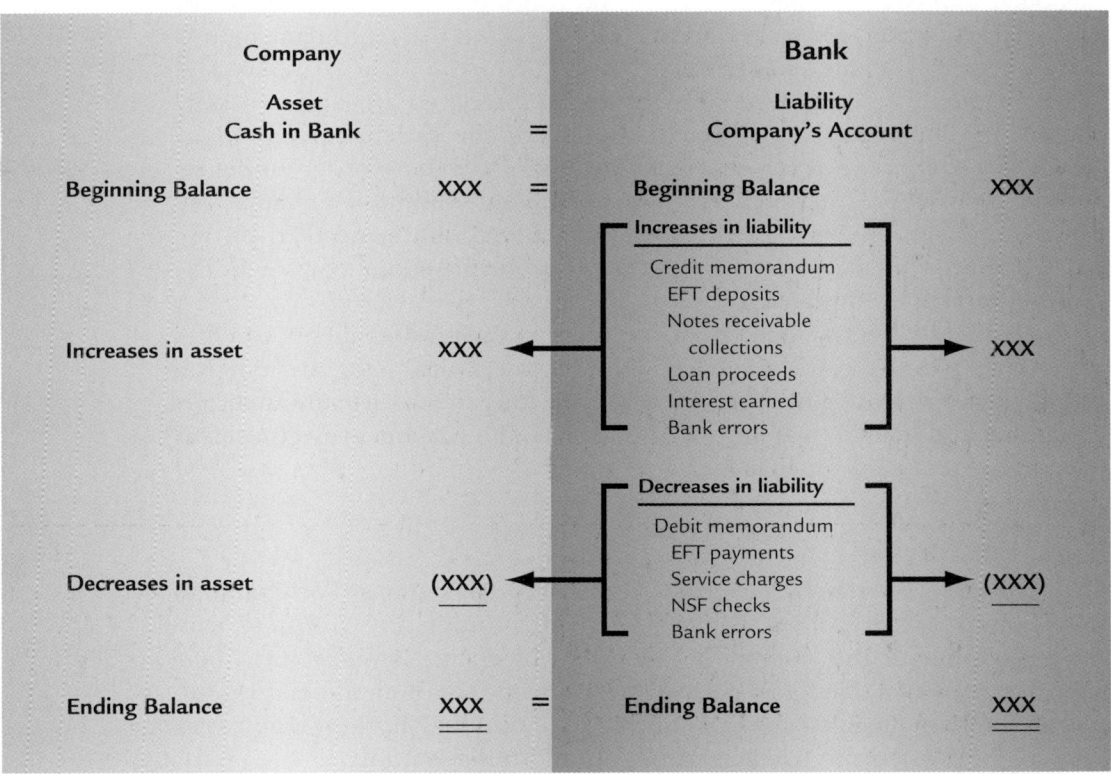

A bank issues credit memos for the following:

1. Deposits made by electronic funds transfer (EFT)
2. Collections of note receivable for the company
3. Proceeds for a loan made to the company by the bank
4. Interest earned on the company's account
5. Correction (if any) of bank errors

A bank issues debit memos for the following:

1. Payments made by electronic funds transfer (EFT)
2. Service charges
3. Customer checks returned for not sufficient funds
4. Correction (if any) of bank errors

Customers' checks returned for not sufficient funds, called *NSF checks,* are customer checks that were initially deposited, but were not paid by the customer's bank. Since the company's bank increased the customer's check to the

EXHIBIT | 5 | **Bank Statement**

MEMBER FDIC		PAGE 1

VALLEY NATIONAL BANK
OF LOS ANGELES

LOS ANGELES, CA 90020-4253   (310)555-5151

ACCOUNT NUMBER	1627042
FROM 6/30/09	TO 7/31/09
BALANCE	4,218.60
22 DEPOSITS	13,749.75
52 WITHDRAWALS	14,698.57
3 OTHER DEBITS	
AND CREDITS	90.00CR
NEW BALANCE	3,359.78

POWER NETWORKING
1000 Belkin Street
Los Angeles, CA 90014-1000

* – – CHECKS AND OTHER DEBITS – – – – – – – – * – – – – – – – DEPOSITS –*–DATE * BALANCE *

							DEPOSITS	DATE	BALANCE
No. 850	819.40	No. 852	122.54				585.75	07/01	3,862.41
No. 854	369.50	No. 853	20.15				421.53	07/02	3,894.29
No. 851	600.00	No. 856	190.70	No. 857	52.50		781.30	07/03	3,832.39
No. 855	25.93	No. 858	160.00				662.50	07/05	4,308.96
No. 860	921.20	NSF	300.00				503.18	07/07	3,590.94

No. 880	32.26	No. 877	535.09			ACH 932.00	07/29	4,136.66
No. 881	21.10	No. 879	732.26	No. 882	126.20	705.21	07/30	3,962.31
		SC	18.00			MS 408.00	07/30	4,352.31
No. 874	26.12	ACH	1,615.13			648.72	07/31	3,359.78

EC — ERROR CORRECTION   ACH — AUTOMATED CLEARING HOUSE
MS — MISCELLANEOUS
NSF — NOT SUFFICIENT FUNDS   SC — SERVICE CHARGE

* * *   * * *   * * *

THE RECONCILEMENT OF THIS STATEMENT WITH YOUR RECORDS IS ESSENTIAL.
ANY ERROR OR EXCEPTION SHOULD BE REPORTED IMMEDIATELY.

company's account when it was deposited, the bank decreases the company's account (issues a debit memo) when the check is returned without payment.

The reason for a credit or debit memo entry is indicated on the bank statement. Exhibit 5 identifies the following types of credit and debit memo entries:

EC: Error correction to correct bank error

NSF: Not sufficient funds check

SC: Service charge

ACH: Automated clearing house entry for electronic funds transfer

MS: Miscellaneous item such as collection of a note receivable on behalf of the company or receipt of a loan by the company from the bank

The above list includes the notation "ACH" for electronic funds transfers. ACH is a network for clearing electronic funds transfers among individuals, companies, and banks.[7] Because electronic funds transfers may be either deposits or payments, ACH entries may indicate either a positive or negative entry to the company's account. Likewise, entries to correct bank errors and miscellaneous items may indicate a positive or negative entry to the company's account.

[7] For further information on ACH, go to **http://www.nacha.org/.** Click on "About Us," and then click on "What is ACH?"

Using the Bank Statement as a Control Over Cash

The bank statement is a primary control that a company uses over cash. A company uses the bank's statement as a control by comparing the company's recording of cash transactions to those recorded by the bank.

The cash balance shown by a bank statement is usually different from the company's cash balance, as shown in Exhibit 6.

EXHIBIT 6   Power Networking's Records and Bank Statement

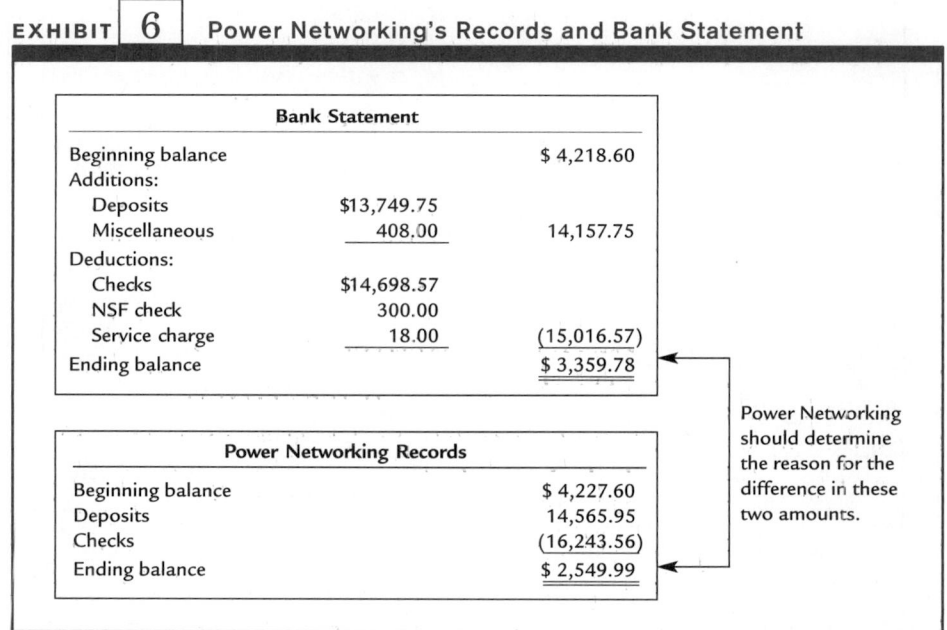

Bank Statement		
Beginning balance		$ 4,218.60
Additions:		
Deposits	$13,749.75	
Miscellaneous	408.00	14,157.75
Deductions:		
Checks	$14,698.57	
NSF check	300.00	
Service charge	18.00	(15,016.57)
Ending balance		$ 3,359.78

Power Networking Records	
Beginning balance	$ 4,227.60
Deposits	14,565.95
Checks	(16,243.56)
Ending balance	$ 2,549.99

Power Networking should determine the reason for the difference in these two amounts.

Differences between the company and bank balances may arise because of a delay by either the company or bank in recording transactions. For example, there is normally a time lag of one or more days between the date a check is written and the date that it is paid by the bank. Likewise, there is normally a time lag between when the company mails a deposit to the bank (or uses the night depository) and when the bank receives and records the deposit.

Differences may also arise because the bank has increased or decreased the company's account for transactions that the company will not know about until the bank statement is received. Finally, differences may arise from errors made by either the company or the bank. For example, the company may incorrectly post to Cash a check written for $4,500 as $450. Likewise, a bank may incorrectly record the amount of a check.

INTEGRITY, OBJECTIVITY, AND ETHICS IN BUSINESS

Check Fraud

Check fraud involves counterfeiting, altering, or otherwise manipulating the information on checks in order to fraudulently cash a check. According to the *National Check Fraud Center,* check fraud and counterfeiting are among the fastest growing problems affecting the financial system, generating over $10 billion in losses annually. Criminals perpetrate the fraud by taking blank checks from your checkbook, finding a canceled check in the garbage, or removing a check you have mailed to pay bills. Consumers can prevent check fraud by carefully storing blank checks, placing outgoing mail in postal mailboxes, and shredding canceled checks.

Bank Reconciliation

Obj 5 Describe and illustrate the use of a bank reconciliation in controlling cash.

A **bank reconciliation** is an analysis of the items and amounts that result in the cash balance reported in the bank statement differing from the balance of the cash account in the ledger. The adjusted cash balance determined in the bank reconciliation is reported on the balance sheet.

A bank reconciliation is usually divided into two sections as follows:

1. The *bank section* begins with the cash balance according to the bank statement and ends with the *adjusted balance*.

2. The *company section* begins with the cash balance according to the company's records and ends with the *adjusted balance*.

The *adjusted balance* from bank and company sections must be equal. The format of the bank reconciliation is shown below.

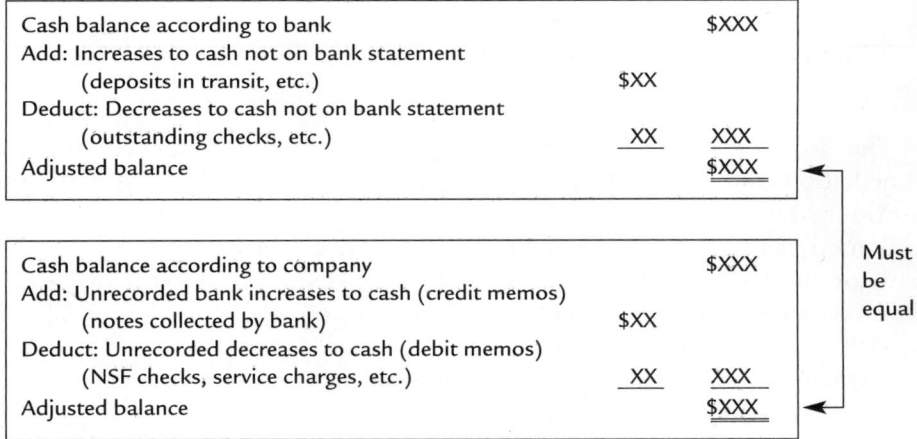

A bank reconciliation is prepared using the following steps:

Bank Section of Reconciliation

Step 1. Enter the *Cash balance according to bank* from the ending cash balance according to the bank statement.

Step 2. *Add deposits not recorded by the bank.* Identify deposits not recorded by the bank by comparing each deposit listed on the bank statement with unrecorded deposits appearing in the preceding period's reconciliation and with the current period's deposits. Examples: Deposits in transit at the end of the period.

Step 3. *Deduct outstanding checks that have not been paid by the bank.* Identify outstanding checks by comparing paid checks with outstanding checks appearing on the preceding period's reconciliation and with recorded checks. Examples: Outstanding checks at the end of the period.

Step 4. Determine the *Adjusted balance* by adding Step 2 and deducting Step 3.

Company Section of Reconciliation

Step 5. Enter the *Cash balance according to company* from the ending cash balance in the ledger.

Step 6. *Add increases to cash (credit memos) that have not been recorded.* Identify the bank credit memos that have not been recorded by comparing the bank statement credit memos to entries in the journal. Examples: A note receivable and interest that the bank has collected for the company.

Step 7. *Deduct decreases to cash (debit memos) that have not been recorded.* Identify the bank debit memos that have not been recorded by comparing the bank statement debit memos to entries in the journal. Examples: Customers' not sufficient funds (NSF) checks; bank service charges.

Step 8. Determine the *Adjusted balance* by adding Step 6 and deducting Step 7.

Step 9. Verify that the Adjusted balances determined in Steps 4 and 8 are equal.

The adjusted balances in the bank and company sections of the reconciliation must be equal. If the balances are not equal, an item has been overlooked and must be found.

Sometimes, the adjusted balances are not equal because either the company or the bank has made an error. In such cases, the error is often discovered by comparing the amount of each item (deposit and check) on the bank statement with that in the company's records.

Any bank or company errors discovered should be added to or deducted from the bank or company section of the reconciliation depending on the nature of the error. For example, assume that the bank incorrectly recorded a company check for $50 as $500. This bank error of $450 ($500 – $50) would be added to the bank balance in the bank section of the reconciliation. In addition, the bank would be notified of the error so that it could be corrected. On the other hand, assume that the company recorded a deposit of $1,200 as $2,100. This company error of $900 ($2,100 – $1,200) would be deducted from the cash balance in the company section of the bank reconciliation. The company would later correct the error in its records.

To illustrate, we will use the bank statement for Power Networking in Exhibit 5. This bank statement shows a balance of $3,359.78 as of July 31. The cash balance in Power Networking's ledger on the same date is $2,549.99. Using the preceding steps, the following reconciling items were identified:

Step 2. Deposit of July 31, not recorded on bank statement: $816.20

Step 3. Outstanding checks:

Check No. 812	$1,061.00
Check No. 878	435.39
Check No. 883	48.60
Total	$1,544.99

Step 6. Note receivable of $400 plus interest of $8 collected by bank, but not recorded by the company as indicated by a credit memo of $408.

Step 7. Check from customer (Thomas Ivey) for $300 returned by bank because of insufficient funds (NSF) as indicated by a debit memo of $300.00.

Bank service charges of $18, but not recorded by the company as indicated by a debit memo of $18.00.

In addition, an error of $9 was discovered. This error occurred when Check No. 879 for $732.26 to Taylor Co., on account, was recorded by the company as $723.26.

The bank reconciliation, based on the Exhibit 5 bank statement and the preceding reconciling items, is shown in Exhibit 7.

EXHIBIT 7 | Bank Reconciliation for Power Networking

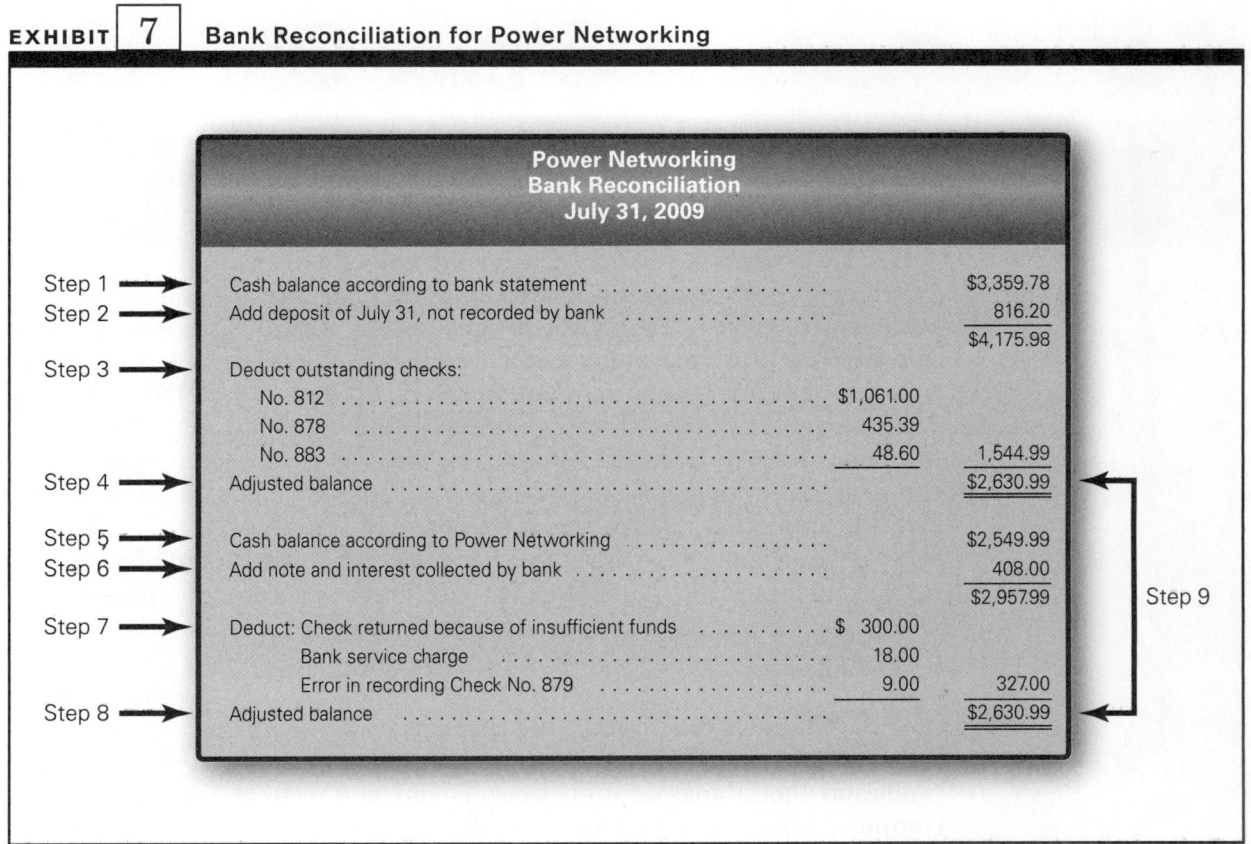

The company's records do not need to be updated for any items in the *bank section* of the reconciliation. This section begins with the cash balance according to the bank statement. However, the bank should be notified of any errors that need to be corrected.

The company's records do need to be updated for any items in the *company section* of the bank reconciliation. For example, entries should be made for any unrecorded bank memos and any company errors.

The effects of the adjustments on the accounts and financial statements of Power Networking, based on the preceding bank reconciliation in Exhibit 7, are as follows:

Statement of Cash Flows		Balance Sheet						Income Statement
		Assets		=	Liabilities	+	Stockholders' Equity	
	Cash	+	Notes Receivable	=			Retained Earnings	
July 31.	408		−400				8	July 31.

Statement of Cash Flows			Income Statement		
July 31. Operating	408		July 31. Interest income	8	

Statement of Cash Flows		Balance Sheet							Income Statement
		Assets		=	Liabilities	+		Stockholders' Equity	
	Cash	+	Accounts Receivable	=	Accounts Payable	+		Retained Earnings	
July 31.	−327		300		−9			−18	July 31.

Statement of Cash Flows			Income Statement		
July 31. Operating	−327		July 31. Misc. expense	−18	

After the preceding entries are recorded, the cash account will have a balance of $2,630.99. This cash balance agrees with the adjusted balance shown on the bank reconciliation. This is the amount of cash on July 31 and is the amount that is reported on Power Networking's July 31 balance sheet.

Businesses may reconcile their bank accounts in a slightly different format from that shown in Exhibit 7. Regardless, the objective is to control cash by reconciling the company's records with the bank statement. In doing so, any errors or misuse of cash may be detected.

To enhance internal control, the bank reconciliation should be prepared by an employee who does not take part in or record cash transactions. Otherwise, mistakes may occur, and it is more likely that cash will be stolen or misapplied. For example, an employee who handles cash and also reconciles the bank statement could steal a cash deposit, omit the deposit from the accounts, and omit it from the reconciliation.

Bank reconciliations are also important computerized systems where deposits and checks are stored in electronic files and records. Some systems use computer software to determine the difference between the bank statement and company cash balances. The software then adjusts for deposits in transit and outstanding checks. Any remaining differences are reported for further analysis.

INTEGRITY, OBJECTIVITY, AND ETHICS IN BUSINESS

Bank Error in Your Favor

You may sometime have a bank error in your favor, such as a misposted deposit. Such errors are not a case of "found money," as in the Monopoly® game. Bank control systems quickly discover most errors and make automatic adjustments. Even so, you have a legal responsibility to report the error and return the money to the bank.

Special-Purpose Cash Funds

Obj 6 Describe the accounting for special-purpose cash funds.

A company often has to pay small amounts for such items as postage, office supplies, or minor repairs. Although small, such payments may occur often enough to total a significant amount. Thus, it is desirable to control such payments. However, writing a check for each small payment is not practical. Instead, a special cash fund, called a **petty cash fund**, is used.

A petty cash fund is established by estimating the amount of payments needed from the fund during a period, such as a week or a month. A check is then written and cashed for this amount. The money obtained from cashing the check is then given to an employee, called the *petty cash custodian*. The petty cash custodian disburses monies from the fund as needed. For control purposes, the company may place restrictions on the maximum amount and the types of payments that can be made from the fund. Each time money is paid from petty cash, the custodian records the details on a petty cash receipts form.

The petty cash fund is normally replenished at periodic intervals, when it is depleted, or reaches a minimum amount. When a petty cash fund is replenished, the accounts are updated by summarizing the petty cash receipts. A check is then written for this amount, payable to Petty Cash.

To illustrate normal petty cash fund entries, assume that a petty cash fund of $500 is established on August 1. The effect on the accounts and financial statements of recording this transaction is as follows:

Statement of Cash Flows	Balance Sheet					Income Statement
	Assets		= Liabilities +		Stockholders' Equity	
	Cash +	Petty Cash				
Aug. 1.	−500	500				

At the end of August, the petty cash receipts indicate expenditures for the following items:

Office supplies	$380
Postage (debit Office Supplies)	22
Store supplies	35
Miscellaneous administrative expense	30
Total	$467

The effect on the accounts and financial statements of replenishing the petty cash fund on August 31 is as follows:

Statement of Cash Flows	Balance Sheet						Income Statement
	Assets			= Liabilities +	Stockholders' Equity		
	Cash +	Office Supplies +	Store Supplies =			Retained Earnings	
Aug. 31.	−467	402	35			−30	Aug. 31.

Statement of Cash Flows		Income Statement	
Aug. 31. Operating	−467	Aug. 31. Misc. admin. expense	−30

Replenishing the petty cash fund restores it to its original amount of $500. There is no adjustment to Petty Cash when the fund is replenished. Petty Cash is adjusted only if the amount of the fund is later increased or decreased.

Companies often use other cash funds for special needs, such as payroll or travel expenses. Such funds are called **special-purpose funds**. For example, each salesperson might be given $1,000 for travel-related expenses. Periodically, each salesperson submits an expense report, and the fund is replenished. Special-purpose funds are established and controlled in a manner similar to that of the petty cash fund.

Obj 7 Describe and illustrate the reporting of cash and cash equivalents in the financial statements.

Financial Statement Reporting of Cash

Cash is normally listed as the first asset in the Current Assets section of the balance sheet. Most companies present only a single cash amount on the balance sheet by combining all their bank and cash fund accounts.

A company may temporarily have excess cash. In such cases, the company normally invests in highly liquid investments in order to earn interest. These investments are called **cash equivalents**.[8] Examples of cash equivalents include U.S. Treasury bills, notes issued by major corporations (referred to as commercial paper), and money market funds. In such cases, companies usually report *Cash and cash equivalents* as one amount on the balance sheet.

To illustrate, **Microsoft Corp.** disclosed the details of its cash and cash equivalents in the notes to its financial statements as follows:

Balance Sheet
June 30, 2008
(In millions)

Assets	
Current assets:	
Cash and cash equivalents	$10,339
Short-term investments	13,323
Total cash and short-term investments	$23,662

The cash and cash equivalents of $10,339 million are further described in the notes to the financial statements, as shown below.

Cash and equivalents:	
Cash	$ 3,274
Mutual funds	835
Commercial paper	787
Certificates of deposit	1,373
U.S. government and agency securities	1839
Corporate notes and bonds	2,122
Municipal securities	109
Total cash and equivalents	$10,339

Banks may require that companies maintain minimum cash balances in their bank accounts. Such a balance is called a **compensating balance**. This is often required by the bank as part of a loan agreement or line of credit. A *line of credit* is a preapproved amount the bank is willing to lend to a customer upon request. Compensating balance requirements are normally disclosed in notes to the financial statements.

---

[8] To be classified a cash equivalent, according to FASB Statement No. 95, the investment is expected to be converted to cash within 90 days.

Key Points

1. **Describe the Sarbanes-Oxley Act of 2002 and its impact on internal controls and financial reporting.**

   The purpose of the Sarbanes-Oxley Act of 2002 is to restore public confidence and trust in the financial statements of companies. Sarbanes-Oxley requires companies to maintain strong and effective internal controls over the recording of transactions and the preparing of financial statements. Sarbanes-Oxley also requires companies and their independent accountants to report on the effectiveness of a company's internal controls.

2. **Describe and illustrate the objectives and elements of internal control.**

   The objectives of internal control are to provide reasonable assurance that (1) assets are safeguarded and used for business purposes, (2) business information is accurate, and (3) laws and regulations are complied with. The elements of internal control are the control environment, risk assessment, control procedures, monitoring, and information and communication.

3. **Describe and illustrate the application of internal controls to cash.**

   One of the most important controls to protect cash received in over-the-counter sales is a cash register. A remittance advice is a control for cash received through the mail. Separating the duties of handling cash and recording cash is also a control. A voucher system is a control system for cash payments that uses a set of procedures for authorizing and recording liabilities and cash payments. Many companies use electronic funds transfers to enhance their control over cash receipts and cash payments.

4. **Describe the nature of a bank account and its use in controlling cash.**

   Businesses use bank accounts as a means of controlling cash. Bank accounts reduce the amount of cash on hand and facilitate the transfer of cash between businesses and locations. In addition, banks send monthly statements to their customers, summarizing all of the transactions for the month. The bank statement allows a business to reconcile the cash transactions recorded in the accounting records to those recorded by the bank.

5. **Describe and illustrate the use of a bank reconciliation in controlling cash.**

   The first section of the bank reconciliation begins with the cash balance according to the bank statement. This balance is adjusted for the company's changes in cash that do not appear on the bank statement and for any bank errors. The second section begins with the cash balance according to the company's records. This balance is adjusted for the bank's changes in cash that do not appear on the company's records and for any company errors. The adjusted balances for the two sections must be equal. No adjustments are necessary on the company's records as a result of the information included in the bank section of the bank reconciliation. However, the items in the company section require adjustments on the company's records.

6. **Describe the accounting for special-purpose cash funds.**

   Businesses often use special-purpose cash funds, such as a petty cash fund or travel funds, to meet specific needs. Each fund is initially established by cashing a check for the amount of cash needed. The cash is then given to a custodian who is authorized to disburse monies from the fund. At periodic intervals or when it is depleted or reaches a minimum amount, the fund is replenished and the disbursements recorded.

7. **Describe and illustrate the reporting of cash and cash equivalents in the financial statements.**

   Cash is listed as the first asset in the Current Assets section of the balance sheet. Companies that have invested excess cash in highly liquid investments usually report *Cash and cash equivalents* on the balance sheet.

Key Terms

Bank reconciliation The analysis that details the items responsible for the difference between the cash balance reported in the bank statement and the cash balance in the ledger.

Bank statement A summary of all transactions mailed to the depositor by the bank each month.

Cash Coins, currency (paper money), checks, money orders, and money on deposit available for unrestricted withdrawal from banks and other financial institutions.

Cash equivalents Highly liquid investments that are usually reported with cash on the balance sheet.

Cash short and over The account used to record the difference between the amount of cash in a cash register and the amount of cash that should be on hand according to the records.

Compensating balance A requirement by some banks that depositors maintain minimum cash balances in their bank accounts.

Electronic funds transfer (EFT) A system in which computers rather than paper (money, checks, etc.) are used to effect cash transactions.

Elements of internal control The control environment, risk assessment, control activities, information and communication, and monitoring.

Employee fraud The intentional act of deceiving an employer for personal gain.

Internal control The policies and procedures used to safeguard assets, ensure accurate business information, and ensure compliance with laws and regulations.

Petty cash fund A special-purpose cash fund to pay relatively small amounts.

Sarbanes-Oxley Act of 2002 An act passed by Congress to restore public confidence and trust in the financial statements of companies.

Special-purpose fund A cash fund used for a special business need.

Voucher Any document that serves as proof of authority to pay cash.

Voucher system A set of procedures for authorizing and recording liabilities and cash payments.

Illustrative Problem

The bank statement for Urethane Company for June 30, 2011, indicates a balance of $9,143.11. All cash receipts are deposited each evening in a night depository, after banking hours.

The accounting records indicate the following summary data for cash receipts and payments for June:

Cash balance as of June 1	$ 3,943.50
Total cash receipts for June	28,971.60
Total amount of checks issued in June	28,388.85

Comparing the bank statement and the accompanying canceled checks and memorandums with the records reveals the following reconciling items:

a. The bank had collected for Urethane Company $1,030 on a customer's note left for collection. The face of the note was $1,000.

b. A deposit of $1,852.21, representing receipts of June 30, had been made too late to appear on the bank statement.

c. Checks outstanding totaled $5,265.27.

d. A check drawn for $139 had been incorrectly charged by the bank as $157.

e. A check for $30 returned with the statement had been recorded in the company's records as $240. The check was for the payment of an obligation to Avery Equipment Company for the purchase of office supplies on account.

f. Bank service charges for June amounted to $18.20.

Instructions

1. Prepare a bank reconciliation for June.

2. Record the effects on the accounts and financial statements that should be made by Urethane Company based upon the bank reconciliation.

Solution

1.

URETHANE COMPANY
Bank Reconciliation
June 30, 2011

Cash balance according to bank statement		$ 9,143.11
Add: Deposit of June 30 not recorded by bank	$1,852.21	
Bank error in charging check as $157 instead of $139	18.00	1,870.21
		$11,013.32
Deduct: Outstanding checks		5,265.27
Adjusted balance		$ 5,748.05
Cash balance according to company's records		$ 4,526.25*
Add: Proceeds of note collected by bank, including $30 interest	$1,030.00	
Error in recording check	210.00	1,240.00
		$ 5,766.25
Deduct: Bank service charges		18.20
Adjusted balance		$ 5,748.05

*$3,943.50 + $28,971.60 – $28,388.85

2.

Statement of Cash Flows	Balance Sheet					Income Statement
	Assets	=	Liabilities	+	Stockholders' Equity	
	Cash +	Notes Receivable =	Accounts Payable	+	Retained Earnings	
June 30.	1,240.00	–1,000.00	210.00		30.00	June 30.

Statement of Cash Flows		Income Statement	
June 30. Operating	1,240.00	June 30. Interest revenue	30.00

Statement of Cash Flows	Balance Sheet					Income Statement
	Assets	=	Liabilities	+	Stockholders' Equity	
	Cash	=			Retained Earnings	
June 30.	–18.20				–18.20	June 30.

Statement of Cash Flows		Income Statement	
June 30. Operating	–18.20	June 30. Misc. admin. exp.	–18.20

Self-Examination Questions (Answers appear at the end of chapter)

1. Which of the following is *not* an element of internal control?

   A. Control environment

   B. Monitoring

   C. Compliance with laws and regulations

   D. Control procedures

2. The bank erroneously charged Tropical Services' account for $450.50 for a check that was correctly written and recorded by Tropical Services as $540.50. To reconcile the bank account of Tropical Services at the end of the month, you would:

   A. add $90 to the cash balance according to the bank statement.

   B. add $90 to the cash balance according to Tropical Services' records.

   C. deduct $90 from the cash balance according to the bank statement.

   D. deduct $90 from the cash balance according to Tropical Services' records.

3. In preparing a bank reconciliation, the amount of checks outstanding would be:

   A. added to the cash balance according to the bank statement.

   B. deducted from the cash balance according to the bank statement.

   C. added to the cash balance according to the company's records.

   D. deducted from the cash balance according to the company's records.

4. Adjustments to the company's records based on the bank reconciliation are required for:

   A. additions to the cash balance according to the company's records.

   B. deductions from the cash balance according to the company's records.

   C. both A and B.

   D. neither A nor B.

5. A petty cash fund is:

   A. used to pay relatively small amounts.

   B. established by estimating the amount of cash needed for disbursements of relatively small amounts during a specified period.

   C. reimbursed when the amount of money in the fund is reduced to a predetermined minimum amount.

   D. all of the above.

Class Discussion Questions

1. (a) Why did Congress pass the Sarbanes-Oxley Act of 2002? (b) What was the purpose of the Sarbanes-Oxley Act of 2002?

2. Define *internal control*.

3. (a) Name and describe the five elements of internal control. (b) Is any one element of internal control more important than another?

4. How does a policy of rotating clerical employees from job to job aid in strengthening the control procedures within the control environment? Explain.

5. Why should the responsibility for a sequence of related operations be divided among different persons? Explain.

6. Why should the employee who handles cash receipts not have the responsibility for maintaining the accounts receivable records? Explain.

7. In an attempt to improve operating efficiency, one employee was made responsible for all purchasing, receiving, and storing of supplies. Is this organizational change wise from an internal control standpoint? Explain.

8. The ticket seller at a movie theater doubles as a ticket taker for a few minutes each day while the ticket taker is on a break. Which control procedure of a business's system of internal control is violated in this situation?

9. Why should the responsibility for maintaining the accounting records be separated from the responsibility for operations? Explain.

10. Assume that Yvonne Dauphin, accounts payable clerk for Bedell Inc., stole $73,250 by paying fictitious invoices for goods that were never received. The clerk set up accounts in the names of the fictitious companies and

cashed the checks at a local bank. Describe a control procedure that would have prevented or detected the fraud.

11. Before a voucher for the purchase of merchandise is approved for payment, supporting documents should be compared to verify the accuracy of the liability. Give an example of a supporting document for the purchase of merchandise.

12. The accounting clerk pays all obligations by prenumbered checks. What are the strengths and weaknesses in the internal control over cash payments in this situation?

13. The balance of Cash is likely to differ from the bank statement balance. What two factors are likely to be responsible for the difference?

14. What is the purpose of preparing a bank reconciliation?

15. Do items reported as a credit memorandum on the bank statement represent (a) additions made by the bank to the company's balance or (b) deductions made by the bank from the company's balance? Explain.

16. Oak Grove Inc. has a petty cash fund of $1,500. (a) Since the petty cash fund is only $1,500, should Oak Grove Inc. implement controls over petty cash? (b) What controls, if any, could be used for the petty cash fund?

17. (a) How are cash equivalents reported in the financial statements? (b) What are some examples of cash equivalents?

Exercises

E5-1
Sarbanes-Oxley internal control report

Obj 1

Using Wikipedia (www.wikipedia.com.), look up the entry for the Sarbanes-Oxley Act. Look over the table of contents and find the section that describes Section 404. What does Section 404 require of management's internal control report?

E5-2
Internal controls

Objs 2, 3

Blake Gable has recently been hired as the manager of Jittery Jim's Canyon Coffee. Jittery Jim's Canyon Coffee is a national chain of franchised coffee shops. During his first month as store manager, Blake encountered the following internal control situations:

a. Blake caught an employee putting a case of 100 single-serving tea bags in her car. Not wanting to create a scene, Blake smiled and said, "I don't think you're putting those tea bags on the right shelf. Don't they belong inside the coffee shop?" The employee returned the tea bags to the stockroom.

b. Jittery Jim's Canyon Coffee has one cash register. Prior to Blake's joining the coffee shop, each employee working on a shift would take a customer order, accept payment, and then prepare the order. Blake made one employee on each shift responsible for taking orders and accepting the customer's payment. Other employees prepare the orders.

c. Since only one employee uses the cash register, that employee is responsible for counting the cash at the end of the shift and verifying that the cash in the drawer matches the amount of cash sales recorded by the cash register. Blake expects each cashier to balance the drawer to the penny *every* time—no exceptions.

State whether you agree or disagree with Blake's method of handling each situation and explain your answer.

E5-3
Objs 2, 3

Anasazi Earth Clothing is a retail store specializing in women's clothing. The store has established a liberal return policy for the holiday season in order to encourage gift purchases. Any item purchased during November and December may be returned through January 31, with a receipt, for cash or exchange. If the

customer does not have a receipt, cash will still be refunded for any item under $100. If the item is more than $100, a check is mailed to the customer.

Whenever an item is returned, a store clerk completes a return slip, which the customer signs. The return slip is placed in a special box. The store manager visits the return counter approximately once every two hours to authorize the return slips. Clerks are instructed to place the returned merchandise on the proper rack on the selling floor as soon as possible.

This year, returns at Anasazi Earth Clothing have reached an all-time high. There are a large number of returns under $100 without receipts.

a. How can sales clerks employed at Anasazi Earth Clothing use the store's return policy to steal money from the cash register?

b. What internal control weaknesses do you see in the return policy that make cash thefts easier?

c. Would issuing a store credit in place of a cash refund for all merchandise returned without a receipt reduce the possibility of theft? List some advantages and disadvantages of issuing a store credit in place of a cash refund.

d. Assume that Anasazi Earth Clothing is committed to the current policy of issuing cash refunds without a receipt. What changes could be made in the store's procedures regarding customer refunds in order to improve internal control?

E5-4

Internal controls

Objs 2, 3

First Kenmore Bank provides loans to businesses in the community through its Commercial Lending Department. Small loans (less than $100,000) may be approved by an individual loan officer, while larger loans (greater than $100,000) must be approved by a board of loan officers. Once a loan is approved, the funds are made available to the loan applicant under agreed-upon terms. The president of First Kenmore Bank has instituted a policy whereby he has the individual authority to approve loans up to $5,000,000. The president believes that this policy will allow flexibility to approve loans to valued clients much quicker than under the previous policy.

As an internal auditor of First Kenmore Bank, how would you respond to this change in policy?

E5-5

Internal controls

Objs 2, 3

One of the largest losses in history from unauthorized securities trading involved a securities trader for the French bank, *Société Générale.* The trader was able to circumvent internal controls and create over $7 billion in trading losses in six months. The trader apparently escaped detection by using knowledge of the bank's internal control systems learned from a previous back-office monitoring job. Much of this monitoring involved the use of software to monitor trades. In addition, traders are usually kept to tight spending limits. Apparently, these controls failed in this case.

What general weaknesses in Société Générale's internal controls contributed to the occurrence and size of the losses?

E5-6

Internal controls

Objs 2, 3

An employee of *JHT Holdings, Inc.,* a trucking company, was responsible for resolving roadway accident claims under $25,000. The employee created fake accident claims and wrote settlement checks of between $5,000 and $25,000 to friends or acquaintances acting as phony "victims." One friend recruited subordinates at his place of work to cash some of the checks. Beyond this, the JHT employee also recruited lawyers, who he paid to represent both the trucking

company and the fake victims in the bogus accident settlements. When the lawyers cashed the checks, they allegedly split the money with the corrupt JHT employee. This fraud went undetected for two years.

Why would it take so long to discover such a fraud?

E5-7

Internal controls

Objs 2, 3

Bizarro Sound Co. discovered a fraud whereby one of its front office administrative employees used company funds to purchase goods, such as computers, digital cameras, compact disk players, and other electronic items, for her own use. The fraud was discovered when employees noticed an increase in delivery frequency from vendors and the use of unusual vendors. After some investigation, it was discovered that the employee would alter the description or change the quantity on an invoice in order to explain the cost on the bill.

What general internal control weaknesses contributed to this fraud?

E5-8

Financial statement fraud

Objs 2, 3

A former chairman, CFO, and controller of **Donnkenny, Inc.,** an apparel company that makes sportswear for Pierre Cardin and Victoria Jones, pleaded guilty to financial statement fraud. These managers used false journal entries to record fictitious sales, hid inventory in public warehouses so that it could be recorded as "sold," and required sales orders to be backdated so that the sale could be moved back to an earlier period. The combined effect of these actions caused $25 million out of $40 million in quarterly sales to be phony.

a. Why might control procedures listed in this chapter be insufficient in stopping this type of fraud?

b. How could this type of fraud be stopped?

E5-9

Internal control of cash receipts

Objs 2, 3

The procedures used for over-the-counter receipts are as follows. At the close of each day's business, the sales clerks count the cash in their respective cash drawers, after which they determine the amount recorded by the cash register and prepare the memo cash form, noting any discrepancies. An employee from the cashier's office counts the cash, compares the total with the memo, and takes the cash to the cashier's office.

a. Indicate the weak link in internal control.

b. How can the weakness be corrected?

E5-10

Internal control of cash receipts

Objs 2, 3

Victor Blackmon works at the drive-through window of Buffalo Bob's Burgers. Occasionally, when a drive-through customer orders, Victor fills the order and pockets the customer's money. He does not ring up the order on the cash register.

Identify the internal control weaknesses that exist at Buffalo Bob's Burgers, and discuss what can be done to prevent this theft.

E5-11

Internal control of cash receipts

Objs 2, 3

The mailroom employees send all remittances and remittance advices to the cashier. The cashier deposits the cash in the bank and forwards the remittance advices and duplicate deposit slips to the Accounting Department.

a. Indicate the weak link in internal control in the handling of cash receipts.

b. How can the weakness be corrected?

E5-12

Entry for cash sales; cash short

Objs 2, 3

The actual cash received from cash sales was $36,183, and the amount indicated by the cash register total was $36,197.

a. What is the amount deposited in the bank for the day's sales?
b. What is the amount recorded for the day's sales?
c. How should the difference be recorded?
d. If a cashier is consistently over or short, what action should be taken?

E5-13

Recording cash sales; cash over

Objs 2, 3

The actual cash received from cash sales was $11,279, and the amount indicated by the cash register total was $11,256.

a. What is the amount deposited in the bank for the day's sales?
b. What is amount recorded for the day's sales?
c. How should the difference be recorded?
d. If a cashier is consistently over or short, what action should be taken?

E5-14

Internal control of cash payments

Objs 2, 3

El Cordova Co. is a small merchandising company with a manual accounting system. An investigation revealed that in spite of a sufficient bank balance, a significant amount of available cash discounts had been lost because of failure to make timely payments. In addition, it was discovered that the invoices for several purchases had been paid twice.

Outline procedures for the payment of vendors' invoices, so that the possibilities of losing available cash discounts and of paying an invoice a second time will be minimized.

E5-15

Internal control of cash payments

Objs 2, 3

Digital Com Company, a communications equipment manufacturer, recently fell victim to a fraud scheme developed by one of its employees. To understand the scheme, it is necessary to review Digital Com's procedures for the purchase of services.

The purchasing agent is responsible for ordering services (such as repairs to a photocopy machine or office cleaning) after receiving a service requisition from an authorized manager. However, since no tangible goods are delivered, a receiving report is not prepared. When the Accounting Department receives an invoice billing Digital Com for a service call, the accounts payable clerk calls the manager who requested the service in order to verify that it was performed.

The fraud scheme involves Matt DuBois, the manager of plant and facilities. Matt arranged for his uncle's company, Urban Industrial Supply and Service, to be placed on Digital Com's approved vendor list. Matt did not disclose the family relationship.

On several occasions, Matt would submit a requisition for services to be provided by Urban Industrial Supply and Service. However, the service requested was really not needed, and it was never performed. Urban would bill Digital Com for the service and then split the cash payment with Matt.

Explain what changes should be made to Digital Com's procedures for ordering and paying for services in order to prevent such occurrences in the future.

E5-16

Bank reconciliation

Obj 5

Identify each of the following reconciling items as: (a) an addition to the cash balance according to the bank statement, (b) a deduction from the cash balance according to the bank statement, (c) an addition to the cash balance according to the company's records, or (d) a deduction from the cash balance according to

the company's records. (None of the transactions reported by bank debit and credit memos have been recorded by the company.)

1. Bank service charges, $15.
2. Check drawn by company for $160 but incorrectly recorded by company as $610.
3. Check for $500 incorrectly charged by bank as $5,000.
4. Check of a customer returned by bank to company because of insufficient funds, $3,000.
5. Deposit in transit, $15,500.
6. Outstanding checks, $9,600.
7. Note collected by bank, $10,000.

E5-17

Entries based on bank reconciliation

Obj 5

Which of the reconciling items listed in Exercise 5-16 are required to be in the company's accounts?

E5-18

Bank reconcilliation

Obj 5

✓ **Adjusted balance:**
$13,680

The following data were accumulated for use in reconciling the bank account of Commander Co. for March:

a. Cash balance according to the company's records at March 31, $13,065.
b. Cash balance according to the bank statement at March 31, $12,750.
c. Checks outstanding, $4,170.
d. Deposit in transit, not recorded by bank, $5,100.
e. A check for $180 in payment of an account was erroneously recorded in the check register as $810.
f. Bank debit memo for service charges, $15.

Prepare a bank reconciliation, using the format shown in Exhibit 7.

E5-19

Entries for bank reconciliation

Obj 5

Using the data presented in Exercise 5-18, record the effects on the accounts and financial statements of the company based upon the bank reconciliation.

E5-20

Entries for note collected by bank

Obj 5

Accompanying a bank statement for Euthenics Company is a credit memo for $18,270, representing the principal ($18,000) and interest ($270) on a note that had been collected by the bank. The company had been notified by the bank at the time of the collection, but had made no recording. Record the adjustment that should be made by the company to bring the accounting records up to date.

E5-21

Bank reconciliation

Obj 5

✓ **Adjusted balance:**
$11,740

An accounting clerk for Grebe Co. prepared the following bank reconciliation:

GREBE CO.
Bank Reconciliation
August 31, 2010

Cash balance according to company's records		$ 4,690
Add: Outstanding checks	$3,110	
Error by Grebe Co. in recording Check No. 1115 as $940 instead of $490	450	
Note for $6,500 collected by bank, including interest	6,630	10,190
	$4,725	$14,880
Deduct: Deposit in transit on August 31		
Bank service charges	30	4,755
Cash balance according to bank statement		$10,125

a. From the bank reconciliation data on the previous page, prepare a new bank reconciliation for Grebe Co., using the format shown in the illustrative problem.

b. If a balance sheet were prepared for Grebe Co. on August 31, 2010, what amount should be reported for cash?

E5-22

Bank reconciliation

Obj 5

✓ **Corrected adjusted balance: $11,960**

Identify the errors in the following bank reconciliation:

RAKESTRAW CO.
Bank Reconciliation
For the Month Ended April 30, 2010

Cash balance according to bank statement			$11,320
Add outstanding checks:			
No. 315		$ 450	
360		615	
364		850	
365		775	2,690
			$14,010
Deduct deposit of April 30, not recorded by bank			3,330
Adjusted balance			$10,680
Cash balance according to company's records			$ 7,003
Add: Proceeds of note collected by bank:			
Principal	$4,000		
Interest	120	$4,120	
Service charges		18	4,138
			$11,141
Deduct: Check returned because of insufficient funds		$ 945	
Error in recording April 20 deposit of $5,300 as $3,500		1,800	2,745
Adjusted balance			$ 8,396

E5-23

Using bank reconciliation to determine cash receipts stolen

Objs 2, 3, 5

First Impressions Co. records all cash receipts on the basis of its cash register tapes. First Impressions Co. discovered during June 2010 that one of its sales clerks had stolen an undetermined amount of cash receipts when she took the daily deposits to the bank. The following data have been gathered for June:

Cash in bank according to the general ledger	$ 7,865
Cash according to the June 30, 2010 bank statement	18,175
Outstanding checks as of June 30, 2010	5,190
Bank service charge for June	25
Note receivable, including interest collected by bank in June	8,400

No deposits were in transit on June 30.

a. Determine the amount of cash receipts stolen by the sales clerk.

b. What accounting controls would have prevented or detected this theft?

E5-24

Recording petty cash fund transactions

Obj 6

Illustrate the effect on the accounts and financial statements of the following transactions:

a. Established a petty cash fund of $1,000.

b. The amount of cash in the petty cash fund is now $315. Replenished the fund, based on the following summary of petty cash receipts: office supplies, $425; miscellaneous selling expense, $220; miscellaneous administrative expense, $40.

E5-25

Recording petty cash fund transactions

Obj 6

Illustrate the effect on the accounts and financial statements of the following transactions:

a. Established a petty cash fund of $800.

b. The amount of cash in the petty cash fund is now $120. Replenished the fund, based on the following summary of petty cash receipts: office supplies, $430; miscellaneous selling expense, $175; miscellaneous administrative expense, $75.

E5-26

Variation in cash flows

Obj 7

Mattel, Inc., designs, manufactures, and markets toy products worldwide. ***Mattel***'s toys include Barbie™ fashion dolls and accessories, Hot Wheels™, and Fisher-Price brands. For a recent year, ***Mattel*** reported the following net cash flows from operating activities (in thousands):

First quarter ending March 31	$ (326,536)
Second quarter ending June 30	(165,047)
Third quarter ending September 30	(9,738)
Fourth quarter December 31	1,243,603

Explain why Mattel reports negative net cash flows from operating activities during the first three quarters, yet reports positive cash flows for the fourth quarter and net positive cash flows for the year.

Problems

P5-1

Evaluate internal control of cash

Objs 2, 3

The following procedures were recently installed by The Louver Shop:

a. Each cashier is assigned a separate cash register drawer to which no other cashier has access.

b. At the end of a shift, each cashier counts the cash in his or her cash register, unlocks the cash register record, and compares the amount of cash with the amount on the record to determine cash shortages and overages.

c. Vouchers and all supporting documents are perforated with a PAID designation after being paid by the treasurer.

d. Disbursements are made from the petty cash fund only after a petty cash receipt has been completed and signed by the payee.

e. All sales are rung up on the cash register, and a receipt is given to the customer. All sales are recorded on a record locked inside the cash register.

f. Checks received through the mail are given daily to the accounts receivable clerk for recording collections on account and for depositing in the bank.

g. The bank reconciliation is prepared by the accountant.

Instructions

Indicate whether each of the procedures of internal control over cash represents (1) a strength or (2) a weakness. For each weakness, indicate why it exists.

P5-2

Bank reconciliation
and entries

Obj 5

SPREADSHEET

✓ 1. Adjusted balance:
  $13,445

The cash account for Interactive Systems at February 28, 2010, indicated a balance of $7,635. The bank statement indicated a balance of $13,333 on February 28, 2010. Comparing the bank statement and the accompanying canceled checks and memos with the records reveals the following reconciling items:

a. Checks outstanding totaled $4,118.
b. A deposit of $4,500, representing receipts of February 28, had been made too late to appear on the bank statement.
c. The bank had collected $5,200 on a note left for collection. The face of the note was $5,000.
d. A check for $290 returned with the statement had been incorrectly recorded by Interactive Systems as $920. The check was for the payment of an obligation to Busser Co. for the purchase of office supplies on account.
e. A check drawn for $415 had been incorrectly charged by the bank as $145.
f. Bank service charges for February amounted to $20.

Instructions

1. Prepare a bank reconciliation.
2. Illustrate the effects on the accounts and financial statements of the bank reconciliation.

P5-3

Bank reconciliation and entries

Obj 5

SPREADSHEET

✓ 1. Adjusted balance:
  $15,430

The cash account for Fred's Sports Co. on June 1, 2010, indicated a balance of $16,515. During June, the total cash deposited was $40,150, and checks written totaled $43,600. The bank statement indicated a balance of $18,175 on June 30, 2010. Comparing the bank statement, the canceled checks, and the accompanying memos with the records revealed the following reconciling items:

a. Checks outstanding totaled $6,840.
b. A deposit of $4,275, representing receipts of June 30, had been made too late to appear on the bank statement.
c. A check for $640 had been incorrectly charged by the bank as $460.
d. A check for $80 returned with the statement had been recorded by Fred's Sports Co. as $800. The check was for the payment of an obligation to Miliski Co. on account.
e. The bank had collected for Fred's Sports Co. $3,240 on a note left for collection. The face of the note was $3,000.
f. Bank service charges for June amounted to $35.
g. A check for $1,560 from ChimTech Co. was returned by the bank because of insufficient funds.

Instructions

1. Prepare a bank reconciliation as of June 30.
2. Illustrate the effects on the accounts and financial statements of the bank reconciliation.

P5-4

Bank reconciliation and entries

Obj 5

SPREADSHEET

✓ 1. Adjusted balance:
  $11,178.59

Rocky Mountain Interiors deposits all cash receipts each Wednesday and Friday in a night depository, after banking hours. The data required to reconcile the bank statement as of July 31 have been taken from various documents and records and are reproduced as follows. The sources of the data are printed in capital letters. All checks were written for payments on account.

BANK RECONCILIATION FOR PRECEDING MONTH (DATED JUNE 30):

Cash balance according to bank statement		$ 9,422.80
Add deposit of June 30, not recorded by bank		780.80
		$10,203.60
Deduct outstanding checks:		
No. 580	$310.10	
No. 602	85.50	
No. 612	92.50	
No. 613	137.50	625.60
Adjusted balance		$ 9,578.00
Cash balance according to company's records		$ 9,605.70
Deduct service charges		27.70
Adjusted balance		$ 9,578.00

CASH ACCOUNT:

Balance as of July 1	$ 9,578.00

CHECKS WRITTEN:

Number and amount of each check issued in July:

Check No.	Amount	Check No.	Amount	Check No.	Amount
614	$243.50	621	$309.50	628	$ 837.70
615	350.10	622	Void	629	329.90
616	279.90	623	Void	630	882.80
617	395.50	624	707.01	631	1,081.56
618	435.40	625	158.63	632	62.40
619	320.10	626	550.03	633	310.08
620	328.87	627	318.73	634	503.30
Total amount of checks issued in July					$8,405.01

MEMBER FDIC

AB AMERICAN NATIONAL BANK OF DETROIT

DETROIT, MI 48201-2500   (313)933-8547

ROCKY MOUNTAIN INTERIORS

ACCOUNT NUMBER		PAGE 1
FROM 7/01/20–	TO 7/31/20–	
BALANCE	9,422.80	
9 DEPOSITS	6,086.35	
20 WITHDRAWALS	8,237.41	
4 OTHER DEBITS AND CREDITS	3,685.00CR	
NEW BALANCE	10,956.74	

* - - - - - CHECKS AND OTHER DEBITS - - - - - *				- DEPOSITS - *	- DATE - *	- BALANCE- *
No.580	310.10	No.612	92.50	780.80	07/01	9,801.00
No.602	85.50	No.614	243.50	569.50	07/03	10,041.50
No.615	350.10	No.616	279.90	701.80	07/06	10,113.30
No.617	395.50	No.618	435.40	819.24	07/11	10,101.64
No.619	320.10	No.620	238.87	580.70	07/13	10,123.37
No.621	309.50	No.624	707.01	MS 4,000.00	07/14	13,106.86
No.625	158.63	No.626	550.03	MS 160.00	07/14	12,558.20
No.627	318.73	No.629	329.90	600.10	07/17	12,509.67
No.630	882.80	No.631	1,081.56	NSF 450.00	07/20	10,095.31
No.628	837.70	No.633	310.08	701.26	07/21	9,648.79
				731.45	07/24	10,380.24
				601.50	07/28	10,981.74
					07/31	10,956.74
		SC	25.00			

EC — ERROR CORRECTION	OD — OVERDRAFT
MS — MISCELLANEOUS	PS — PAYMENT STOPPED
NSF — NOT SUFFICIENT FUNDS	SC — SERVICE CHARGE

* * *   * * *   * * *

THE RECONCILEMENT OF THIS STATEMENT WITH YOUR RECORDS IS ESSENTIAL.
ANY ERROR OR EXCEPTION SHOULD BE REPORTED IMMEDIATELY.

CASH RECEIPTS FOR MONTH OF JULY   6,158.60
DUPLICATE DEPOSIT TICKETS:
    Date and amount of each deposit in July:

5.4

Date	Amount	Date	Amount	Date	Amount
July 2	$569.50	July 12	$508.70	July 23	$731.45
5	701.80	16	600.10	26	601.50
9	819.24	19	701.26	31	925.05

Instructions

1. Prepare a bank reconciliation as of July 31. If errors in recording deposits or checks are discovered, assume that the errors were made by the company. Assume that all deposits are from cash sales. All checks are written to satisfy accounts payable.

2. Illustrate the effects on the accounts and financial statements of the bank reconciliation.

3. What is the amount of Cash that should appear on the balance sheet as of July 31?

4. Assume that a canceled check for $125 has been incorrectly recorded by the bank as $1,250. Briefly explain how the error would be included in a bank reconciliation and how it should be corrected.

Activities

A5-1

Ethics and professional conduct in business

ETHICS

During the preparation of the bank reconciliation for New Concepts Co., Peter Fikes, the assistant controller, discovered that City National Bank incorrectly recorded a $710 check written by New Concepts Co. as $170. Peter has decided not to notify the bank but wait for the bank to detect the error. Peter plans to record the $540 error as Other Income if the bank fails to detect the error within the next three months.

Discuss whether Peter is behaving in a professional manner.

A5-2

Internal controls

The following is an excerpt from a conversation between two sales clerks, Ross Maas and Shu Lyons. Both Ross and Shu are employed by Hawkins Electronics, a locally owned and operated electronics retail store.

Ross: Did you hear the news?

Shu: What news?

Ross: Jane and Rachel were both arrested this morning.

Shu: What? Arrested? You're putting me on!

Ross: No, really! The police arrested them first thing this morning. Put them in handcuffs, read them their rights—the whole works. It was unreal!

Shu: What did they do?

Ross: Well, apparently they were filling out merchandise refund forms for fictitious customers and then taking the cash.

Shu: I guess I never thought of that. How did they catch them?

Ross: The store manager noticed that returns were twice that of last year and seemed to be increasing. When he confronted Jane, she became flustered and admitted to taking the cash, apparently over $7,000 in just three months. They're going over the last six months' transactions to try to determine how much Rachel stole. She apparently started stealing first.

Suggest appropriate control procedures that would have prevented or detected the theft of cash.

A5-3
Internal controls

The following is an excerpt from a conversation between the store manager of Yoder Brothers Grocery Stores, Lori Colburn, and Terry Whipple, president of Yoder Brothers Grocery Stores.

Terry: Lori, I'm concerned about this new scanning system.

Lori: What's the problem?

Terry: Well, how do we know the clerks are ringing up all the merchandise?

Lori: That's one of the strong points about the system. The scanner automatically rings up each item, based on its bar code. We update the prices daily, so we're sure that the sale is rung up for the right price.

Terry: That's not my concern. What keeps a clerk from pretending to scan items and then simply not charging his friends? If his friends were buying 10–15 items, it would be easy for the clerk to pass through several items with his finger over the bar code or just pass the merchandise through the scanner with the wrong side showing. It would look normal for anyone observing. In the old days, we at least could hear the cash register ringing up each sale.

Lori: I see your point.

Suggest ways that Yoder Brothers Grocery Stores could prevent or detect the theft of merchandise as described.

A5-4
Ethics and professional conduct in business

ETHICS

Ryan Egan and Jack Moody are both cash register clerks for Organic Markets. Lee Sorrell is the store manager for Organic Markets. The following is an excerpt of a conversation between Ryan and Jack:

Ryan: Jack, how long have you been working for Organic Markets?

Jack: Almost five years this November. You just started two weeks ago . . . right?

Ryan: Yes. Do you mind if I ask you a question?

Jack: No, go ahead.

Ryan: What I want to know is, have they always had this rule that if your cash register is short at the end of the day, you have to make up the shortage out of your own pocket?

Jack: Yes, as long as I've been working here.

Ryan: Well, it's the pits. Last week I had to pay in almost $40.

Jack: It's not that big a deal. I just make sure that I'm not short at the end of the day.

Ryan: How do you do that?

Jack: I just shortchange a few customers early in the day. There are a few jerks that deserve it anyway. Most of the time, their attention is elsewhere and they don't think to check their change.

Ryan: What happens if you're over at the end of the day?

Jack: Lee lets me keep it as long as it doesn't get to be too large. I've not been short in over a year. I usually clear about $20 to $30 extra per day.

Discuss this case from the viewpoint of proper controls and professional behavior.

A5-5

Bank reconciliation and internal control

The records of Anacker Company indicate a July 31 cash balance of $9,400, which includes undeposited receipts for July 30 and 31. The cash balance on the bank statement as of July 31 is $6,575. This balance includes a note of $4,000 plus $160 interest collected by the bank but not recorded in the journal. Checks outstanding on July 31 were as follows: No. 370, $580; No. 379, $615; No. 390, $900; No. 1148, $225; No. 1149, $300; and No. 1151, $750.

On July 3, the cashier resigned, effective at the end of the month. Before leaving on July 31, the cashier prepared the following bank reconciliation:

Cash balance per books, July 31		$ 9,400
Add outstanding checks:		
No. 1148	$225	
1149	300	
1151	750	1,175
		$10,575
Less undeposited receipts		4,000
Cash balance per bank, July 31		$ 6,575
Deduct unrecorded note with interest		4,160
True cash, July 31		$ 2,415

```
Calculator Tape of Outstanding Checks:
          0*
        225 +
        300 +
        750 +
      1,175 *
```

Subsequently, the owner of Anacker Company discovered that the cashier had stolen an unknown amount of undeposited receipts, leaving only $1,000 to be deposited on July 31. The owner, a close family friend, has asked your help in determining the amount that the former cashier has stolen.

1. Determine the amount the cashier stole from Anacker Company. Show your computations in good form.
2. How did the cashier attempt to conceal the theft?
3. a. Identify two major weaknesses in internal controls that allowed the cashier to steal the undeposited cash receipts.
   b. Recommend improvements in internal controls, so that similar types of thefts of undeposited cash receipts can be prevented.

A5-6

Observe internal controls over cash

GROUP

Select a business in your community and observe its internal controls over cash receipts and cash payments. The business could be a bank or a bookstore, restaurant, department store, or other retailer. In groups of three or four, identify and discuss the similarities and differences in each business's cash internal controls.

Answers to Self-Examination Questions

1. **C** Compliance with laws and regulations (answer C) is an objective, not an element, of internal control. The control environment (answer A), monitoring (answer B), control procedures (answer D), risk assessment, and information and communication are the five elements of internal control.

2. **C** The error was made by the bank, so the cash balance according to the bank statement needs to be adjusted. Since the bank deducted $90 ($540.50 − $450.50) too little, the error of $90 should be deducted from the cash balance according to the bank statement (answer C).

3. **B** On any specific date, the cash account in a company's ledger may not agree with the account in the bank's ledger because of delays and/or errors by either party in recording transactions. The purpose of a bank reconciliation, therefore, is to determine the reasons for any differences between the two account balances. All errors should then be corrected by the company or the bank, as appropriate. In arriving at the adjusted cash balance according to the bank statement, outstanding checks must be deducted (answer B) to adjust for checks that have been written by the company but that have not yet been presented to the bank for payment.

4. **C** All reconciling items that are added to and deducted from the cash balance according to the company's records on the bank reconciliation (answer C) require that adjustments be recorded by the company to correct errors made in recording transactions or to bring the cash account up to date for delays in recording transactions.

5. **D** To avoid the delay, annoyance, and expense that is associated with paying all obligations by check, relatively small amounts (answer A) are paid from a petty cash fund. The fund is established by estimating the amount of cash needed to pay these small amounts during a specified period (answer B), and it is then reimbursed when the amount of money in the fund is reduced to a predetermined minimum amount (answer C).

Receivables and Inventories

6

Learning Objectives

After studying this chapter, you should be able to:

Obj 1 Describe the common classifications of receivables.

Obj 2 Describe the nature of and the accounting for uncollectible receivables.

Obj 3 Describe the direct write-off method of accounting for uncollectible receivables.

Obj 4 Describe the allowance method of accounting for uncollectible receivables.

Obj 5 Describe the common classifications of inventories.

Obj 6 Describe three inventory cost flow assumptions and how they impact the financial statements.

Obj 7 Compare and contrast the use of the three inventory costing methods.

Obj 8 Describe how receivables and inventory are reported on the financial statements.

What is the role of receivables in business? Unlike the individual consumer purchasing a DVD at **Wal-Mart** for cash or by **Master-Card** or **Visa,** a business normally purchases merchandise on account. That is, the seller records a receivable and invoices the buyer for payment at a later time. For example, **The Hershey Company** will record a receivable and invoice **Kroger** supermarkets for delivery of chocolate candy to various stores. Kroger will pay for the candy after delivery according to the terms of the invoice.

What is the role of inventory in business? From a consumer's perspective, inventory allows us to compare items, touch items, purchase on impulse, and take immediate delivery of a product on purchase. For example, at **Best Buy** you can inspect digital television sets before deciding which set best suits your needs and tastes. To support Wal-Mart's need for immediate product shipments, **Procter & Gamble** holds an inventory of Tide®. Inventory also provides protection against disruptions in production and transportation. For example, an unexpected strike by a supplier's employees can halt production for a manufacturer or cause lost sales for a merchandiser. Inventory also allows a business to meet unexpected increases in the demand for its product.

In this chapter, accounting and reporting issues related to receivables and inventories are described and illustrated. In doing so, the effects on the financial statements of estimating uncollectible receivables and inventory cost flow assumptions are emphasized.

Classification of Receivables

The receivables that result from sales on account are normally accounts receivable or notes receivable. The term **receivables** includes all money claims against other entities, including people, companies, and other organizations. Receivables are usually a significant portion of the total current assets.

Accounts Receivable

The most common transaction creating a receivable is selling merchandise or services on account (on credit). The receivable is recorded as an increase to Accounts Receivable. Such **accounts receivable** are normally collected within a short period, such as 30 or 60 days. They are classified on the balance sheet as a current asset.

Notes Receivable

Notes receivable are amounts that customers owe for which a formal, written instrument of credit has been issued. If notes receivable are expected to be collected within a year, they are classified on the balance sheet as a current asset.

Notes are often used for credit periods of more than 60 days. For example, an automobile dealer may require a down payment at the time of sale and accept a note or a series of notes for the remainder. Such notes usually provide for monthly payments.

A note has some advantages over an account receivable. By signing a note, the debtor recognizes the debt and agrees to pay it according to its terms. Thus, a note is a stronger legal claim.

A promissory note receivable is a written promise to pay the face amount, usually with interest, on demand or at a date in the future.[1] Characteristics of a promissory note are as follows:

1. The *maker* is the party making the promise to pay.
2. The *payee* is the party to whom the note is payable.

Obj 1 Describe the common classifications of receivables.

An annual report of ***La-Z-Boy Incorporated*** reported that receivables made up over 48% of La-Z-Boy's current assets.

INTEGRITY, OBJECTIVITY, AND ETHICS IN BUSINESS

Receivables Fraud

Financial reporting frauds are often tied to accounts receivable, because receivables allow companies to record revenue before cash is received. Take, for example, the case of entrepreneur Michael Weinstein, who acquired **Coated Sales, Inc.** with the dream of growing the small specialty company into a major corporation. To acquire funding that would facilitate this growth, Weinstein had to artificially boost the company's sales. He accomplished this by adding millions in false accounts receivable to existing customer accounts.

The company's auditors began to sense a problem when they called one of the company's customers to confirm a large order. When the customer denied placing the order, the auditors began to investigate the company's receivables more closely. Their analysis revealed a fraud which overstated profits by $55 million and forced the company into bankruptcy, costing investors and creditors over $160 million.

Source: Joseph T. Wells, "Follow Fraud to the Likely Perpetrator," *The Journal of Accountancy*, March 2001.

---

[1] You may see references to non-interest-bearing notes. Such notes are not widely used and carry an assumed or implicit interest rate.

3. The *face amount* is the amount the note is written for on its face.

4. The *issuance date* is the date a note is issued.

5. The *due date* or *maturity date* is the date the note is to be paid.

6. The *term* of a note is the amount of time between the issuance and due dates.

7. The *interest rate* is that rate of interest that must be paid on the face amount for the term of the note.

Exhibit 1 illustrates a promissory note.

EXHIBIT 1   Promissory Note

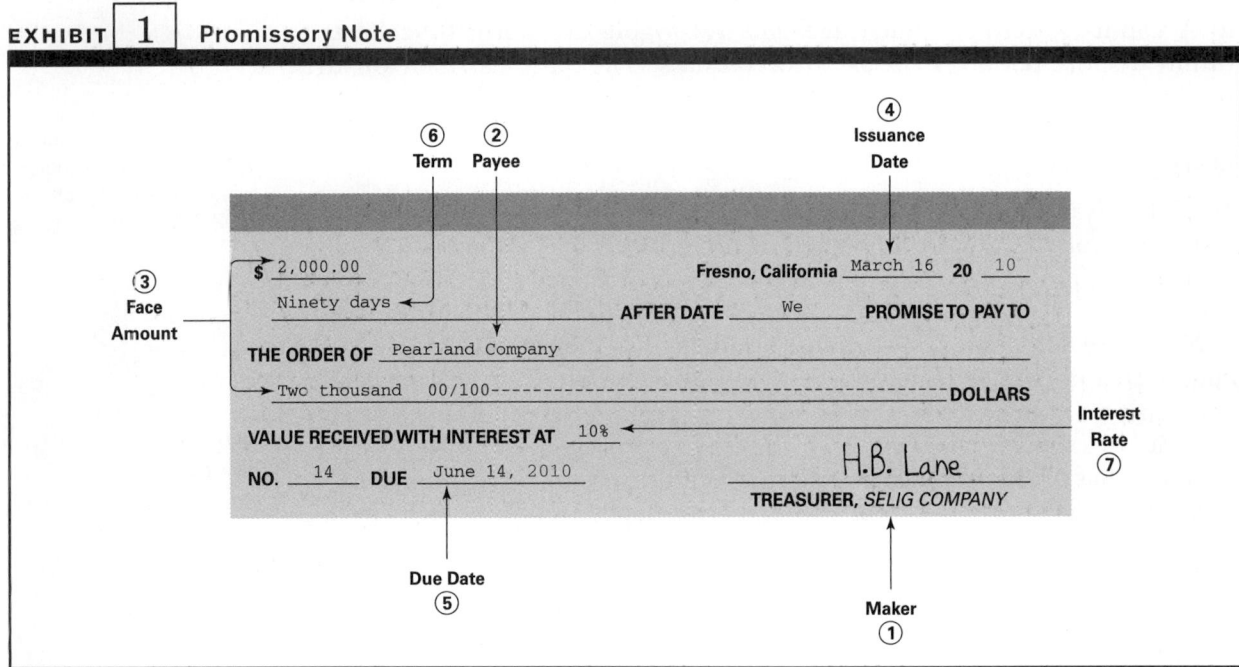

The maker of the note is Selig Company, and the payee is Pearland Company. The face value of the note is $2,000, and the issuance date is March 16, 2010. The term of the note is 90 days, which results in a due date of June 14, 2010, as shown below.

Days in March	31 days
Minus issuance date of note	16
Days remaining in March	15 days
Add days in April	30
Add days in May	31
Add days in June (due date of June 14)	14
Term of note	90 days

DUE DATE OF 90-DAY NOTE

MARCH 16-31   **APRIL** 1-30   **MAY** 1-31   **JUNE** 1-14

15 days   + 30 days   + 31 days   + 14 days

Mar. 16   **Total of 90 days**   June 14

In Exhibit 1, the term of the note is 90 days and has an interest rate of 10%. The interest on a note is computed as follows:

$$\text{Interest} = \text{Face Amount} \times \text{Interest Rate} \times (\text{Term}/360 \text{ days})$$

The interest rate is stated on an annual (yearly) basis, while the term is expressed as days. Thus, the interest on the note in Exhibit 1 is computed as follows:

$$\text{Interest} = \$2,000 \times 10\% \times (90/360) = \$50$$

To simplify, 360 days per year are used in this chapter. In practice, companies such as banks and mortgage lenders use the exact number of days in a year, 365.

The **maturity value** is the amount that must be paid at the due date of the note, which is the sum of the face amount and the interest. The maturity value of the note in Exhibit 1 is $2,050 ($2,000 + $50).

Notes may be used to settle a customer's account receivable. Notes and accounts receivable that result from sales transactions are sometimes called *trade receivables*. All notes and accounts receivable in this chapter are assumed to be from sales transactions.

Other Receivables

Other receivables include interest receivable, taxes receivable, and receivables from officers or employees. Other receivables are normally reported separately on the balance sheet. If they are expected to be collected within one year, they are classified as current assets. If collection is expected beyond one year, they are classified as noncurrent assets and reported under the caption *Investments*.

Uncollectible Receivables

In prior chapters, the accounting for sales of merchandise or services on account (on credit) was described and illustrated. A major issue that has not yet been discussed is that some customers will not pay their accounts. That is, some accounts receivable will be uncollectible.

Companies may shift the risk of uncollectible receivables to other companies. For example, some retailers do not accept sales on account, but will only accept cash or credit cards. Such policies shift the risk to the credit card companies.

Companies may also sell their receivables. This is often the case when a company issues its own credit card. For example, Macy's and JCPenney issue their own credit cards. Selling receivables is called *factoring* the receivables. The buyer of the receivables is called a *factor*. An advantage of factoring is that the company selling its receivables immediately receives cash for operating and other needs. Also, depending on the factoring agreement, some of the risk of uncollectible accounts is shifted to the factor.

Regardless of how careful a company is in granting credit, some credit sales will be uncollectible. The operating expense recorded from uncollectible receivables is called **bad debt expense**, *uncollectible accounts expense*, or *doubtful accounts expense*.

Your credit card balances that are not paid at the end of the month incur an interest charge expressed as a percent per month. Interest charges of 1½% per month are common. Such charges approximate an annual interest rate of 18% per year (1½% × 12). Thus, if you can borrow money at less than 18%, you are better off borrowing the money to pay off the credit card balance.

If you have purchased an automobile on credit, you probably signed a note. From your viewpoint, the note is a note payable. From the creditor's viewpoint, the note is a note receivable.

Obj 2 Describe the nature of and the accounting for uncollectible receivables.

There is no general rule for when an account becomes uncollectible. Some indications that an account may be uncollectible include the following:

1. The receivable is past due.
2. The customer does not respond to the company's attempts to collect.
3. The customer files for bankruptcy.
4. The customer closes its business.
5. The company cannot locate the customer.

Adams, Stevens & Bradley, Ltd. is a collection agency that operates on a contingency basis. That is, its fees are based on what it collects.

If a customer doesn't pay, a company may turn the account over to a collection agency. After the collection agency attempts to collect payment, any remaining balance in the account is considered worthless.

The two methods of accounting for uncollectible receivables are as follows:

1. The **direct write-off method** records bad debt expense only when an account is determined to be worthless.
2. The **allowance method** records bad debt expense by estimating uncollectible accounts at the end of the accounting period.

The direct write-off method is often used by small companies and companies with few receivables.[2] Generally accepted accounting principles (GAAP), however, require companies with a large amount of receivables to use the allowance method. As a result, most well-known companies such as ***General Electric, Pepsi, Intel,*** and ***FedEx*** use the allowance method.

Obj 3 Describe the direct write-off method of accounting for uncollectible receivables.

Direct Write-Off Method for Uncollectible Accounts

Under the direct write-off method, bad debt expense is not recorded until the customer's account is determined to be worthless. At that time, the customer's account receivable is written off.

To illustrate, assume that a $4,200 account receivable from D. L. Ross has been determined to be uncollectible. The effect on the accounts and financial statements of writing off the account is as follows:

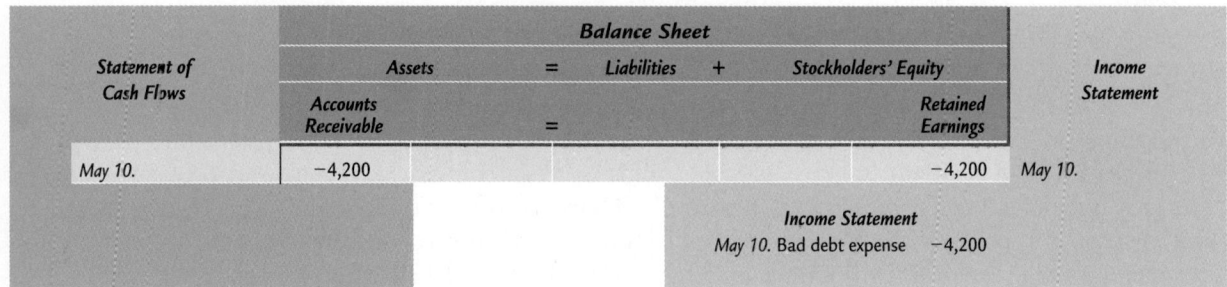

An account receivable that has been written off may be later collected. In such cases, the account is reinstated by reversing the write-off. The cash received in payment is then recorded as a receipt on account.

To illustrate, assume that the D. L. Ross account of $4,200 written off on May 10 is later collected on November 21. The effect on the accounts

---

[2] The direct write-off method is also required for federal income tax purposes.

and financial statements of the reinstatement and the receipt of cash is as follows:

Statement of Cash Flows	Balance Sheet						Income Statement
	Assets	=	Liabilities	+	Stockholders' Equity		
	Accounts Receivable	=			Retained Earnings		
Nov. 21.	4,200				4,200		Nov. 21.

Income Statement
Nov. 21. Bad debt expense   4,200

Statement of Cash Flows	Balance Sheet						Income Statement
	Assets	=	Liabilities	+	Stockholders' Equity		
	Cash	+	Accounts Receivable				
Nov. 21.	4,200		−4,200				

Statement of Cash Flows
Nov. 21. Operating   4,200

The direct write-off method is used by businesses that sell most of their goods or services for cash and accept only MasterCard or Visa, which are recorded as cash sales. In such cases, receivables are a small part of the current assets and any bad debt expense would be small. Examples of such businesses are a restaurant, a convenience store, and a small retail store.

Allowance Method for Uncollectible Accounts

Obj 4 Describe the allowance method of accounting for uncollectible receivables.

The allowance method estimates the uncollectible accounts receivable at the end of the accounting period. Based on this estimate, Bad Debt Expense is recorded by an adjustment.

To illustrate, assume that ExTone Company began operations August 1. As of the end of its accounting period on December 31, 2009, ExTone has an accounts receivable balance of $200,000. This balance includes some past due accounts. Based on industry averages, ExTone estimates that $30,000 of the December 31 accounts receivable will be uncollectible. However, on December 31, ExTone doesn't know which customer accounts will be uncollectible. Thus, specific customer accounts cannot be decreased or credited. Instead, a contra asset account, **Allowance for Doubtful Accounts**, is used.

Using the $30,000 estimate, the effect on the accounts and financial statements of recording the adjustment on December 31 is shown below:

Statement of Cash Flows	Balance Sheet						Income Statement
	Assets	=	Liabilities	+	Stockholders' Equity		
	Allow. for − Doubtful Acc'ts.	=			Retained Earnings		
Dec. 31.	−30,000				−30,000		Dec. 31.

Income Statement
Dec. 31. Bad debt expense   −30,000

The preceding adjustment affects the income statement and balance sheet. On the income statement, the $30,000 of Bad Debt Expense will be matched against the related revenues of the period. On the balance sheet, the value of the receivables is reduced to the amount that is expected to be collected or realized. This amount, $170,000 ($200,000 – $30,000), is called the **net realizable value** of the receivables.

After the preceding adjustment is recorded, Accounts Receivable still has a balance of $200,000. This balance is the total amount owed by customers on account on December 31 and is supported by the individual customer accounts.[3] The accounts receivable contra account, Allowance for Doubtful Accounts, has a negative balance of $30,000.

Write-Offs to the Allowance Account

When a customer's account is identified as uncollectible, it is written off against the allowance account. This requires the company to remove the specific accounts receivable and an equal amount from the allowance account. For example, the effect on the accounts and financial statements on January 21, 2011, of writing off John Parker's account of $6,000 with ExTone Company is as follows:

Statement of Cash Flows	Balance Sheet					Income Statement
	Assets		=	Liabilities	+	Stockholders' Equity	
	Accounts Receivable	− Allow. for Doubtful Acc'ts.					
Jan. 21.	−6,000	6,000					

At the end of a period, the Allowance for Doubtful Accounts will normally have a balance. This is because the Allowance for Doubtful Accounts is based upon an estimate. As a result, the total write-offs to the allowance account during the period will rarely equal the balance of the account at the beginning of the period. The allowance account will have a negative balance at the

INTEGRITY, OBJECTIVITY, AND ETHICS IN BUSINESS

Seller Beware

A company in financial distress will still try to purchase goods and services on account. In these cases, rather than "buyer beware," it is more like "seller beware." Sellers must be careful in advancing credit to such companies, because trade creditors have low priority for cash payments in the event of bankruptcy. To help suppliers, third-party services specialize in evaluating financially distressed customers. These services analyze credit risk for these firms by evaluating recent management payment decisions (who is getting paid and when), court actions (if in bankruptcy), and other supplier credit tightening or suspension actions. Such information helps monitor and adjust trade credit amounts and terms with the financially distressed customer.

[3] The individual customer accounts are often maintained in a separate file or record called a *subsidiary ledger.* The sum of the individual customer accounts equals the balance of the accounts receivable reported in the balance sheet.

end of the period if the write-offs during the period are less than the beginning balance. It will have a positive balance if the write-offs exceed the beginning balance. However, after the end-of-period adjustment is recorded, Allowance for Doubtful Accounts should always have a negative balance.

An account receivable that has been written off against the allowance account may be collected later. Like the direct write-off method, the account is reinstated by reversing the write-off. The cash received in payment is then recorded as a receipt on account.

To illustrate, assume that Nancy Smith's account of $5,000 which was written off on April 2 is later collected on June 10. ExTone Company records the reinstatement and the collection is as follows:

Statement of Cash Flows	Balance Sheet						Income Statement
	Assets		=	Liabilities	+	Stockholders' Equity	
	Accounts Receivable	− Allow. for Doubtful Acc'ts.					
June 10.	5,000	−5,000					

Statement of Cash Flows	Balance Sheet						Income Statement
	Assets		=	Liabilities	+	Stockholders' Equity	
	Cash	+ Accounts Receivable					
June 10.	5,000	−5,000					

Statement of Cash Flows
June 10. Operating 5,000

Estimating Uncollectibles

The allowance method requires an estimate of uncollectible accounts at the end of the period. This estimate is normally based on past experience, industry averages, and forecasts of the future.

The two methods used to estimate uncollectible accounts are as follows:

1. percent of sales method
2. analysis of receivables method

Percent of Sales Method

Since accounts receivable are created by credit sales, uncollectible accounts can be estimated as a percent of credit sales. If the portion of credit sales to sales is relatively constant, the percent may be applied to total sales or net sales.

To illustrate, assume the following data for ExTone Company on December 31, 2010, before any adjustments:

Balance of Accounts Receivable	$ 240,000
Balance of Allowance for Doubtful Accounts	−3,250
Total credit sales	3,000,000
Bad debt as a percent of credit sales	¾%

Bad Debt Expense of $22,500 is estimated as follows:

Bad Debt Expense = Credit Sales × Bad Debt as a Percent of Credit Sales

Bad Debt Expense = $3,000,000 × ¾% = $22,500

The effect of the adjustment on the accounts and financial statements on December 31 is as follows:

Statement of Cash Flows	Balance Sheet					Income Statement
	Assets	=	Liabilities	+	Stockholders' Equity	
	Allow. for −Doubtful Acc'ts.	=			Retained Earnings	
Dec. 31.	−22,500				−22,500	Dec. 31.

Income Statement
Dec. 31. Bad debt expense −22,500

After the adjustment, Bad Debt Expense will have an adjusted balance of $22,500. Allowance for Doubtful Accounts will have a negative adjusted balance of −$25,750 ($3,250 + $22,500).

Under the percent of sales method, the amount of the adjustment is always the amount estimated for Bad Debt Expense. In the preceding example, this amount was $22,500.

Analysis of Receivables Method

The analysis of receivables method is based on the assumption that the longer an account receivable is outstanding, the less likely that it will be collected. The analysis of receivables method is applied as follows:

Step 1. The due date of each account receivable is determined.

Step 2. The number of days each account is past due is determined. This is the number of days between the due date of the account and the date of the analysis.

Step 3. Each account is placed in an aged class according to its days past due. Typical aged classes include the following:

Not past due

1–30 days past due

31–60 days past due

61–90 days past due

91–180 days past due

181–365 days past due

Over 365 days past due

Step 4. The totals for each aged class are determined.

Step 5. The total for each aged class is multiplied by an estimated percentage of uncollectible accounts for that class.

Step 6. The estimated total of uncollectible accounts is determined as the sum of the uncollectible accounts for each aged class.

The preceding steps are summarized in an aging schedule, and this overall process is called **aging the receivables**.

The percentage of uncollectible accounts will vary across companies and industries. For example, in their recent annual reports, **JCPenney** reported 1.7% of its receivables as uncollectible, **Deere & Company** (manufacturer of John Deere tractors, etc.) reported only 1.0% of its dealer receivables as uncollectible, and **HCA Inc.**, a hospital management company, reported 42% of its receivables as uncollectible.

To illustrate, assume that ExTone Company uses the analysis of receivables method instead of the percent of sales method. ExTone prepared an aging schedule for its accounts receivable of $240,000 as of December 31, 2010, as shown in Exhibit 2.

EXHIBIT 2 Aging of Receivables Schedule
December 31, 2010

	A	B	C	D	E	F	G	H	I
1			Not			Days Past Due			
2			Past						Over
3	Customer	Balance	Due	1–30	31–60	61–90	91–180	181–365	365
4	Ashby & Co.	1,500			1,500				
5	B. T. Barr	6,100					3,500	2,600	
6	Brock Co.	4,700	4,700						
21									
22	Saxon Woods Co.	600					600		
23	Total	240,000	125,000	64,000	13,100	8,900	5,000	10,000	14,000
24	Percent uncollectible		2%	5%	10%	20%	30%	50%	80%
25	Estimate of uncollectible accounts	26,490	2,500	3,200	1,310	1,780	1,500	5,000	11,200

Steps 1–3 (rows 4–22)
Step 4 → 23
Step 5 → 24
Step 6 → 25

Assume that ExTone Company sold merchandise to Saxon Woods Co. on August 29 with terms 2/10, n/30. Thus, the due date (Step 1) of Saxon Woods' account is September 28, as shown below.

Credit terms, net	30 days
Less: Aug. 29 to Aug. 30	2 days
Days in September	28 days

As of December 31, Saxon Woods' account is 94 days past due (Step 2), as shown below.

Number of days past due in September	2 days (30 – 28)
Number of days past due in October	31 days
Number of days past due in November	30 days
Number of days past due in December	31 days
Total number of days past due	94 days

Exhibit 2 shows that the $600 account receivable for Saxon Woods Co. was placed in the 91–180 days past due class (Step 3).

The total for each of the aged classes is determined (Step 4). Exhibit 2 shows that $125,000 of the accounts receivable are not past due, while $64,000 are 1–30 days past due. ExTone Company applies a different estimated percentage of uncollectible accounts to the totals of each of the aged classes (Step 5). As shown in Exhibit 2, the percent is 2% for accounts not past due, while the percent is 80% for accounts over 365 days past due.

The sum of the estimated uncollectible accounts for each aged class (Step 6) is the estimated uncollectible accounts on December 31, 2010. This is the

desired adjusted balance for Allowance for Doubtful Accounts. For ExTone Company, this amount is $26,490, as shown in Exhibit 2.

Comparing the estimate of $26,490 with the unadjusted balance of the allowance account determines the amount of the adjustment for Bad Debt Expense. For ExTone, the unadjusted balance of the allowance account is a negative balance of –$3,250. The amount to be added to this balance is therefore –$23,240 ($26,490 – $3,250).

The effect of the adjustment of $23,240 on the accounts and financial statements of ExTone Company is shown below:

Statement of Cash Flows	Balance Sheet					Income Statement
	Assets	=	Liabilities	+	Stockholders' Equity	
	Allow. for –Doubtful Acc'ts.	=			Retained Earnings	
Dec. 31.	–23,240				–23,240	Dec. 31.

Income Statement
Dec. 31. Bad debt expense   –23,240

After the preceding adjustment, Bad Debt Expense will have an adjusted balance of $23,240. Allowance for Doubtful Accounts will have an adjusted balance of $26,490, and the net realizable value of the receivables is $213,510 ($240,000 – $26,490).

Under the analysis of receivables method, the amount of the adjustment is the amount that will yield an adjusted balance for Allowance for Doubtful Accounts equal to that estimated by the aging schedule.

Comparing Estimation Methods

Both the percent of sales and analysis of receivables methods estimate uncollectible accounts. However, each method has a slightly different focus and financial statement emphasis.

Under the percent of sales method, Bad Debt Expense is the focus of the estimation process. The percent of sales method places more emphasis on matching revenues and expenses and thus emphasizes the income statement. That is, the amount of the adjusting entry is based on the estimate of Bad Debt Expense for the period. Allowance for Doubtful Accounts is then adjusted by this amount.

Under the analysis of receivables method, Allowance for Doubtful Accounts is the focus of the estimation process. The analysis of receivables method places more emphasis on the net realizable value of the receivables and thus emphasizes the balance sheet. That is, the amount of the adjusting entry is the amount that will yield an adjusted balance for Allowance for Doubtful Accounts equal to that estimated by the aging schedule. Bad Debt Expense is then adjusted by this amount.

Exhibit 3 summarizes these differences between the percent of sales and the analysis of receivables methods. Exhibit 3 also shows the results of the ExTone Company illustration for the percent of sales and analysis of receivables methods. The amounts shown in Exhibit 3 assume an unadjusted negative balance of –$3,250 for Allowance for Doubtful Accounts. While the methods

EXHIBIT 3 | **Differences Between Estimation Methods**

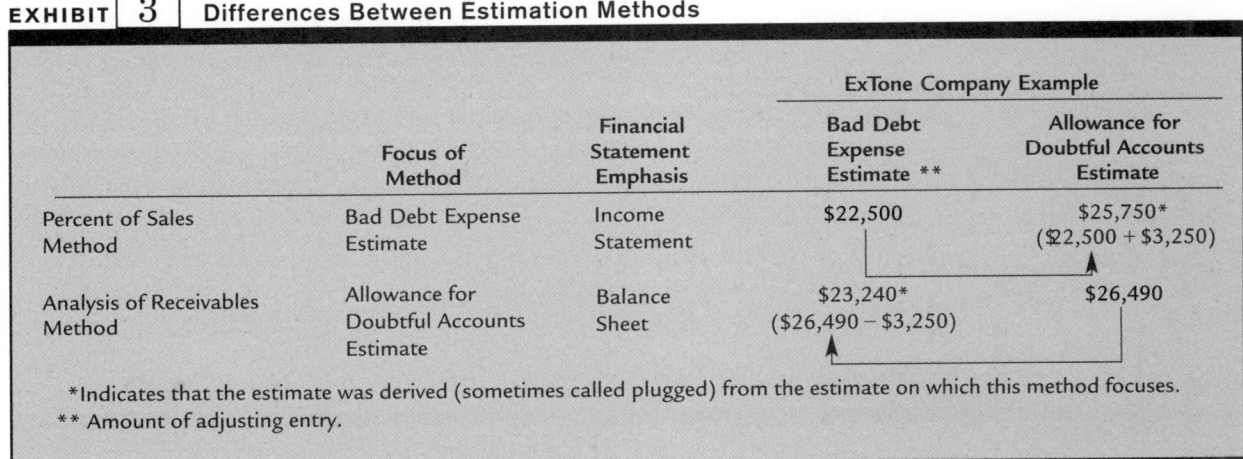

	Focus of Method	Financial Statement Emphasis	ExTone Company Example	
			Bad Debt Expense Estimate **	Allowance for Doubtful Accounts Estimate
Percent of Sales Method	Bad Debt Expense Estimate	Income Statement	$22,500	$25,750* ($22,500 + $3,250)
Analysis of Receivables Method	Allowance for Doubtful Accounts Estimate	Balance Sheet	$23,240* ($26,490 − $3,250)	$26,490

*Indicates that the estimate was derived (sometimes called plugged) from the estimate on which this method focuses.

** Amount of adjusting entry.

normally yield different amounts for any one period, over several periods the amounts should be similar.

Inventory Classification for Merchandisers and Manufacturers

Obj 5 Describe the common classifications of inventories.

In Chapter 4, a merchandiser was defined as a company that purchases products for resale, such as apparel, consumer electronics, hardware, or food items. Merchandise on hand (not sold) at the end of the period is a current asset called **merchandise inventory**. Inventory sold becomes the *cost of merchandise sold*. Merchandise inventory is a large asset for most merchandising companies, as illustrated for some well-known merchandising companies in Exhibit 4.

EXHIBIT 4 | **Size of Merchandise Inventory for Merchandising Businesses**

	Merchandise Inventory as a Percentage of Current Assets	Merchandise Inventory as a Percentage of Total Assets
Wal-Mart	72%	22%
Best Buy	44	30
Home Depot	71	25
Kroger	68	22

As illustrated in earlier chapters, the cost of merchandise is its purchase price, less any purchase discounts. Merchandise inventory also includes other costs, such as freight, import duties, property taxes, and insurance costs.

Manufacturing companies convert raw materials into final products, which are often sold to merchandising businesses. A manufacturing company has three types of inventory:

1. **Materials inventory** consists of the cost of raw materials used in manufacturing a product.

2. **Work-in-process inventory** consists of the costs for partially completed product.

3. **Finished goods inventory** consists of all the costs for completed product.

The manufacturing costs for *Hershey* candy bars, illustrated in Exhibit 5, are as follows:

1. Materials inventory consists of cocoa and sugar.

2. Work-in-process inventory consists of material costs that have been put into production as well as labor costs and overhead costs. Overhead costs consist of costs such as electricity and depreciation on factory equipment.

3. Finished goods inventory consists of candy bars, which are made up of material, labor, and overhead costs.

EXHIBIT 5   Manufacturing Inventories

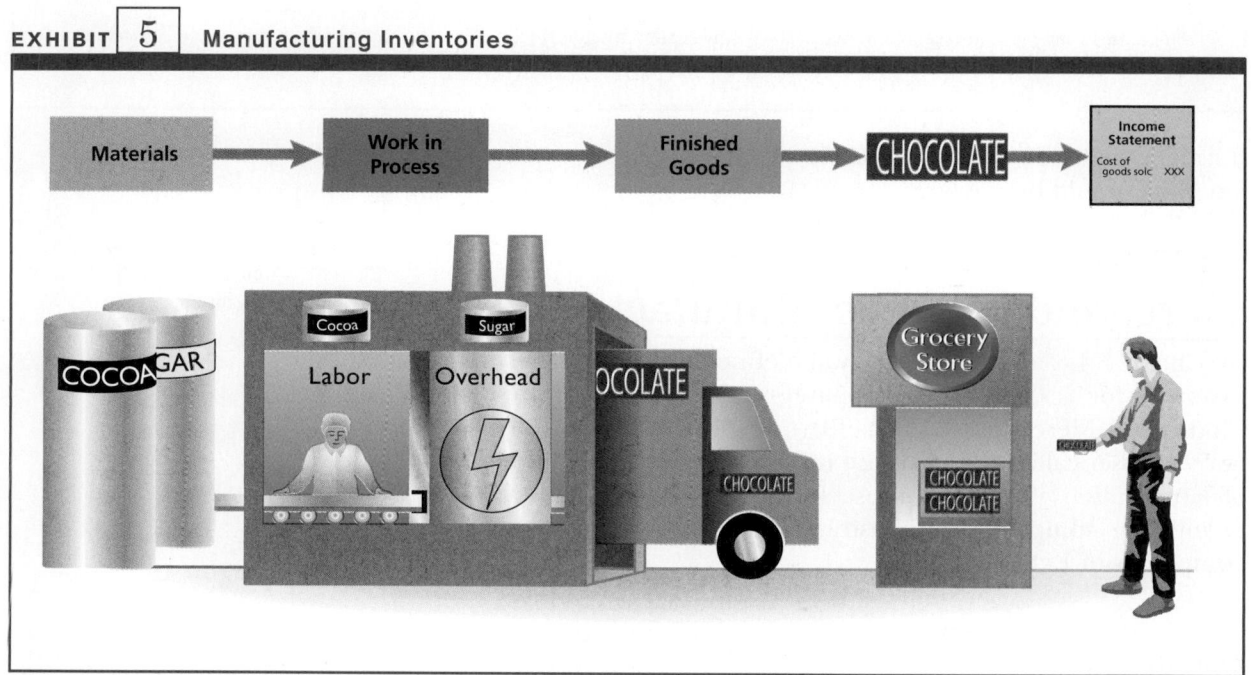

When the finished goods are sold, the costs are transferred to cost of goods sold on the income statement. Manufacturers normally use the term **cost of goods sold** rather than cost of merchandise sold to describe the cost of products sold.

Manufacturing inventories are normally disclosed in the footnotes to the financial statements. For example, The Hershey Company reported inventories of $730,311,000 as follows:

Materials	$215,309,000
Work in process	95,986,000
Finished goods	419,016,000
Total inventories	$730,311,000

In this chapter, inventory accounting and analysis issues for a merchandising company are described and illustrated. However, much of this discussion also applies to manufacturing companies.

How Businesses Make Money

The Consumer Electronic Wars: Best Buy versus Circuit City

How did *Best Buy* compete against the now defunct *Circuit City Stores Inc.* in the intensely competitive consumer electronics market? It didn't just follow a 'me too' method but approached the market by trying to find a way to distinguish itself from Circuit City. First, a warmer color and lighting scheme, featuring light yellows, was chosen over Circuit City's darker color scheme. Second, it opened up bigger stores to provide extra space for the "software" of home electronics. Best Buy believes that more space devoted to CD music, DVD movies, and computer software creates customer foot traffic that eventually translates into other sales. Third, Best Buy introduced a "do-it-yourself" emphasis on the sales floor. Rather than using commissioned salespersons, Best Buy believes that noncommissioned sales personnel can support floor sales. That is, it believes that customers don't need an expert to sell them a product. As a result, the selling expenses as a percent of revenues are reduced. Has the emphasis worked? Over the last 5 years, Best Buy has grown from $15,189 million to $27,433 million in sales, an 81% increase, while Circuit City has gone out of business.

Inventory Cost Flow Assumptions

Obj 6 Describe three inventory cost flow assumptions and how they impact the financial statements.

An accounting issue arises when identical units of merchandise are acquired at different unit costs during a period. In such cases, when an item is sold, it is necessary to determine its cost using a cost flow assumption and related inventory cost flow method. Three common cost flow assumptions and related inventory cost flow methods are shown below.

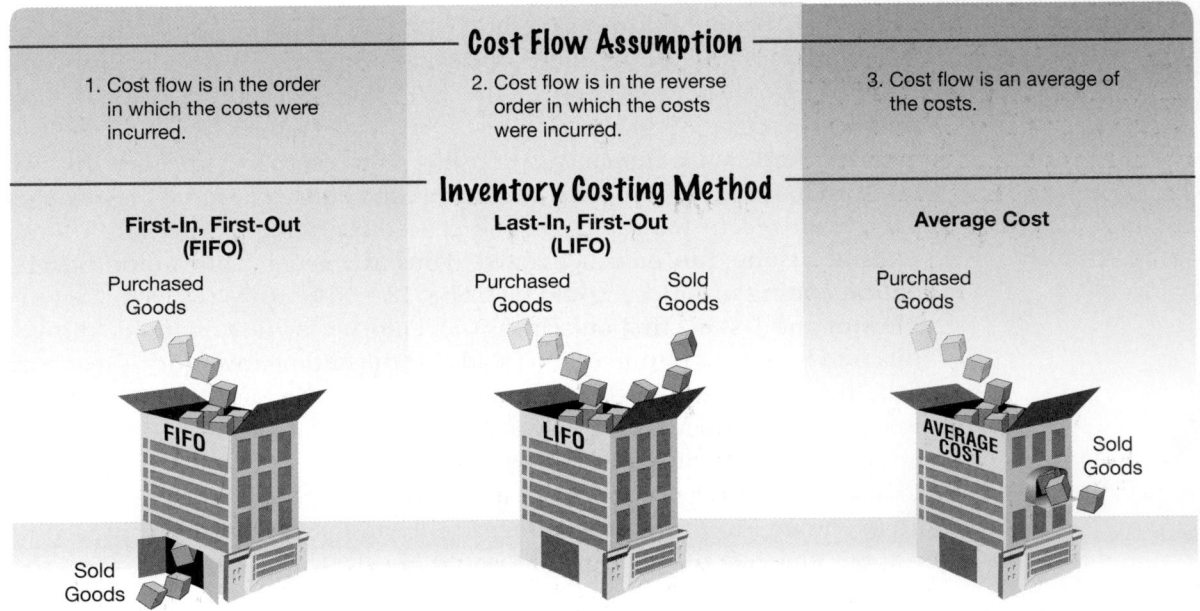

To illustrate, assume that three identical units of merchandise are purchased during May, as follows:

			Units	Cost
May	10	Purchase	1	$ 9
	18	Purchase	1	13
	24	Purchase	1	14
Total			3	$36

Average cost per unit: $12 ($36 ÷ 3 units)

Assume that one unit is sold on May 30 for $20. Depending upon which unit was sold, the gross profit varies from $11 to $6 as shown below.

	May 10 Unit Sold	May 18 Unit Sold	May 24 Unit Sold
Sales	$20	$20	$20
Cost of merchandise sold	9	13	14
Gross profit	$11	$ 7	$ 6
Ending inventory	$27	$23	$22
	($13 + $14)	($9 + $14)	($9 + $13)

Under the **specific identification inventory cost flow method**, the unit sold is identified with a specific purchase. The ending inventory is made up of the remaining units on hand. Thus, the gross profit, cost of merchandise sold, and ending inventory can vary as shown above. For example, if the May 18 unit was sold, the cost of merchandise sold is $13, the gross profit is $7, and the ending inventory is $23.

The specific identification method is normally used by automobile dealerships, jewelry stores, and art galleries.

The specific identification method is not practical unless each inventory unit can be separately identified. For example, an automobile dealer may use the specific identification method since each automobile has a unique serial number. However, most businesses cannot identify each inventory unit separately. In such cases, one of the following three inventory cost flow methods is used.

Under the **first-in, first-out (FIFO) inventory cost flow method**, the first units purchased are assumed to be sold and the ending inventory is made up of the most recent purchases. In the preceding example, the May 10 unit would be assumed to have been sold. Thus, the gross profit would be $11, and the ending inventory would be $27 ($13 + $14).

Under the **last-in, first-out (LIFO) inventory cost flow method**, the last units purchased are assumed to be sold and the ending inventory is made up of the first purchases. In the preceding example, the May 24 unit would be assumed to have been sold. Thus, the gross profit would be $6, and the ending inventory would be $22 ($9 + $13).

Under the **average inventory cost flow method**, the cost of the units sold and in ending inventory is an average of the purchase costs. In the preceding example, the cost of the unit sold would be $12 ($36 ÷ 3 units), the gross profit would be $8 ($20 − $12), and the ending inventory would be $24 ($12 ÷ 2 units).

The three inventory cost flow methods, FIFO, LIFO, and average, are shown in Exhibit 6.

EXHIBIT | 6 | Inventory Costing Methods

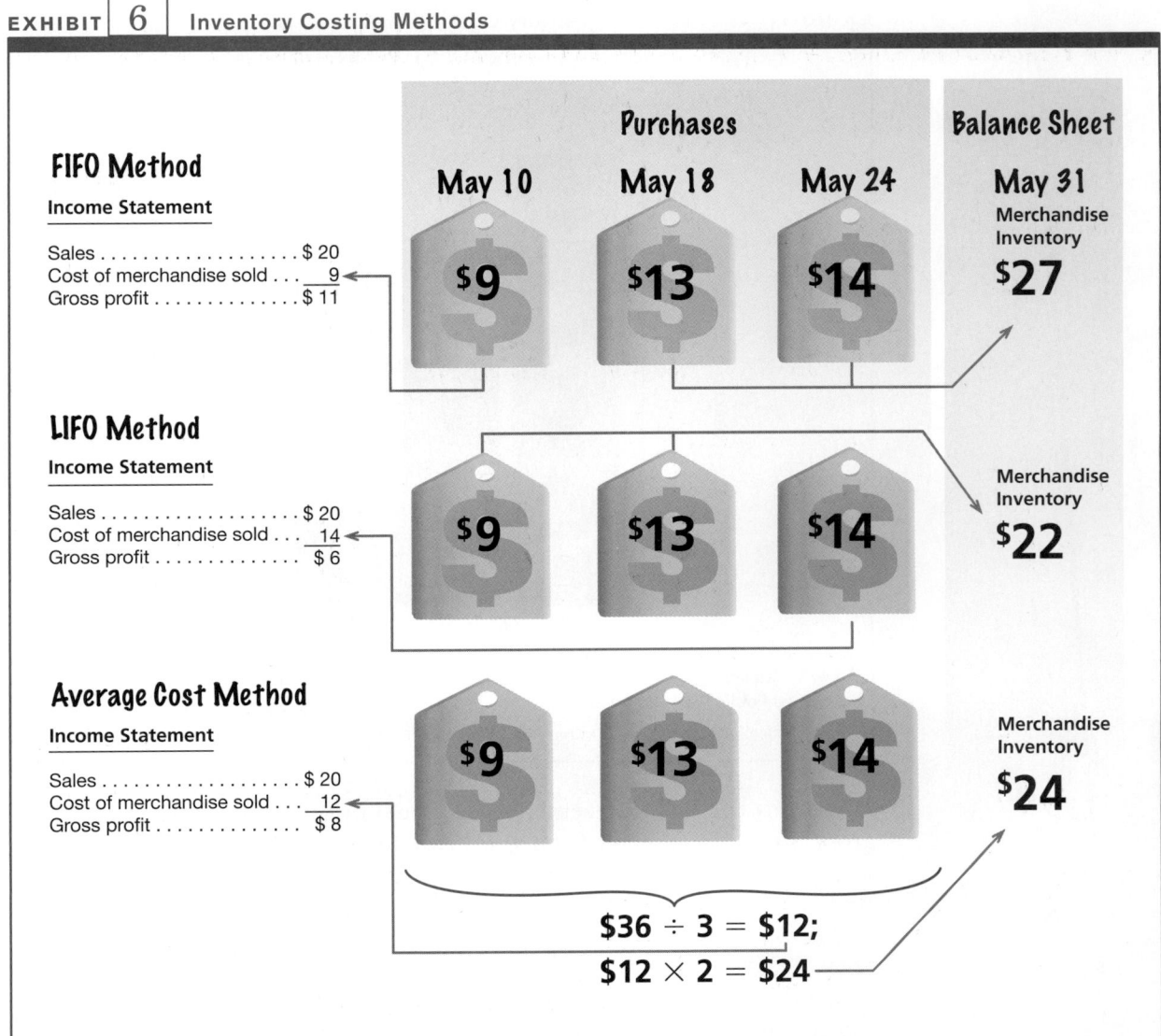

Exhibit 7 shows the frequency with which the FIFO, LIFO, and average methods are used.

Comparing Inventory Costing Methods

Obj 7 Compare and contrast the use of the three inventory costing methods.

As illustrated in Exhibit 6, when prices change, the different inventory costing methods affect the income statement and balance sheet differently. That is, the methods yield different amounts for (1) the cost of the merchandise sold for the period, (2) the gross profit (and net income) for the period, and (3) the ending inventory.

Use of the First-In, First-Out (FIFO) Method

When the FIFO method is used during a period of inflation or rising prices, the earlier unit costs are lower than the more recent unit costs. Much of the benefit of the larger amount of gross profit is lost, however, because the inventory must be replaced at ever higher prices. In fact, the balance sheet will report the ending merchandise inventory at an amount that is about the

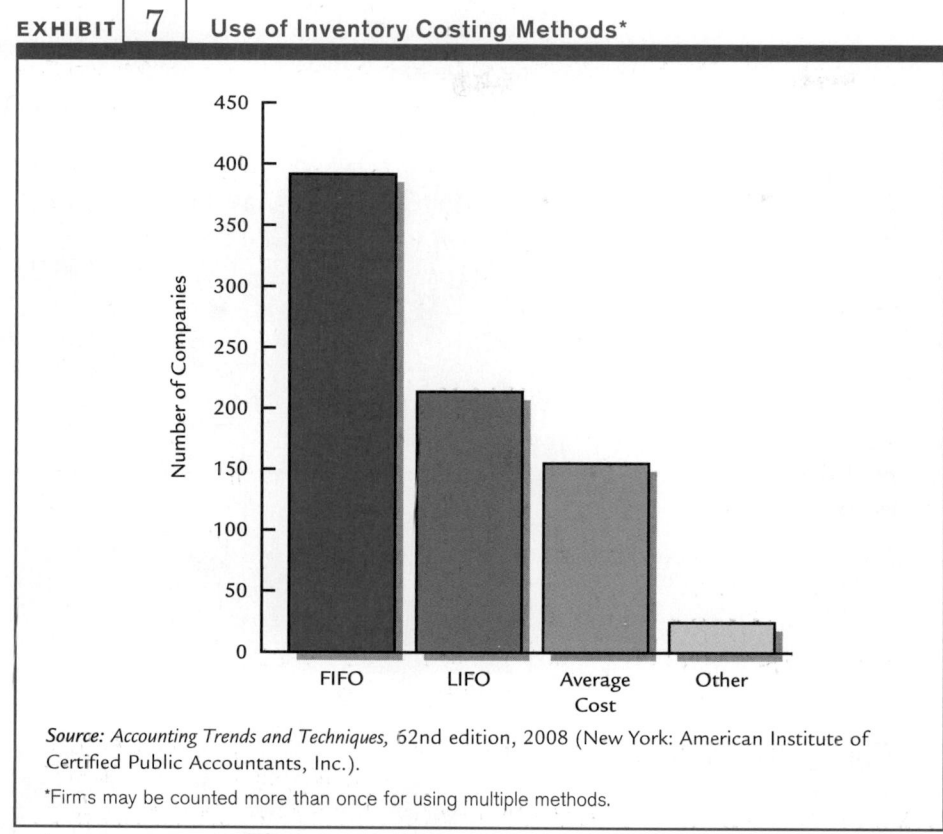

EXHIBIT 7   Use of Inventory Costing Methods*

Source: Accounting Trends and Techniques, 62nd edition, 2008 (New York: American Institute of Certified Public Accountants, Inc.).

*Firms may be counted more than once for using multiple methods.

same as its current replacement cost. When prices are increasing, the larger gross profits that result from the FIFO method are often called *inventory profits* or *illusory profits.* In a period of deflation or declining prices, the effect is just the opposite.

Use of the Last-In, First-Out (LIFO) Method

When the LIFO method is used during a period of inflation or rising prices, the results are opposite those of the other two methods. The LIFO method will yield a higher amount of cost of merchandise sold, a lower amount of gross profit, and a lower amount of inventory at the end of the period than will the other two methods. The reason for these effects is that the cost of the most recently acquired units is about the same as the cost of their replacement. In a period of inflation, the more recent unit costs are higher

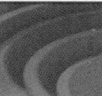

INTEGRITY, OBJECTIVITY, AND ETHICS IN BUSINESS

Where's the Bonus?

Managers are often given bonuses based on reported earnings numbers. This can create a conflict. LIFO can improve the value of the company through lower taxes. However, in periods of rising costs (prices), LIFO also produces a lower earnings number and therefore lower management bonuses. Ethically, managers should select accounting procedures that will maximize the value of the firm, rather than their own compensation. Compensation specialists can help avoid this ethical dilemma by adjusting the bonus plan for the accounting procedure differences.

than the earlier unit costs. Thus, it can be argued that the LIFO method more nearly matches current costs with current revenues.

The rules used for external financial reporting need not be the same as those used for income tax reporting. One exception to this general rule is the use of LIFO. If a company elects to use LIFO inventory valuation for tax purposes, then the company must also use LIFO for external financial reporting. This is called the **LIFO conformity rule**. Thus, in periods of rising prices, LIFO offers an income tax savings because it reports the lowest amount of net income of the three methods. Many managers elect to use LIFO because of the tax savings, even though the reported earnings will be lower.

The ending inventory on the balance sheet may be quite different from its current replacement cost (or FIFO estimate).[4] In such cases, the financial statements will include a note that states the estimated difference between the LIFO inventory and the inventory if FIFO had been used. This difference is called the **LIFO reserve**. An example of such a note for *Deere & Company* is shown below.

Most inventories owned by Deere & Company and its United States equipment subsidiaries are valued at cost, on the LIFO basis. ... If all inventories had been valued on a FIFO basis, estimated inventories by major classification at October 31 in millions of dollars would have been as follows:

INVENTORIES

	2008	2007
Raw materials and supplies	$ 1,170	$ 882
Work-in-process	519	425
Finished machines and parts	2,677	2,263
Total FIFO value	4,366	3,570
Less (LIFO reserve) adjustment to LIFO value	1,324	1,233
Inventories	$ 3,042	$ 2,337

As shown above, the LIFO reserve may be quite large. For Deere & Company, the LIFO reserve is over 30% ($1,324 ÷ $4,366) of the total FIFO inventory for 2008.

The wide differences in the percent of LIFO reserve to FIFO are a result of two major factors: (1) price inflation of the inventory and (2) the age of the inventory. Generally, old LIFO inventory combined with rapid price inflation will result in large LIFO reserves.

If a business sells some of its old LIFO inventory, the LIFO reserve is said to be liquidated. Since old LIFO inventory is normally at low prices, selling old LIFO inventory will result in a lower cost of merchandise sold and a higher gross profit and net income.

Whenever LIFO inventory is liquidated, investors and analysts should be careful in interpreting the income statement. In such cases, most investors and analysts will adjust earnings to what they would have been under FIFO.

Use of the Average Cost Method

As you might have already reasoned, the average cost method is, in a sense, a compromise between FIFO and LIFO. The effect of price trends is averaged in determining the cost of merchandise sold and the ending inventory. For a series of purchases, the average cost will be the same, regardless of the direction of price trends. For example, reversing the sequence of unit costs

[4] The FIFO estimate is replacement cost, which is often similar to FIFO.

presented in Exhibit 6 would not affect the reported cost of merchandise sold, gross profit, or ending inventory.

Obj 8 Describe how receivables and inventory are reported on the financial statements.

Reporting Receivables and Inventory

Receivables and inventory are reported as current assets on the balance sheet, as shown in Exhibit 8. In addition, generally accepted accounting principles require that supplementary information for these accounts be reported in the footnotes accompanying the financial statements. This section focuses on the financial statement and footnote reporting requirements for receivables and inventory.

EXHIBIT | 8 | Receivables and Inventory in Balance Sheet

CRABTREE CO. Balance Sheet December 31, 20—		
Assets		
Current assets:		
Cash and cash equivalents		$119,500
Notes receivable		250,000
Accounts receivable	$445,000	
Less allowance for doubtful accounts	15,000	430,000
Interest receivable		14,500
Merchandise inventory—at lower of cost (first-in, first-out method) or market		216,300

Receivables

All receivables expected to be realized in cash within a year are presented in the Current Assets section of the balance sheet. These assets are normally listed in the order of their liquidity, that is, the order in which they are expected to be converted to cash during normal operations. The receivables are presented on *Starbucks'* balance sheet, as shown here.[5]

Assets (in millions)	Sep. 28, 2008	Sep. 30, 2009
Current assets:		
Cash and cash equivalents	$ 269.8	$ 281.3
Marketable securities	52.5	157.4
Accounts receivable, net of allowances of $4.5 and $3.2, respectively	329.5	287.9
Inventories	692.8	691.7
Prepaid expenses and other current assets	403.4	278.2
Total current assets	1,748.0	1,696.5

Starbucks reports net accounts receivable of $329.5 and $287.9. The allowances for doubtful accounts of $4.5 and $3.2 are subtracted from the total accounts receivable to arrive at the net receivables. Alternatively, the allowances for each year could be shown in a note to the financial statements.

[5] Adapted from Starbucks Corporation amended 10-K for the year ended September 28, 2008.

Other disclosures related to receivables are presented either on the face of the financial statements or in the accompanying notes.[6] Such disclosures include the market (fair) value of the receivables if significantly different from the reported value. In addition, if unusual credit risks exist within the receivables, the nature of the risks should be disclosed. For example, if the majority of the receivables are due from one customer or are due from customers located in one area of the country or one industry, these facts should be disclosed.

Starbucks did not report any unusual credit risks related to its receivables. However, the following credit risk disclosure was adapted from the 2008 financial statements of Deere & Company:

> *Trade accounts and notes receivable have significant concentrations of credit risk in the agricultural, commercial and consumer, and construction and forestry sectors.... On a geographic basis, there is not a disproportionate concentration of credit risk in any area.*

Inventory

Merchandise inventory is usually presented in the Current Assets section of the balance sheet, following receivables. The method of determining the cost of the inventory (FIFO, LIFO, or average) should be shown. It is not unusual for large businesses with varied activities to use different costing methods for different segments of their inventories. The details may be disclosed in parentheses on the balance sheet or in a footnote to the financial statements.

Valuation at Net Realizable Value

Merchandise that is out of date, spoiled, or damaged can often be sold only at a price below its original cost. Such merchandise should be valued at its **net realizable value**. Net realizable value is determined as follows:

Net Realizable Value = Estimated Selling Price – Direct Costs of Disposal

Direct costs of disposal include selling expenses such as special advertising or sales commissions on the sale. To illustrate, assume the following data about an item of damaged merchandise:

Original cost	$1,000
Estimated selling price	800
Selling expenses	150

The merchandise should be valued at its net realizable value of $650 as shown below.

Net Realizable Value = $800 – $150 = $650

Inventory is valued at other than cost when (1) the cost of replacing items in inventory is below the recorded cost, and (2) the inventory is not salable at normal sales prices. This latter case may be due to imperfections, shop wear, style changes, or other causes. In either situation, the method of valuing the inventories (cost or lower of cost or market) should also be disclosed on the balance sheet.

Digital Theater Systems Inc. reported the following inventory write-downs: "... an inventory write-down of $3,871,000 (was recorded) due to ... technological obsolescence."

---

[6] *Statement of Financial Accounting Standards No. 105,* "Disclosures of Information about Financial Instruments with Off-Balance Sheet Risk and Financial Instruments with Concentrations of Credit Risk," and *No. 107,* "Disclosures about Fair Value of Financial Instruments" (Norwalk, CT: Financial Accounting Standards Board).

Valuation at Lower of Cost or Market

Dell Inc. recorded over $39.3 million of charges (expenses) in writing down its inventory of notebook computers. The remaining inventories of computers were then sold at significantly reduced prices.

If the cost of replacing inventory is lower than its recorded purchase cost, the **lower-of-cost-or-market (LCM) method** is used to value the inventory. *Market,* as used in *lower of cost or market,* is the cost to replace the inventory. The market value is based on normal quantities that would be purchased from suppliers.

The lower-of-cost-or-market method can be applied in one of three ways. The cost, market price, and any declines could be determined for the following:

1. each item in the inventory

2. each major class or category of inventory

3. total inventory as a whole

The amount of any price decline is included in the cost of merchandise sold. This, in turn, reduces gross profit and net income in the period in which the price declines occur. This matching of price declines to the period in which they occur is the primary advantage of using the lower-of-cost-or-market method.

To illustrate, assume the following data for 400 identical units of Item A in inventory on December 31, 2010:

Unit purchased cost	$10.25
Replacement cost on December 31, 2010	9.50

Since Item A could be replaced at $9.50 a unit, $9.50 is used under the lower-of-cost-or-market method.

Exhibit 9 illustrates applying the lower-of-cost-or-market method to each inventory item (A, B, C, and D). As applied on an item-by-item basis, the total lower of cost or market is $15,070, which is a market decline of $450 ($15,520 − $15,070). This market decline of $450 is included in the cost of merchandise sold.

EXHIBIT 9   Determining Inventory at Lower of Cost or Market

	A	B	C	D	E	F	G
1			Unit	Unit		Total	
2		Inventory	Cost	Market			Lower
3	Item	Quantity	Price	Price	Cost	Market	of C or M
4	A	400	$10.25	$ 9.50	$ 4,100	$ 3,800	$ 3,800
5	B	120	22.50	24.10	2,700	2,892	2,700
6	C	600	8.00	7.75	4,800	4,650	4,650
7	D	280	14.00	14.75	3,920	4,130	3,920
8	Total				$15,520	$15,472	$15,070
9							

In Exhibit 9, Items A, B, C, and D could be viewed as a class of inventory items. If the lower-of-cost-or-market method is applied to the class, the inventory would be valued at $15,472, which is a market decline of $48 ($15,520 − $15,472). Likewise, if Items A, B, C, and D make up the total inventory, the lower-of-cost-or-market method as applied to the total inventory would be the same amount, $15,472.

Key Points

1. **Describe the common classifications of receivables.**

   The term *receivables* includes all money claims against other entities, including people, business firms, and other organizations. Receivables are normally classified as accounts receivable, notes receivable, or other receivables.

2. **Describe the nature of and the accounting for uncollectible receivables.**

   The two methods of accounting for uncollectible receivables are the direct write-off method and the allowance method. The direct write-off method recognizes the expense only when the account is judged to be uncollectible. The allowance method provides in advance for uncollectible receivables.

3. **Describe the direct write-off method of accounting for uncollectible receivables.**

   Under the direct write-off method, writing off an account increases Bad Debt Expense and decreases Accounts Receivable. Neither an allowance account nor an adjustment is needed at the end of the period.

4. **Describe the allowance method of accounting for uncollectible receivables.**

   A year-end adjustment provides for (1) the reduction of the value of the receivables to the amount of cash expected to be realized from them in the future and (2) the allocation to the current period of the expected expense resulting from such reduction. The adjustment increases Bad Debt Expense and Allowance for Doubtful Accounts. When an account is believed to be uncollectible, it is written off against the allowance account.

   When the estimate of uncollectibles is based on the amount of sales for the period, the adjustment is made without regard to the balance of the allowance account. When the estimate of uncollectibles is based on the amount and the age of the receivable accounts at the end of the period, the adjustment is recorded so that the balance of the allowance account will equal the estimated uncollectibles at the end of the period.

   The allowance account, which will have a negative balance after the adjustment has been posted, is a contra asset account. The bad debt expense is generally reported on the income statement as an operating expense.

5. **Describe the common classifications of inventories.**

   The inventory of a merchandiser is called merchandise inventory. The cost of merchandise inventory that is sold is reported on the income statement. Manufacturers typically have three types of inventory: materials, work in process, and finished goods. When finished goods are sold, the cost is reported on the income statement as cost of goods sold.

6. **Describe three inventory cost flow assumptions and how they impact the financial statements.**

   The three common cost flow assumptions used in business are the (1) first-in, first-out method, (2) last-in, first-out method, and (3) average cost method. Each method normally yields different amounts for the cost of merchandise sold and the ending merchandise inventory. Thus, the choice of a cost flow assumption directly affects the financial statements.

7. **Compare and contrast the use of the three inventory costing methods.**

   The three inventory costing methods will normally yield different amounts for (1) the ending inventory, (2) the cost of the merchandise sold for the period, and (3) the gross profit (and net income) for the period. During periods of inflation, the FIFO method yields the lowest amount for the cost of merchandise sold, the highest amount for gross profit (and net income), and the highest amount for the ending inventory. The LIFO method yields the opposite results. During periods of deflation, the preceding effects are reversed. The average cost method yields results that are between those of FIFO and LIFO.

8. **Describe how receivables and inventory are reported on the financial statements.**

   All receivables that are expected to be realized in cash within a year are presented in the Current Assets section of the balance sheet. It is normal to list the assets in the order of their liquidity, which is the order in which they can be converted to cash in normal operations. In addition to the allowance for doubtful

accounts, additional receivable disclosures include the market (fair) value and unusual credit risks.

Inventory is normally presented in the Current Assets section of the balance sheet following receivables. If the market price of an item of inventory is lower than its cost, the lower market price is used to compute the value of the item. Market price is the cost to replace the merchandise on the inventory date. It is possible to apply the lower of cost or market to each item in the inventory, to major classes or categories, or to the inventory as a whole.

Merchandise that can be sold only at prices below cost should be valued at net realizable value, which is the estimated selling price less any direct costs of disposal.

Key Terms

Accounts receivable Receivables created by selling merchandise or services on credit.

Aging the receivables The process of analyzing the accounts receivable and classifying them according to various age groupings, with the due date being the base point for determining age.

Allowance for doubtful accounts The contra asset account for accounts receivable.

Allowance method The method of accounting for uncollectible accounts that provides an expense for uncollectible receivables in advance of their write-off.

Average inventory cost flow method The method of inventory costing that is based upon the assumption that costs should be charged against revenue by using the weighted average unit cost of the items sold.

Bad debt expense The operating expense incurred because of the failure to collect receivables.

Cost of goods sold The cost of the manufactured product sold.

Direct write-off method The method of accounting for uncollectible accounts that recognizes the expense only when accounts are judged to be worthless.

Finished goods inventory The cost of finished products on hand that have not been sold.

First-in, first-out (FIFO) inventory method A method of inventory costing based on the assumption that the costs of merchandise sold should be charged against revenue in the order in which the costs were incurred.

Last-in, first-out (LIFO) inventory method A method of inventory costing based on the assumption that the most recent merchandise inventory costs should be charged against revenue.

LIFO conformity rule A financial reporting rule requiring a firm that elects to use LIFO inventory valuation for tax purposes to also use LIFO for external financial reporting.

LIFO reserve A required disclosure for LIFO firms, showing the difference between inventory valued under FIFO and inventory valued under LIFO.

Lower-of-cost-or-market (LCM) method A method of valuing inventory that reports the inventory at the lower of its cost or current market value (replacement cost).

Materials inventory The cost of materials that have not yet entered into the manufacturing process.

Maturity value The amount that is due at the maturity or due date of a note.

Merchandise inventory Merchandise on hand (not sold) at the end of an accounting period.

Net realizable value For a receivable, the amount of cash expected to be realized in the future. For inventory, the estimated selling price of an item of inventory less any direct costs of disposal, such as sales commissions.

Notes receivable Written claims against debtors who promise to pay the amount of the note plus interest at an agreed upon rate.

Receivables All money claims against other entities, including people, business firms, and other organizations.

Specific identification inventory cost flow method An inventory cost flow method where the cost of each inventory unit is separately identified.

Work-in-process (WIP) inventory The direct materials costs, the direct labor costs, and the factory overhead costs that have entered into the manufacturing process but are associated with products that have not been finished.

Illustrative Problem

Stewart Co. is a construction supply company that uses the allowance method of accounting for uncollectible accounts receivable. It is estimated that 3% of the credit sales of $1,375,000 for the year ended December 31 will be uncollectible. In addition, Stewart Co.'s beginning inventory and purchases during the year ended December 31, 2010, were as follows:

		Units	Unit Cost	Total Cost
January 1	Inventory	1,000	$50.00	$ 50,000
March 10	Purchase	1,200	52.50	63,000
August 30	Purchase	800	55.00	44,000
November 26	Purchase	2,000	56.00	112,000
Total		5,000		$269,000

Instructions

1. Determine the amount of the adjustment for uncollectible accounts as of December 31, 2010.

2. Illustrate the effects of the adjustment for uncollectible accounts on the accounts and financial statements of Stewart Co.

3. If the balance of Allowance for Doubtful Accounts was a negative $7,500, would the amount of adjustment determined in (1) change?

4. Assuming that 3,300 units were sold during the year, determine the cost of inventory on December 31, 2010, using each of the following inventory costing methods:

   a. first-in, first-out

   b. last-in, first-out

   c. average cost

Solution

1. $41,250 ($1,375,000 × 3%)

2.

	Balance Sheet				
Statement of Cash Flows	Assets	= Liabilities +		Stockholders' Equity	Income Statement
	Allow. for − Doubtful Acc'ts.	=		Retained Earnings	
Dec. 31.	−41,250			−41,250	Dec. 31.

Income Statement
Dec. 31. Bad debt expense −41,250

3. No. Under the percent of sales method the amount of the adjustment is determined without considering the balance of the Allowance for Doubtful Accounts. Under the analysis of receivables method, however, the balance of the Allowance for Doubtful Accounts does affect the amount of the adjustment.

4. a. First-in, first-out method: 1,700 units at $56 = $95,200

b. Last-in, first-out method:

1,000 units at $50.00	$50,000
700 units at $52.50	36,750
1,700	$86,750

c. Average cost method:

Average cost per unit: $269,000 ÷ 5,000 units = $53.80

Inventory, December 31, 2008: 1,700 units at $53.80 = $91,460

Self-Examination Questions (Answers appear at the end of chapter)

1. At the end of the fiscal year, before the accounts are adjusted, Accounts Receivable has a balance of $200,000 and Allowance for Doubtful Accounts has a negative balance of $2,500. If the estimate of uncollectible accounts determined by aging the receivables is $8,500, the amount of bad debt expense is:

   A. $2,500

   B. $6,000

   C. $8,500

   D. $11,000

2. At the end of the fiscal year, Accounts Receivable has a balance of $100,000 and Allowance for Doubtful Accounts has a negative balance of $7,000. The expected net realizable value of the accounts receivable is:

   A. $7,000

   B. $93,000

   C. $100,000

   D. $107,000

3. The direct labor cost should be recognized first in which inventory account?

   A. Materials Inventory

   B. Merchandise Inventory

   C. Finished Goods Inventory

   D. Work in Process Inventory

4. The following units of a particular item were available for sale during the period:

Beginning inventory	40 units at $20
First purchase	50 units at $21
Second purchase	50 units at $22
Third purchase	50 units at $23

   What is the unit cost of the 35 units on hand at the end of the period as determined under the FIFO costing method?

   A. $20

   B. $21

   C. $22

   D. $23

5. If merchandise inventory is being valued at cost and the price level is steadily rising, the method of costing that will yield the highest net income is:

   A. LIFO

   B. FIFO

   C. average

   D. periodic

Class Discussion Questions

1. What are the three classifications of receivables?

2. What types of transactions give rise to accounts receivable?

3. In what section of the balance sheet should a note receivable be listed if its term is (a) 120 days, (b) 6 years?

4. Give two examples of other receivables.

5. Gallatin's Hardware is a small hardware store in the rural township of Willow Creek that rarely extends credit to its customers in the form of an account receivable. The few customers that are allowed to carry accounts receivable are long-time residents of Willow Creek and have a history of doing business at Gallatin's. What method of accounting for uncollectible receivables should Gallatin's Hardware use? Why?

6. Which of the two methods of accounting for uncollectible accounts provides for the recognition of the expense at the earlier date?

7. What kind of an account (asset, liability, etc.) is Allowance for Doubtful Accounts?

8. After the accounts are adjusted at the end of the fiscal year, Accounts Receivable has a balance of $298,150 and Allowance for Doubtful Accounts has a negative balance of $31,200. Describe how the Accounts Receivable and the Allowance for Doubtful Accounts are reported on the balance sheet.

9. A firm has consistently adjusted its allowance account at the end of the fiscal year by adding a fixed percent of the period's net sales on account. After 8 years, the balance in Allowance for Doubtful Accounts has become very large in relationship to the balance in Accounts Receivable. Give two possible explanations.

10. How are manufacturing inventories different from those of a merchandiser?

11. Do the terms *FIFO* and *LIFO* refer to techniques used in determining quantities of the various classes of merchandise on hand? Explain.

12. Does the term *last-in* in the LIFO method mean that the items in the inventory are assumed to be the most recent (last) acquisitions? Explain.

13. If merchandise inventory is being valued at cost and the price level is steadily rising, which of the three methods of costing—FIFO, LIFO, or average cost—will yield (a) the highest inventory cost, (b) the lowest inventory cost, (c) the highest gross profit, (d) the lowest gross profit?

14. Which of the three methods of inventory costing—FIFO, LIFO, or average cost—will in general yield an inventory cost most nearly approximating current replacement cost?

15. If inventory is being valued at cost and the price level is steadily rising, which of the three methods of costing—FIFO, LIFO, or average cost—will yield the lowest annual income tax expense? Explain.

16. What is the LIFO reserve, and why would an analyst be careful in interpreting the earnings of a company that has liquidated some of its LIFO reserve?

17. Under what section should accounts receivable be reported on the balance sheet?

18. Because of imperfections, an item of merchandise cannot be sold at its normal selling price. How should this item be valued for financial statement purposes?

19. How is the method of determining the cost of inventory and the method of valuing it disclosed in the financial statements?

Exercises

E6-1

Classifications of receivables

Obj 1

Boeing is one of the world's major aerospace firms, with operations involving commercial aircraft, military aircraft, missiles, satellite systems, and information and battle management systems. As of December 31, 2008, Boeing had $2,675 million of receivables involving U.S. government contracts and $1,041 million of receivables involving commercial aircraft customers, such as *Delta Air Lines* and *United Airlines.*

Should Boeing report these receivables separately in the financial statements, or combine them into one overall accounts receivable amount? Explain.

E6-2

Determine due date and interest on notes

Obj 1

SPREADSHEET

✓ d. May 5. $225

Determine the due date and the amount of interest due at maturity on the following notes:

	Date of Note	Face Amount	Interest Rate	Term of Note
a.	October 1	$10,500	8%	60 days
b.	August 30	18,000	10	120 days
c.	May 30	12,000	12	90 days
d.	March 6	15,000	9	60 days
e.	May 23	9,000	10	60 days

E6-3

Nature of uncollectible accounts

Obj 2

✓ a. 19.9%

The *MGM Mirage* owns and operates casinos including the MGM Grand and the Bellagio in Las Vegas, Nevada. For a recent year, the MGM Mirage reported accounts and notes receivable of $452,945,000 and allowance for doubtful accounts of $90,024,000.

Johnson & Johnson manufactures and sells a wide range of health care products including Band-Aids and Tylenol. For a recent year, Johnson & Johnson reported accounts receivable of $9,444,000,000 and allowance for doubtful accounts of $193,000,000.

a. Compute the percentage of the allowance for doubtful accounts to the accounts and notes receivable for the MGM Mirage.

b. Compute the percentage of the allowance for doubtful accounts to the accounts receivable for Johnson & Johnson.

c. Discuss possible reasons for the difference in the two ratios computed in (a) and (b).

E6-4

Uncollectible accounts, using direct write-off method

Obj 3

Illustrate the effects on the accounts and financial statements of the following transactions in the accounts of Laser Tech Co., a hospital supply company that uses the direct write-off method of accounting for uncollectible receivables:

May 10. Received $10,000 on an account and wrote off the remainder owed of $31,500 as uncollectible.

Dec. 2. Reinstated the account that had been written off on May 10 and received $31,500 cash in full payment.

E6-5

Uncollectible receivables, using allowance method

Obj 4

Illustrate the effects on the accounts and financial statements of the following transactions in the accounts of Food Unlimited Company, a restaurant supply company that uses the allowance method of accounting for uncollectible receivables:

Mar. 31. Received $5,000 on an account and wrote off the remainder owed of $8,200 as uncollectible.

Sept. 3. Reinstated the account that had been written off on March 31 and received $8,200 cash in full payment.

E6-6

Writing off accounts receivable

Objs 3, 4

Tech Savvy, a computer consulting firm, has decided to write off the $8,375 balance of an account owed by a customer. Illustrate the effects on the accounts and financial statements to record the write-off (a) assuming that the direct write-off method is used, and (b) assuming that the allowance method is used.

E6-7

Estimating doubtful accounts

Obj 4

Fonda Bikes Co. is a wholesaler of motorcycle supplies. An aging of the company's accounts receivable on December 31, 2010, and a historical analysis of the percentage of uncollectible accounts in each age category are as follows:

Age Interval	Balance	Percent Uncollectible
Not past due	$567,000	½%
1–30 days past due	58,000	3
31–60 days past due	29,000	7
61–90 days past due	20,500	15
91–180 days past due	15,000	40
Over 180 days past due	10,500	75
	$700,000	

Estimate what the proper balance of the allowance for doubtful accounts should be as of December 31, 2010.

E6-8

Entry for uncollectible accounts

Obj 4

Using the data in Exercise 6-7, assume that the allowance for doubtful accounts for Fonda Bikes Co. had a negative balance of −$4,145 as of December 31, 2010.

Illustrate the effects of the adjustment for uncollectible accounts as of December 31, 2010, on the accounts and financial statements.

E6-9

Providing for doubtful accounts

Obj 4

✓ a. $23,500

✓ b. $24,800

At the end of the current year, the accounts receivable account has a balance of $825,000 and net sales for the year total $9,400,000. Determine the amount of the adjusting entry to provide for doubtful accounts under each of the following assumptions:

a. The allowance account before adjustment has a negative balance of −$11,200. Bad debt expense is estimated at ¼ of 1% of net sales.

b. The allowance account before adjustment has a negative balance of −$11,200. An aging of the accounts in the customer ledger indicates estimated doubtful accounts of $36,000.

c. The allowance account before adjustment has a positive balance of $6,000. Bad debt expense is estimated at ½ of 1% of net sales.

d. The allowance account before adjustment has a positive balance of $6,000. An aging of the accounts in the customer ledger indicates estimated doubtful accounts of $49,500.

E6-10

Effect of doubtful accounts on net income

Objs 3, 4

During its first year of operations, Master Plumbing Supply Co. had net sales of $3,500,000, wrote off $50,000 of accounts as uncollectible using the direct write-off method, and reported net income of $390,500. Determine what the net income would have been if the allowance method had been used, and the company estimated that 1¾% of net sales would be uncollectible.

E6-11

Effect of doubtful accounts on net income

Objs 3, 4

✓ b. $24,750

Using the data in Exercise 6-10, assume that during the second year of operations Master Plumbing Supply Co. had net sales of $4,200,000, wrote off $60,000 of accounts as uncollectible using the direct write-off method, and reported net income of $425,000.

a. Determine what net income would have been in the second year if the allowance method (using 1¾% of net sales) had been used in both the first and second years.

b. Determine what the balance of Allowance for Doubtful Accounts would have been at the end of the second year if the allowance method had been used in both the first and second years.

E6-12

Manufacturing inventories

Obj 5

Qualcomm Incorporated is a leading developer and manufacturer of digital wireless telecommunications products and services. Qualcomm reported the following inventories on September 28, 2008, in the notes to its financial statements:

	(In millions) September 28, 2008
Raw materials	$ 27
Work in process	199
Finished goods	295
	$521

a. Why does Qualcomm report three different inventories?
b. What costs are included in each of the three classes of inventory?

E6-13

Film costs of Dreamworks

Obj 5

Dreamworks Animation SKG Inc. shows "film costs" as an asset on its balance sheet. In the notes to its financial statements, the following disclosure was made:

	December 31,	
Film Costs (in thousands)	2008	2007
In release:		
Animated feature films(1)	$326,861	$263,514
Television special	3,124	4,210
In production:		
Animated feature films	251,066	239,450
Television special	7,207	—
In development	49,985	34,743
Total film costs	$638,243	$541,917

a. Interpret the film cost asset categories.
b. How are these classifications similar or dissimilar to the inventory classifications used in a manufacturing firm?

E6-14

Inventory by three methods

Obj 6

✓ b. $6,414

The units of an item available for sale during the year were as follows:

Jan. 1	Inventory	27 units at $120
Feb. 17	Purchase	54 units at $138
July 21	Purchase	63 units at $156
Nov. 23	Purchase	36 units at $165

There are 50 units of the item in the physical inventory at December 31. The periodic inventory system is used. Determine the inventory cost by (a) the first-in, first-out method, (b) the last-in, first-out method, and (c) the average cost method.

E6-15

Inventory by three methods; cost of merchandise sold

SPREADSHEET

Obj 6

✓ a. Merchandise inventory, $2,508

The units of an item available for sale during the year were as follows:

Jan. 1	Inventory	42 units at $60
Mar. 10	Purchase	58 units at $65
Aug. 30	Purchase	20 units at $68
Dec. 12	Purchase	30 units at $70

There are 36 units of the item in the physical inventory at December 31. The periodic inventory system is used. Determine the inventory cost and the cost of merchandise sold by three methods, presenting your answers in the following form:

	Cost	
Inventory Method	Merchandise Inventory	Merchandise Sold
a. First-in, first-out	$	$
b. Last-in, first-out		
c. Average cost		

E6-16

Comparing inventory methods

Obj 7

Assume that a firm separately determined inventory under FIFO and LIFO and then compared the results.

1. In each space below, place the correct sign [less than (<), greater than (>), or equal (=)] for each comparison, assuming periods of rising prices.

   a. FIFO inventory ___ LIFO inventory
   b. FIFO cost of goods sold ___ LIFO cost of goods sold
   c. FIFO net income ___ LIFO net income
   d. FIFO income tax ___ LIFO income tax

2. Why would management prefer to use LIFO over FIFO in periods of rising prices?

E6-17

Receivables in the balance sheet

Obj 8

List any errors you can find in the following partial balance sheet:

JENNETT COMPANY
Balance Sheet
December 31, 2010

Assets

Current assets:		
Cash		$ 95,000
Notes receivable	$250,000	
Less interest receivable	15,000	235,000
Account receivable	$398,000	
Plus allowance for doubtful accounts	36,000	434,000

E6-18

Lower-of-cost-or-market inventoryReceivables in the balance sheet

Obj 8

SPREADSHEET

✓ LCM: $16,990

On the basis of the following data, determine the value of the inventory at the lower of cost or market. Assemble the data in the form illustrated in Exhibit 9.

Commodity	Inventory Quantity	Unit Cost Price	Unit Market Price
Aquarius	20	$ 80	$ 92
Capricorn	50	70	65
Leo	8	300	280
Scorpio	30	40	30
Taurus	100	90	94

E6-19

Merchandise inventory on the balance sheet

Obj 8

Based on the data in Exercise 6-18 and assuming that cost was determined by the FIFO method, show how the merchandise inventory would appear on the balance sheet.

Problems

P6-1

Allowance method for doubtful accounts

Obj 4

SPREADSHEET

✓ 1. Estimate of
doubtful accounts,
$67,210

Wigs Plus Company supplies wigs and hair care products to beauty salons throughout California and the Pacific Northwest. The accounts receivable clerk for Wigs Plus prepared the following aging-of-receivables schedule as of the end of business on December 31, 2010:

	A	B	C	D	E	F	G	H
1			Not		Days Past Due			
2			Past					
3	Customer	Balance	Due	1–30	31–60	61–90	91–120	Over 120
4	Alpha Beauty	20,000	20,000					
5	Blonde Wigs	11,000			11,000			
30	Zahn's Beauty	2,900		2,900				
31	Totals	925,550	506,000	219,500	102,950	36,100	36,000	25,000

Wigs Plus Company has a past history of uncollectible accounts by age category, as follows:

Age Class	Percent Uncollectible
Not past due	2%
1–30 days past due	4
31–60 days past due	10
61–90 days past due	15
91–120 days past due	35
Over 120 days past due	80

Instructions

1. Estimate the allowance for doubtful accounts, based on the aging-of-receivables schedule.
2. Assume that the allowance for doubtful accounts for Wigs Plus Company has a negative balance of −$1,710 before adjustment on December 31, 2010. Illustrate the effect on the accounts and financial statements of the adjustment for uncollectible accounts.
3. Wigs Plus Company reported credit sales of $4,000,000 during 2010. Assume that instead of using the analysis of receivables method of estimating uncollectible accounts, Wigs Plus Company uses the percent of sales method and estimates that 1.75% of sales will be uncollectible. Illustrate the effect on the accounts and financial statements of the adjustment for uncollectible accounts using the percent of sales method.
4. Assume that on February 10, 2011, Wigs Plus wrote off the $3,500 account of Lasting Images as uncollectible. Illustrate the effect on the accounts and financial statements of the write-off of the Lasting Images account.
5. Assume that on May 17, 2011, Lasting Images paid $3,500 on its account. Illustrate the effect on the accounts and financial statements of reinstating and collecting the Lasting Images account.

6. Assume that instead of using the allowance method, Wigs Plus uses the direct write-off method. Illustrate the effect on the accounts and financial statements of the following:

a. The write-off of the Lasting Images account on February 10, 2011.

b. The reinstatement and collection of the Lasting Images account on May 17, 2011.

7. Does *Amazon.com* use the direct write-off or allowance method of accounting for uncollectible accounts receivable? Explain.

P6-2

Estimate uncollectible accounts

Obj 4

✓ (a) 2007, $15,300

For several years, Halsey Co.'s sales have been on a "cash only" basis. On January 1, 2007, however, Halsey Co. began offering credit on terms of n/30. The amount of the adjusting entry to record the estimated uncollectible receivables at the end of each year has been ¼ of 1% of credit sales, which is the rate reported as the average for the industry. Credit sales and the year-end credit balances in Allowance for Doubtful Accounts for the past four years are as follows:

Year	Credit Sales	Allowance for Doubtful Accounts
2007	$6,120,000	$ 6,390
2008	6,300,000	11,880
2009	6,390,000	17,000
2010	6,540,000	24,600

Javier Cernao, president of Halsey Co., is concerned that the method used to account for and write off uncollectible receivables is unsatisfactory. He has asked for your advice in the analysis of past operations in this area and for recommendations for change.

1. Determine the amount of (a) the addition to Allowance for Doubtful Accounts and (b) the accounts written off for each of the four years.

2. a. Advise Javier Cernao as to whether the estimate of ¼ of 1% of credit sales appears reasonable.

b. Assume that after discussing (a) with Javier Cernao, he asked you what action might be taken to determine what the balance of Allowance for Doubtful Accounts should be at December 31, 2010, and what possible changes, if any, you might recommend in accounting for uncollectible receivables. How would you respond?

P6-3

Compare two methods of accounting for uncollectible receivables

Objs 3, 4

✓ 1. Year 4: Balance of allowance account, end of year, $13,350

J. J. Technology Company, which operates a chain of 30 electronics supply stores, has just completed its fourth year of operations. The direct write-off method of recording bad debt expense has been used during the entire period. Because of substantial increases in sales volume and the amount of uncollectible accounts, the firm is considering changing to the allowance method. Information is requested as to the effect that an annual provision of ½% of sales would have had on the amount of bad debt expense reported for each of the past four years. It is also considered desirable to know what the balance of Allowance for Doubtful Accounts would have been at the end of each year. The following data have been obtained from the accounts:

Year	Sales	Uncollectible Accounts Written Off	Year of Origin of Accounts Receivable Written Off as Uncollectible			
			1st	2nd	3rd	4th
1st	$1,300,000	$ 1,200	$1,200			
2nd	1,750,000	3,000	1,400	$1,600		
3rd	3,000,000	13,000	3,800	3,000	$6,200	
4th	3,600,000	17,700		4,000	6,100	$7,600

Instructions

1. Assemble the desired data, using the following column headings:

	Bad Debt Expense			
Year	Expense Actually Reported	Expense Based on Estimate	Increase (Decrease) in Amount of Expense	Balance of Allowance Account, End of Year

2. Experience during the first four years of operations indicated that the receivables were either collected within two years or had to be written off as uncollectible. Does the estimate of ½% of sales appear to be reasonably close to the actual experience with uncollectible accounts originating during the first two years? Explain.

P6-4

Inventory by three cost flow methods

Objs 6, 7

SPREADSHEET

✓ 1. $15,583

Details regarding the inventory of appliances at January 1, 2010, purchases invoices during the year, and the inventory count at December 31, 2010, of Arctic Appliances are summarized as follows:

Model	Inventory, January 1	Purchases Invoices			Inventory Count, December 31
		1st	2nd	3rd	
BB900	27 at $213	21 at $215	18 at $222	18 at $225	30
C911	10 at 60	6 at 65	2 at 65	2 at 70	4
L100	6 at 305	3 at 310	3 at 316	4 at 317	4
N201	2 at 520	2 at 527	2 at 530	2 at 535	4
Q73	6 at 520	8 at 531	4 at 549	6 at 542	7
Z120	—	4 at 222	4 at 232	—	2
ZZRF	8 at 70	12 at 72	16 at 74	14 at 78	12

Instructions

1. Determine the cost of the inventory on December 31, 2010, by the first-in, first-out method. Present data in columnar form, using the following headings:

Model	Quantity	Unit Cost	Total Cost

If the inventory of a particular model comprises one entire purchase plus a portion of another purchase acquired at a different unit cost, use a separate line for each purchase.

2. Determine the cost of the inventory on December 31, 2010, by the last-in, first-out method, following the procedures indicated in (1).
3. Determine the cost of the inventory on December 31, 2010, by the average cost method, using the columnar headings indicated in (1).
4. Discuss which method (FIFO or LIFO) would be preferred for income tax purposes in periods of (a) rising prices and (b) declining prices.

P6-5

Lower-of-cost-or-market inventory

Obj 8

SPREADSHEET

✓ Total LCM, $43,703

Data on the physical inventory of Winesap Company as of December 31, 2010, are presented below.

Description	Inventory Quantity	Unit Market Price
AC172	38	$ 56
BE43	18	180
CJ9	30	120
E34	125	26
F17	18	550
G68	60	15
K41	5	390
Q79	375	6
RZ13	90	18
S60	6	235
W21	140	18
XR90	15	745

Quantity and cost data from the last purchases invoice of the year and the next-to-the-last purchases invoice are summarized as follows:

Description	Last Purchases Invoice		Next-to-the-Last Purchases Invoice	
	Quantity Purchased	Unit Cost	Quantity Purchased	Unit Cost
AC172	25	$ 60	30	$ 58
BE43	35	175	20	180
CJ9	18	130	25	128
E34	150	25	100	24
F17	10	565	10	560
G68	100	15	100	14
K41	10	385	5	384
Q79	500	6	500	6
RZ13	80	22	50	21
S60	5	250	4	260
W21	100	20	75	19
XR90	9	750	9	740

Instructions

Determine the inventory at cost and also at the lower of cost or market, using the first-in, first-out method. Record the appropriate unit costs on an inventory sheet and complete the pricing of the inventory. When there are two different unit costs applicable to an item, proceed as follows:

1. Draw a line through the quantity, and insert the quantity and unit cost of the last purchase.

2. On the following line, insert the quantity and unit cost of the next-to-the-last purchase.

3. Total the cost and market columns and insert the lower of the two totals in the Lower of C or M column. The first item on the inventory sheet has been completed below as an example.

Inventory Sheet
December 31, 2010

Description	Inventory Quantity	Unit Cost Price	Unit Market Price	Total Cost	Total Market	Lower of C or M
AC172	~~38~~ 25	$60	$56	$1,500	$1,400	
	13	58		754	728	
				$2,254	$2,128	$2,128

Activities

A6-1

Ethics and professional conduct in business

ETHICS

Mirna Gaymer, vice president of operations for Rocky Mountain County Bank, has instructed the bank's computer programmer to use a 365-day year to compute interest on depository accounts (payables). Mirna also instructed the programmer to use a 360-day year to compute interest on loans (receivables).

Discuss whether Mirna is behaving in a professional manner.

A6-2

Collecting accounts receivable

The following is an excerpt from a conversation between the office manager, Mark Cottman, and the president of Horowitz Construction Supplies Co., Rosa Mullin. Horowitz sells building supplies to local contractors.

Mark: Rosa, we're going to have to do something about these overdue accounts receivable. One-third of our accounts are over 60 days past due, and I've had accounts that have stayed open for almost a year!

Rosa: I didn't realize it was that bad. Any ideas?

Mark: Well, we could stop giving credit. Make everyone pay with cash or a credit card. We accept MasterCard and Visa already, but only the walk-in customers use them. Almost all of the contractors put purchases on their bills.

Rosa: Yes, but we've been allowing credit for years. As far as I know, all of our competitors allow contractors credit. If we stopped giving credit, we'd lose many of our contractors. They'd just go elsewhere. You know, some of these guys run up bills as high as $60,000 or $80,000. There's no way they could put that kind of money on a credit card.

Mark: That's a good point. But we've got to do something.

Rosa: How many of the contractor accounts do you actually end up writing off as uncollectible?

Mark: Not many. Almost all eventually pay. It's just that they take so long!

Suggest one or more solutions to Horowitz Construction Supplies Co.'s problem concerning the collection of accounts receivable.

A6-3

Ethics and professional
conduct in business

ETHICS

Ebba Co. is experiencing a decrease in sales and operating income for the fiscal year ending December 31, 2010. Cody Bryant, controller of Ebba Co., has suggested that all orders received before the end of the fiscal year be shipped by midnight, December 31, 2010, even if the shipping department must work overtime. Since Ebba Co. ships all merchandise FOB shipping point, it would record all such shipments as sales for the year ending December 31, 2010, thereby offsetting some of the decreases in sales and operating income.

Discuss whether Cody Bryant is behaving in a professional manner.

A6-4

LIFO and inventory flow

The following is an excerpt from a conversation between Chad Lindy, the warehouse manager for House of Foods Wholesale Co., and its accountant, Summer Roseberry. Wholesale operates a large regional warehouse that supplies produce and other grocery products to grocery stores in smaller communities.

Chad: Summer, can you explain what's going on here with these monthly statements?

Summer: Sure, Chad. How can I help you?

Chad: I don't understand this last-in, first-out inventory procedure. It just doesn't make sense.

Summer: Well, what it means is that we assume that the last goods we receive are the first ones sold. So the inventory is made up of the items we purchased first.

Chad: Yes, but that's my problem. It doesn't work that way! We always distribute the oldest produce first. Some of that produce is perishable! We can't keep any of it very long or it'll spoil.

Summer: Chad, you don't understand. We only assume that the products we distribute are the last ones received. We don't actually have to distribute the goods in this way.

Chad: I always thought that accounting was supposed to show what really happened. It all sounds like "make believe" to me! Why not report what really happens?

Respond to Chad's concerns.

Answers to Self-Examination Questions

1. **B** The estimate of uncollectible accounts, $8,500 (answer C), is the amount of the desired balance of Allowance for Doubtful Accounts after adjustment. The amount of the current provision to be made for bad debt expense is thus $6,000 (answer B), which is the amount that must be added to the Allowance for Doubtful Accounts negative balance of $2,500 (answer A), so that the account will have the desired balance of $8,500.

2. **B** The amount expected to be realized from accounts receivable is the balance of Accounts Receivable, $100,000, less the balance of Allowance for Doubtful Accounts, $7,000, or $93,000 (answer B).

3. **D** The direct labor costs are introduced into production initially as work in process. Once the units are completed, these costs are transferred to finished goods inventory (answer C). Materials inventory (answer A) includes only material costs, not direct labor cost. Merchandise inventory (answer B) is not used in a manufacturing setting, hence does not include direct labor cost.

4. **D** The FIFO method of costing is based on the assumption that costs should be charged against revenue in the order in which they were incurred (first-in, first-out). Thus, the most recent costs are assigned to inventory. The 35 units would be assigned a unit cost of $23 (answer D).

5. **B** When the price level is steadily rising, the earlier unit costs are lower than recent unit costs. Under the FIFO method (answer B), these earlier costs are matched against revenue to yield the highest possible net income. The periodic inventory system (answer D) is a system and not a method of costing.

Fixed Assets and Intangible Assets

Learning Objectives

After studying this chapter, you should be able to:

Obj 1 Define, classify, and account for the cost of fixed assets.

Obj 2 Compute depreciation using the straight-line and double-declining-balance methods.

Obj 3 Describe the accounting for the disposal of fixed assets.

Obj 4 Describe the accounting for depletion of natural resources.

Obj 5 Describe the accounting for intangible assets.

Obj 6 Describe how depreciation expense is reported in an income statement and prepare a balance sheet that includes fixed assets and intangible assets.

Do you remember purchasing your first car? You probably didn't buy your first car like you would download songs from iTunes. Purchasing a new or used car is expensive. In addition, you would drive (use) the car for the next 3–5 years or longer. As a result, you might spend hours or weeks considering different makes and models, safety ratings, warranties, and operating costs before deciding on the final purchase.

Like buying her first car, Lovie Yancey spent a lot of time before deciding to open her first restaurant. In 1952, she created the biggest, juiciest hamburger that anyone had ever seen. She called it a Fatburger. The **Fatburger** restaurant initially started as a 24-hour operation to cater to the schedules of professional musicians. As a fan of popular music and its performers, Yancey played rhythm and blues, jazz, and blues recordings for her customers. Fatburger's popularity with entertainers was illustrated when its name was used in a 1992 rap by Ice Cube. "Two in the mornin' got the Fatburger," Cube said, in "It Was a Good Day," a track on his *Predator* album.

The demand for this incredible burger was such that, in 1980, Ms. Yancey decided to offer Fatburger franchise opportunities. In 1990, with the goal of expanding Fatburger throughout the world, Fatburger Inc. purchased the business from Ms. Yancey. Today, Fatburger has grown to a multi-restaurant chain with owners and investors such as talk show host Montel Williams, former Cincinnati Bengals' tackle Willie Anderson, comedian David Spade, and musicians Cher, Janet Jackson, and Pharrell.

So, how much would it cost you to open a Fatburger restaurant? The total investment begins at over $750,000 per restaurant. Thus, in starting a Fatburger restaurant, you would be making a significant investment that would affect your life for years to come. For more information see **http://www.fatburger.com**.

This chapter discusses the accounting for investments in fixed assets such as those used to open a Fatburger restaurant. How to determine the portion of the fixed asset that becomes an expense over time is also discussed. Finally, the accounting for the disposal of fixed assets and accounting for intangible assets such as patents and copyrights are discussed.

Obj 1 Define, classify, and
account for the cost of fixed
assets.

Nature of Fixed Assets

Fixed assets are long-term or relatively permanent assets such as equipment, machinery, buildings, and land. Other descriptive titles for fixed assets are *plant assets* or *property, plant, and equipment*. Fixed assets have the following characteristics:

1. They exist physically and thus are *tangible* assets.
2. They are owned and used by the company in its normal operations.
3. They are not offered for sale as part of normal operations.

Exhibit 1 shows the percent of fixed assets to total assets for some select companies. As shown in Exhibit 1, fixed assets are often a significant portion of the total assets of a company.

EXHIBIT 1   Fixed Assets as a Percent of Total Assets—Selected Companies

	Fixed Assets as a Percent of Total Assets
Alcoa Inc.	40%
ExxonMobil Corporation	60
Ford Motor Company	35
Kroger	55
Marriott International, Inc.	31
United Parcel Service, Inc.	53
Verizon Communications	45
Walgreen Co.	46
Wal-Mart	53

Classifying Costs

A cost that has been incurred may be classified as a fixed asset, an investment, or an expense. Exhibit 2 shows how to determine the proper classification of a cost and thus how it should be recorded.

As shown in Exhibit 2, classifying a cost involves the following steps:

Step 1. Is the purchased item (cost) long-lived?

If *yes*, the item is capitalized as an asset on the balance sheet as either a fixed asset or an investment. Proceed to Step 2.

If *no*, the item is classified and recorded as an *expense*.

Step 2. Is the asset used in normal operations?

If *yes*, the asset is classified and recorded as a *fixed asset*.

If *no*, the asset is classified and recorded as an *investment*.

Costs that are classified and recorded as fixed assets include the purchase of land, buildings, or equipment. Such assets normally last more than a year and are used in the normal operations. However, standby equipment for use during peak periods or when other equipment breaks down is still classified as a fixed asset even though it is not used very often. In contrast, fixed assets that have been abandoned or are no longer used in operations are not fixed assets.

Although fixed assets may be sold, they should not be offered for sale as part of normal operations. For example, cars and trucks offered for sale by

EXHIBIT | 2 | **Classifying Costs**

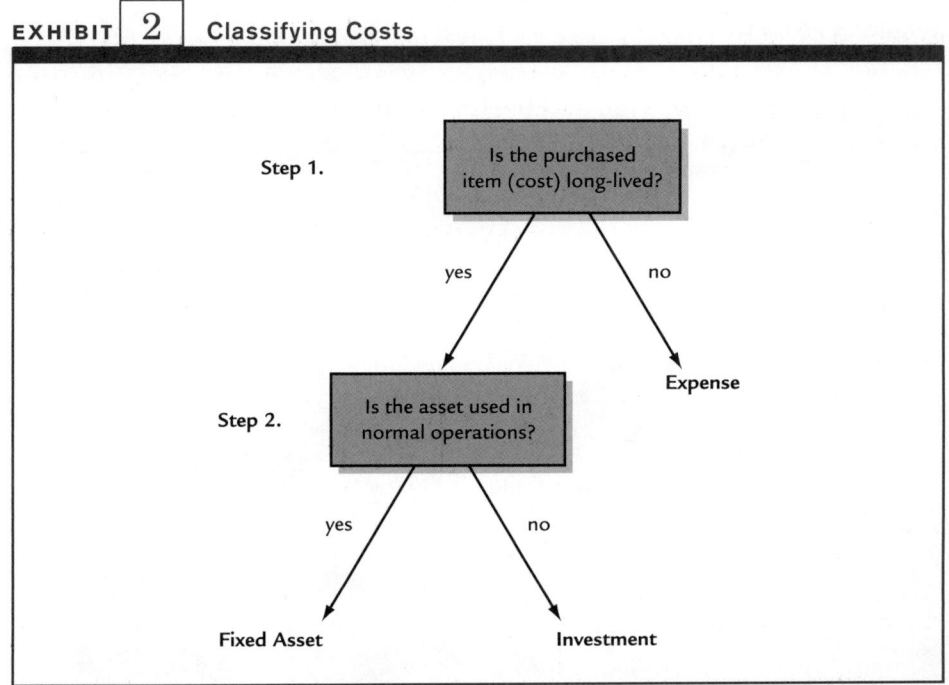

an automotive dealership are not fixed assets of the dealership. On the other hand, a tow truck used in the normal operations of the dealership is a fixed asset of the dealership.

Investments are long-lived assets that are not used in the normal operations and are held for future resale. Such assets are reported on the balance sheet in a section entitled *Investments*. For example, undeveloped land acquired for future resale would be classified and reported as an investment, not land.

The Cost of Fixed Assets

The costs of acquiring fixed assets include all amounts spent to get the asset in place and ready for use. For example, freight costs and the costs of installing equipment are part of the asset's total cost.

Exhibit 3 summarizes some of the common costs of acquiring fixed assets. These costs are recorded by increasing the related fixed asset account, such as Land,[1] Building, Land Improvements, or Machinery and Equipment.

Only costs necessary for preparing the fixed asset for use are included as a cost of the asset. Unnecessary costs that do not increase the asset's usefulness are recorded as an expense. For example, the following costs are recorded as an expense:

1. Vandalism

2. Mistakes in installation

3. Uninsured theft

4. Damage during unpacking and installing

5. Fines for not obtaining proper permits from governmental agencies

A company may incur costs associated with constructing a fixed asset such as a new building. The direct costs incurred in the construction, such as

---

[1] As discussed here, land is assumed to be used only as a location or site and not for its mineral deposits or other natural resources.

EXHIBIT | **3** | **Costs of Acquiring Fixed Assets**

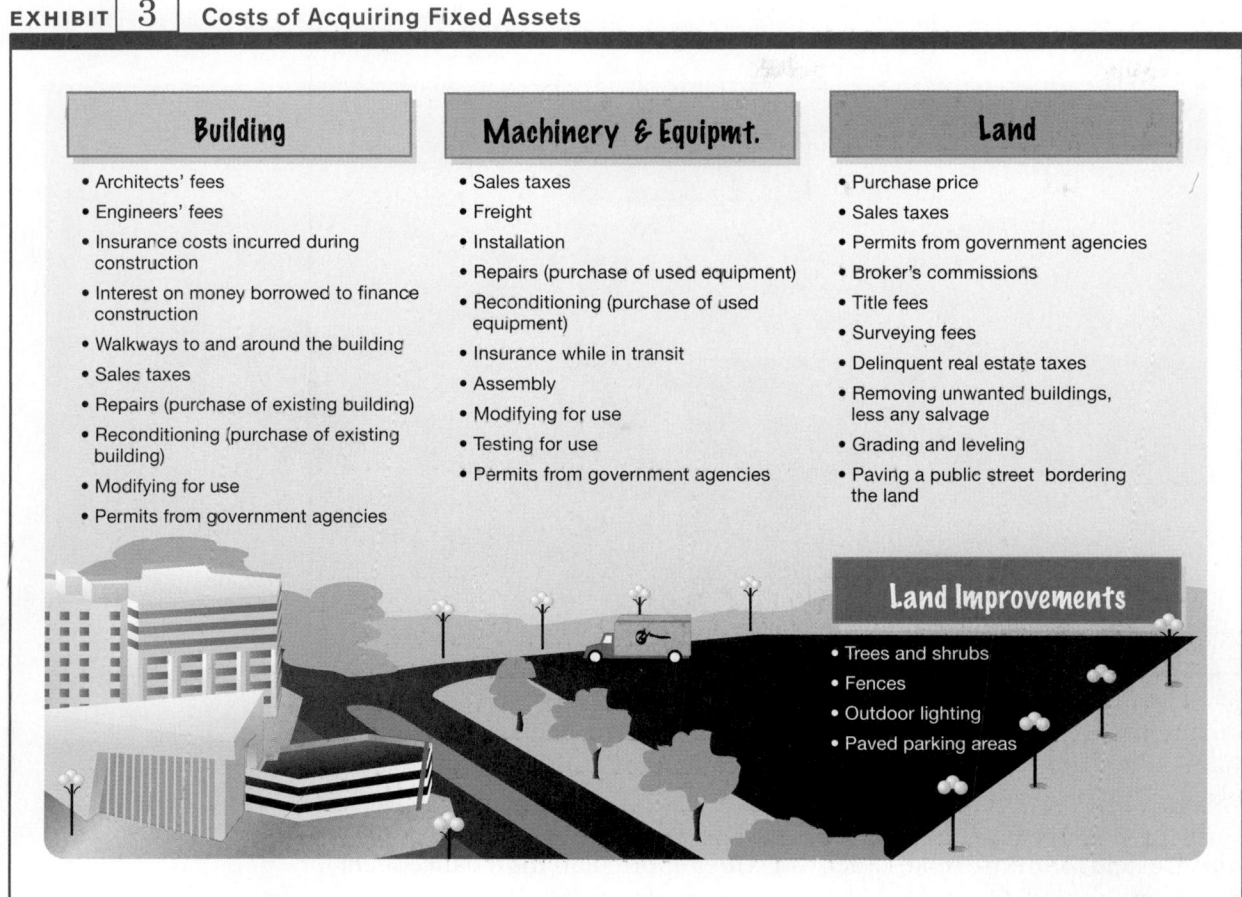

Building
- Architects' fees
- Engineers' fees
- Insurance costs incurred during construction
- Interest on money borrowed to finance construction
- Walkways to and around the building
- Sales taxes
- Repairs (purchase of existing building)
- Reconditioning (purchase of existing building)
- Modifying for use
- Permits from government agencies

Machinery & Equipmt.
- Sales taxes
- Freight
- Installation
- Repairs (purchase of used equipment)
- Reconditioning (purchase of used equipment)
- Insurance while in transit
- Assembly
- Modifying for use
- Testing for use
- Permits from government agencies

Land
- Purchase price
- Sales taxes
- Permits from government agencies
- Broker's commissions
- Title fees
- Surveying fees
- Delinquent real estate taxes
- Removing unwanted buildings, less any salvage
- Grading and leveling
- Paving a public street bordering the land

Land Improvements
- Trees and shrubs
- Fences
- Outdoor lighting
- Paved parking areas

Intel Corporation recently reported almost $3 billion of construction in progress, which was 7% of its total fixed assets.

labor and materials, should be capitalized by increasing an account entitled Construction in Progress. When the construction is complete, the costs are reclassified by decreasing Construction in Progress and increasing the proper fixed asset account such as Building. For some companies, construction in progress can be significant.

Capital and Revenue Expenditures

Once a fixed asset has been acquired and placed in service, costs may be incurred for ordinary maintenance and repairs. In addition, costs may be incurred for improving an asset or for extraordinary repairs that extend the asset's useful life. Costs that benefit only the current period are called **revenue expenditures**. Costs that improve the asset or extend its useful life are **capital expenditures**.

Ordinary Maintenance and Repairs

Costs related to the ordinary maintenance and repairs of a fixed asset are recorded as an expense of the current period. Such expenditures are *revenue expenditures* and are recorded as increases to Repairs and Maintenance Expense. For example, $300 paid for a tune-up of a delivery truck is recorded as an increase in Repairs and Maintenance Expense and a decrease in Cash of $300.

INTEGRITY, OBJECTIVITY, AND ETHICS IN BUSINESS

Capital Crime

One of the largest alleged accounting frauds in history involved the improper accounting for capital expenditures. **WorldCom**, the second largest telecommunications company in the United States at the time, improperly treated maintenance expenditures on its telecommunications network as capital expenditures.

As a result, the company had to restate its prior years' earnings downward by nearly $4 billion to correct this error. The company declared bankruptcy within months of disclosing the error, and the CEO was sentenced to 25 years in prison.

Asset Improvements

After a fixed asset has been placed in service, costs may be incurred to improve the asset. For example, the service value of a delivery truck might be improved by adding a $5,500 hydraulic lift to allow for easier and quicker loading of cargo. Such costs are *capital expenditures* and are recorded as increases to the fixed asset account. In the case of the hydraulic lift, the expenditure is recorded as an increase in Delivery Truck and a decrease in Cash of $5,500. Because the cost of the delivery truck has increased, depreciation for the truck would also change over its remaining useful life.

Extraordinary Repairs

After a fixed asset has been placed in service, costs may be incurred to extend the asset's useful life. For example, the engine of a forklift that is near the end of its useful life may be overhauled at a cost of $4,500, extending its useful life by eight years. Such costs are *capital expenditures* and are recorded as a decrease in an accumulated depreciation account. In the case of the forklift, the expenditure is recorded as a decrease in Accumulated Depreciation—Forklift and a decrease in Cash of $4,500. Because the forklift's remaining useful life has changed, depreciation for the forklift would also change based on the new book value of the forklift.

The accounting for revenue and capital expenditures is summarized below.

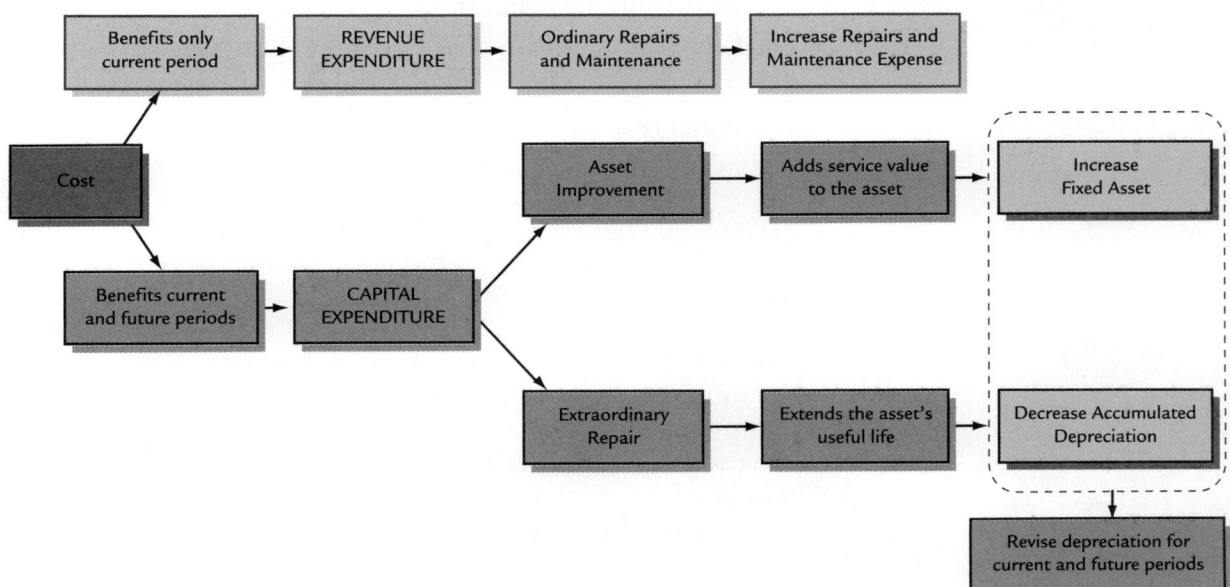

Accounting for Depreciation

Fixed assets, with the exception of land, lose their ability, over time, to provide services. Thus, the cost of fixed assets such as equipment and buildings should be recorded as an expense over their useful lives. This periodic recording of the cost of fixed assets as an expense is called **depreciation**. Because land has an unlimited life, it is not depreciated.

> The adjusting entry to record depreciation increases Depreciation Expense and increases Accumulated Depreciation.

The adjustment to record depreciation increases *Depreciation Expense* and a *contra asset* account entitled *Accumulated Depreciation* or *Allowance for Depreciation*. The use of a contra asset account allows the original cost to remain unchanged in the fixed asset account.

Depreciation can be caused by physical or functional factors.

1. *Physical depreciation* factors include wear and tear during use or from exposure to weather.

2. *Functional depreciation* factors include obsolescence and changes in customer needs that cause the asset to no longer provide services for which it was intended. For example, equipment may become obsolete due to changing technology.

Two common misunderstandings that exist about *depreciation* as used in accounting include:

1. Depreciation does not measure a decline in the market value of a fixed asset. Instead, depreciation is an allocation of a fixed asset's cost to expense over the asset's useful life. Thus, the book value of a fixed asset (cost less accumulated depreciation) usually does not agree with the asset's market value. This is justified in accounting because a fixed asset is for use in a company's operations rather than for resale.

2. Depreciation does not provide cash to replace fixed assets as they wear out. This misunderstanding may occur because depreciation, unlike most expenses, does not require an outlay of cash when it is recorded.

Would you have more cash if you depreciated your car? The answer is no. Depreciation does not affect your cash flows. Likewise, depreciation does not affect the cash flows of a business. However, depreciation is subtracted in determining net income.

Factors in Computing Depreciation Expense

Three factors determine the depreciation expense for a fixed asset. These three factors are as follows:

1. The asset's initial cost
2. The asset's expected useful life
3. The asset's estimated residual value

The initial *cost* of a fixed asset is determined using the concepts discussed and illustrated earlier in this chapter.

The *expected useful life* of a fixed asset is estimated at the time the asset is placed into service. Estimates of expected useful lives are available from industry trade associations. The Internal Revenue Service also publishes guidelines for useful lives, which may be helpful for financial reporting purposes. However, it is not uncommon for different companies to use a different useful life for similar assets.

The **residual value** of a fixed asset at the end of its useful life is estimated at the time the asset is placed into service. Residual value is

JCPenney depreciates buildings over 50 years, while *Tandy Corporation* depreciates buildings over 10–40 years.

sometimes referred to as *scrap value, salvage value,* or *trade-in value.* The difference between a fixed asset's initial cost and its residual value is called the asset's *depreciable cost.* The depreciable cost is the amount of the asset's cost that is allocated over its useful life as depreciation expense. If a fixed asset has no residual value, then its entire cost should be allocated to depreciation.

Exhibit 4 shows the relationship between depreciation expense and a fixed asset's initial cost, expected useful life, and estimated residual value.

EXHIBIT 4   **Depreciation Expense Factors**

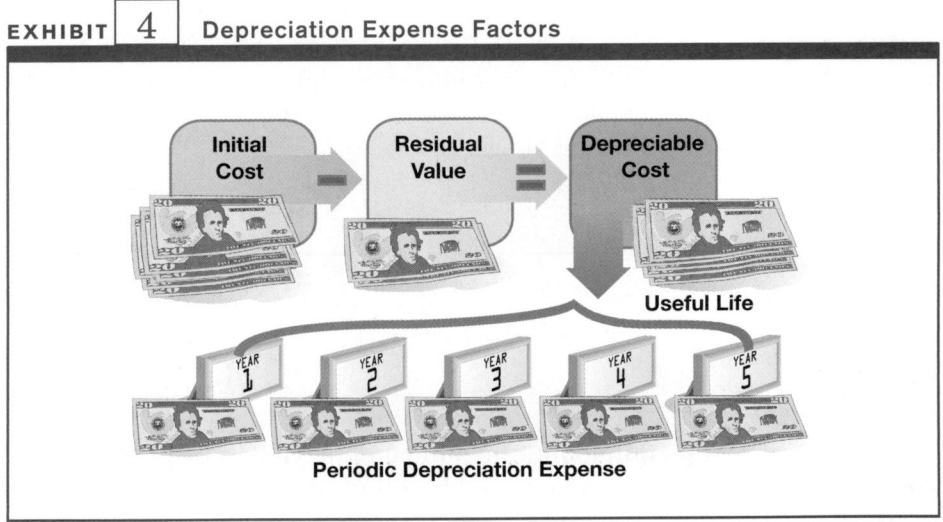

For an asset placed into or taken out of service during the first half of a month, many companies compute depreciation on the asset for the entire month. That is, the asset is treated as having been purchased or sold on the first day of *that* month. Likewise, purchases and sales during the second half of a month are treated as having occurred on the first day of the *next* month. To simplify, this practice is used in this chapter.

The two depreciation methods often used are:

1. Straight-line depreciation
2. Double-declining-balance depreciation

It is not necessary that a company use one method of computing depreciation for all of its fixed assets. For example, a company may use one method for depreciating equipment and another method for depreciating buildings. A company may also use different methods for determining income and property taxes.

Straight-Line Method

The **straight-line method** provides for the same amount of depreciation expense for each year of the asset's useful life. The straight-line method is the most widely used depreciation method.

To illustrate, assume that equipment was purchased on January 1 as follows:

Initial cost	$24,000
Expected useful life	5 years
Estimated residual value	$ 2,000

The annual straight-line depreciation of $4,400 is computed below.

$$\text{Annual Depreciation} = \frac{\text{Cost} - \text{Residual Value}}{\text{Useful Life}} = \frac{\$24,000 - \$2,000}{5 \text{ Years}} = \$4,400$$

If an asset is used for only part of a year, the annual depreciation is pro-rated. For example, assume that the preceding equipment was purchased and placed into service on October 1. The depreciation for the year ending December 31 would be $1,100, computed as follows:

First-Year Partial Depreciation = $4,400 × 3/12 = $1,100

The computation of straight-line depreciation may be simplified by converting the annual depreciation to a percentage of depreciable cost.[2] The straight-line percentage is determined by dividing 100% by the number of years of expected useful life, as shown below.

Expected Years of Useful Life	Straight-Line Percentage
5 years	20% (100%/5)
8 years	12.5% (100%/8)
10 years	10% (100%/10)
20 years	5% (100%/20)
25 years	4% (100%/25)

For the preceding equipment, the annual depreciation of $4,400 can be computed by multiplying the depreciable cost of $22,000 by 20% (100%/5).

As shown above, the straight-line method is simple to use. When an asset's revenues are about the same from period to period, straight-line depreciation provides a good matching of depreciation expense with the asset's revenues.

Double-Declining-Balance Method

The **double-declining-balance method** provides for a declining periodic expense over the expected useful life of the asset. The double-declining-balance method is applied in three steps.

Step 1. Determine the straight-line percentage using the expected useful life.

Step 2. Determine the double-declining-balance rate by multiplying the straight-line rate from Step 1 by two.

Step 3. Compute the depreciation expense by multiplying the double-declining-balance rate from Step 2 times the book value of the asset.

To illustrate, the equipment purchased in the preceding example is used to compute double-declining-balance depreciation. For the first year, the depreciation is $9,600, as shown below.

Step 1. Straight-line percentage = 20% (100%/5)

Step 2. Double-declining-balance rate = 40% (20%×2)

Step 3. Depreciation expense = $9,600 ($24,000×40%)

---

[2] The depreciation rate may also be expressed as a fraction. For example, the annual straight-line rate for an asset with a three-year useful life is 1/3.

For the first year, the book value of the equipment is its initial cost of $24,000. After the first year, the **book value** (cost minus accumulated depreciation) declines and thus the depreciation also declines. The double-declining-balance depreciation for the full five-year life of the equipment is shown below.

Year	Cost	Acc. Dep. at Beginning of Year	Book Value at Beginning of Year		Double-Declining-Balance Rate	Depreciation for Year	Book Value at End of Year
1	$24,000		$24,000.00	×	40%	$9,600.00	$14,400.00
2	24,000	$ 9,600.00	14,400.00	×	40%	5,760.00	8,640.00
3	24,000	15,360.00	8,640.00	×	40%	3,456.00	5,184.00
4	24,000	18,816.00	5,184.00	×	40%	2,073.60	3,110.40
5	24,000	20,889.60	3,110.40		—	1,110.40	2,000.00

When the double-declining-balance method is used, the estimated residual value is *not* considered. However, the asset should not be depreciated below its estimated residual value. In the above example, the estimated residual value was $2,000. Therefore, the depreciation for the fifth year is $1,110.40 ($3,110.40 − $2,000.00) instead of $1,244.16 (40% × $3,110.40).

Like straight-line depreciation, if an asset is used for only part of a year, the annual depreciation is prorated. For example, assume that the preceding equipment was purchased and placed into service on October 1. The depreciation for the year ending December 31 would be $2,400, computed as follows:

$$\text{First-Year Partial Depreciation} = \$9,600 \times 3/12 = \$2,400$$

The depreciation for the second year would then be $8,640, computed as follows:

$$\text{Second-Year Depreciation} = \$8,640 = [40\% \times (\$24,000 - \$2,400)]$$

The double-declining-balance method provides a higher depreciation in the first year of the asset's use, followed by declining depreciation amounts. For this reason, the double-declining-balance method is called an **accelerated depreciation method.**

An asset's revenues are often greater in the early years of its use than in later years. In such cases, the double-declining-balance method provides a good matching of depreciation expense with the asset's revenues.

Comparing Depreciation Methods

The depreciation methods are summarized in Exhibit 5. Both methods allocate a portion of the total cost of an asset to an accounting period, while never depreciating an asset below its residual value. The straight-line method provides for the same periodic amounts of depreciation expense over the life of the asset. The double-declining-balance method provides for a higher depreciation amount in the first year of the asset's use, followed by declining amounts.

EXHIBIT **5**   Summary of Depreciation Methods

Method	Useful Life	Depreciable Cost	Depreciation Rate	Depreciation Expense
Straight-line	Years	Cost less residual value	Straight-line rate*	Constant
Double-declining-balance	Years	Declining book value, but not below residual value	Straight-line rate* × 2	Declining

*Straight-line rate = (1/Useful life)

The depreciation for the straight-line and double-declining-balance methods is shown in Exhibit 6. The depreciation in Exhibit 6 is based on the equipment purchased in our prior illustrations.

EXHIBIT **6**   Comparing Depreciation Methods

	Depreciation Expense	
Year	Straight-Line Method	Double-Declining-Balance Method
1	$ 4,400*	$9,600.00 ($24,000 × 40%)
2	4,400	5,760.00 ($14,400 × 40%)
3	4,400	3,456.00 ($ 8,640 × 40%)
4	4,400	2,073.60 ($ 5,184 × 40%)
5	4,400	1,110.40**
Total	$22,000	$22,000.00

*$4,400 = ($24,000 − $2,000)/5 years
**$3,110.40 − $2,000.00 because the equipment cannot be depreciated below its residual value.

Depreciation for Federal Income Tax

Tax Code Section 179 allows a business to deduct a portion of the cost of qualified property in the year it is placed into service.

The Internal Revenue Code uses the *Modified Accelerated Cost Recovery System (MACRS)* to compute depreciation for tax purposes. MACRS has eight classes of useful life and depreciation rates for each class. Two of the most common classes are the five-year class and the seven-year class.[3] The five-year class includes automobiles and light-duty trucks. The seven-year class includes most machinery and equipment. Depreciation for these two classes is similar to that computed using the double-declining-balance method.

In using the MACRS rates, residual value is ignored. Also, all fixed assets are assumed to be put in and taken out of service in the middle of the year. For the five-year-class assets, depreciation is spread over six years, as shown below.

Year	MACRS 5-Year-Class Depreciation Rates
1	20.0%
2	32.0
3	19.2
4	11.5
5	11.5
6	5.8
	100.0%

[3] Real estate is in either a 27½-year or a 31½-year class and is depreciated by the straight-line method.

To simplify, a company will sometimes use MACRS for both financial statement and tax purposes. This is acceptable if MACRS does not result in significantly different amounts than would have been reported using one of the depreciation methods discussed in this chapter.

Disposal of Fixed Assets

Obj 3 Describe the accounting for the disposal of fixed assets.

Fixed assets that are no longer useful may be discarded or sold.[4] In such cases, the fixed asset is removed from the accounts. Just because a fixed asset is fully depreciated, however, does not mean that it should be removed from the accounts.

If a fixed asset is still being used, its cost and accumulated depreciation should remain in the records even if the asset is fully depreciated. This maintains accountability. If the asset was removed from the records, the accounts would contain no evidence of the continued existence of the asset. In addition, cost and accumulated depreciation data on such assets are often needed for property tax and income tax reports.

> The entry to record the disposal of a fixed asset removes the cost of the asset and its accumulated depreciation from the accounts.

Discarding Fixed Assets

If a fixed asset is no longer used and has no residual value, it is discarded. To illustrate, assume that fully depreciated equipment acquired at a cost of $25,000 is discarded on February 14, 2010. The effect on the accounts and financial statements is as follows:

Statement of Cash Flows	Balance Sheet						Income Statement
	Assets		=	Liabilities	+	Stcokholders' Equity	
	Equipment	− Acc. Dep.— Equip.					
Feb. 14.	−25,000	25,000					

If an asset has not been fully depreciated, depreciation should be recorded before removing the asset from the accounting records. To illustrate, assume that equipment costing $6,000 with no estimated residual value is depreciated at a straight-line rate of 10%. On December 31, 2009, the accumulated depreciation balance, after adjusting entries, is $4,750. On March 24, 2010, the asset is removed from service and discarded. The effect of recording the depreciation for the three months of 2010 before the asset is discarded is as follows:

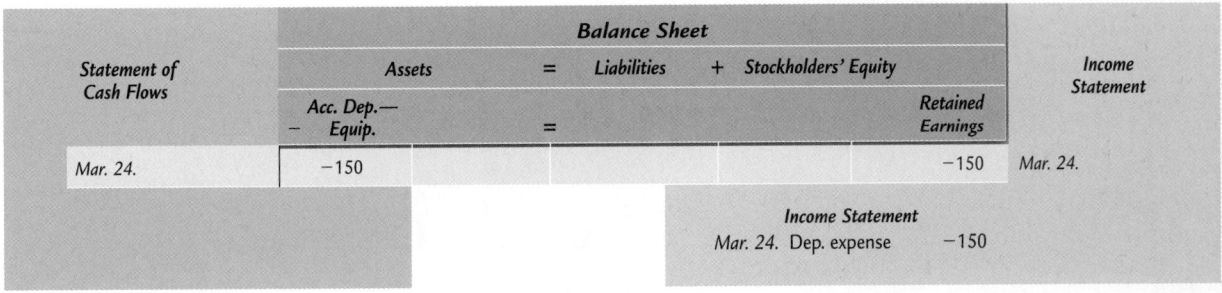

Statement of Cash Flows	Balance Sheet						Income Statement
	Assets	=	Liabilities	+	Stockholders' Equity		
	− Acc. Dep.— Equip.	=				Retained Earnings	
Mar. 24.	−150					−150	Mar. 24.

Income Statement	
Mar. 24. Dep. expense	−150

---

[4] The accounting for the exchange of fixed assets is described and illustrated in advanced accounting courses.

The effect on the accounts and financial statements of discarding the equipment is as follows:

Statement of Cash Flows	Balance Sheet							Income Statement
	Assets		=	Liabilities	+	Stockholders' Equity		
	Equipment	Acc. Dep.— Equip. =					Retained Earnings	
Mar. 24.	−6,000	4,900					−1,100	Mar. 24.

	Income Statement	
	Mar. 24. Loss on disposal of equip.	−1,100

The loss of −$1,100 is recorded because the balance of the accumulated depreciation account ($4,900) is less than the balance in the equipment account ($6,000). Losses on the discarding of fixed assets are nonoperating items and are normally reported in the Other expense section of the income statement.

Selling Fixed Assets

The entry to record the sale of a fixed asset is similar to the entries for discarding an asset. The only difference is that the receipt of cash is also recorded. If the selling price is more than the book value of the asset, a gain is recorded. If the selling price is less than the book value, a loss is recorded.

To illustrate, assume that equipment is purchased at a cost of $10,000 with no estimated residual value and is depreciated at a straight-line rate of 10%. The equipment is sold for cash on October 12 of the eighth year of its use. The balance of the accumulated depreciation account as of the preceding December 31 is $7,000. The effect on the accounts and financial statements of updating depreciation for the nine months of the current year is as follows:

Statement of Cash Flows	Balance Sheet							Income Statement
	Assets		=	Liabilities	+	Stockholders' Equity		
	Acc. Dep.— − Equip.		=				Retained Earnings	
Oct. 12.	−750						−750	Oct. 12.

	Income Statement	
	Oct. 12. Dep. exp.—equip.	−750

After the current depreciation is recorded, the book value of the asset is $2,250 ($10,000 − $7,750). The effect of the sale, assuming three different selling prices, is as follows:

Sold at book value, for $2,250. No gain or loss.

Statement of Cash Flows	Balance Sheet						Income Statement
	Assets			=	Liabilities	+	Stockholders' Equity
	Cash +	Equipment −	Acc. Dep.— Equip.				
Oct. 12.	2,250	−10,000	7,750				

Statement of Cash Flows	
Oct. 12. Investing	2,250

Sold below book value, for $1,000. Loss of $1,250.

Statement of Cash Flows	Balance Sheet						Income Statement
	Assets			=	Liabilities	+ Stcokholders' Equity	
	Cash	+ Equipment	− Acc. Dep.— Equip.	=		Retained Earnings	
Oct. 12.	1,000	−10,000	7,750			−1,250	Oct. 12.

| Statement of Cash Flows | | Income Statement | |
| Oct. 12. Investing | 1,000 | Oct. 12. Loss on disposal of equip. −1,250 | |

Sold above book value, for $2,800. Gain of $550.

Statement of Cash Flows	Balance Sheet						Income Statement
	Assets			=	Liabilities	+ Stcokholders' Equity	
	Cash	+ Equipment	− Acc. Dep.— Equip.	=		Retained Earnings	
Oct. 12.	2,800	−10,000	7,750			550	Oct. 12.

| Statement of Cash Flows | | Income Statement | |
| Oct. 12. Investing | 2,800 | Oct. 12. Gain on disposal of equip. 550 | |

Natural Resources

Obj 4 Describe the accounting for depletion of natural resources.

The fixed assets of some companies include timber, metal ores, minerals, or other natural resources. As these resources are harvested or mined and then sold, a portion of their cost is debited to an expense account. This process of transferring the cost of natural resources to an expense account is called **depletion**.

Depletion is determined as follows:[5]

Step 1. Determine the depletion rate as:

$$\text{Depletion Rate} = \frac{\text{Cost of Resource}}{\text{Estimated Total Units of Resource}}$$

Step 2. Multiply the depletion rate by the quantity extracted from the re-source during the period.

$$\text{Depletion Expense} = \text{Depletion Rate} \times \text{Quantity Extracted}$$

To illustrate, assume that Karst Company purchased mining rights as follows:

Cost of mineral deposit	$400,000
Estimated total units of resource	1,000,000 tons
Tons mined during year	90,000 tons

[5] It is assumed that there is no significant residual value left after all the natural resource is extracted.

The depletion expense of $36,000 for the year is computed, as shown below.

Step 1.

$$\text{Depletion Rate} = \frac{\text{Cost of Resource}}{\text{Estimated Total Units of Resource}}$$

$$= \frac{\$400,000}{1,000,000 \text{ Tons}} = \$0.40 \text{ per Ton}$$

Step 2.

$$\text{Depletion Expense} = \$0.40 \text{ per Ton} \times 90,000 \text{ Tons} = \$36,000$$

The effect of the depletion on the accounts and financial statements is shown below.

Statement of Cash Flows	Balance Sheet					Income Statement
	Assets	=	Liabilities	+	Stockholders' Equity	
	− Acc. Depletion	=			Retained Earnings	
Dec. 31.	−36,000				−36,000	Dec. 31.

Income Statement
Dec. 31. Depletion exp. −36,000

Like the accumulated depreciation account, Accumulated Depletion is a *contra asset* account. It is reported on the balance sheet as a deduction from the cost of the mineral deposit.

Intangible Assets

Obj 5 Describe the accounting for intangible assets.

Patents, copyrights, trademarks, and goodwill are long-lived assets that are used in the operations of a business and are not held for sale. These assets are called **intangible assets** because they do not exist physically.

The accounting for intangible assets is similar to that for fixed assets. The major issues are:

1. Determining the initial cost
2. Determining the **amortization**, which is the amount of cost to transfer to expense

Apple, Inc., amortizes intangible assets over 3–10 years.

Amortization results from the passage of time or a decline in the usefulness of the intangible asset.

Patents

Manufacturers may acquire exclusive rights to produce and sell goods with one or more unique features. Such rights are granted by **patents**, which the federal government issues to inventors. These rights continue in effect for 20 years. A business may purchase patent rights from others, or it may obtain patents developed by its own research and development.

The initial cost of a purchased patent, including any legal fees, is recorded by increasing an asset account. This cost is written off, or amortized, over the

years of the patent's expected useful life. The expected useful life of a patent may be less than its legal life. For example, a patent may become worthless due to changing technology or consumer tastes.

Patent amortization is normally computed using the straight-line method. The amortization is recorded by increasing an amortization expense account and decreasing the patents account. A separate contra asset account is usually *not* used for intangible assets.

To illustrate, assume that at the beginning of its fiscal year, a company acquires patent rights for $100,000. Although the patent will not expire for 14 years, its remaining useful life is estimated as five years. The effect of the amortization of the patent at the end of the fiscal year is as follows:

Statement of Cash Flows	Balance Sheet						Income Statement
	Assets	=	Liabilities	+	Stockholders' Equity		
	Patents	=				Retained Earnings	
Dec. 31.	−20,000					−20,000	Dec. 31.

Income Statement
Dec. 31. Amortization exp.—
       patents   −20,000

Some companies develop their own patents through research and development. In such cases, any *research and development costs* are usually recorded as current operating expenses in the period in which they are incurred. This accounting for research and development costs is justified on the basis that any future benefits from research and development are highly uncertain.

Copyrights and Trademarks

The exclusive right to publish and sell a literary, artistic, or musical composition is granted by a **copyright**. Copyrights are issued by the federal government and extend for 70 years beyond the author's death. The costs of a copyright include all costs of creating the work plus any other costs of obtaining the copyright. A copyright that is purchased is recorded at the price paid for it. Copyrights are amortized over their estimated useful lives.

A **trademark** is a name, term, or symbol used to identify a business and its products. Most businesses identify their trademarks with ® in their advertisements and on their products.

Under federal law, businesses can protect their trademarks by registering them for 10 years and renewing the registration for 10-year periods. Like a copyright, the legal costs of registering a trademark are recorded as an asset.

If a trademark is purchased from another business, its cost is recorded as an asset. In such cases, the cost of the trademark is considered to have an indefinite useful life. Thus, trademarks are not amortized. Instead, trademarks are reviewed periodically for impaired value. When a trademark is impaired, the trademark should be written down and a loss recognized.

Sony Corporation of America amortizes its artist contracts and music catalogs over 16 years and 21 years, respectively.

Coke® is one of the world's most recognizable trademarks. As stated in *LIFE*, "Two-thirds of the earth is covered by water; the rest is covered by Coke. If the French are known for wine and the Germans for beer, America achieved global beverage dominance with fizzy water and caramel color."

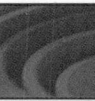

INTEGRITY, OBJECTIVITY, AND ETHICS IN BUSINESS

21st Century Pirates

Pirated software is a major concern of software companies. For example, during a recent global sweep, **Microsoft Corporation** seized nearly 5 million units of counterfeit Microsoft software with an estimated retail value of $1.7 billion. U.S. copyright laws and practices are sometimes ignored or disputed in other parts of the world.

Businesses must honor the copyrights held by software companies by eliminating pirated software from corporate computers. **The Business Software Alliance** (BSA) represents the largest software companies in campaigns to investigate illegal use of unlicensed software by businesses. The BSA estimates software industry losses of nearly $12 billion annually from software piracy. Employees using pirated software on business assets risk bringing legal penalties to themselves and their employers.

Goodwill

eBay recorded an impairment of $1.39 billion in the goodwill created from its purchase of **Skype**™.

Goodwill refers to an intangible asset of a business that is created from such favorable factors as location, product quality, reputation, and managerial skill. Goodwill allows a business to earn a greater rate of return than normal.

Generally accepted accounting principles (GAAP) allow goodwill to be recorded only if it is objectively determined by a transaction. An example of such a transaction is the purchase of a business at a price in excess of the fair value of its net assets (assets – liabilities). The excess is recorded as goodwill and reported as an intangible asset.

Unlike patents and copyrights, goodwill is not amortized. However, a loss should be recorded if the future prospects of the purchased firm become impaired. This loss would normally be disclosed in the Other expense section of the income statement.

To illustrate, assume that on December 31 FaceCard Company has determined that $250,000 of the goodwill created from the purchase of Electronic Systems is impaired. The effect on the accounts and financial statements is as follows:

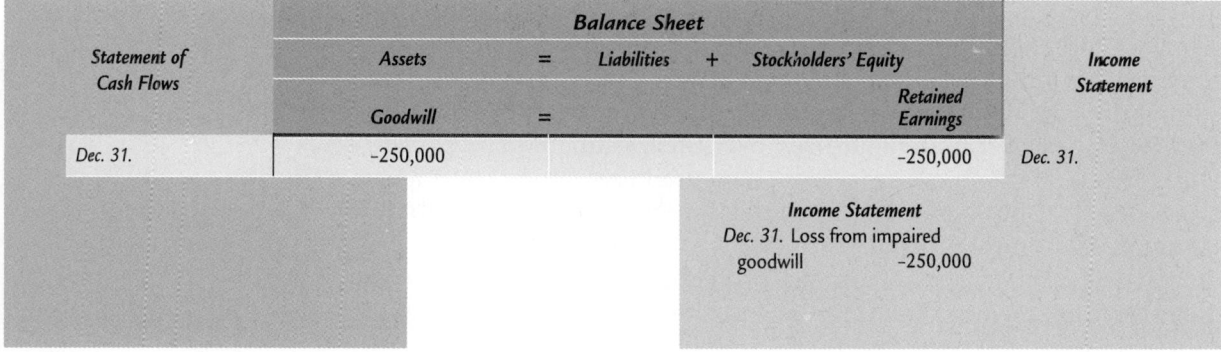

Exhibit 7 shows intangible asset disclosures for 600 large firms. Goodwill is the most often reported intangible asset. This is because goodwill arises from merger transactions, which are common.

EXHIBIT 7 | Frequency of Intangible Asset Disclosures for 600 Firms

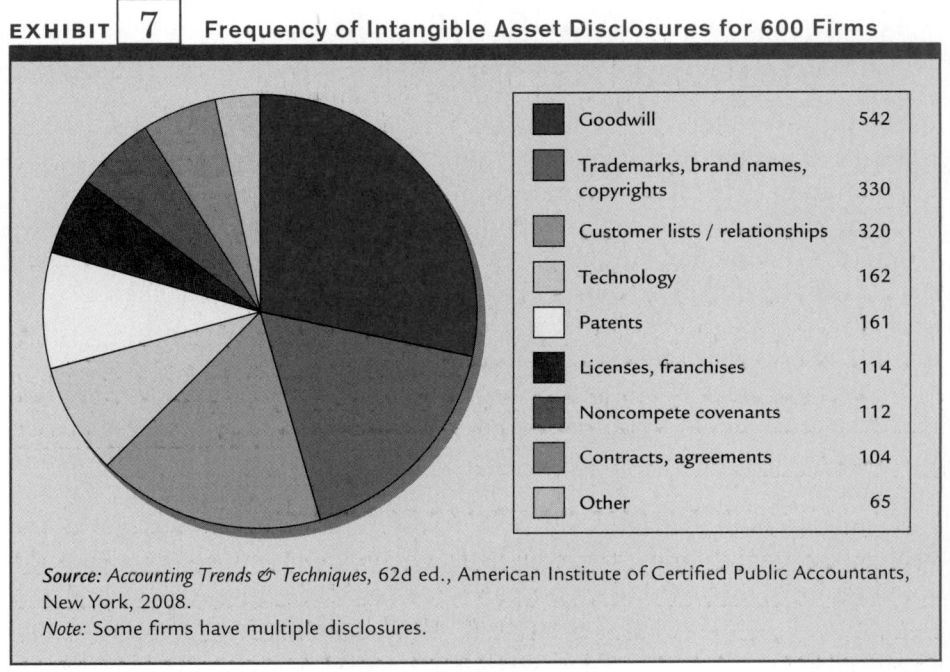

Goodwill	542
Trademarks, brand names, copyrights	330
Customer lists / relationships	320
Technology	162
Patents	161
Licenses, franchises	114
Noncompete covenants	112
Contracts, agreements	104
Other	65

Source: Accounting Trends & Techniques, 62d ed., American Institute of Certified Public Accountants, New York, 2008.
Note: Some firms have multiple disclosures.

Exhibit 8 summarizes the characteristics of intangible assets.

EXHIBIT 8 | Comparison of Intangible Assets

Intangible Asset	Description	Amortization Period	Periodic Expense
Patent	Exclusive right to benefit from an innovation	Estimated useful life not to exceed legal life	Amortization expense
Copyright	Exclusive right to benefit from a literary, artistic, or musical composition	Estimated useful life not to exceed legal life	Amortization expense
Trademark	Exclusive use of a name, term, or symbol	None	Impairment loss if fair value less than carrying value (impaired)
Goodwill	Excess of purchase price of a business over the fair value of its net assets (assets – liabilities)	None	Impairment loss if fair value less than carrying value (impaired)

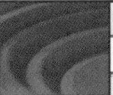

INTEGRITY, OBJECTIVITY, AND ETHICS IN BUSINESS

When Does Goodwill Become Worthless?

The timing and amount of goodwill write-offs can be very subjective. Managers and their accountants should fairly estimate the value of goodwill and record goodwill impairment when it occurs. It would be unethical to delay a write-down of goodwill when it is determined that the asset is impaired.

Obj 6 Describe how depreciation expense is reported in an income statement and prepare a balance sheet that includes fixed assets and intangible assets.

Financial Reporting for Fixed Assets and Intangible Assets

In the income statement, depreciation and amortization expense should be reported separately or disclosed in a note. A description of the methods used in computing depreciation should also be reported.

In the balance sheet, each class of fixed assets should be disclosed on the face of the statement or in the notes. The related accumulated depreciation should also be disclosed, either by class or in total. The fixed assets may be shown at their *book value* (cost less accumulated depreciation), which can also be described as their *net* amount.

If there are many classes of fixed assets, a single amount may be presented in the balance sheet, supported by a note with a separate listing. Fixed assets may be reported under the more descriptive caption of property, plant, and equipment.

The cost of mineral rights or ore deposits is normally shown as part of the Fixed assets section of the balance sheet. The related accumulated depletion should also be disclosed. In some cases, the mineral rights are shown net of depletion on the face of the balance sheet, accompanied by a note that discloses the amount of the accumulated depletion.

Intangible assets are usually reported in the balance sheet in a separate section immediately following fixed assets. The balance of each major class of intangible assets should be disclosed at an amount net of amortization taken to date. Exhibit 9 is a partial balance sheet that shows the reporting of fixed assets and intangible assets.

EXHIBIT 9   Fixed Assets and Intangible Assets in the Balance Sheet

DISCOVERY MINING CO.
Balance Sheet
December 31, 2010

Assets

	Cost	Accum. Depr.	Book Value		
Total current assets					$ 462,500
Property, plant, and equipment:					
Land	$ 30,000	—	$ 30,000		
Buildings	110,000	$ 26,000	84,000		
Factory equipment	650,000	192,000	458,000		
Office equipment	120,000	13,000	107,000		
	$ 910,000	$ 231,000		$679,000	
	Cost	Accum. Depl.	Book Value		
Mineral deposits:					
Alaska deposit	$1,200,000	$ 800,000	$ 400,000		
Wyoming deposit	750,000	200,000	550,000		
	$1,950,000	$ 1,000,000		950,000	
Total property, plant, and equipment					1,629,000
Intangible assets:					
Patents				$ 75,000	
Goodwill				50,000	
Total intangible assets					125,000

How Businesses Make Money

Hub-and-Spoke or Point-to-Point?

Southwest Airlines Co. uses a simple fare structure, featuring low, unrestricted, unlimited, everyday coach fares. These fares are made possible by Southwest's use of a point-to-point, rather than a hub-and-spoke, business approach. *United Airlines, Inc.*, *Delta Air Lines*, and *American Airlines* employ a hub-and-spoke approach in which an airline establishes major hubs that serve as connecting links to other cities. For example, Delta has established major connecting hubs in Atlanta and Salt Lake City. In contrast, Southwest focuses on point-to-point service between selected cities with over 400 one-way, nonstop city pairs with an average length of just over 600 miles and average flying time of 1.8 hours. As a result, Southwest minimizes connections, delays, and total trip time.

Southwest also focuses on serving conveniently located satellite or downtown airports, such as Dallas Love Field, Houston Hobby, and Chicago Midway. Because these airports are normally less congested than hub airports, Southwest is better able to maintain high employee productivity and reliable on-time performance. This operating approach permits the company to achieve high utilization of its fixed assets, such as its 737 aircraft. For example, aircraft are scheduled to minimize time spent at the gate, thereby reducing the number of aircraft and gate facilities that would otherwise be required.

AP PHOTO/MATT SLOCUM

Key Points

1. **Define, classify, and account for the cost of fixed assets.**

   Fixed assets are long-term tangible assets that are owned by the business and are used in the normal operations of the business. Examples of fixed assets are equipment, buildings, and land. The initial cost of a fixed asset includes all amounts spent to get the asset in place and ready for use. For example, sales tax, freight, insurance in transit, and installation costs are all included in the cost of a fixed asset. Once a fixed asset has been acquired and placed in service, revenue and capital expenditures may be incurred. Expenditures related to the ordinary maintenance and repairs of a fixed asset are revenue expenditures and are recorded as an expense of the current period. Expenditures to improve an asset are capital expenditures and are recorded as increases to the fixed asset account. Expenditures to extend the asset's useful life are capital expenditures and are recorded as a decrease in accumulated depreciation.

2. **Compute depreciation using the straight-line and double-declining-balance methods.**

   In computing depreciation, three factors need to be considered: (1) the fixed asset's initial cost, (2) the useful life of the asset, and (3) the residual value of the asset.

   The straight-line method spreads the initial cost less the residual value equally over the useful life. The double-declining-balance method is applied by multiplying the declining book value of the asset by twice the straight-line rate.

3. **Describe the accounting for the disposal of fixed assets.**

   The recording of disposals of fixed assets will vary. In all cases, however, any depreciation for the current period should be recorded, and the book value of the asset is then removed from the accounts. Removing the book value from the accounts decreases the asset's accumulated depreciation account and the asset account for the cost of the asset. For assets

retired from service, a loss may be recorded for any remaining book value of the asset.

When a fixed asset is sold, the book value is removed and the cash or other asset received is also recorded. If the selling price is more than the book value of the asset, the transaction results in a gain. If the selling price is less than the book value, there is a loss.

4. Describe the accounting for depletion of natural resources.

The amount of periodic depletion is computed by multiplying the quantity of minerals extracted during the period by a depletion rate. The depletion rate is computed by dividing the cost of the mineral deposit by its estimated size. Recording depletion increases a depletion expense account and an accumulated depletion account.

5. Describe the accounting for intangible assets.

Long-term assets that are without physical attributes but are used in the business are classified as intangible assets. Examples of intangible assets are patents, copyrights, trademarks, and goodwill. The initial cost of an intangible asset should be recorded by increasing an asset account. For patents and copyrights, this cost should be written off, or amortized, over the years of the asset's expected usefulness by increasing an expense account and decreasing the intangible asset account. Trademarks and goodwill are not amortized, but are written down only on impairment.

6. Describe how depreciation expense is reported in an income statement and prepare a balance sheet that includes fixed assets and intangible assets.

The amount of depreciation expense and the method or methods used in computing depreciation should be disclosed in the financial statements. In addition, each major class of fixed assets should be disclosed, along with the related accumulated depreciation. Intangible assets are usually presented in the balance sheet in a separate section immediately following fixed assets. Each major class of intangible assets should be disclosed at an amount net of the amortization recorded to date.

Key Terms

Accelerated depreciation method A depreciation method that provides for a higher depreciation amount in the first year of the asset's use, followed by a gradually declining amount of depreciation.

Amortization The periodic transfer of the cost of an intangible asset to expense.

Book value The cost of a fixed asset minus accumulated depreciation on the asset.

Capital expenditures The costs of acquiring fixed assets, adding a component, or replacing a component of fixed assets.

Copyright An exclusive right to publish and sell a literary, artistic, or musical composition.

Depletion The process of transferring the cost of natural resources to an expense account.

Depreciation The systematic periodic transfer of the cost of a fixed asset to an expense account during its expected useful life.

Double-declining-balance method A method of depreciation that provides periodic depreciation expense based on the declining book value of a fixed asset over its estimated life.

Fixed assets Long-lived or relatively permanent tangible assets that are used in the normal business operations; sometimes called *plant assets.*

Goodwill An intangible asset of a business that is created from favorable factors such as location, product quality, reputation, and managerial skill, as verified from a merger transaction.

Patents Exclusive rights to produce and sell goods with one or more unique features.

Residual value The estimated value of a fixed asset at the end of its useful life.

Revenue expenditures Costs that benefit only the current period or costs incurred for normal maintenance and repairs of fixed assets.

Straight-line method A method of depreciation that provides for equal periodic depreciation expense over the estimated life of a fixed asset.

Trademark A name, term, or symbol used to identify a business and its products.

Illustrative Problem

McCollum Company, a furniture wholesaler, acquired new equipment at a cost of $150,000 at the beginning of the fiscal year. The equipment has an estimated life of five years and an estimated residual value of $12,000. Ellen McCollum, the president, has requested information regarding alternative depreciation methods.

Instructions

Determine the annual depreciation for each of the five years of estimated useful life of the equipment, the accumulated depreciation at the end of each year, and the book value of the equipment at the end of each year by (a) the straight-line method and (b) the double-declining-balance method.

Solution

	Year	Depreciation Expense	Accumulated Depreciation, End of Year	Book Value, End of Year
a.	1	$27,600*	$ 27,600	$122,400
	2	27,600	55,200	94,800
	3	27,600	82,800	67,200
	4	27,600	110,400	39,600
	5	27,600	138,000	12,000

*$27,600 = ($150,000 – $12,000) ÷ 5

	Year	Depreciation Expense	Accumulated Depreciation, End of Year	Book Value, End of Year
b.	1	$60,000**	$ 60,000	$ 90,000
	2	36,000	96,000	54,000
	3	21,600	117,600	32,400
	4	12,960	130,560	19,440
	5	7,440***	138,000	12,000

**$60,000 = $150,000 × 40%
***The asset is not depreciated below the estimated residual value of $12,000.

Self-Examination Questions (Answers appear at the end of chapter)

1. Which of the following expenditures incurred in connection with acquiring machinery is a proper addition to the asset account?
   A. Freight
   B. Installation costs
   C. Both A and B
   D. Neither A nor B

2. What is the amount of depreciation, using the double-declining-balance method (twice the straight-line rate), for the second year of use for equipment costing $9,000, with an estimated residual value of $600 and an estimated life of three years?

   A. $6,000
   B. $3,000
   C. $2,000
   D. $400

3. An example of an accelerated depreciation method is:
   A. Straight-line
   B. Double-declining-balance
   C. Units-of-production
   D. Depletion balance

4. Hyde Inc. purchased mineral rights estimated at 2,500,000 tons near Great Falls, Montana, for $3,600,000 on August 7, 2010. During the remainder of the year, Hyde mined 175,000 tons of ore. What is the depletion expense for 2010?

   A. $121,528
   B. $252,000
   C. $1,500,000
   D. $3,600,000

5. Which of the following is an example of an intangible asset?

   A. Patents
   B. Goodwill
   C. Copyrights
   D. All of the above

Class Discussion Questions

1. Which of the following qualities are characteristic of fixed assets? (a) tangible, (b) capable of repeated use in the operations of the business, (c) held for sale in the normal course of business, (d) used rarely in the operations of the business, (e) long-lived.

2. Mancini Outfitters Co. has a fleet of automobiles and trucks for use by salespersons and for delivery of office supplies and equipment. East Village Auto Sales Co. has automobiles and trucks for sale. Under what caption would the automobiles and trucks be reported on the balance sheet of (a) Mancini Outfitters Co., (b) East Village Auto Sales Co.?

3. Just Animals Co. acquired an adjacent vacant lot with the hope of selling it in the future at a gain. The lot is not intended to be used in Just Animals' business operations. Where should such real estate be listed in the balance sheet?

4. My Mother's Closet Company solicited bids from several contractors to construct an addition to its office building. The lowest bid received was for $375,000. My Mother's Closet Company decided to construct the addition itself at a cost of $298,500. What amount should be recorded in the building account?

5. Distinguish between the accounting for capital expenditures and revenue expenditures.

6. Immediately after a used truck is acquired, a new motor is installed and the tires are replaced at a total cost of $3,175. Is this a capital expenditure or a revenue expenditure?

7. Classify each of the following expenditures as either a revenue or capital expenditure: (a) installation of a video messaging system on a semitrailer, (b) changing oil in a delivery truck, (c) purchase of a color copier.

8. Are the amounts at which fixed assets are reported in the balance sheet their approximate market values as of the balance sheet date? Discuss.

9. a. Does the recognition of depreciation in the accounts provide a special cash fund for the replacement of fixed assets? Explain.

   b. Describe the nature of depreciation as the term is used in accounting.

10. Pac Vac Company purchased a machine that has a manufacturer's suggested life of 15 years. The company plans to use the machine on a special project that will last 12 years. At the completion of the project, the machine will be sold. Over how many years should the machine be depreciated?

11. Is it necessary for a business to use the same method of computing depreciation (a) for all classes of its depreciable assets, (b) in the financial statements and in determining income taxes?

12. a. Under what conditions is the use of an accelerated depreciation method most appropriate?

    b. Why is an accelerated depreciation method often used for income tax purposes?

    c. What is the Modified Accelerated Cost Recovery System (MACRS), and under what conditions is it used?

13. For some of the fixed assets of a business, the balance in Accumulated Depreciation is

exactly equal to the cost of the asset. (a) Is it permissible to record additional depreciation on the assets if they are still useful to the company? Explain. (b) When should the cost and the accumulated depreciation be removed from the accounts?

14. How is depletion determined?

15. a. Over what period of time should the cost of a patent acquired by purchase be amortized?

   b. In general, what is the required accounting treatment for research and development costs?

   c. How should goodwill be amortized?

Exercises

E7-1

Costs of acquiring fixed assets

Obj 1

Catherine Simpkins owns and operates Speedy Print Co. During February, Speedy Print Co. incurred the following costs in acquiring two printing presses. One printing press was new, and the other was used by a business that recently filed for bankruptcy.

Costs related to new printing press:

1. Sales tax on purchase price
2. Freight
3. Special foundation
4. Insurance while in transit
5. New parts to replace those damaged in unloading
6. Fee paid to factory representative for installation

Costs related to used printing press:

7. Fees paid to attorney to review purchase agreement
8. Freight
9. Installation
10. Repair of vandalism during installation
11. Replacement of worn-out parts
12. Repair of damage incurred in reconditioning the press

   a. Indicate which costs incurred in acquiring the new printing press should be recorded as an increase to the asset account.
   b. Indicate which costs incurred in acquiring the used printing press should be recorded as an increase to the asset account.

E7-2

Determine cost of land

Obj 1

Bridger Ski Co. has developed a tract of land into a ski resort. The company has cut the trees, cleared and graded the land and hills, and constructed ski lifts. (a) Should the tree cutting, land clearing, and grading costs of constructing the ski slopes be recorded as an increase in the land account? (b) If such costs are recorded as an increase in Land, should they be depreciated?

E7-3

Determine cost of land

Obj 1

✓ $327,425

Fastball Delivery Company acquired an adjacent lot to construct a new warehouse, paying $30,000 and giving a short-term note for $270,000. Legal fees paid were $1,425, delinquent taxes assumed were $12,000, and fees paid to remove an old building from the land were $18,500. Materials salvaged from the demolition of the building were sold for $4,500. A contractor was paid $910,000 to construct a new warehouse. Determine the cost of the land to be reported on the balance sheet.

E7-4

Capital and revenue expenditures

Obj 1

Connect Lines Co. incurred the following costs related to trucks and vans used in operating its delivery service:

1. Replaced a truck's suspension system with a new suspension system that allows for the delivery of heavier loads.
2. Installed a hydraulic lift to a van.
3. Repaired a flat tire on one of the vans.
4. Overhauled the engine on one of the trucks purchased three years ago.
5. Removed a two-way radio from one of the trucks and installed a new radio with a greater range of communication.
6. Rebuilt the transmission on one of the vans that had been driven 40,000 miles. The van was no longer under warranty.
7. Changed the radiator fluid on a truck that had been in service for the past four years.
8. Tinted the back and side windows of one of the vans to discourage theft of contents.
9. Changed the oil and greased the joints of all the trucks and vans.
10. Installed security systems on four of the newer trucks.

Classify each of the costs as a capital expenditure or a revenue expenditure.

E7-5

Capital and revenue expenditures

Obj 1

Jaime Baldwin owns and operates Love Transport Co. During the past year, Jaime incurred the following costs related to an 18-wheel truck:

1. Changed engine oil.
2. Installed a wind deflector on top of the cab to increase fuel mileage.
3. Replaced fog and cab light bulbs.
4. Modified the factory-installed turbo charger with a special-order kit designed to add 50 more horsepower to the engine performance.
5. Replaced a headlight that had burned out.
6. Removed the old CB radio and replaced it with a newer model with a greater range.
7. Replaced the old radar detector with a newer model that detects additional frequencies now used by many of the state patrol radar guns. The detector is wired directly into the cab, so that it is partially hidden. In addition, Jaime fastened the detector to the truck with a locking device that prevents its removal.
8. Replaced the hydraulic brake system that had begun to fail during his latest trip through the Rocky Mountains.
9. Installed a television in the sleeping compartment of the truck.
10. Replaced a shock absorber that had worn out.

Classify each of the costs as a capital expenditure or a revenue expenditure.

E7-6

Nature of depreciation

Obj 2

Legacy Ironworks Co. reported $3,175,000 for equipment and $2,683,000 for accumulated depreciation—equipment on its balance sheet.

Does this mean (a) that the replacement cost of the equipment is $3,175,000 and (b) that $2,683,000 is set aside in a special fund for the replacement of the equipment? Explain.

E7-7

Straight-line depreciation rates

Obj 2

✓ c. 10%

Convert each of the following estimates of useful life to a straight-line depreciation rate, stated as a percentage, assuming that the residual value of the fixed asset is to be ignored: (a) 2 years, (b) 8 years, (c) 10 years, (d) 20 years, (e) 25 years, (f) 40 years, (g) 50 years.

E7-8

Straight-line depreciation

Obj 2

✓ $3,350

A refrigerator used by a meat processor has a cost of $93,750, an estimated residual value of $10,000, and an estimated useful life of 25 years. What is the amount of the annual depreciation computed by the straight-line method?

E7-9

Depreciation by two methods

Obj 2

✓ a. $3,750

A Kubota tractor acquired on January 9 at a cost of $75,000 has an estimated useful life of 20 years. Assuming that it will have no residual value, determine the depreciation for each of the first two years (a) by the straight-line method and (b) by the double-declining-balance method.

E7-10

Depreciation by two methods

Obj 2

✓ a. $19,000

A storage tank acquired at the beginning of the fiscal year at a cost of $172,000 has an estimated residual value of $20,000 and an estimated useful life of eight years. Determine the following: (a) the amount of annual depreciation by the straight-line method and (b) the amount of depreciation for the first and second year computed by the double-declining-balance method.

E7-11

Partial-year depreciation

Obj 2

✓ a. First year, $2,000

Sandblasting equipment acquired at a cost of $85,000 has an estimated residual value of $5,000 and an estimated useful life of 10 years. It was placed in service on October 1 of the current fiscal year, which ends on December 31. Determine the depreciation for the current fiscal year and for the following fiscal year by (a) the straight-line method and (b) the double-declining-balance method.

E7-12

Book value of fixed assets

Obj 2

The following data were taken from recent annual reports of **Interstate Bakeries Corporation (IBC)**. Interstate Bakeries produces, distributes, and sells fresh bakery products nationwide through supermarkets, convenience stores, and its 67 bakeries and 1,500 thrift stores.

	May 31, 2008	June 2, 2007
Land and buildings	$359,133,000	$ 390,147,000
Machinery and equipment	820,484,000	865,398,000
Accumulated depreciation	715,162,000	713,820,000

a. Compute the book value of the fixed assets for 2008 and 2007 and explain the differences, if any.

b. Would you normally expect the book value of fixed assets to increase or decrease during the year?

E7-13

Sale of asset

Obj 3

✓ a. $350,000

Equipment acquired on January 3, 2007, at a cost of $504,000, has an estimated useful life of 12 years, has an estimated residual value of $42,000, and is depreciated by the straight-line method.

a. What was the book value of the equipment at December 31, 2010, the end of the year?

b. Assuming that the equipment was sold on April 1, 2010, for $315,000, illustrate the effects on the accounts and financial statements of (1) depreciation for the three months until the sale date, and (2) the sale of the equipment.

E7-14

Disposal of fixed asset

Obj 3

Equipment acquired on January 3, 2007, at a cost of $265,500, has an estimated useful life of eight years and an estimated residual value of $31,500.

a. What was the annual amount of depreciation for the years 2007, 2008, and 2009, using the straight-line method of depreciation?
b. What was the book value of the equipment on January 1, 2010?
c. Assuming that the equipment was sold on January 4, 2010, for $168,500, illustrate the effects on the accounts and financial statements of the sale.
d. Assuming that the equipment was sold on January 4, 2010, for $180,000 instead of $168,500, illustrate the effects on the accounts and financial statements of the sale.

E7-15

Recording depletion

Obj 4

✓ a. $2,475,000

Cikan Mining Co. acquired mineral rights for $16,200,000. The mineral deposit is estimated at 90,000,000 tons. During the current year, 13,750,000 tons were mined and sold.

a. Determine the amount of depletion expense for the current year.
b. Illustrate the effects on the accounts and financial statements of the depletion expense.

E7-16

Recording amortization

Obj 5

✓ a. $57,500

Isolution Company acquired patent rights on January 4, 2007, for $750,000. The patent has a useful life equal to its legal life of 15 years. On January 7, 2010, Isolution successfully defended the patent in a lawsuit at a cost of $90,000.

a. Determine the patent amortization expense for the current year ended December 31, 2010.
b. Illustrate the effects on the accounts and financial statements to recognize the amortization.

E7-17

Goodwill impairment

Obj 5

On January 1, 2007, Hoffman Financial, Inc., purchased the assets of AMG Insurance Co. for $100,000,000, a price reflecting a $25,000,000 goodwill premium. On December 31, 2010, Hoffman determined that the goodwill from the AMG acquisition was impaired and had a value of only $6,000,000.

a. Determine the book value of the goodwill on December 31, 2010, prior to making the impairment adjustment.
b. Illustrate the effects on the accounts and financial statements of the December 31, 2010, adjustment for the goodwill impairment.

E7-18

Book value of fixed assets

Obj 6

Apple, Inc., designs, manufactures, and markets personal computers and related software. Apple also manufactures and distributes music players (iPod™) along with related accessories and services, including the online distribution of third-party music. The following information was taken from a recent annual report of Apple:

Property, Plant, and Equipment (in millions):

	Current Year	Preceding Year
Land and buildings	$626	$361
Machinery, equipment, and internal-use software	595	470
Office furniture and equipment	94	81
Other fixed assets related to leases	760	569
Accumulated depreciation and amortization	794	664

a. Compute the book value of the fixed assets for the current year and the preceding year and explain the differences, if any.

b. Would you normally expect the book value of fixed assets to increase or decrease during the year?

E7-19

Balance sheet presentation

Obj 6

List the errors you find in the following partial balance sheet:

HOBART COMPANY
Balance Sheet
December 31, 2010

Assets

Total current assets $ 350,000

	Replacement Cost	Accumulated Depreciation	Book Value	
Property, plant, and equipment:				
Land	$ 60,000	$ 12,000	$ 48,000	
Buildings	156,000	45,600	110,400	
Factory equipment	330,000	175,200	154,800	
Office equipment	72,000	48,000	24,000	
Patents	48,000	—	48,000	
Goodwill	27,000	3,000	24,000	
Total property plant, and equipment	$693,000	$283,800		409,200

Problems

P7-1

Allocate payments and receipts to fixed asset accounts

Obj 1

SPREADSHEET

✓ Land, $469,450

The following payments and receipts are related to land, land improvements, and buildings acquired for use in a wholesale apparel business. The receipts are identified by an asterisk.

a. Finder's fee paid to real estate agency		$ 4,000
b. Cost of real estate acquired as a plant site: Land		375,000
	Building	25,000
c. Fee paid to attorney for title search		2,500
d. Delinquent real estate taxes on property, assumed by purchaser		31,750
e. Architect's and engineer's fees for plans and supervision		36,000
f. Cost of removing building purchased with land in (b)		10,000
g. Proceeds from sale of salvage materials from old building		3,000*
h. Cost of filling and grading land		15,200
i. Premium on one-year insurance policy during construction		5,400
j. Money borrowed to pay building contractor		600,000*
k. Special assessment paid to city for extension of water main to the property		9,000
l. Cost of repairing windstorm damage during construction		3,000
m. Cost of repairing vandalism damage during construction		1,800
n. Cost of trees and shrubbery planted		12,000
o. Cost of paving parking lot to be used by customers		14,500
p. Interest incurred on building loan during construction		33,000
q. Proceeds from insurance company for windstorm and vandalism damage		4,500*
r. Payment to building contractor for new building		700,000
s. Refund of premium on insurance policy (j) canceled after 10 months		450*

Instructions

1. Assign each payment and receipt to Land (unlimited life), Land Improvements (limited life), Building, or Other Accounts. Indicate receipts by an asterisk. Identify each item by letter and list the amounts in columnar form, as follows:

Item	Land	Land Improvements	Building	Other Accounts

2. Determine the increases to Land, Land Improvements, and Building.
3. The costs assigned to the land, which is used as a plant site, will not be depreciated, while the costs assigned to land improvements will be depreciated. Explain this seemingly contradictory application of the concept of depreciation.

P7-2

Compare three depreciation methods

Obj 2

SPREADSHEET

✓ a. 2009: straight-line depreciation, $86,000

Newbirth Coatings Company purchased waterproofing equipment on January 2, 2009, for $380,000. The equipment was expected to have a useful life of four years, and a residual value of $36,000.

Instructions

Determine the amount of depreciation expense for the years ended December 31, 2009, 2010, 2011, and 2012, by (a) the straight-line method and (b) the double-declining-balance method. Also determine the total depreciation expense for the four years by each method. The following columnar headings are suggested for recording the depreciation expense amounts:

	Depreciation Expense	
Year	Straight-Line Method	Double-Declining-Balance Method

P7-3

Depreciation by two methods; partial years

Obj 2

SPREADSHEET

✓ a. 2008, $7,600

Razor Sharp Company purchased tool sharpening equipment on July 1, 2008, for $48,600. The equipment was expected to have a useful life of three years, and a residual value of $3,000.

Instructions

Determine the amount of depreciation expense for the years ended December 31, 2008, 2009, 2010, and 2011, by (a) the straight-line method and (b) the double-declining-balance method.

P7-4

Depreciation by two methods; sale of fixed asset

Objs 2, 3

SPREADSHEET

✓ 1. b. Year 1, $72,000 depreciation expense

New tire retreading equipment, acquired at a cost of $144,000 at the beginning of a fiscal year, has an estimated useful life of four years and an estimated residual value of $10,800. The manager requested information regarding the effect of alternative methods on the amount of depreciation expense each year. On the basis of the data presented to the manager, the double-declining-balance method was selected.

In the first week of the fourth year, the equipment was sold for $19,750.

Instructions

1. Determine the annual depreciation expense for each of the estimated four years of use, the accumulated depreciation at the end of each year, and the book value of the equipment at the end of each year by (a) the straight-line method and (b) the double-declining-balance method. The following columnar headings are suggested for each schedule:

Year	Depreciation Expense	Accumulated Depreciation, End of Year	Book Value, End of Year

2. Illustrate the effects on the accounts and financial statements of the sale.
3. Illustrate the effects on the accounts and financial statements of the sale, assuming a sale price of $14,900 instead of $19,750.

P7-5

Amortization and depletion entries

Objs 4, 5

✓ 1. b. $33,750

Data related to the acquisition of timber rights and intangible assets during the current year ended December 31 are as follows:

a. On December 31, the company determined that $20,000,000 of goodwill was impaired.
b. Governmental and legal costs of $675,000 were incurred on June 30 in obtaining a patent with an estimated economic life of 10 years. Amortization is to be for one-half year.
c. Timber rights on a tract of land were purchased for $1,665,000 on February 16. The stand of timber is estimated at 9,000,000 board feet. During the current year, 2,400,000 board feet of timber were cut and sold.

Instructions

1. Determine the amount of the amortization, depletion, or impairment for the current year for each of the foregoing items.
2. Illustrate the effects on the accounts and financial statements of the adjustments for each item.

Activities

A7-1

Ethics and professional conduct in business

ETHICS

Esteban Appleby, CPA, is an assistant to the controller of Summerfield Consulting Co. In his spare time, Esteban also prepares tax returns and performs general accounting services for clients. Frequently, Esteban performs these services after his normal working hours, using Summerfield Consulting Co.'s computers and laser printers. Occasionally, Esteban's clients will call him at the office during regular working hours.

Discuss whether Esteban is performing in a professional manner.

A7-2

Financial vs. tax depreciation

The following is an excerpt from a conversation between two employees of Quantum Technologies, Pat Gapp and Faye Dalby. Pat is the accounts payable clerk, and Faye is the cashier.

Pat: Faye, could I get your opinion on something?

Faye: Sure, Pat.

Pat: Do you know Julie, the fixed assets clerk?

Faye: I know who she is, but I don't know her real well. Why?

Pat: Well, I was talking to her at lunch last Monday about how she liked her job, etc. You know, the usual … and she mentioned something about having to keep two sets of books … one for taxes and one for the financial statements. That can't be good accounting, can it? What do you think?

Faye: Two sets of books? It doesn't sound right.

Pat: It doesn't seem right to me either. I was always taught that you had to use generally accepted accounting principles. How can there be two sets of books? What can be the difference between the two?

How would you respond to Faye and Pat if you were Julie?

A7-3

Effect of depreciation on net income

Lonesome Dove Construction Co. specializes in building replicas of historic houses. Mike Jahn, president of Lonesome Dove Construction, is considering the purchase of various items of equipment on July 1, 2008, for $200,000. The equipment would have a useful life of five years and no residual value. In the past, all equipment has been leased. For tax purposes, Mike is considering depreciating the equipment by the straight-line method. He discussed the matter with his CPA and learned that, although the straight-line method could be elected, it was to his advantage to use the Modified Accelerated Cost Recovery System (MACRS) for tax purposes. He asked for your advice as to which method to use for tax purposes.

1. Compute depreciation for each of the years (2008, 2009, 2010, 2011, 2012, and 2013) of useful life by (a) the straight-line method and (b) MACRS. In using the straight-line method, one-half year's depreciation should be computed for 2008 and 2013. Use the MACRS rates presented in the chapter.
2. Assuming that income before depreciation and income tax is estimated to be $500,000 uniformly per year and that the income tax rate is 40%, compute the net income for each of the years 2008, 2009, 2010, 2011, 2012, and 2013, if (a) the straight-line method is used and (b) MACRS is used.
3. What factors would you present for Mike's consideration in the selection of a depreciation method?

A7-4

Shopping for a delivery truck

GROUP PROJECT

You are planning to acquire a delivery truck for use in your business for five years. In groups of three or four, explore a local dealer's purchase and leasing options for the truck. Summarize the costs of purchasing versus leasing, and list other factors that might help you decide whether to buy or lease the truck.

A7-5

Applying for patents, copyrights, and trademarks

INTERNET PROJECT

Go to the Internet and review the procedures for applying for a patent, a copyright, and a trademark. One Internet site that is useful for this purpose is **www.idresearch.com**, which is linked from the text's Web site at **www.cengage.com/accounting/warren**. Prepare a written summary of these procedures.

A7-6

Ethics and professional
conduct in business

ETHICS

The following is an excerpt from a conversation between the chief executive officer, Harry Balmer, and the chief financial officer, Connie Kenner, of BKX Group Inc.:

Harry (CEO): Connie, as you know, the auditors are coming in to audit our year-end financial statements pretty soon. Do you see any problems on the horizon?

Connie (CFO): Well, you know about our "famous" Robert Company acquisition of a couple of years ago. We booked $5,000,000 of goodwill from that acquisition, and the accounting rules require us to recognize any impairment of goodwill.

Harry (CEO): Uh-oh.

Connie (CFO): Yeah right. We had to shut the old Robert Company operations down this year because those products were no longer selling. Thus, our auditor is going to insist that we write off the $5,000,000 of goodwill to reflect the impaired value.

Harry (CEO): We can't have that—at least not this year! Do everything you can to push back on this one. We just can't take that kind of a hit this year. The most we could stand is $3,000,000. Connie, keep the write-off to $3,000,000 and promise anything in the future. Then we'll deal with that when we get there.

How should Connie respond to the CEO?

Answers to Self-Examination Questions

1. **C** All amounts spent to get a fixed asset (such as machinery) in place and ready for use are proper additions to the asset account. In the case of machinery acquired, the freight (answer A) and the installation costs (answer B) are both (answer C) proper charges to the machinery account.

2. **C** The periodic charge for depreciation under the double-declining-balance method for the second year is determined by first computing the depreciation charge for the first year. The depreciation for the first year of $6,000 (answer A) is computed by multiplying the cost of the equipment, $9,000, by ⅔ (the straight-line rate of ⅓ multiplied by 2). The depreciation for the second year of $2,000 (answer C) is then determined by multiplying the book value at the end of the first year, $3,000 (the cost of $9,000 minus the first-year depreciation of $6,000), by ⅔. The third year's depreciation is $400 (answer D). It is determined by multiplying the book value at the end of the second year, $1,000, by ⅔, thus yielding $667. However, the equipment cannot be depreciated below

its residual value of $600; thus, the third-year depreciation is $400 ($1,000 − $600).

3. **B** A depreciation method that provides for a higher depreciation amount in the first year of the use of an asset and a gradually declining periodic amount thereafter is called an accelerated depreciation method. The double-declining-balance method (answer B) is an example of such a method.

4. **B** $252,000. The depletion expense is determined by first computing a depletion rate. For Hyde Inc. the depletion rate is $1.44 per ton ($3,600,000/2,500,000 tons). The depletion rate of $1.44 per ton is then multiplied by the number of tons mined during the year, or 175,000 tons, to determine the depletion expense of $252,000 (175,000 tons × $1.44).

5. **D** Long-lived assets that are useful in operations, not held for sale, and without physical qualities are called intangible assets. Patents, goodwill, and copyrights are examples of intangible assets (answer D).

Liabilities and Stockholders' Equity

8

Banks and other financial institutions provide loans or credit to buyers for purchases of various items. Using credit to purchase items is probably as old as commerce itself. In fact, the Babylonians were lending money to support trade as early as 1300 B.C. The use of credit provides *individuals* convenience and buying power. Credit cards provide individuals convenience over writing checks and make purchasing over the Internet easier. Credit cards also provide individuals control over cash by providing documentation of their purchases through receipt of monthly credit card statements and by allowing them to avoid carrying large amounts of cash and to purchase items before they are paid.

Short-term credit is also used by *businesses* to provide convenience in purchasing items for manufacture or resale. More importantly, short-term credit gives a business control over the payment for goods and services. For example, **Panera Bread,** a chain of bakery-cafés located throughout the United States, uses short-term trade credit, or accounts payable, to purchase ingredients for making bread products in its bakeries. Short-term trade credit gives Panera control over cash payments by separating the purchase function from the payment function. Thus, the employee responsible for purchasing the bakery ingredients is separated from the employee responsible for paying for the purchase. This separation of duties can help prevent unauthorized purchases or payments.

In addition to accounts payable, a business like Panera Bread can also have current liabilities related to payroll, payroll taxes, short-term notes, and contingencies. Each of these types of current liabilities is described and illustrated in this chapter.

Panera Bread also uses long-term debt and stock to finance its operations and to raise funds for future expansion of its business. In this chapter, the use of bond and stock financing is described and illustrated.

Financing Operations

Obj 1 Describe how businesses finance their operations.

A company may finance its operations through debt, equity, or both. Debt financing includes all liabilities of the company. For example, most companies have accounts payable due to vendors and other suppliers. In effect, these vendors and suppliers are helping finance the company. A company may also issue notes or bonds to finance its operations. In contrast to accounts payable, notes and bonds normally require the periodic payment of interest.

Some equity financing is used by all companies. A proprietorship or partnership obtains equity financing from investments by its owner(s). A corporation obtains equity financing by issuing stock.

The preceding chapters focused primarily on the income statement and the asset side of the balance sheet. This chapter focuses on the right side of the accounting equation: the liabilities and stockholders' equity. The next section focuses on current liabilities, notes payable, taxes, contingencies, and payroll. This is followed by a discussion of bond and stock financing.

Liabilities

Obj 2 Describe and illustrate current liabilities, notes payable, taxes, contingencies, and payroll.

Liabilities are debts owed to others. Liabilities that are to be paid out of current assets and are due within a short time are reported as **current liabilities** on the balance sheet. Liabilities due beyond one year are classified as **long-term liabilities**. In addition, in some cases a company incurs a liability, called a **contingent liability**, if certain events occur in the future.

Current Liabilities

Most current liabilities arise from two basic transactions:

1. Receiving goods or services prior to making payment
2. Receiving payment prior to delivering goods or services

An example of the first type of transaction is an account payable arising from a purchase of merchandise for resale. An example of the second type of transaction is unearned rent arising from the receipt of rent in advance.

Earlier chapters described and illustrated the accounting for accounts payable and unearned liabilities transactions. The remainder of this section focuses on notes payable, tax liabilities, contingencies, and payroll liabilities.

Notes Payable

Notes payable are often issued to:

1. satisfy an account payable
2. purchase merchandise or other assets

The issuer of the note is called the borrower while the party receiving the note is called the lender. The lender accounts for the note as a note receivable, which was described and illustrated in Chapter 6.[1]

---

[1] The effect on the accounts and financial statements by a lender who accepts a note is exactly opposite that for the issuer of the note.

To illustrate the effects on the accounts and financial statements of issuing a note, assume the following:

Face value of note:	$1,000
Interest rate:	12%
Date of note:	August 1, 2010
Term of note:	90 days
Due date of note:	October 30

The effect on the accounts and financial statements of issuing and paying the note is as follows.

Issuing a 90-day, 12% note on account on August 1.

Statement of Cash Flows	Balance Sheet						Income Statement
	Assets	=	Liabilities		+	Stockholders' Equity	
			Accounts Payable	+	Notes Payable		
Aug. 1.			−1,000		1,000		

Paying of note on October 30.

Statement of Cash Flows	Balance Sheet						Income Statement
	Assets	=	Liabilities	+	Stockholders' Equity		
	Cash	=	Notes Payable	+	Retained Earnings		
Oct. 30.	−1,030		−1,000			−30	Oct. 30.

Statement of Cash Flows			Income Statement	
Oct. 30. Operating	−1,030		Oct. 30. Interest expense	−30

The interest expense is reported in the Other expense section of the income statement for the year ended December 31, 2010. If the accounting period ends before the maturity date of the note, interest expense to the end of the period is recorded by an adjustment.

Income Taxes

Under the United States tax code, corporations must pay federal income taxes.[2] Most corporations normally pay estimated federal income taxes in four installments throughout the year.

To illustrate, assume that a corporation, with a calendar-year accounting period, estimates its income tax expense for the year as $84,000. The effect on the accounts and the financial statements of the first of the four estimated tax payments of $21,000 (¼ of $84,000) is as follows:

---

[2] A corporation may also be required to pay state and local income taxes. To simplify, the discussion in this chapter is limited to federal income taxes. However, the basic concepts also apply to other income taxes.

Statement of Cash Flows	Balance Sheet						Income Statement
	Assets	=	Liabilities	+	Stockholders' Equity		
	Cash	=				Retained Earnings	
April 5.	−21,000					−21,000	April 5.

| Statement of Cash Flows | | | Income Statement | |
| April 5. Operating | −21,000 | | April 5. Income tax exp. | −21,000 |

At year-end, the actual taxable income and related tax are determined. If additional taxes are owed, the additional liability is recorded. If the total estimated tax payments are more than the tax liability, the overpayment is recorded as an increase in Income Tax Receivable and a decrease in Income Tax Expense.

The **taxable income** of a corporation is determined according to the tax laws. Since tax laws differ from generally accepted accounting principles, the income before taxes reported on the income statement is usually different from taxable income as shown in Exhibit 1.

EXHIBIT | 1 | Taxable Income and Income Before Taxes

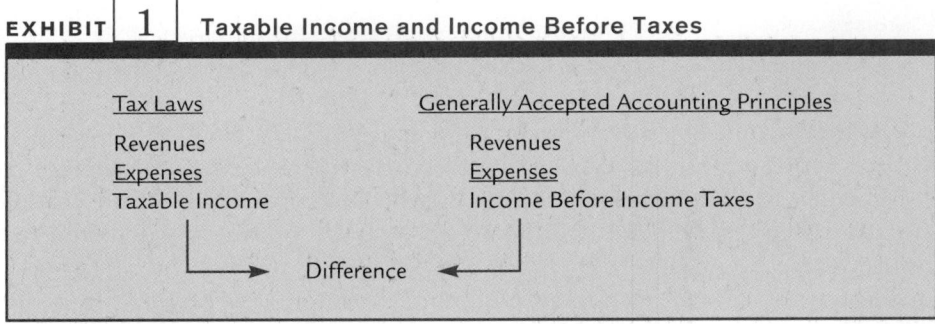

The tax implication of a difference may need to be allocated between financial statement periods. The difference may be created because items are recognized in one period for tax purposes and in another period for income statement purposes. Such differences, called **temporary differences**, reverse or turn around in later years. For example, such differences may be caused by a company using MACRS (Modified Accelerated Cost Recovery System) depreciation for tax purposes and the straight-line method for financial reporting purposes.

Since temporary differences reverse in later years, they do not change or reduce the total amount of taxable income over the life of a business. For example, MACRS recognizes more depreciation in the early years but less depreciation in the later years. However, the total depreciation expense is the same for MACRS and the straight-line method over the life of the asset.

Temporary differences do not change the total amount of taxes paid. Only the timing of when taxes are to be paid is affected. Companies normally use tax planning to delay or defer the payment of taxes to later years. As a result, at the end of each year, most corporations will have two tax liabilities as follows:

1. Current income tax liability, which is due on the current year's taxable income

2. Postponed or deferred tax liability, which is due in the future when the temporary differences reverse

To illustrate, assume the following data for the first year of a corporation's operations:

Income before income taxes (income statement)	$300,000
Less temporary differences	200,000
Taxable income (tax return)	$100,000
Income tax rate	40%

Based on the preceding data, the income tax expense reported on the income statement is $120,000 ($300,000 × 40%). However, the current income tax liability (income tax due for the year) reported on the corporate tax return is only $40,000 ($100,000 × 40%). The $80,000 ($120,000 − $40,000) difference is the deferred tax liability that will be paid in future years as shown below.

Income tax expense based on $300,000 reported income at 40%	$120,000
Income tax payable based on $100,000 taxable income at 40%	40,000
Income tax deferred to future years	$ 80,000

On the income statement, income tax expense of $120,000 ($300,000 × 40%) is reported. This is done so that the current year's expenses (including income tax) are properly matched against the current year's revenue. Of this amount, $40,000 is currently due and $80,000 will be due in (deferred to) future years.

The effect on the accounts and financial statements of recording the preceding tax expense is as follows:

Statement of Cash Flows	Balance Sheet						Income Statement
	Assets	=	Liabilities		+	Stockholders' Equity	
			Income Tax Pay.	+	Deferred Income Tax Pay.	+	Retained Earnings	
			40,000		80,000		−120,000	

Income Statement
Income tax exp.   −120,000

The balance of deferred income tax payable is reported as a liability. The amount due within one year is reported as a current liability and the remainder is reported as a long-term liability.[3]

Differences between taxable income and income (before taxes) reported on the income statement may also arise because some revenues are exempt from tax or some expenses are not deductible. Such differences, called **permanent differences,** create no special financial reporting issues. This is because the amount of income tax determined according to the tax laws is the same amount reported on the income statement.

---

[3] In some cases, a deferred tax asset can arise for tax benefits to be received in the future. Such items as well as additional disclosures for deferred taxes are discussed in advanced accounting texts.

Contingent Liabilities

Some liabilities may arise from past transactions if certain events occur in the future. These *potential* liabilities are called **contingent liabilities.**

As shown in Exhibit 2, the accounting for contingent liabilities depends on the following two factors:

1. Likelihood of occurring: Probable, reasonably possible, or remote
2. Measurement: Estimable or not estimable

EXHIBIT | 2 | **Accounting Treatment of Contingent Liabilities**

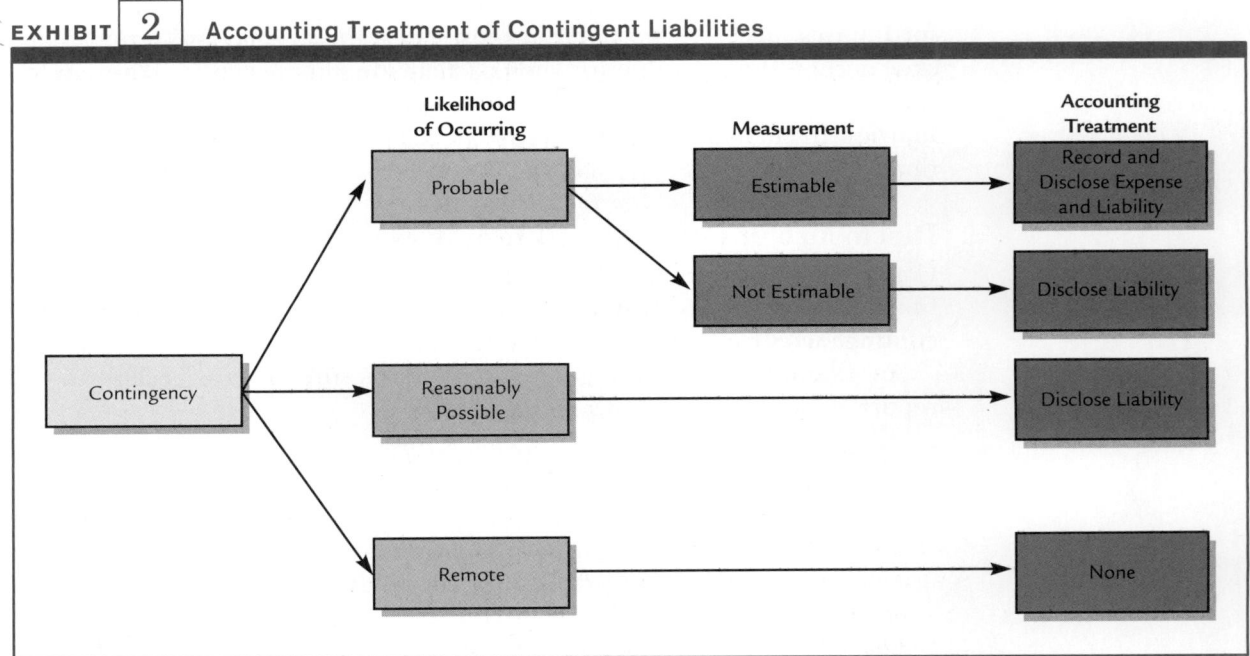

Probable and Estimable

If a contingent liability is *probable* and the amount of the liability can be *reasonably estimated,* it is recorded and disclosed. The liability is recorded by increasing an expense and a liability.

To illustrate, assume that during June a company sold a product for $60,000 that includes a 36-month warranty for repairs. The average cost of repairs over the warranty period is 5% of the sales price.

Warranty expense of $3,000 ($60,000 × 55) is recorded by increasing Warranty Expense and increasing Product Warranty Payable. In doing so, the warranty expense is recorded in the same period in which the related product sale is recorded. In other words, the warranty expense is matched with the related revenue (sales). When a defective product is repaired, the repair costs are recorded by decreasing Product Warranty Payable and decreasing Cash, Supplies, or other appropriate accounts.

The estimated costs of warranty work on new car sales are a contingent liability for *Ford Motor Company*.

Probable and Not Estimable

A contingent liability may be probable, but cannot be estimated. In this case, the contingent liability is disclosed in the notes to the financial statements. For ·example, a company may have accidentally polluted a local river by dumping waste products. At the end of the period, the cost of the cleanup and any fines may not be able to be estimated.

Reasonably Possible

A contingent liability may be only possible. For example, a company may have lost a lawsuit for infringing on another company's patent rights. However, the verdict is under appeal and the company's lawyers feel that the verdict will be reversed or significantly reduced. In this case, the contingent liability is disclosed in the notes to the financial statements.

Remote

A contingent liability may be remote. For example, a ski resort may be sued for injuries incurred by skiers. In most cases, the courts have found that a skier accepts the risk of injury when participating in the activity. Thus, unless the ski resort is grossly negligent, the resort will not incur a liability for ski injuries. In such cases, no disclosure needs to be made in the notes to the financial statements.

Disclosure of Contingent Liabilities

Common examples of contingent liabilities disclosed in notes to the financial statements are litigation, environmental matters, guarantees, and contingencies from the sale of receivables.

An example of a contingent liability disclosure from a recent annual report of *Google Inc.* is shown below.

> –Certain entities have also filed copyright claims against us, alleging that certain of our products, including Google Web Search, Google News, Google Image Search, and Google Book Search, infringe their rights. Adverse results in these lawsuits may include awards of damages and may also result in, or even compel, a change in our business practices, which could result in a loss of revenue for us or otherwise harm our business.
> –Although the results of litigation and claims cannot be predicted with certainty, we believe that the final outcome of the matters discussed above will not have a material adverse effect on our business....

Professional judgment is necessary in distinguishing among classes of contingent liabilities. This is especially the case when distinguishing between probable and reasonably possible contingent liabilities.

Payroll

The term **payroll** refers to the amount paid to employees for the services they provide during a period. Payroll can include either salaries or wages or both. *Salary* refers to payment for managerial, administrative, or similar

---

INTEGRITY, OBJECTIVITY, AND ETHICS IN BUSINESS

Today's Mistakes Can Be Tomorrow's Liability

Environmental and public health claims are quickly growing into some of the largest contingent liabilities facing companies. For example, tobacco, asbestos, and environmental cleanup claims have reached billions of dollars and have led to a number of corporate bankruptcies. Managers must be careful that today's decisions do not become tomorrow's nightmare.

services. The rate of salary is normally expressed in terms of a month or a year. *Wages* refers to payment for manual labor, both skilled and unskilled. The rate of wages is normally stated on an hourly or weekly basis.

The total earnings of an employee for a payroll period, including bonuses and overtime pay, is called **gross pay**. From this amount is subtracted one or more deductions to arrive at the net pay. **Net pay** is the amount the employer must pay the employee. The deductions for federal taxes are usually the largest deduction. Deductions may also be required for state or local income taxes. Still other deductions may be made for FICA tax, medical insurance, contributions to pensions, and items authorized by individual employees.

The FICA tax withheld from employees contributes to two federal programs. The first program, called *social security*, is for old age, survivors, and disability insurance (OASDI). The second program, called *Medicare*, is health insurance for senior citizens. The FICA tax rate and the amounts subject to the tax are established annually by law.[4]

To illustrate recording payroll, assume that McDermott Co. had a gross payroll of $13,800 for the week ending April 11. Assume that the FICA tax was 7.5% of the gross payroll and that federal and state withholding was $1,655 and $280, respectively. The effect on the accounts and financial statements of McDermott Co. of recording the payroll follows:

Statement of Cash Flows	Balance Sheet					Income Statement
	Assets =	Liabilities			+ Stockholders' Equity	
	Cash =	FICA Tax Payable +	Employee Federal Income Tax Payable +	Employee State Income Tax Payable +	Retained Earnings	
April 11.	−10,830	1,035	1,655	280	−13,800	April 11.

Statement of Cash Flows		Income Statement	
April 11. Operating	−10,830	April 11. Wages and salary exp.	−13,800

The FICA, federal, and state taxes withheld from the employees' earnings are not expenses to the employer. Rather, these amounts are withheld on the behalf of employees. These amounts must be remitted periodically to the state and federal agencies.

Most employers are subject to federal and state payroll taxes. Such taxes are an operating expense of the business. For example, employers are required to match employees' contributions to social security and Medicare. In addition, most businesses must pay federal and state unemployment taxes.

The Federal Unemployment Tax Act (FUTA) provides for temporary payments to those who become unemployed as a result of layoffs or other causes beyond their control. The FUTA tax rate and maximum earnings of each employee subject to the tax are established annually by law.

State Unemployment Tax Acts (SUTA) provide for payments to unemployed workers. The amounts paid as benefits are obtained, for the most

[4] The social security tax portion of the FICA tax is limited to a specific amount of the annual compensation for each individual. The 2009 limitation is $106,800. The Medicare portion is not subject to a limitation. To simplify, it is assumed that all compensation is within the social security limitation. By doing so, the social security and Medicare can be expressed as a single rate of 7.5%. The single rate for 2009 is 7.65%.

part, from a tax on employers only. The employment experience and the status of each employer's tax account are reviewed annually, and the tax rates are adjusted accordingly by each state.

The employer's payroll taxes become liabilities when the related payroll is *paid* to employees. The prior payroll information of McDermott Co. indicates that the amount of FICA tax withheld is $1,035 on April 11. Since the employer must match the employees' FICA contributions, the employer's social security payroll tax will also be $1,035. Furthermore, assume that the FUTA and SUTA taxes are $145 and $25, respectively. The effect on the accounts and financial statements of McDermott Co. of recording the payroll tax liabilities for the week follows.

Statement of Cash Flows	Balance Sheet					Income Statement
	Assets =	Liabilities			+ Stockholders' Equity	
		FICA Tax Payable +	FUTA Tax Payable +	SUTA Tax Payable +	Retained Earnings	
April 11.		1,035	145	25	−1,205	April 11.

Income Statement
April 11. Payroll tax exp.   −1,205

Payroll tax liabilities are paid to appropriate taxing authorities on a quarterly basis by decreasing Cash and the related taxes payable.

Many companies provide their employees a variety of benefits in addition to salary and wages earned. Such **fringe benefits** can take many forms, including vacations, pension plans, and health, life, and disability insurance coverage. When the employer pays part or all of the cost of the fringe benefits, these costs must be recognized as expenses. To properly match revenues and expenses, the estimated cost of these benefits should be recorded as an expense during the period in which the employee earns the benefit. In recording the expense, the related liability is also recorded.

Bonds

Obj 3 Describe and illustrate the financing of operations through issuance of bonds.

Many large corporations finance their operations through the issuance of bonds. A **bond** is simply a form of an interest-bearing note. Like a note, a bond requires periodic interest payments, with the face amount payable at the maturity date.

A corporation that issues bonds enters into a contract, called a **bond indenture** or trust indenture, with the bondholders. A bond issue is normally divided into a number of individual bonds. Usually the face value of each bond, called the *principal,* is $1,000 or a multiple of $1,000. The interest on bonds may be payable annually, semiannually, or quarterly. Most bonds pay interest semiannually.

The prices of bonds are quoted on bond exchanges as a percentage of the bonds' face value. Thus, investors could purchase or sell bonds quoted at $109\frac{7}{8}$ for $1,098.75. Likewise, bonds quoted at 110 could be purchased or sold for $1,100.

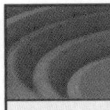

INTEGRITY, OBJECTIVITY, AND ETHICS IN BUSINESS

Résumé Padding

Misrepresenting your accomplishments on your résumé could come back to haunt you. In one case, the Chief Financial Officer (CFO) of **Veritas Software** was forced to resign his position when it was discovered that he had lied about earning an MBA from Stanford University, when in actuality he had earned only an undergraduate degree from Idaho State University.

Source: Reuters News Service, October 4, 2002

When a corporation issues bonds, the price that buyers are willing to pay for the bonds depends on these three factors:

1. The face amount of the bonds due at the maturity date
2. The periodic interest to be paid on the bonds
3. The market rate of interest

The periodic interest to be paid on the bonds is identified in the bond indenture and is expressed as a percentage of the face amount of the bond. This percentage or rate of interest is called the **contract rate** or *coupon rate*. The **market rate of interest**, sometimes called the *effective rate of interest,* is determined by transactions between buyers and sellers of similar bonds. If the contract rate of interest is the same as the market rate of interest, the bonds sell for their face amount.

To illustrate, assume that on January 1 a corporation issues for cash $100,000 of 12%, 5-year bonds, with interest of $6,000 payable semiannually. The market rate of interest at the time the bonds are issued is 12%.

Since the contract rate and the market rate of interest are the same, the bonds will sell at their face amount. The effect on the accounts and financial statements of issuing the bonds, paying the semiannual interest, and paying off the bonds at the maturity date is shown here.

Issuance of bonds payable at face amount on January 1.

Statement of Cash Flows	Balance Sheet				Income Statement
	Assets	=	Liabilities	+ Stockholders' Equity	
	Cash	=	Bonds Payable		
Jan. 1.	100,000		100,000		

Statement of Cash Flows	
Jan. 1. Financing	100,000

Payment of semiannual interest on June 30. (Interest: $100,000 \times 0.12 \times \frac{1}{2} = \$6,000$)

Statement of Cash Flows	Balance Sheet				Income Statement
	Assets	=	Liabilities	+ Stockholders' Equity	
	Cash	=		Retained Earnings	
June 30.	−6,000			−6,000	June 30.

Statement of Cash Flows		Income Statement	
June 30. Operating	−6,000	June 30. Interest expense	−6,000

Payment of face value of bond at maturity.

Statement of Cash Flows	Balance Sheet						Income Statement
	Assets	=	Liabilities	+	Stockholders' Equity		
	Cash	=	Bonds Payable				
Dec. 31.	−100,000		−100,000				

Statement of Cash Flows	
Dec. 31. Financing	−100,000

The market and contract rates of interest determine whether the selling price of a bond will be equal to, less than, or more than the bond's face amount.

1. Market Rate = Contract Rate

    Selling Price = Face Amount of Bonds

2. Market Rate > Contract Rate

    Selling Price < Face Amount of Bonds

    The face amount of bonds less the selling price is called a **discount on bonds payable**.

3. Market Rate < Contract Rate

    Selling Price > Face Amount of Bonds

    The selling price less the face amount of the bonds is called a **premium on bonds payable**.

A bond sells at a discount because buyers are only willing to pay less than the face amount for bonds whose contract rate is less than the market rate. A bond sells at a premium because buyers are willing to pay more than the face amount for bonds whose contract rate is higher than the market rate.

Generally accepted accounting principles require that bond discounts and premiums be amortized to Interest Expense over the life of the bond. The amortization of a discount increases Interest Expense, and the amortization of a premium reduces Interest Expense.

Stock

Obj 4 Describe and illustrate the financing of operations through issuance of stock.

A major means of equity financing for a corporation is issuing stock. The equity in the assets that results from issuing stock is called *paid-in capital* or *contributed capital*. Another major means of equity financing for a corporation's operations is through retaining net income in the business, called *retained earnings*. The accounting for retained earnings has been described and illustrated in earlier chapters.

The number of shares of stock that a corporation is authorized to issue is stated in its charter filed in its state of incorporation. The term *issued* refers to the shares issued to the stockholders. A corporation may reacquire some of the stock that it has issued. The stock remaining in the hands of stockholders is then called **outstanding stock**. The relationship between authorized, issued, and outstanding stock is shown in the margin.

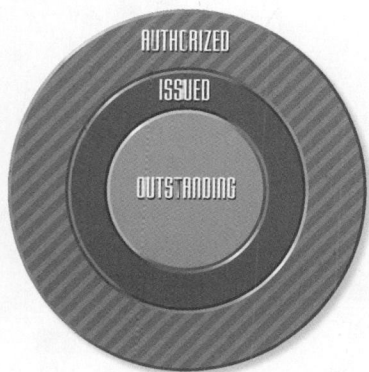

Number of shares authorized, issued, and outstanding

Shares of stock are often assigned a monetary amount, called **par**. Upon request, a corporation may issue stock certificates to stockholders to document their ownership. Printed on a stock certificate is the par value of the stock, the name of the stockholder, and the number of shares owned. Stock can also be issued without par, in which case it is called *no-par stock*. Some states require the board of directors to assign a **stated value** to no-par stock.

Because corporations have limited liability, creditors have no claim against the personal assets of stockholders. However, some state laws require that corporations maintain a minimum stockholder contribution to protect creditors. This minimum amount is called *legal capital*. The amount of required legal capital varies among the states, but it usually includes the amount of par or stated value of the shares of stock issued.

The major rights that accompany ownership of a share of stock are as follows:

1. The right to vote in matters concerning the corporation
2. The right to share in distributions of earnings
3. The right to share in assets on liquidation

Common and Preferred Stock

When only one class of stock is issued, it is called **common stock**. Each share of common stock has equal rights.

A corporation may also issue one or more classes of stock with various preference rights such as a preference to dividends. Such stock is called **preferred stock**. The dividend rights of preferred stock are stated either as dollars per share or as a percent of par. For example, a $50 par value preferred stock with a $4 per share dividend may be described as either:

$4 preferred stock, $50 par

    or

8% preferred stock, $50 par

The payment of dividends is authorized by the corporation's board of directors. When authorized, the directors are said to have *declared* a dividend. Because they have first rights (preference) to any dividends, preferred stockholders have a greater chance of receiving dividends than common stockholders. However, since dividends are normally based on earnings, a corporation cannot guarantee dividends even to preferred stockholders.

Issuance of Stock

Because different classes of stock have different rights, a separate account is used for recording the amount of each class of stock issued to investors. Stock is often issued by a corporation at a price other than its par. This is because the par value of a stock is simply its legal capital.

The price at which stock is sold depends on a variety of factors such as:

1. The financial condition, earnings record, and dividend record of the corporation
2. Investor expectations of the corporation's potential earning power
3. General business and economic conditions and prospects

Normally, stock is issued for a price that is more than its par. In this case, it is sold at a **premium on stock**.[5] Thus, if stock with a par of $50 is issued for a price of $60, the stock is sold at a premium of $10.

When stock is issued at a premium, Cash (or other asset) is increased for the amount received. Common Stock or Preferred Stock is then increased for the par amount. The excess of the amount received over par is a part of the capital contributed by the stockholders of the corporation. This amount is recorded in an account entitled Paid-In Capital in Excess of Par.

To illustrate, assume that Caldwell Company issues 2,000 shares of $1 par common stock for cash at $55 on November 1. The effects on the accounts and financial statements follow:

Statement of Cash Flows	Balance Sheet						Income Statement
	Assets	=	Liabilities	+	Stockholders' Equity		
	Cash	=			Common Stock	+ Paid-In Capital in Excess of Par	
Nov. 1.	110,000				2,000	108,000	

Statement of Cash Flows		
Nov. 1. Financing	110,000	

When stock is issued in exchange for assets other than cash, such as land, buildings, and equipment, the assets acquired are recorded at their fair market value. If this value cannot be objectively determined, the fair market price of the stock issued may be used.

In most states, both preferred and common stock may be issued without a par value. When no-par stock is issued, the entire proceeds are recorded in the stock account. In some states, no-par stock may be assigned a stated value per share. The stated value is recorded like a par value, and the excess of the amount received over the stated value is recorded in Paid-In Capital in Excess of Stated Value.

Reacquired Stock

Treasury stock is stock that a corporation has issued and then reacquired. A corporation may reacquire (purchase) its own stock for a variety of reasons including:

1. To provide shares for resale to employees
2. To reissue as bonuses to employees
3. To support the market price of the stock

The purchase of treasury stock increases Treasury Stock and decreases Cash by the cost of the repurchased shares. At the end of the year, the balance of the treasury stock account is reported as a reduction of stockholders' equity. When treasury stock is sold or reissued, Cash is increased by the proceeds from the sale and Treasury Stock is decreased by the cost of its repurchase. Any difference increases or decreases an account called Paid-In Capital from Treasury Stock.

---

[5] When stock is issued for a price that is less than its par, the stock is sold at a discount. Many states do not permit stock to be issued at a discount. In others, it may be done only under unusual conditions. For these reasons, we assume that stock is sold at par or at a premium in the reminder of this text.

Dividends

Obj 5 Describe and illustrate the accounting for cash and stock dividends.

When a board of directors declares a cash dividend, it authorizes the distribution of cash to stockholders. When a board of directors declares a stock dividend, it authorizes the distribution of its stock. In both cases, declaring a dividend decreases the retained earnings of the corporation.[6]

Cash Dividends

A cash distribution of earnings by a corporation to its shareholders is a **cash dividend**. Although dividends may be paid in other assets, cash dividends are the most common.

Three conditions for a cash dividend are as follows:

1. Sufficient retained earnings
2. Sufficient cash
3. Formal action by the board of directors

There must be a sufficient (large enough) balance in Retained Earnings to declare a cash dividend. However, a large Retained Earnings balance does not mean that there is cash available to pay dividends. This is because the balances of Cash and Retained Earnings are often unrelated.

Even if there are sufficient retained earnings and cash, a corporation's board of directors is not required to pay dividends. Nevertheless, many corporations pay quarterly cash dividends to make their stock more attractive to investors. *Special* or *extra* dividends may also be paid when a corporation experiences higher than normal profits.

Three dates included in a dividend announcement are as follows:

1. Date of declaration
2. Date of record
3. Date of payment

The *date of declaration* is the date the board of directors formally authorizes the payment of the dividend. On this date, the corporation incurs the liability to pay the amount of the dividend.

The *date of record* is the date the corporation uses to determine which stockholders will receive the dividend. During the period of time between the date of declaration and the date of record, the stock price is quoted as selling *with-dividends*. This means that any investors purchasing the stock before the date of record will receive the dividend.

The *date of payment* is the date the corporation will pay the dividend to the stockholders who owned the stock on the date of record. During the period of time between the record date and the payment date, the stock price is quoted as selling *ex-dividends*. This means that since the date of record has passed, any new investors will not receive the dividend.

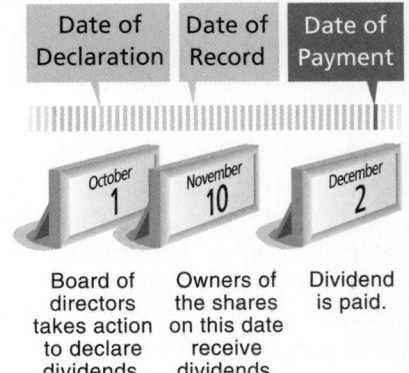

---

[6] In rare cases, when a corporation is reducing its operations or going out of business, a dividend may be a distribution of paid-in capital. Such a dividend is called a liquidating dividend.

To illustrate, assume that on *December 1* Hiber Corporation's board of directors declares the following quarterly cash dividend. The date of record is *December 10,* and the date of payment is *January 2.*

	Dividend per Share	Total Dividends
Preferred stock, $100 par, 5,000 shares outstanding	$2.50	$12,500
Common stock, $10 par, 100,000 shares outstanding	$0.30	30,000
Total		$42,500

The effect of the declaration of the dividend on the accounts and financial statements is as follows:

Statement of Cash Flows	Balance Sheet					Income Statement
	Assets	=	Liabilities	+	Stockholders' Equity	
			Cash Dividends Payable	+	Retained Earnings	
Dec. 1.			42,500		−42,500	

Note that the date of record, December 10, does not affect the accounts or the financial statements since this date merely determines which stockholders will receive the dividend. The payment of the dividend on January 2 decreases Cash and Dividends Payable.

If a corporation holding treasury stock declares a cash dividend, the dividends are not paid on the treasury shares. To do so would place the corporation in the position of earning income through dealing with itself. For example, if Hiber Corporation in the preceding illustration had held 5,000 shares of its own common stock, the cash dividends on the common stock would have been $28,500 [(100,000 × 5,000) × $0.30] instead of $30,000.

INTEGRITY, OBJECTIVITY, AND ETHICS IN BUSINESS

The Professor Who Knew Too Much

A major Midwestern university released a quarterly "American Customer Satisfaction Index" based on its research of customers of popular U.S. products and services. Before the release of the index to the public, the professor in charge of the research bought and sold stocks of some of the companies in the report. The professor was quoted as saying that he thought it was important to test his theories of customer satisfaction with "real" [his own] money.

Is this proper or ethical? Apparently, the dean of the Business School didn't think so. In a statement to the press, the dean stated: "I have instructed anyone affiliated with the (index) not to make personal use of information gathered in the course of producing the quarterly index, prior to the index's release to the general public, and they [the researchers] have agreed."

Sources: Jon E. Hilsenrath and Dan Morse, "Researcher Uses Index to Buy, Short Stocks," *The Wall Street Journal,* February 18, 2003; and Jon E. Hilsenrath, "Satisfaction Theory: Mixed Results," *The Wall Street Journal,* February 19, 2003.

Stock Dividends

A **stock dividend** is a distribution of shares of stock to stockholders. Stock dividends are normally declared only on common stock and issued to common stockholders.

The effect of a stock dividend on the stockholders' equity of the issuing corporation is to transfer retained earnings to paid-in capital. For public corporations, the amount transferred from the retained earnings account to the paid-in capital account is normally the fair value (market price) of the shares issued in the stock dividend.[7]

A stock dividend does not change the assets, liabilities, or total stockholders' equity of a corporation. Likewise, a stock dividend does not change an individual stockholder's proportionate interest (equity) in the corporation.

To illustrate, assume a stockholder owns 1,000 of a corporation's 10,000 shares outstanding. If the corporation declares a 6% stock dividend, the stockholder's proportionate interest will not change, as shown below.

	Before Stock Dividend	After Stock Dividend
Total shares issued	10,000	10,600 [10,000 + (10,000 × 6%)]
Number of shares owned	1,000	1,060 [1,000 + (1,000 × 6%)]
Proportionate ownership	10% (1,000/10,000)	10% (1,060/10,600)

Stock Splits

Obj 6 Describe the effects of stock splits on the financial statements.

A **stock split** is a process by which a corporation reduces the par or stated value of its common stock and issues a proportionate number of additional shares. A stock split applies to all common shares including the unissued, issued, and treasury shares.

A major objective of a stock split is to reduce the market price per share of the stock. This, in turn, attracts more investors to the stock and broadens the types and numbers of stockholders.

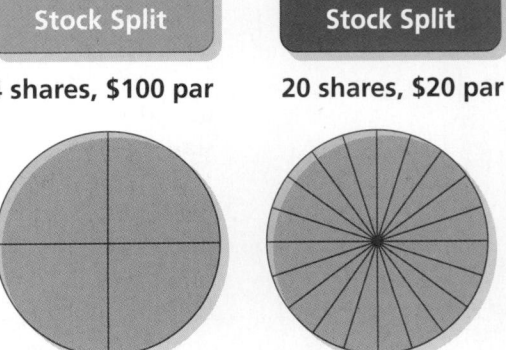

Before Stock Split — 4 shares, $100 par — $400 total par value

After 5:1 Stock Split — 20 shares, $20 par — $400 total par value

To illustrate, assume that Rojek Corporation has 10,000 shares of $100 par common stock outstanding with a current market price of $150 per share. The board of directors declares the following stock split:

1. Each common shareholder will receive 5 shares for each share held. This is called a 5-for-1 stock split. As a result, 50,000 shares (10,000 shares × 5) will be outstanding.

2. The par of each share of common stock will be reduced to $20 ($100/5).

The par value of the common stock outstanding is $1,000,000 both before and after the stock split as shown below.

	Before Split	After Split
Number of shares	10,000	50,000
Par value per share	× $100	× $20
Total	$1,000,000	$1,000,000

[7] The use of fair market value is justified as long as the number of shares issued for the stock dividend is small (less than 25% of the shares outstanding).

When **Nature's Sunshine Products, Inc.,** declared a 2-for-1 stock split, the company president said: *We believe the split will place our stock price in a range attractive to both individual and institutional investors, broadening the market for the stock.*

In addition, each Rojek Corporation shareholder owns the same total par amount of stock before and after the stock split. For example, a stockholder who owned 4 shares of $100 par stock before the split (total par of $400) would own 20 shares of $20 par stock after the split (total par of $400). Only the number of shares and the par value per share have changed.

Since there are more shares outstanding after the stock split, the market price of the stock should decrease. For example, in the preceding example, there would be 5 times as many shares outstanding after the split. Thus, the market price of the stock would be expected to fall from $150 to about $30 ($150/5).

Stock splits do not affect any financial statement accounts since only the par (or stated) value and number of shares outstanding have changed. However, the details of stock splits are normally disclosed in the notes to the financial statements.

Obj 7 Describe financial statement reporting of liabilities and stockholders' equity.

Reporting Liabilities and Stockholders' Equity

Liabilities that are expected to be paid within one year are presented in the Current Liabilities section of the balance sheet. Thus, any notes or bonds payable maturing within one year are reported as current liabilities. However, if the notes or bonds are to be paid from noncurrent assets or if the notes or bonds are going to be refinanced, they are reported as noncurrent liabilities. The detailed descriptions, including terms, due dates, and interest rates for notes or bonds, are reported either on the balance sheet or in a footnote. Also, the fair market value of notes or bonds is disclosed. Exhibit 3 illustrates the reporting of liabilities on the balance sheet.

Contingent liabilities that are probable but cannot be reasonably estimated or are only possible are disclosed in the footnotes to the financial statements.

Although stockholders' equity is reported on the balance sheet, significant changes in stockholders' equity during the year should also be disclosed. Changes in retained earnings are often presented in a separate retained earnings statement. Changes in paid-in capital during the year may be reported on the face of the balance sheet or in the footnotes. Some companies prepare a separate statement of stockholders' equity that includes changes in both paid-in capital and retained earnings. An example of a statement of stockholders' equity is shown in Exhibit 4.

Obj 8 Analyze the impact of debt or equity financing on earnings per share.

Earnings per Share

One of the many factors that influence the decision of whether to finance operations using debt or equity is the effect on earnings per share. Earnings per share is a major profitability measure that is reported in the financial statements and is followed closely by the financial press. As a result, corporate managers closely monitor the impact of decisions on earnings per share.

EXHIBIT 3 Partial Balance Sheet with Liabilities and Stockholders' Equity

ESCOE CORPORATION
Balance Sheet
December 31, 2010

Liabilities

Current liabilities:

Accounts payable	$ 488,200	
Notes payable (9% due on March 1, 2011)	250,000	
Accrued interest payable	15,000	
Accrued salaries and wages payable	13,500	
Other accrued liabilities	9,850	
Total current liabilities		$ 776,550

Long-term liabilities:

Debenture 8% bonds payable, due December 31, 2023 (Market value $950,000)		1,000,000
Total liabilities		$1,776,550

Stockholders' Equity

Paid-in capital:

Preferred 10% stock, $50 par (20,000 shares authorized and issued)	$1,000,000	
Common stock, $20 par (250,000 shares authorized, 100,000 shares issued)	2,000,000	
Additional paid-in capital in excess of par	520,000	
Total paid-in capital	$ 3,520,000	
Retained earnings	4,580,500	
Total	$ 8,100,500	
Deduct treasury stock (1,000 shares at cost)	75,000	
Total stockholders' equity		8,025,500
Total liabilities and stockholders' equity		$9,802,050

EXHIBIT 4 Statement of Stockholders' Equity

TELEX INC.
Statement of Stockholders' Equity
For the Year Ended December 31, 2010

	Preferred Stock	Common Stock	Paid-In Capital in Excess of Par—Common Stock	Retained Earnings	Treasury (Common) Stock	Total
Balance, January 1	$5,000,000	$10,000,000	$3,000,000	$2,000,000	$(500,000)	$19,500,000
Net income				850,000		850,000
Dividends on preferred stock				(250,000)		(250,000)
Dividends on common stock				(400,000)		(400,000)
Issuance of additional common stock		500,000	50,000			550,000
Purchase of treasury stock					(30,000)	(30,000)
Balance, December 31	$5,000,000	$10,500,000	$3,050,000	$2,200,000	$(530,000)	$20,220,000

Earnings per share (EPS) measures the income earned by each share of common stock.[8] It is computed as follows:

$$\text{Earning per Share} = \frac{\text{Net Income} - \text{Preferred Dividends}}{\text{Number of Common Shares Outstanding}}$$

To illustrate, assume the following data for Lincoln Corporation:

	2011	2010
Shares of common stock outstanding	50,000	50,000
Shares of 9%, $100 par preferred stock outstanding	100,000	100,000
Net income	$ 91,000	$ 76,500

The earnings per share for 2011 and 2010 is computed below:

2011:

$$\text{Earnings per Share} = \frac{\text{Net Income} - \text{Preferred Dividends}}{\text{Number of Common Shares Outstanding}}$$
$$= \frac{\$91,000 - \$9,000}{50,000 \text{ Shares}} = \$1.64 \text{ per Share}$$

2010:

$$\text{Earnings per Share} = \frac{\text{Net Income} - \text{Preferred Dividends}}{\text{Number of Common Shares Outstanding}}$$
$$= \frac{\$76,000 - \$9,000}{50,000 \text{ Shares}} = \$1.35 \text{ per Share}$$

To illustrate the financing of long-term operations, assume Huckadee Corporation is considering the following plans to issue debt and equity:

	Plan 1		Plan 2		Plan 3	
	Amount	Percent	Amount	Percent	Amount	Percent
Issue 12% bonds	—	0%	—	0%	$2,000,000	50%
Issue 9% preferred stock, $50 par value	—	0	$2,000,000	50	1,000,000	25
Issue common stock, $10 par value	$4,000,000	100	2,000,000	50	1,000,000	25
Total amount of financing	$4,000,000	100%	$4,000,000	100%	$4,000,000	100%

Each of the preceding plans finances some of the corporation's operations by issuing common stock. However, the percentage financed by common stock varies from 100% (Plan 1) to 25% (Plan 3).

In addition, assume the following data for Huckadee Corporation:

1. Earnings before interest and income taxes are $800,000.

2. The tax rate is 40%.

3. All bonds or stocks are issued at their par or face amount.

The effect of the preceding financing plans on Huckadee's net income and earnings per share is shown in Exhibit 5. Exhibit 5 indicates that Plan 3 yields the highest earnings per share on common stock and thus is the most

---

[8] Earnings per share is further discussed in Chapter 9, "Financial Statement Analysis."

EXHIBIT 5 | **Effect of Alternative Financing Plans—$800,000 Earnings**

	Plan 1	Plan 2	Plan 3
12% bonds	—	—	$ 2,000,000
Preferred 9% stock, $50 par	—	$ 2,000,000	1,000,000
Common stock, $10 par	$ 4,000,000	2,000,000	1,000,000
Total	$ 4,000,000	$ 4,000,000	$ 4,000,000
Earnings before interest and income tax	$ 800,000	$ 800,000	$ 800,000
Deduct interest on bonds	—	—	240,000
Income before income tax	$ 800,000	$ 800,000	$ 560,000
Deduct income tax	320,000	320,000	224,000
Net income	$ 480,000	$ 480,000	$ 336,000
Dividends on preferred stock	—	180,000	90,000
Available for dividends on common stock	$ 480,000	$ 300,000	$ 246,000
Shares of common stock outstanding	÷ 400,000	÷ 200,000	÷ 100,000
Earnings per share on common stock	$ 1.20	$ 1.50	$ 2.46

attractive for common stockholders. If the estimated earnings are more than $800,000, the difference between the earnings per share to common stockholders under Plans 1 and 3 is even greater.[9]

If smaller earnings occur, however, Plans 1 and 2 become more attractive to common stockholders. To illustrate, the effect of earnings of $440,000 rather than $800,000 is shown in Exhibit 6.

In addition to earnings per share, the corporation should consider other factors in deciding among the financing plans. For example, once bonds are

EXHIBIT 6 | **Effect of Alternative Financing Plans—$440,000 Earnings**

	Plan 1	Plan 2	Plan 3
12% bonds	—	—	$2,000,000
Preferred 9% stock, $50 par	—	$2,000,000	1,000,000
Common stock, $10 par	$4,000,000	2,000,000	1,000,000
Total	$4,000,000	$4,000,000	$4,000,000
Earnings before interest and income tax	$ 440,000	$ 440,000	$ 440,000
Deduct interest on bonds	—	—	240,000
Income before income tax	$ 440,000	$ 440,000	$ 200,000
Deduct income tax	176,000	176,000	80,000
Net income	$ 264,000	$ 264,000	$ 120,000
Dividends on preferred stock	—	180,000	90,000
Available for dividends on common stock	$ 264,000	$ 84,000	$ 30,000
Shares of common stock outstanding	÷400,000	÷200,000	÷100,000
Earnings per share on common stock	$ 0.66	$ 0.42	$ 0.30

[9] The higher earnings per share under Plan 3 is due to a finance concept known as leverage. This concept is discussed further in Chapter 9.

issued, the interest and the face value of the bonds at maturity must be paid. If these payments are not made, the bondholders could seek court action and force the company into bankruptcy. In contrast, a corporation is not legally obligated to pay dividends on preferred or common stock.

Key Points

1. **Describe how businesses finance their operations.**

   A business must finance its operations through either debt or equity. Debt financing includes all liabilities owed by a business, including both current and long-term liabilities. A corporation may also finance its operations by issuing stock. Corporations may issue different classes of stock that contain different rights and privileges, such as rights to dividend payments.

2. **Describe and illustrate current liabilities, notes payable, taxes, contingencies, and payroll.**

   Liabilities that are to be paid out of current assets and are due within a short time, usually within one year, are called *current liabilities*. Most current liabilities arise from either receiving goods or services prior to making payment or receiving payment prior to delivering goods or services. Current liabilities can also arise from notes payable, taxes, contingencies, and payroll. Warranties are examples of liabilities arising from contingencies. Wages and salaries payable and employee and employer payroll taxes are examples of liabilities arising from payroll. Deferred income taxes arise from temporary differences between taxable income and income before taxes as reported on the income statement.

3. **Describe and illustrate the financing of operations through issuance of bonds.**

   Many large corporations finance their operations through the issuance of bonds. A bond is simply a form of an interest-bearing note that requires periodic interest payments and the repayment of the face amount at the maturity date. When the contract rate of interest differs from the market rate of interest, bonds are issued at discounts or premiums. The amortization of discounts and premiums affects interest expense.

4. **Describe and illustrate the financing of operations through issuance of stock.**

   A corporation may finance its operations by issuing either preferred or common stock. Preferred stock has preferential rights, including the right to receive dividends ahead of the common stockholders. When stock is issued at a premium, Cash or another asset account is increased for the amount received. Common Stock or Preferred Stock is increased for the par amount. The excess of the amount paid over par is a part of the paid-in capital and is normally recorded in an account entitled Paid-In Capital in Excess of Par.

   Stock that a corporation has once issued and then reacquires is called *treasury stock*. It decreases stockholders' equity.

5. **Describe and illustrate the accounting for cash and stock dividends.**

   When a board of directors declares a cash dividend, it authorizes the distribution of a portion of the corporation's cash to stockholders. When a board of directors declares a stock dividend, it authorizes the distribution of a portion of the stock. In both cases, the declaration of a dividend reduces the retained earnings of the corporation.

6. **Describe the effects of stock splits on the financial statements.**

   Corporations sometimes reduce the par or stated value of their common stock and issue a proportionate number of additional shares in what is called a *stock split*. Since a stock split changes only the par or stated value and the number of shares outstanding, it is not recorded. However, the details of stock splits are normally disclosed in the notes to the financial statements.

7. Describe financial statement reporting of liabilities and stockholders' equity.

Liabilities that are expected to be paid within one year are presented in the Current Liabilities section of the balance sheet. Notes or bonds payable not maturing within one year should be shown as noncurrent liabilities. The detailed descriptions including terms, due dates, and interest rates for notes or bonds should be reported either on the balance sheet or in an accompanying footnote. Also, the fair market value of notes or bonds should be disclosed. The notes should disclose any contingent liabilities that cannot be reasonably estimated or are only possible. Significant changes in stockholders' equity during the year should also be reported.

8. Analyze the impact of debt or equity financing on earnings per share.

One of the many factors that influence the decision of whether to finance operations using debt or equity is the effect of each alternative on earnings per share. If a corporation has issued only common stock, earnings per share is computed by dividing net income by the number of shares of common stock outstanding. If preferred and common stock have been issued, the net income must first be reduced by the amount of preferred dividends.

Key Terms

Bond A form of interest-bearing note used by corporations to borrow on a long-term basis.

Bond indenture The contract between a corporation issuing bonds and the bondholders.

Cash dividend A cash distribution of earnings by a corporation to its shareholders.

Common stock The basic type of stock issued to stockholders of a corporation when a corporation has issued only one class of stock.

Contingent liabilities Potential liabilities if certain events occur in the future.

Contract rate The periodic interest to be paid on the bonds that is identified in the bond indenture; expressed as a percentage of the face amount of the bond.

Current liabilities Liabilities that are to be paid out of current assets and are due within a short time, usually within one year.

Discount on bonds payable The excess of the face amount of bonds over their issue price.

Earnings per share (EPS) A measure of profitability computed by dividing net income, reduced by preferred dividends, by the number of shares outstanding.

Fringe benefits Benefits provided to employees in addition to wages and salaries.

Gross pay The total earnings of an employee for a payroll period.

Long-term liabilities Liabilities due beyond one year or liabilities that will be paid out of noncurrent assets.

Market rate of interest The effective rate of interest at the time the bonds were issued.

Net pay Gross pay less payroll deductions; the amount the employer is obligated to pay the employee.

Outstanding stock The stock in the hands of stockholders.

Par The monetary amount printed on a stock certificate.

Payroll The total amount paid to employees for a certain period.

Preferred stock A class of stock with preferential rights over common stock.

Premium on bonds payable The excess of the issue price of bonds over their face amount.

Premium on stock The excess of the issue price of a stock over its par value.

Stated value A value, similar to par value, approved by the board of directors of a corporation for no-par stock.

Stock dividend A distribution of shares of stock to a corporation's stockholders.

Stock split The reduction in the par or stated value of common stock and issuance of a proportionate number of additional shares.

Taxable income The income of a corporation that is subject to taxes as determined according to the tax laws.

Temporary differences Differences between taxable income and income before income taxes that are created because items are recognized in one period for tax purposes and in another period for income statement purposes.

Treasury stock Stock that a corporation has once issued and then reacquires.

Illustrative Problem

Differences between the accounting methods applied to accounts and financial reports and those used in determining taxable income yielded the following amounts for the first four years of a corporation's operations:

	First Year	Second Year	Third Year	Fourth Year
Income before income taxes	$400,000	$480,000	$600,000	$520,000
Taxable income	300,000	420,000	630,000	600,000

The income tax rate for each of the four years was 40% of taxable income, and each year's taxes were promptly paid.

Instructions

1. Determine for each year the amounts described by the following captions, presenting the information in the form indicated:

Year	Income Tax Deducted on Income Statement	Income Tax Payments for the Year	Deferred Income Tax Payable Year's Addition (Deduction)	Year-End Balance

2. Total the first three amount columns.

Solution

1. and 2.

Year	Income Tax Deducted on Income Statement	Income Tax Payments for the Year	Deferred Income Tax Payable Year's Addition (Deduction)	Year-End Balance
First	$160,000	$120,000	$ 40,000	$40,000
Second	192,000	168,000	24,000	64,000
Third	240,000	252,000	(12,000)	52,000
Fourth	208,000	240,000	(32,000)	20,000
Total	$800,000	$780,000	$ 20,000	

Self-Examination Questions *(Answers appear at the end of chapter)*

1. A business issued a $5,000, 60-day, 12% note to the bank. The amount due at maturity is:

   A. $4,900
   B. $5,000
   C. $5,100
   D. $5,600

2. Which of the following taxes are employers usually not required to withhold from employees?

   A. Federal income tax
   B. Federal unemployment compensation tax
   C. FICA tax
   D. State and local income tax

3. Employers do not incur an expense for which of the following payroll taxes?

A. FICA tax

B. Federal unemployment compensation tax

C. State unemployment compensation tax

D. Employees' federal income tax

4. If a corporation plans to issue $1,000,000 of 12% bonds when the market rate for similar bonds is 10%, the bonds can be expected to sell at:

A. Their face amount

B. A premium

C. A discount

D. A price below their face amount

5. A corporation has issued 25,000 shares of $100 par common stock and holds 3,000 of these shares as treasury stock. If the corporation declares a $2 per share cash dividend, what amount will be recorded as cash dividends?

A. $22,000

B. $25,000

C. $44,000

D. $50,000

Class Discussion Questions

1. What two types of transactions cause most current liabilities?

2. When are short-term notes payable issued?

3. When should the liability associated with a product warranty be recorded? Discuss.

4. *Deere & Company,* a company well known for manufacturing farm equipment, reported more than $800 million of product warranties in recent financial statements. How would costs of repairing a defective product be recorded?

5. *Delta Air Lines'* SkyMiles program allows frequent flyers to earn credit toward free tickets and other amenities. (a) Does Delta Air Lines have a contingent liability for award redemption by its SkyMiles members? (b) When should a contingent liability be recorded?

6. For each of the following payroll-related taxes, indicate whether it generally applies to (1) employees only, (2) employers only, or (3) both employees and employers:

   a. Federal income tax

   b. Federal unemployment compensation tax

   c. Medicare tax

   d. Social security tax

   e. State unemployment compensation tax

7. To match revenues and expenses properly, should the expense for employee vacation pay be recorded in the period during which the vacation privilege is earned or during the period in which the vacation is taken? Discuss.

8. Identify the two distinct obligations incurred by a corporation when issuing bonds.

9. A corporation issues $25,000,000 of 5% bonds to yield an effective interest rate of 7½%.

   a. Was the amount of cash received from the sale of the bonds more or less than $25,000,000?

   b. Identify the following amounts related to the bond issue: (1) face amount, (2) market rate of interest, (3) contract rate of interest, and (4) maturity amount.

10. The following data relate to a $5,000,000, 6% bond issue for a selected semiannual interest period:

Bond carrying amount at beginning of period	$5,350,000
Interest paid at end of period	300,000
Interest expense allocable to the period	285,500

   (a) Were the bonds issued at a discount or at a premium? (b) What expense account was decreased to amortize the discount or premium?

11. Of two corporations organized at approximately the same time and engaged in competing businesses, one issued $100 par common stock, and the other issued $5 par common stock. Do the par designations

provide any indication as to which stock is preferable as an investment? Explain.

12. When a corporation issues stock at a premium, is the premium income? Explain.

13. a. In what respect does treasury stock differ from unissued stock?

    b. How should treasury stock be presented on the balance sheet?

14. A corporation reacquires 25,000 shares of its own $100 par common stock for $3,000,000, recording it at cost. (a) What effect does this transaction have on revenue or expense of the period? (b) What effect does it have on stockholders' equity?

15. The treasury stock in Question 14 is resold for $3,250,000. (a) What is the effect on the corporation's revenue of the period? (b) What is the effect on stockholders' equity?

16. A corporation with preferred stock and common stock outstanding has a substantial balance in its retained earnings account at the beginning of the current fiscal year. Although net income for the current year is sufficient to pay the preferred dividend of $30,000 each quarter and a common dividend of $75,000 each quarter, the board of directors declares dividends only on the preferred stock. Suggest possible reasons that the board passes the dividends on the common stock.

17. An owner of 250 shares of Reynolds Spring Company common stock receives a stock dividend of 20 shares. (a) What is the effect of the stock dividend on the stockholder's proportionate interest (equity) in the corporation? (b) How does the total equity of 270 shares compare with the total equity of 250 shares before the stock dividend?

18. What is the primary purpose of a stock split?

Exercises

E8-1

Current liabilities

Objs 2, 7

✓ Total current liabilities, $790,000

I-Generation Co. sold 14,000 annual subscriptions of *Climber's World* for $60 during December 2010. These new subscribers will receive monthly issues, beginning in January 2011. In addition, the business had taxable income of $400,000 during the first calendar quarter of 2011. The federal tax rate is 40%. A quarterly tax payment will be made on April 7, 2011.

Prepare the Current Liabilities section of the balance sheet for I-Generation Co. on March 31, 2011.

E8-2

Recording income taxes

Obj 2

A business issued a 30-day, 4% note for $60,000 to a creditor on account. Illustrate the effects on the accounts and financial statements of recording (a) the issuance of the note and (b) the payment of the note at maturity, including interest.

E8-3

Recording income taxes

Obj 2

Illustrate the effects on the accounts and financial statements of recording the following selected transactions of Bronson Leather Co.:

Apr. 15. Paid the first installment of the estimated income tax for the current fiscal year ending December 31, $120,000. No entry had been made to record the liability.

Dec. 31. Recorded the estimated income tax liability for the year just ended and the deferred income tax liability, based on the April 15 transaction and the following data:

Income tax rate	40%
Income before income tax	$1,100,000
Taxable income according to tax return	$ 950,000

Assume that the June 15 and September 15 installments of $120,000 were also paid.

E8-4

Deferred income taxes

Obj 2

Mattress System Inc. recognized service revenue of $500,000 on its financial statements in 2009. Assume, however, that the tax code requires this amount to be recognized for tax purposes in 2010. The taxable income for 2009 and 2010 is $1,800,000 and $2,400,000, respectively. Assume a tax rate of 40%.

Illustrate the effects on the accounts and financial statements of the tax expense, deferred taxes, and taxes payable for 2009 and 2010, respectively.

E8-5

Accrued product warranty

Obj 2

Awesome Audio Works, Inc. warrants its products for one year. The estimated product warranty is 2% of sales. Assume that sales were $500,000 for January. In February, a customer received warranty repairs requiring $2,500 of parts.

a. Determine the warranty liability at January 31, the end of the first month of the current year.
b. What accounts are decreased for the warranty work provided in February?

E8-6

Accrued product warranty

Obj 2

Ford Motor Company disclosed estimated product warranty payable for 2008 and 2007 as follows:

	December 31	
	2008	2007
	(in millions)	
Product warranty payable	$3,840	$4,862

Ford's sales were $154,379 million in 2007 and decreased to $129,166 million in 2008. Assume that the total paid on warranty claims during 2008 was $3,076 million.

a. Illustrate the effects on the accounts and financial statements for the 2008 product warranty expense.
b. Assuming $3,076 million in warranty claims paid during 2008, explain the $1,022 million decrease in the total warranty liability from 2007 to 2008.

E8-7

Contingent liabilities

Obj 2

Several months ago, Welker Chemical Company experienced a hazardous materials spill at one of its plants. As a result, the Environmental Protection Agency (EPA) fined the company $410,000. The company is contesting the fine. In addition, an employee is seeking $400,000 damages related to the spill. Lastly, a homeowner has sued the company for $260,000. The homeowner lives 30 miles from the plant, but believes that the incident has reduced the home's resale value by $260,000.

Welker's legal counsel believes that it is probable that the EPA fine will stand. In addition, counsel indicates that an out-of-court settlement of $170,000 has recently been reached with the employee. The final papers will be signed next week. Counsel believes that the homeowner's case is much weaker and will be decided in favor of Welker. Other litigation related to the spill is possible, but the damage amounts are uncertain.

a. Illustrate the effects of the contingent liabilities associated with the hazardous materials spill on the accounts and financial statements.
b. Prepare a note disclosure relating to this incident.

E8-8

Contingent liabilities

Obj 2

The following note accompanied recent financial statements for ***Goodyear Tire and Rubber Company:***

> *We are a defendant in numerous lawsuits alleging various asbestos-related personal injuries purported to result from alleged exposure to certain asbestos products manufactured by us or present in certain of our facilities. Typically, these lawsuits have been brought against multiple defendants in state and federal courts. To date, we have disposed of approximately 72,100 claims by defending and obtaining the dismissal thereof or by entering into a settlement. The sum of our accrued asbestos-related liability,... including legal costs totaled approximately $325 million through December 31, 2008....*

a. Illustrate the effects on the accounts and financial statements of recording the contingent liability of $325,000,000.
b. Why was the contingent liability recorded?

E8-9

Calculate payroll

Obj 2

✓ b. Net pay, $2,061

An employee earns $40 per hour and 1.75 times that rate for all hours in excess of 40 hours per week. Assume that the employee worked 60 hours during the week, and that the gross pay prior to the current week totaled $58,000. Assume further that the social security tax rate was 6.0% (on earnings up to $100,000), the Medicare tax rate was 1.5%, and federal income tax to be withheld was $714.

a. Determine the gross pay for the week.
b. Determine the net pay for the week.

E8-10

Summary payroll data

Obj 2

✓ (3) Total earnings, $400,000

In the following summary of data for a payroll period, some amounts have been intentionally omitted:

Earnings:	
1. At regular rate	?
2. At overtime rate	$ 60,000
3. Total earnings	?
Deductions:	
4. FICA tax	29,200
5. Income tax withheld	99,600
6. Medical insurance	14,000
7. Union dues	?
8. Total deductions	147,800
9. Net amount paid	252,200
Accounts increased:	
10. Factory Wages	210,000
11. Sales Salaries	?
12. Office Salaries	80,000

Calculate the amounts omitted in lines (1), (3), (7), and (11).

E8-11

Recording payroll taxes

Obj 2

According to a summary of the payroll of Newman Publishing Co., $600,000 was subject to the 7.5% FICA tax. Also, $50,000 was subject to state and federal unemployment taxes.

a. Calculate the employer's payroll taxes, using the following rates: state unemployment, 4.3%; federal unemployment, 0.8%.
b. Illustrate the effects on the accounts and financial statements of recording the accrual of payroll taxes.

E8-12

Accrued vacation pay

Obj 2

A business provides its employees with varying amounts of vacation per year, depending on the length of employment. The estimated amount of the current year's vacation pay is $375,000. Illustrate the effects on the accounts and financial statements of the adjustment required on January 31, the end of the first month of the current year, to record the accrued vacation pay.

E8-13

Bond price

Obj 3

Walt Disney 7% bonds due in 2032 were selling for 118.29 as for March, 29, 2009. Were the bonds selling at a premium or at a discount? Explain.

E8-14

Issuing bonds

Obj 3

Grodski Inc. produces and distributes fiber optic cable for use by telecommunications companies. Grodski Inc. issued $24,000,000 of 20-year, 10% bonds on April 1 at their face amount, with interest payable on April 1 and October 1. The fiscal year of the company is the calendar year. Illustrate the effects on the accounts and financial statements of recording the following selected transactions for the current year:

April 1.   Issued the bonds for cash at their face amount.
 Oct. 1.   Paid the interest on the bonds.
Dec. 31.   Recorded accrued interest for three months.

E8-15

Dividends per share

Objs 4, 5

✓ Preferred stock, Ist year: $2.00

Fairmount Inc., a developer of radiology equipment, has stock outstanding as follows: 15,000 shares of 2% preferred stock of $150 par, and 50,000 shares of $5 par common. During its first four years of operations, the following amounts were distributed as dividends: first year, $30,000; second year, $42,000; third year, $90,000; fourth year, $120,000. Calculate the dividends per share on each class of stock for each of the four years.

E8-16

Dividends per share

Objs 4, 5

✓ Preferred stock, 3rd year: $0.25

Michelangelo Inc., a software development firm, has stock outstanding as follows: 20,000 shares of 1% preferred stock of $25 par, and 25,000 shares of $100 par common. During its first four years of operations, the following amounts were distributed as dividends: first year, $3,000; second year, $4,000; third year, $30,000; fourth year, $80,000. Calculate the dividends per share on each class of stock for each of the four years.

E8-17

Issuing par stock

Obj 4

On February 10, Peerless Rocks Inc., a marble contractor, issued for cash 40,000 shares of $10 par common stock at $34, and on May 9, it issued for cash 100,000 shares of $5 par preferred stock at $7.

a. Illustrate the effects on the accounts and financial statements of the February 10 and May 9 transactions.
b. What is the total amount invested (total paid-in capital) by all stockholders as of May 9?

E8-18

Issuing stock for assets other than cash

Obj 4

On January 30, Lift Time Corporation, a wholesaler of hydraulic lifts, acquired land in exchange for 18,000 shares of $10 par common stock with a current market price of $15.

Illustrate the effect on the accounts and financial statements of the purchase of the land.

E8-19

Treasury stock transactions

Obj 4

Beaverhead Creek Inc. bottles and distributes spring water. On March 4 of the current year, Beaverhead Creek reacquired 5,000 shares of its common stock at $90 per share.

a. What is the balance of Treasury Stock on December 31 of the current year?
b. Where will the balance of Treasury Stock be reported on the balance sheet?
c. For what reasons might Beaverhead Creek have purchased the treasury stock?

E8-20

Treasury stock transactions

Obj 4

Augusta Gardens Inc. develops and produces spraying equipment for lawn maintenance and industrial uses. On August 30 of the current year, Augusta Gardens Inc. reacquired 17,500 shares of its common stock at $42 per share.

a. What is the balance of Treasury Stock on December 31 of the current year?
b. How will the balance in Treasury Stock be reported on the balance sheet?

E8-21

Treasury stock transactions

Obj 4

Sweet Water Inc. bottles and distributes spring water. On July 15 of the current year, Sweet Water Inc. reacquired 24,000 shares of its common stock at $60 per share.

a. What is the balance of Treasury Stock on December 31 of the current year?
b. Where will the balance of Treasury Stock be reported on the balance sheet?
c. For what reasons might Sweet Water Inc. have purchased the treasury stock?

E8-22

Cash dividends

Obj 5

The dates of importance in connection with a cash dividend declared and paid of $69,500 on a corporation's common stock are May 3, June 17, and August 1. Illustrate the effects on the accounts and financial statements for each date.

E8-23

Effect of cash dividend and stock split

Objs 5, 6

Indicate whether the following actions would (+) increase, (−) decrease, or (0) not affect Pillar Falls Inc.'s total assets, liabilities, and stockholders' equity:

	Assets	Liabilities	Stockholders' Equity
(1) Declaring a cash dividend	_____	_____	_____
(2) Paying the cash dividend declared in (1)	_____	_____	_____
(3) Authorizing and issuing stock certificates in a stock split	_____	_____	_____
(4) Declaring a stock dividend	_____	_____	_____
(5) Issuing stock certificates for the stock dividend declared in (4)	_____	_____	_____

E8-24

Effect of stock split

Obj 6

Ma Restaurant Corporation wholesales ovens and ranges to restaurants throughout the Southwest. Ma Restaurant Corporation, which had 40,000 shares of common stock outstanding, declared a 4-for-1 stock split (3 additional shares for each share issued).

a. What will be the number of shares outstanding after the split?
b. If the common stock had a market price of $300 per share before the stock split, what would be an approximate market price per share after the split?

E8-25

Stockholders' equity section of balance sheet

Obj 7

✓ Total stockholders' equity, $4,350,000

The following accounts and their balances appear in the ledger of Newberry Properties Inc. on June 30 of the current year:

Common Stock, $75 par	$1,350,000
Paid-In Capital in Excess of Par	108,000
Paid-In Capital from Sale of Treasury Stock	12,000
Retained Earnings	2,950,000
Treasury Stock	70,000

Prepare the Stockholders' Equity section of the balance sheet as of June 30. Forty thousand shares of common stock are authorized, and 875 shares have been reacquired.

E8-26

Stockholders' equity section of balance sheet

Obj 7

✓ Total stockholders' equity, $5,985,000

Race Car Inc. retails racing products for BMWs, Porsches, and Ferraris. The following accounts and their balances appear in the ledger of Race Car Inc. on April 30, the end of the current year:

Common Stock, $10 par	$ 400,000
Paid-In Capital in Excess of Par—Common Stock	120,000
Paid-In Capital in Excess of Par—Preferred Stock	90,000
Paid-In Capital from Sale of Treasury Stock—Common	30,000
Preferred 4% Stock, $50 par	1,500,000
Retained Earnings	3,900,000
Treasury Stock—Common	55,000

Fifty thousand shares of preferred and 200,000 shares of common stock are authorized. There are 5,000 shares of common stock held as treasury stock.

Prepare the Stockholders' Equity section of the balance sheet as of April 30, the end of the current year.

E8-27

Effect of financing on earnings per share

Obj 8

✓ a. $0.50

Miller Co., which produces and sells skiing equipment, is financed as follows:

Bonds payable, 10% (issued at face amount)	$10,000,000
Preferred 1% stock, $10 par	10,000,000
Common stock, $25 par	10,000,000

Income tax is estimated at 40% of income.

Determine the earnings per share of common stock, assuming that the income before bond interest and income tax is (a) $3,000,000, (b) $4,000,000, and (c) $5,000,000.

E8-28

Evaluate alternative financing plans

Obj 8

Based on the data in Exercise 8-27, discuss factors other than earnings per share that should be considered in evaluating such financing plans.

Problems

P8-1

Income tax allocation

Obj 8

✓ 1. Year-end balance, 3rd year, $30,000

Differences between the accounting methods applied to accounts and financial reports and those used in determining taxable income yielded the following amounts for the first four years of a corporation's operations:

	First Year	Second Year	Third Year	Fourth Year
Income before income taxes	$625,000	$750,000	$1,250,000	$1,000,000
Taxable income	500,000	700,000	1,350,000	1,075,000

The income tax rate for each of the four years was 40% of taxable income, and each year's taxes were promptly paid.

Instructions

1. Determine for each year the amounts described by the following captions, presenting the information in the form indicated:

Year	Income Tax Deducted on Income Statement	Income Tax Payments for the Year	Deferred Income Tax Payable	
			Year's Addition (Deduction)	Year-End Balance

2. Total the first three amount columns.
3. Illustrate the effects of recording the current and deferred tax liabilities on the accounts and financial statements for the first year.

P8-2

Recording payroll and payroll taxes

Obj 2

✓ 1. $37,800

The following information about the payroll for the week ended March 17 was obtained from the records of Butte Mining Co.:

Salaries:		Deductions:	
Sales salaries	$244,000	Income tax withheld	$88,704
Warehouse salaries	135,000	U.S. savings bonds	11,088
Office salaries	125,000	Group insurance	9,072
	$504,000		

Tax rates assumed:
  FICA tax, 7.5% of employee annual earnings
  State unemployment (employer only), 4.2%
  Federal unemployment (employer only), 0.8%

Instructions

1. For the March 17 payroll, determine the employee FICA tax payable.
2. Illustrate the effect on the accounts and financial statements of paying and recording the March 17 payroll.
3. Determine the following amounts for the employer payroll taxes related to the March 17 payroll: (a) FICA tax payable, (b) state unemployment tax payable, and (c) federal unemployment tax payable.
4. Illustrate the effect on the accounts and financial statements of recording the liability for the March 17 payroll taxes.

P8-3

Present value; bond premium; bonds payable transactions

Obj 3

Sierra Vaults Corporation produces and sells burial vaults. On July 1, 2010, Sierra Vaults Corporation issued $18,000,000 of 10-year, 6% bonds at par. Interest on the bonds is payable semiannually on December 31 and June 30. The fiscal year of the company is the calendar year.

Instructions

1. Illustrate the effects of the issuance of the bonds on July 1, 2010, on the accounts and financial statements.
2. Illustrate the effects of the first semiannual interest payment on December 31, 2010, on the accounts and financial statements.
3. Illustrate the effects of the payment of the face value of bonds at maturity on the accounts and financial statements.
4. If the market rate of interest were 7% on July 1, 2010, would the bonds have sold at a discount or premium?

P8-4

Stock transactions for corporate expansion

Obj 4

Sheldon Optics produces medical lasers for use in hospitals. The accounts and their balances appear in the ledger of Sheldon Optics on October 31 of the current year as follows:

Preferred 2% Stock, $80 par (50,000 shares authorized, 25,000 shares issued)	$ 2,000,000
Paid-In Capital in Excess of Par—Preferred Stock	75,000
Common Stock, $100 par (500,000 shares authorized, 50,000 shares issued)	5,000,000
Paid-In Capital in Excess of Par—Common Stock	600,000
Retained Earnings	16,750,000

At the annual stockholders' meeting on December 7, the board of directors presented a plan for modernizing and expanding plant operations at a cost of approximately $5,300,000. The plan provided (a) that the corporation borrow $2,000,000, (b) that 15,000 shares of the unissued preferred stock be issued through an underwriter, and (c) that a building, valued at $1,850,000, and the land on which it is located, valued at $162,500, be acquired in accordance with preliminary negotiations by the issuance of 17,500 shares of common stock. The plan was approved by the stockholders and accomplished by the following transactions:

Jan. 10. Borrowed $2,000,000 from Whitefish National Bank, giving a 7% mortgage note.

21. Issued 15,000 shares of preferred stock, receiving $84.50 per share in cash.

31. Issued 17,500 shares of common stock in exchange for land and a building, according to the plan.

No other transactions occurred during January.

Instructions

Illustrate the effects on the accounts and financial statements of each of the preceding transactions.

P8-5

Dividends on preferred and common stock

Objs 4, 5

SPREADSHEET

✓ 1. Preferred dividends in 2006: $18,000

Bridger Bike Corp. manufactures mountain bikes and distributes them through retail outlets in Montana, Idaho, Oregon, and Washington. Bridger Bike Corp. has declared the following annual dividends over a six-year period ending December 31 of each year: 2005, $5,000; 2006, $18,000; 2007, $45,000; 2008, $45,000; 2009, $60,000; and 2010, $67,000. During the entire period, the outstanding stock of the company was composed of 10,000 shares of 4% preferred stock, $50 par, and 25,000 shares of common stock, $1 par.

Instructions

1. Determine the total dividends and the per-share dividends declared on each class of stock for each of the six years. Summarize the data in tabular form, using the following column headings:

Year	Total Dividends	Preferred Dividends		Common Dividends	
		Total	Per Share	Total	Per Share
2005	$ 5,000				
2006	18,000				
2007	45,000				
2008	45,000				
2009	60,000				
2010	67,000				

2. Calculate the average annual dividend per share for each class of stock for the six-year period. Round to the nearest cent.

3. Assuming that the preferred stock was sold at $86 and common stock was sold at $22.75 at the beginning of the six-year period, calculate the average annual percentage return on initial shareholders' investment, based on the average annual dividend per share (a) for preferred stock and (b) for common stock.

P8-6

Effect of financing on earnings per share

Obj 8

SPREADSHEET

✓ 1. Plan 3: $2.60

Three different plans for financing a $10,000,000 corporation are under consideration by its organizers. Under each of the following plans, the securities will be issued at their par or face amount, and the income tax rate is estimated at 40% of income.

	Plan 1	Plan 2	Plan 3
10% bonds	—	—	$ 5,000,000
Preferred 10% stock, $40 par	—	$ 5,000,000	2,500,000
Common stock, $10 par	$10,000,000	5,000,000	2,500,000
Total	$10,000,000	$10,000,000	$10,000,000

Instructions

1. Determine for each plan the earnings per share of common stock, assuming that the income before bond interest and income tax is $2,000,000.

2. Determine for each plan the earnings per share of common stock, assuming that the income before bond interest and income tax is $950,000.

3. Discuss the advantages and disadvantages of each plan.

Activities

A8-1

Ethics and professional conduct in business

ETHICS

Fio Barellis was discussing summer employment with Sara Rida, president of Xanadu Construction Service:

Sara: I'm glad that you're thinking about joining us for the summer. We could certainly use the help.

Fio: Sounds good. I enjoy outdoor work, and I could use the money to help with next year's school expenses.

Sara: I've got a plan that can help you out on that. As you know, I'll pay you $12 per hour, but in addition, I'd like to pay you with cash. Since you're only working for the summer, it really doesn't make sense for me to go to the trouble of formally putting you on our payroll system. In fact, I do some jobs for my clients on a strictly cash basis, so it would be easy to just pay you that way.

Fio: Well, that's a bit unusual, but I guess money is money.

Sara: Yeah, not only that, it's tax-free!

Fio: What do you mean?

Sara: Didn't you know? Any money that you receive in cash is not reported to the IRS on a W-2 form; therefore, the IRS doesn't know about the income—hence, it's the same as tax-free earnings.

a. Why does Sara Rida want to conduct business transactions using cash (not check or credit card)?

b. How should Fio respond to Sara's suggestion?

A8-2

Contingent liabilities

INTERNET PROJECT

Altria Group, Inc., has over 24 pages dedicated to describing contingent liabilities in the notes to recent financial statements. These pages include extensive descriptions of multiple contingent liabilities. Use the Internet to research Altria Group, Inc., at **http://www.altria.com**.

a. What are the major business units of Altria Group?

b. Based on your understanding of this company, why would Altria Group require 11 pages of contingency disclosure?

A8-3

Issuing stock

Biosciences Unlimited Inc. began operations on January 2, 2010, with the issuance of 100,000 shares of $50 par common stock. The sole stockholders of Biosciences Unlimited Inc. are Rafel Baltis and Dr. Oscar Hansel, who organized Biosciences Unlimited Inc. with the objective of developing a new flu vaccine. Dr. Hansel claims that the flu vaccine, which is nearing the final development stage, will protect individuals against 90% of the flu types that have been medically identified. To complete the project, Biosciences Unlimited Inc. needs $10,000,000 of additional funds. The local banks have been unwilling to loan the funds because of the lack of sufficient collateral and the riskiness of the business. The following is a conversation between Rafel Baltis, the chief executive officer of Biosciences Unlimited Inc., and Dr. Oscar Hansel, the leading researcher:

Rafel: What are we going to do? The banks won't loan us any more money, and we've got to have $10 million to complete the project. We are so close! It would be a disaster to quit now. The only thing I can think of is to issue additional stock. Do you have any suggestions?

Oscar: I guess you're right. But if the banks won't loan us any more money, how do you think we can find any investors to buy stock?

Rafel: I've been thinking about that. What if we promise the investors that we will pay them 2% of net sales until they have received an amount equal to what they paid for the stock?

Oscar: What happens when we pay back the $10 million? Do the investors get to keep the stock? If they do, it'll dilute our ownership.

Rafel: How about, if after we pay back the $10 million, we make them turn in their stock for $100 per share? That's twice what they paid for it, plus they would have already gotten all their money back. That's a $100 profit per share for the investors.

Oscar: It could work. We get our money, but don't have to pay any interest, dividends, or the $50 until we start generating net sales. At the same time, the investors could get their money back plus $50 per share.

Rafel: We'll need current financial statements for the new investors. I'll get our accountant working on them and contact our attorney to draw up a legally binding contract for the new investors. Yes, this could work.

In late 2010, the attorney and the various regulatory authorities approved the new stock offering, and 200,000 shares of common stock were privately sold to new investors at the stock's par of $50.

In preparing financial statements for 2010, Rafel Baltis and Emma Cavins, the controller for Biosciences Unlimited Inc., have the following conversation:

Emma: Rafel, I've got a problem.

Rafel: What's that, Emma?

Emma: Issuing common stock to raise that additional $10 million was a great idea. But …

Rafel: But what?

Emma: I've got to prepare the 2010 annual financial statements, and I am not sure how to classify the common stock.

Rafel: What do you mean? It's common stock.

Emma: I'm not so sure. I called the auditor and explained how we are contractually obligated to pay the new stockholders 2% of net sales until $50 per share is paid. Then, we may be obligated to pay them $100 per share.

Rafel: So …

Emma: So the auditor thinks that we should classify the additional issuance of $10 million as debt, not stock! And, if we put the $10 million on the balance sheet as debt, we will violate our other loan agreements with the banks. And, if these agreements are violated, the banks may call in all our debt immediately. If they do that, we are in deep trouble. We'll probably have to file for bankruptcy. We just don't have the cash to pay off the banks.

1. Discuss the arguments for and against classifying the issuance of the $10 million of stock as debt.
2. What do you think might be a practical solution to this classification problem?

A8-4

Profiling a corporation

GROUP PROJECT

INTERNET PROJECT

Select a public corporation you are familiar with or which interests you. Using the Internet, your school library, and other sources, develop a short (one to two pages) profile of the corporation. Include in your profile the following information:

1. Name of the corporation
2. State of incorporation
3. Nature of its operations
4. Total assets for the most recent balance sheet
5. Total revenues for the most recent income statement
6. Net income for the most recent income statement
7. Classes of stock outstanding
8. Market price of the stock outstanding
9. High and low price of the stock for the past year
10. Dividends paid for each share of stock during the past year

In groups of three or four, discuss each corporate profile. Select one of the corporations, assuming that your group has $100,000 to invest in its stock. Summarize why your group selected the corporation it did and how financial

accounting information may have affected your decision. Keep track of the performance of your corporation's stock for the remainder of the term.

Note: Most major corporations maintain "home pages" on the Internet. This home page provides a variety of information on the corporation and often includes the corporation's financial statements. In addition, the New York Stock Exchange Web site (**http://www.nyse.com**) includes links to the home pages of many listed companies. Financial statements can also be accessed using EDGAR, the electronic archives of financial statements filed with the Securities and Exchange Commission (SEC).

SEC documents can also be retrieved using the EdgarScan™ service at **http://www.sec.gov/edgar/searchedgar/webusers.htm**. To obtain annual report information, key in a company name in the appropriate space. Edgar will list the reports available to you for the company you've selected. Select the most recent annual report filing, identified as a 10-K or 10-K405.

A8-5

Preferred stock vs. bonds

Beacon Inc. has decided to expand its operations to owning and operating long-term health care facilities. The following is an excerpt from a conversation between the chief executive officer, Frank Forrest, and the vice president of finance, Rachel Tucker.

Frank: Rachel, have you given any thought to how we're going to finance the acquisition of St. Seniors Health Care?

Rachel: Well, the two basic options, as I see it, are to issue either preferred stock or bonds. The equity market is a little depressed right now. The rumor is that the Federal Reserve Bank's going to increase the interest rates either this month or next.

Frank: Yes, I've heard the rumor. The problem is that we can't wait around to see what's going to happen. We'll have to move on this next week if we want any chance to complete the acquisition of St. Seniors.

Rachel: Well, the bond market is strong right now. Maybe we should issue debt this time around.

Frank: That's what I would have guessed as well. St. Seniors's financial statements look pretty good, except for the volatility of its income and cash flows. But that's characteristic of the industry.

Discuss the advantages and disadvantages of issuing preferred stock versus bonds.

A8-6

Financing business expansion

You hold a 25% common stock interest in the family-owned business, a vending machine company. Your sister, who is the manager, has proposed an expansion of plant facilities at an expected cost of $7,500,000. Two alternative plans have been suggested as methods of financing the expansion. Each plan is briefly described as follows:

Plan 1. Issue $7,500,000 of 10-year, 8% notes at face amount.
Plan 2. Issue an additional 100,000 shares of $10 par common stock at $40 per share, and $3,500,000 of 10-year, 8% notes at face amount.

The balance sheet as of the end of the previous fiscal year is as follows:

THACKER, INC.
Balance Sheet
December 31, 2010

Assets	
Current assets	$ 4,000,000
Property, plant, and equipment	6, 000,000
Total assets	$10,000,000

Liabilities and Stockholders' Equity	
Liabilities	$ 3,000,000
Common stock, $5	1,000,000
Paid-in capital in excess of par	100,000
Retained earnings	5,900,000
Total liabilities and stockholders' equity	$10,000,000

Net income has remained relatively constant over the past several years. The expansion program is expected to increase yearly income before bond interest and income tax from $750,000 in the previous year to $1,000,000 for this year. Your sister has asked you, as the company treasurer, to prepare an analysis of each financing plan.

1. Prepare a table indicating the expected earnings per share on the common stock under each plan. Assume an income tax rate of 40%. Round to the nearest cent.
2. a. Discuss the factors that should be considered in evaluating the two plans.
   b. Which plan offers the greater benefit to the present stockholders? Give reasons for your opinion.

A8-7

Bond ratings

INTERNET PROJECT

Moody's Investors Service maintains a Web site at **http://www.moodys.com**. One of the services offered at this site is a listing of announcements of recent bond rating changes. Visit this site and read over some of these announcements. Write down several of the reasons provided for rating downgrades and upgrades. If you were a bond investor or bond issuer, would you care if Moody's changed the rating on your bonds? Why or why not?

Answers to Self-Examination Questions

1. **C** The maturity value is $5,100, determined as follows:

Face amount of note	$5,000
Plus interest ($5,000 × 0.12 × 60/360)	100
Maturity value	$5,100

2. **B** Employers are usually required to withhold a portion of their employees' earnings for payment of federal income taxes (answer A), FICA tax (answer C), and state and local income taxes (answer D).

Generally, federal unemployment compensation taxes (answer B) are levied against the employer only and thus are not deducted from employee earnings.

3. **D** The employer incurs an expense for FICA tax (answer A), federal unemployment compensation tax (answer B), and state unemployment compensation tax (answer C). The employees' federal income tax (answer D) is not an expense of the employer. It is withheld from the employees' earnings.

4. **B** Since the contract rate on the bonds is higher than the prevailing market rate, a rational investor would be willing to pay more than the face amount, or a premium (answer B), for the bonds. If the contract rate and the market rate were equal, the bonds could be expected to sell at their face amount (answer A). Likewise, if the market rate is higher than the contract rate, the bonds would sell at a price below their face amount (answer D) or at a discount (answer C).

5. **C** If a corporation that holds treasury stock declares a cash dividend, the dividends are not paid on the treasury shares. To do so would place the corporation in the position of earning income through dealing with itself. Thus, the corporation will record $44,000 (answer C) as cash dividends [(25,000 shares issued less 3,000 shares held as treasury stock) × $2 per share dividend].

Financial Statement Analysis

9

Learning Objectives

After studying this chapter, you should be able to:

Obj 1 Describe basic financial statement analytical methods.

Obj 2 Use financial statement analysis to assess the solvency of a business.

Obj 3 Use financial statement analysis to assess the profitability of a business.

Obj 4 Describe the contents of corporate annual reports.

"Just do it." These three words identify one of the most recognizable brands in the world, Nike. While this phrase inspires athletes to "compete and achieve their potential," it also defines the company.

Nike began in 1964 as a partnership between University of Oregon track coach Bill Bowerman and one of his former student-athletes, Phil Knight. The two began by selling shoes imported from Japan out of the back of Knight's car to athletes at track and field events. As sales grew, the company opened retail outlets and began to develop its own shoes. In 1971 the company, originally named Blue Ribbon Sports, commissioned a graphic design student at Portland State University to develop the Nike Swoosh logo for a fee of $35. In 1978 the company changed its name to Nike, and in 1980, it sold its first shares of stock to the public.

Nike would have been a great company in which to have invested. If you had invested in Nike's common stock back in 1990, you would have paid $5.00 per share. As the book goes to press, Nike's stock sells for $65.62 per share. Unfortunately, you can't invest using hindsight.

How then should you select companies to invest in? Like any significant purchase, you should do some research to guide your investment decision. If you were buying a car, for example, you might go to **Edmunds.com** to obtain reviews, ratings, prices, specifications, options, and fuel economy across a number of vehicles. In deciding whether to invest in a company, you can use financial analysis to gain insight into a company's past performance and future prospects. This chapter describes and illustrates common financial data that can be analyzed to assist you in making investment decisions such as whether or not to invest in Nike's stock.

Source: http://www.nikebiz.com/

Basic Analytical Methods

Obj 1 Describe basic financial statement analytical methods.

Users analyze a company's financial statements using a variety of analytical methods. Three such methods are as follows:

1. Horizontal analysis
2. Vertical analysis
3. Common-sized statements

Horizontal Analysis

The percentage analysis of increases and decreases in related items in comparative financial statements is called **horizontal analysis**. Each item on the most recent statement is compared with the related item on one or more earlier statements in terms of the following:

1. *Amount* of increase or decrease
2. *Percent* of increase or decrease

When comparing statements, the earlier statement is normally used as the base for computing increases and decreases.

Exhibit 1 illustrates horizontal analysis for the December 31, 2010 and 2009 balance sheets of Lincoln Company. In Exhibit 1, the December 31, 2009 balance sheet (the earliest year presented) is used as the base.

EXHIBIT 1   Comparative Balance Sheet—Horizontal Analysis

LINCOLN COMPANY Comparative Balance Sheet December 31, 2010 and 2009				
	Dec. 31, 2010	Dec. 31, 2009	Increase (Decrease) Amount	Percent
Assets				
Current assets	$ 550,000	$ 533,000	$ 17,000	3.2%
Long-term investments	95,000	177,500	(82,500)	(46.5%)
Property, plant, and equipment (net)	444,500	470,000	(25,500)	(5.4%)
Intangible assets	50,000	50,000	—	—
Total assets	$ 1,139,500	$ 1,230,500	$ (91,000)	(7.4%)
Liabilities				
Current liabilities	$ 210,000	$ 243,000	$ (33,000)	(13.6%)
Long-term liabilities	100,000	200,000	(100,000)	(50.0%)
Total liabilities	$ 310,000	$ 443,000	$(133,000)	(30.0%)
Stockholders' Equity				
Preferred 6% stock, $100 par	$ 150,000	$ 150,000	—	—
Common stock, $10 par	500,000	500,000	—	—
Retained earnings	179,500	137,500	$ 42,000	30.5%
Total stockholders' equity	$ 829,500	$ 787,500	$ 42,000	5.3%
Total liabilities and stockholders' equity	$ 1,139,500	$ 1,230,500	$ (91,000)	(7.4%)

Exhibit 1 indicates that total assets decreased by $91,000(7.4%), liabilities decreased by $133,000(30.0%), and stockholders' equity increased by $42,000(5.3%). It appears that most of the decrease in long-term liabilities of $100,000 was achieved through the sale of long-term investments.

The balance sheets in Exhibit 1 may be expanded or supported by a separate schedule that includes the individual asset and liability accounts. For example, Exhibit 2 is a supporting schedule of Lincoln's current asset accounts.

EXHIBIT 2   Comparative Schedule of Current Assets—Horizontal Analysis

LINCOLN COMPANY
Comparative Schedule of Current Assets
December 31, 2010 and 2009

	Dec. 31, 2010	Dec. 31, 2009	Increase (Decrease) Amount	Percent
Cash	$ 90,500	$ 64,700	$ 25,800	39.9%
Temporary investments	75,000	60,000	15,000	25.0%
Accounts receivable (net)	115,000	120,000	(5,000)	(4.2%)
Inventories	264,000	283,000	(19,000)	(6.7%)
Prepaid expenses	5,500	5,300	200	3.8%
Total current assets	$550,000	$533,000	$ 17,000	3.2%

Exhibit 2 indicates that while cash and temporary investments increased, accounts receivable and inventories decreased. The decrease in accounts receivable could be caused by improved collection policies, which would increase cash. The decrease in inventories could be caused by increased sales.

Exhibit 3 illustrates horizontal analysis for the 2010 and 2009 income statements of Lincoln Company. Exhibit 3 indicates an increase in sales of $296,500, or 24.0%. However, the percentage increase in sales of 24.0% was accompanied by an even greater percentage increase in the cost of goods

EXHIBIT 3   Comparative Income Statement—Horizontal Analysis

LINCOLN COMPANY
Comparative Income Statement
For the Years Ended December 31, 2010 and 2009

	2010	2009	Increase (Decrease) Amount	Percent
Sales	$ 1,530,500	$ 1,234,000	$ 296,500	24.0%
Sales returns and allowances	32,500	34,000	(1,500)	(4.4%)
Net sales	$ 1,498,000	$ 1,200,000	$ 298,000	24.8%
Cost of goods sold	1,043,000	820,000	223,000	27.2%
Gross profit	$ 455,000	$ 380,000	$ 75,000	19.7%
Selling expenses	$ 191,000	$ 147,000	$ 44,000	29.9%
Administrative expenses	104,000	97,400	6,600	6.8%
Total operating expenses	$ 295,000	$ 244,400	$ 50,600	20.7%
income from operations	$ 160,000	$ 135,600	$ 24,400	18.0%
Other income	8,500	11,000	(2,500)	(22.7%)
	$ 168,500	$ 146,600	$ 21,900	14.9%
Other expense (interest)	6,000	12,000	(6,000)	(50.0%)
Income before income tax	$ 162,500	$ 134,600	$ 27,900	20.7%
Income tax expense	71,500	58,100	13,400	23.1%
Net income	$ 91,000	$ 76,500	$ 14,500	19.0%

(merchandise) sold of 27.2%.[1] Thus, gross profit increased by only 19.7% rather than by the 24.0% increase in sales.

Exhibit 3 also indicates that selling expenses increased by 29.9%. Thus, the 24.0% increases in sales could have been caused by an advertising campaign, which increased selling expenses. Administrative expenses increased by only 6.8%, total operating expenses increased by 20.7%, and income from operations increased by 18.0%. Interest expense decreased by 50.0%. This decrease was probably caused by the 50.0% decrease in long-term liabilities (Exhibit 1). Overall, net income increased by 19.0%, a favorable result.

Exhibit 4 illustrates horizontal analysis for the 2010 and 2009 retained earnings statements of Lincoln Company. Exhibit 4 indicates that retained earnings increased by 30.5% for the year. The increase is due to net income of $91,000 for the year, less dividends of $49,000.

EXHIBIT 4 Comparative Retained Earnings Statement—Horizontal Analysis

LINCOLN COMPANY
Comparative Retained Earnings Statement
For the Years Ended December 31, 2010 and 2009

	2010	2009	Increase (Decrease) Amount	Percent
Retained earnings, January 1	$ 137,500	$ 100,000	$ 37,500	37.5%
Net income for the year	91,000	76,500	14,500	19.0%
Total	$ 228,500	$ 176,500	$ 52,000	29.5%
Dividends:				
On preferred stock	$ 9,000	$ 9,000	—	—
On common stock	40,000	30,000	$ 10,000	33.3%
Total	$ 49,000	$ 39,000	$ 10,000	25.6%
Retained earnings, December 31	$ 179,500	$ 137,500	$ 42,000	30.5%

Vertical Analysis

The percentage analysis of the relationship of each component in a financial statement to a total within the statement is called **vertical analysis**. Although vertical analysis is applied to a single statement, it may be applied on the same statement over time. This enhances the analysis by showing how the percentages of each item have changed over time.

In vertical analysis of the balance sheet, the percentages are computed as follows:

1. Each asset item is stated as a percent of the total assets.

2. Each liability and stockholders' equity item is stated as a percent of the total liabilities and stockholders' equity.

Exhibit 5 illustrates the vertical analysis of the December 31, 2010 and 2009 balance sheets of Lincoln Company. Exhibit 5 indicates that current assets have increased from 43.3% to 48.3% of total assets. Long-term investments decreased from 14.4% to 8.3% of total assets. Stockholders' equity increased from 64.0% to 72.8% with a comparable decrease in liabilities.

[1] The term *cost of goods sold* is often used in practice in place of *cost of merchandise sold.* Such usage is followed in this chapter.

EXHIBIT `5`   Comparative Balance Sheet–Vertical Analysis

LINCOLN COMPANY Comparative Balance Sheet December 31, 2010 and 2009				
	Dec. 31, 2010		Dec. 31, 2009	
	Amount	Percent	Amount	Percent
Assets				
Current assets	$ 550,000	48.3%	$ 533,000	43.3%
Long-term investments	95,000	8.3	177,500	14.4
Property, plant, and equipment (net)	444,500	39.0	470,000	38.2
Intangible assets	50,000	4.4	50,000	4.1
Total assets	$ 1,139,500	100.0%	$ 1,230,500	100.0%
Liabilities				
Current liabilities	$ 210,000	18.4%	$ 243,000	19.7%
Long-term liabilities	100,000	8.8	200,000	16.3
Total liabilities	$ 310,000	27.2%	$ 443,000	36.0%
Stockholders' Equity				
Preferred 6% stock, $100 par	$ 150,000	13.2%	$ 150,000	12.2%
Common stock, $10 par	500,000	43.9	500,000	40.6
Retained earnings	179,500	15.7	137,500	11.2
Total stockholders' equity	$ 829,500	72.8%	$ 787,500	64.0%.
Total liabilities and stockholders' equity	$ 1,139,500	100.0%	$ 1,230,500	100.0%

In a vertical analysis of the income statement, each item is stated as a percent of net sales. Exhibit 6 illustrates the vertical analysis of the 2010 and 2009 income statements of Lincoln Company.

Exhibit 6 indicates a decrease of the gross profit rate from 31.7% in 2009 to 30.4% in 2010. Although this is only a 1.3 percentage point (31.7% – 30.4%)

EXHIBIT `6`   Comparative Income Statement–Vertical Analysis

LINCOLN COMPANY Comparative Income Statement For the Years Ended December 31, 2010 and 2009				
	2010		2009	
	Amount	Percent	Amount	Percent
Sales	$ 1,530,500	102.2%	$1,234,000	102.8%
Sales returns and allowances	32,500	2.2	34,000	2.8
Net sales	$ 1,498,000	100.0%	$1,200,000	100.0%
Cost of goods sold	1,043,000	69.6	820,000	68.3
Gross profit	$ 455,000	30.4%	$ 380,000	31.7%
Selling expenses	$ 191,000	12.8%	$ 147,000	12.3%
Administrative expenses	104,000	6.9	97,400	8.1
Total operating expenses	$ 295,000	19.7%	$ 244,400	20.4%
Income from operations	$ 160,000	10.7%	$ 135,600	11.3%
Other income	8,500	0.6	11,000	0.9
	$ 168,500	11.3%	$ 146,600	12.2%
Other expense (interest)	6,000	0.4	12,000	1.0
Income before income tax	$ 162,500	10.9%	$ 134,600	11.2%
Income tax expense	71,500	4.8	58,100	4.8
Net income	$ 91,000	6.1%	$ 76,500	6.4%

decrease, in dollars of potential gross profit, it represents a decrease of about $19,500 (1.3% × $1,498,000). Thus, a small percentage decrease can have a large dollar effect.

Common-Sized Statements

In a **common-sized statement**, all items are expressed as percentages with no dollar amounts shown. Common-sized statements are often useful for comparing one company with another or for comparing a company with industry averages.

Exhibit 7 illustrates common-sized income statements for Lincoln Company and Madison Corporation.

EXHIBIT 7   Common-Sized Income Statement

	Lincoln Company	Madison Corporation
Sales	102.2%	102.3%
Sates returns and allowances	2.2	2.3
Net sates	100.0%	100.0%
Cost of goods sold	69.6	70.0
Gross profit	30.4%	30.0%
Selling expenses	12.8%	11.5%
Administrative expenses	6.9	4.1
Total operating expenses	19.7%	15.6%
income from operations	10.7%	14.4%
Other income	0.6	0.6
	11.3%	15.0%
Other expense (interest)	0.4	0.5
income before income tax	10.9%	14.5%
Income tax expense	4.8	5.5
Net income	6.1%	9.0%

Exhibit 7 indicates that Lincoln Company has a slightly higher rate of gross profit (30.4%) than Madison Corporation (30.0%). However, Lincoln has a higher percentage of selling expenses (12.8%) and administrative expenses (6.9%) than does Madison (11.5% and 4.1%). As a result, the income from operations of Lincoln (10.7%) is less than that of Madison (14.4%).

The unfavorable difference of 3.7 (14.4% – 10.7%) percentage points in income from operations would concern the managers and other stakeholders of Lincoln. The underlying causes of the difference should be investigated and possibly corrected. For example, Lincoln Company may decide to outsource some of its administrative duties so that its administrative expenses are more comparative to those of Madison Corporation.

Other Analytical Measures

Other relationships may be expressed in ratios and percentages. Often, these relationships are compared within the same statement

The percentages of gross profit and net income to sales for a recent fiscal year for **Target** and **Wal-Mart** are shown below.

	Target	Wal-Mart
Gross profit to sales	36.9%	24.8%
Net income to sales	5.1%	3.2%

Wal-Mart has a significantly lower gross profit margin percentage than does Target, which is likely due to Wal-Mart's aggressive pricing strategy. However, Target's gross profit margin advantage shrinks when comparing the net income to sales ratio. Target must have larger selling and administrative expenses to sales than does Wal-Mart. Even so, Target's net income to sales is still 1.9 percentage points better than Wal-Mart's net income to sales.

and thus are a type of vertical analysis. Comparing these items with items from earlier periods is a type of horizontal analysis.

Analytical measures are not ends in themselves. They are only guides in evaluating financial and operating data. Many other factors, such as trends in the industry and general economic conditions, should also be considered when analyzing a company.

Obj 2 Use financial statement analysis to assess the solvency of a business.

Solvency Analysis

All users of financial statements are interested in the ability of a company to do the following:

1. Meet its financial obligations (debts), called **solvency**

2. Earn income, called **profitability**

Solvency and profitability are interrelated. For example, a company that cannot pay its debts will have difficulty obtaining credit. A lack of credit will, in turn, limit the company's ability to purchase merchandise or expand operations, which decreases its profitability.

Solvency analysis focuses on the ability of a company to pay its liabilities. It is normally assessed using the following:

1. Current position analysis
> Working capital
> Current ratio
> Quick ratio

2. Accounts receivable analysis
> Accounts receivable turnover
> Number of days' sales in receivables

3. Inventory analysis
> Inventory turnover
> Number of days' sales in inventory

4. The ratio of fixed assets to long-term liabilities

5. The ratio of liabilities to stockholders' equity

6. The number of times interest charges are earned

The Lincoln Company financial statements presented earlier are used to illustrate the preceding analyses.

One popular printed source for industry ratios is *Annual Statement Studies* from **Risk Management Association**. Online analysis is available from **Zacks Investment Research** site.

Current Position Analysis

A company's ability to pay its current liabilities is called **current position analysis**. It is of special interest to short-term creditors and includes the computation and analysis of the following:

1. Working capital

2. Current ratio

3. Quick ratio

Working Capital

A company's **working capital** is computed as follows:

Working Capital = Current Assets − Current Liabilities

To illustrate, the working capital for Lincoln Company for 2010 and 2009 is computed below.

	2010	2009
Current assets	$550,000	$533,000
Less current liabilities	210,000	243,000
Working capital	$340,000	$290,000

The working capital is used to evaluate a company's ability to pay current liabilities. A company's working capital is often monitored monthly, quarterly, or yearly by creditors and other debtors. However, it is difficult to use working capital to compare companies of different sizes. For example, working capital of $250,000 may be adequate for a local hardware store, but it would be inadequate for *The Home Depot.*

Current Ratio

The **current ratio**, sometimes called the *working capital ratio* or *bankers' ratio,* is computed as follows:

$$\text{Current Ratio} = \frac{\text{Current Assets}}{\text{Current Liabilities}}$$

To illustrate, the current ratio for Lincoln Company is computed below.

	2010	2009
Current assets	$550,000	$533,000
Current liabilities	$210,000	$243,000
Current ratio	2.6 ($550,000/$210,000)	2.2 ($533,000/$243,000)

The current ratio is a more reliable indicator of the ability to pay current liabilities than is working capital. To illustrate, assume that as of December 31, 2010, the working capital of a competitor is much greater than $340,000, but its current ratio is only 1.3. Considering these facts alone, Lincoln Company, with its current ratio of 2.6, is in a more favorable position to obtain short-term credit than the competitor, which has the greater amount of working capital.

Quick Ratio

One limitation of working capital and the current ratio is that they do not consider the makeup of the current assets. Because of this, two companies may have the same working capital and current ratios, but differ significantly in their ability to pay their current liabilities.

To illustrate, the current assets and liabilities for Lincoln Company and Jefferson Corporation as of December 31, 2010, are as follows:

	Lincoln Company	Jefferson Corporation
Current assets:		
Cash	$ 90,500	$ 45,500
Temporary investments	75,000	25,000
Accounts receivable (net)	115,000	90,000
Inventories	264,000	380,000
Prepaid expenses	5,500	9,500
Total current assets	$550,000	$550,000
Total current assets	$550,000	$550,000
Less current liabilities	210,000	210,000
Working capital	$340,000	$340,000
Current ratio ($550,000/$210,000)	2.6	2.6

Lincoln and Jefferson both have a working capital of $340,000 and current ratios of 2.6. Jefferson, however, has more of its current assets in inventories. These inventories must be sold and the receivables collected before all the current liabilities can be paid. This takes time. In addition, if the market for its product declines, Jefferson may have difficulty selling its inventory. This, in turn, could impair its ability to pay its current liabilities.

In contrast, Lincoln's current assets contain more cash, temporary investments, and accounts receivable, which can easily be converted to cash. Thus, Lincoln is in a stronger current position than Jefferson to pay its current liabilities.

A ratio that measures the "instant" debt-paying ability of a company is the **quick ratio**, sometimes called the *acid-test ratio*. The quick ratio is computed as follows:

$$\text{Quick Ratio} = \frac{\text{Quick Assets}}{\text{Current Liabilities}}$$

Quick assets are cash and other current assets that can be easily converted to cash. Quick assets normally include cash, temporary investments, and receivables.

To illustrate, the quick ratio for Lincoln Company is computed below.

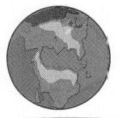

Microsoft Corporation maintains a high quick ratio—1.9 for a recent year. Microsoft's stable and profitable software business has allowed it to develop a strong cash position coupled with no short-term notes payable.

	2010	2009
Quick assets:		
Cash	$ 90,500	$ 64,700
Temporary investments	75,000	60,000
Accounts receivable (net)	115,000	120,000
Total quick assets	$280,500	$244,700
Current liabilities	$210,000	$243,000
Quick ratio	1.3*	1.0**

*1.3 = $280,500 ÷ $210,000
**1.0 = $244,700 ÷ $243,000

Accounts Receivable Analysis

A company's ability to collect its accounts receivable is called **accounts receivable analysis**. It includes the computation and analysis of the following:

1. Accounts receivable turnover
2. Number of days' sales in receivables

Collecting accounts receivable as quickly as possible improves a company's solvency. In addition, the cash collected from receivables may be used to improve or expand operations. Quick collection of receivables also reduces the risk of uncollectible accounts.

Accounts Receivable Turnover

The **accounts receivable turnover** is computed as follows:

$$\text{Accounts Receivable Turnover} = \frac{\text{Net Sales}^2}{\text{Average Accounts Receivable}}$$

(handwritten: (BOY A/R + EOY A/R)/2)

To illustrate, the accounts receivable turnover for Lincoln Company for 2010 and 2009 is computed below.

	2010	2009
Net sales	$1,498,000	$1,200,000
Accounts receivable (net):		
Beginning of year	$ 120,000	$ 140,000
End of year	115,000	120,000
Total	$ 235,000	$ 260,000
Average accounts receivable	$117,500 ($235,000 ÷ 2)	$130,000 ($260,000 ÷ 2)
Accounts receivable turnover	12.7 ($1,498,000 ÷ $117,500)	9.2 ($1,200,000 ÷ $130,000)

The increase in Lincoln's accounts receivable turnover from 9.2 to 12.7 indicates that the collection of receivables has improved during 2010. This may be due to a change in how credit is granted, collection practices, or both.

For Lincoln Company, the average accounts receivable was computed using the accounts receivable balance at the beginning and the end of the year. When sales are seasonal and thus vary throughout the year, monthly balances of receivables are often used. Also, if sales on account include notes receivable as well as accounts receivable, notes and accounts receivables are normally combined for analysis.

Number of Days' Sales in Receivables

The **number of days' sales in receivables** is computed as follows:

(handwritten: both accounts; from 2009 & 2010 ÷ by 2)

$$\text{Number of Days' Sales in Receivables} = \frac{\text{Average Accounts Receivable}}{\text{Average Daily Sales}}$$

---

[2] If known, *credit* sales should be used in the numerator. Because credit sales are not normally known by external users, net sales is used in the numerator.

where

$$\text{Average Daily Sales} = \frac{\text{Net Sales}}{365 \text{ days}}$$

To illustrate, the number of days' sales in receivables for Lincoln Company is computed below.

	2010	**2009**
Average accounts receivable	$117,500 ($235,000 ÷ 2)	$130,000 ($260,000 ÷ 2)
Average daily sales	$4,104 ($1,498,000 ÷ 365)	$3,288 ($1,200,000 ÷ 365)
Number of days' sales in receivables	28.6 ($117,500 ÷ $4,104)	39.5 ($130,000 ÷ $3,288)

The number of days' sales in receivables is an estimate of the time (in days) that the accounts receivable have been outstanding. The number of days' sales in receivables is often compared with a company's credit terms to evaluate the efficiency of the collection of receivables.

To illustrate, if Lincoln's credit terms are 2/10, n/30, then Lincoln was very *inefficient* in collecting receivables in 2009. In other words, receivables should have been collected in 30 days or less, but were being collected in 39.5 days. Although collections improved during 2010 to 28.6 days, there is probably still room for improvement. On the other hand, if Lincoln's credit terms are n/45, then there is probably little room for improving collections.

Inventory Analysis

A company's ability to manage its inventory effectively is evaluated using **inventory analysis**. It includes the computation and analysis of the following:

1. Inventory turnover
2. Number of days' sales in inventory

Excess inventory decreases solvency by tying up funds (cash) in inventory. In addition, excess inventory increases insurance expense, property taxes, storage costs, and other related expenses. These expenses further reduce funds that could be used elsewhere to improve or expand operations.

Excess inventory also increases the risk of losses because of price declines or obsolescence of the inventory. On the other hand, a company should keep enough inventory in stock so that it doesn't lose sales because of lack of inventory.

Inventory Turnover

The **inventory turnover** is computed as follows:

$$\text{Inventory Turnover} = \frac{\text{Cost of Goods Sold}}{\text{Average Inventory}}$$

[handwritten annotations: "from 2009 & 2010 then ÷ by 2", "both years"]

To illustrate, the inventory turnover for Lincoln Company for 2010 and 2009 is computed below.

	2010	2009
Cost of goods sold	$1,043,000	$820,000
Inventories:		
Beginning of year	$ 283,000	$311,000
End of year	264,000	283,000
Total	$ 547,000	$594,000
Average inventory	$273,500 ($547,000 ÷ 2)	$297,000 ($594,000 ÷ 2)
Inventory turnover	3.8 ($1,043,000 ÷ $273,500)	2.8 ($820,000 ÷ $297,000)

The increase in Lincoln's inventory turnover from 2.8 to 3.8 indicates that the management of inventory has improved in 2010. The inventory turnover improved because of an increase in the cost of goods sold, which indicates more sales, and a decrease in the average inventories.

What is considered a good inventory turnover varies by type of inventory, companies, and industries. For example, grocery stores have a higher inventory turnover than jewelers or furniture stores. Likewise, within a grocery store, perishable foods have a higher turnover than the soaps and cleansers.

Number of Days' Sales in Inventory

The **number of days' sales in inventory** is computed as follows:

$$\text{Number of Days' Sales in Inventory} = \frac{\text{Average Inventory}}{\text{Average Daily Cost of Goods Sold}}$$

where

$$\text{Average Daily Cost of Goods Sold} = \frac{\text{Cost of Goods Sold}}{365 \text{ days}}$$

To illustrate, the number of days' sales in inventory for Lincoln Company is computed below.

	2010	2009
Average inventory	$273,500 ($547,000 ÷ 2)	$297,000 ($594,000 ÷ 2)
Average daily cost of goods sold	$2,858 ($1,043,000 ÷ 365)	$2,247 ($820,000 ÷ 365)
Number of days' sales in inventory	95.7 ($273,500 ÷ $2,858)	132.2 ($297,000 ÷ $2,247)

The number of days' sales in inventory is a rough measure of the length of time it takes to purchase, sell, and replace the inventory. Lincoln's number of days' sales in inventory improved from 132.2 days to 95.7 days during 2010. This is a major improvement in managing inventory.

Ratio of Fixed Assets to Long-Term Liabilities

The **ratio of fixed assets to long-term liabilities** provides a measure of whether noteholders or bondholders will be paid. Since fixed assets are often pledged as security for long-term notes and bonds, it is computed as follows:

$$\text{Ratio of Fixed Assets to Long-Term Liabilities} = \frac{\text{Fixed Assets (net)}}{\text{Long-Term Liabilities}}$$

To illustrate, the ratio of fixed assets to long-term liabilities for Lincoln Company is computed below.

	2010	2009
Fixed assets (net)	$444,500	$470,000
Long-term liabilities	$100,000	$200,000
Ratio of fixed assets to long-term liabilities	4.4 ($444,500 ÷ $100,000)	2.4 ($470,000 ÷ $200,000)

During 2010, Lincoln's ratio of fixed assets to long-term liabilities increased from 2.4 to 4.4. This increase was due primarily to Lincoln paying off one-half of its long-term liabilities in 2010.

Ratio of Liabilities to Stockholders' Equity

The **ratio of liabilities to stockholders' equity** measures how much of the company is financed by debt and equity. It is computed as follows:

$$\text{Ratio of Liabilities to Stockholders' Equity} = \frac{\text{Total Liabilities}}{\text{Total Stockholders' Equity}}$$

To illustrate, the ratio of liabilities to stockholders' equity for Lincoln Company is computed below.

	2010	2009
Total liabilities	$310,000	$443,000
Total stockholders' equity	$829,500	$787,500
Ratio of liabilities to stockholders' equity	0.4 ($310,000 ÷ $829,500)	0.6 ($443,000 ÷ $787,500)

The ratio of liabilities to stockholders' equity varies across industries as in the following examples:

Continental Airlines   31.6
Procter & Gamble   1.1

Lincoln's ratio of liabilities to stockholders' equity decreased from 0.6 to 0.4 during 2010. This is an improvement and indicates that Lincoln's creditors have an adequate margin of safety.

Number of Times Interest Charges Earned

The **number of times interest charges are earned**, sometimes called the *fixed charge coverage ratio*, measures the risk that interest payments will not be made if earnings decrease. It is computed as follows:

$$\text{Number of Times Interest Charges Are Earned} = \frac{\text{Income Before Income Tax} + \text{Interest Expense}}{\text{Interest Expense}}$$

Interest expense is paid before income taxes. In other words, interest expense is deducted in determining taxable income and, thus, income tax. For this reason, income *before taxes* is used in computing the number of times interest charges are earned.

The *higher* the ratio, the more likely interest payments will be paid if earnings decrease. To illustrate, the number of times interest charges are earned for Lincoln Company is computed below.

	2010	2009
Income before income tax	$162,500	$134,600
Add interest expense	6,000	12,000
Amount available to pay interest	$168,500	$146,600
Number of times interest charges earned	28.1 ($168,500 ÷ $6,000)	12.2 ($146,600 ÷ $12,000)

The number of times interest charges are earned improved from 12.2 to 28.1 during 2010. This indicates that Lincoln Company has sufficient earnings to pay interest expense.

The number of times interest charges are earned can be adapted for use with dividends on preferred stock. In this case, the *number of times preferred dividends are earned* is computed as follows:

$$\text{Number of Times Preferred Dividends Are Earned} = \frac{\text{Net Income}}{\text{Preferred Dividends}}$$

Since dividends are paid after taxes, net income is used in computing the number of times preferred dividends are earned. The *higher* the ratio, the more likely preferred dividend payments will be paid if earnings decrease.

Profitability Analysis

Profitability analysis focuses on the ability of a company to earn profits. This ability is reflected in the company's operating results, as reported in its income statement. The ability to earn profits also depends on the assets the company has available for use in its operations, as reported in its balance sheet. Thus, income statement and balance sheet relationships are often used in evaluating profitability.

Common profitability analyses include the following:

1. Ratio of net sales to assets
2. Rate earned on total assets
3. Rate earned on stockholders' equity
4. Rate earned on common stockholders' equity
5. Earnings per share on common stock
6. Price-earnings ratio
7. Dividends per share
8. Dividend yield

Obj 3 Use financial statement analysis to assess the profitability of a business.

Ratio of Net Sales to Assets

The **ratio of net sales to assets** measures how effectively a company uses its assets. It is computed as follows:

$$\text{Ratio of Net Sales to Assets} = \frac{\text{Net Sales}}{\text{Average Total Assets (excluding long-term investments)}}$$

As shown above, any long-term investments are excluded in computing the ratio of net sales to assets. This is because long-term investments are unrelated to normal operations and net sales.

To illustrate, the ratio of net sales to assets for Lincoln Company is computed below.

	2010	2009
Net sales	$ 1,498,000	$ 1,200,000
Total assets (excluding long-term investments):		
Beginning of year	$ 1,053,000	$ 1,010,000
End of year	1,044,500	1,053,000
Total	$ 2,097,500	$ 2,063,000
Average total assets	$1,048,750 ($2,097,500 ÷ 2)	$1,031,500 ($2,063,000 ÷ 2)
Ratio of net sales to assets	1.4 ($1,498,000 ÷ $1,048,750)	1.2 ($1,200,000 ÷ $1,031,500)

For Lincoln Company, the average total assets was computed using total assets (excluding long-term investments) at the beginning and the end of the year. The average total assets could also be based on monthly or quarterly averages.

The ratio of net sales to assets indicates that Lincoln's use of its operating assets has improved in 2010. This was primarily due to the increase in net sales in 2010.

Rate Earned on Total Assets

The **rate earned on total assets** measures the profitability of total assets, without considering how the assets are financed. In other words, this rate is not affected by the portion of assets financed by creditors or stockholders. It is computed as follows:

$$\text{Rate Earned on Total Assets} = \frac{\text{Net Income + Interest Expense}}{\text{Average Total Assets}}$$

The rate earned on total assets is computed by adding interest expense to net income. By adding interest expense to net income, the effect of whether the assets are financed by creditors (debt) or stockholders (equity) is eliminated. Because net income includes any income earned from long-term investments, the average total assets includes long-term investments as well as the net operating assets.

To illustrate, the rate earned on total assets by Lincoln Company is computed below.

	2010	2009
Net income	$ 91,000	$ 76,500
Plus interest expense	6,000	12,000
Total	$ 97,000	$ 88,500
Total assets:		
Beginning of year	$ 1,230,500	$ 1,187,500
End of year	1,139,500	1,230,500
Total	$ 2,370,000	$ 2,418,000
Average total assets	$1,185,000 ($2,370,000 ÷ 2)	$1,209,000 ($2,418,000 ÷ 2)
Rate earned on total assets	8.2% ($97,000 ÷ $1,185,000)	7.3% ($88,500 ÷ $1,209,000)

The rate earned on total assets improved from 7.3% to 8.2% during 2010.

The *rate earned on operating assets* is sometimes computed when there are large amounts of nonoperating income and expense. It is computed as follows:

$$\text{Rate Earned on Operating Assets} = \frac{\text{Income from Operations}}{\text{Average Operating Assets}}$$

Since Lincoln Company does not have a significant amount of nonoperating income and expense, the rate earned on operating assets is not illustrated.

Rate Earned on Stockholders' Equity

The **rate earned on stockholders' equity** measures the rate of income earned on the amount invested by the stockholders. It is computed as follows:

$$\text{Rate Earned on Stockholders' Equity} = \frac{\text{Net Income}}{\text{Average Total Stockholders' Equity}}$$

both years ÷ 2

To illustrate, the rate earned on stockholders' equity for Lincoln Company is computed below.

	2010	2009
Net income	$91,000	$76,500
Stockholders' equity:		
Beginning of year	$ 787,500	$ 750,000
End of year	829,500	787,500
Total	$1,617,000	$1,537,500
Average stockholders' equity	$808,500 ($1,617,000 ÷ 2)	$768,750 ($1,537,500 ÷ 2)
Rate earned on stockholders' equity	11.3% ($91,000 ÷ $808,500)	10.0% ($76,500 ÷ $768,750)

The rate earned on stockholders' equity improved from 10.0% to 11.3% during 2010.

Leverage involves using debt to increase the return on an investment. The rate earned on stockholders' equity is normally higher than the rate earned on total assets. This is because of the effect of leverage.

For Lincoln Company, the effect of leverage for 2010 is 3.1%, computed as follows:

Rate earned on stockholders' equity	11.3%
Less rate earned on total assets	8.2
Effect of leverage	3.1%

Exhibit 8 shows the 2010 and 2009 effects of leverage for Lincoln Company.

EXHIBIT 8 | Effect of Leverage

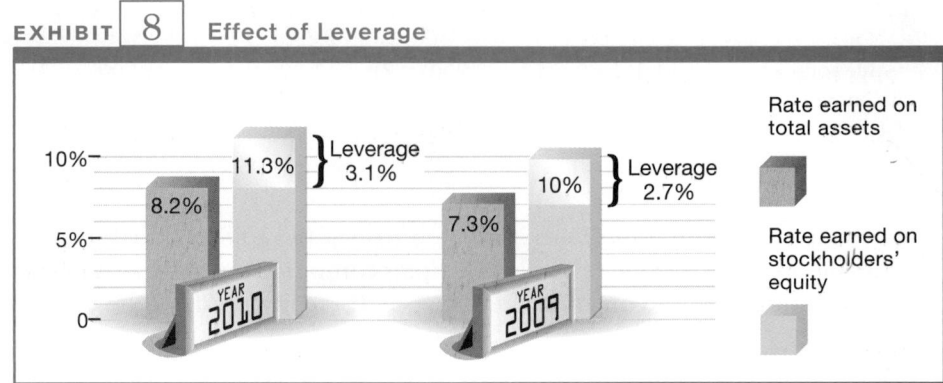

Rate Earned on Common Stockholders' Equity

The **rate earned on common stockholders' equity** measures the rate of profits earned on the amount invested by the common stockholders. It is computed as follows:

$$\text{Rate Earned on Common Stockholders' Equity} = \frac{\text{Net Income} - \text{Preferred Dividends}}{\text{Average Common Stockholders' Equity}}$$

Because preferred stockholders rank ahead of the common stockholders in their claim on earnings, any preferred dividends are subtracted from net income in computing the rate earned on common stockholders' equity.

To illustrate, the rate earned on common stockholders' equity for Lincoln Company is computed below.

	2010	2009
Net income	$91,000	$76,500
Less preferred dividends	9,000	9,000
Total	$82,000	$67,500
Common stockholders' equity:		
Beginning of year	$ 637,500	$ 600,000
End of year	679,500	637,500
Total	$1,317,000	$1,237,500
Average common stockholders' equity	$ 658,500 ($1,317,000 ÷ 2)	$618,750 ($1,237,500 ÷ 2)
Rate earned on common stockholders' equity	12.5% ($82,000 ÷ $658,500)	10.9% ($67,500 ÷ $618,750)

Lincoln Company had $150,000 of 6% preferred stock outstanding on December 31, 2010 and 2009. Thus, preferred dividends of $9,000

($150,000 × 6%) were deducted from net income. Lincoln's common stockholders' equity was determined as follows:

| | December 31 | | |
	2010	2009	2008
Common stock, $10 par	$500,000	$500,000	$500,000
Retained earnings	179,500	137,500	100,000
Common stockholders' equity	$679,500	$637,500	$600,000

The retained earnings on December 31, 2008, of $100,000 is the same as the retained earnings on January 1, 2009, as shown in Lincoln's retained earnings statement in Exhibit 4.

Lincoln Company's rate earned on common stockholders' equity improved from 10.9% to 12.5% in 2010. This rate differs from the rates earned by Lincoln Company on total assets and stockholders' equity as shown below.

	2010	2009
Rate earned on total assets	8.2%	7.3%
Rate earned on stockholders' equity	11.3%	10.0%
Rate earned on common stockholders' equity	12.5%	10.9%

These rates differ because of leverage, as discussed in the preceding section.

Earnings per Share on Common Stock

Earnings per share (EPS) on common stock measures the share of profits that are earned by a share of common stock. Generally accepted accounting principles (GAAP) require the reporting of earnings per share in the income statement.[3] As a result, earnings per share (EPS) is often reported in the financial press. It is computed as follows:

$$\text{Earnings per Share (EPS) on Common Stock} = \frac{\text{Net Income} - \text{Preferred Dividends}}{\text{Shares of Common Stock Outstanding}}$$

When preferred and common stock are outstanding, preferred dividends are subtracted from net income to determine the income related to the common shares.

To illustrate, the earnings per share (EPS) of common stock for Lincoln Company is computed below.

	2010	2009
Net income	$91,000	$76,500
Preferred dividends	9,000	9,000
Total	$82,000	$67,500
Shares of common stock outstanding	50,000	50,000
Earnings per share on common stock	$1.64 ($82,000 ÷ 50,000)	$1.35 ($67,500 ÷ 50,000)

[3] *Statement of Financial Accounting Standards No. 128,* "Earnings per Share" (Norwalk, CT: Financial Accounting Standards Board, 1997).

As shown on the previous page, Lincoln's earnings per share (EPS) on common stock improved from $1.35 to $1.64 during 2010.

Lincoln Company had $150,000 of 6% preferred stock outstanding on December 31, 2010 and 2009. Thus, preferred dividends of $9,000 ($150,000 × 6%) are deducted from net income in computing earnings per share on common stock.

Lincoln did not issue any additional shares of common stock in 2010. If Lincoln had issued additional shares in 2010, a weighted average of common shares outstanding during the year would have been used.

Lincoln Company has a simple capital structure with only common stock and preferred stock outstanding. Many corporations, however, have complex capital structures with various types of equity securities outstanding, such as convertible preferred stock, stock options, and stock warrants. In such cases, the possible effects of such securities on the shares of common stock outstanding are considered in reporting earnings per share. These possible effects are reported separately as *earnings per common share assuming dilution* or *diluted earnings per share*.[4] This topic is described and illustrated in advanced accounting courses and textbooks.

Price-Earnings Ratio

The **price-earnings (P/E) ratio** on common stock measures a company's future earnings prospects. It is often quoted in the financial press and is computed as follows:

$$\text{Price-Earnings (P/E) Ratio} = \frac{\text{Market Price per Share of Common Stock}}{\text{Earnings per Share on Common Stock}}$$

To illustrate, the price-earnings (P/E) ratio for Lincoln Company is computed below.

	2010	2009
Market price per share of common stock	$41.00	$27.00
Earnings per share on common stock	$ 1.64	$ 1.35
Price-earnings ratio on common stock	25 ($41 ÷ $1.64)	20 ($27 ÷ $1.35)

The dividends per share, dividend yield, and P/E ratio of a common stock are normally quoted on the daily listing of stock prices in *The Wall Street Journal* and on Yahoo!'s finance Web site.

The price-earnings ratio improved from 20 to 25 during 2010. In other words, a share of common stock of Lincoln Company was selling for 20 times earnings per share at the end of 2009. At the end of 2010, the common stock was selling for 25 times earnings per share. This indicates that the market expects Lincoln to experience favorable earnings in the future.

Dividends per Share

Dividends per share measures the extent to which earnings are being distributed to common shareholders. It is computed as follows:

$$\text{Dividends per Share} = \frac{\text{Dividends}}{\text{Shares of Common Stock Outstanding}}$$

---

[4] Ibid., pars. 11–39.

To illustrate, the dividends per share for Lincoln Company are computed below.

	2010	2009
Dividends	$40,000	$30,000
Shares of common stock outstanding	50,000	50,000
Dividends per share of common stock	$0.80 ($40,000 ÷ 50,000)	$0.60 ($30,000 ÷ 50,000)

The dividends per share of common stock increased from $0.60 to $0.80 during 2010.

Dividends per share are often reported with earnings per share. Comparing the two per-share amounts indicates the extent to which earnings are being retained for use in operations. To illustrate, the dividends and earnings per share for Lincoln Company are shown in Exhibit 9.

EXHIBIT 9 **Dividends and Earnings per Share of Common Stock**

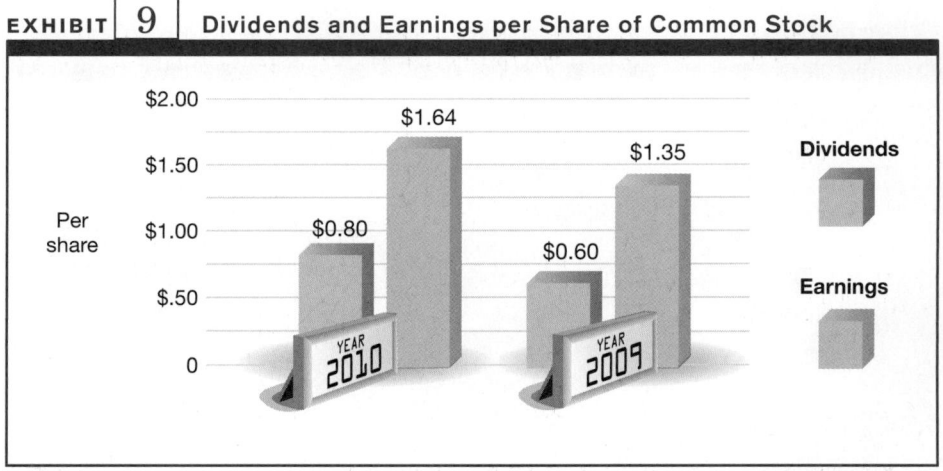

Dividend Yield

The **dividend yield** on common stock measures the rate of return to common stockholders from cash dividends. It is of special interest to investors, whose objective is to earn revenue (dividends) from their investment. It is computed as follows:

$$\text{Dividend Yield} = \frac{\text{Dividends per Share of Common Stock}}{\text{Market Price per Share of Common Stock}}$$

To illustrate, the dividend yield for Lincoln Company is computed below.

	2010	2009
Dividends per share of common stock	$ 0.80	$ 0.60
Market price per share of common stock	$41.00	$27.00
Dividend yield on common stock	2.0% ($0.80 ÷ $41)	2.2% ($0.60 ÷ $27)

The dividend yield declined slightly from 2.2% to 2.0% in 2010. This decline was primarily due to the increase in the market price of Lincoln's common stock.

Summary of Analytical Measures

Exhibit 10 shows a summary of the solvency and profitability measures discussed in this chapter. The type of industry and the company's operations usually affect which measures are used. In many cases, additional measures are used for a specific industry. For example, airlines use *revenue per passenger mile* and *cost per available seat* as profitability measures. Likewise, hotels use *occupancy rates* as a profitability measure.

The analytical measures shown in Exhibit 10 are a useful starting point for analyzing a company's solvency and profitability. However, they are not a substitute for sound judgment. For example, the general economic and business environment should always be considered in analyzing a company's future prospects. In addition, any trends and interrelationships among the measures should be carefully studied.

EXHIBIT 10   **Summary of Analytical Measures**

	Method of Computation	Use
Solvency measures:		
Working Capital	Current Assets − Current Liabilities	To indicate the ability to meet currently maturing obligations
Current Ratio	$\dfrac{\text{Current Assets}}{\text{Current Liabilities}}$	
Quick Ratio	$\dfrac{\text{Quick Assets}}{\text{Current Liabilities}}$	To indicate instant debt-paying
Accounts Receivable Turnover	$\dfrac{\text{Net Sales}}{\text{Average Accounts Receivable}}$	To assess the efficiency in collecting receivables and in the management of credit
Numbers of Days' Sales in Receivables	$\dfrac{\text{Average Accounts Receivable}}{\text{Average Daily Sales}}$	
Inventory Turnover	$\dfrac{\text{Cost of Goods Sold}}{\text{Average Inventory}}$	To assess the efficiency in the management of inventory
Number of Days' Sales in Inventory	$\dfrac{\text{Average Inventory}}{\text{Average Daily Cost of Goods Sold}}$	
Ratio of Fixed Assets to Long-Term Liabilities	$\dfrac{\text{Fixed Assets (net)}}{\text{Long-Term Liabilities}}$	To indicate the margin of safety to long-term creditors
Ratio of Liabilities to Stockholders' Equity	$\dfrac{\text{Total Liabilities}}{\text{Total Stockholders' Equity}}$	To indicate the margin of safety to creditors
Number of Times Interest Charges Are Earned	$\dfrac{\text{Income Before Income Tax + Interest Expense}}{\text{Interest Expense}}$	To assess the risk to debtholders in terms of number of times interest charges were earned

(Continued)

EXHIBIT 10 │ **Summary of Analytical Measures** *(Continued)*

	Method of Computation	Use
Profitability measures:		
Ratio of Net Sales to Assets	$\dfrac{\text{Net Sales}}{\text{Average Total Assets (excluding long-term investments)}}$	To assess the effectiveness in the use of assets
Rate Earned on Total Assets	$\dfrac{\text{Net Income + Interest Expense}}{\text{Average Total Assets}}$	To assess the profitability of the assets
Rate Earned on Stockholders' Equity	$\dfrac{\text{Net Income}}{\text{Average Total Stockholders' Equity}}$	To assess the profitability of the investment by stockholders
Rate Earned on Common Stockholders' Equity	$\dfrac{\text{Net Income} - \text{Preferred Dividends}}{\text{Average Common Stockholders' Equity}}$	To assess the profitability of the investment by common stockholders
Earnings per Share on Common Stock	$\dfrac{\text{Net Income} - \text{Preferred Dividends}}{\text{Shares of Common Stock Outstanding}}$	
Price-Earnings Ratio	$\dfrac{\text{Market Price per Share of Common Stock}}{\text{Earnings per Share on Common Stock}}$	To indicate future earnings prospects, based on the relationship between market value of common stock and earnings
Dividends per Share	$\dfrac{\text{Dividends}}{\text{Shares of Common Stock Outstanding}}$	To indicate the extent to which earnings are being distributed to common stockholders
Dividend Yield	$\dfrac{\text{Dividends per Share of Common Stock}}{\text{Market Price per Share of Common Stock}}$	To indicate the rate of return to common stockholders in terms of dividends

INTEGRITY, OBJECTIVITY, AND ETHICS IN BUSINESS

One Bad Apple

A recent survey by *CFO* magazine reported that 47% of chief financial officers have been pressured by the chief executive officer to use questionable accounting. In addition, only 38% of those surveyed feel less pressure to use aggressive accounting today than in years past, while 20% believe there is more pressure.

Perhaps more troublesome is the chief financial officers' confidence in the quality of financial information, with only 27% being "very confident" in the quality of financial information presented by public companies.

Source: D. Durfee, "It's Better (and Worse) Than You Think," CFO, May 3, 2004.

Corporate Annual Reports

Obj 4 Describe the contents of corporate annual reports.

Public corporations issue annual reports summarizing their operating activities for the past year and plans for the future. Such annual reports include the financial statements and the accompanying notes. In addition, annual reports normally include the following sections:

1. Management's discussion and analysis
2. Report on internal control
3. Report on fairness of the financial statements

Management's Discussion and Analysis

Management's Discussion and Analysis (MD&A) is required in annual reports filed with the Securities and Exchange Commission. It includes management's analysis of current operations and its plans for the future. Typical items included in the MD&A include the following:

1. Management's analysis and explanations of any significant changes between the current and prior years' financial statements.

2. Important accounting principles or policies that could affect interpretation of the financial statements, including the effect of changes in accounting principles or the adoption of new accounting principles.

3. Management's assessment of the company's liquidity and the availability of capital to the company.

4. Significant risk exposures that might affect the company.

5. Any "off-balance-sheet" arrangements such as leases not included directly in the financial statements. Such arrangements are discussed in advanced accounting courses and textbooks.

How Businesses Make Money

Investing Strategies

How do people make investment decisions? Investment decisions, like any major purchase, must meet the needs of the buyer. For example, if you have a family of five and are thinking about buying a new car, you probably wouldn't buy a two-seat sports car. It just wouldn't meet your objectives or fit your lifestyle. Alternatively, if you are a young single person, a minivan might not meet your immediate needs. Investors buy stocks in the same way, buying stocks that match their investment style and their financial needs. Two common approaches are value and growth investing.

Value Investing

Value investors search for undervalued stocks. That is, the investor tries to find companies whose value is not reflected in their stock price. These are typically quiet, "boring" companies with excellent financial performance that are temporarily out of favor in the stock market. This investment approach assumes that the stock's price will eventually rise to match the company's value. The most successful investor of all time, Warren Buffett, uses this approach almost exclusively. Naturally, the key to successful value investing is to accurately determine a stock's value. This will often include analyzing a company's financial ratios, as discussed in this chapter, compared to target ratios and industry norms. For example, the stock of **Deckers Outdoor Corporation,** the maker of TEVA™ sport sandals, was selling for $27.43 on December 27, 2005, a value relative to its earnings per share of $2.58. Over the next two years, the company's stock price increased more than 500%, reaching $166.50.

Growth Investing

The growth investor tries to identify companies that have the potential to grow sales and earnings through new products, markets, or opportunities. Growth companies are often newer companies that are still unproven but that possess unique technologies or capabilities. The strategy is to purchase these companies before their potential becomes obvious, hoping to profit from relatively large increases in the company's stock price. This approach, however, carries the risk that the growth may not occur. Growth investors use many of the ratios discussed in this chapter to identify high-potential growth companies. For example, in March 2005, **Research in Motion Limited,** maker of the popular BlackBerry® handheld mobile device, reported earnings per share of $0.37, and the company's stock price was trading near $62 per share. In the following two years, the company's sales increased by 125%, earnings increased to $1.14 per share, and the company's stock price rose above $135 per share.

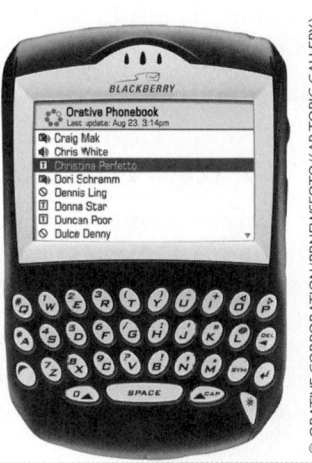

Report on Internal Control

The Sarbanes-Oxley Act of 2002 requires management to prepare a report on internal control. The report states management's responsibility for establishing and maintaining internal control. In addition, management's assessment of the effectiveness of internal controls over financial reporting is included in the report.

Sarbanes-Oxley also requires a public accounting firm to verify management's conclusions on internal control. Thus, two reports on internal control, one by management and one by a public accounting firm, are included in the annual report. In some situations, these may be combined into a single report on internal control.

Report on Fairness of the Financial Statements

All publicly held corporations are required to have an independent audit (examination) of their financial statements. The Certified Public Accounting (CPA) firm that conducts the audit renders an opinion, called the *Report of Independent Registered Public Accounting Firm,* on the fairness of the statements.

An opinion stating that the financial statements present fairly the financial position, results of operations, and cash flows of the company is said to be an *unqualified opinion,* sometimes called a *clean opinion.* Any report other than an unqualified opinion raises a "red flag" for financial statement users and requires further investigation as to its cause.

Appendix

Unusual Items on the Income Statement

Generally accepted accounting principles require that unusual items be reported separately on the income statement. This is because such items do not occur frequently and often are unrelated to current operations. Without separate reporting of these items, users of the financial statements might be misled about current and future operations.

Unusual items affecting the current period's income statement include the following:

1. Discontinued operations
2. Extraordinary items

Discontinued Operations

A company may discontinue a segment of its operations by selling or abandoning the operations. For example, a retailer might decide to sell its product only online and thus discontinue selling its merchandise at its retail outlets (stores).

Any gain or loss on discontinued operations is reported on the income statement as a *Gain (or loss) from discontinued operations.* It is reported immediately following *Income from continuing operations.*[5]

---

[5] *Statement of Financial Accounting Standards No. 144,* "Accounting for the Impairment or Disposal of Long-Lived Assets" (Norwalk, CT: Financial Accounting Standards Board, 2001).

To illustrate, assume that Jones Corporation produces and sells electrical products, hardware supplies, and lawn equipment. Because of lack of profits, Jones discontinues its electrical products operation and sells the remaining inventory and other assets at a loss of $100,000. Exhibit 11 illustrates the reporting of the loss on discontinued operations.[6]

EXHIBIT 11   Unusual Items in the Income Statement

JONES CORPORATION Income Statement For the Year Ended December 31, 2010	
Net sales	$ 2,350,000
Cost of merchandise sold	5.800,000
Gross profit	$ 6,550,000
Selling and administrative expenses	5,240,000
Income from continuing operations before income tax	$ 1,310,000
Income tax expense	620,000
Income from continuing operations	$ 690,000
Loss on discontinued operations	100,000
Income before extraordinary items	$ 590,000
Extraordinary items:	
Gain on condemnation of land	150,000
Net income	$ 740,000

In addition, a note accompanying the income statement should describe the operations sold including such details as the date operations were discontinued, the assets sold, and the effect (if any) on current and future operations.

Extraordinary Items

An **extraordinary item** is defined as an event or transaction with the following characteristics:

1. Unusual in nature

2. Infrequent in occurrence

Gains and losses from natural disasters such as floods, earthquakes, and fires are normally reported as extraordinary items, provided that they occur infrequently. Gains or losses from land or buildings taken (condemned) for public use are also reported as extraordinary items.

Any gain or loss from extraordinary items is reported on the income statement as *Gain (or loss) from extraordinary item*. It is reported immediately following *Income from continuing operations* and any *Gain (or loss) on discontinued operations*.

To illustrate, assume that land owned by Jones Corporation was condemned by the local government. The condemnation of the land resulted in a gain of $150,000. Exhibit 11 illustrates the reporting of the extraordinary gain.[7]

---

[6] The gain or loss on discontinued operations is reported net of any tax effects. To simplify, the tax effects are not specifically identified in Exhibit 11.

[7] The gain or loss on extraordinary operations is reported net of any tax effects.

Reporting Earnings per Share

Earnings per common share should be reported separately for discontinued operations and extraordinary items. Assuming 200,000 shares of common stock are outstanding, a partial income statement for Jones Corporation is shown in Exhibit 12.

EXHIBIT 12   Income Statement with Earnings per Share

JONES CORPORATION Income Statement For the Year Ended December 31, 2010	
Earnings per common share:	
Income from continuing operations	$ 3.45
Loss on discontinued operations	0.50
Income before extraordinary items	$ 2.95
Extraordinary items:	
Gain on condemnation of land	0.75
Net income	$ 3.70

Exhibit 12 reports earnings per common share for income from continuing operations, discontinued operations, and extraordinary items. However, only earnings per share for income from continuing operations and net income are required by generally accepted accounting principles (GAAP). The other per-share amounts may be presented in the notes to the financial statements.[8]

Key Points

1. Describe basic financial statement analytical methods.

   The analysis of percentage increases and decreases in related items in comparative financial statements is called horizontal analysis. The analysis of percentages of component parts to the total in a single statement is called vertical analysis. Financial statements in which all amounts are expressed in percentages for purposes of analysis are called common-sized statements.

2. Use financial statement analysis to assess the solvency of a business.

   The primary focus of financial statement analysis is the assessment of solvency and profitability. All users are interested in the ability of a business to pay its debts as they come due (solvency) and to earn income (profitability). Solvency analysis is normally assessed by examining the following balance sheet relationships: (1) current position analysis, (2) accounts receivable analysis, (3) inventory analysis, (4) the ratio of fixed assets to long-term liabilities, (5) the ratio of liabilities to stockholders' equity, and (6) the number of times interest charges are earned.

3. Use financial statement analysis to assess the profitability of a business.

   Profitability analysis focuses mainly on the relationship between operating results (income statement) and resources available (balance sheet). Major analyses used in assessing

[8] Statement of *Financial Standards No. 128*, op. cit., pars. 36 and 37.

profitability include (1) the ratio of net sales to assets, (2) the rate earned on total assets, (3) the rate earned on stockholders' equity, (4) the rate earned on common stockholders' equity, (5) earnings per share on common stock, (6) the price-earnings ratio, (7) dividends per share, and (8) dividend yield.

4. Describe the contents of corporate annual reports.

Corporate annual reports normally include financial statements and the accompanying notes, the Management's Discussion and Analysis, and the Report on Fairness of the Financial Statements.

Key Terms

Accounts receivable analysis The analysis of a company's ability to collect its accounts receivable.

Accounts receivable turnover The relationship between net sales and accounts receivable computed by dividing the net sales by the average net accounts receivable; measures how frequently during the year the accounts receivable are being converted to cash.

Common-sized statement A financial statement in which all items are expressed only in relative terms.

Current position analysis The analysis of a company's ability to pay its current liabilities.

Current ratio A financial ratio that is computed by dividing current assets by current liabilities.

Dividend yield A ratio, computed by dividing the annual dividends paid per share of common stock by the market price per share at a specific date, which indicates the rate of return to stockholders in term of cash dividend distributions.

Dividends per share Measures the extent to which earnings are being distributed to common shareholders.

Earnings per share (EPS) on common stock Net income per share of common stock outstanding during a period.

Extraordinary item An event or transaction reported on the income statement that is (1) unusual in nature and (2) infrequent in occurrence.

Horizontal analysis Financial analysis that compares an item in a current statement with the same item in prior statements.

Inventory analysis A company's ability to manage its inventory effectively.

Inventory turnover The relationship between the volume of goods sold and inventory, computed by dividing the cost of goods sold by the average inventory.

Management's Discussion and Analysis (MD&A) An annual report disclosure that provides management's analysis of the results of operations and financial condition.

Number of days' sales in inventory The relationship between the volume of sales and inventory, computed by dividing the inventory at the end of the year by the average daily cost of goods sold.

Number of days' sales in receivables The relationship between sales and accounts receivable, computed by dividing the average accounts receivable by the average daily sales.

Number of times interest charges are earned A ratio that measures creditor margin of safety for interest payments, calculated as income before interest and taxes divided by interest expense.

Price-earnings (P/E) ratio The ratio of the market price per share of common stock, at a specific date, to the annual earnings per share.

Profitability The ability of a firm to earn income.

Quick assets Cash and other current assets that can be quickly converted to cash, such as marketable securities and receivables.

Quick ratio A financial ratio that measures the ability to pay current liabilities with quick assets (cash, marketable securities, accounts receivable).

Rate earned on stockholders' equity A measure of profitability computed by dividing net income by average total stockholders' equity.

Rate earned on common stockholders' equity A measure of profitability computed by dividing net income less preferred dividends by average common stockholders' equity.

Rate earned on total assets A measure of the profitability of assets, without regard to the equity of creditors and stockholders in the assets.

Ratio of fixed assets to long-term liabilities A leverage ratio that measures the margin of safety

of long-term creditors, calculated as the net fixed assets divided by the long-term liabilities.

Ratio of liabilities to stockholders' equity A comprehensive leverage ratio that measures the relationship of the claims of creditors to stockholders' equity.

Ratio of net sales to assets Ratio that measures how effectively a company uses its assets, computed as net sales divided by average total assets.

Solvency The ability of a firm to pay its debts as they come due.

Vertical analysis An analysis that compares each item in a current statement with a total amount within the same statement.

Working capital The excess of the current assets of a business over its current liabilities.

Illustrative Problem

Rainbow Paint Co.'s comparative financial statements for the years ending December 31, 2010 and 2009, are as follows. The market price of Rainbow Paint Co.'s common stock was $30 on December 31, 2009, and $25 on December 31, 2010.

Rainbow Paint Co.
Comparative Income Statement
For the Years Ended December 31, 2010 and 2009

	2010	2009
Sales	$5,125,000	$3,257,600
Sales returns and allowances	125,000	57,600
Net sales	$5,000,000	$3,200,000
Cost of goods sold	3,400,000	2,080,000
Gross profit	$1,600,000	$1,120,000
Selling expenses	$ 650,000	$ 464,000
Administrative expenses	325,000	224,000
Total operating expenses	$ 975,000	$ 688,000
Income from operations	$ 625,000	$ 432,000
Other income	25,000	19,200
	$ 650,000	$ 451,200
Other expenses (interest)	105,000	64,000
Income before income tax	$ 545,000	$ 387,200
Income tax expenses	300,000	176,000
Net income	$ 245,000	$ 211,200

Rainbow Paint Co.
Comparative Retained Earnings Statement
For the Years Ended December 31, 2010 and 2009

	2010	2009
Retained earnings, January 1	$ 723,000	$ 581,800
Add net income for year	245,000	211,200
Total	$ 968,000	$ 793,000
Deduct dividends:		
On preferred stock	$ 40,000	$ 40,000
On common stock	45,000	30,000
Total	$ 85,000	$ 70,000
Retained earnings, December 31	$ 883,000	$ 723,000

Rainbow Paint Co.
Comparative Balance Sheet
December 31, 2010 and 2009

	Dec. 31, 2010	Dec. 31, 2009
Assets		
Current assets:		
Cash	$ 175,000	$ 125,000
Temporary investments	150,000	50,000
Accounts receivable (net)	425,000	325,000
Inventories	720,000	480,000
Prepaid expenses	30,000	20,000
Total current assets	$ 1,500,000	$ 1,000,000
Long-term investments	250,000	225,000
Property, plant, and equipment (net)	2,093,000	1,948,000
Total assets	$ 3,843,000	$ 3,173,000
Liabilities		
Current liabilities	$ 750,000	$ 650,000
Long-term liabilities:		
Mortgage note payable, 10%, due 2013	$ 410,000	—
Bonds payable, 8%, due 2016	800,000	$ 800,000
Total long-term liabilities	$ 1,210,000	$ 800,000
Total liabilities	$ 1,960,000	$ 1,450,000
Stockholders' Equity		
Preferred 8% stock, $100 par	$ 500,000	$ 500,000
Common stock, $10 par	500,000	500,000
Retained earnings	883,000	723,000
Total stockholders' equity	$ 1,883,000	$ 1,723,000
Total liabilities and stockholders' equity	$ 3,843,000	$ 3,173,000

Instructions

Determine the following measures for 2010:

1. Working capital
2. Current ratio
3. Quick ratio
4. Accounts receivable turnover
5. Number of days' sales in receivables
6. Inventory turnover
7. Number of days' sales in inventory
8. Ratio of fixed assets to long-term liabilities
9. Ratio of liabilities to stockholders' equity
10. Number of times interest charges are earned
11. Number of times preferred dividends earned
12. Ratio of net sales to assets
13. Rate earned on total assets
14. Rate earned on stockholders' equity
15. Rate earned on common stockholders' equity
16. Earnings per share on common stock
17. Price-earnings ratio
18. Dividends per share
19. Dividend yield

Solution

(Ratios are rounded to the nearest single digit after the decimal point.)

1. Working capital: $750,000
   $1,500,000 − $750,000

2. Current ratio: 2.0
   $1,500,000 ÷ $750,000

3. Quick ratio: 1.0
   $750,000 ÷ $750,000

4. Accounts receivable turnover: 13.3
   $5,000,000 ÷ [($425,000 + $325,000) ÷ 2]

5. Number of days' sales in receivables: 27.4 days
   $5,000,000 ÷ 365 days = $13,699
   $375,000 ÷ $13,699

6. Inventory turnover: 5.7
   $3,400,000 ÷ [($720,000 + $480,000) ÷ 2]

7. Number of days' sales in inventory: 64.4 days
   $3,400,000 ÷ 365 days = $9,315
   $600,000 ÷ $9,315

8. Ratio of fixed assets to long-term liabilities: 1.7
   $2,093,000 ÷ $1,210,000

9. Ratio of liabilities to stockholders' equity: 1.0
   $1,960,000 ÷ $1,883,000

10. Number of times interest charges are earned: 6.2
    ($545,000 + $105,000) ÷ $105,000

11. Number of times preferred dividends earned: 6.1
    $245,000 ÷ $40,000

12. Ratio of net sales to assets: 1.5
    $5,000,000 ÷ [($3,593,000 + $2,948,000) ÷ 2]

13. Rate earned on total assets: 10.0%
    ($245,000 + $105,000) ÷ [($3,843,000 + $3,173,000) ÷ 2]

14. Rate earned on stockholders' equity: 13.6%
    $245,500 ÷ [($1,883,000 + $1,723,000) ÷ 2]

15. Rate earned on common stockholders' equity: 15.7%
    ($245,000 − $40,000) ÷ [($1,383,000 + $1,223,000) ÷ 2]

16. Earnings per share on common stock: $4.10
    ($245,000 − $40,000) ÷ 50,000 shares

17. Price-earnings ratio: 6.1
    $25 ÷ $4.10

18. Dividends per share: $0.90
    $45,000 ÷ 50,000 shares

19. Dividend yield: 3.6%
    $0.90 ÷ $25

Self-Examination Questions (Answers appear at the end of chapter)

1. What type of analysis is indicated by the following?

	Amount	Percent
Current assets	$100,000	20%
Property, plant, and equipment	400,000	80
Total assets	$500,000	100%

   A. Vertical analysis

   B. Horizontal analysis

   C. Profitability analysis

   D. Contribution margin analysis

2. Which of the following measures indicates the ability of a firm to pay its current liabilities?

   A. Working capital

   B. Current ratio

   C. Quick ratio

   D. All of the above

3. The ratio determined by dividing total current assets by total current liabilities is the:

   A. current ratio.

   B. working capital ratio.

   C. bankers' ratio.

   D. all of the above.

4. The ratio of the quick assets to current liabilities, which indicates the "instant" debt-paying ability of a firm, is the:

   A. current ratio.

   B. working capital ratio.

   C. quick ratio.

   D. bankers' ratio.

5. A measure useful in evaluating efficiency in the management of inventories is the:

   A. working capital ratio.

   B. quick ratio.

   C. number of days' sales in inventory.

   D. ratio of fixed assets to long-term liabilities.

Class Discussion Questions

1. What is the difference between horizontal and vertical analysis of financial statements?

2. What is the advantage of using comparative statements for financial analysis rather than statements for a single date or period?

3. The current year's amount of net income (after income tax) is 20% larger than that of the preceding year. Does this indicate an improved operating performance? Discuss.

4. How would you respond to a horizontal analysis that showed an expense increasing by over 80%?

5. How would the current and quick ratios of a service business compare?

6. For Gray Corporation, the working capital at the end of the current year is $10,000 more than the working capital at the end of the preceding year, reported as follows:

	Current Year	Preceding Year
Current assets:		
Cash, temporary investments, and receivables	$ 80,000	$ 84,000
Inventories	120,000	66,000
Total current assets	$200,000	$ 150,000
Current liabilities	100,000	60,000
Working capital	$100,000	$ 90,000

   Has the current position improved? Explain.

7. Why would the accounts receivable turnover ratio be different between *Wal-Mart* and *Procter & Gamble*?

8. A company that grants terms of n/45 on all sales has a yearly accounts receivable turnover, based on monthly averages, of 5. Is this a satisfactory turnover? Discuss.

9. a. Why is it advantageous to have a high inventory turnover?

   b. Is it possible for the inventory turnover to be too high? Discuss.

   c. Is it possible to have a high inventory turnover and a high number of days' sales in inventory? Discuss.

10. What do the following data taken from a comparative balance sheet indicate about the company's ability to borrow additional funds on a long-term basis in the current year as compared to the preceding year?

	Current Year	Preceding Year
Fixed assets (net)	$480,000	$540,000
Total long-term liabilities	120,000	180,000

11. a. How does the rate earned on total assets differ from the rate earned on stockholders' equity?

    b. Which ratio is normally higher? Explain.

12. a. Why is the rate earned on stockholders' equity by a thriving business ordinarily higher than the rate earned on total assets?

    b. Should the rate earned on common stockholders' equity normally be higher or lower than the rate earned on total stockholders' equity? Explain.

13. The net income (after income tax) of McCants Inc. was $20 per common share in the latest year and $80 per common share for the preceding year. At the beginning of the latest year, the number of shares outstanding was doubled by a stock split. There were no other changes in the amount of stock outstanding. What were the earnings per share in the preceding year, adjusted for comparison with the latest year?

14. The price-earnings ratio for the common stock of Breeden Company was 12 at December 31, the end of the current fiscal year. What does the ratio indicate about the selling price of the common stock in relation to current earnings?

15. Why would the dividend yield differ significantly from the rate earned on common stockholders' equity?

16. Favorable business conditions may bring about certain seemingly unfavorable ratios, and unfavorable business operations may result in apparently favorable ratios. For example, Grochoske Company increased its sales and net income substantially for the current year, yet the current ratio at the end of the year is lower than at the beginning of the year. Discuss some possible causes of the apparent weakening of the current position, while sales and net income have increased substantially.

17. Describe two reports provided by independent auditors in the annual report to shareholders.

Exercises

E9-1

Vertical analysis of income statement

Obj 1

SPREADSHEET

✓ a. 2010 net income: $5,000; 1.0% of sales

Revenue and expense data for Rogan Technologies Co. are as follows:

	2010	2009
Sales	$500,000	$440,000
Cost of goods sold	325,000	242,000
Selling expenses	70,000	79,200
Administrative expenses	75,000	70,400
Income tax expense	25,000	26,400

a. Prepare an income statement in comparative form, stating each item for both 2010 and 2009 as a percent of sales. Round to one decimal place.

b. Comment on the significant changes disclosed by the comparative income statement.

E9-2

Vertical analysis of income statement

Obj 1

SPREADSHEET

✓ a. Year 2 income from continuing operations, 30.7% of revenues

The following comparative income statement (in thousands of dollars) for two recent years was adapted from the annual report of *Speedway Motorsports, Inc.*, owner and operator of several major motor speedways, such as the Atlanta, Texas, and Las Vegas Motor Speedways.

	Year 2	Year 1
Revenues:		
Admissions	$175,208	$177,352
Event-related revenue	183,404	168,359
NASCAR broadcasting revenue	162,715	140,956
Other operating revenue	46,038	57,401
Total revenue	$567,365	$544,068
Expenses and other:		
Direct expense of events	$ 95,990	$ 97,042
NASCAR purse and sanction fees	105,826	96,306
Other direct expenses	113,141	102,535
General and administrative	78,070	73,281
Total expenses and other	$393,027	$369,164
Income from continuing operations	$174,338	$174,904

a. Prepare a comparative income statement for Years 1 and 2 in vertical form, stating each item as a percent of revenues. Round to one decimal place.
b. Comment on the significant changes.

E9-3

Common-sized income statement

Obj 1

SPREADSHEET

✓ a. Sorenson net income: $84,000; 4.2% of sales

Revenue and expense data for the current calendar year for Sorenson Electronics Company and for the electronics industry are as follows. The Sorenson Electronics Company data are expressed in dollars. The electronics industry averages are expressed in percentages.

	Sorenson Electronics Company	Electronics Industry Average
Sales	$2,050,000	102.5%
Sales returns and allowances	50,000	2.5
Net sales	$2,000,000	100.0%
Cost of goods sold	1,100,000	61.0
Gross profit	$ 900,000	39.0%
Selling expenses	$ 560,000	23.0%
Administrative expenses	220,000	10.0
Total operating expenses	$ 780,000	33.0%
Operating income	$ 120,000	6.0%
Other income	44,000	2.2
	$ 164,000	8.2%
Other expense	20,000	1.0
Income before income tax	$ 144,000	7.2%
Income tax expense	60,000	5.0
Net income	$ 84,000	2.2%

a. Prepare a common-sized income statement comparing the results of operations for Sorenson Electronics Company with the industry average. Round to one decimal place.
b. As far as the data permit, comment on significant relationships revealed by the comparisons.

E9-4

Vertical analysis of balance sheet

Obj 1

SPREADSHEET

✓ Retained earnings, Dec. 31, 2010, 34.0%

Balance sheet data for Hanes Company on December 31, the end of the fiscal year, are shown below.

	2010	2009
Current assets	320,000	200,000
Property, plant, and equipment	560,000	560,000
Intangible assets	120,000	40,000
Current liabilities	210,000	120,000
Long-term liabilities	350,000	300,000
Common stock	100,000	100,000
Retained earnings	340,000	280,000

Prepare a comparative balance sheet for 2010 and 2009, stating each asset as a percent of total assets and each liability and stockholders' equity item as a percent of the total liabilities and stockholders' equity. Round to one decimal place.

E9-5

Horizontal analysis of the income statement

Obj 1

SPREADSHEET

✓ a. Net income increase, 95.0%

Income statement data for Grendel Images Company for the years ended December 31, 2010 and 2009, are as follows:

	2010	2009
Sales	$196,000	$160,000
Cost of goods sold	170,100	140,000
Gross profit	$ 25,900	$ 20,000
Selling expenses	$ 12,200	$ 10,000
Administrative expenses	9,750	8,000
Total operating expenses	$ 21,950	$ 18,000
Income before income tax	$ 3,950	$ 2,000
Income tax expense	2,000	1,000
Net income	$ 1,950	$ 1,000

a. Prepare a comparative income statement with horizontal analysis, indicating the increase (decrease) for 2010 when compared with 2009. Round to one decimal place.
b. What conclusions can be drawn from the horizontal analysis?

E9-6

Current position analysis

Obj 2

✓ a. 2010 working capital, $1,000,000

The following data were taken from the balance sheet of Bock Suppliers Company:

	Dec. 31, 2010	Dec. 31, 2009
Cash	$ 295,000	$ 210,000
Temporary investments	315,000	230,000
Accounts and notes receivable (net)	290,000	250,000
Inventories	405,000	309,000
Prepaid expenses	195,000	105,000
Total current assets	$1,500,000	$1,104,000
Accounts and notes payable (short-term)	$ 290,000	$ 320,000
Accrued liabilities	210,000	140,000
Total current liabilities	$ 500,000	$ 460,000

a. Determine for each year (1) the working capital, (2) the current ratio, and (3) the quick ratio. Round ratios to one decimal place.
b. What conclusions can be drawn from these data as to the company's ability to meet its currently maturing debts?

E9-7

Current position analysis

Obj 2

✓ a. (1) Year 1 current ratio, 1.1

PepsiCo, Inc., the parent company of Frito-Lay™ snack foods and Pepsi beverages, had the following current assets and current liabilities at the end of two recent years:

	Year 2 (in millions)	Year 1 (in millions)
Cash and cash equivalents	$1,651	$1,716
Short-term investments, at cost	1,171	3,166
Accounts and notes receivable, net	3,725	3,261
Inventories	1,926	1,693
Prepaid expenses and other current assets	657	618
Short-term obligations	274	2,889
Accounts payable and other current liabilities	6,496	5,971
Income taxes payable	90	546

a. Determine the (1) current ratio and (2) quick ratio for both years. Round to one decimal place.

b. What conclusions can you draw from these data?

E9-8

Current position analysis

Obj 2

The bond indenture for the 10-year, 10% debenture bonds dated January 2, 2009, required working capital of $142,000, a current ratio of 1.7, and a quick ratio of 1.2 at the end of each calendar year until the bonds mature. At December 31, 2010, the three measures were computed as follows:

1. Current assets:		
Cash	$170,000	
Temporary investments	80,000	
Accounts and notes receivable (net)	200,000	
Inventories	60,000	
Prepaid expenses	40,000	
Intangible assets	208,000	
Property, plant and equipment	92,000	
Total current assets (net)		$850,000
Current liabilities:		
Accounts and short-term notes payable	$160,000	
Accrued liabilities	340,000	
Total current liabilities		500,000
Working capital		$350,000
2. Current ratio	1.7	$850,000 ÷ $500,000
3. Quick ratio	1.2	$192,000 ÷ $160,000

a. List the errors in the determination of the three measures of current position analysis.

b. Is the company satisfying the terms of the bond indenture?

E9-9

Accounts receivable analysis

Obj 2

✓ a. Accounts receivable turnover. 2010, 6.4

The following data are taken from the financial statements of McKee Technology Inc. Terms of all sales are 2/10, n/60.

	2010	2009	2008
Accounts receivable, end of year	$147,500	$158,000	$165,000
Net sales on account	975,000	900,000	

a. For 2010 and 2009, determine (1) the accounts receivable turnover and (2) the number of days' sales in receivables. Round to nearest dollar and one decimal place.

b. What conclusions can be drawn from these data concerning accounts receivable and credit policies?

E9-10

Accounts receivable analysis

Obj 2

Xavier Stores Company and Lestrade Stores, Inc., are large retail department stores. Both companies offer credit to their customers through their own credit card operations. Information from the financial statements for both companies for two recent years is as follows (all numbers are in millions):

	Xavier	Lestrade
Merchandise sales	$28,000	$65,000
Credit card receivables—beginning	2,750	15,000
Credit card receivables—ending	2,250	11,000

a. Determine (1) the accounts receivable turnover and (2) the number of days' sales in receivables for both companies. Round to one decimal place.

b. Compare the two companies with regard to their credit card policies.

E9-11

Inventory analysis

Obj 2

✓ a. Inventory turnover, current year, 7.4

The following data were extracted from the income statement of Brecca Systems Inc.:

	Current Year	Preceding Year
Sales	$1,139,600	$1,192,320
Beginning inventories	80,000	64,000
Cost of goods sold	569,800	662,400
Ending inventories	74,000	80,000

a. Determine for each year (1) the inventory turnover and (2) the number of days' sales in inventory. Round to nearest dollar and one decimal place.

b. What conclusions can be drawn from these data concerning the inventories?

E9-12

Inventory analysis

Obj 2

✓ a. Dell inventory turnover, 76.8

Dell Inc. and *Hewlett-Packard Company (HP)* compete with each other in the personal computer market. Dell's primary strategy is to assemble computers to customer orders, rather than for inventory. Thus, for example, Dell will build and deliver a computer within four days of a customer entering an order on a Web page. Hewlett-Packard, on the other hand, builds some computers prior to receiving an order, then sells from this inventory once an order is received. Below is selected financial information for both companies from a recent year's financial statements (in millions):

	Dell Inc.	Hewlett-Packard Company
Sales	$57,420	$73,557
Cost of goods sold	47,904	69,427
Inventory, beginning of period	588	6,877
Inventory, end of period	660	7,750

a. Determine for both companies (1) the inventory turnover and (2) the number of days' sales in inventory. Round to one decimal place.

b. Interpret the inventory ratios by considering Dell's and Hewlett-Packard's operating strategies.

E9-13

Ratio of liabilities to stockholders' equity and number of times interest charges earned

Obj 2

✓ **a. Ratio of liabilities to stockholders' equity, Dec. 31, 2010, 0.6**

The following data were taken from the financial statements of Weal Construction Inc. for December 31, 2010 and 2009:

	Dec. 31, 2010	Dec. 31, 2009
Accounts payable	$ 300,000	$ 280,000
Current maturities of serial bonds payable	400,000	400,000
Serial bonds payable, 10%, issued 2005, due 2015	2,000,000	2,400,000
Common stock, $1 par value	100,000	100,000
Paid-in capital in excess of par	1,000,000	1,000,000
Retained earnings	3,400,000	2,750,000

The income before income tax was $720,000 and $560,000 for the years 2010 and 2009, respectively.

a. Determine the ratio of liabilities to stockholders' equity at the end of each year. Round to one decimal place.

b. Determine the number of times the bond interest charges are earned during the year for both years. Round to one decimal place.

c. What conclusions can be drawn from these data as to the company's ability to meet its currently maturing debts?

E9-14

Ratio of liabilities to stockholders' equity and number of times interest charges earned

Obj 2

✓ **a. Hasbro, 0.9**

Hasbro and *Mattel, Inc.*, are the two largest toy companies in North America. Condensed liabilities and stockholders' equity from a recent balance sheet are shown for each company as follows (in thousands):

	Hasbro	Mattel
Current liabilities	$ 905,873	$1,582,520
Long-term debt	494,917	635,714
Other liabilities	—	304,676
Total liabilities	$1,400,790	$2,522,910
Shareholders' equity:		
Common stock	$ 104,847	$ 441,369
Additional paid in capital	322,254	1,613,307
Retained earnings	2,020,348	1,652,140
Accumulated other comprehensive loss and other equity items	11,186	(276,861)
Treasury stock, at cost	(920,475)	(996,981)
Total stockholders' equity	$1,538,160	$2,432,974
Total liabilities and stockholder's equity	$2,938,950	$4,955,884

The income from operations and interest expense from the income statement for both companies were as follows:

	Hasbro	Mattel
Income from operations	$376,363	$728,818
Interest expense	27,521	79,853

a. Determine the ratio of liabilities to stockholders' equity for both companies. Round to one decimal place.

b. Determine the number of times interest charges are earned for both companies. Round to one decimal place.

c. Interpret the ratio differences between the two companies.

E9-15

Ratio of liabilities to stockholders' equity and ratio of fixed assets to long-term liabilities

Obj 2

✓ a. H.J. Heinz, 4.4

Recent balance sheet information for two companies in the food industry, **H.J. Heinz Company** and **The Hershey Company,** are as follows (in thousands of dollars):

	H.J. Heinz	Hershey
Net property, plant, and equipment	$1,998,153	$1,651,300
Current liabilities	2,505,106	1,453,538
Long-term debt	4,413,641	1,248,128
Other long-term liabilities	1,272,596	486,473
Stockholders' equity	1,841,683	683,423

a. Determine the ratio of liabilities to stockholders' equity for both companies. Round to one decimal place.

b. Determine the ratio of fixed assets to long-term liabilities for both companies. Round to one decimal place.

c. Interpret the ratio differences between the two companies.

E9-16

Ratio of net sales to assets

Obj 3

✓ a. YRC Worldwide, 1.7

Three major segments of the transportation industry are motor carriers, such as **YRC Worldwide;** railroads, such as **Union Pacific;** and transportation arrangement services, such as **C.H. Robinson Worldwide Inc.** Recent financial statement information for these three companies is shown as follows (in thousands of dollars):

	YRC Worldwide	Union Pacific	C.H. Robinson Worldwide Inc.
Net sales	$9,918,690	$15,578,000	$6,566,194
Average total assets	5,829,713	36,067,500	1,513,381

a. Determine the ratio of net sales to assets for all three companies. Round to one decimal place.

b. Assume that the ratio of net sales to assets for each company represents that company's respective industry segment. Interpret the differences in the ratio of net sales to assets in terms of the operating characteristics of each of the respective segments.

E9-17

Profitability ratios

Obj 3

✓ a. Rate earned on total assets, 2010, 12.0%

The following selected data were taken from the financial statements of The Sigemund Group Inc. for December 31, 2010, 2009, and 2008:

	December 31		
	2010	2009	2008
Total assets	$3,000,000	$2,700,000	$2,400,000
Notes payable (10% interest)	1,000,000	1,000,000	1,000,000
Common stock	400,000	400,000	400,000
Preferred $6 stock, $100 par (no change during year)	200,000	200,000	200,000
Retained earnings	1,126,000	896,000	600,000

The 2010 net income was $242,000, and the 2009 net income was $308,000. No dividends on common stock were declared between 2008 and 2010.

a. Determine the rate earned on total assets, the rate earned on stockholders' equity, and the rate earned on common stockholders' equity for the years 2009 and 2010. Round to one decimal place.

b. What conclusions can be drawn from these data as to the company's profitability?

E9-18

Profitability ratios

Obj 3

✓ a. 2006 rate earned on total assets, fiscal year ended 2/3/2007 9.5%

Ann Taylor Retail, Inc., sells professional women's apparel through company-owned retail stores. Recent financial information for Ann Taylor is provided below (all numbers in thousands).

	Year 3	Year 2
Net income	$142,982	$81,872
Interest expense	2,230	2,083

	Year 3	Year 2	Year 1
Total assets	$1,568,503	$1,492,906	$1,327,338
Total stockholders' equity	1,049,911	1,034,482	926,744

Assume the apparel industry average rate earned on total assets is 8.2%, and the average rate earned on stockholders' equity is 10.0% for year 3.

a. Determine the rate earned on total assets for Ann Taylor for Years 3 and 2. Round to one digit after the decimal place.
b. Determine the rate earned on stockholders' equity for Ann Taylor for Year 3 and 2. Round to one decimal place.
c. Evaluate the two-year trend for the profitability ratios determined in (a) and (b).
d. Evaluate Ann Taylor's profit performance relative to the industry.

E9-19

Six measures of solvency or profitability

Objs 2, 3

✓ c. Ratio of net sales to assets, 5.0

The following data were taken from the financial statements of Heston Enterprises Inc. for the current fiscal year. Assuming that long-term investments totaled $2,100,000 throughout the year and that total assets were $4,000,000 at the beginning of the year, determine the following: (a) ratio of fixed assets to long-term liabilities, (b) ratio of liabilities to stockholders' equity, (c) ratio of net sales to assets, (d) rate earned on total assets, (e) rate earned on stockholders' equity, and (f) rate earned on common stockholders' equity. Round to one decimal place.

Property, plant, and equipment (net)			$ 1,600,000
Liabilities:			
Current liabilities		$ 200,000	
Mortgage note payable, 10%, issued 1999, due 2015		1,000,000	
Total liabilities			$ 1,200,000
Stockholders' equity:			
Preferred $10 stock, $100 par (no change during year)			$ 1,000,000
Common stock, $10 par (no change during year)			1,000,000
Retained earnings:			
Balance, beginning of year	$800,000		
Net income	400,000	$1,200,000	
Preferred dividends	$100,000		
Common dividends	100,000	200,000	
Balance, end of year			1,000,000
Total stockholders' equity			$ 3,000,000
Net sales			$10,000,000
Interest expense			$ 100,000

E9-20

Six measures of solvency or profitability

Objs 2, 3

✓ d. Price-earnings ratio, 10.0

The balance sheet for Bearing Industries Inc. at the end of the current fiscal year indicated the following:

Bonds payable, 10% (issued in 2000, due in 2020)	$4,000,000
Preferred $5 stock, $100 par	1,000,000
Common stock, $10 par	2,000,000

Income before income tax was $1,000,000, and income taxes were $150,000 for the current year. Cash dividends paid on common stock during the current year totaled $200,000. The common stock was selling for $40 per share at the end of the year. Determine each of the following: (a) number of times bond interest charges are earned, (b) number of times preferred dividends are earned, (c) earnings per share on common stock, (d) price-earnings ratio, (e) dividends per share of common stock, and (f) dividend yield. Round to one decimal place except earnings per share, which should be rounded to two decimal places.

E9-21

Earnings per share, price-earnings ratio, dividend yield

Obj 3

✓ b. Price-earnings ratio, 12.5

The following information was taken from the financial statements of Finn Resources Inc. for December 31 of the current fiscal year:

Common stock, $20 par value (no change during the year)	$5,000,000
Preferred $10 stock, $40 par (no change during the year)	800,000

The net income was $600,000 and the declared dividends on the common stock were $125,000 for the current year. The market price of the common stock is $20 per share.

For the common stock, determine (a) the earnings per share, (b) the price-earnings ratio, (c) the dividends per share, and (d) the dividend yield. Round to one decimal place except earnings per share, which should be rounded to two decimal places.

E9-22

Price-earnings ratio; dividend yield

Obj 3

The table below shows the stock price, earnings per share, and dividends per share for three companies as of October 2007:

	Price	Earnings per Share	Dividends per Share
Bank of America Corporation	$52.99	$4.59	$2.12
eBay Inc	33.51	0.57	0.00
The Coca-Cola Company	47.76	2.16	1.24

a. Determine the price-earnings ratio and dividend yield for the three companies. Round to one decimal place.
b. Explain the differences in these ratios across the three companies.

E9-23

Earnings per share

Appendix

✓ b. Earnings per share on common stock, $23.40

The net income reported on the income statement of Goth Co. was $2,500,000. There were 100,000 shares of $10 par common stock and 40,000 shares of $4 preferred stock outstanding throughout the current year. The income statement included two extraordinary items: a $500,000 gain from condemnation of land and a $200,000 loss arising from flood damage, both after applicable income tax. Determine the per-share figures for common stock for (a) income before extraordinary items and (b) net income.

E9-24

Extraordinary item

Appendix

Assume that the amount of each of the following items is material to the financial statements. Classify each item as either normally recurring (NR) or unusual items. If unusual item then specify if it is a discontinued item (DI) or extraordinary (E).

a. Loss on the disposal of equipment considered to be obsolete because of the development of new technology.
b. Uncollectible accounts expense.
c. Gain on sale of land condemned by the local government for a public works project.
d. Interest revenue on notes receivable.
e. Uninsured loss on building due to hurricane damage. The building was purchased by the company in 1910 and had not previously incurred hurricane damage.
f. Loss on sale of investments in stocks and bonds.
g. Uninsured flood loss. (Flood insurance is unavailable because of periodic flooding in the area.)

E9-25

Income statement and earnings per share for extraordinary items and discontinued operations

Appendix

Brady, Inc., reports the following for 2010:

Income from continuing operations before income tax	$500,000
Extraordinary property loss from hurricane	$ 60,000*
Loss from discontinued operations	$ 90,000*
Weighted average number of shares outstanding	40,000
Applicable tax rate	40%

*Net of any tax effect.

a. Prepare a partial income statement for Brady, Inc., beginning with income from continuing operations before income tax.
b. Assuming 200,000 shares, calculate the earnings per common share for Brady, Inc., including per-share amounts for unusual items.

Problems

P9-1

Horizontal analysis for income statement

SPREADSHEET

Obj 1

✓ 1. Net sales, 10.0% increase

For 2010, Wiglaf Technology Company reported its most significant decline in net income in years. At the end of the year, C. S. Lewis, the president, is presented with the following condensed comparative income statement:

Wiglaf Technology Company
Comparative Income Statement
For the Years Ended December 31, 2010 and 2009

	2010	2009
Sales	$560,000	$500,000
Sales returns and allowances	37,500	25,000
Net sales	$522,500	$475,000
Cost of goods sold	372,000	300,000
Gross profit	$150,500	$175,000
Selling expenses	$ 52,000	$ 40,000
Administrative expenses	30,500	25,000
Total operating expenses	$ 82,500	$ 65,000
Income from operations	$ 68,000	$110,000
Other income	3,000	2,000
Income before income tax	$ 71,000	$112,000
Income tax expense	5,500	5,000
Net income	$ 65,500	$107,000

Instructions

1. Prepare a comparative income statement with horizontal analysis for the two-year period, using 2009 as the base year. Round to one decimal place.

2. To the extent the data permit, comment on the significant relationships revealed by the horizontal analysis prepared in (1).

P9-2

Vertical analysis for income statement

SPREADSHEET

Obj 1

✓ 1. Net income, 2010, 16.0%

For 2010, Othere Technology Company initiated a sales promotion campaign that included the expenditure of an additional $20,000 for advertising. At the end of the year, George Wallace, the president, is presented with the following condensed comparative income statement:

Othere Technology Company
Comparative Income Statement
For the Years Ended December 31, 2010 and 2009

	2010	2009
Sales	$714,000	$612,000
Sales returns and allowances	14,000	12,000
Net sales	$700,000	$600,000
Cost of goods sold	322,000	312,000
Gross profit	$378,000	$288,000
Selling expenses	$154,000	$120,000
Administrative expenses	70,000	66,000
Total operating expenses	$224,000	$186,000
Income from operations	$154,000	$102,000
Other income	28,000	24,000
Income before income tax	$182,000	$126,000
Income tax	70,000	60,000
Net income	$112,000	$ 66,000

Instructions

1. Prepare a comparative income statement for the two-year period, presenting an analysis of each item in relationship to net sales for each of the years. Round to one decimal place.
2. To the extent the data permit, comment on the significant relationships revealed by the vertical analysis prepared in (1).

P9-3

Effect of transactions on current position analysis

SPREADSHEET

Obj 2

✓ 2. c. Current ratio, 2.6

Data pertaining to the current position of Boole Company are as follows:

Cash	$240,000
Temporary investments	120,000
Accounts and notes receivable (net)	360,000
Inventories	380,000
Prepaid expenses	20,000
Accounts payable	140,000
Notes payable (short-term)	200,000
Accrued expenses	60,000

Instructions

1. Compute (a) the working capital, (b) the current ratio, and (c) the quick ratio. Round to one decimal place.
2. List the following captions on a sheet of paper:

Transaction	Working Capital	Current Ratio	Quick Ratio

Compute the working capital, the current ratio, and the quick ratio after each of the following transactions, and record the results in the appropriate columns. Consider each transaction separately and assume that only that transaction affects the data given above. Round to one decimal place.

a. Sold temporary investments at no gain or loss, $45,000.
b. Paid accounts payable, $80,000.
c. Purchased goods on account, $50,000.
d. Paid notes payable, $100,000.
e. Declared a cash dividend, $80,000.
f. Declared a common stock dividend on common stock, $22,500.
g. Borrowed cash from bank on a long-term note, $200,000.
h. Received cash on account, $67,500.
i. Issued additional shares of stock for cash, $400,000.
j. Paid cash for prepaid expenses, $40,000.

P9-4

Nineteen measures of solvency and profitability

SPREADSHEET

Objs 2, 3

✓ 5. Number of days' sales in receivables, 53.7

The comparative financial statements of Optical Solutions Inc. are as follows. The market price of Optical Solutions Inc. common stock was $60.00 on December 31, 2010.

Optical Solutions Inc.
Comparative Retained Earnings Statement
For the Years Ended December 31, 2010 and 2009

	2010	2009
Retained earnings, January 1	$ 604,000	$306,000
Add net income for year	428,000	314,000
Total	$1,032,000	$620,000
Deduct dividends:		
On preferred stock	$ 4,000	$ 4,000
On common stock	12,000	12,000
Total	$ 16,000	$ 16,000
Retained earnings, December 31	$1,016,000	$604,000

Optical Solutions Inc.
Comparative Income Statement
For the Years Ended December 31, 2010 and 2009

	2010	2009
Sales	$1,608,000	$1,481,600
Sales returns and allowances	5,920	6,000
Net sales	$1,602,080	$1,475,600
Cost of goods sold	480,200	499,200
Gross profit	$1,121,880	$ 976,400
Selling expenses	$ 324,000	$ 352,000
Administrative expenses	234,000	211,200
Total operating expenses	$ 558,000	$ 563,200
Income from operations	$ 563,880	$ 413,200
Other income	24,000	19,200
	$ 587,880	$ 432,400
Other expense (interest)	110,720	80,000
Income before income tax	$ 477,160	$ 352,400
Income tax expense	49,160	38,400
Net income	$ 428,000	$ 314,000

Optical Solutions Inc.
Comparative Balance Sheet
December 31, 2010 and 2009

	Dec. 31, 2010	Dec. 31, 2009
Assets		
Current assets:		
Cash	$ 240,000	$ 162,400
Temporary investments	364,000	328,800
Accounts receivable (net)	260,000	211,200
Inventories	208,000	66,400
Prepaid expenses	44,000	23,200
Total current assets	$1,116,000	$ 792,000
Long-term investments	204,800	256,000
Property, plant, and equipment (net).	1,539,200	976,000
Total assets.	$2,860,000	$2,024,000
Liabilities		
Current liabilities	$ 360,000	$ 320,000
Long-term liabilities:		
Mortgage note payable, 8%, due 2015	$ 384,000	—
Bonds payable, 10%, due 2019	800,000	$ 800,000
Total long-term liabilities	$1,184,000	$ 800,000
Total liabilities.	$1,544,000	$1,120,000
Stockholders' Equity		
Preferred $2.00 stock, $50 par	$ 100,000	$ 100,000
Common stock, $5 par	200,000	200,000
Retained earnings	1,016,000	604,000
Total stockholders' equity	$1,316,000	$ 904,000
Total liabilities and stockholders' equity.	$2,860,000	$2,024,000

Instructions

Determine the following measures for 2010, rounding to one decimal place:

1. Working capital
2. Current ratio
3. Quick ratio
4. Accounts receivable turnover
5. Number of days' sales in receivables
6. Inventory turnover
7. Number of days' sales in inventory
8. Ratio of fixed assets to long-term liabilities
9. Ratio of liabilities to stockholders' equity
10. Number of times interest charges earned
11. Number of times preferred dividends earned
12. Ratio of net sales to assets
13. Rate earned on total assets
14. Rate earned on stockholders' equity
15. Rate earned on common stockholders' equity
16. Earnings per share on common stock
17. Price-earnings ratio
18. Dividends per share of common stock
19. Dividend yield

P9-5

Solvency and profitability trend analysis

Objs 2, 3

Lancelot Company has provided the following comparative information:

	2010	2009	2008	2007	2006
Net income	$ 1,930,500	$1,287,000	$ 975,000	$ 650,000	$ 500,000
Interest expense	400,200	345,000	300,000	240,000	200,000
Income tax expense	477,360	318,240	244,800	163,200	120,000
Total assets (ending balance)	11,498,760	8,845,200	6,804,000	5,040,000	4,200,000
Total stockholders' equity (ending balance)	6,742,500	4,812,000	3,525,000	2,550,000	1,900,000
Average total assets	10,171,980	7,824,600	5,922,000	4,620,000	3,600,000
Average stockholders' equity	5,777,250	4,168,500	3,037,500	2,225,000	1,650,000

You have been asked to evaluate the historical performance of the company over the last five years.

Selected industry ratios have remained relatively steady at the following levels for the last five years:

	2006–2010
Rate earned on total assets	15%
Rate earned on stockholders' equity	18%
Number of times interest charges earned	3.5
Ratio of liabilities to stockholders' equity	1.4

Instructions

1. Prepare four line graphs with the ratio on the vertical axis and the years on the horizontal axis for the following four ratios (rounded to one decimal place):

   a. Rate earned on total assets

   b. Rate earned on stockholders' equity

   c. Number of times interest charges earned

   d. Ratio of liabilities to stockholders' equity

   Display both the company ratio and the industry benchmark on each graph. That is, each graph should have two lines.

2. Prepare an analysis of the graphs in (1).

Activities

A9-1

Analysis of financing corporate growth

Assume that the president of Garden Isle Brewery made the following statement in the Annual Report to Shareholders:

> "The founding family and majority shareholders of the company do not believe in using debt to finance future growth. The founding family learned from hard experience during Prohibition and the Great Depression that debt can cause loss of flexibility and eventual loss of corporate control. The company will not place itself at such risk. As such, all future growth will be financed either by stock sales to the public or by internally generated resources."

As a public shareholder of this company, how would you respond to this policy?

A9-2

Receivables and inventory turnover

Tylee Industries, Inc., has completed its fiscal year on December 31, 2010. The auditor, Holly Marcum, has approached the CFO, Doug Bliss, regarding the year-end receivables and inventory levels of Tylee Industries. The following conversation takes place:

Holly: We are beginning our audit of Tylee Industries and have prepared ratio analyses to determine if there have been significant changes in operations or financial position. This helps us guide the audit process. This analysis indicates that the inventory turnover has decreased from 4.5 to 2.1, while the accounts receivable turnover has decreased from 10 to 6. I was wondering if you could explain this change in operations.

Doug: There is little need for concern. The inventory represents computers that we were unable to sell during the holiday buying season. We are confident, however, that we will be able to sell these computers as we move into the next fiscal year.

Holly: What gives you this confidence?

Doug: We will increase our advertising and provide some very attractive price concessions to move these machines. We have no choice. Newer technology is already out there, and we have to unload this inventory.

Holly: ... and the receivables?

Doug: As you may be aware, the company is under tremendous pressure to expand sales and profits. As a result, we lowered our credit standards to our commercial customers so that we would be able to sell products to a broader customer base. As a result of this policy change, we have been able to expand sales by 35%.

Holly: Your responses have not been reassuring to me.

Doug: I'm a little confused. Assets are good, right? Why don't you look at our current ratio? It has improved, hasn't it? I would think that you would view that very favorably.

Why is Holly concerned about the inventory and accounts receivable turnover ratios and Doug's responses to them? What action may Holly need to take? How would you respond to Doug's last comment?

A9-3

Vertical analysis

The condensed income statements through income from operations for *Dell Inc.* and *Apple Inc.*, are reproduced below for recent fiscal years (numbers in millions of dollars).

	Dell Inc.	Apple Inc.
Sales (net)	$57,420	$24,006
Cost of sales	44,904	15,852
Gross profit	$12,516	$ 8,154
Selling, general, and administrative expenses	$ 5,948	$ 2,963
Research and development	498	782
Operating expenses	$ 6,446	$ 3,745
Income from operations	$ 6,070	$ 4,409

Prepare comparative common-sized statements, rounding percents to one decimal place. Interpret the analyses.

A9-4

Profitability and stockholder ratios

Harley-Davidson, Inc., is a leading motorcycle manufacturer in the United States. The company manufactures and sells a number of different types of motorcycles, a complete line of motorcycle parts, and brand-related accessories, clothing, and collectibles. In recent years, Harley-Davidson has attempted to expand its dealer network and product lines internationally.

The following information is available for three recent years (in millions except per-share amounts):

	Year 3	Year 2	Year 1
Net income (loss)	$ 960	$ 890	$ 761
Preferred dividends	$ 0.00	$ 0.00	$ 0.00
Interest expense	$36.15	$22.72	$17.64
Shares outstanding for computing earnings per share	280	295	302
Cash dividend per share	$ 0.63	$ 0.41	$ 0.20
Average total assets	$5,369	$5,203	$4,392
Average stockholders' equity	$3,151	$3,088	$2,595
Average stock price per share	$56.12	$54.14	$46.87

1. Calculate the following ratios for each year:
   a. Rate earned on total assets
   b. Rate earned on stockholders' equity
   c. Earnings per share
   d. Dividend yield
   e. Price-earnings ratio

2. What is the ratio of average liabilities to average stockholders' equity for Year 3?

3. Explain the direction of the dividend yield and price-earnings ratio in light of Harley-Davidson's profitability trend.

4. Based on these data, evaluate Harley-Davidson's strategy to expand to international markets.

A9-5

Comprehensive profitability and solvency analysis

Marriott International, Inc., and *Hilton Hotels Corporation* are two major owners and managers of lodging and resort properties in the United States. Abstracted income statement information for the two companies is as follows for a recent year:

	Marriott (in millions)	Hilton (in millions)
Operating profit before other expenses and interest	$1,011	$1,274
Other income (expenses)	7	62
Interest expense	(124)	(498)
Income before income taxes	894	838
Income tax expense	286	266
Net income	$ 608	$ 572

Balance sheet information is as follows:

	Marriott (in millions)	Hilton (in millions)
Total liabilities	$5,970	$12,754
Total stockholders' equity	2,618	3,727
Total liabilities and stockholders' equity	$8,588	$16,481

The average liabilities, stockholders' equity, and total assets were as follows:

	Marriott	Hilton
Average total liabilities	$7,250	$ 9,343
Average total stockholders' equity	2,935	3,269
Average total assets	6,933	12,612

1. Determine the following ratios for both companies (round to one decimal place after the whole percent):

   a. Rate earned on total assets

   b. Rate earned on total stockholders' equity

   c. Number of times interest charges are earned

   d. Ratio of liabilities to stockholders' equity

2. Analyze and compare the two companies, using the information in (1).

Answers to Self-Examination Questions

1. **A** Percentage analysis indicating the relationship of the component parts to the total in a financial statement, such as the relationship of current assets to total assets (20% to 100%) in the question, is called vertical analysis (answer A). Percentage analysis of increases and decreases in corresponding items in comparative financial statements is called horizontal analysis (answer B). An example of horizontal analysis would be the presentation of the amount of current assets in the preceding balance sheet, along with the amount of current assets at the end of the current year, with the increase or decrease in current assets between the periods expressed as a percentage. Profitability analysis (answer C) is the analysis of a firm's ability to earn income. Contribution margin analysis (answer D) is discussed in a later managerial accounting chapter.

2. **D** Various solvency measures, categorized as current position analysis, indicate a firm's ability to meet currently maturing obligations. Each measure contributes to the analysis of a firm's current position and is most useful when viewed with other measures and when compared with similar measures for other periods and for other firms. Working capital (answer A) is the excess of current assets over current liabilities; the current ratio (answer B) is the ratio of current assets to current liabilities; and the quick ratio (answer C) is the ratio of the sum of cash, receivables, and temporary investments to current liabilities.

3. **D** The ratio of current assets to current liabilities is usually called the current ratio (answer A). It is sometimes called the working capital ratio (answer B) or bankers' ratio (answer C).

4. **C** The ratio of the sum of cash, receivables, and temporary investments (sometimes called quick assets) to current liabilities is called the quick ratio (answer C) or acid-test ratio. The current ratio (answer A), working capital ratio (answer B), and bankers' ratio (answer D) are terms that describe the ratio of current assets to current liabilities.

5. **C** The number of days' sales in inventory (answer C), which is determined by dividing the average inventory by the average daily cost of goods sold, expresses the relationship between the cost of goods sold and inventory. It indicates the efficiency in the management of inventory. The working capital ratio (answer A) indicates the ability of the business to meet currently maturing obligations (debt). The quick ratio (answer B) indicates the "instant" debt-paying ability of the business. The ratio of fixed assets to long-term liabilities (answer D) indicates the margin of safety for long-term creditors.

Accounting Systems for Manufacturing Businesses

Learning Objectives
After studying this chapter, you should be able to:

Obj 1 Distinguish the activities of a manufacturing business from those of a merchandising or service business.

Obj 2 Define and illustrate materials, factory labor, and factory overhead costs.

Obj 3 Describe cost accounting systems used by manufacturing businesses.

Obj 4 Describe and illustrate a job order cost accounting system.

Obj 5 Use job order cost information for decision making.

Obj 6 Describe the flow of costs for a service business that uses a job order cost accounting system.

Obj 7 Describe just-in-time manufacturing practices.

Obj 8 Describe and illustrate the use of activity-based costing in a service business.

D an Donegan, guitarist for the rock band *Disturbed*, entertains millions of fans each year playing his guitar. His guitar was built by **Washburn Guitars** in Chicago. Washburn Guitars is well-known in the music industry and has been in business for over 120 years.

Staying in business for 120 years requires a thorough understanding of how to manufacture high-quality guitars. In addition, it requires knowledge of how to account for the costs of making guitars. For example, Washburn needs cost information to answer the following questions:

How much should be charged for its guitars?

How many guitars does it have to sell in a year to cover its costs and earn a profit?

How many employees should the company have working on each stage of the manufacturing process?

How would purchasing automated equipment affect the costs of its guitars?

Washburn Guitars can answer these questions with the aid of cost information. This chapter introduces cost concepts used in managerial accounting that help answer questions like those above. In addition, the development of cost information and its use in manufacturing a product will be described and illustrated.

This chapter begins by describing the nature of manufacturing businesses. We then introduce basic cost terms and describe accounting systems for manufacturing businesses. Using this as a basis, a job order cost accounting system is described and illustrated. This chapter concludes by focusing on recent trends in manufacturing and the design of manufacturing accounting systems.

Nature of Manufacturing Businesses

Obj 1 Distinguish the activities of a manufacturing business from those of a merchandising or service business.

Chapters 2 and 3 described and illustrated accounting systems for service businesses. Chapter 4 described and illustrated accounting systems for merchandising businesses. This chapter focuses on manufacturing businesses. Examples of manufacturing businesses include *General Motors* and *Intel Corporation.*

The revenue activities of a service business involve providing services to customers. The revenue activities of a merchandising business involve the buying and selling of merchandise. In contrast, a manufacturing business first produces the products it sells. A manufacturing business converts materials into finished products through the use of machinery and labor.

Like merchandising businesses, a manufacturing business reports sales from selling its products. The cost of the products sold is normally reported as **cost of goods sold**, whereas a merchandising business reports these costs as cost of merchandise sold. The subtraction of the cost of goods sold from sales is reported as gross profit. Operating expenses are deducted from gross profit to arrive at net income.

Materials, products in the process of being manufactured, and finished products are reported on the manufacturer's balance sheet as inventories. Like merchandise inventory, these inventories are reported as current assets.

Manufacturing Cost Terms

Obj 2 Define and illustrate materials, factory labor, and factory overhead costs.

Managers rely on managerial accountants to provide useful *cost* information to support decision making. What is a cost? A **cost** is a payment of cash or its equivalent or the commitment to pay cash in the future for the purpose of generating revenues. A cost provides a benefit that is used immediately or deferred to a future period of time. If the benefit is used immediately, then the cost is an expense, such as salary expense. If the benefit is deferred, then the cost is an asset, such as equipment. As the asset is used, an expense, such as depreciation expense, is recognized.

This section illustrates manufacturing costs for Legend Guitars, a manufacturing firm. A *manufacturing business* converts materials into a finished product through the use of machinery and labor. Legend Guitars manufactures guitars as shown in Exhibit 1.

EXHIBIT 1   **Guitar Making Operations of Legend Guitars**

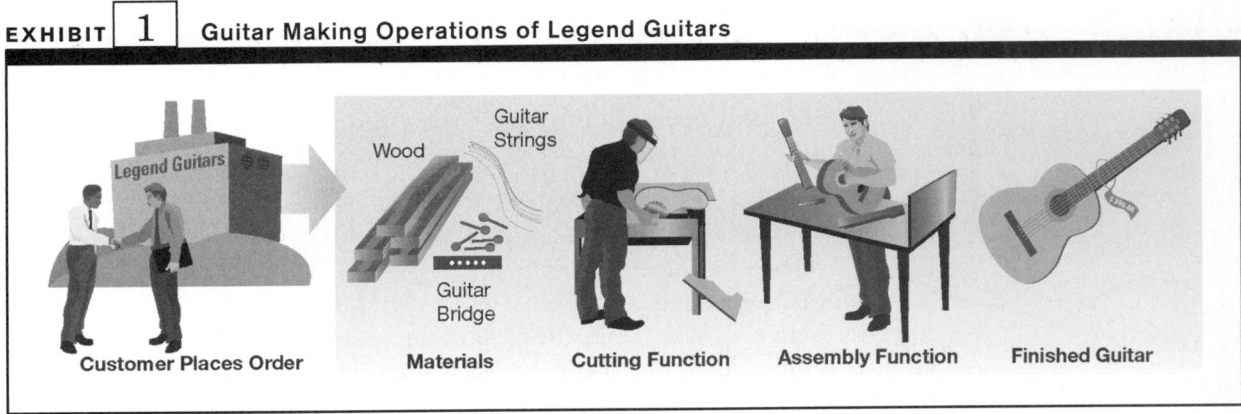

Customer Places Order   Materials   Cutting Function   Assembly Function   Finished Guitar

Legend's guitar-making process begins when a customer places an order for a guitar. Once the order is accepted, the manufacturing process begins by obtaining the necessary materials. An employee then cuts the body and neck of the guitar out of raw lumber. Once the wood is cut, the body and neck of the guitar are assembled. When the assembly is complete, the guitar is painted and finished.

The cost of a manufactured product includes the cost of materials used in making the product. In addition, the cost of a manufactured product includes the cost of converting the materials into a finished product. For example, Legend Guitars uses employees and machines to convert wood (and other supplies) into finished guitars. Thus, the cost of a finished guitar (the cost object) includes the following:

1. Direct materials cost

2. Direct labor cost

3. Factory overhead cost

Direct Materials Cost

Manufactured products begin with raw materials that are converted into finished products. The cost of any material that is an integral part of the finished product is classified as a **direct materials cost.** For Legend Guitars, direct materials cost includes the cost of the wood used in producing each guitar. Other examples of direct materials costs include the cost of electronic components for a television, silicon wafers for microcomputer chips, and tires for an automobile.

To be classified as a direct materials cost, the cost must be *both* of the following:

1. An integral part of the finished product

2. A significant portion of the total cost of the product

For Legend Guitars, the cost of the guitar strings is not a direct materials cost. This is because the cost of guitar strings is an insignificant part of the total cost of each guitar. Instead, the cost of guitar strings is classified as a factory overhead cost, which is discussed later.

Materials costs such as the cost of the guitar strings are referred to as indirect materials costs. Another example of an indirect cost for Legend Guitars is glue. As noted above, indirect materials costs are included in factory overhead.

Direct Labor Cost

Most manufacturing processes use employees to convert materials into finished products. The cost of employee wages that is an integral part of the finished product is classified as **direct labor cost**. For Legend Guitars, direct labor cost includes the wages of the employees who cut each guitar out of raw lumber and assemble it. Other examples of direct labor costs include mechanics' wages for repairing an automobile, machine operators' wages for manufacturing tools, and assemblers' wages for assembling a laptop computer.

Like a direct materials cost, a direct labor cost must be *both* of the following:

1. An integral part of the finished product
2. A significant portion of the total cost of the product

For Legend Guitars, the wages of the janitors who clean the factory are not a direct labor cost. This is because janitorial costs are not an integral part or a significant cost of each guitar. Instead, janitorial costs are classified as a factory overhead cost, which is discussed next.

Such labor costs as janitorial costs are referred to as indirect labor costs. Another example of an indirect labor cost for Legend Guitars is salaries of maintenance employees and plant supervisors. As noted above, indirect labor costs are included in factory overhead.

Factory Overhead Cost

Costs other than direct materials cost and direct labor cost that are incurred in the manufacturing process are combined and classified as **factory overhead cost**. Factory overhead is sometimes called *manufacturing overhead* or *factory burden*.

All factory overhead costs are indirect costs of the product. Some factory overhead costs include the following:

1. Heating and lighting the factory
2. Repairing and maintaining factory equipment
3. Property taxes on factory buildings and land
4. Insurance on factory buildings
5. Depreciation on factory plant and equipment

As manufacturing processes have become more automated, direct labor costs have become so small that they are often included as part of factory overhead.

Factory overhead cost also includes materials and labor costs that do not enter directly into the finished product. Examples include the cost of oil used to lubricate machinery and the wages of janitorial and supervisory employees. Also, if the costs of direct materials or direct labor are not a significant portion of the total product cost, these costs may be classified as factory overhead costs.

For Legend Guitars, the costs of guitar strings and janitorial wages are factory overhead costs. Additional factory overhead costs of making guitars are as follows:

1. Sandpaper
2. Buffing compound
3. Glue
4. Power (electricity) to run the machines
5. Depreciation of the machines and building
6. Salaries of production supervisors

Prime Costs and Conversion Costs

Direct materials, direct labor, and factory overhead costs may be grouped together for analysis and reporting. Two such common groupings are as follows:

1. **Prime costs**, which consist of direct materials and direct labor costs

2. **Conversion costs**, which consist of direct labor and factory overhead costs

Conversion costs are the costs of converting the materials into a finished product. Direct labor is both a prime cost and a conversion cost, as shown in Exhibit 2.

EXHIBIT **2**   Prime Costs and Conversion Costs

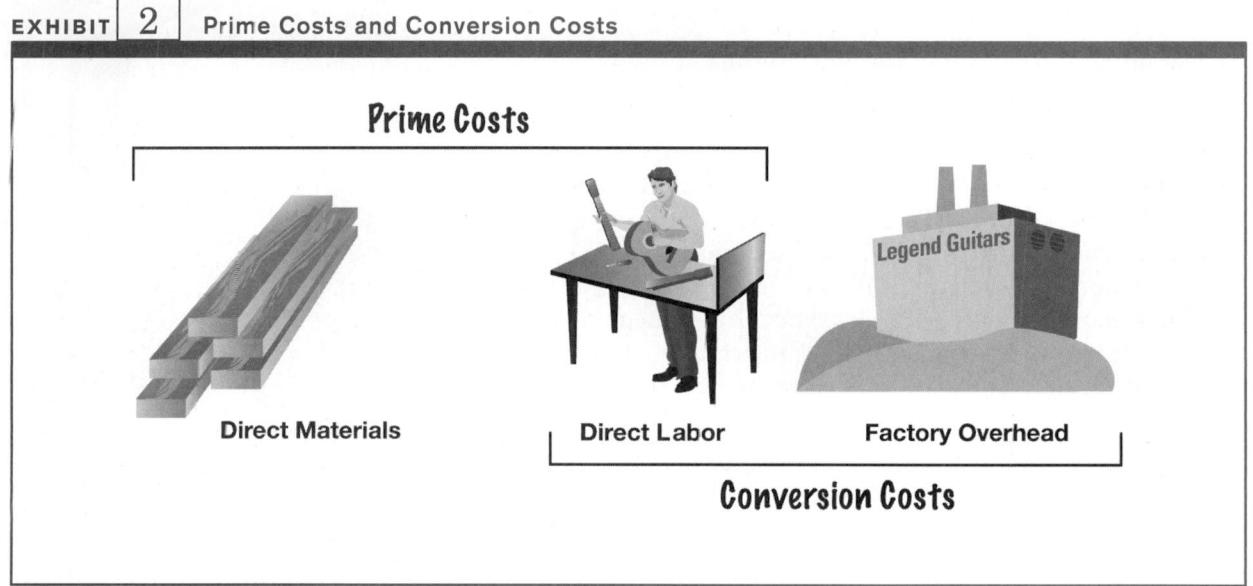

Product Costs and Period Costs

For financial reporting purposes, costs are classified as product costs or period costs.

1. **Product costs** consist of manufacturing costs: direct materials, direct labor, and factory overhead.

2. **Period costs** consist of selling and administrative expenses. *Selling expenses* are incurred in marketing the product and delivering the product to customers. *Administrative expenses* are incurred in managing the company and are not directly related to the manufacturing or selling functions.

Examples of product costs and period costs for Legend Guitars are presented in Exhibit 3.

To facilitate control, selling and administrative expenses may be reported by level of responsibility. For example, selling expenses may be reported by products, salespersons, departments, divisions, or territories. Likewise, administrative expenses may be reported by areas such as human resources, computer services, legal, accounting, or finance.

The impact on the financial statements of product and period costs is summarized in Exhibit 4. As product costs are incurred, they are recorded and reported on the balance sheet as *inventory*. When the inventory is sold, the cost of the manufactured product sold is reported as *cost of goods sold* on the income statement. Period costs are reported as *expenses* on the income statement in the period in which they are incurred and thus never appear on the balance sheet.

EXHIBIT 3 | Examples of Product Costs and Period Costs—Legend Guitars

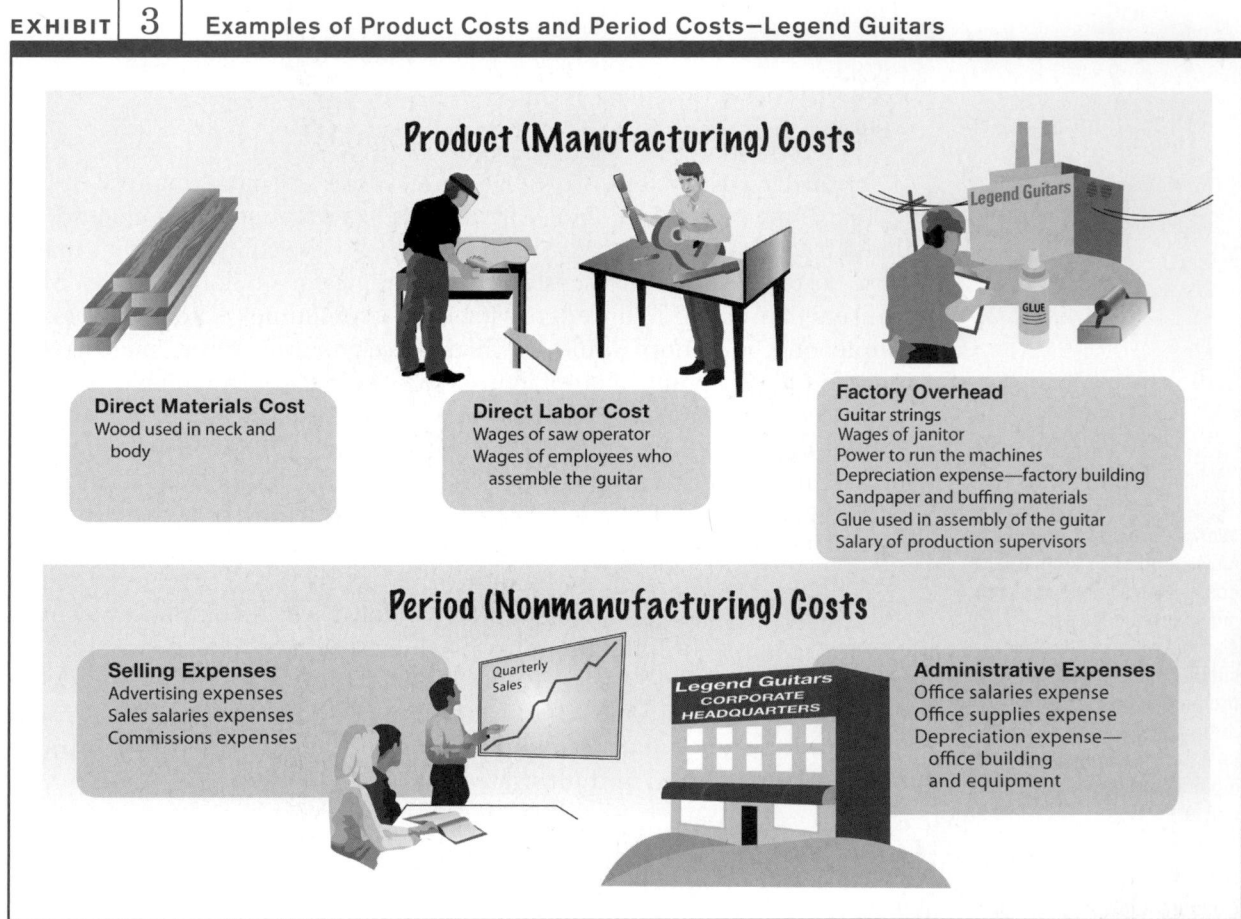

EXHIBIT 4 | Product Costs, Period Costs, and the Financial Statements

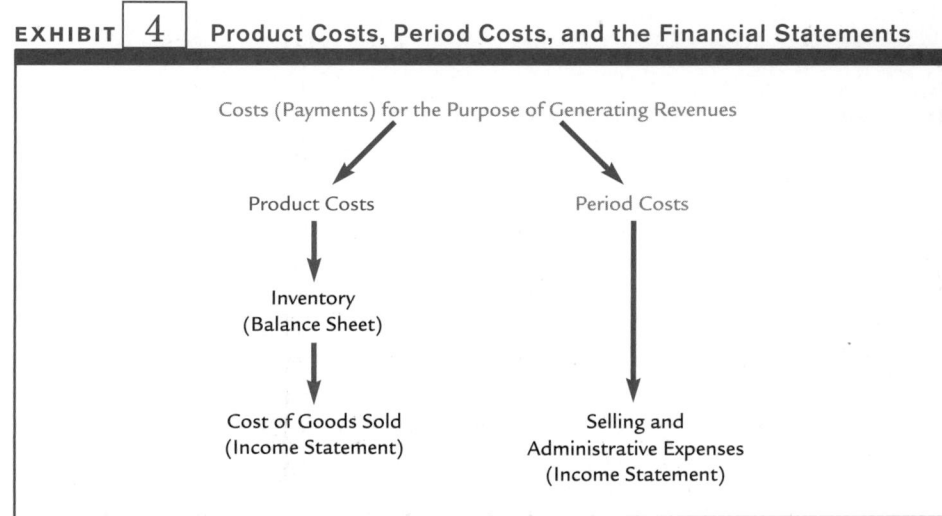

Cost Accounting System Overview

Obj 3 Describe cost accounting systems used by manufacturing businesses.

Cost accounting systems measure, record, and report product costs. Managers use product costs for setting product prices, controlling operations, and developing financial statements.

The two main types of cost accounting systems for manufacturing operations are:

1. Job order cost systems
2. Process cost systems

A **job order cost system** provides product costs for each quantity of product that is manufactured. Each quantity of product that is manufactured is called a *job*. Job order cost systems are often used by companies that manufacture custom products for customers or batches of similar products. Manufacturers that use a job order cost system are sometimes called *job shops*. An example of a job shop would be an apparel manufacturer, such as **Levi Strauss & Co.**, or a guitar manufacturer such as Washburn Guitars.

A **process cost system** provides product costs for each manufacturing department or process. Process cost systems are often used by companies that manufacture units of a product that are indistinguishable from each other and are manufactured using a continuous production process. Examples would be oil refineries, paper producers, chemical processors, and food processors.

Job order and process cost systems are widely used. A company may use a job order cost system for some of its products and a process cost system for other products.

In this chapter, the job order cost system is illustrated. As a basis for illustration, Legend Guitars, a manufacturer of guitars, is used. The process cost system is described and illustrated in Appendix B.

Job Order Cost Systems for Manufacturing Businesses

A job order cost system records and summarizes manufacturing costs by jobs. The flow of manufacturing costs in a job order system is illustrated in Exhibit 5.

Warner Bros. and other movie studios use job order cost systems to accumulate movie production and distribution costs. Costs such as actor salaries, production costs, movie print costs, and marketing costs are accumulated in a job account for a particular movie.

Obj 4 Describe and illustrate a job order cost accounting system.

EXHIBIT 5   **Flow of Manufacturing Costs**

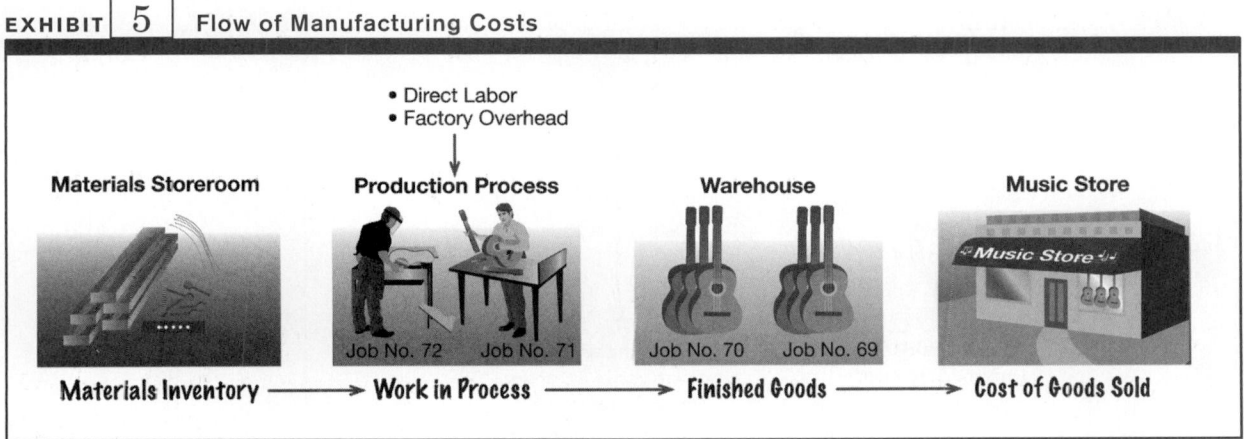

The **materials inventory**, sometimes called *raw materials inventory*, consists of the costs of the direct and indirect materials that have not yet entered the manufacturing process. For Legend Guitars, the materials inventory would consist of wood, guitar strings, guitar bridges, and glue.

The **work-in-process inventory** consists of direct materials costs, direct labor costs, and factory overhead costs that have entered the manufacturing

process but are associated with products that have not been completed. For example, although the materials for Jobs 71 and 72 have been added, they are still in the production process. Thus, Jobs 71 and 72 are in Work-in-Process Inventory as shown in Exhibit 5.

The **finished goods inventory** consists of completed jobs that have not been sold. Jobs 69 and 70 have been completed and are included in Finished Goods Inventory as shown in Exhibit 5.

Upon sale, a manufacturer records the cost of the sale as *cost of goods sold*. An example is the guitars sold to the music store in Exhibit 5. The cost of goods sold for a manufacturer is comparable to the cost of merchandise sold for a merchandising business.

In a job order cost accounting system, perpetual inventory records are maintained for materials, work-in-process, and finished goods inventories. For example, materials inventory is supported by subsidiary inventory accounts that record the increase, decrease, and amount on hand for each type of material. These subsidiary materials accounts are kept in a ledger, called a **subsidiary ledger**. The sum of the subsidiary ledger accounts equals the balance of the materials account, called the **controlling account**.[1]

The controlling accounts and subsidiary ledgers for materials, work-in-process, and finished goods inventories are illustrated below for Legend Guitars.

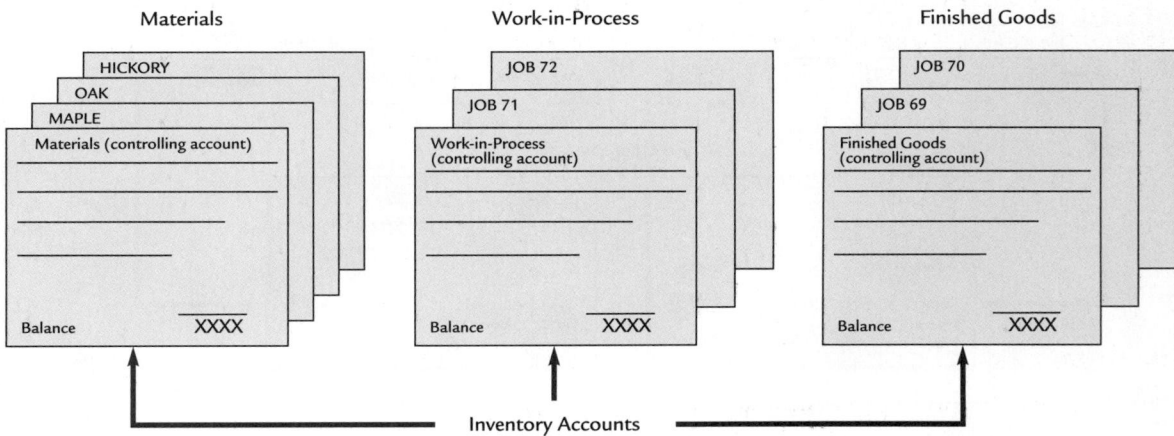

Materials

The materials account is a controlling account. A separate account for each type of material is maintained in a subsidiary **materials ledger**.

Exhibit 6 shows Legend Guitars' materials subsidiary ledger account for maple. Increases and decreases to the account are as follows:

1. Increases are based on *receiving reports* such as Receiving Report No. 196 for $10,500, which is supported by the supplier's invoice.

2. Decreases are based on *materials requisitions* such as Requisition No. 672 for $2,000 for Job 71 and Requisition No. 704 for $11,000 for Job 72.

Many companies use bar code scanning devices in place of receiving reports to record and electronically transmit incoming materials data.

---

[1] In addition to inventory, controlling accounts and subsidiary ledgers are also normally maintained for accounts receivable; accounts payable; property, plant, and equipment; and capital stock.

EXHIBIT 6 | Materials Information and Cost Flows

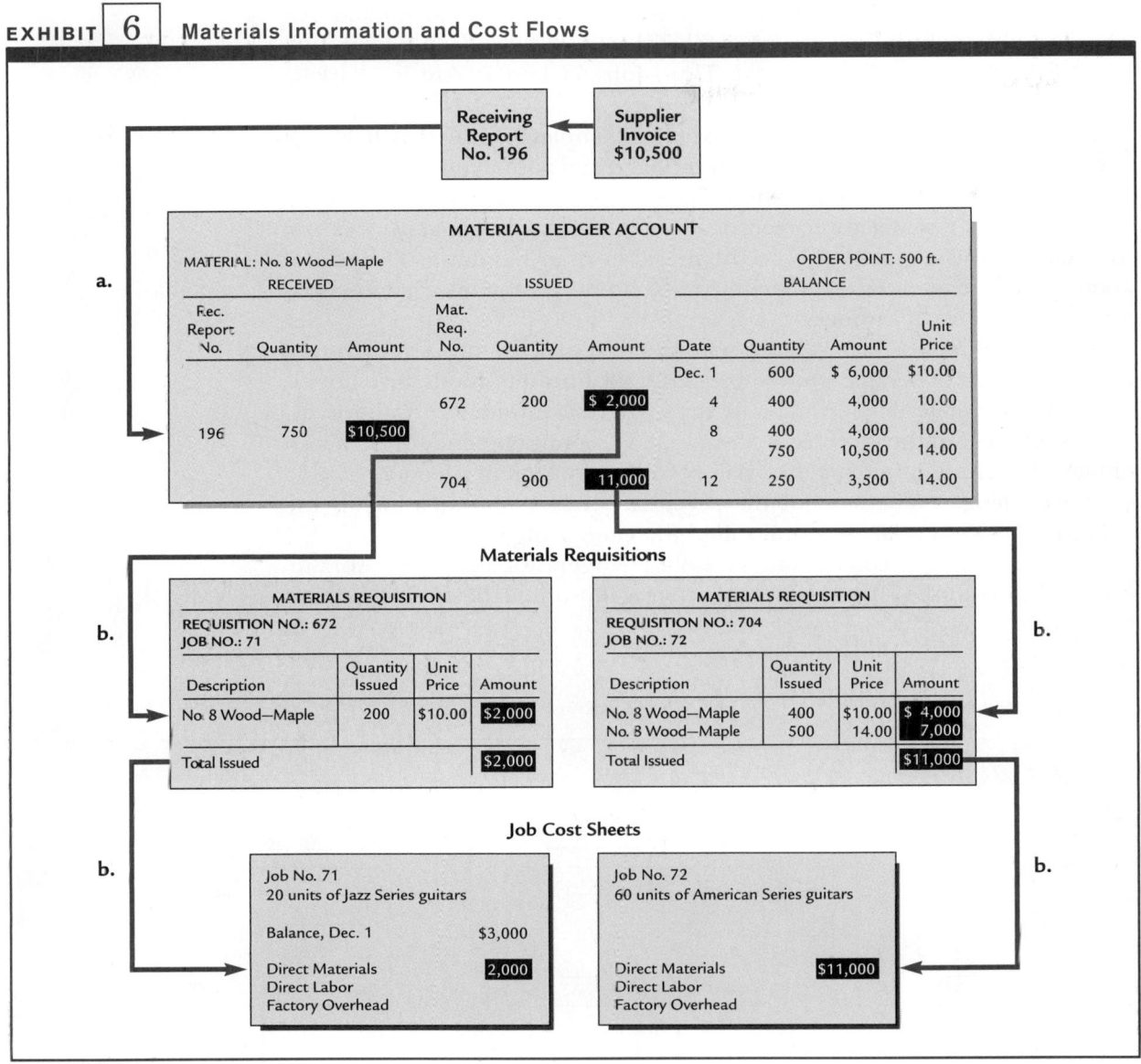

A **receiving report** is prepared when materials that have been ordered are received and inspected. The quantity received and the condition of the materials are entered on the receiving report. When the supplier's invoice is received, it is compared to the receiving report. If there are no discrepancies, the purchase is recorded.

The effect on the accounts and financial statements of recording the supplier invoice and receiving report No. 196 is shown below.

Statement of Cash Flows	Balance Sheet					Income Statement
	Assets	=	Liabilities	+	Stockholders' Equity	
	Materials	=	Accounts Payable			
d.	10,500		10,500			

The storeroom releases materials for use in manufacturing when a **materials requisition** is received. An example of a materials requisition is shown in Exhibit 6.

The materials requisitions for each job serve as the basis for recording materials used. For direct materials, the quantities and amounts from the materials requisitions are recorded on job cost sheets. **Job cost sheets**, which are illustrated in Exhibit 6, make up the work-in-process subsidiary ledger.

Exhibit 6 shows the posting of $2,000 of direct materials to Job 71 and $11,000 of direct materials to Job 72.[2] Job 71 is an order for 20 units of Jazz Series guitars, while Job 72 is an order for 60 units of American Series guitars.

A summary of the materials requisitions is used as a basis for recording the materials of $13,000 ($2,000 + $11,000) used for the month. The effect on the accounts and financial statements of the materials used in December is shown below.

For many manufacturing firms, the direct materials cost can be greater than 50% of the total cost to manufacture a product. This is why controlling materials costs is very important.

Statement of Cash Flows	Balance Sheet						Income Statement
	Assets		=	Liabilities	+	Stockholders' Equity	
	Materials	+	Work in Process				
b.	−13,000		13,000				

Many companies use computerized information processes to record the use of materials. In such cases, storeroom employees electronically record the release of materials, which automatically updates the materials ledger and job cost sheets.

INTEGRITY, OBJECTIVITY, AND ETHICS IN BUSINESS

Phony Invoice Scams

A popular method for defrauding a company is to issue a phony invoice. The scam begins by initially contacting the target firm to discover details of key business contacts, business operations, and products. The swindler then uses this information to create a fictitious invoice. The invoice will include names, figures, and other details to give it the appearance of legitimacy. This type of scam can be avoided if invoices are matched with receiving documents prior to issuing a check.

Factory Labor

When employees report for work, they may use *clock cards, in-and-out cards,* or *electronic badges* to clock in. When employees work on an individual job, they use **time tickets**. Exhibit 7 illustrates time tickets for Jobs 71 and 72.

Exhibit 7 shows that on December 13, 2010, D. McInnis spent six hours working on Job 71 at an hourly rate of $10 for a cost of $60 (6 hrs. × $10). Exhibit 7 also indicates that a total of 350 hours was spent by employees on Job 71 during December for a total cost of $3,500. This total direct labor cost of $3,500 is recorded on the job cost sheet for Job 71, as shown in Exhibit 7.

---

[2] To simplify, Exhibit 6 and this chapter use the first-in, first-out cost flow method.

EXHIBIT 7   Labor Information and Cost Flows

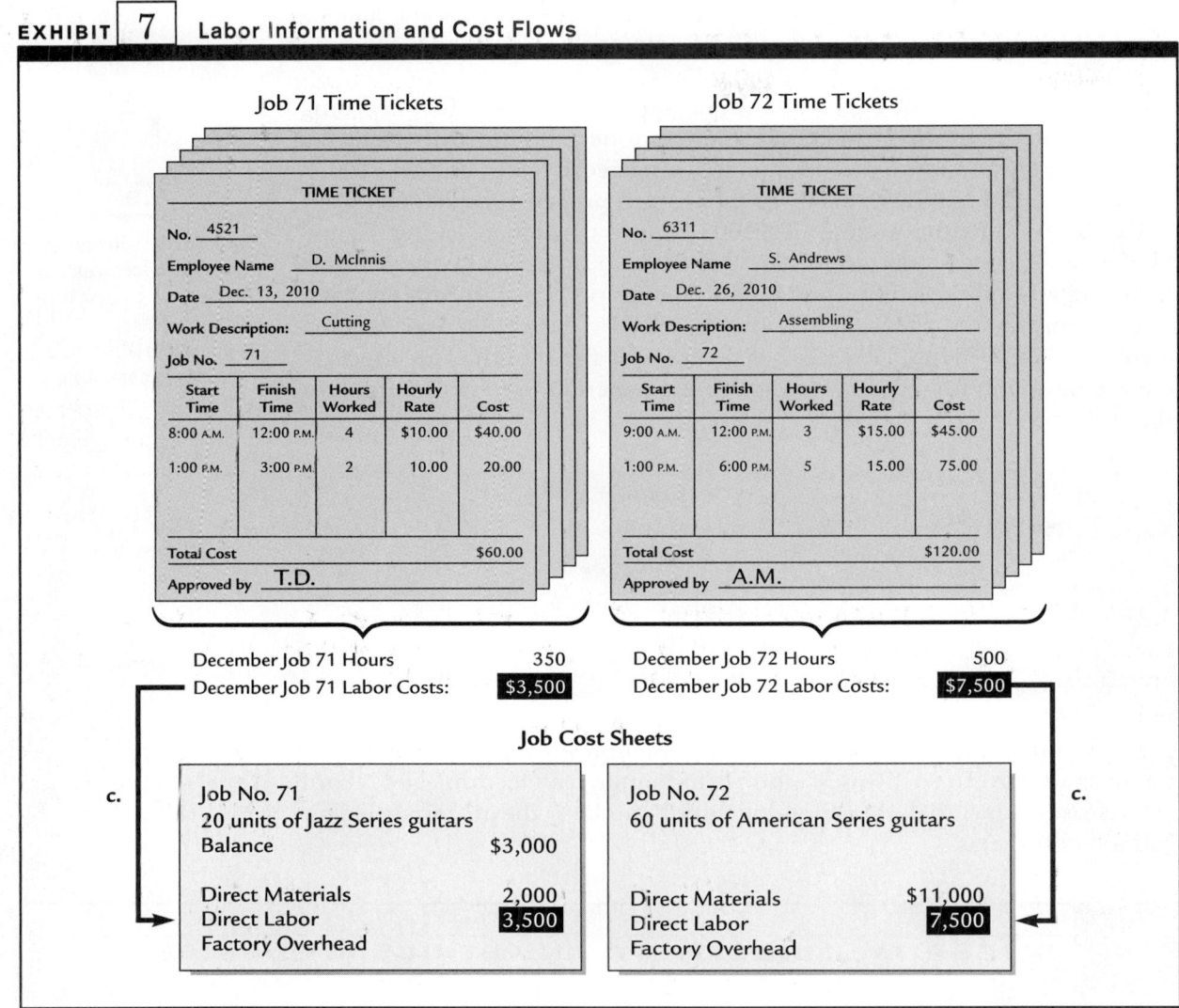

Likewise, Exhibit 7 shows that on December 26, 2010, S. Andrews spent eight hours on Job 72 at an hourly rate of $15 for a cost of $120 (8 hrs. × $15). A total of 500 hours was spent by employees on Job 72 during December for a total cost of $7,500. This total direct labor cost of $7,500 is posted to the job cost sheet for Job 72, as shown in Exhibit 7.

A summary of the time tickets is used as the basis for recording direct labor of $11,000 ($3,500 + $7,500) for the month. The direct labor costs that flow into production increase Work in Process and Wages Payable. The effect on the accounts and financial statements of recording the direct labor for December is shown below.

Statement of Cash Flows	Balance Sheet					Income Statement
	Assets	=	Liabilities	+	Stockholders' Equity	
	Work in Process	=	Wages Payable			
c.	11,000		11,000			

As with direct materials, many businesses use computerized information processing to record direct labor. In such cases, employees may log their time directly into computer terminals at their workstations. In other cases, employees may be issued magnetic cards, much like credit cards, to log in and out of work assignments.

INTEGRITY, OBJECTIVITY, AND ETHICS IN BUSINESS

Ghost Employees

Companies must guard against the fraudulent creation and cashing of payroll checks. Numerous payroll frauds involve supervisors adding fictitious employees to or failing to remove departing employees from the payroll and then cashing the check. This type of fraud can be minimized by requiring proper authorization and approval of employee additions, removals, or changes in pay rates.

Factory Overhead Cost

Factory overhead includes all manufacturing costs except direct materials and direct labor. A summary of factory overhead costs comes from a variety of sources including the following:

1. *Indirect materials* comes from a summary of materials requisitions.
2. *Indirect labor* comes from the salaries of production supervisors and the wages of other employees such as janitors.
3. *Factory power* comes from utility bills.
4. *Factory depreciation* comes from Accounting Department computations of depreciation.

Shell Group uses a magnetic card system to track the work of maintenance crews in its refinery operations.

To illustrate the recording of factory overhead, assume that Legend Guitars incurred $4,600 of overhead in December. The effect on the accounts and financial statements is shown below.

Statement of Cash Flows	Balance Sheet						Income Statement
	Assets			=	Liabilities	+ Stockholders' Equity	
	Materials	+ Factory Overhead	− Accumulated Depreciation	=	Wages Payable	+ Utilities Payable	
d.	−500	4,600	−1,200		2,000	900	

Allocating Factory Overhead

Factory overhead is different from direct labor and direct materials in that it is *indirectly* related to the jobs. That is, factory overhead costs cannot be identified with or traced to specific jobs. For this reason, factory overhead costs are allocated to jobs. The process by which factory overhead or other costs are assigned to a cost object, such as a job, is called **cost allocation**.

The factory overhead costs are *allocated* to jobs using a common measure related to each job. This measure is called an **activity base**, *allocation base*, or

activity driver. The activity base used to allocate overhead should reflect the consumption or use of factory overhead costs. For example, production supervisor salaries could be allocated on the basis of direct labor hours or direct labor cost of each job.

Predetermined Factory Overhead Rate

Factory overhead costs are normally allocated or *applied* to jobs using a **predetermined factory overhead rate**. The predetermined factory overhead rate is computed as follows:

$$\frac{\text{Predetermined Factory}}{\text{Overhead Rate}} = \frac{\text{Estimated Total Factory Overhead Costs}}{\text{Estimated Activity Base}}$$

To illustrate, assume that Legend Guitars estimates the total factory overhead cost as $50,000 for the year and the activity base as 10,000 direct labor hours. The predetermined factory overhead rate of $5 per direct labor hour is computed as follows:

$$\frac{\text{Predetermined Factory}}{\text{Overhead Rate}} = \frac{\text{Estimated Total Factory Overhead Costs}}{\text{Estimated Activity Base}}$$

$$\frac{\text{Predetermined Factory}}{\text{Overhead Rate}} = \frac{\$50,000}{10,000 \text{ direct labor hours}} = \$5 \text{ per direct hour}$$

As shown above, the predetermined overhead rate is computed using *estimated* amounts at the beginning of the period. This is because managers need timely information on the product costs of each job. If a company waited until all overhead costs were known at the end of the period, the allocated factory overhead would be accurate, but not timely. Only through timely reporting can managers adjust manufacturing methods or product pricing.

Many companies are using a method for accumulating and allocating factory overhead costs. This method, called **activity-based costing**, uses a different overhead rate for each type of factory overhead activity, such as inspecting, moving, and machining. Activity-based costing is discussed and illustrated at the end of this chapter.

A survey conducted by the Cost Management Group of the Institute for Management Accountants found that 20% of survey respondents had adopted activity-based costing.

Applying Factory Overhead to Work in Process

Legend Guitars applies factory overhead using a rate of $5 per direct labor hour. The factory overhead applied to each job is recorded on the job cost sheets, as shown in Exhibit 8.

Exhibit 8 shows that 850 direct labor hours were used in Legend Guitars' December operations. Based on the time tickets, 350 hours can be traced to Job 71, and 500 hours can be traced to Job 72.

Using a factory overhead rate of $5 per direct labor hour, $4,250 of factory overhead is applied as follows:

	Direct Labor Hours	Factory Overhead Rate	Factory Overhead Applied
Job 71	350	$5	$1,750 (350 hrs. × $5)
Job 72	500	$5	2,500 (500 hrs. × $5)
Total	850		$4,250

As shown in Exhibit 8, the applied overhead is recorded on each job cost sheet. Factory overhead of $1,750 is posted to Job 71, which results in a total

EXHIBIT 8 | Applying Factory Overhead to Jobs

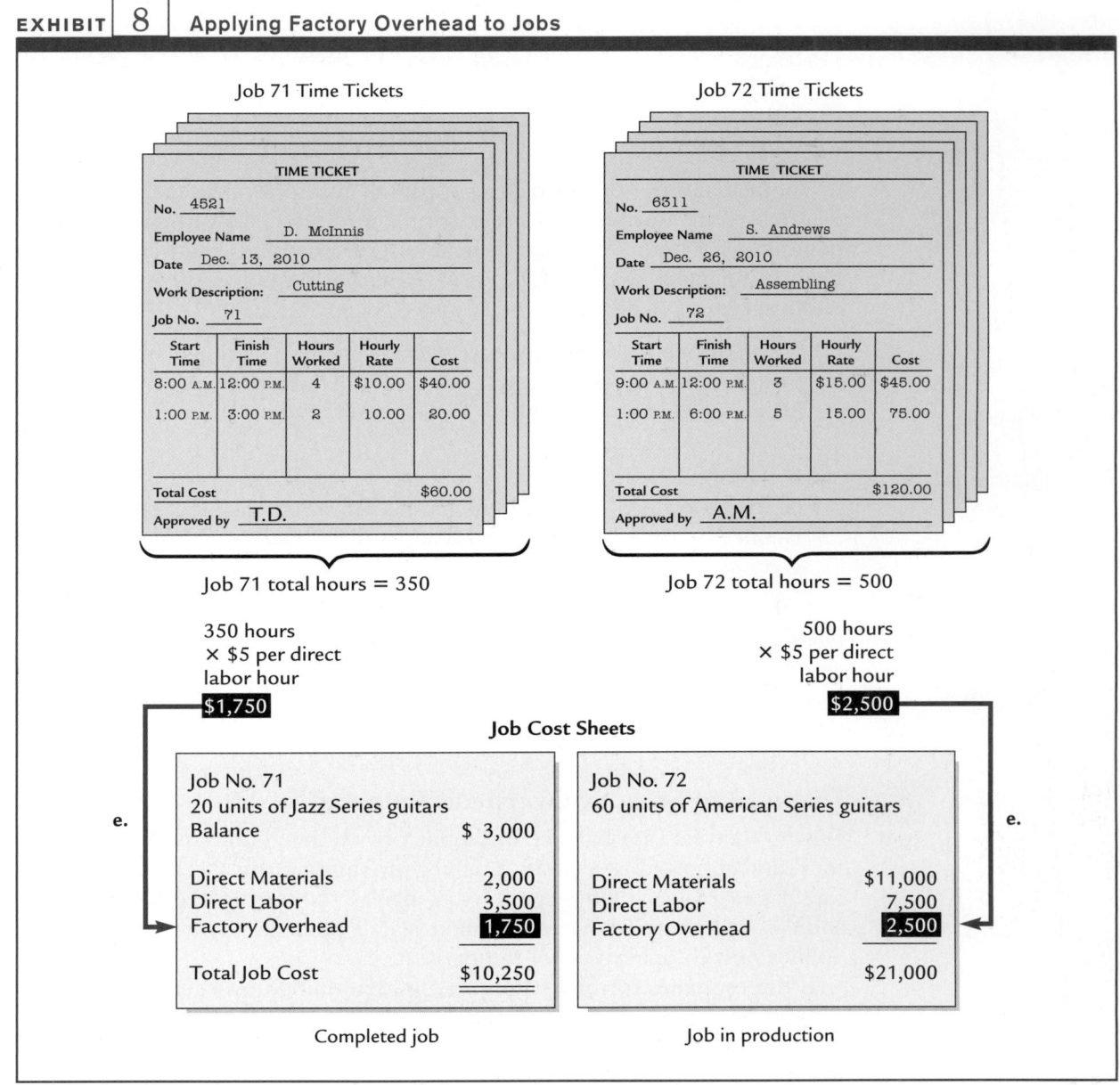

product cost on December 31, 2010, of $10,250. Factory overhead of $2,500 is posted to Job 72, which results in a total product cost on December 31, 2010, of $21,000.

The factory overhead costs applied to production increase the work in process account and decrease the factory overhead account. The effect of applying the $4,250 ($1,750 + $2,500) of factory overhead to production on the accounts and financial statements for Legend Guitars is shown below.

Statement of Cash Flows	Balance Sheet					Income Statement
	Assets		= Liabilities	+	Stockholders' Equity	
	Work in Process	+ Factory Overhead				
e.	4,250	−4,250				

To summarize, the factory overhead account is:

1. Increased for the *actual overhead* costs incurred, as shown earlier for transaction (d) on page 373.
2. Decreased for the *applied overhead,* as shown in the previous page for transaction (e).

The actual and applied overhead usually differ because the actual overhead costs are normally different from the estimated overhead costs. Depending on whether actual overhead is greater or less than applied overhead, the factory overhead account will either have a positive or negative ending balance as follows:

1. If the applied overhead is *less than* the actual overhead incurred, the factory overhead account will have a positive balance. This positive balance is called **underapplied factory overhead** or *underabsorbed factory overhead.*
2. If the applied overhead is *more than* the actual overhead incurred, the factory overhead account will have a negative balance. This negative balance is called **overapplied factory overhead** or *overabsorbed factory overhead.*

If the balance of factory overhead (either underapplied or overapplied) becomes large, the balance and related overhead rate should be investigated. For example, a large balance could be caused by changes in manufacturing methods. In this case, the factory overhead rate should be revised.

Disposal of Factory Overhead Balance

During the year, the balance in the factory overhead account is carried forward and reported as a positive or negative amount on the monthly (interim) balance sheets. However, any balance in the factory overhead account should not be carried over to the next year. This is because any such balance applies only to operations of the current year.

If the estimates for computing the predetermined overhead rate are reasonably accurate, the ending balance of Factory Overhead should be relatively small. For this reason, the balance of Factory Overhead at the end of the year is disposed of by transferring it to the cost of goods sold account as follows:[3]

1. An ending positive balance (underapplied overhead) in the factory overhead account is disposed of by increasing Cost of Goods Sold and decreasing Factory Overhead.
2. An ending negative balance (overapplied overhead) in the factory overhead account is disposed of by increasing Factory Overhead and decreasing Cost of Goods Sold.

To illustrate, the effect on the accounts and financial statements of eliminating an underapplied (positive) overhead balance of $150 at the end of the year for Legend Guitars is as shown on the next page:

---

[3] An ending balance in the factory overhead account may also be allocated among the work in process, finished goods, and cost of goods sold accounts. This brings these accounts into agreement with the actual costs incurred. This approach is rarely used and is only required for large ending balances in the factory overhead account. For this reason, it will not be used in this text.

Statement of Cash Flows	Balance Sheet					Income Statement
	Assets	=	Liabilities	+	Stockholders' Equity	
	Factory Overhead	=			Retained Earnings	
f.	−150				−150	f.

	Income Statement	
	f. Cost of goods sold	−150

Work in Process

During the period, Work in Process is increased for the following:

1. Direct materials cost
2. Direct labor cost
3. Applied factory overhead cost

To illustrate, the balance of work in process for Legend Guitars on December 1, 2010 (beginning balance) was $3,000. This balance relates to Job 71, which was the only job in process on this date. During December, Work in Process was increased for the following:

1. Direct materials cost of $13,000 [transaction (b)] based on materials requisitions.
2. Direct labor cost of $11,000 [transaction (c)] based on time tickets.
3. Applied factory overhead of $4,250 [transaction (e)] based on the pre-determined overhead rate of $5 per direct labor hour.

The preceding increases in Work in Process are supported by the job cost sheets for Jobs 71 and 72, as shown in Exhibit 9.

During December, Job 71 was completed. Upon completion, the product costs (direct materials, direct labor, factory overhead) are totaled. This total is divided by the number of units produced to determine the cost per unit. Thus, the 20 Jazz Series guitars produced as Job 71 cost $512.50 ($10,250/20) per guitar.

After completion, Job 71 is transferred from Work in Process to Finished Goods. For Job 71, this transfer of costs affects the accounts and financial statements as follows:

Statement of Cash Flows	Balance Sheet					Income Statement
	Assets		=	Liabilities	+ Stockholders' Equity	
	Work in Process	+ Finished Goods				
g.	−10,250	10,250				

Job 72 was started in December, but was not completed by December 31, 2010. Thus, Job 72 is still part of work in process on December 31, 2010. As shown in Exhibit 9, the balance of the job cost sheet for Job 72 ($21,000) is also the December 31, 2010 balance of Work in Process.

EXHIBIT 9   Job Cost Sheets and the Work in Process Controlling Accounts

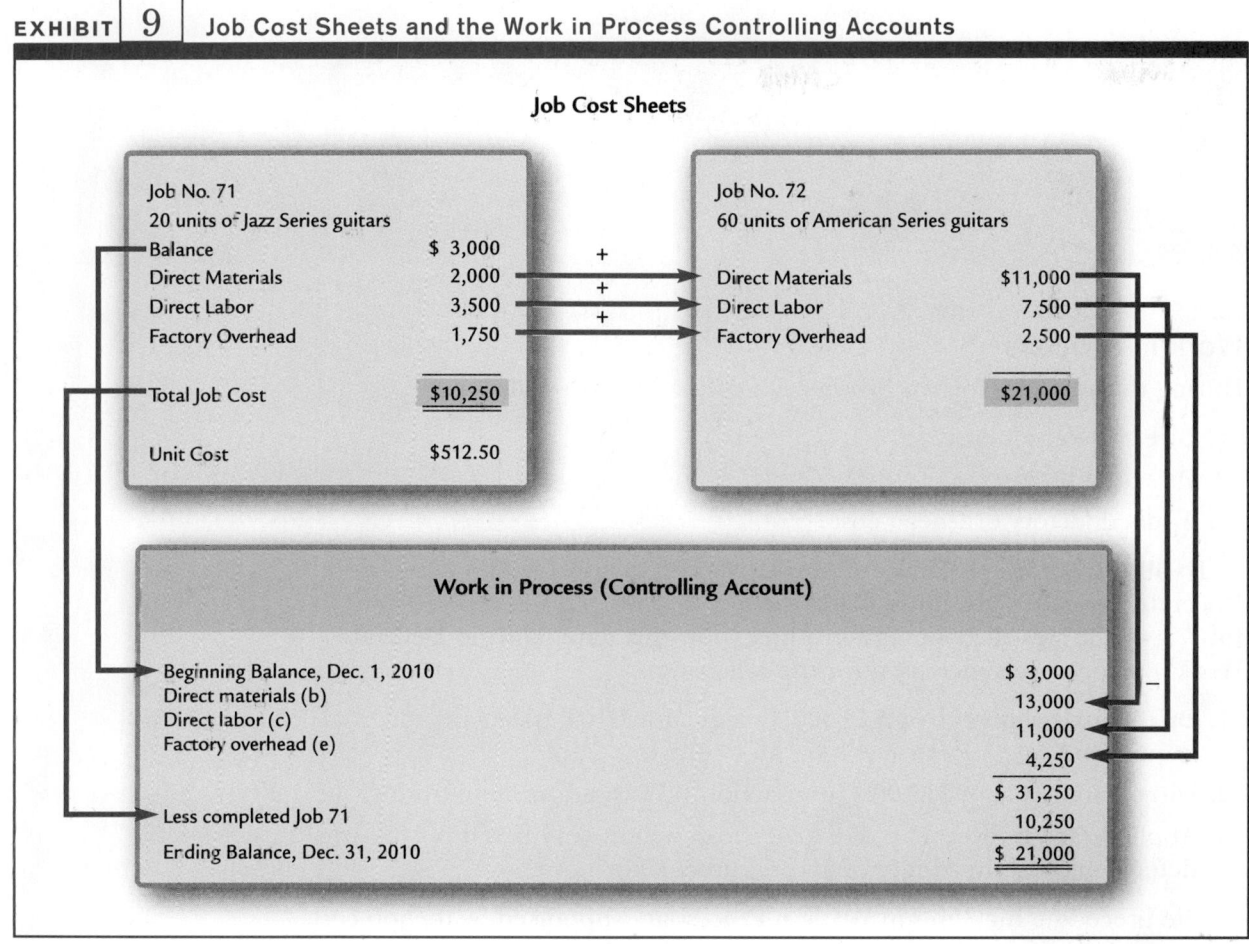

Finished Goods

The finished goods account is a controlling account for the subsidiary **finished goods ledger** or *stock ledger*. Each account in the finished goods ledger contains cost data for the units manufactured, units sold, and units on hand.

Exhibit 10 illustrates the finished goods ledger account for Jazz Series guitars.

EXHIBIT 10   Finished Goods Ledger Account

ITEM: *Jazz Series guitars*

Manufactured			Shipped			Balance			
Job Order No.	Quantity	Amount	Ship Order No.	Quantity	Amount	Date	Quantity	Amount	Unit Cost
						Dec. 1	40	$20,000	$500.00
			643	40	$20,000	9	—	—	—
71	20	$10,250				31	20	10,250	512.50

Exhibit 10 indicates that there were 40 Jazz Series guitars on hand on December 1, 2010. During the month, 20 additional Jazz guitars were completed and transferred to Finished Goods from the completion of Job 71. In addition, the beginning inventory of 40 Jazz guitars were sold during the month.

Sales and Cost of Goods Sold

Sales for a manufacturing business and a merchandising business have the same effect on the accounts and financial statements. To illustrate, assume that Legend Guitars sold the 40 Jazz Series guitars during December for $850 per unit. These guitars have a cost of $500 per unit. The cost data can be obtained from the finished goods ledger. The effect of selling the 40 Jazz guitars on the accounts and financial statements is as follows:

	Balance Sheet							
Statement of Cash Flows	Assets		=	Liabilities	+	Stockholders' Equity		Income Statement
	Accounts Receivable	+ Finished Goods =					Retained Earnings	
h.	34,000	−20,000					14,000	h.

Income Statement	
h. Sales	34,000
Cost of goods sold	−20,000
Net income	14,000

Period Costs

Period costs are used in generating revenue during the current period, but are not involved in the manufacturing process. Period costs are recorded as expenses of the current period as either selling or administrative expenses.

Selling expenses are incurred in marketing the product and delivering sold products to customers. Administrative expenses are incurred in managing the company, but are not related to the manufacturing or selling functions.

Service companies, such as telecommunications, insurance, banking, broadcasting, and hospitality, typically have a large portion of their total costs as period costs with few product costs.

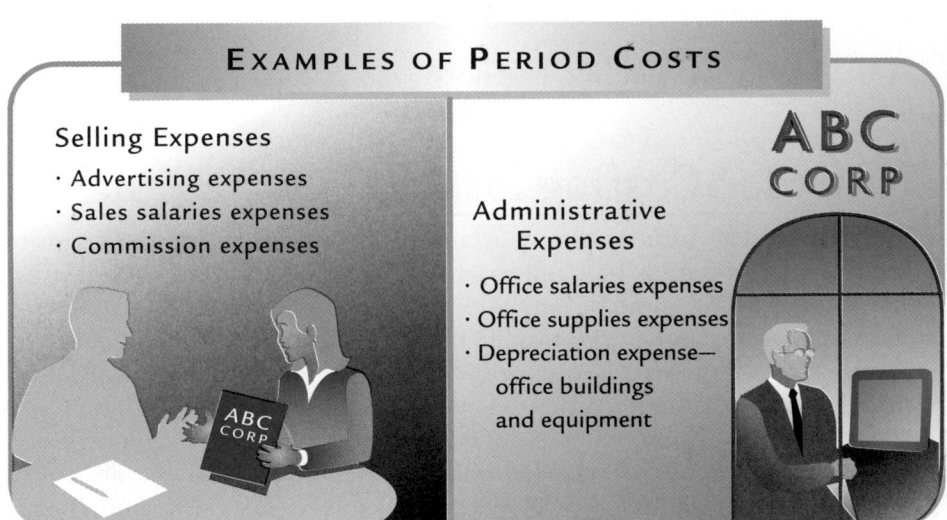

EXAMPLES OF PERIOD COSTS

Selling Expenses
· Advertising expenses
· Sales salaries expenses
· Commission expenses

Administrative Expenses
· Office salaries expenses
· Office supplies expenses
· Depreciation expense—office buildings and equipment

ABC CORP

During December Legend Guitars incurred sales salaries of $2,000 and office salaries of $1,500. The effect on the accounts and financial statements of recording the December salaries is as follows:

Statement of Cash Flows			Balance Sheet				Income Statement
	Assets	=	Liabilities	+	Stockholders' Equity		
			Salaries Payable	+	Retained Earnings		
i.			3,500		−3,500	i.	

Income Statement	
i. Sales salaries exp.	−2,000
Office salaries exp.	−1,500
Net income	−3,500

Summary of Cost Flows for Legend Guitars

Exhibit 11 shows the cost flows through the manufacturing accounts of Legend Guitars for December. In Exhibit 11, increases are shown on the left side and decreases are shown on the right side of the accounts. In addition, summary details of the following subsidiary ledgers are shown:

1. *Materials Ledger*—the subsidiary ledger for Materials.
2. *Job Cost Sheets*—the subsidiary ledger for Work in Process.
3. *Finished Goods Ledger*—the subsidiary ledger for Finished Goods.

Entries in the accounts shown in Exhibit 11 are identified by letters. These letters refer to the entries described and illustrated in the chapter. Entry (h) is not shown because it does not involve a cost flow.

As shown in Exhibit 11, the balances of Materials, Work in Process, and Finished Goods are supported by their subsidiary ledgers. These balances are as follows:

Controlling Account	Balance and Total of Related Subsidiary Ledger
Materials	$ 3,500
Work in Process	21,000
Finished Goods	10,250

The income statement for Legend Guitars is shown in Exhibit 12 on page 380.

Obj 5 Use job order cost information for decision making.

Job Order Costing for Decision Making

A job order cost accounting system accumulates and records product costs by jobs. The resulting total and unit product costs can be compared to similar jobs, compared over time, or compared to expected costs. In this way, a job order cost system can be used by managers for cost evaluation and control.

To illustrate, Exhibit 13 on page 380 shows the direct materials used for Jobs 54 and 63 for Legend Guitars. The wood used in manufacturing guitars is measured in board feet. Since Jobs 54 and 63 produced the same type and number of guitars, the direct materials cost per unit should be about the same. However, the materials cost per guitar for Job 54 is $100, while for Job 63 it is $125. Thus, the materials costs are significantly more for Job 63.

EXHIBIT 11 Flow of Manufacturing Costs for Legend Guitars

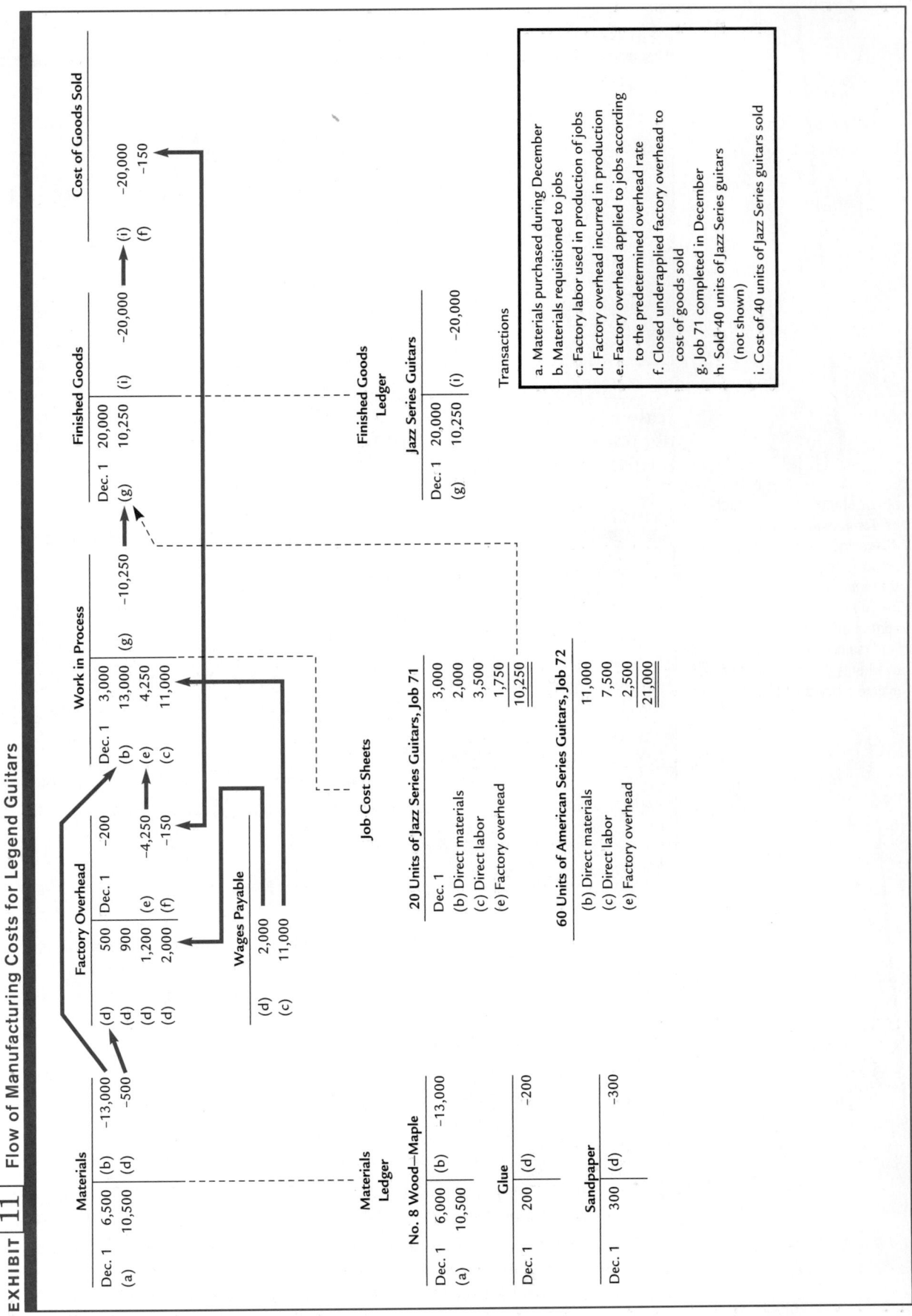

EXHIBIT 12 Income Statement of Legend Guitars

LEGEND GUITARS Income Statement For the Month Ended December 31, 2010		
Sales		$34,000
Cost of goods sold		20,150
Gross profit		$13,850
Selling and administrative expenses:		
Sales salaries expenses	$2,000	
Office salaries expense	1,500	
Total selling and administrative expenses		3,500
Income from operations		$10,350

The job cost sheets shown in Exhibit 13 can be analyzed for possible reasons for the increased materials cost for Job 63. Since the materials price did not change ($10 per board foot), the increased materials cost must be related to wood consumption.

Major electric utilities such as *Tennessee Valley Authority*, *Consolidated Edison Inc.*, and *Pacific Gas and Electric Company* use job order accounting to control the costs associated with major repairs and overhauls that occur during maintenance shutdowns.

EXHIBIT 13 Comparing Data from Job Cost Sheets

Job 54
Item: 40 Jazz Series guitars

	Materials Quantity (board feet)	Materials Price	Materials Amount
Direct materials:			
No. 8 Wood—Maple	400	$10.00	$4,000
Direct materials per guitar			$ 100

Job 63
Item: 40 Jazz Series guitars

	Materials Quantity (board feet)	Materials Price	Materials Amount
Direct materials:			
No. 8 Wood—Maple	500	$10.00	$5,000
Direct materials per guitar			$ 125

Comparing wood consumed for Jobs 54 and 63 shows that 400 board feet were used in Job 54 to produce 40 guitars. In contrast, Job 63 used 500 board feet to produce the same number of guitars. Thus, an investigation should be undertaken to determine the cause of the extra 100 board feet used for Job 63. Possible explanations could include the following:

1. A new employee, who was not properly trained, cut the wood for Job 63. As a result, there was excess waste and scrap.

2. The wood used for Job 63 was purchased from a new supplier. The wood was of poor quality, which created excessive waste and scrap.

3. The cutting tools needed repair and were not properly maintained. As a result, the wood was miscut, which created excessive waste and scrap.

4. The instructions attached to the job were incorrect. The wood was cut according to the instructions. The incorrect instructions were discovered later in assembly. As a result, the wood had to be recut and the initial cuttings scrapped.

Job Order Cost Systems for Professional Service Businesses

Obj 6 Describe the flow of costs for a service business that uses a job order cost accounting system.

A job order cost accounting system may be used for a professional service business. For example, an advertising agency, an attorney, and a physician provide services to individual customers, clients, or patients. In such cases, the customer, client, or patient can be viewed as a job for which costs are accumulated and reported.

The primary product costs for a service business are direct labor and overhead costs. Any materials or supplies used in rendering services are normally insignificant. As a result, materials and supply costs are included as part of the overhead cost.

Like a manufacturing business, direct labor and overhead costs of rendering services to clients are accumulated in a work in process account. *Work in Process* is supported by a cost ledger with a job cost sheet for each client.

When a job is completed and the client is billed, the costs are transferred to a cost of services account. *Cost of Services* is similar to the cost of merchandise sold account for a merchandising business or the cost of goods sold account for a manufacturing business. A finished goods account and related finished goods ledger are not necessary. This is because the revenues for the services are recorded only after the services are provided.

The flow of costs through a service business using a job order cost accounting system is shown in Exhibit 14.

EXHIBIT 14 | **Flow of Costs Through a Service Business**

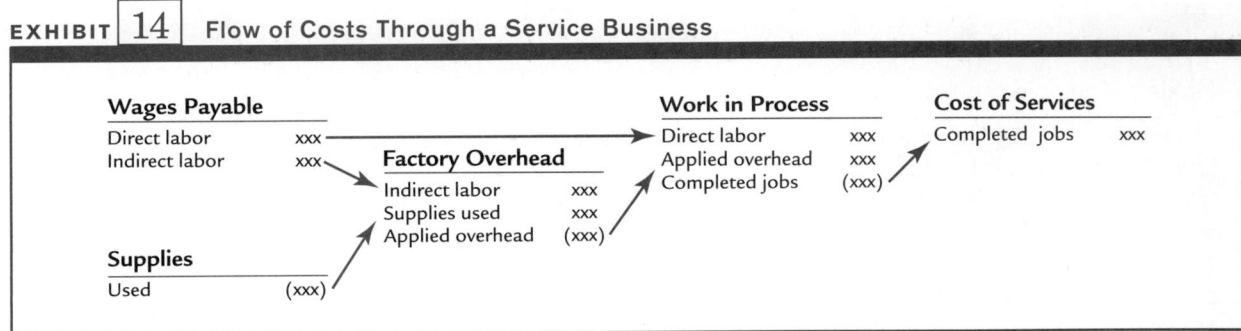

In practice, other considerations unique to service businesses may need to be considered. For example, a service business may bill clients on a weekly or monthly basis rather than when a job is completed. In such cases, a portion of the costs related to each billing is transferred from the work in process account to the cost of services account. A service business may also bill clients for services in advance, which would be accounted for as deferred revenue until the services are completed.

Just-in-Time Practices

Obj 7 Describe just-in-time manufacturing practices.

The objective of most manufacturers is to produce products with high quality, low cost, and instant availability. In attempting to achieve this objective, many manufacturers have implemented just-in-time processing. **Just-in-time processing (JIT)**, sometimes called *lean manufacturing*, is a philosophy that focuses on reducing time and cost, and eliminating poor quality.

Exhibit 15 lists just-in-time manufacturing and the traditional manufacturing practices. Each of the just-in-time practices is discussed in this section.

EXHIBIT 15   Operating Principles of Just-in-Time versus Traditional Manufacturing

Issue	Just-in-Time Manufacturing	Traditional Manufacturing
Inventory	Reduces inventory.	Increases inventory to protect against process problems.
Lead time	Reduces lead time.	Increases lead time to protect against uncertainty.
Setup time	Reduces setup time.	Disregards setup time as an improvement priority.
Production layout	Emphasizes product-oriented layout.	Emphasizes process-oriented layout.
Role of the employee	Emphasizes team-oriented employee involvement.	Emphasizes work of individuals, following manager instructions.
Production scheduling policy	Emphasizes pull manufacturing.	Emphasizes push manufacturing.
Quality	Emphasizes zero defects.	Tolerates defects.
Suppliers and customers	Emphasizes supply chain management.	Treats suppliers and customers as "arm's-length," independent entities.

Reducing Inventory

Just-in-time (JIT) manufacturing views inventory as wasteful and unnecessary. As a result, JIT emphasizes reducing or eliminating inventory.

How Businesses Make Money

Making Money in the Movie Business

Movie making is a high risk venture. The movie must be produced and marketed before the first dollar is received from the box office. If the movie is a hit, then all is well; but if the movie is a bomb, money will be lost. This is termed a "Blockbuster" business strategy and is common in businesses that have large up-front costs in the face of uncertain follow-up revenues, such as pharmaceuticals, video games, and publishing.

The profitability of a movie depends on its revenue and cost. A movie's cost is determined using job order costing; however, how costs are assigned to a movie is often complex and may be subject to disagreement. For example, in Hollywood's competitive environment, studios often negotiate payments to producers and actors based on a percentage of the film's gross revenues.

This is termed "contingent compensation." As movies become hits, compensation costs increase in proportion to the movie's revenues, which eats into a hit's profitability.

As the dollars involved get bigger, disagreements often develop between movie studios and actors or producers over the amount of contingent compensation. For example, the producer of the 2002 hit movie *Chicago* sued **Miramax Film Corp.** for failing to include foreign receipts and DVD sales in the revenue that was used to determine his payments. The controversial nature of contingent compensation is illustrated by the suit's claim that the accounting for contingent compensation leads to confusing and meaningless results.

GARY BUSS/TAXI/GETTY IMAGES

Under traditional manufacturing, inventory often hides underlying production problems. For example, if machine breakdowns occur, work-in-process inventories can be used to keep production running in other departments while the machines are being repaired. Likewise, inventories can be used to hide problems caused by a shortage of trained employees, unreliable suppliers, or poor quality.

In contrast, just-in-time manufacturing attempts to solve and remove production problems. In this way, raw materials, work-in-process, and finished goods inventories are reduced or eliminated.

The role of inventory in manufacturing can be illustrated using a river. Inventory is the water in a river. The rocks at the bottom of the river are production problems. When the water (inventory) is high, the rocks (production problems) at the bottom of the river are hidden. As the water level (inventory) drops, the rocks (production problems) become visible, one by one. JIT manufacturing reduces the water level (inventory), exposes the rocks (production problems), and removes the rocks so that the river can flow smoothly.

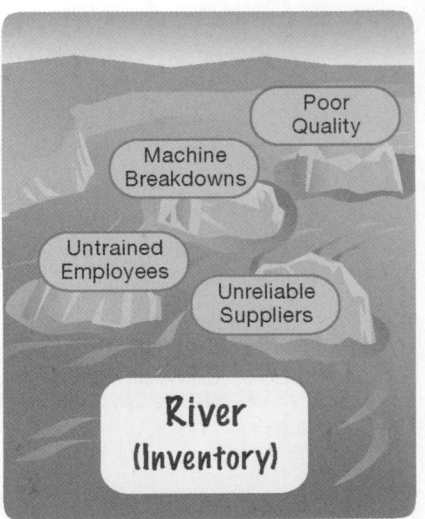

INTEGRITY, OBJECTIVITY, AND ETHICS IN BUSINESS

The Inventory Shift

Some managers take a shortcut to reducing inventory by shifting inventory to their suppliers. With this tactic, the hard work of improving processes is avoided. Enlightened managers realize that such tactics often have short-lived savings. Suppliers will eventually increase their prices to compensate for the additional inventory holding costs, thus resulting in no savings. Therefore, shifting a problem doesn't eliminate a problem.

Reducing Lead Times

Lead time, sometimes called *throughput time,* measures the time between when a product enters production (is started) and when it is completed (finished). In other words, lead time measures how long it takes to manufacture a product. For example, if a product enters production at 1:00 P.M. and is completed at 5:00 P.M., the lead time is four hours.

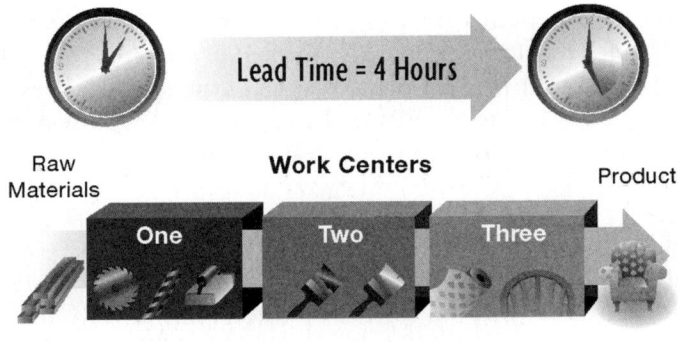

The lead time can be classified as one of the following:

1. **Value-added lead time,** which is the time spent in converting raw materials into a finished unit of product
2. **Non-value-added lead time,** which is the time spent while the unit of product is waiting to enter the next production process or is moved from one process to another

Exhibit 16 illustrates value-added and non-value-added lead time.

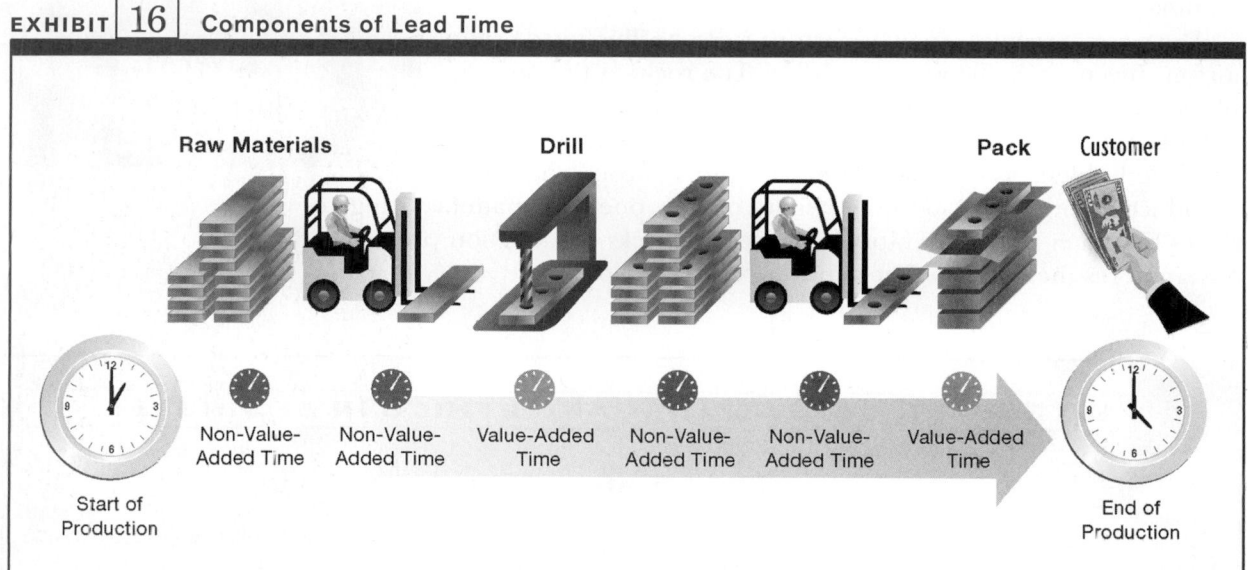

The time spent drilling and packing the unit of product is value-added time. The time spent waiting to enter the next process or the time spent moving the unit of product from one process to another is non-valued-added time.

Just-in-time manufacturing reduces or eliminates non-value-added time. In contrast, traditional manufacturing processes may have a value-added ratio as small as 5%.

Crown Audio reduced the lead time between receiving a customer order and delivering it from 30 days to 12 hours by using just-in-time principles.

Reducing Setup Time

A **setup** is the effort spent preparing an operation or process for a production run. If setups are long and costly, the batch size (number of units) for the related production run is normally large. Large batch sizes allow setup costs to be spread over more units and thus reduce the cost per unit. However, large batch sizes increase inventory and lead time.

Emphasizing Product-Oriented Layout

Manufacturing processes can be organized around a product, which is called a **product-oriented layout** (or *product cells*). Alternatively, manufacturing processes can be organized around a process, which is called a **process-oriented layout.**

How Businesses Make Money

P&G's "Pit Stops"

What do **Procter & Gamble** and **Formula One** racing have in common? The answer begins with P&G's Packing Department, which is where detergents and other products are filled on a "pack line." Containers move down the pack line and are filled with products from a packing machine. When it was time to change from a 36-oz. to a 54-oz. *Tide* box, for example, the changeover involved stopping the line, adjusting guide rails, retrieving items from the tool room, placing items back in the tool room, changing and cleaning the pack heads, and performing routine maintenance. Changing the pack line could be a very difficult process and typically took up to several hours.

Management realized that it was important to reduce this time significantly in order to become more flexible and cost efficient in packing products. Where could they learn how to do setups faster? They turned to Formula One racing, reasoning that a pit stop was much like a setup. As a result, P&G videotaped actual Formula One pit stops. These videos were used to form the following principles for conducting a fast setup:

- Position the tools near their point of use on the line prior to stopping the line, to reduce time going back and forth to the tool room.
- Arrange the tools in the exact order of work, so that no time is wasted looking for a tool.
- Have each employee perform a very specific task during the setup.
- Design the workflow so that employees don't interfere with each other.
- Have each employee in position at the moment the line is stopped.
- Train each employee, and practice, practice, practice.
- Put a stop watch on the setup process.
- Plot improvements over time on a visible chart.

As a result of these changes, P&G was able to reduce pack-line setup time from several hours to 20 minutes. This allowed it to reduce lead time and to improve the cost performance of the Packing Department.

AP PHOTO/PAUL SAKUMA

Just-in-time normally organizes manufacturing around products rather than processes. Organizing work around products reduces:

1. Moving materials and products between processes
2. Work-in-process inventory
3. Lead time
4. Production costs

In addition, a product-oriented layout improves coordination among operations.

Yamaha manufactures musical instruments such as trumpets, horns, saxophones, clarinets, and flutes using product-oriented layouts.

Emphasizing Employee Involvement

Employee involvement is a management approach that grants employees the responsibility and authority to make decisions about operations. Employee involvement is often applied in a just-in-time operation by organizing employees into *product cells*. Within each product cell, employees are organized as teams where the employees are *cross-trained* to perform any operation within the product cell.

To illustrate, employees learn how to operate several different machines within their product cell. In addition, team members are trained to perform functions traditionally performed by centralized service departments. For example, product cell employees may perform their own equipment maintenance, quality control, and housekeeping.

Sony has organized a small team of four employees to completely assemble a camcorder, doing everything from soldering to testing. The new line reduces assembly time from 70 minutes to 15 minutes per camera.

Kenney Manufacturing Company, a manufacturer of window shades, estimated that 50% of its window shade process was non-value-added. By using pull manufacturing and changing the line layout, it was able to reduce inventory by 82% and lead time by 84%.

Emphasizing Pull Manufacturing

Pull manufacturing (or *make-to-order*) is an important just-in-time practice. In pull manufacturing, products are manufactured only as they are needed by the customer. Products can be thought of as being pulled through the manufacturing process. In other words, the status of the next operation determines when products are moved or produced. If the next operation is busy, production stops so that work in process does not pile up in front of the busy operation. When the next operation is ready, the product is moved to that operation.

A system used in pull manufacturing is *kanban*, which is Japanese for "cards." Electronic cards or containers signal production quantities to be filled by the preceding operation. The cards link the customer's order for a product back through each stage of production. In other words, when a consumer orders a product, a kanban card triggers the manufacture of the product.

In contrast, the traditional approach to manufacturing is based on estimated customer demand. This principle is called **push manufacturing** (or make-to-stock) manufacturing. In push manufacturing, products are manufactured according to a production schedule that is based upon estimated sales. The schedule "pushes" product into inventory before customer orders are received. As a result, push manufacturers normally have more inventory than pull-manufacturers.

Emphasizing Zero Defects

Just-in-time manufacturing attempts to eliminate poor quality. Poor quality creates:

1. Scrap
2. Rework, which is fixing product made wrong the first time
3. Disruption in the production process
4. Dissatisfied customers
5. Warranty costs and expenses

Motorola has claimed over $17 billion in savings from Six Sigma.

One way to improve product quality and manufacturing processes is Six Sigma. **Six Sigma** was developed by ***Motorola Corporation*** and consists of five steps: define, measure, analyze, improve, and control (DMAIC).[4] Since its development, Six Sigma has been adopted by thousands of organizations worldwide.

Toyota Motor often works with supply chain partners to maximize the use of just-in-time.

Emphasizing Supply Chain Management

Supply chain management coordinates and controls the flow of materials, services, information, and finances with suppliers, manufacturers, and customers. Supply chain management partners with suppliers using long-term agreements. These agreements ensure that products are delivered with the right quality, at the right cost, at the right time.

To enhance the interchange of information between suppliers and customers, supply chain management often uses:

---

[4] The term "Six Sigma" refers to a statistical property where a process has less than 3.4 defects per one million items.

1. **Electronic data interchange (EDI)**, which uses computers to electronically communicate orders, relay information, and make or receive payments from one organization to another

2. **Radio frequency identification devices (RFID)**, which are electronic tags (chips) placed on or embedded within products that can be read by radio waves that allow instant monitoring of product location

3. **Enterprise resource planning (ERP)** systems, which are used to plan and control internal and supply chain operations

Hyundai/Kia Motors Group will use 20 million RFID tags annually to track automotive parts through the supply chain.

Activity-Based Costing

In today's complex manufacturing systems, product costs can be distorted if inappropriate factory overhead rates are used. One way to avoid this distortion is by using the *activity-based costing (ABC) method*. This approach allocates factory overhead more accurately than does the single, plantwide overhead rate that was illustrated earlier in this chapter.

Obj 8 Describe and illustrate the use of activity-based costing in a service business.

The activity-based costing method uses cost of activities to determine product costs. Under this method, factory overhead costs are initially accounted for in **activity cost pools**. These cost pools are related to a given activity, such as machine usage, inspections, moving, production setups, and engineering activities.

In order to simplify, a service business is used to illustrate the principles of activity-based costing. Like manufacturing businesses, service companies need to determine the cost of services in order to make pricing, promotional, and other decisions. Many service companies find that a single overhead rate can lead to service cost distortions. Thus, many service companies are now using activity-based costing for determining the cost of providing services to customers.

To illustrate, assume that Hopewell Hospital uses activity-based costing to allocate hospital overhead to patients. Hopewell Hospital applies activity-based costing by:

1. Identifying activity cost pools
2. Determining activity rates for each cost pool
3. Allocating overhead costs to patients based upon activity usage

Hopewell Hospital has identified the following activity cost pools:

1. Admission
2. Radiological testing
3. Operating room
4. Pathological testing
5. Dietary and laundry

Owens & Minor, a medical distributor, uses activity-based costing information to price distribution services to customers, based on the number of orders and the number of items per order.

Each activity cost pool has an estimated patient activity-base usage. Based on the budgeted costs for each activity and related estimated activity-base usage, the activity rates shown in Exhibit 17 were developed.

To illustrate, assume the following data for radiological testing:

Budgeted costs	$960,000
Total estimated activity-base usage	3,000 images

The activity rate of $320 per radiological image is computed as:

$$\text{Radiological Testing Activity Rate} = \frac{\text{Budgeted Activity Cost}}{\text{Activity-Base Usage}}$$

$$= \frac{\$960,000}{3,000 \text{ images}} = \$320 \text{ per image}$$

EXHIBIT **17**   Activity-Based Costing Method—Hopewell Hospital

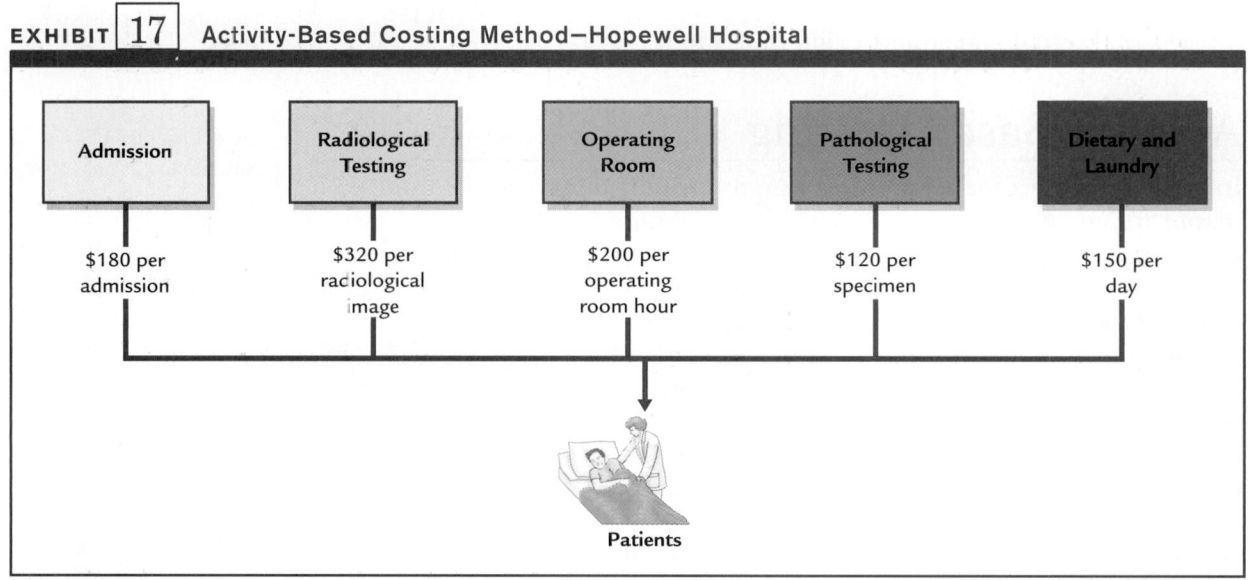

The activity rates for the other activities are determined in a similar manner. These activity rates along with the patient activity usage are used to allocate costs to patients as follows:

Activity Cost Allocated to Patient = Patient Activity Usage × Activity Rate

To illustrate, assume that Mia Wilson was a patient of the hospital. The hospital overhead services (activities) performed for Mia Wilson are shown below.

	Patient (Mia Wilson) Activity Usage
Admission	1 admission
Radiological testing	2 images
Operating room	4 hours
Pathological testing	1 specimen
Dietary and laundry	7 days

Based on the preceding services (activities), the Hopewell Hospital overhead costs allocated to Mia Wilson total $2,790, as computed below.

	A	B	C	D	E	F
1		Patient Name: Mia Wilson				
2		Activity-Base		Activity		Activity
3	**Activity**	**Usage**	×	**Rate**	=	**Cost**
4						
5	Admission	1 admission		$180 /admission		$ 180
6	Radiological testing	2 images		$320 /image		640
7	Operating room	4 hours		$200 /hour		800
8	Pathological testing	1 specimen		$120 /specimen		120
9	Dietary and laundry	7 days		$150 /day		1,050
10	Total					$2,790
11						

The patient activity costs can be combined with the direct costs, such as drugs and supplies. These costs and the related revenues can be reported for each patient in a patient (customer) profitability report. A partial patient profitability report for Hopewell Hospital is shown in Exhibit 18.

EXHIBIT 18 | **Customer Profitability Report**

Hopewell Hospital
Patient (Customer) Profitability Report
For the Period Ending December 31, 2010

	Adcock, Kim	Birini, Brian	Conway, Don		Wilson, Mia
Revenues	$9,500	$ 21,400	$5,050		$3,300
Less patient costs:					
Drugs and supplies	$ 400	$ 1,000	$ 300		$ 200
Admission	180	180	180		180
Radiological testing	1,280	2,560	1,280		640
Operating room	2,400	6,400	1,600		800
Pathological testing	240	600	120		120
Dietary and laundry	4,200	14,700	1,050		1,050
Total patient costs	$8,700	$ 25,440	$4,530		$2,990
Income from operations	$ 800	$ (4,040)	$ 520		$ 310

Exhibit 18 can be used by hospital administrators for decisions on pricing or services. For example, there was a large loss on services provided to Brian Birini. Investigation might reveal that some of the services provided to Birini were not reimbursed by insurance. As a result, Hopewell might lobby the insurance company to reimburse these services or request higher insurance reimbursement on other services.

INTEGRITY, OBJECTIVITY, AND ETHICS IN BUSINESS

University and Community Partnership—Learning Your ABC's

Students at Harvard's Kennedy School of Government joined with the city of Somerville, Massachusetts, in building an activity-based cost system for the city. The students volunteered several hours a week in four-person teams, interviewing city officials within 18 departments. The students were able to determine activity costs, such as the cost of filling a pothole, processing a building permit, or responding to a four-alarm fire. Their study was used by the city in forming the city budget. As stated by some of the students participating in this project: "It makes sense to use the resources of the university for community building. ... Real-world experience is a tremendous thing to have in your back pocket. We learned from the mayor and the fire chief, who are seasoned professionals in their own right."

Source: Kennedy School Bulletin, Spring 2005, "Easy as A-B-C: Students Take on the Somerville Budget Overhaul."

How Businesses Make Money

Finding the Right Niche

Businesses often attempt to divide a market into its unique characteristics, called market segmentation. Once a market segment is identified, product, price, promotion, and location strategies are tailored to fit that market. This is a better approach for many products and services than following a "one size fits all" strategy. Activity-based costing can be used to help tailor organizational effort toward different segments. For example, *Fidelity Investments* uses activity-based costing to tailor its sales and marketing strategies to different wealth segments. Thus, a higher wealth segment could rely on personal sales activities, while less wealthy segments would rely on less costly sales activities, such as mass mail. The following table lists popular forms of segmentation and their common characteristics:

Form of Segmentation	Characteristics
Demographic	Age, education, gender, income, race
Geographic	Region, city, country
Psychographic	Lifestyle, values, attitudes
Benefit	Benefits provided
Volume	Light vs. heavy use

Examples for each of these forms of segmentation are as follows:

Demographic: Fidelity Investments tailors sales and marketing strategies to different wealth segments.

Geographic: Pro sports teams offer merchandise in their home cities.

Psychographic: **The Body Shop** markets all-natural beauty products to consumers who value cosmetic products that have not been animal-tested.

Benefit: **Cold Stone Creamery** sells a premium ice cream product with customized toppings.

Volume: **Delta Air Lines** provides additional benefits, such as class upgrades, free air travel, and boarding priority, to its frequent fliers.

Key Points

1. **Distinguish the activities of a manufacturing business from those of a merchandising or service business.**

   A manufacturing business must first produce the products it sells. A manufacturing business converts materials into a finished product through the use of machinery and labor. Materials, products in the process of being manufactured, and finished products are reported on the balance sheet as inventories under the Current Assets caption.

2. **Define and illustrate materials, factory labor, and factory overhead costs.**

   A manufacturer converts materials into a finished product by using machinery and labor. The cost of materials that are an integral part of the manufactured product is direct materials cost. The cost of wages of employees who are involved in converting materials into the manufactured product is direct labor cost. Costs other than direct materials and direct labor costs are factory overhead costs, including indirect materials and labor. Direct labor and factory overhead are termed conversion costs. Direct materials, direct labor, and factory overhead costs are associated with products and are called product costs.

3. **Describe cost accounting systems used by manufacturing businesses.**

   A cost accounting system accumulates product costs. The cost accounting system is used by management to determine the proper product cost for inventory valuation on the financial statements, to support product pricing decisions, and to identify opportunities for cost reduction and improved production efficiency. The two primary cost accounting systems are job order and process cost systems.

4. Describe and illustrate a job order cost accounting system.

A job order cost system provides for a separate record of the cost of each particular quantity of product that passes through the factory. Direct materials, direct labor, and factory overhead costs are accumulated in a subsidiary cost ledger, in which each account is represented by a job cost sheet. Work in Process is the controlling account for the cost ledger. As a job is finished, its costs are transferred to the finished goods ledger, for which Finished Goods is the controlling account.

5. Use job order cost information for decision making.

Job order cost information can support pricing and cost analysis. Managers can use job cost information to identify unusual trends and areas for cost improvement.

6. Describe the flow of costs for a service business that uses a job order cost accounting system.

A cost flow diagram for a service business using a job order cost accounting system is shown in Exhibit 14. For a service business, the cost of materials or supplies used is normally included as part of the overhead. The direct labor and overhead costs of rendering services are accumulated in a work in process account. When a job is completed and the client is billed, the costs are transferred to a cost of services account.

7. Describe just-in-time manufacturing practices.

The just-in-time manufacturing philosophy uses different principles than do traditional manufacturing methods. Just-in-time attempts to reduce lead time while traditional methods attempt to lengthen lead time to provide a time buffer for uncertainty. Just-in-time emphasizes a product-oriented production layout rather than a process-oriented layout. Just-in-time emphasizes a team-oriented work environment; the traditional approach is more individual oriented. Just-in-time views setup time reduction as a high-priority item. With reduced setup times, just-in-time manufacturers can emphasize pull manufacturing rather than push manufacturing. Just-in-time manufacturers must emphasize high quality, since there is very little inventory to protect production against quality problems. Finally, just-in-time manufacturers emphasize supplier partnering to improve the quality and delivery of incoming materials.

8. Describe and illustrate the use of activity-based costing in a service business.

Activity-based costing can be applied in service settings to determine the cost of individual service offerings. Service costs are determined by multiplying activity rates by the amount of activity-base quantities consumed by the customer using the service offering. Such information can support service pricing and profitability analysis.

Key Terms

Activity base (driver) A measure of activity that is related to changes in cost and is used in the denominator in calculating the predetermined factory overhead rate to assign factory overhead costs to cost objects.

Activity-based costing An accounting framework based on determining the cost of activities and allocating these costs to products using activity rates.

Activity cost pools Cost accumulations that are associated with a given activity, such as machine usage, inspections, moving, and production setups.

Conversion costs The combination of direct labor and factory overhead costs.

Controlling account The account in the general ledger that summarizes the balances of the accounts in the subsidiary ledger.

Cost A payment of cash (or a commitment to pay cash in the future) for the purpose of generating revenues.

Cost accounting system A system used to accumulate manufacturing costs for decision-making and financial reporting purposes.

Cost allocation The process of assigning indirect costs to a cost object, such as a job.

Cost of goods sold The cost of the manufactured product sold.

Direct labor cost Wages of factory workers who are directly involved in converting materials into a finished product.

Direct materials cost The cost of materials that are an integral part of the finished product.

Electronic data interchange (EDI) An information technology that allows different business organizations to use computers to communicate orders, relay information, and make or receive payments.

Employee involvement A philosophy that grants employees the responsibility and authority to make their own decisions about their operations.

Enterprise resource planning A system used to plan and control internal and supply chain operations.

Factory overhead cost All of the costs of operating the factory except for direct materials and direct labor.

Finished goods inventory The cost of finished products on hand that have not been sold.

Finished goods ledger The subsidiary ledger that contains the individual accounts for each kind of commodity or product produced.

Job cost sheet An account in the work-in-process subsidiary ledger in which the costs charged to a particular job order are recorded.

Job order cost system A type of cost accounting system that provides for a separate record of the cost of each particular quantity of product that passes through the factory.

Just-in-time (JIT) processing A business philosophy that focuses on eliminating time, cost, and poor quality within manufacturing processes.

Lead time Starting a unit of product into the beginning of a process and its completion.

Materials inventory The cost of materials that have not yet entered into the manufacturing process.

Materials ledger The subsidiary ledger containing the individual accounts for each type of material.

Materials requisition The form or electronic transmission used by a manufacturing department to authorize the issuance of materials from the storeroom.

Non-value-added lead time The time that units wait in inventories, move unnecessarily, and wait during machine breakdowns.

Overapplied factory overhead The amount of factory overhead applied in excess of the actual factory overhead costs incurred for production during a period.

Period costs Those costs that are used up in generating revenue during the current period and that are not involved in the manufacturing process.

Predetermined factory overhead rate The rate used to apply factory overhead costs to the goods manufactured. The rate is determined from budgeted overhead cost and estimated activity usage data at the beginning of the fiscal period.

Process cost system A type of cost accounting system in which costs are accumulated by department or process within a factory.

Process-oriented layout Organizing work in a plant or administrative function around processes (tasks).

Prime costs The combination of direct materials and direct labor costs.

Product costs The three components of manufacturing costs: direct materials, direct labor, and factory overhead costs.

Product-oriented layout Organizing work in a plant or administrative function around products; sometimes referred to as *product cells.*

Pull manufacturing A just-in-time method wherein customer orders trigger the release of finished goods, which triggers production, which triggers release of materials from suppliers.

Push manufacturing Materials are released into production and work in process is released into finished goods in anticipation of future sales.

Radio frequency identification devices Electronic tags(chips) placed on or embedded within products that can be read by radio waves and that allow instant monitoring of product location.

Receiving report The form or electronic transmission used by the receiving personnel to indicate that materials have been received and inspected.

Setup The effort required to prepare an operation for a new production run.

Six Sigma A method of improving product quality and manufacturing processes developed by Motorola Corporation that consists of five steps: define, measure, analyze, improve, and control.

Subsidiary ledger A ledger containing individual accounts with a common characteristic.

Supply chain management The coordination and control of materials, services, information, and finances as they move in a process from the supplier, through the manufacturer, wholesaler, and retailer to the consumer.

Time tickets The form on which the amount of time spent by each employee and the labor costs incurred for each individual job, or for factory overhead, are recorded.

Underapplied factory overhead The actual factory overhead costs incurred in excess of the amount of factory overhead applied for production during a period.

Value-added lead time The time required to manufacture a unit of product or other output.

Work-in-process inventory The direct materials costs, the direct labor costs, and the factory overhead costs that have entered into the manufacturing process but are associated with products that have not been finished.

Illustrative Problem

Derby Music Company specializes in producing and packaging compact discs (CDs) for the music recording industry. Derby uses a job order cost system. The following data summarize the operations related to production for March, the first month of operations:

a. Materials purchased on account, $15,500.

b. Materials requisitioned and labor used:

	Materials	Factory Labor
Job No. 100	$2,650	$1,770
Job No. 101	1,240	650
Job No. 102	980	420
Job No. 103	3,420	1,900
Job No. 104	1,000	500
Job No. 105	2,100	1,760
For general factory use	450	650

c. Factory overhead costs incurred on account, $2,700.

d. Depreciation of machinery, $1,750.

e. Factory overhead is applied at a rate of 70% of direct labor cost.

f. Jobs completed: Nos. 100, 101, 102, 104.

g. Jobs 100, 101, and 102 were shipped, and customers were billed for $8,100, $3,800, and $3,500, respectively.

Instructions

1. Prepare a schedule summarizing manufacturing costs by job during the month. Use the following form:

Job	Direct Materials	Direct Labor	Factory Overhead	Total

2. Prepare a schedule of jobs finished.

3. Prepare a schedule of jobs sold.

4. Prepare a schedule of completed jobs on hand at the end of the month.

5. Prepare a schedule of unfinished jobs at the end of the month.

Solution

1. Schedule of manufacturing costs incurred during month:

Job	Direct Materials	Direct Labor	Factory Overhead	Total
Job No. 100	$ 2,650	$1,770	$1,239	$ 5,659
Job No. 101	1,240	650	455	2,345
Job No. 102	980	420	294	1,694
Job No. 103	3,420	1,900	1,330	6,650
Job No. 104	1,000	500	350	1,850
Job No. 105	2,100	1,760	1,232	5,092
	$11,390	$7,000	$4,900	$23,290

2. Schedule of the cost of jobs finished:

Job	Direct Materials	Direct Labor	Factory Overhead	Total
Job No. 100	$2,650	$1,770	$1,239	$ 5,659
Job No. 101	1,240	650	455	2,345
Job No. 102	980	420	294	1,694
Job No. 104	1,000	500	350	1,850
				$11,548

3. Schedule of the cost of jobs sold:

Job No. 100	$5,659
Job No. 101	2,345
Job No. 102	1,694
	$9,698

4.

Schedule of Completed Jobs

Job No. 104:	
Direct materials	$1,000
Direct labor	500
Factory overhead	350
Balance of Finished Goods, March, 31	$1,850

5.

Schedule of Unfinished Jobs

Job	Direct Materials	Direct Labor	Factory Overhead	Total
Job No. 103	$3,420	$1,900	$1,330	$ 6,650
Job No. 105	2,100	1,760	1,232	5,092
Balance of Work in Process, March 31				$ 11,742

Self-Examination Questions (Answers appear at the end of chapter)

1. Which of the following is *not* considered a cost of manufacturing a product?

    A. Direct materials cost

    B. Factory overhead cost

    C. Sales salaries

    D. Direct labor cost

2. Which of the following costs would be included as part of the factory overhead costs of a computer manufacturer?

    A. The cost of memory chips

    B. Depreciation of testing equipment

    C. Wages of computer assemblers

    D. The cost of disk drives

3. A company estimated $420,000 of factory overhead cost and 16,000 direct labor hours for the period. During the period, a job was completed with $4,500 of direct materials and $3,000 of direct labor. The direct labor rate was $15 per hour. What is the factory overhead applied to this job?

    A. $2,100

    B. $5,250

    C. $78,750

    D. $420,000

4. If the factory overhead account has a negative balance, factory overhead is said to be:

    A. underapplied.

    B. overapplied.

    C. underabsorbed.

    D. in error.

5. Which of the following is *not* a characteristic of the just-in-time philosophy?

    A. Product-oriented layout

    B. Push manufacturing (make-to-stock)

    C. Short lead times

    D. Reducing setup time as a critical improvement priority

Class Discussion Questions

1. For a company that produces desktop computers, would memory chips be considered a direct or an indirect materials cost of each computer produced?

2. How is product cost information used by managers?

3. a. Name two principal types of cost accounting systems.

    b. Which system provides for a separate record of each particular quantity of product that passes through the factory?

    c. Which system accumulates the costs for each department or process within the factory?

4. What kind of firm would use a job order cost system?

5. *Hewlett-Packard Company* assembles ink jet printers in which a high volume of standardized units are assembled and tested. Is the job order cost system appropriate in this situation?

6. How does the use of the materials requisition help control the issuance of materials from the storeroom?

7. a. Differentiate between the clock card and the time ticket.

    b. Why should the total time reported on an employee's time tickets for a payroll period be compared with the time reported on the employee's clock cards for the same period?

8. Describe the source of the data for increasing Work in Process for (a) direct materials, (b) direct labor, and (c) factory overhead.

9. Discuss how the predetermined factory overhead rate can be used in job order cost accounting to assist management in pricing jobs.

10. a. How is a predetermined factory overhead rate calculated?

    b. Name three common bases used in calculating the rate.

11. a. What is (1) overapplied factory overhead and (2) underapplied factory overhead?

   b. If the factory overhead account has a positive balance, was factory overhead underapplied or overapplied?

12. At the end of the fiscal year, there was a relatively minor balance in the factory overhead account. What procedure can be used for disposing of the balance in the account?

13. What is the difference between a product cost and a period cost?

14. How can job cost information be used to identify cost improvement opportunities?

15. Describe how a job order cost system can be used for professional service businesses.

16. What is the benefit of just-in-time processing?

17. What are some examples of non-value-added lead time?

18. Why do just-in-time manufacturers favor pull or make-to-order manufacturing?

19. Why would a just-in-time manufacturer strive to produce zero defects?

20. How is supplier partnering different from traditional supplier relationships?

21. How can activity-based costing be used in service companies?

Exercises

E10-1

Classifying costs as materials, labor, or factory overhead

Obj 2

Indicate whether each of the following costs of an airplane manufacturer would be classified as direct materials cost, direct labor cost, or factory overhead cost:

a. Controls for flight deck
b. Aircraft engines
c. Depreciation of welding equipment
d. Welding machinery lubricants
e. Salary of test pilot
f. Steel used in landing gear
g. Wages of assembly line worker
h. Tires

E10-2

Classifying costs as materials, labor, or factory overhead

Obj 2

Indicate whether the following costs of *Colgate-Palmolive Company* would be classified as direct materials cost, direct labor cost, or factory overhead cost:

a. Wages paid to Packaging Department employees
b. Maintenance supplies
c. Plant manager salary for the Morristown, Tennessee, toothpaste plant
d. Packaging materials
e. Depreciation on production machinery
f. Salary of process engineers
g. Depreciation on the Clarksville, Indiana, soap plant
h. Resins for soap and shampoo products
i. Scents and fragrances
j. Wages of production line employees

E10-3

Classifying costs as factory overhead

Obj 2

Which of the following items are properly classified as part of factory overhead for *Caterpillar*?

a. Factory supplies used in the Morganton, North Carolina, engine parts plant
b. Amortization of patents on new assembly process
c. Steel plate

d. Vice president of finance's salary

e. Sales incentive fees to dealers

f. Depreciation on Peoria, Illinois, headquarters building

g. Interest expense on debt

h. Plant manager's salary at Aurora, Illinois, manufacturing plant

i. Consultant fees for a study of production line employee productivity

j. Property taxes on the Danville, Kentucky, tractor tread plant

E10-4

Classifying costs as product or period costs

Objs 2, 4

For apparel manufacturer ***Ann Taylor, Inc.***, classify each of the following costs as either a product cost or a period cost:

a. Sales commissions

b. Advertising expenses

c. Fabric used during production

d. Property taxes on factory building and equipment

e. Depreciation on sewing machines

f. Factory janitorial supplies

g. Depreciation on office equipment

h. Wages of sewing machine operators

i. Repairs and maintenance costs for sewing machines

j. Salary of production quality control supervisor

k. Salaries of distribution center personnel

l. Research and development costs

m. Oil used to lubricate sewing machines

n. Corporate controller's salary

o. Utility costs for office building

p. Travel costs of salespersons

q. Factory supervisors' salaries

E10-5

Concepts and terminology

Objs 2, 4

From the choices presented in the parentheses, choose the appropriate term for completing each of the following sentences:

a. Advertising expenses are usually viewed as (period, product) costs.

b. The balance sheet of a manufacturer would include an account for (cost of goods sold, work-in-process inventory).

c. Materials that are an integral part of the manufactured product are classified as (direct materials, materials inventory).

d. An example of factory overhead is (plant depreciation, sales office depreciation).

e. Implementing automatic factory robotics equipment normally (increases, decreases) the factory overhead component of product costs.

f. Direct labor costs combined with factory overhead costs are called (product, conversion) costs.

g. The wages of an assembly worker are normally considered a (period, product) cost.

h. Payments of cash or its equivalent or the commitment to pay cash in the future for the purpose of generating revenues are (costs, expenses).

E10-6

Transactions in a job order cost system

Obj 4

Five selected transactions for the current month are indicated by letters in the following accounts in a job order cost accounting system:

Materials	Work in Process
(a) decrease	(a) increase
	(b) increase
	(c) increase
	(d) decrease

Wages Payable	Finished Goods
(b) increase	(d) increase
	(e) decrease

Factory Overhead	Cost of Goods Sold
(a) increase	(e) increase
(b) increase	
(c) decrease	

Describe each of the five transactions.

E10-7

Cost flow relationships

Obj 4

✓ c. $629,500

The following information is available for the first month of operations of Url Inc., a manufacturer of art and craft items:

Sales	$1,200,000
Gross profit	320,000
Indirect labor	110,000
Indirect materials	45,000
Other factory overhead	20,000
Materials purchased	610,000
Total manufacturing costs for the period	1,325,000
Materials inventory, end of period	45,000

Using the above information, determine the following:

a. Cost of goods sold
b. Direct materials cost
c. Direct labor cost

E10-8

Cost of materials issuances

Obj 4

✓ b. $1,320

An incomplete subsidiary ledger of wire cable for May is as follows:

RECEIVED			ISSUED				BALANCE		
Receiving Report Number	Quantity	Unit Price	Materials Requisition Number	Quantity	Amount	Date	Quantity	Amount	Unit Price
						May 1	300	$2,400	$8.00
24	210	$10.00				May 2			
			101	340		May 6			
30	140	12.00				May 12			
			114	200		May 21			

a. Complete the materials issuances and balances for the wire cable subsidiary ledger.
b. Determine the balance of wire cable at the end of August.
c. Determine the total amount of materials transferred to work-in-process for August.
d. Explain how the materials ledger might be used as an aid in maintaining inventory quantities on hand.

E10-9

Recording issuing of materials

Obj 4

Materials issued for the current month are as follows:

Requisition No.	Material	Job No.	Amount
101	Steel	210	$25,400
102	Plastic	215	19,600
103	Glue	Indirect	1,450
104	Rubber	222	1,200
105	Aluminium	231	52,400

a. Determine the amount of materials transferred to work-in-process and factory overhead for the current month.

b. Illustrate the effect on the accounts and financial statements of the materials transferred in (a).

E10-10

Entries for materials

Obj 4

✓ c. Fabric, $33,500

Bullock Furniture Company manufactures furniture. Bullock uses a job order cost system. Balances on June 1 from the materials ledger are as follows:

Fabric	$ 25,000
Polyester filling	7,500
Lumber	56,000
Glue	2,400

The materials purchased during June are summarized from the receiving reports as follows:

Fabric	$126,000
Polyester filling	175,000
Lumber	345,000
Glue	12,000

Materials were requisitioned to individual jobs as follows:

	Fabric	Polyester Filling	Lumber	Glue	Total
Job 101	$ 47,500	$ 60,000	$160,000		$267,500
Job 102	36,500	54,000	140,000		230,500
Job 103	33,500	44,000	78,000		155,500
Factory overhead—indirect materials				$13,000	13,000
Total	$117,500	$158,000	$378,000	$13,000	$666,500

The glue is not a significant cost, so it is treated as indirect materials (factory overhead).

a. Determine the total purchase of materials in June.

b. Determine the amounts of materials transferred to Work in Process and Factory Overhead for the requisition of materials in June.

c. Determine the June 30 balances that would be shown in the materials ledger accounts.

E10-11

Recording factory labor costs

Obj 4

A summary of the time tickets for the current month follows:

Job No.	Amount	Job No.	Amount
201	$ 2,100	220	$3,650
204	1,750	224	2,240
205	3,200	228	1,460
Indirect labor	11,200	236	9,875

a. Determine the amounts of factory labor costs transferred to Work in Process and Factory Overhead for the current month.

b. Illustrate the effect on the accounts and financial statements of the factory labor costs transferred in (a).

E10-12

Recording factory labor costs

Obj 4

The weekly time tickets indicate the following distribution of labor hours for three direct labor employees:

	Hours			
	Job 201	Job 202	Job 203	Process Improvement
John Washington	20	10	7	3
George Jefferson	10	15	13	2
Thomas Adams	12	14	10	4

The direct labor rate earned by the three employees is as follows:

Washington	$20
Jefferson	22
Adams	18

The process improvement category includes training, quality improvement, housekeeping, and other indirect tasks.

a. Determine the amounts of factory labor costs transferred to Work in Process and Factory Overhead for the week.

b. Assume that Jobs 201 and 202 were completed but not sold during the week and that Job 203 remained incomplete at the end of the week. How would the direct labor costs for all three jobs be reflected on the financial statements at the end of the week?

E10-13

Recording direct labor and factory overhead

Obj 4

Moura Industries Inc. manufactures recreational vehicles. Moura uses a job order cost system. The time tickets from August jobs are summarized below.

Job 410	$3,400
Job 411	1,700
Job 412	1,400
Job 413	2,500
Factory supervision	1,900

Factory overhead is applied to jobs on the basis of a predetermined overhead rate of $25 per direct labor hour. The direct labor rate is $15 per hour.

a. Determine the total factory labor costs transferred to Work in Process and Factory Overhead for August.

b. Determine the amount of factory overhead applied to production for August.

c. Illustrate the effects of the factory overhead applied in (b) on the accounts and financial statements.

E10-14

Factory overhead rates and account balances

Obj 4

✓ b. $40.00 per direct labor hour

Hudson Company operates two factories. The company applies factory overhead to jobs on the basis of machine hours in Factory 1 and on the basis of direct labor hours in Factory 2. Estimated factory overhead costs, direct labor hours, and machine hours are as follows:

	Factory 1	Factory 2
Estimated factory overhead cost for fiscal year beginning June 1	$475,000	$600,000
Estimated direct labor hours for year		15,000
Estimated machine hours for year	20,000	
Actual factory overhead costs for June	$ 38,000	$ 52,000
Actual direct labor hours for June		1,350
Actual machine hours for June	1,560	

a. Determine the factory overhead rate for Factory 1.

b. Determine the factory overhead rate for Factory 2.

c. Determine the factory overhead applied to production in each factory for June.

d. Determine the balances of the factory accounts for each factory as of June 30, and indicate whether the amounts represent overapplied or underapplied factory overhead.

E10-15

Predetermined factory overhead rate

Obj 4

Willie's Engine Shop uses a job order cost system to determine the cost of performing engine repair work. Estimated costs and expenses for the coming period are as follows:

Engine parts	$ 875,000
Shop direct labor	640,000
Shop and repair equipment depreciation	45,000
Shop supervisor salaries	125,800
Shop property tax	22,600
Shop supplies	16,600
Advertising expense	17,800
Administrative office salaries	75,000
Administrative office depreciation expense	10,000
Total costs and expenses	$1,827,800

The average shop direct labor rate is $16 per hour. Determine the predetermined shop overhead rate per direct labor hour.

E10-16

Predetermined factory overhead rate

Obj 4

✓ a. $205 per hour

The Medical Center has a single operating room that is used by local physicians to perform surgical procedures. The cost of using the operating room is accumulated by each patient procedure and includes the direct materials costs (drugs and medical devices), physician surgical time, and operating room

overhead. On November 1 of the current year, the annual operating room overhead is estimated to be:

Disposable supplies	$150,000
Depreciation expense	27,000
Utilities	15,500
Nurse salaries	225,500
Technician wages	74,000
Total operating room overhead	$492,000

The overhead costs will be assigned to procedures based on the number of surgical room hours. The Medical Center expects to use the operating room an average of eight hours per day, six days per week. In addition, the operating room will be shut down two weeks per year for general repairs.

a. Determine the predetermined operating room overhead rate for the year.
b. Gretchen Kelton had a 6-hour procedure on November 10. How much operating room overhead would be charged to her procedure, using the rate determined in part (a)?
c. During November, the operating room was used 192 hours. The actual overhead costs incurred for November were $38,500. Determine the overhead under- or overapplied for the period.

E10-17

Recording jobs completed

Obj 4

✓ b. $13,500

The following account appears in the ledger after only part of the postings have been completed for January:

Work in Process	
Balance, January 1	$14,200
Direct materials	115,400
Direct labor	124,500
Factory overhead	65,400

Jobs finished during January are summarized as follows:

Job 710	$62,500	Job 727	$ 35,400
Job 714	75,600	Job 732	132,500

a. Determine the cost of jobs completed.
b. Determine the cost of the unfinished jobs at January 31.

E10-18

Determining manufacturing costs

Obj 4

✓ d. $ 31,160

Munch Printing Inc. began printing operations on July 1. Jobs 10 and 11 were completed during the month, and all costs applicable to them were recorded on the related cost sheets. Jobs 12 and 13 are still in process at the end of the month, and all applicable costs except factory overhead have been recorded on the related cost sheets. In addition to the materials and labor charged directly to the jobs, $1,200 of indirect materials and $14,500 of indirect labor were used during the month. The cost sheets for the four jobs entering production during the month are as follows, in summary form:

Job 10			Job 11	
Direct materials	12,400		Direct materials	5,800
Direct labor	4,750		Direct labor	2,450
Factory overhead	3,800		Factory overhead	1,960
Total	20,950		Total	10,210

Job 12			Job 13	
Direct materials	17,400		Direct materials	3,500
Direct labor	5,250		Direct labor	700
Factory overhead			Factory overhead	

Determine each of the following for July:

a. Direct and indirect materials used.
b. Direct and indirect labor used.
c. Factory overhead applied (a single overhead rate is used based on direct labor cost).
d. Cost of completed Jobs 10 and 11.

E10-19

Financial statements of a manufacturing firm

Obj 4

SPREADSHEET

✓ a. Income from operations, $99,600

The following events took place for Salsa Inc. during May 2010, the first month of operations, as a producer of road bikes:

- Purchased $244,000 of materials.
- Used $210,000 of direct materials in production.
- Incurred $180,000 of direct labor wages.
- Applied factory overhead at a rate of 75% of direct labor cost.
- Transferred $510,000 of work in process to finished goods.
- Sold goods with a cost of $485,000.
- Sold goods for $870,000.
- Incurred $210,000 of selling expenses.
- Incurred $75,400 of administrative expenses.

a. Prepare the May income statement for Salsa. Assume that Salsa uses the perpetual inventory method.
b. Determine the inventory balances at the end of the first month of operations.

E10-20

Decision making with job order costs

Obj 5

Letson Manufacturing Inc. is a job shop. The management of Letson Manufacturing uses the cost information from the job sheets to assess its cost performance. Information on the total cost, product type, and quantity of items produced is as follows:

Date	Job No.	Quantity	Product	Amount
Jan. 2	1	240	Alpha	$ 6,000
Jan. 15	22	1,100	Beta	8,800
Feb. 3	38	800	Beta	8,000
Mar. 7	56	400	Alpha	8,800
Mar. 24	65	1,500	Gamma	6,000
May 19	74	1,750	Gamma	10,500
June 12	87	350	Alpha	6,300
Aug. 18	92	2,200	Gamma	19,800
Sept. 2	100	600	Beta	4,800
Nov. 14	110	500	Alpha	7,000
Dec. 12	116	2,000	Gamma	24,000

a. Develop a graph for *each* product (three graphs), with Job No. (in date order) on the horizontal axis and unit cost on the vertical axis. Use this information to determine Letson Manufacturing's cost performance over time for the three products.

b. What additional information would you require to investigate Letson Manufacturing's cost performance more precisely?

E10-21

Decision making with job order costs

Obj 5

Duncan Trophies Inc. uses a job order cost system for determining the cost to manufacture award products (plaques and trophies). Among the company's products is an engraved plaque that is awarded to participants who complete an executive education program at a local university. The company sells the plaque to the university for $160 each.

Each plaque has a brass plate engraved with the name of the participant. Engraving requires approximately 20 minutes per name. Improperly engraved names must be redone. The plate is screwed to a walnut backboard. This assembly takes approximately 10 minutes per unit. Improper assembly must be redone using a new walnut backboard.

During the first half of the year, the university had two separate executive education classes. The job cost sheets for the two separate jobs indicated the following information:

Job 201	April 12		
	Cost per Unit	**Units**	**Job Cost**
Direct materials:			
Wood	$32.00/unit	60 units	$ 1,920
Brass	24.00/unit	60 units	1,440
Engraving labor	60.00/hr.	20 hrs.	1,200
Assembly labor	45.00/hr.	10 hrs.	450
Factory overhead	36.00/hr.	30 hrs.	1,050
			$ 6,060
Plaques shipped			÷ 60
Cost per plaque			$101.00

Job 212	May 6		
	Cost per Unit	**Units**	**Job Cost**
Direct materials:			
Wood	$ 32.00/unit	48 units	$ 1,536
Brass	24.00/unit	48 units	1,152
Engraving labor	60.00/hr.	28 hrs.	1,680
Assembly labor	45.00/hr.	14 hrs.	630
Factory overhead	35.00/hr.	42 hrs.	1,470
			$ 6,468
Plaques shipped			÷ 42
Cost per plaque			$ 154.00

a. Why did the cost per plaque increase from $101.00 to $154.00?

b. What improvements would you recommend for Duncan Trophies Inc.?

E10-22

Job order cost accounting entries for a service business

Obj 6

✓ d. Cost of Services Completed, $777,500

The Ad Guys Inc. provides advertising services for clients across the nation. The Ad Guys is presently working on four projects, each for a different client. The Ad Guys accumulates costs for each account (client) on the basis of both direct costs and allocated indirect costs. The direct costs include the charged time of

professional personnel and media purchases (air time and ad space). Overhead is allocated to each project as a percentage of media purchases. The predetermined overhead rate is 50% of media purchases.On June 1, the four advertising projects had the following accumulated costs:

	June 1 Balances
Clinton Bank	$80,000
Pryor Airlines	24,000
O'Ryan Hotels	56,000
Marshall Beverages	34,000

During June, The Ad Guys incurred the following direct labor and media purchase costs related to preparing advertising for each of the four accounts:

	Direct Labor	Media Purchases
Clinton Bank	$ 56,000	$ 210,000
Pryor Airlines	25,000	185,000
O'Ryan Hotels	110,000	135,000
Marshall Beverages	125,000	101,000
Total	$316,000	$ 631,000

At the end of June, both the Clinton Bank and Pryor Airlines campaigns were completed. The costs of completed campaigns are debited to the cost of services account.

Determine each of the following for the month:

a. Direct labor costs.
b. Media purchases.
c. Overhead applied.
d. Completion of Clinton Bank and Pryor Airlines campaigns.

E10-23

Just-in-time principles

Obj 7

The chief executive officer (CEO) of Gemini Inc. has just returned from a management seminar describing the benefits of the just-in-time philosophy. The CEO issued the following statement after returning from the conference:

This company will become a just-in-time manufacturing company. Presently, we have too much inventory. To become just-in-time we need to eliminate the excess inventory. Therefore, I want all employees to begin reducing inventories until we are just-in-time. Thank you for your cooperation.

How would you respond to the CEO's statement?

E10-24

Just-in-time as a strategy

Obj 7

The American textile industry has moved much of its operations offshore in the pursuit of lower labor costs. Textile imports have risen from 2% of all textile production in 1962 to over 70% in 2008. Offshore manufacturers make long runs of standard mass-market apparel items. These are then brought to the United States in container ships, requiring significant time between original order and delivery. As a result, retail customers must accurately forecast market demands for imported apparel items.

Assuming that you work for a U.S.-based textile company, how would you recommend responding to the low-cost imports?

E10-25

Lead time reduction–service company

Obj 7

AAA Insurance Company takes ten days to make payments on insurance claims. Claims are processed through three departments: Data Input, Claims Audit, and Claims Adjustment. The three departments are on different floors, approximately one hour apart from each other. Claims are processed in batches of 50. Each batch of 50 claims moves through the three departments on a wheeled cart. Management is concerned about customer dissatisfaction caused by the long lead time for claim payments.

How might this process be changed so that the lead time could be reduced significantly?

E10-26

Just-in-time principles

Obj 7

Galaxy Shirt Company manufactures various styles of men's casual wear. Shirts are cut and assembled by a workforce that is paid by piece rate. This means that workers are paid according to the amount of work completed during a period of time. To illustrate, if the piece rate is $0.10 per sleeve assembled, and the worker assembles 700 sleeves during the day, then the worker would be paid $70 (700 × $0.10) for the day's work.

The company is considering adopting a just-in-time manufacturing philosophy by organizing work cells around various types of products and employing pull manufacturing. However, no change is expected in the compensation policy. On this point, the manufacturing manager stated the following:

> *Piecework compensation provides an incentive to work fast. Without it, the workers will just goof off and expect a full day's pay. We can't pay straight hourly wages—at least not in this industry.*

How would you respond to the manufacturing manager's comments?

E10-27

Supply chain management

Obj 7

The following is an excerpt from a recent article discussing supplier relationships with the Big Three North American automakers.

> *"The Big Three select suppliers on the basis of lowest price and annual price reductions," said Neil De Koker, president of the Original Equipment Suppliers Association. "They look globally for the lowest parts prices from the lowest cost countries," De Koker said. "There is little trust and respect. Collaboration is missing." Japanese auto makers want long-term supplier relationships. They select suppliers as a person would a mate. The Big Three are quick to beat down prices with methods such as electronic auctions or rebidding work to a competitor. The Japanese are equally tough on price but are committed to maintaining supplier continuity. "They work with you to arrive at a competitive price, and they are willing to pay because they want long-term partnering," said Carl Code, a vice president at Ernie Green Industries. "They [**Honda** and **Toyota**] want suppliers to make enough money to stay in business, grow and bring them innovation." The Big Three's supply chain model is not much different from the one set by Henry Ford. In 1913, he set up the system of independent supplier firms operating at arm's length on short-term contracts. One consequence of the Big Three's low-price-at-all-costs mentality is that suppliers are reluctant to offer them their cutting-edge technology out of fear the contract will be resourced before the research and development costs are recouped.*

a. Contrast the Japanese supply chain model with that of the Big Three.
b. Why might a supplier prefer the Japanese model?
c. What benefits might accrue to the Big Three by adopting the Japanese supply chain practices?

Source: Robert Sherefkin and Amy Wilson, "Suppliers Prefer Japanese Business Model," Rubber & Plastics News, March 17, 2003, Vol. 24, No. 11.

E10-28

Employee involvement

Obj 7

Quickie Designs Inc. uses teams in the manufacture of lightweight wheelchairs. Two features of its team approach are team hiring and peer reviews. Under team hiring, the team recruits, interviews, and hires new team members from within the organization. Using peer reviews, the team evaluates each member of the team with regard to quality, knowledge, teamwork, goal performance, attendance, and safety. These reviews provide feedback to the team member for improvement.

How do these two team approaches differ from using managers to hire and evaluate employees?

E10-29

Activity-based costing for a hospital

Obj 8

SPREADSHEET

✓ a. Patient Lawson, $2,380

St. Luke Hospital plans to use activity-based costing to assign hospital indirect costs to the care of patients. The hospital has identified the following activities and activity rates for the hospital indirect costs:

Activity	Activity Rate
Room and meals	$170 per day
Radiology	$240 per image
Pharmacy	$40 per physician order
Chemistry lab	$75 per test
Operating room	$720 per operating room hour

The records of two representative patients were analyzed, using the activity rates. The activity information associated with the two patients is as follows:

	Patient Lawson	Patient Masters
Number of days	3 days	8 days
Number of images	2 images	5 images
Number of physician orders	4 orders	6 orders
Number of tests	2 tests	5 tests
Number of operating room hours	1.5 hours	5.5 hours

a. Determine the activity cost associated with each patient.
b. Why is the total activity cost different for the two patients?

E10-30

Activity-based costing in an insurance company

Obj 8

SPREADSHEET

✓ a. Auto, $1,000,050

Shield Insurance Company carries three major lines of insurance: auto, workers' compensation, and homeowners. The company has prepared the following report for 2011:

Shield Insurance Company
Product Profitability Report
For the Year Ended December 31, 2011

	Auto	Workers' Compensation	Homeowners
Premium revenue	$5,600,000	$4,800,000	$7,200,000
Less estimated claims	3,920,000	3,360,000	5,040,000
Underwriting income	$1,680,000	$1,440,000	$2,160,000
Underwriting income as a percent of premium revenue	30%	30%	30%

Management is concerned that the administrative expenses may make some of the insurance lines unprofitable. However, the administrative expenses have not been allocated to the insurance lines. The controller has suggested that the

administrative expenses could be assigned to the insurance lines using activity-based costing. The administrative expenses are comprised of five activities. The activities and their rates are as follows:

	Activity Rates
New policy processing	$160 per new policy
Cancellation processing	$240 per cancellation
Claim audits	$500 per claim audit
Claim disbursements processing	$120 per disbursement
Premium collection processing	$ 25 per premium collected

Activity-base usage data for each line of insurance were retrieved from the corporate records and are shown below.

	Auto	Workers' Comp.	Homeowners
Number of new policies	1,100	1,250	3,200
Number of canceled policies	450	200	1,600
Number of audited claims	320	100	700
Number of claim disbursements	400	180	750
Number of premiums collected	7,500	1,500	12,000

a. Complete the product profitability report through the administrative activities. Determine the income from operations as a percent of premium revenue, rounded to one decimal place.
b. Interpret the report.

Problems

P10-1

Classifying costs

Objs 2, 4

The following is a list of costs that were incurred in the production and sale of lawn mowers:

a. Attorney fees for drafting a new lease for headquarters offices.
b. Commissions paid to sales representatives, based on the number of lawn mowers sold.
c. Property taxes on the factory building and equipment.
d. Hourly wages of operators of robotic machinery used in production.
e. Salary of vice president of marketing.
f. Gasoline engines used for lawn mowers.
g. Factory cafeteria cashier's wages.
h. Electricity used to run the robotic machinery.
i. Maintenance costs for new robotic factory equipment, based on hours of usage.
j. License fees for use of patent for lawn mower blade, based on the number of lawn mowers produced.
k. Salary of factory supervisor.
l. Steel used in producing the lawn mowers.
m. Telephone charges for company controller's office.
n. Paint used to coat the lawn mowers.
o. Straight-line depreciation on the robotic machinery used to manufacture the lawn mowers.
p. Tires for lawn mowers.
q. Engine oil used in mower engines prior to shipment.
r. Cash paid to outside firm for janitorial services for factory.
s. Cost of advertising in a national magazine.

t. Salary of quality control supervisor who inspects each lawn mower before it is shipped.
u. Plastic for outside housing of lawn mowers.
v. Steering wheels for lawn mowers.
w. Filter for spray gun used to paint the lawn mowers.
x. Cost of boxes used in packaging lawn mowers.
y. Premiums on insurance policy for factory buildings.
z. Payroll taxes on hourly assembly line employees.

Instructions

Classify each cost as either a product cost or a period cost. Indicate whether each product cost is a direct materials cost, a direct labor cost, or a factory overhead cost. Indicate whether each period cost is a selling expense or an administrative expense. Use the following tabular headings for your answer, placing an "X" in the appropriate column.

	Product Costs			Period Costs	
Cost	Direct Materials Cost	Direct Labor Cost	Factory Overhead Expense	Selling Expense	Administrative Expense

P10-2

Entries and schedules for unfinished jobs and completed jobs

Obj 4

SPREADSHEET

✓ 5. Work in Process balance, $22,290

Staircase Equipment Company uses a job order cost system. The following data summarize the operations related to production for April 2010, the first month of operations:

a. Materials purchased on account, $23,400.
b. Materials requisitioned and factory labor used:

Job	Materials	Factory Labor
No. 201	$2,350	$2,200
No. 202	2,875	2,970
No. 203	1,900	1,490
No. 204	6,450	5,460
No. 205	4,100	4,150
No. 206	2,980	2,650
For general factory use	860	3,250

c. Factory overhead costs incurred on account, $4,500.
d. Depreciation of machinery and equipment, $1,560.
e. The factory overhead rate is $50 per machine hour. Machine hours used:

Job	Machine Hours
No. 201	18
No. 202	30
No. 203	24
No. 204	75
No. 205	33
No. 206	20
Total	200

f. Jobs completed: 201, 202, 203, and 205.
g. Jobs were shipped and customers were billed as follows: Job 201, $6,540; Job 202, $8,820; Job 203, $11,880.

Instructions

1. Prepare a schedule summarizing manufacturing costs by job for April. Use the following form:

Job	Direct Materials	Direct Labor	Factory Overhead	Total

2. Prepare a schedule of jobs finished in April.
3. Prepare a schedule of jobs sold in April. What account does this schedule support for the month of April?
4. Prepare a schedule of completed jobs on hand as of April 30, 2010. What account does this schedule support?
5. Prepare a schedule of unfinished jobs as of April 30, 2010. What account does this schedule support?

P10-3

Job order cost sheet

Objs 4, 5

SPREADSHEET

Lynch Furniture Company refinishes and reupholsters furniture. Lynch uses a job order cost system. When a prospective customer asks for a price quote on a job, the estimated cost data are inserted on an unnumbered job cost sheet. If the offer is accepted, a number is assigned to the job, and the costs incurred are recorded in the usual manner on the job cost sheet. After the job is completed, reasons for the variances between the estimated and actual costs are noted on the sheet. The data are then available to management in evaluating the efficiency of operations and in preparing quotes on future jobs. On May 10, 2010, an estimate of $1,530.00 for reupholstering a chair and couch was given to Queen Mercury. The estimate was based on the following data:

Estimated direct materials:	
40 meters at $12 per meter	$ 480.00
Estimated direct labor:	
24 hours at $15 per hour	360.00
Estimated factory overhead (50% of direct labor cost)	180.00
Total estimated costs	$1,020.00
Markup (50% of production costs)	510.00
Total estimate	$1,530.00

On May 16, the chair and couch were picked up from the residence of Queen Mercury, 10 Rhapsody Lane, Lake Forest, with a commitment to return them on June 12. The job was completed on June 8.

The related materials requisitions and time tickets are summarized as follows:

Materials Requisition No.	Description	Amount
210	24 meters at $12	$288
212	21 meters at $12	252

Time Ticket No.	Description	Amount
H25	18 hours at $14.50	$261.00
H34	9 hours at $14.50	130.50

Instructions

1. Prepare a job order cost sheet showing the estimate given to the customer. Use the format shown below.
2. Assign number 10-206 to the job, record the costs incurred, and complete the job order cost sheet. Comment on the reasons for the variances between actual costs and estimated costs. For this purpose, assume that five meters of materials were spoiled, the factory overhead rate has been proved to be satisfactory, and an inexperienced employee performed the work.

JOB ORDER COST SHEET

Customer _____   Date _____
Address _____   Date wanted _____
_____   Date completed _____
Item _____   Job No. _____

ESTIMATE

Direct Materials		Direct Labor		Summary	
	Amount		Amount		Amount
____ meter at $____	_____	____ hours at $____	_____	Direct materials	_____
____ meter at $____	_____	____ hours at $____	_____	Direct labor	_____
____ meter at $____	_____	____ hours at $____	_____	Factory overhead	_____
____ meter at $____	_____	____ hours at $____	_____	Total cost	_____
Total	_____	Total	_____		

ACTUAL

Direct Materials			Direct Labor			Summary	
Mat. Req. No.	Description	Amount	Mat. Req. No.	Description	Amount	Item	Amount
____	_____	_____	____	_____	_____	Direct materials	_____
____	_____	_____	____	_____	_____	Direct labor	_____
____	_____	_____	____	_____	_____	Factory overhead	_____
____	_____	_____	____	_____	_____	Total cost	_____
Total		_____	Total		_____		

P10-4

Analyzing manufacturing cost accounts

Obj 4

SPREADSHEET

✓ G. $282,130

Big Wave Company manufactures surf boards in a wide variety of sizes and styles. The following incomplete ledger accounts refer to transactions that are summarized for July:

Materials			
July	1	Balance	30,000
	31	Purchase	120,000
	31	Requisitions	(A)

Work in Process

July	1	Balance	(B)
	31	Materials	(C)
	31	Direct labor	(D)
	31	Factory overhead applied	(E)
	31	Completed jobs	(F)

Finished Goods

July	1	Balance	0
	31	Completed jobs	(F)
	31	Cost of goods sold	(G)

Wages Payable

July	31	Wages incurred	120,000

Factory Overhead

July	1	Balance	22,000
	31	Indirect labor	(H) 24000
	31	Indirect materials	16,000
	31	Other overhead	95,000
	31	Factory overhead applied	(E) 153600

In addition, the following information is available:

a. Materials and direct labor were applied to six jobs in July:

Job No.	Style	Quantity	Direct Materials	Direct Labor
No. 21	X-10	200	$ 20,000	$ 15,000
No. 22	X-20	400	34,000	26,000
No. 23	X-50	200	14,000	8,000
No. 24	T-20	250	30,000	25,000
No. 25	X-40	180	22,000	17,500
No. 26	T-10	140	8,000	4,500
	Total	1,370	$128,000	$ 96,000

b. Factory overhead is applied to each job at a rate of 160% of direct labor cost.

c. The July 1 Work in Process balance consisted of two jobs, as follows:

Job No.	Style	Work in Process, July 1
Job 21	X-10	$ 6,000
Job 22	X-20	16,000
Total		$22,000

d. Customer jobs completed and units sold in July were as follows:

Job No.	Style	Completed in July	Units Sold in July
No. 21	X-10	X	160
No. 22	X-20	X	320
No. 23	X-50		0
No. 24	T-20	X	210
No. 25	X-40	X	150
No. 26	T-10		0

Instructions

1. Determine the missing amounts associated with each letter. Provide supporting calculations by completing a table with the following headings:

Job No.	Quantity	July 1 Work in Process	Direct Materials	Direct Labor	Factory Overhead	Total Cost	Unit Cost	Units Sold	Cost of Goods Sold

2. Determine the July 31 balances for each of the inventory accounts and factory overhead.

P10-5

Flow of costs and income statement

Obj 4

✓ 1. Income from operations, $3,300,000

Digital Tunes Inc. is in the business of developing, promoting, and selling musical talent on compact disc (CD). The company signed a new group, called *Smashing Britney,* on January 1, 2010. For the first six months of 2010, the company spent $4,000,000 on a media campaign for *Smashing Britney* and $1,200,000 in legal costs. The CD production began on February 1, 2010.

Digital Tunes uses a job order cost system to accumulate costs associated with a CD title. The unit direct materials cost for the CD is:

Blank CD	$1.80
Jewel case	0.60
Song lyric insert	0.60

The production process is straightforward. First, the blank CDs are brought to a production area where the digital soundtrack is copied onto the CD. The copying machine requires one hour per 2,400 CDs.

After the CDs are copied, they are brought to an assembly area where an employee packs the CD with a jewel case and song lyric insert. The direct labor cost is $0.25 per unit.

The CDs are sold to record stores. Each record store is given promotional materials, such as posters and aisle displays. Promotional materials cost $40 per record store. In addition, shipping costs average $0.25 per CD.

Total completed production was 1,000,000 units during the year. Other information is as follows:

Number of customers (record stores)	42,500
Number of CDs sold	850,000
Wholesale price (to record store) per CD	$16

Factory overhead cost is applied to jobs at the rate of $1,200 per copy machine hour. There were an additional 25,000 copied CDs, packages, and inserts waiting to be assembled on December 31, 2010.

Instructions

1. Prepare an annual income statement for the *Smashing Britney* CD, including supporting calculations, from the information above.

2. Determine the balances in the work in process and finished goods inventory for the *Smashing Britney* CD on December 31, 2010.

Activities

A10-1

Ethics and professional conduct in business

ETHICS

Earnhart Manufacturing Company allows employees to purchase, at cost, manufacturing materials, such as metal and lumber, for personal use. To purchase materials for personal use, an employee must complete a materials requisition form, which must then be approved by the employee's immediate supervisor. Gretchen MacCauley, an assistant cost accountant, charges the employee an amount based on Earnhart's net purchase cost.

Gretchen MacCauley is in the process of replacing a deck on her home and has requisitioned lumber for personal use, which has been approved in accordance with company policy. In computing the cost of the lumber, Gretchen reviewed all the purchase invoices for the past year. She then used the lowest price to compute the amount due the company for the lumber.

Discuss whether Gretchen behaved in an ethical manner.

A10-2

Financial vs. managerial accounting

The following statement was made by the vice president of finance of Orville Inc.: "The managers of a company should use the same information as the shareholders of the firm. When managers use the same information in guiding their internal operations as shareholders use in evaluating their investments, the managers will be aligned with the stockholders' profit objectives."

Respond to the vice president's statement.

A10-3

Classifying costs

The Nerd Squad provides computer repair services for the community. Jane Doe's computer was not working, and she called The Nerd Squad for a home repair visit. The Nerd Squad's technician arrived at 2:00 P.M. to begin work. By 4:00 P.M. the problem was diagnosed as a failed circuit board. Unfortunately, the technician did not have a new circuit board in the truck, since the technician's previous customer had the same problem, and a board was used on that visit. Replacement boards were available back at The Nerd Squad's shop. Therefore, the technician drove back to the shop to retrieve a replacement board. From 4:00 to 5:00 P.M., The Nerd Squad's technician drove the round trip to retrieve the replacement board from the shop.

At 5:00 P.M. the technician was back on the job at Jane's home. The replacement procedure is somewhat complex, since a variety of tests must be performed once the board is installed. The job was completed at 6:00 P.M.

Jane's repair bill showed the following:

Circuit board	$ 60
Labor charges	255
Total	$315

Jane was surprised at the size of the bill and asked for some greater detail supporting the calculations. The Nerd Squad responded with the following explanations:

Cost of materials:	
Purchase price of circuit board	$45
Markup on purchase price to cover storage and handling	15
Total materials charge	$60

The labor charge per hour is detailed as follows:

2:00–3:00 P.M.	$ 55
3:00–4:00 P.M.	45
4:00–5:00 P.M.	65
5:00–6:00 P.M.	90
Total labor charge	$255

Further explanations in the differences in the hourly rates are as follows:

First hour:	
Base labor rate	$25
Fringe benefits	10
Overhead (other than storage and handling)	10
Total base labor rate	$45
Additional charge for first hour of any job to cover the cost of vehicle depreciation, fuel, and employee time in transit. A 30-minute transit time is assumed.	10
	$55
Third hour:	
Base labor rate	$45
The trip back to the shop includes vehicle depreciation and fuel; therefore, a charge was added to the hourly rate to cover these costs. The round trip took an hour.	20
	$65
Fourth hour:	
Base labor rate	$45
Overtime premium for time worked in excess of an eight-hour day (starting at 5:00 P.M.) is equal to the base rate.	45
	$90

1. If you were in Jane's position, how would you respond to the bill? Are there parts of the bill that appear incorrect to you? If so, what argument would you employ to convince The Nerd Squad that the bill is too high?
2. Use the headings below to construct a table. Fill in the table by first listing the costs identified in the activity in the left-hand column. For each cost, place a check mark in the appropriate column identifying the correct cost classification. Assume that each service call is a job.

Cost	Direct Materials	Direct Labor	Overhead

A10-4

Managerial analysis

The controller of the plant of Berry Building Supplies prepared a graph of the unit costs from the job cost reports for Product X-S1. The graph appeared as follows:

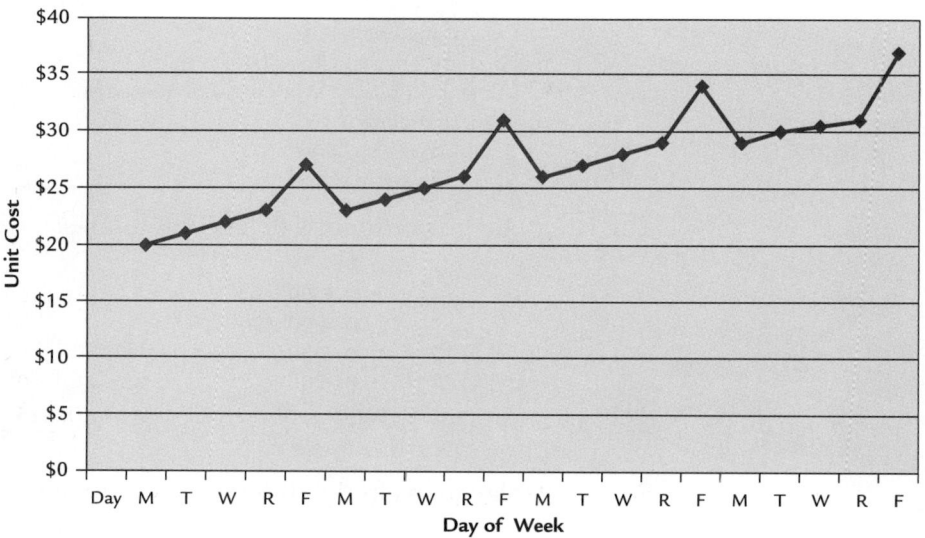

How would you interpret this information? What further information would you request?

A10-5

Factory overhead rate

Digital-Tech Inc., a specialized equipment manufacturer, uses a job order costing system. The overhead is allocated to jobs on the basis of direct labor hours. The overhead rate is now $2,500 per direct labor hour. The design engineer thinks that this is illogical. The design engineer has stated the following:

> *Our accounting system doesn't make any sense to me. It tells me that every labor hour carries an additional burden of $2,500. This means that direct labor makes up only 7% of our total product cost, yet it drives all our costs. In addition, these rates give my design engineers incentives to "design out" direct labor by using machine technology. Yet, over the past years as we have had less and less direct labor, the overhead rate keeps going up and up. I won't be surprised if next year the rate is $3,000 per direct labor hour. I'm also concerned because small errors in our estimates of the direct labor content can have a large impact on our estimated costs. Just a 30-minute error in our estimate of assembly time is worth $1,250. Small mistakes in our direct labor time estimates really swing our bids around. I think this puts us at a disadvantage when we are going after business.*

1. What is the engineer's concern about the overhead rate going "up and up"?
2. What did the engineer mean about the large overhead rate being a disadvantage when placing bids and seeking new business?
3. What do you think is a possible solution?

A10-6

Classifying costs

GROUP

With a group of students, visit a local copy and graphics shop or a pizza restaurant. As you observe the operation, consider the costs associated with running the business. As a group, identify as many costs as you can and classify them according to the following table headings:

Cost	Direct Materials	Direct Labor	Overhead	Selling Expense

A10-7

Just-in-time principles

Hilton Inc. manufactures electric space heaters. While the CEO, Azra Khan, is visiting the production facility, the following conversation takes place with the plant manager, Paul Lopez:

Azra: As I walk around the facility, I can't help noticing all the materials inventories. What's going on?

Paul: I have found our suppliers to be very unreliable in meeting their delivery commitments. Thus, I keep a lot of materials on hand so as to not risk running out and shutting down production.

Azra: Not only do I see a lot of materials inventory, but there also seems to be a lot of finished goods inventory on hand. Why is this?

Paul: As you know, I am evaluated on maintaining a low cost per unit. The one way that I am able to reduce my unit costs is by producing as many space heaters as possible. This allows me to spread my fixed costs over a larger base. When orders are down, the excess production builds up as inventory, as we are seeing now. But don't worry—I'm really keeping our unit costs down this way.

Azra: I'm not so sure. It seems that this inventory must cost us something.

Paul: Not really. I'll eventually use the materials and we'll eventually sell the finished goods. By keeping the plant busy, I'm using our plant assets wisely. This is reflected in the low unit costs that I'm able to maintain.

If you were Azra Kahn, how would you respond to Paul Lopez? What recommendations would you provide Paul Lopez?

Answers to Self-Examination Questions

1. **C** Sales salaries (answer C) is a selling expense and is not considered a cost of manufacturing a product. Direct materials cost (answer A), factory overhead cost (answer B), and direct labor cost (answer D) are costs of manufacturing a product.

2. **B** Depreciation of testing equipment (answer B) is included as part of the factory overhead costs of the computer manufacturer. The cost of memory chips (answer A) and the cost of disk drives (answer D) are both considered a part of direct materials cost. The wages of computer assemblers (answer C) are part of direct labor costs.

3. **B**

$$\text{Predetermined factory overhead rate} = \frac{\text{Estimated total factory overhead costs}}{\text{Estimated activity base}}$$

$$\text{Predetermined factory overhead rate} = \frac{\$420,000}{16,000 \text{ dlh}} = \$26.25$$

$$\text{Hours applied to the job} : \frac{\$3,000}{\$15 \text{ per hour}} = 200 \text{ hours}$$

Factory overhead applied to the job:

200 hours × $26.25 = $5,250

4. **B** If the amount of factory overhead applied during a particular period exceeds the actual overhead costs, the factory overhead account will have a negative balance and is said to be overapplied (answer B) or overabsorbed. If the amount applied is less than the actual costs, the account will have a positive balance and is said to be underapplied (answer A) or underabsorbed (answer C). Since an "estimated" predetermined overhead rate is used to apply overhead, a negative balance does not necessarily represent an error (answer D).

5. **B** The just-in-time philosophy embraces a product-oriented layout (answer A), making lead times short (answer C) and reducing setup times (answer D). Pull manufacturing, the opposite of push manufacturing (answer B), is also a just-in-time principle.

Cost Behavior and Cost-Volume-Profit Analysis

Learning Objectives

After studying this chapter, you should be able to:

Obj 1 Classify costs as variable costs, fixed costs, or mixed costs.

Obj 2 Compute the contribution margin, the contribution margin ratio, and the unit contribution margin.

Obj 3 Determine the break-even point and sales necessary to achieve a target profit.

Obj 4 Using a cost-volume-profit chart and a profit-volume chart, determine the break-even point and sales necessary to achieve a target profit.

Obj 5 Compute the break-even point for a company selling more than one product, the operating leverage, and the margin of safety.

How do you decide whether you are going to buy or rent a video game? It probably depends on how much you think you are going to use the game. If you are going to play the game a lot, you are probably better off buying the game than renting. The one-time cost of buying the game would be much less expensive than the cost of multiple rentals. If, on the other hand, you are uncertain about how frequently you are going to play the game, it may be less expensive to rent. The cost of an individual rental is much less than the cost of purchase. Understanding how the costs of rental and purchase behave affects your decision.

Understanding how costs behave is also important to companies like ***Netflix,*** an online DVD movie rental service. For a fee, Netflix customers can directly download movies directly to their computer. Alternatively, customers can select DVDs from their own computer, and have the DVDs delivered to their home along with a prepaid return envelope. Customers can keep the DVDs as long as they want, but must return the DVDs before they rent additional movies. The number of DVDs that members can check out at one time varies between one and three, depending on their subscription plan.

In order to entice customers to subscribe, Netflix had to invest in a well-stocked library of DVD titles, and build a warehouse to hold and distribute these titles. These costs do not change with the number of subscriptions. But how many subscriptions does Netflix need in order to make a profit? That depends on the price of each subscription, the costs incurred with each DVD rental, and the costs associated with maintaining the DVD library.

As with Netflix, understanding how costs behave and the relationship among costs, profits, and volume is important for all businesses. This chapter discusses commonly used methods for classifying costs according to how they change. Techniques that management can use to evaluate costs in order to make sound business decisions are also discussed.

Obj 1 Classify costs as variable costs, fixed costs, or mixed costs.

Cost Behavior

Cost behavior is the manner in which a cost changes as a related activity changes. The behavior of costs is useful to managers for a variety of reasons. For example, knowing how costs behave allows managers to predict profits as sales and production volumes change. Knowing how costs behave is also useful for estimating costs, which affects a variety of decisions such as whether to replace a machine.

Understanding the behavior of a cost depends on:

1. Identifying the activities that cause the cost to change. These activities are called **activity bases** (or *activity drivers*).

2. Specifying the range of activity over which the changes in the cost are of interest. This range of activity is called the **relevant range**.

To illustrate, assume that a hospital is concerned about planning and controlling patient food costs. A good activity base is the number of patients who *stay* overnight in the hospital. The number of patients who are *treated* is not as good an activity base since some patients are outpatients and thus do not consume food. Once an activity base is identified, food costs can then be analyzed over the range of the number of patients who normally stay in the hospital (the relevant range).

Costs are normally classified as variable costs, fixed costs, or mixed costs.

Variable Costs

Variable costs are costs that vary in proportion to changes in the activity base. When the activity base is units produced, direct materials and direct labor costs are normally classified as variable costs.

To illustrate, assume that Jason Sound Inc. produces stereo systems. The parts for the stereo systems are purchased from suppliers for $10 per unit and are assembled by Jason Sound Inc. For Model JS-12, the direct materials costs for the relevant range of 5,000 to 30,000 units of production are shown below.

Number of Units of Model JS-12 Produced	Direct Materials Cost per Unit	Total Direct Materials Cost
5,000 units	$10	$50,000
10,000	10	100,000
15,000	10	150,000
20,000	10	200,000
25,000	10	250,000
30,000	10	300,000

As shown above, variable costs have the following characteristics:

1. *Cost per unit* remains the same regardless of changes in the activity base. For Model JS-12, the cost per unit is $10.

2. *Total cost* changes in proportion to changes in the activity base. For Model JS-12, the direct materials cost for 10,000 units ($100,000) is twice the direct materials cost for 5,000 units ($50,000).

Exhibit 1 illustrates how the variable costs for direct materials for Model JS-12 behave in total and on a per-unit basis as production changes.

EXHIBIT 1 Variable Cost Graphs

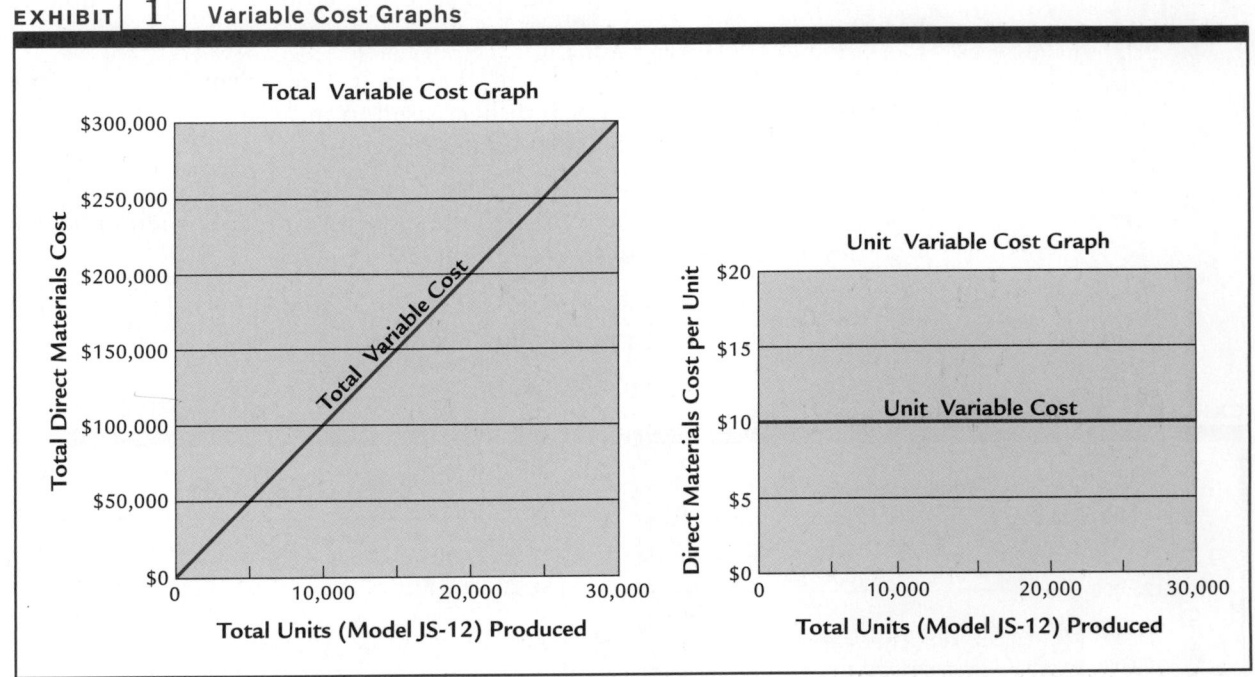

Some examples of variable costs and their related activity bases for various types of businesses are shown below.

Type of Business	Cost	Activity Base
University	Instructor salaries	Number of classes
Passenger airline	Fuel	Number of miles flown
Manufacturing	Direct materials	Number of units produced
Hospital	Nurse wages	Number of patients
Hotel	Maid wages	Number of guests
Bank	Teller wages	Number of banking transactions

Fixed Costs

Fixed costs are costs that remain the same in total dollar amount as the activity base changes. When the activity base is units produced, many factory overhead costs such as straight-line depreciation are classified as fixed costs.

To illustrate, assume that Minton Inc. manufactures, bottles, and distributes perfume. The production supervisor is Jane Sovissi, who is paid a salary of $75,000 per year. For the relevant range of 50,000 to 300,000 bottles of perfume, the total fixed cost of $75,000 does not vary as production increases. However, the fixed cost per bottle decreases as the units produced increase; thus, the fixed cost is spread over a larger number of bottles, as shown below.

Number of Bottles of Perfume Produced	Total Salary for Jane Sovissi	Salary per Bottle of Perfume Produced
50,000 bottles	$75,000	$1,500
100,000	75,000	0.750
150,000	75,000	0.500
200,000	75,000	0.375
250,000	75,000	0.300
300,000	75,000	0.250

As shown on the preceding page, fixed costs have the following characteristics:

1. *Cost per unit* changes inversely to changes in the activity base. For Jane Sovissi's salary, the cost per unit decreased from $1.50 for 50,000 bottles produced to $0.25 for 300,000 bottles produced.

2. *Total cost* remains the same regardless of changes in the activity base. Jane Sovissi's salary of $75,000 remained the same regardless of whether 50,000 bottles or 300,000 bottles were produced.

Exhibit 2 illustrates how Jane Sovissi's salary (fixed cost) behaves in total and on a per-unit basis as production changes.

EXHIBIT **2** **Fixed Cost Graphs**

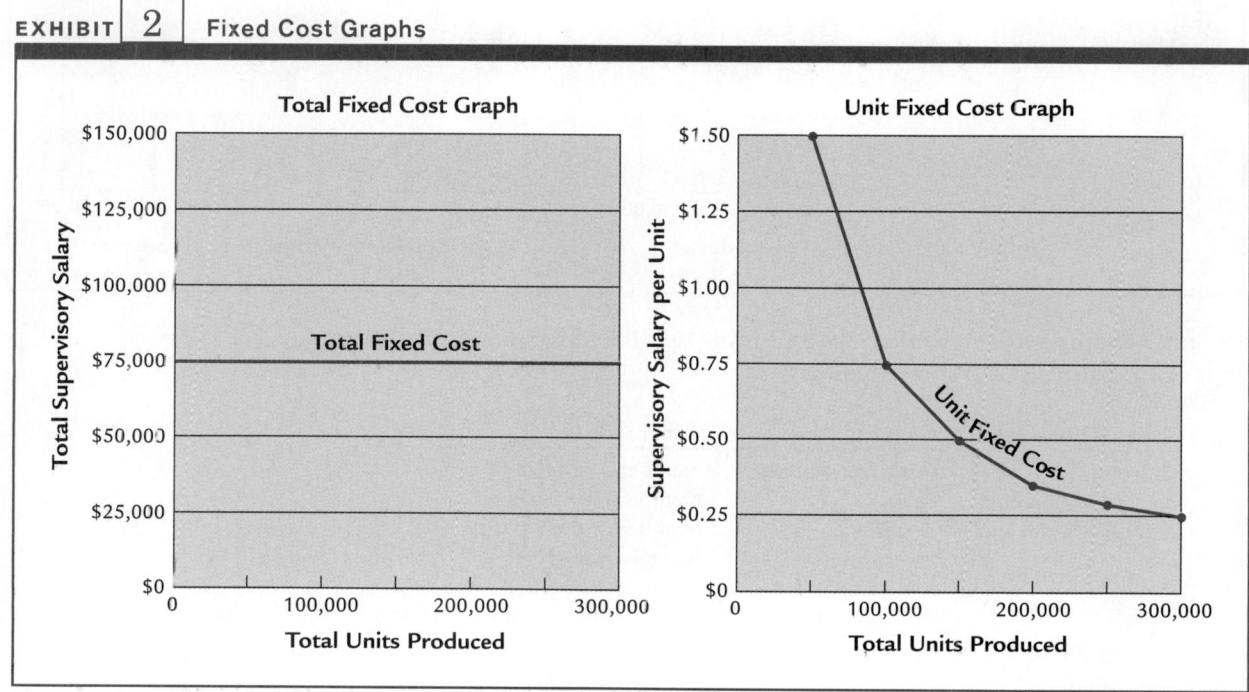

Some examples of fixed costs and their related activity bases for various types of businesses are shown below.

Type of Business	Fixed Cost	Activity Base
University	Building (straight-line) depreciation	Number of students
Passenger airline	Airplane (straight-line) depreciation	Number of miles flown
Manufacturing	Plant manager salary	Number of units produced
Hospital	Property insurance	Number of patients
Hotel	Property taxes	Number of guests
Bank	Branch manager salary	Number of customer accounts

A salesperson's compensation can be a mixed cost comprised of a salary (fixed portion) plus a commission as a percent of sales (variable portion).

Mixed Costs

Mixed costs are costs that have characteristics of both a variable and a fixed cost. Mixed costs are sometimes called *semivariable* or *semifixed* costs.

To illustrate, assume that Simpson Inc. manufactures sails, using rented machinery. The rental charges are as follows:

Rental Charge = $15,000 per year

+ $1 times each machine hour over 10,000 hours

The rental charges for various hours used within the relevant range of 8,000 hours to 40,000 hours are as follows:

Hours Used	Rental Charge
8,000 hours	$15,000
12,000	$17,000 {$15,000 + [(12,000 hrs. − 10,000 hrs.) × $1]}
20,000	$25,000 {$15,000 + [(20,000 hrs. − 10,000 hrs.) × $1]}
40,000	$45,000 {$15,000 + [(40,000 hrs. − 10,000 hrs.) × $1]}

Exhibit 3 illustrates the preceding mixed cost behavior.

EXHIBIT 3 Mixed Costs

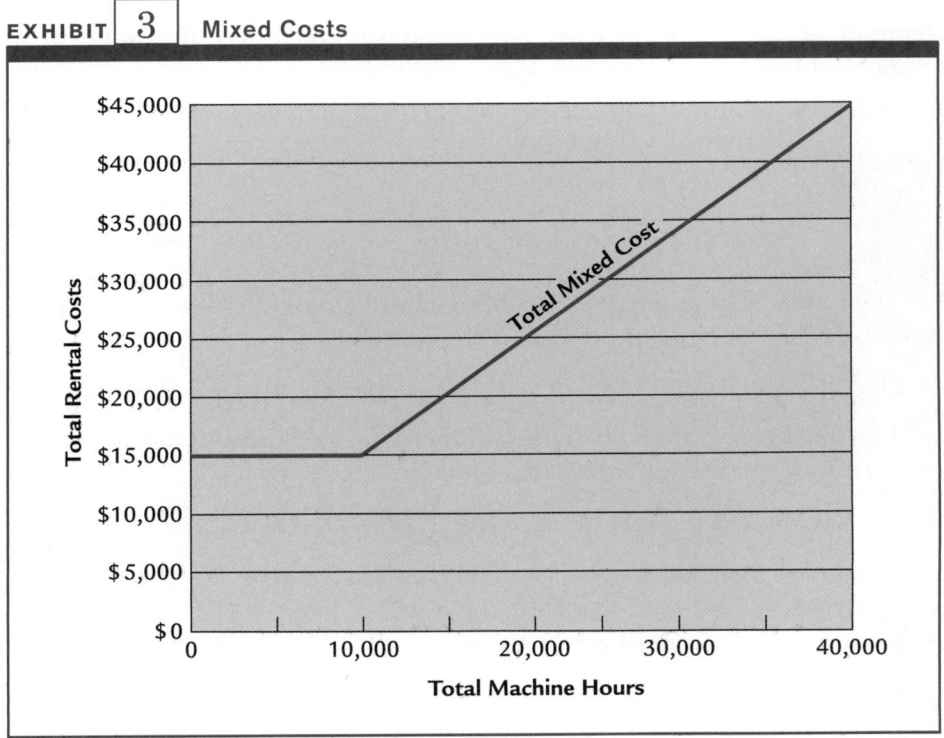

For purposes of analysis, mixed costs are usually separated into their fixed and variable components. The **high-low method** is a cost estimation method that may be used for this purpose.[1] The high-low method uses the highest and lowest activity levels and their related costs to estimate the variable cost per unit and the fixed cost.

To illustrate, assume that the Equipment Maintenance Department of Kason Inc. incurred the following costs during the past five months:

	Production	Total Cost
June	1,000 units	$45,550
July	1,500	52,000
August	2,100	61,500
September	1,800	57,500
October	750	41,250

The number of units produced is the activity base, and the relevant range is the units produced between June and October. For Kason Inc., the

[1] Other methods of estimating costs, such as the scattergraph method and the least squares method, are discussed in cost accounting textbooks.

difference between the units produced and total costs at the highest and lowest levels of production are as follows:

	Production	Total Cost
Highest level	2,100 units	$61,500
Lowest level	750	41,250
Difference	1,350 units	$20,250

The total fixed cost does not change with changes in production. Thus, the $20,250 difference in the total cost is the change in the total variable cost. Dividing this difference of $20,250 by the difference in production is an estimate of the variable cost per unit. For Kason Inc., this estimate is $15, as computed below.

$$\text{Variable Cost per Unit} = \frac{\text{Difference in Total Cost}}{\text{Difference in Production}}$$

$$\text{Variable Cost per Unit} = \frac{\$20,250}{1,350 \text{ units}} = \$15 \text{ per unit}$$

The fixed cost is estimated by subtracting the total variable costs from the total costs for the units produced as shown below.

Fixed Cost = Total Costs − (Variable Cost per Unit × Units Produced)

The fixed cost is the same at the highest and the lowest levels of production as shown below for Kason Inc.

Highest level (2,100 units)

Fixed Cost = Total Costs − (Variable Cost per Unit × Units Produced)
Fixed Cost = $61,500 − ($15 × 2,100 units)
Fixed Cost = $61,500 − $31,500
Fixed Cost = $30,000

Lowest level (750 units)

Fixed Cost = Total Costs − (Variable Cost per Unit × Units Produced)
Fixed Cost = $41,250 − ($15 × 750 units)
Fixed Cost = $41,250 − $11,250
Fixed Cost = $30,000

Using the variable cost per unit and the fixed cost, the total equipment maintenance cost for Kason Inc. can be computed for various levels of production as follows:

Total Cost = (Variable Cost per Unit × Units Produced) + Fixed Costs

Total Cost = ($15 × Units Produced) + $30,000

To illustrate, the estimated total cost of 2,000 units of production is $60,000, as computed below:

Total Cost = ($15 × Units Produced) + $30,000
Total Cost = ($15 × 2,000 units) + $30,000 = $30,000 + $30,000
Total Cost = $60,000

Summary of Cost Behavior Concepts

The cost behavior of variable costs and fixed costs is summarized below.

	Effect of Changing Activity Level	
Cost	**Total Amount**	**Per-Unit Amount**
Variable	Increases and decreases proportionately with activity level.	Remains the same regardless of activity level.
Fixed	Remains the same regardless of activity level.	Increases and decreases inversely with activity level.

Mixed costs contain a fixed cost component that is incurred even if nothing is produced. For analysis, the fixed and variable cost components of mixed costs are separated using the high-low method.

Some examples of variable, fixed, and mixed costs for the activity base *units produced* are as follows:

Variable Cost	**Fixed Cost**	**Mixed Cost**
Direct materials	Straight-line depreciation	Quality Control Department salaries
Direct labor	Property taxes	Purchasing Department salaries
Electricity expense	Production supervisor salaries	Maintenance expenses
Supplies	Insurance expense	Warehouse expenses

One method of reporting variable and fixed costs is called **variable costing** or *direct costing*. Under variable costing, only the variable manufacturing costs (direct materials, direct labor, and variable factory overhead) are included in the product cost. The fixed factory overhead is treated as an expense of the period in which it is incurred. Variable costing is described and illustrated in advanced accounting courses.

Cost-Volume-Profit Relationships

Obj 2 Compute the contribution margin, the contribution margin ratio, and the unit contribution margin.

Cost-volume-profit analysis is the examination of the relationships among selling prices, sales and production volume, costs, expenses, and profits. Cost-volume-profit analysis is useful for managerial decision making. Some of the ways cost-volume-profit analysis may be used include:

1. Analyzing the effects of changes in selling prices on profits
2. Analyzing the effects of changes in costs on profits
3. Analyzing the effects of changes in volume on profits
4. Setting selling prices
5. Selecting the mix of products to sell
6. Choosing among marketing strategies

Contribution Margin

Contribution margin is especially useful because it provides insight into the profit potential of a company. **Contribution margin** is the excess of sales over variable costs, as shown below.

$$\text{Contribution Margin} = \text{Sales} - \text{Variable Costs}$$

To illustrate, assume the following data for Lambert Inc.:

Sales	50,000 units
Sales price per unit	$20 per unit
Variable cost per unit	$12 per unit
Fixed costs	$300,000

Exhibit 4 illustrates an income statement for Lambert Inc. prepared in a contribution margin format.

EXHIBIT 4   Contribution Margin Income Statement

Sales (50,000 units × $20)	$1,000,000
Variable costs (50,000 units × $12)	600,000
Contribution margin (50,000 units × $8)	$ 400,000
Fixed costs	300,000
Income from operations	$ 100,000

Lambert's contribution margin of $400,000 is available to cover the fixed costs of $300,000. Once the fixed costs are covered, any additional contribution margin increases income from operations.

The graphic to the left illustrates the contribution margin and its effect on profits. The fixed costs are a bucket and the contribution margin is water filling the bucket. Once the bucket is filled, the overflow represents income from operations. Up until the point of overflow, the contribution margin contributes to fixed costs (filling the bucket).

Contribution Margin Ratio

The contribution margin can also be expressed as a percentage. The **contribution margin ratio**, sometimes called the *profit-volume ratio*, indicates the percentage of each sales dollar available to cover fixed costs and to provide income from operations. The contribution margin ratio is computed as follows:

$$\text{Contribution Margin Ratio} = \frac{\text{Contribution Margin}}{\text{Sales}}$$

The contribution margin ratio is 40% for Lambert Inc., as computed below.

$$\text{Contribution Margin Ratio} = \frac{\text{Contribution Margin}}{\text{Sales}}$$

$$\text{Contribution Margin Ratio} = \frac{\$400,000}{\$1,000,000} = 40\%$$

The contribution margin ratio is most useful when the increase or decrease in sales volume is measured in sales *dollars.* In this case, the change

in sales dollars multiplied by the contribution margin ratio equals the change in income from operations, as shown below.

Change in Income from Operations = Change in Sales Dollars
$\qquad\qquad\qquad\qquad\qquad$ × Contribution Margin Ratio

To illustrate, if Lambert Inc. adds $80,000 in sales orders, its income from operations will increase by $32,000, as computed below.

Change in Income from Operations = Change in Sales Dollars
$\qquad\qquad\qquad\qquad\qquad$ × Contribution Margin Ratio

$\qquad$ Change in Income from Operations = $80,000 × 40% = $32,000

The preceding analysis is confirmed by the following contribution margin income statement of Lambert Inc.:

Sales	$1,080,000
Variable costs ($1,080,000 × 60%)	648,000
Contribution margin ($1,080,000 × 40%)	$ 432,000
Fixed costs	300,000
Income from operations	$ 132,000

[handwritten margin note: 40% Sales / 60% Sales / 150,000]

Income from operations increased from $100,000 to $132,000 when sales increased from $1,000,000 to $1,080,000. Variable costs as a percentage of sales are equal to 100% minus the contribution margin ratio. Thus, in the above income statement, the variable costs are 60% (100% – 40%) of sales, or $648,000 ($1,080,000 × 60%). The total contribution margin, $432,000, can also be computed directly by multiplying the total sales by the contribution margin ratio ($1,080,000 × 40%).

In the preceding analysis, factors other than sales volume, such as variable cost per unit and sales price, are assumed to remain constant. If such factors change, their effect must also be considered.

The contribution margin ratio is also useful in developing business strategies. For example, assume that a company has a high contribution margin ratio and is producing below 100% of capacity. In this case, a large increase in income from operations can be expected from an increase in sales volume. Therefore, the company might consider implementing a special sales campaign to increase sales. In contrast, a company with a small contribution margin ratio will probably want to give more attention to reducing costs before attempting to promote sales.

Unit Contribution Margin

The unit contribution margin is also useful for analyzing the profit potential of proposed decisions. The **unit contribution margin** is computed as follows:

Unit Contribution Margin = Sales Price per Unit − Variable Cost per Unit

To illustrate, if Lambert Inc.'s unit selling price is $20 and its variable cost per unit is $12, the unit contribution margin is $8 as shown below.

Unit Contribution Margin = Sales Price per Unit − Variable Cost per Unit
Unit Contribution Margin = $20 − $12 = $8

[handwritten note: 60% 40%]

The unit contribution margin is most useful when the increase or decrease in sales volume is measured in sales *units* (quantities). In this case, the change in sales volume (units) multiplied by the unit contribution margin equals the change in income from operations, as shown below.

Change in Income from Operations = Change in Sales Units
$\qquad\qquad\qquad\qquad$ × Unit Contribution Margin

To illustrate, assume that Lambert Inc.'s sales could be increased by 15,000 units, from 50,000 units to 65,000 units. Lambert's income from operations would increase by $120,000 (15,000 units × $8), as shown below.

Change in Income from Operations = Change in Sales Units
$\qquad\qquad\qquad\qquad$ × Unit Contribution Margin

Change in Income from Operations = 15,000 units × $8 = $120,000

The preceding analysis is confirmed by the following contribution margin income statement of Lambert Inc., which shows that income increased to $220,000 when 65,000 units are sold.

A room night at **Hilton Hotels** has a high contribution margin. The high contribution margin per room night is necessary to cover the high fixed costs for the hotel.

Sales (65,000 units × $20)	$1,300,000
Variable costs (65,000 units × $12)	780,000
Contribution margin (65,000 units × $8)	$ 520,000
Fixed costs	300,000
Income from operations	$ 220,000

The prior income statement in Exhibit 4 on page 426 indicates income of $100,000 when 50,000 units are sold. Thus, selling an additional 15,000 units increases income by $120,000 ($220,000 − $100,000).

Unit contribution margin analysis is useful information for managers. For example, in the preceding illustration, Lambert Inc. could spend up to $120,000 for special advertising or other product promotions to increase sales by 15,000 units. For example, if Lambert Inc. spent $90,000 to increase sales by 15,000, then income would increase by $30,000 ($120,000 − $90,000).

Obj 3 Determine the break-even point and sales necessary to achieve a target profit.

Mathematical Approach to Cost-Volume-Profit Analysis

The mathematical approach to cost-volume-profit analysis uses equations to determine the following:

1. Sales necessary to break even
2. Sales necessary to make a target or desired profit

Break-Even Point

The **break-even point** is the level of operations at which a company's revenues and expenses are equal. At break-even, a company reports neither

an income nor a loss from operations. The break-even point in *sales units* is computed as follows:

$$\text{Break-Even Sales (units)} = \frac{\text{Fixed Costs}}{\text{Unit Contribution Margin}}$$

To illustrate, assume the following data for Baker Corporation:

Fixed costs	$90,000
Unit selling price	$25
Unit variable cost	15
Unit contribution margin	$10

[handwritten: 150,000]
[handwritten: 40% of sales]
[handwritten: 60% of sales]

The break-even point is 9,000 units, as shown below.

$$\text{Break-Even Sales (units)} = \frac{\text{Fixed Costs}}{\text{Unit Contribution Margin}}$$

$$= \frac{\$90,000}{\$10} = 9,000\ \text{units}$$

The following income statement verifies the break-even point of 9,000 units:

Sales (9,000 units × $25)		$225,000
Variable costs (9,000 units × $15)	60	135,000
Contribution margin	40	$ 90,000
Fixed costs		90,000
Income from operations		$ 0

When the owner of a shopping center was asked how he was doing, he said, "My properties are *almost* fully rented." The questioner commented, "That must be pretty good." The shopping center owner responded, "Maybe so. But as you know, the profit is in the *almost.*" This exchange reveals an important business principle: Income from operations is earned only after the break-even point is reached.

As shown in the preceding income statement, the break-even point is $225,000 (9,000 units × $25) of sales. The break-even point in *sales dollars* can be determined directly as follows:

$$\text{Break-Even Sales (dollars)} = \frac{\text{Fixed Costs}}{\text{Contribution Margin Ratio}}$$

The contribution margin ratio can be computed using the unit contribution margin and unit selling price as follows:

$$\text{Contribution Margin Ratio} = \frac{\text{Unit Contribution Margin}}{\text{Unit Selling Price}}$$

The contribution margin ratio for Baker Corporation is 40%, as shown below.

$$\text{Contribution Margin Ratio} = \frac{\text{Unit Contribution Margin}}{\text{Unit Selling Price}} = \frac{\$10}{\$25} = 40\%$$

[handwritten: 150,000]

Thus, the break-even sales dollars for Baker Corporation of $225,000 can be computed directly as follows:

$$\text{Break-Even Sales (dollars)} = \frac{\text{Fixed Costs}}{\text{Contribution Margin Ratio}} = \frac{\$90,000}{40\%} = \$225,000$$

The break-even point is affected by changes in the fixed costs, unit variable costs, and the unit selling price.

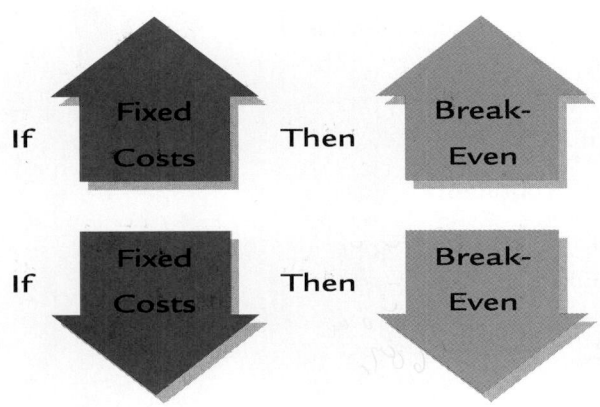

Effect of Changes in Fixed Costs

Fixed costs do not change in total with changes in the level of activity. However, fixed costs may change because of other factors such as changes in property tax rates or factory supervisors' salaries.

Changes in fixed costs affect the break-even point as follows:

1. Increases in fixed costs increase the break-even point.

2. Decreases in fixed costs decrease the break-even point.

To illustrate, assume that Bishop Co. is evaluating a proposal to budget an additional $100,000 for advertising. The data for Bishop Co. are as follows:

	Current	Proposed
Unit selling price	$90	$90
Unit variable cost	70	70
Unit contribution margin	$20	$20
Fixed costs	$600,000	$700,000

Indian Airlines Limited renegotiated leases on Airbus aircraft from $2,500,000 to $1,400,000 per month. This reduction in monthly fixed costs reduced the airline's break-even passenger volume.

Bishop Co.'s break-even point *before* the additional advertising expense of $100,000 is 30,000 units, as shown below.

$$\text{Break-Even Sales (units)} = \frac{\text{Fixed Costs}}{\text{Unit Contribution Margin}}$$

$$= \frac{\$600,000}{\$20} = 30,000 \text{ units}$$

Bishop Co.'s break-even point *after* the additional advertising expense of $100,000 is 35,000 units, as shown below.

$$\text{Break-Even Sales (units)} = \frac{\text{Fixed Costs}}{\text{Unit Contribution Margin}}$$

$$= \frac{\$700,000}{\$20} = 35,000 \text{ units}$$

As shown above, the $100,000 increase in advertising (fixed costs) requires an additional 5,000 units (35,000 − 30,000) of sales to break even.[2] In other words, an increase in sales of 5,000 units is required in order to generate an additional $100,000 of total contribution margin (5,000 units × $20) to cover the increased fixed costs.

Effect of Changes in Unit Variable Costs

Unit variable costs do not change with changes in the level of activity. However, unit variable costs may be affected by other factors such as changes in the cost per unit of direct materials.

Changes in unit variable costs affect the break-even point as follows:

1. Increases in unit variable costs increase the break-even point.

2. Decreases in unit variable costs decrease the break-even point.

---

[2] The increase of 5,000 units can also be computed by dividing the increase in fixed costs of $100,000 by the unit contribution margin, $20, as follows: 5,000 units = $100,000/$20.

To illustrate, assume that Park Co. is evaluating a proposal to pay an additional 2% commission on sales to its salespeople as an incentive to increase sales. The data for Park Co. are as follows:

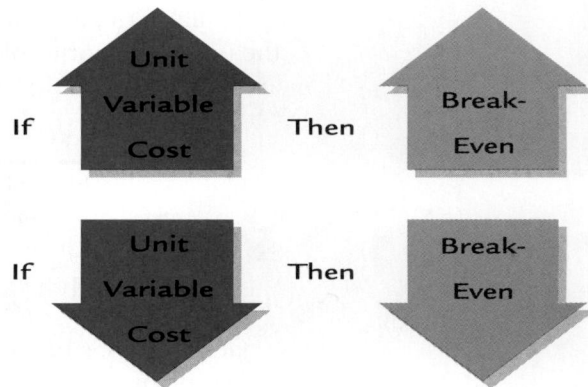

	Current	Proposed
Unit selling price	$250	$250
Unit variable cost	145	150
Unit contribution margin	$105	$100
Fixed costs	$840,000	$840,000

Park Co.'s break-even point *before* the additional 2% commission is 8,000 units, as shown below.

$$\text{Break-Even Sales (units)} = \frac{\text{Fixed Costs}}{\text{Unit Contribution Margin}}$$
$$= \frac{\$840,000}{\$105} = 8,000 \text{ units}$$

Increases in fuel prices increase the break-even freight load for the **Union Pacific** railroad.

If the 2% sales commission proposal is adopted, unit variable costs will increase by $5 ($250 × 2%) from $145 to $150 per unit. This increase in unit variable costs will decrease the unit contribution margin from $105 to $100 ($250 − $150). Thus, Park Co.'s break-even point *after* the additional 2% commission is 8,400 units, as shown below.

$$\text{Break-Even Sales (units)} = \frac{\text{Fixed Costs}}{\text{Unit Contribution Margin}}$$
$$= \frac{\$840,000}{\$100} = 8,400 \text{ units}$$

As shown above, an additional 400 units of sales will be required in order to break even. This is because if 8,000 units are sold, the new unit contribution margin of $100 provides only $800,000 (8,000 units × $100) of contribution margin. Thus, $40,000 more contribution margin is necessary to cover the total fixed costs of $840,000. This additional $40,000 of contribution margin is provided by selling 400 more units (400 units × $100).

Effect of Changes in Unit Selling Price

Changes in the unit selling price affect the unit contribution margin and thus the break-even point. Specifically, changes in the unit selling price affect the break-even point as follows:

1. Increases in the unit selling price decrease the break-even point.
2. Decreases in the unit selling price increase the break-even point.

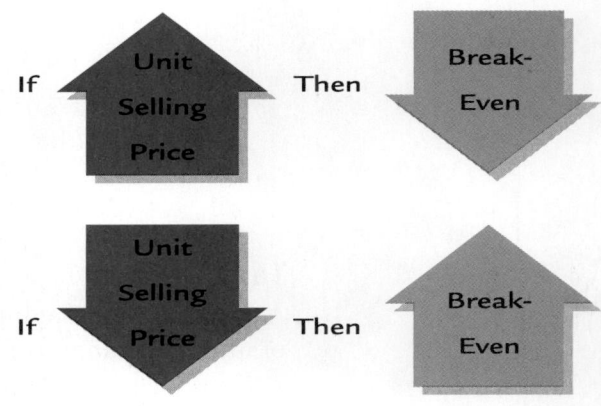

To illustrate, assume that Graham Co. is evaluating a proposal to increase the unit selling price of its product from $50 to $60. The data for Graham Co. are as follows:

	Current	Proposed
Unit selling price	$50	$60
Unit variable cost	30	30
Unit contribution margin	$20	$30
Fixed costs	$600,000	$600,000

Graham Co.'s break-even point *before* the price increase is 30,000 units, as shown below.

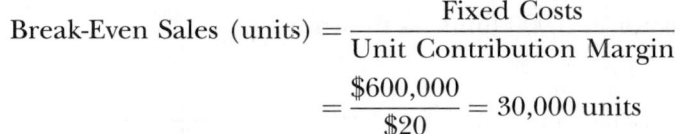

$$\text{Break-Even Sales (units)} = \frac{\text{Fixed Costs}}{\text{Unit Contribution Margin}}$$

$$= \frac{\$600,000}{\$20} = 30,000 \text{ units}$$

The increase of $10 per unit in the selling price increases the unit contribution margin by $10. Thus, Graham Co.'s break-even point *after* the price increase is 20,000 units, as shown below.

$$\text{Break-Even Sales (units)} = \frac{\text{Fixed Costs}}{\text{Unit Contribution Margin}}$$

$$= \frac{\$600,000}{\$30} = 20,000 \text{ units}$$

As shown above, the price increase of $10 increased the unit contribution margin by $10, which decreased the break-even point by 10,000 units (30,000 units − 20,000 units).

Summary of Effects of Changes on Break-Even Point

The break-even point in sales changes in the same direction as changes in the variable cost per unit and fixed costs. In contrast, the break-even point in sales changes in the opposite direction as changes in the unit selling price. These changes on the break-even point in sales are summarized below.

Type of Change	Direction of Change	Effect of Change on Break-Even Sales
Fixed cost	Increase	Increase
	Decrease	Decrease
Unit variable cost	Increase	Increase
	Decrease	Decrease
Unit selling price	Increase	Decrease
	Decrease	Increase

Target Profit

At the break-even point, sales and costs are exactly equal. However, the goal of most companies is to make a profit.

The *Golf Channel* went from a premium cable service price of $6.95 per month to a much lower basic cable price, causing its break-even point to increase from 6 million to 19 million subscribers. The price change was successful, however, since the subscriber numbers exceeded the new break-even point.

By modifying the break-even equation, the sales required to earn a target or desired amount of profit may be computed. For this purpose, target profit is added to the break-even equation as shown below.

$$\text{Sales (units)} = \frac{\text{Fixed Costs} + \text{Target Profit}}{\text{Unit Contribution Margin}}$$

To illustrate, assume the following data for Waltham Co.:

Fixed costs	$200,000
Target profit	100,000
Unit selling price	$75
Unit variable cost	45
Unit contribution margin	$30

The sales necessary to earn the target profit of $100,000 would be 10,000 units, computed as follows:

$$\text{Sales (units)} = \frac{\text{Fixed Costs} + \text{Target Profit}}{\text{Unit Contribution Margin}}$$

$$= \frac{\$200,000 + \$100,000}{\$30} = 10,000 \text{ units}$$

The following income statement verifies this computation:

Sales (10,000 units × $75)	$750,000
Variable costs (10,000 units × $45)	450,000
Contribution margin (10,000 units × $30)	$300,000
Fixed costs	200,000
Income from operations	$100,000

← Target profit

How Businesses Make Money

Breaking Even on Howard Stern

Satellite radio, one of the fastest growing forms of entertainment, has seen remarkable growth in recent years. Customers are able to choose from a variety of types of music and talk radio and listen from just about anywhere in the country with limited commercials. The satellite radio market is dominated by **Sirius XM Radio Inc.** Prior to its merger with **XM Radio**, Sirius tripled its customer base by diversifying its product line and signing high-profile talk personalities. As part of this strategy, Sirius signed a five-year $500 million contract in 2005 with radio "shock jock" Howard Stern. But how did Sirius determine that adding the self-proclaimed "King of All Media" to its play list was worth such a large amount of money? It used break-even analysis. Prior to signing with Sirius, 12 million listeners tuned in to Stern's show on **Infinity Broadcasting Corporation.** At the time the contract was signed, Sirius had about 600,000 subscribers. The company estimated that it would need 1 million of Stern's fans to subscribe to Sirius in order to break even on the $500 million fixed cost of the contract. Initial projections estimated that Stern's show would attract as many as 10 million listeners. It appears that the company's strategy worked as Sirius's subscriber base had grown to 3.3 million customers by the end of 2005.

As shown in the preceding income statement, sales of $750,000 (10,000 units × $75) are necessary to earn the target profit of $100,000. The sales of $750,000 needed to earn the target profit of $100,000 can be computed directly using the contribution margin ratio, as shown below.

$$\text{Contribution Margin Ratio} = \frac{\text{Unit Contribution Margin}}{\text{Unit Selling Price}} = \frac{\$30}{\$75} = 40\%$$

$$\text{Sales (dollars)} = \frac{\text{Fixed Costs} + \text{Target Profit}}{\text{Contribution Margin Ratio}}$$

$$= \frac{\$200,000 + \$100,000}{40\%} = \frac{\$300,000}{40\%} = \$750,000$$

INTEGRITY, OBJECTIVITY, AND ETHICS IN BUSINESS

Orphan Drugs

Each year, pharmaceutical companies develop new drugs that cure a variety of physical conditions. In order to be profitable, drug companies must sell enough of a product to exceed break even for a reasonable selling price. Break-even points, however, create a problem for drugs targeted at rare diseases, called "orphan drugs." These drugs are typically expensive to develop and have low sales volumes, making it impossible to achieve break even. To ensure that orphan drugs are not overlooked, Congress passed the Orphan Drug Act, which provides incentives for pharmaceutical companies to develop drugs for rare diseases that might not generate enough sales to reach break even. The program has been a great success. Since 1982, over 200 orphan drugs have come to market, including **Jacobus Pharmaceuticals Company, Inc.**'s drug for the treatment of tuberculosis and **Novartis AG**'s drug for the treatment of Paget's disease.

Obj 4 Using a cost-volume-profit chart and a profit-volume chart, determine the break-even point and sales necessary to achieve a target profit.

Graphic Approach to Cost-Volume-Profit Analysis

Cost-volume-profit analysis can be presented graphically as well as in equation form. Many managers prefer the graphic form because the operating profit or loss for different levels of sales can readily be seen.

Cost-Volume-Profit (Break-Even) Chart

A **cost-volume-profit chart**, sometimes called a *break-even chart,* graphically shows sales, costs, and the related profit or loss for various levels of units sold. It assists in understanding the relationship among sales, costs, and operating profit or loss.

To illustrate, the cost-volume-profit chart in Exhibit 5 is based on the following data:

Total fixed costs	$100,000
Unit selling price	$50
Unit variable cost	30
Unit contribution margin	$20

EXHIBIT 5 | **Cost-Volume-Profit Chart**

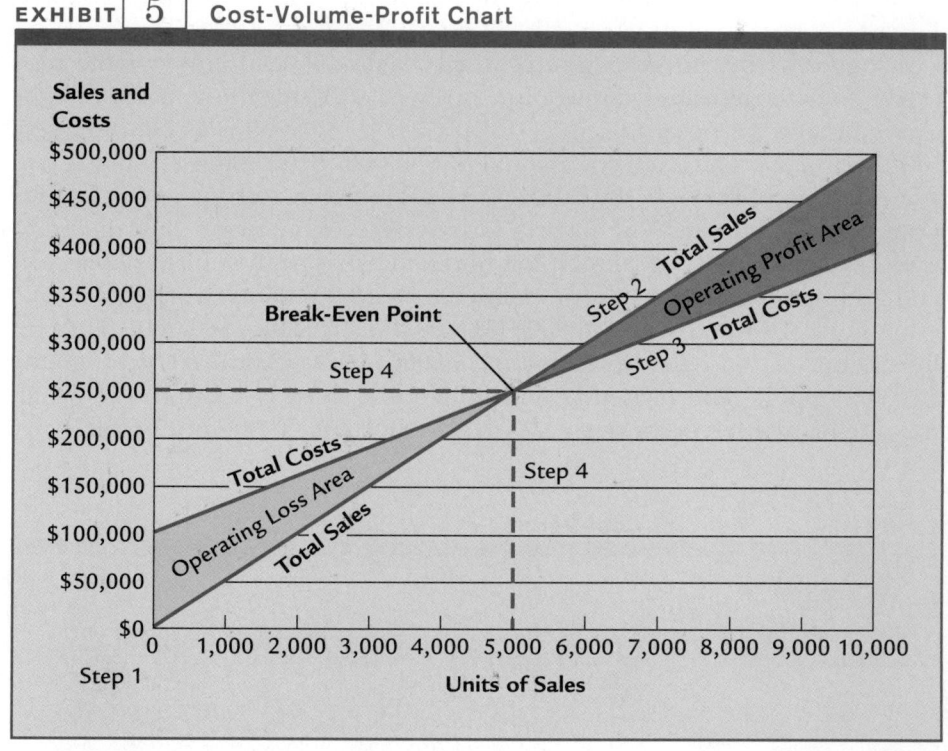

The cost-volume-profit chart in Exhibit 5 is constructed using the following steps:

Step 1. Volume in units of sales is indicated along the horizontal axis. The range of volume shown is the relevant range in which the company expects to operate. Dollar amounts of total sales and costs are indicated along the vertical axis.

Step 2. A sales line is plotted by beginning at zero on the left corner of the graph. A second point is determined by multiplying any units of sales on the horizontal axis by the unit sales price of $50. For example, for 10,000 units of sales, the total sales would be $500,000 (10,000 units × $50). The sales line is drawn upward to the right from zero through the $500,000 point.

Step 3. A cost line is plotted by beginning with total fixed costs, $100,000, on the vertical axis. A second point is determined by multiplying any units of sales on the horizontal axis by the unit variable costs and adding the fixed costs. For example, for 10,000 units of sales, the total estimated costs would be $400,000 [(10,000 units × $30) + $100,000]. The cost line is drawn upward to the right from $100,000 on the vertical axis through the $400,000 point.

Step 4. The break-even point is the intersection point of the total sales and total cost lines. A vertical dotted line drawn downward at the intersection point indicates the units of sales at the break-even point. A horizontal dotted line drawn to the left at the intersection point indicates the sales dollars and costs at the break-even point.

In Exhibit 5, the break-even point is $250,000 of sales, which represents sales of 5,000 units. Operating profits will be earned when sales levels are to the right of the break-even point (*operating profit area*). Operating losses will

be incurred when sales levels are to the left of the break-even point (*operating loss area*).

Changes in the unit selling price, total fixed costs, and unit variable costs can be analyzed by using a cost-volume-profit chart. Using the data in Exhibit 5, assume that a proposal to reduce fixed costs by $20,000 is to be evaluated. In this case, the total fixed costs would be $80,000 ($100,000 − $20,000).

As shown in Exhibit 6, the total cost line is redrawn, starting at the $80,000 point (total fixed costs) on the vertical axis. A second point is determined by multiplying any units of sales on the horizontal axis by the unit variable costs and adding the fixed costs. For example, for 10,000 units of sales, the total estimated costs would be $380,000 [(10,000 units × $30) + $80,000]. The cost line is drawn upward to the right from $80,000 on the vertical axis through the $380,000 point. The revised cost-volume-profit chart in Exhibit 6 indicates that the break-even point decreases to $200,000 and 4,000 units of sales.

EXHIBIT 6 | Revised Cost-Volume-Profit Chart

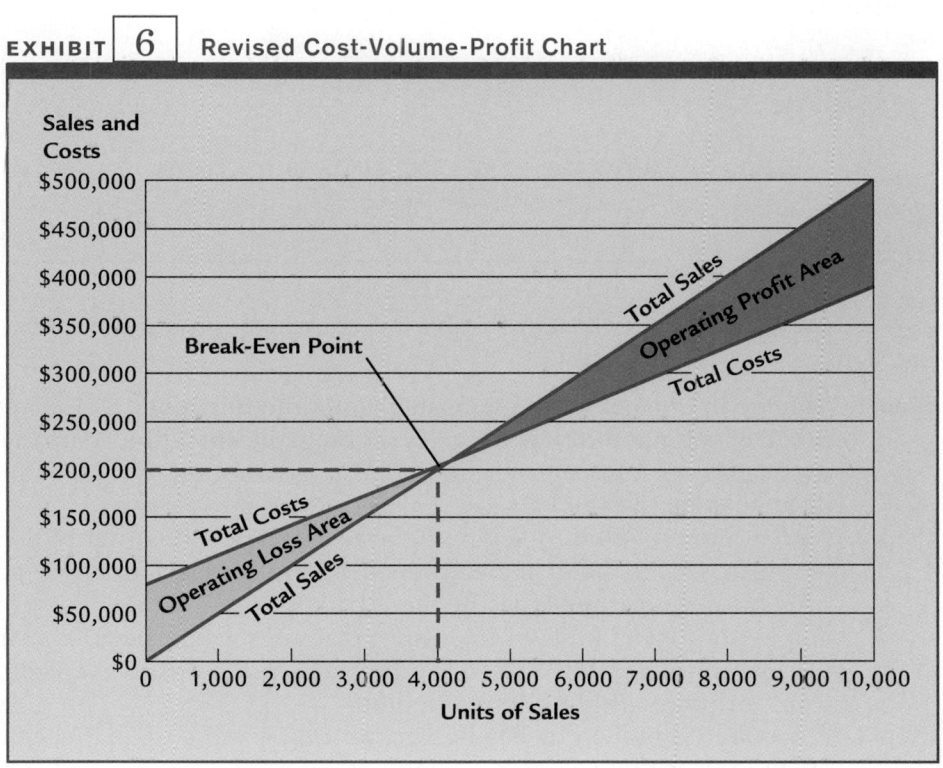

Profit-Volume Chart

Another graphic approach to cost-volume-profit analysis is the profit-volume chart. The **profit-volume chart** plots only the difference between total sales and total costs (or profits). In this way, the profit-volume chart allows managers to determine the operating profit (or loss) for various levels of units sold.

To illustrate, the profit-volume chart in Exhibit 7 is based on the same data as used in Exhibit 5. These data are as follows:

Total fixed costs	$100,000
Unit selling price	$50
Unit variable cost	30
Unit contribution margin	$20

EXHIBIT 7 | **Profit-Volume Chart**

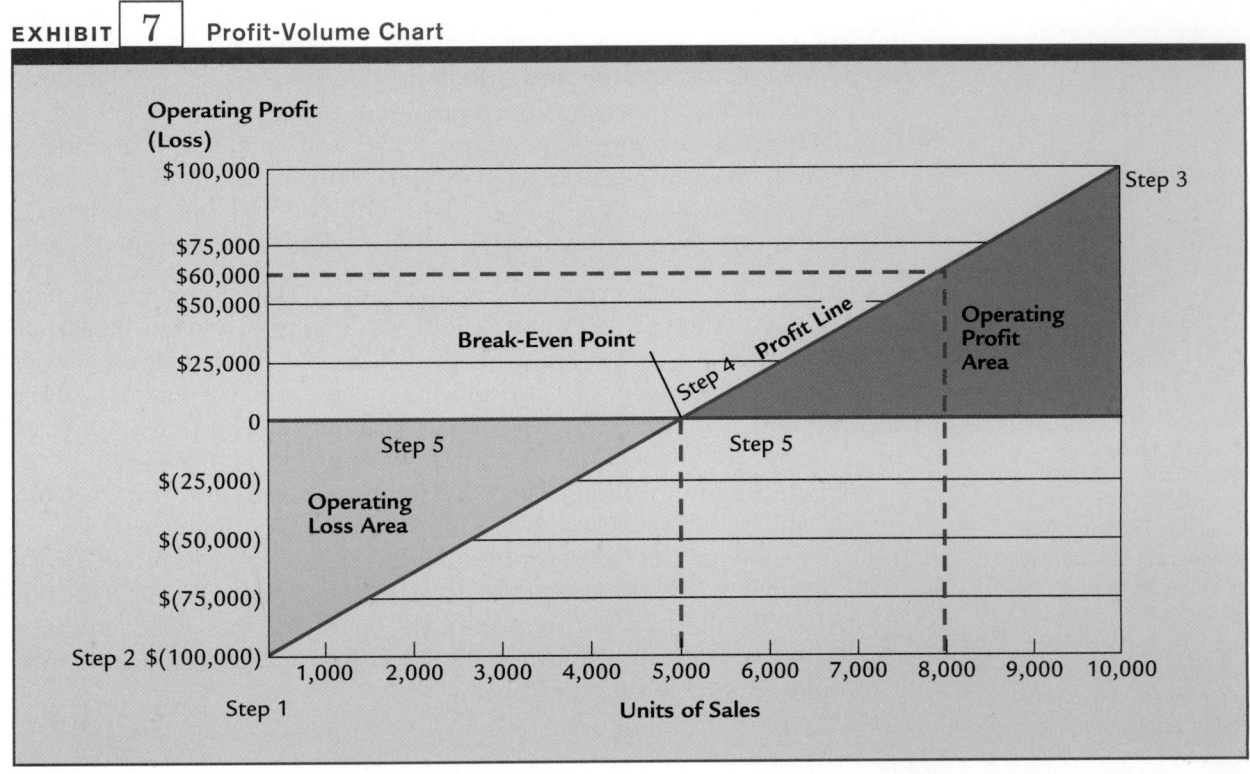

The maximum operating loss is equal to the fixed costs of $100,000. Assuming that the maximum units that can be sold within the relevant range is 10,000 units, the maximum operating profit is $100,000, as shown below.

Sales (10,000 units × $50)	$500,000
Variable costs (10,000 units × $30)	300,000
Contribution margin (10,000 units × $20)	$200,000
Fixed costs	100,000
Operating profit	$100,000 ← Maximum profit

The profit-volume chart in Exhibit 7 is constructed using the following steps:

Step 1. Volume in units of sales is indicated along the horizontal axis. The range of volume shown is the relevant range in which the company expects to operate. In Exhibit 7, the maximum units of sales is 10,000 units. Dollar amounts indicating operating profits and losses are shown along the vertical axis.

Step 2. A point representing the maximum operating loss is plotted on the vertical axis at the left. This loss is equal to the total fixed costs at the zero level of sales. Thus, the maximum operating loss is equal to the fixed costs of $100,000.

Step 3. A point representing the maximum operating profit within the relevant range is plotted on the right. Assuming that the maximum

Many NBA franchises, such as the **Los Angeles Lakers,** state that their financial goal is to break even during the regular season and to make their profit during the playoffs, or basketball's so called "second season." The deeper the team goes into the playoffs, the greater the operating profit earned above break even from additional ticket sales and TV revenues.

unit sales within the relevant range is 10,000 units, the maximum operating profit is $100,000.

Step 4. A diagonal profit line is drawn connecting the maximum operating loss point with the maximum operating profit point.

Step 5. The profit line intersects the horizontal zero operating profit line at the break-even point in units of sales. The area indicating an operating profit is identified to the right of the intersection, and the area indicating an operating loss is identified to the left of the intersection.

In Exhibit 7, the break-even point is 5,000 units of sales, which is equal to total sales of $250,000 (5,000 units × $50). Operating profit will be earned when sales levels are to the right of the break-even point (*operating profit area*). Operating losses will be incurred when sales levels are to the left of the break-even point (*operating loss area*). For example, at sales of 8,000 units, an operating profit of $60,000 will be earned, as shown in Exhibit 7.

Changes in the unit selling price, total fixed costs, and unit variable costs on profit can be analyzed using a profit-volume chart. Using the data in Exhibit 7, assume the effect on profit of an increase of $20,000 in fixed costs is to be evaluated. In this case, the total fixed costs would be $120,000 ($100,000 + $20,000), and the maximum operating loss would also be $120,000. At the maximum sales of 10,000 units, the maximum operating profit would be $80,000, as shown below.

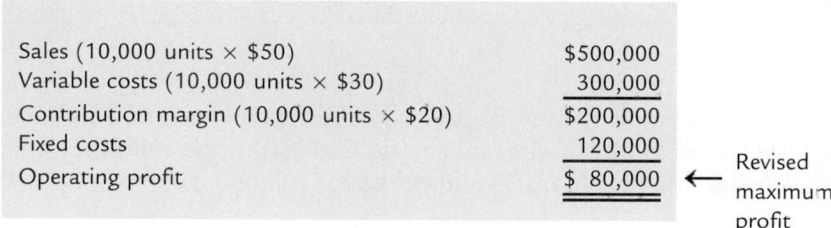

Sales (10,000 units × $50)	$500,000
Variable costs (10,000 units × $30)	300,000
Contribution margin (10,000 units × $20)	$200,000
Fixed costs	120,000
Operating profit	$ 80,000	← Revised maximum profit

A revised profit-volume chart is constructed by plotting the maximum operating loss and maximum operating profit points and drawing the revised profit line. The original and the revised profit-volume charts are shown in Exhibit 8.

The revised profit-volume chart indicates that the break-even point is 6,000 units of sales. This is equal to total sales of $300,000 (6,000 units × $50). The operating loss area of the chart has increased, while the operating profit area has decreased.

Use of Computers in Cost-Volume-Profit Analysis

With computers, the graphic approach and the mathematical approach to cost-volume-profit analysis are easy to use. Managers can vary assumptions regarding selling prices, costs, and volume and can observe the effects of each change on the break-even point and profit. Such an analysis is called a *"what if" analysis* or *sensitivity analysis*.

Assumptions of Cost-Volume-Profit Analysis

Cost-volume-profit analysis depends on several assumptions. These assumptions simplify cost-volume-profit analysis. Since they are often valid for the relevant range of operations, cost-volume-profit analysis is useful for decision making.[3]

---

[3] The impact of violating these assumptions is discussed in advanced accounting texts.

EXHIBIT 8 Original Profit-Volume Chart and Revised Profit-Volume Chart

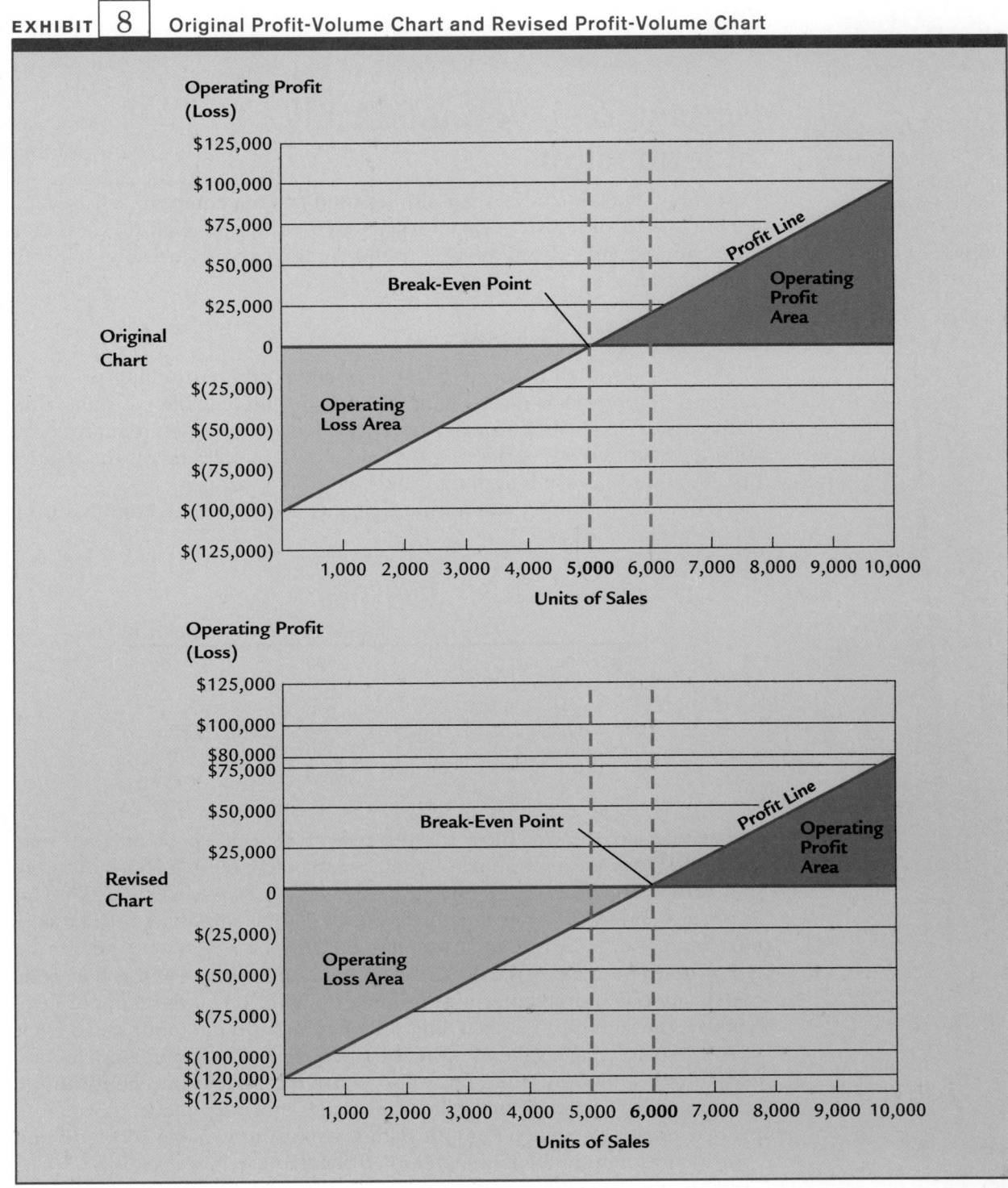

The primary assumptions of cost-volume-profit analysis are listed below.

1. Total sales and total costs can be represented by straight lines.

2. Within the relevant range of operating activity, the efficiency of operations does not change.

3. Costs can be divided into fixed and variable components.

4. The sales mix is constant.

5. There is no change in the inventory quantities during the period.

Obj 5 Compute the break-even point for a company selling more than one product, the operating leverage, and the margin of safety.

Special Cost-Volume-Profit Relationships

Cost-volume-profit analysis can also be used when a company sells several products with different costs and prices. In addition, operating leverage and the margin of safety are useful in analyzing cost-volume-profit relationships.

Sales Mix Considerations

Many companies sell more than one product at different selling prices. In addition, the products normally have different unit variable costs and thus different unit contribution margins. In such cases, break-even analysis can still be performed by considering the sales mix. The **sales mix** is the relative distribution of sales among the products sold by a company.

To illustrate, assume that Cascade Company sold Products A and B during the past year as follows:

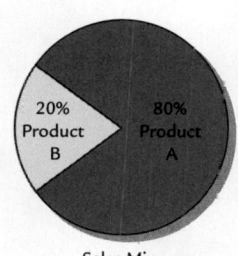

Sales Mix

Total fixed costs	$200,000	
	Product A	**Product B**
Unit selling price	$90	$140
Unit variable cost	70	95
Unit contribution margin	$20	$ 45
Units sold	8,000	2,000
Sales mix	80%	20%

The sales mix for Products A and B is expressed as a percentage of total units sold. For Cascade Company, a total of 10,000 (8,000 + 2,000) units were sold during the year. Therefore, the sales mix is 80% (8,000/10,000) for Product A and 20% for Product B (2,000/10,000) as shown above. The sales mix could also be expressed as the ratio 80:20.

For break-even analysis, it is useful to think of Products A and B as components of one overall enterprise product called E. The unit selling price of E equals the sum of the unit selling prices of each product multiplied by its sales mix percentage. Likewise, the unit variable cost and unit contribution margin of E equal the sum of the unit variable costs and unit contribution margins of each product multiplied by its sales mix percentage.

For Cascade Company, the unit selling price, unit variable cost, and unit contribution margin for E are computed as follows:

Product E		**Product A**		**Product B**
Unit selling price of E	$100	= ($90 × 0.8)	+	($140 × 0.2)
Unit variable cost of E	75	= ($70 × 0.8)	+	($95 × 0.2)
Unit contribution margin of E	$ 25	= ($20 × 0.8)	+	($45 × 0.2)

The break-even point of 8,000 units of E can be determined in the normal manner as shown below.

$$\text{Break-Even Sales (units) for } E = \frac{\text{Fixed Costs}}{\text{Unit Contribution Margin}}$$

$$= \frac{\$200,000}{\$25} = 8,000 \text{ units}$$

Since the sales mix for Products A and B is 80% and 20% respectively, the break-even quantity of A is 6,400 units (8,000 units × 80%) and B is 1,600 units (8,000 units × 20%).

The preceding break-even analysis is verified by the following income statement:

	Product A	Product B	Total
Sales:			
6,400 units × $90	$576,000		$576,000
1,600 units × $140		$224,000	224,000
Total sales	$576,000	$224,000	$800,000
Variable costs:			
6,400 units × $70	$448,000		$448,000
1,600 units × $95		$152,000	152,000
Total variable costs	$448,000	$152,000	$600,000
Contribution margin	$128,000	$ 72,000	$200,000
Fixed costs			200,000
Income from operations			$ 0

← Break-even point

The daily break-even attendance at *Universal Studios* theme areas depends on how many tickets were sold at an *advance purchase discount rate* vs. the full gate rate. Likewise, the break-even point for an overseas flight of *Delta Air Lines* will be influenced by the number of first class, business class, and economy class tickets sold for the flight.

The effects of changes in the sales mix on the break-even point can be determined by assuming a different sales mix. The break-even point of E can then be recomputed.

Operating Leverage

The relationship of a company's contribution margin to income from operations is measured by **operating leverage**. A company's operating leverage is computed as follows:

$$\text{Operating Leverage} = \frac{\text{Contribution Margin}}{\text{Income from Operations}}$$

The difference between contribution margin and income from operations is fixed costs. Thus, companies with high fixed costs will normally have a high operating leverage. Examples of such companies include airline and automotive companies. Low operating leverage is normal for companies that are labor intensive, such as professional service companies, which have low fixed costs.

One type of business that has high operating leverage is what is called a "network" business—one in which service is provided over a network that moves either goods or information. Examples of network businesses include *American Airlines*, *Verizon Communications*, *Yahoo!*, and *Google*.

To illustrate operating leverage, assume the following data for Jones Inc. and Wilson Inc.:

	Jones Inc.	Wilson Inc.
Sales	$400,000	$400,000
Variable costs	300,000	300,000
Contribution margin	$100,000	$100,000
Fixed costs	80,000	50,000
Income from operations	$ 20,000	$ 50,000

As shown above, Jones Inc. and Wilson Inc. have the same sales, the same variable costs, and the same contribution margin. However, Jones Inc. has larger fixed costs than Wilson Inc. and thus a higher operating leverage. The operating leverage for each company is computed as follows:

Jones Inc.

$$\text{Operating Leverage} = \frac{\text{Contribution Margin}}{\text{Income from Operations}} = \frac{\$100,000}{\$20,000} = 5$$

Wilson Inc.

$$\text{Operating Leverage} = \frac{\text{Contribution Margin}}{\text{Income from Operations}} = \frac{\$100,000}{\$50,000} = 2$$

Operating leverage can be used to measure the impact of changes in sales on income from operations. Using operating leverage, the effect of changes in sales on income from operations is computed as follows:

$$\frac{\text{Percent Change in}}{\text{Income from Operations}} = \frac{\text{Percent Change}}{\text{in Sales}} \times \frac{\text{Operating}}{\text{Leverage}}$$

To illustrate, assume that sales increased by 10%, or $40,000 ($400,000 × 10%), for Jones Inc. and Wilson Inc. The percent increase in income from operations for Jones Inc. and Wilson Inc. is computed below.

Jones Inc.

$$\frac{\text{Percent Change in}}{\text{Income from Operations}} = \frac{\text{Percent Change}}{\text{in Sales}} \times \frac{\text{Operating}}{\text{Leverage}}$$

$$\frac{\text{Percent Change in}}{\text{Income from Operations}} = 10\% \times 5 = 50\%$$

Wilson Inc.

$$\frac{\text{Percent Change in}}{\text{Income from Operations}} = \frac{\text{Percent Change}}{\text{in Sales}} \times \frac{\text{Operating}}{\text{Leverage}}$$

$$\frac{\text{Percent Change in}}{\text{Income from Operations}} = 10\% \times 2 = 20\%$$

As shown above, Jones Inc.'s income from operations increases by 50%, while Wilson Inc.'s income from operations increases by only 20%. The

validity of this analysis is shown in the following income statements for Jones Inc. and Wilson Inc. based on the 10% increase in sales:

	Jones Inc.	Wilson Inc.
Sales	$440,000	$440,000
Variable costs	330,000	330,000
Contribution margin	$110,000	$110,000
Fixed costs	80,000	50,000
Income from operations	$ 30,000	$ 60,000

The preceding income statements indicate that Jones Inc.'s income from operations increased from $20,000 to $30,000, a 50% increase ($10,000/ $20,000). In contrast, Wilson Inc.'s income from operations increased from $50,000 to $60,000, a 20% increase ($10,000/$50,000).

Because even a small increase in sales will generate a large percentage increase in income from operations, Jones Inc. might consider ways to increase sales. Such actions could include special advertising or sales promotions. In contrast, Wilson Inc. might consider ways to increase operating leverage by reducing variable costs.

The impact of a change in sales on income from operations for companies with high and low operating leverage can be summarized as follows:

Operating Leverage	Percentage Impact on Income from Operations from a Change in Sales
High	Large
Low	Small

Margin of Safety

The **margin of safety** indicates the possible decrease in sales that may occur before an operating loss results. Thus, if the margin of safety is low, even a small decline in sales revenue may result in an operating loss.

The margin of safety may be expressed in the following ways:

1. Dollars of sales

2. Units of sales

3. Percent of current sales

To illustrate, assume the following data:

Sales	$250,000
Sales at the break-even point	200,000
Unit selling price	25

The margin of safety in dollars of sales is $50,000 ($250,000 – $200,000). The margin of safety in units is 2,000 units ($50,000/$25). The margin of safety expressed as a percent of current sales is 20%, as computed below.

$$\text{Margin of Safety} = \frac{\text{Sales} - \text{Sales at Break-Even Point}}{\text{Sales}}$$

$$= \frac{\$250,000 - \$200,000}{\$250,000} = \frac{\$50,000}{\$250,000} = 20\%$$

Therefore, the current sales may decline $50,000, 2,000 units, or 20% before an operating loss occurs.

Key Points

1. Classify costs as variable costs, fixed costs, or mixed costs.

   Cost behavior refers to the manner in which a cost changes as a related activity changes. Variable costs are costs that vary in total in proportion to changes in the level of activity. Fixed costs are costs that remain the same in total dollar amount as the level of activity changes. A mixed cost has attributes of both a variable and a fixed cost.

2. Compute the contribution margin, the contribution margin ratio, and the unit contribution margin.

   The contribution margin concept is useful in business planning because it gives insight into the profit potential of a firm. The contribution margin is the excess of sales revenues over variable costs. The contribution margin ratio is computed as follows:

$$\text{Contribution Margin Ratio} = \frac{\text{Sales} - \text{Variable Costs}}{\text{Sales}}$$

   The unit contribution margin is the excess of the unit selling price over the unit variable cost.

3. Determine the break-even point and sales necessary to achieve a target profit.

   The mathematical approach to cost-volume-profit analysis uses the unit contribution margin concept and equations to determine the break-even point and the volume necessary to achieve a target profit for a business.

4. Using a cost-volume-profit chart and a profit-volume chart, determine the break-even point and sales necessary to achieve a target profit.

   A cost-volume-profit chart focuses on the relationships among costs, sales, and operating profit or loss. Preparing and using a cost-volume-profit chart to determine the break-even point and the volume necessary to achieve a target profit are illustrated in this chapter.

   The profit-volume chart focuses on profits rather than on revenues and costs. Preparing and using a profit-volume chart to determine the break-even point and the volume necessary to achieve a target profit are illustrated in this chapter.

5. Compute the break-even point for a company selling more than one product, the operating leverage, and the margin of safety.

   Computing the break-even point for a business selling two or more products is based on a specified sales mix. Given the sales mix, the break-even point can be computed, using the methods illustrated in this chapter.

   Operating leverage is useful in measuring the impact of changes in sales on income from operations without preparing formal income statements. It is computed as follows:

$$\text{Operating Leverage} = \frac{\text{Contribution Margin}}{\text{Income from Operations}}$$

   The margin of safety is useful in evaluating past operations and in planning future operations.

   The margin of safety as a percentage of current sales is computed as follows:

$$\text{Margin of safety} = \frac{\text{Sales} - \text{Sales at Break-Even Point}}{\text{Sales}}$$

Key Terms

Activity base (driver) An activity that causes a cost to change.

Break-even point The level of business operations at which revenues and expired costs are equal.

Contribution margin Sales less variable cost of goods sold and variable selling and administrative expenses.

Contribution margin ratio The percentage of each sales dollar that is available to cover the fixed costs and provide income from operations.

Cost behavior The manner in which a cost changes in relation to its activity base (driver).

Cost-volume-profit analysis The systematic examination of the relationships among costs, expenses, sales, and operating profit or loss.

Cost-volume-profit chart A chart used to assist management in understanding the relationships among costs, expenses, sales, and operating profit or loss.

Fixed costs Costs that tend to remain the same in amount, regardless of variations in the level of activity.

High-low method A technique that uses the highest and lowest total cost as a basis for estimating the variable cost per unit and the fixed cost component of a mixed cost.

Margin of safety The difference between current sales revenue and the sales at the break-even point.

Mixed costs Costs with both variable and fixed characteristics.

Operating leverage A measure of the relative mix of a business's variable costs and fixed costs, computed as contribution margin divided by income from operations.

Profit-volume chart A chart used to assist management in understanding the relationship between profit and volume.

Relevant range The range of activity over which changes in cost are of interest to management.

Sales mix The relative distribution of sales among the various products available for sale.

Unit contribution margin The dollars available from each unit of sales to cover fixed costs and provide income from operations.

Variable costing Often referred to as *direct costing*, it is a method of reporting variable and fixed costs that includes only the variable manufacturing costs in the cost of the product.

Variable costs Costs that vary in total dollar amount as the level of activity changes.

Illustrative Problem

Wyatt Inc. expects to maintain the same inventories at the end of the year as at the beginning of the year. The estimated fixed costs for the year are $288,000, and the estimated variable costs per unit are $14. It is expected that 60,000 units will be sold at a price of $20 per unit. Maximum sales within the relevant range are 70,000 units.

Instructions

1. What is (a) the contribution margin ratio and (b) the unit contribution margin?
2. Determine the break-even point in units.
3. Construct a cost-volume-profit chart, indicating the break-even point.
4. Construct a profit-volume chart, indicating the break-even point.
5. What is the margin of safety?

Solution

1. a. $$\text{Contribution Margin Ratio} = \frac{\text{Sales} - \text{Variable Costs}}{\text{Sales}}$$

$$\text{Contribution Margin Ratio} = \frac{(60,000 \text{ units} \times \$20) - (60,000 \text{ units} \times \$14)}{(60,000 \text{ units} \times \$20)}$$

$$\text{Contribution Margin Ratio} = \frac{\$1,200,000 - \$840,000}{\$1,200,000} = \frac{\$360,000}{\$1,200,000}$$

$$\text{Contribution Margin Ratio} = 30\%$$

   b. Unit Contribution Margin = Unit Selling Price − Unit Variable Costs
   Unit Contribution Margin = $20 − $14 = $6

2. $$\text{Break-Even Sales (units)} = \frac{\text{Fixed Costs}}{\text{Unit Contribution Margin}}$$

$$\text{Break-Even Sales (units)} = \frac{\$288,000}{\$6} = 48,000 \text{ units}$$

3. **Sales and Costs**

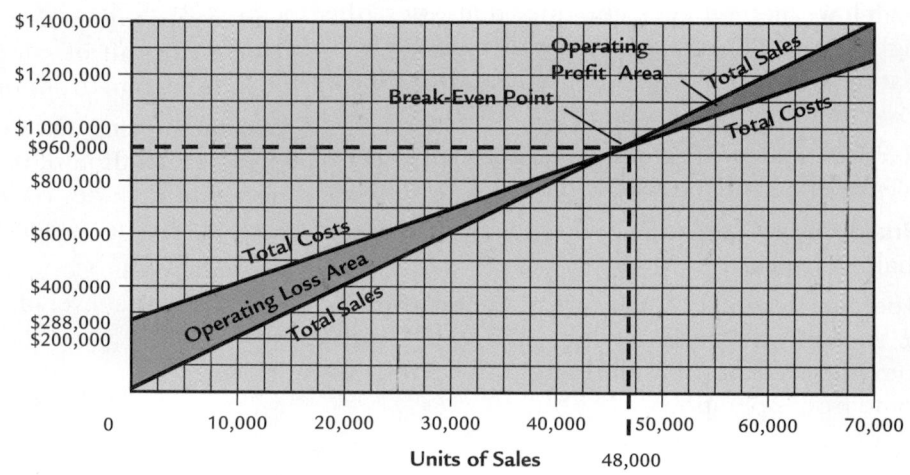

4. **Operating Profit (Loss)**

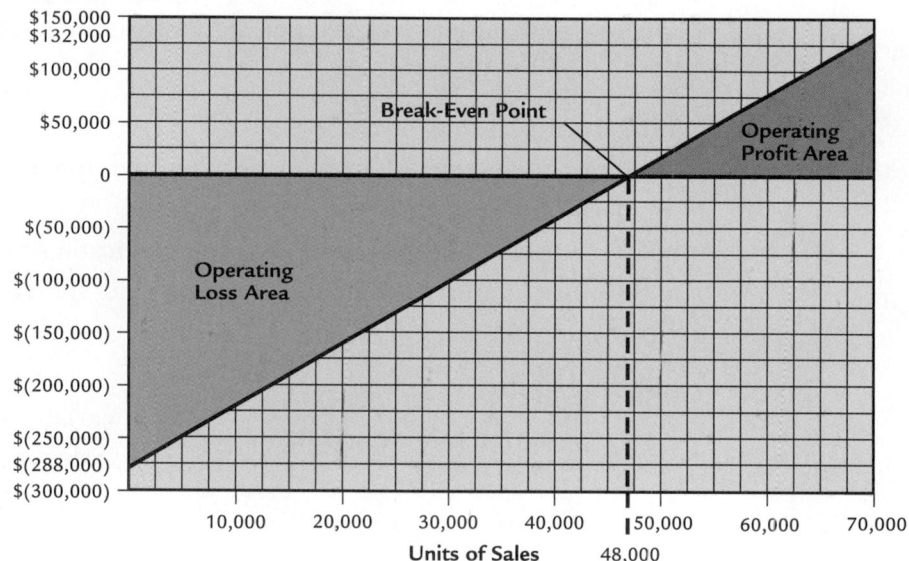

5. **Margin of Safety:**

Expected sales (60,000 units × $20)	$1,200,000
Break-even point (48,000 units × $20)	960,000
Margin of safety	$ 240,000

or

$$\text{Margin of Safety (units)} = \frac{\text{Margin of Safety (dollars)}}{\text{Unit Contribution Margin}}$$

or

12,000 units ($240,000/$20)

or

$$\text{Margin of Safety} = \frac{\text{Sales} - \text{Sales at Break-Even Point}}{\text{Sales}}$$

$$\text{Margin of Safety} = \frac{\$240,000}{\$1,200,000} = 20\%$$

Self-Examination Questions (Answers appear at the end of chapter)

1. Which of the following statements describes variable costs?

   A. Costs that vary on a per-unit basis as the level of activity changes.

   B. Costs that vary in total in direct proportion to changes in the level of activity.

   C. Costs that remain the same in total dollar amount as the level of activity changes.

   D. Costs that vary on a per-unit basis, but remain the same in total as the level of activity changes.

2. If sales are $500,000, variable costs are $200,000, and fixed costs are $240,000, what is the contribution margin ratio?

   A. 40%

   B. 48%

   C. 52%

   D. 60%

3. If the unit selling price is $16, the unit variable cost is $12, and fixed costs are $160,000, what are the break-even sales (units)?

   A. 5,714 units

   B. 10,000 units

   C. 13,333 units

   D. 40,000 units

4. Based on the data presented in Question 3, how many units of sales would be required to realize income from operations of $20,000?

   A. 11,250 units

   B. 35,000 units

   C. 40,000 units

   D. 45,000 units

5. Based on the following operating data, what is the operating leverage?

Sales	$600,000
Variable costs	240,000
Contribution margin	$360,000
Fixed costs	160,000
Income from operations	$200,000

   A. 0.8

   B. 1.2

   C. 1.8

   D. 4.0

Class Discussion Questions

1. Describe how total variable costs and unit variable costs behave with changes in the level of activity.

2. How would each of the following costs be classified if units produced is the activity base?

    a. Direct materials costs

    b. Direct labor costs

    c. Electricity costs of $0.35 per kilowatt-hour

3. Describe the behavior of (a) total fixed costs and (b) unit fixed costs as the level of activity increases.

4. How would each of the following costs be classified if units produced is the activity base?

    a. Salary of factory supervisor ($70,000 per year)

    b. Straight-line depreciation of plant and equipment

    c. Property rent of $6,000 per month on plant and equipment

5. In cost analyses, how are mixed costs treated?

6. Which of the following graphs illustrates how total fixed costs behave with changes in total units produced?

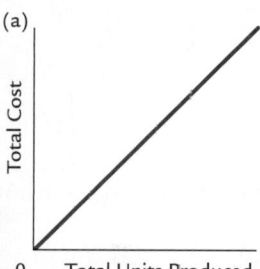

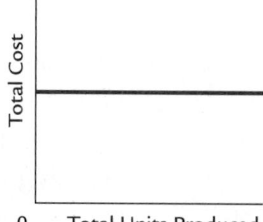

7. Which of the following graphs illustrates how unit variable costs behave with changes in total units produced?

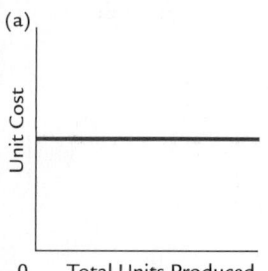

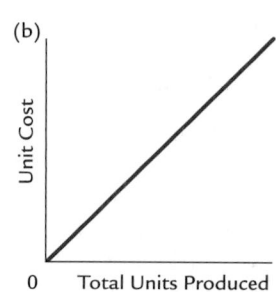

8. Which of the following graphs best illustrates fixed costs per unit as the activity base changes?

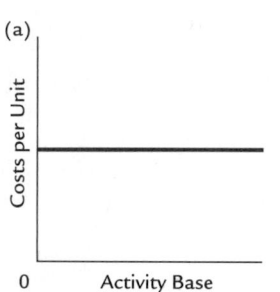

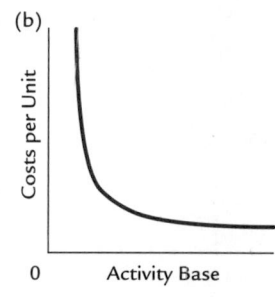

9. In applying the high-low method of cost estimation, how is the total fixed cost estimated?

10. If fixed costs increase, what would be the impact on the (a) contribution margin? (b) income from operations?

11. An examination of the accounting records of Clowney Company disclosed a high contribution margin ratio and production at a level below maximum capacity. Based on this information, suggest a likely means of improving income from operations. Explain.

12. If the unit cost of direct materials is decreased, what effect will this change have on the break-even point?

13. If insurance rates are increased, what effect will this change in fixed costs have on the break-even point?

14. Both Austin Company and Hill Company had the same sales, total costs, and income from operations for the current fiscal year; yet Austin Company had a lower break-even point than Hill Company. Explain the reason for this difference in break-even points.

15. The reliability of cost-volume-profit (CVP) analysis depends on several key assumptions. What are those primary assumptions?

16. How does the sales mix affect the calculation of the break-even point?

17. What does operating leverage measure, and how is it computed?

Exercises

E11-1

Classify costs

Obj 1

Following is a list of various costs incurred in producing toy robotic helicopters. With respect to the production and sale of these toy helicopters, classify each cost as either variable, fixed, or mixed.

1. Oil used in manufacturing equipment
2. Hourly wages of inspectors
3. Electricity costs, $0.20 per kilowatt-hour
4. Property insurance premiums, $1,500 per month plus $0.006 for each dollar of property over $2,000,000
5. Janitorial costs, $4,000 per month
6. Pension cost, $0.80 per employee hour on the job
7. Computer chip (purchased from a vendor)
8. Hourly wages of machine operators
9. Straight-line depreciation on the production equipment
10. Metal
11. Packaging
12. Rent on warehouse, $10,000 per month plus $10 per square foot of storage used
13. Plastic
14. Property taxes, $100,000 per year on factory building and equipment
15. Salary of plant manager

E11-2

Identify cost graphs

Obj 1

The following cost graphs illustrate various types of cost behavior:

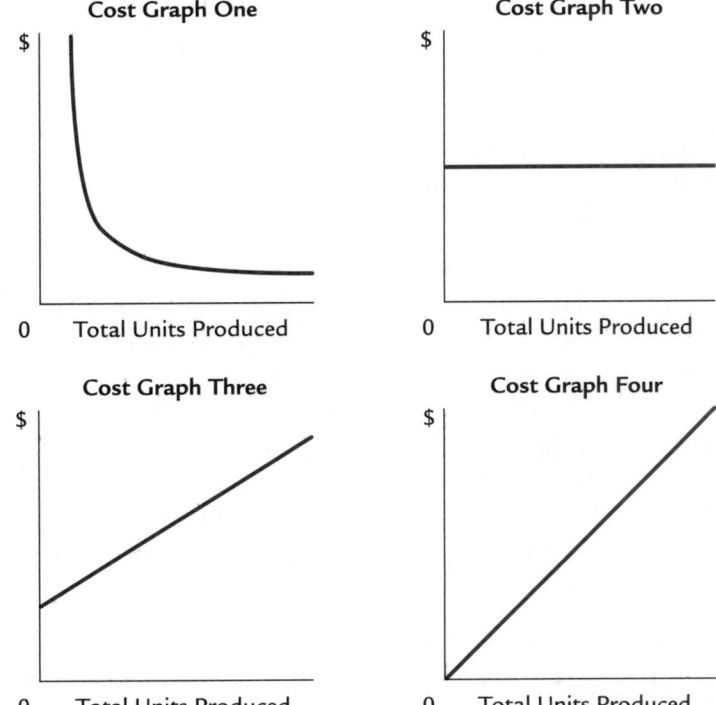

For each of the following costs, identify the cost graph that best illustrates its cost behavior as the number of units produced increases.

a. Total direct materials cost
b. Electricity costs of $2,000 per month plus $0.09 per kilowatt-hour
c. Per-unit direct labor cost
d. Salary of quality control supervisor, $10,000 per month
e. Per-unit cost of straight-line depreciation on factory equipment

E11-3

Identify activity bases

Obj 1

For a major university, match each cost in the following table with the activity base most appropriate to it. An activity base may be used more than once, or not used at all.

Cost:	Activity Base:
1. Housing personnel wages	a. Number of financial aid applications
2. Student records office salaries	b. Number of enrolled students and alumni
3. Financial aid office salaries	c. Student credit hours
4. School supplies	d. Number of student/athletes
5. Instructor salaries	e. Number of enrollment applications
6. Admissions office salaries	f. Number of students living on campus

E11-4

Identify activity bases

Obj 1

From the following list of activity bases for an automobile dealership, select the base that would be most appropriate for each of these costs: (1) preparation costs (cleaning, oil, and gasoline costs) for each car received, (2) salespersons' commission of 4% of the sales price for each car sold, and (3) administrative costs for ordering cars.

a. Dollar amount of cars sold
b. Number of cars received
c. Dollar amount of cars on hand
d. Number of cars on hand
e. Dollar amount of cars ordered
f. Dollar amount of cars received
g. Number of cars ordered
h. Number of cars sold

E11-5

Identify fixed and variable costs

Obj 1

Intuit Inc. develops and sells software products for the personal finance market, including popular titles such as Quicken® and TurboTax®. Classify each of the following costs and expenses for this company as either variable or fixed to the number of units produced and sold:

a. Shipping expenses
b. Property taxes on general offices
c. Straight-line depreciation of computer equipment
d. Salaries of human resources personnel
e. President's salary
f. Advertising
g. Sales commissions
h. CDs
i. Packaging costs
j. Salaries of software developers
k. Wages of telephone order assistants
l. User's guides

E11-6

Relevant range and fixed and variable costs

Obj 1

✓ a. $0.32

Robo-Tech Inc. manufactures components for computer games within a relevant range of 200,000 to 320,000 disks per year. Within this range, the following partially completed manufacturing cost schedule has been prepared:

Components produced	200,000	250,000	320,000
Total costs:			
Total variable costs	$ 64,000	(d)	(j)
Total fixed costs	80,000	(e)	(k)
Total costs	$144,000	(f)	(l)
Cost per unit:			
Variable cost per unit	(a)	(g)	(m)
Fixed cost per unit	(b)	(h)	(n)
Total cost per unit	(c)	(i)	(o)

Complete the cost schedule, identifying each cost by the appropriate letter (a) through (o).

E11-7

High-low method

Obj 1

SPREADSHEET

✓ a. $16.00 per unit

Shatner Inc. has decided to use the high-low method to estimate the total cost and the fixed and variable cost components of the total cost. The data for various levels of production are as follows:

Units Produced	Total Costs
7,500	$600,000
12,500	725,000
20,000	800,000

a. Determine the variable cost per unit and the fixed cost.
b. Based on part (a), estimate the total cost for 10,000 units of production.

E11-8

High-low method for service company

Obj 1

SPREADSHEET

✓ Fixed cost, $160,000

Blowing Rock Railroad decided to use the high-low method and operating data from the past six months to estimate the fixed and variable components of transportation costs. The activity base used by Blowing Rock Railroad is a measure of railroad operating activity, termed "gross-ton miles," which is the total number of tons multiplied by the miles moved.

	Transportation Costs	Gross-Ton Miles
January	$760,000	275,000
February	850,000	310,000
March	600,000	200,000
April	810,000	300,000
May	680,000	240,000
June	875,000	325,000

Determine the variable cost per gross-ton mile and the fixed cost.

E11-9

Contribution margin ratio

Obj 2

✓ a. 84%

a. Bert Company budgets sales of $1,250,000, fixed costs of $450,000, and variable costs of $200,000. What is the contribution margin ratio for Bert Company?
b. If the contribution margin ratio for Ernie Company is 40%, sales were $750,000, and fixed costs were $225,000, what was the income from operations?

E11-10

Contribution margin and contribution margin ratio

Obj 2

✓ b. 34.9%

For a recent year, *McDonald's* company-owned restaurants had the following sales and expenses (in millions):

Sales	$16,083
Food and packaging	$ 5,350
Payroll	4,185
Occupancy (rent, depreciation, etc.)	4,006
General, selling, and administrative expenses	2,340
	$15,881
Income from operations	$ 202

Assume that the variable costs consist of food and packaging, payroll, and 40% of the general, selling, and administrative expenses.

a. What is McDonald's contribution margin? Round to the nearest million.
b. What is McDonald's contribution margin ratio? Round to one decimal place.
c. How much would income from operations increase if same-store sales increased by $500 million for the coming year, with no change in the contribution margin ratio or fixed costs?

E11-11

Break-even sales and sales to realize income from operations

Obj 3

✓ b. 21,200 units

For the current year ending March 31, Jwork Company expects fixed costs of $440,000, a unit variable cost of $50, and a unit selling price of $75.

a. Compute the anticipated break-even sales (units).
b. Compute the sales (units) required to realize income from operations of $90,000.

E11-12

Break-even sales

Obj 3

✓ a. 76,149,219 barrels

Anheuser-Busch Companies, Inc., reported the following operating information for a recent year (in millions):

Net sales	$15,717.1
Cost of goods sold	$10,165.0
Marketing and distribution	2,832.5
	$12,997.5
Income from operations	$ 2,719.6*

*Before special items

In addition, Anheuser-Busch sold 125 million barrels of beer during the year. Assume that variable costs were 75% of the cost of goods sold and 40% of marketing and distribution expenses. Assume that the remaining costs are fixed. For the following year, assume that Anheuser-Busch expects pricing, variable costs per barrel, and fixed costs to remain constant, except that new distribution and general office facilities are expected to increase fixed costs by $150 million.

Rounding to the nearest cent:

a. Compute the break-even sales (barrels) for the current year.
b. Compute the anticipated break-even sales (barrels) for the following year.

E11-13

Break-even sales

Obj 3

✓ a. 10,500 units

Currently, the unit selling price of a product is $280, the unit variable cost is $230, and the total fixed costs are $525,000. A proposal is being evaluated to increase the unit selling price to $300.

a. Compute the current break-even sales (units).
b. Compute the anticipated break-even sales (units), assuming that the unit selling price is increased and all costs remain constant.

E11-14

Break-even analysis

Obj 3

The Dash Club of Tampa, Florida, collected recipes from members and published a cookbook entitled *Life of the Party*. The book will sell for $25 per copy. The chairwoman of the cookbook development committee estimated that the club needed to sell 10,000 books to break even on its $90,000 investment. What is the variable cost per unit assumed in the Dash Club's analysis?

E11-15

Break-even analysis

Obj 3

Media outlets such as **ESPN** and **Fox Sports** often have Web sites that provide in-depth coverage of news and events. Portions of these Web sites are restricted to members who pay a monthly subscription to gain access to exclusive news and commentary. These Web sites typically offer a free trial period to introduce viewers to the Web site. Assume that during a recent fiscal year, ESPN.com spent $1,800,000 on a promotional campaign for its Web site, offering two free months of service for new subscribers. In addition, assume the following information:

Number of months an average new customer stays with the service (including the two free months)	25 months
Revenue per month per customer subscription	$10.00
Variable cost per month per customer subscription	$ 2.00

Determine the number of new customer accounts needed to break even on the cost of the promotional campaign. In forming your answer, (1) treat the cost of the promotional campaign as a fixed cost, and (2) treat the revenue less variable cost per account for the subscription period as the unit contribution margin.

E11-16

Break-even analysis

Obj 3

SPREADSHEET

✓

Sprint Nextel is one of the largest digital wireless service providers in the United States. In a recent year, it had approximately 41.5 million direct subscribers (accounts) that generated revenue of $40,146 million. Costs and expenses for the year were as follows (in millions):

Cost of revenue	$17,191
Selling, general, and administrative expenses	12,673
Depreciation	5,711

Assume that 75% of the cost of revenue and 35% of the selling, general, and administrative expenses are variable to the number of direct subscribers (accounts).

a. What is Sprint Nextel's break-even number of accounts, using the data and assumptions above? Round units to one decimal place (in millions).

b. How much revenue per account would be sufficient for Sprint Nextel to break even if the number of accounts remained constant?

E11-17

Cost-volume-profit chart

Obj 4

✓ b. $360,000

For the coming year, Paladin Inc. anticipates fixed costs of $120,000, a unit variable cost of $60, and a unit selling price of $90. The maximum sales within the relevant range are $900,000.

a. Construct a cost-volume-profit chart.

b. Estimate the break-even sales (dollars) by using the cost-volume-profit chart constructed in part (a).

c. What is the main advantage of presenting the cost-volume-profit analysis in graphic form rather than equation form?

E11-18

Profit-volume chart

Obj 4

✓ b. $180,000

Using the data for Paladin Inc. in Exercise 11-17, (a) determine the maximum possible operating loss, (b) compute the maximum possible income from operations, (c) construct a profit-volume chart, and (d) estimate the break-even sales (units) by using the profit-volume chart constructed in part (c).

E11-19

Break-even chart

Obj 4

Name the following chart, and identify the items represented by the letters (a) through (f).

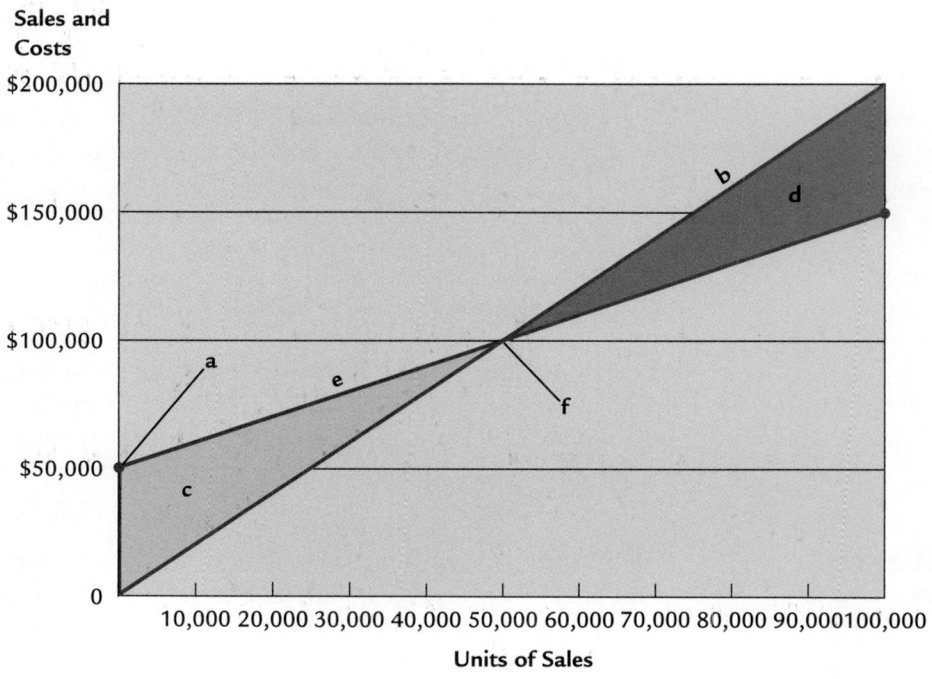

E11-20

Break-even chart

Obj 4

Name the following chart, and identify the items represented by the letters (a) through (f).

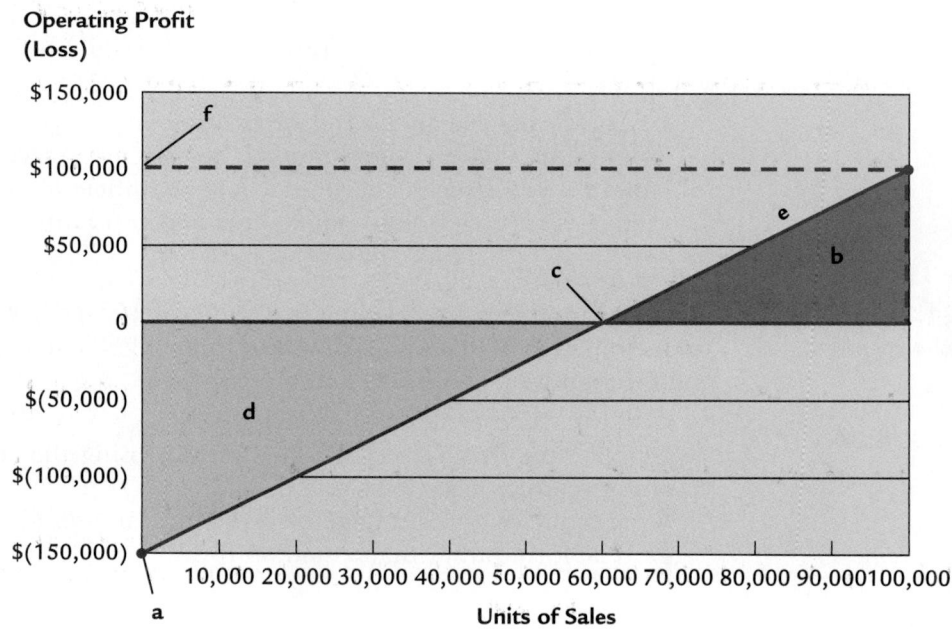

E11-21

Sales mix and break-even sales

Obj 5

✓ a. 10,000 units

New Wave Technology Inc. manufactures and sells two products, MP3 players and satellite radios. The fixed costs are $300,000, and the sales mix is 40% MP3 players and 60% satellite radios. The unit selling price and the unit variable cost for each product are as follows:

Products	Unit Selling Price	Unit Variable Cost
MP3 players	$ 60.00	$45.00
Satellite radios	100.00	60.00

a. Compute the break-even sales (units) for the overall product, E.
b. How many units of each product, MP3 players and satellite radios, would be sold at the break-even point?

E11-22

Break-even sales and sales mix for a service company

Obj 5

✓ a. 50 seats

Southwest Blue Airways provides air transportation services between Seattle and San Diego. A single Seattle to San Diego round-trip flight has the following operating statistics:

Fuel	$7,000
Flight crew salaries	5,400
Airplane depreciation	2,600
Variable cost per passenger—business class	50
Variable cost per passenger—economy class	40
Round-trip ticket price—business class	550
Round-trip ticket price—economy class	290

It is assumed that the fuel, crew salaries, and airplane depreciation are fixed, regardless of the number of seats sold for the round-trip flight.

a. Compute the break-even number of seats sold on a single round-trip flight for the overall product. Assume that the overall product is 20% business class and 80% economy class tickets.
b. How many business class and economy class seats would be sold at the break-even point?

E11-23

Margin of safety

Obj 5

✓ a. (2) 25%

a. If Fama Company, with a break-even point at $360,000 of sales, has actual sales of $480,000, what is the margin of safety expressed (1) in dollars and (2) as a percentage of sales?
b. If the margin of safety for Watkins Company was 25%, fixed costs were $1,200,000 and variable costs were 75% of sales, what was the amount of actual sales (dollars)? (*Hint:* Determine the break-even in sales dollars first.)

E11-24

Break-even and margin of safety relationships

Obj 5

At a recent staff meeting, the management of Guthold Gaming Technologies, Inc., was considering discontinuing the Evegi line of electronic games from the product line. The chief financial analyst reported the following current monthly data for the Evegi:

Units of sales	85,000
Break-even units	100,000
Margin of safety in units	7,000

For what reason would you question the validity of these data?

E11-25

Operating leverage

Obj 5

✓ a. Varner, 3.00

Varner Inc. and King Inc. have the following operating data:

	Varner	King
Sales	$300,000	$600,000
Variable costs	120,000	360,000
Contribution margin	$180,000	$240,000
Fixed costs	120,000	80,000
Income from operations	$ 60,000	$160,000

a. Compute the operating leverage for Varner Inc. and King Inc.
b. How much would income from operations increase for each company if the sales of each increased by 20%?
c. Why is there a difference in the increase in income from operations for the two companies? Explain.

Problems

P11-1

Classify costs

Obj 1

West Coast Apparel Co. manufactures a variety of clothing types for distribution to several major retail chains. The following costs are incurred in the production and sale of blue jeans:

a. Salary of production vice president
b. Property taxes on property, plant, and equipment
c. Electricity costs of $0.12 per kilowatt-hour
d. Salesperson's salary, $30,000 plus 2% of the total sales
e. Consulting fee of $100,000 paid to industry specialist for marketing advice
f. Shipping boxes used to ship orders
g. Dye
h. Thread
i. Salary of designers
j. Brass buttons
k. Janitorial supplies, $2,000 per month
l. Legal fees paid to attorneys in defense of the company in a patent infringement suit, $40,000 plus $150 per hour
m. Straight-line depreciation on sewing machines
n. Insurance premiums on property, plant, and equipment, $50,000 per year plus $4 per $20,000 of insured value over $10,000,000
o. Hourly wages of machine operators
p. Fabric
q. Rental costs of warehouse, $4,000 per month plus $3 per square foot of storage used
r. Rent on experimental equipment, $40,000 per year
s. Leather for patches identifying the brand on individual pieces of apparel
t. Supplies

Instructions

Classify the preceding costs as either fixed, variable, or mixed. Use the following tabular headings and place an "X" in the appropriate column. Identify each cost by letter in the cost column.

Cost	Fixed Cost	Variable Cost	Mixed Cost

P11-2

Break-even sales under present and proposed conditions

Objs 2, 3

✓ 2. (a) $50.00

Battonkill Company, operating at full capacity, sold 112,800 units at a price of $150 per unit during 2010. Its income statement for 2010 is as follows:

Sales		$16,920,000
Cost of goods sold		6,000,000
Gross profit		$10,920,000
Expenses:		
Selling expenses	$3,000,000	
Administrative expenses	1,800,000	
Total expenses		4,800,000
Income from operations		$ 6,120,000

The division of costs between fixed and variable is as follows:

	Fixed	Variable
Cost of sales	40%	60%
Selling expenses	50%	50%
Administrative expenses	70%	30%

Management is considering a plant expansion program that will permit an increase of $1,500,000 in yearly sales. The expansion will increase fixed costs by $200,000, but will not affect the relationship between sales and variable costs.

Instructions

1. Determine for 2010 the total fixed costs and the total variable costs.
2. Determine for 2010 (a) the unit variable cost and (b) the unit contribution margin.
3. Compute the break-even sales (units) for 2010.
4. Compute the break-even sales (units) under the proposed program.
5. Determine the amount of sales (units) that would be necessary under the proposed program to realize the $6,120,000 of income from operations that was earned in 2010.
6. Determine the maximum income from operations possible with the expanded plant.
7. If the proposal is accepted and sales remain at the 2010 level, what will the income or loss from operations be for 2011?
8. Based on the data given, would you recommend accepting the proposal? Explain.

P11-3

Break-even sales and cost-volume-profit chart

Objs 3, 4

✓ 1. 30,000 units

For the coming year, Tolstoy Company anticipates a unit selling price of $100, a unit variable cost of $30, and fixed costs of $2,100,000.

Instructions

1. Compute the anticipated break-even sales (units).
2. Compute the sales (units) required to realize income from operations of $350,000.
3. Construct a cost-volume-profit chart, assuming maximum sales of 50,000 units within the relevant range.
4. Determine the probable income (loss) from operations if sales total 40,000 units.

P11-4

Break-even sales and cost-volume-profit chart

Objs 3, 4

✓ 1. 3,400 units

Last year, Douthett Inc. had sales of $2,400,000, based on a unit selling price of $600. The variable cost per unit was $440, and fixed costs were $544,000. The maximum sales within Douthett's relevant range are 5,000 units. Douthett is considering a proposal to spend an additional $80,000 on billboard advertising during the current year in an attempt to increase sales and utilize unused capacity.

Instructions

1. Construct a cost-volume-profit chart indicating the break-even sales for last year. Verify your answer, using the break-even equation.
2. Using the cost-volume-profit chart prepared in part (1), determine (a) the income from operations for last year and (b) the maximum income from operations that could have been realized during the year. Verify your answers arithmetically.
3. Construct a cost-volume-profit chart indicating the break-even sales for the current year, assuming that a noncancelable contract is signed for the additional billboard advertising. No changes are expected in the unit selling price or other costs. Verify your answer, using the break-even equation.
4. Using the cost-volume-profit chart prepared in part (3), determine (a) the income from operations if sales total 4,000 units and (b) the maximum income from operations that could be realized during the year. Verify your answers arithmetically.

P11-5

Sales mix and break-even sales

Obj 5

✓ 1. 3,000 units

Data related to the expected sales of snowboards and skis for Winter Sports Inc. for the current year, which is typical of recent years, are as follows:

Products	Unit Selling Price	Unit Variable Cost	Sales Mix
Snowboards	$250.00	$170.00	40%
Skis	340.00	160.00	60%

The estimated fixed costs for the current year are $420,000.

Instructions

1. Determine the estimated units of sales of the overall product necessary to reach the break-even point for the current year.
2. Based on the break-even sales (units) in part (1), determine the unit sales of both snowboards and skis for the current year.
3. Assume that the sales mix was 60% snowboards and 40% skis. Compare the break-even point with that in part (1). Why is it so different?

P11-6

Contribution margin, break-even sales, cost-volume-profit chart, margin of safety, and operating leverage

Objs 2, 3, 4, 5

SPREADSHEET

✓ 2. 50%

Soldner Health Care Products Inc. expects to maintain the same inventories at the end of 2010 as at the beginning of the year. The total of all production costs for the year is therefore assumed to be equal to the cost of goods sold. With this in mind, the various department heads were asked to submit estimates of the costs for their departments during 2010. A summary report of these estimates is as follows:

	Estimated Fixed Cost	Estimated Variable Cost (per unit sold)
Production costs:		
Direct materials	—	$18.00
Direct labor	—	12.00
Factory overhead	$318,000	9.00
Selling expenses:		
Sales salaries and commissions	65,500	4.00
Advertising	22,500	—
Travel	5,000	—
Miscellaneous selling expense	5,500	3.50
Administrative expenses:		
Office and officers'salaries	65,000	—
Supplies	8,000	1.50
Miscellaneous administrative expense	10,500	2.00
Total	$500,000	$50.00

It is expected that 20,000 units will be sold at a price of $100 a unit. Maximum sales within the relevant range are 25,000 units.

Instructions

1. Prepare an estimated income statement for 2010.
2. What is the expected contribution margin ratio?
3. Determine the break-even sales in units.
4. Construct a cost-volume-profit chart indicating the break-even sales.
5. What is the expected margin of safety in dollars and as a percentage of sales?
6. Determine the operating leverage.

Activities

A11-1

Ethics and professional conduct in business

ETHICS

Jeff Zengel is a financial consultant to Rae Properties Inc., a real estate syndicate. Rae Properties Inc. finances and develops commercial real estate (office buildings). The completed projects are then sold as limited partnership interests to individual investors. The syndicate makes a profit on the sale of these partnership interests. Jeff provides financial information for the offering prospectus, which is a document that provides the financial and legal details of the limited partnership offerings. In one of the projects, the bank has financed the construction of a commercial office building at a rate of 8% for the first four years, after which time the rate jumps to 12% for the remaining 21 years of the mortgage. The interest costs are one of the major ongoing costs of a real estate project. Jeff has reported prominently in the prospectus that the break-even occupancy for the first four years is 60%. This is the amount of office space that must be leased to cover the interest and general upkeep costs over the first four years. The 60% break even is very low and thus communicates a low risk to potential investors. Jeff uses the 60% break-even rate as a major marketing tool in selling the limited partnership interests. Buried in the fine print of the prospectus is additional information that would allow an astute investor to determine that the break-even occupancy will jump to 90% after the fourth year because of the

contracted increase in the mortgage interest rate. Jeff believes prospective investors are adequately informed as to the risk of the investment.

Comment on the ethical considerations of this situation.

A11-2

Break-even sales, contribution margin

"For a student, a grade of 65 percent is nothing to write home about. But for the airline … [industry], filling 65 percent of the seats … is the difference between profit and loss.

The [economy] might be just strong enough to sustain all the carriers on a cash basis, but not strong enough to bring any significant profitability to the industry…. For the airlines …, the emphasis will be on trying to consolidate routes and raise ticket prices…"

The airline industry is notorious for boom and bust cycles. Why is airline profitability very sensitive to these cycles? Do you think that during a down cycle the strategy to consolidate routes and raise ticket prices is reasonable? What would make this strategy succeed or fail? Why?

Source: Edwin McDowell, *"Empty Seats, Empty Beds, Empty Pockets,"* The New York Times, *January 6, 1992, p. C3.*

A11-3

Break-even analysis

Techno Games Inc. has finished a new video game, *Mountain Bike Challenge.* Management is now considering its marketing strategies. The following information is available:

Anticipated sales price per unit	$40
Variable cost per unit*	$20
Anticipated volume	400,000
Production costs	$6,000,000
Anticipated advertising	$2,000,000

*The cost of the video game, packaging, and copying costs.

Two managers, David Hunter and Jamie Berry, had the following discussion of ways to increase the profitability of this new offering:

David: I think we need to think of some way to increase our profitability. Do you have any ideas?

Jamie: Well, I think the best strategy would be to become aggressive on price.

David: How aggressive?

Jamie: If we drop the price to $28 per unit and maintain our advertising budget at $2,000,000, I think we will generate sales of 1,500,000 units.

David: I think that's the wrong way to go. You're giving too much up on price. Instead, I think we need to follow an aggressive advertising strategy.

Jamie: How aggressive?

David: If we increase our advertising to a total of $6,000,000, we should be able to increase sales volume to 1,300,000 units without any change in price.

Jamie: I don't think that's reasonable. We'll never cover the increased advertising costs.

Which strategy is best: Do nothing? Follow the advice of Jamie Berry? Or follow David Hunter's strategy?

A11-4

Variable costs and activity bases in decision making

The owner of Banner-Tech, a printing company, is planning direct labor needs for the upcoming year. The owner has provided you with the following information for next year's plans:

	One Color	Two Color	Three Color	Four Color	Total
Number of banners	99	125	176	200	600

Each color on the banner must be printed one at a time. Thus, for example, a four-color banner will need to be run through the printing operation four separate times. The total production volume last year was 300 banners, as shown below.

	One Color	Two Color	Three Color	Total
Number of banners	76	103	121	300

As you can see, the four-color banner is a new product offering for the upcoming year. The owner believes that the expected 300-unit increase in volume from last year means that direct labor expenses should increase by 100% (300/300). What do you think?

A11-5

Variable costs and activity bases in decision making

Sales volume has been dropping at La Cross Publishing Company. During this time, however, the Shipping Department manager has been under severe financial constraints. The manager knows that most of the Shipping Department's effort is related to pulling inventory from the warehouse for each order and performing the paperwork. The paperwork involves preparing shipping documents for each order. Thus, the pulling and paperwork effort associated with each sales order is essentially the same, regardless of the size of the order. The Shipping Department manager has discussed the financial situation with senior management. Senior management has responded by pointing out that sales volume has been dropping, so that the amount of work in the Shipping Department should be dropping. Thus, senior management told the Shipping Department manager that costs should be decreasing in the department.

The Shipping Department manager prepared the following information:

Month	Sales Volume	Number of Customer Orders	Sales Volume per Order
January	$168,000	700	240
February	165,600	720	230
March	160,600	730	220
April	150,000	750	200
May	149,150	785	190
June	148,000	800	185
July	147,600	820	180
August	147,000	840	175

Given this information, how would you respond to senior management?

A11-6

Break-even analysis

Break-even analysis is one of the most fundamental tools for managing any kind of business unit. Consider the management of your school. In a group, brainstorm some applications of break-even analysis at your school. Identify three areas where break-even analysis might be used. For each area, identify the revenues, variable costs, and fixed costs that would be used in the calculation.

Answers to Self-Examination Questions

1. **B** Variable costs vary in total in direct proportion to changes in the level of activity (answer B). Costs that vary on a per-unit basis as the level of activity changes (answer A) or remain constant in total dollar amount as the level of activity changes (answer C), or both (answer D), are fixed costs.

2. **D** The contribution margin ratio indicates the percentage of each sales dollar available to cover the fixed costs and provide income from operations and is determined as follows:

$$\text{Contribution Margin Ratio} = \frac{\text{Sales} - \text{Variable Costs}}{\text{Sales}}$$

$$\text{Contribution Margin Ratio} = \frac{\$500,000 - \$200,000}{\$500,000}$$

$$= 60\%$$

3. **D** The break-even sales of 40,000 units (answer D) is computed as follows:

$$\text{Break-Even Sales (units)} = \frac{\text{Fixed Costs}}{\text{Unit Contribution Margin}}$$

$$\text{Break-Even Sales (units)} = \frac{\$160,000}{\$4} = 40,000 \text{ units}$$

4. **D** Sales of 45,000 units are required to realize income from operations of $20,000, computed as follows:

$$\text{Sales (units)} = \frac{\text{Fixed Costs} + \text{Target Profit}}{\text{Unit Contribution Margin}}$$

$$\text{Sales (units)} = \frac{\$160,000 + \$20,000}{\$4} = 45,000 \text{ units}$$

5. **C** The operating leverage is 1.8, computed as follows:

$$\text{Operating Leverage} = \frac{\text{Contribution Margin}}{\text{Income from Operations}}$$

$$\text{Operating Leverage} = \frac{\$360,000}{\$200,000} = 1.8$$

Differential Analysis and Product Pricing

12

Learning Objectives
After studying this chapter, you should be able to:

Obj 1 Prepare differential analysis reports for a variety of managerial decisions.

Obj 2 Determine the selling price of a product, using the total cost, product cost, and variable cost concepts.

Obj 3 Compute the relative profitability of products in bottleneck production processes.

Many of the decisions that you make depend on comparing the estimated costs of alternatives. The payoff from such comparisons is described in the following report from a University of Michigan study.

Richard Nisbett and two colleagues quizzed Michigan faculty members and university seniors on such questions as how often they walk out on a bad movie, refuse to finish a bad meal, or abandon a research project. They believe that people who cut their losses this way are following sound economic rules: calculating the net benefits of alternative courses of action, writing off past costs that can't be recovered, and weighing the opportunity to use future time and effort more profitably elsewhere.

Dr. Nisbett concedes that for many Americans, cost-benefit rules often appear to conflict with such traditional principles as "never give up" and "waste not, want not."

Managers must also apply cost-benefit rules in making decisions affecting their business. **RealNetworks, Inc.**, the Internet-based music and game company, like most companies must choose between alternatives. Examples of decisions faced by RealNetworks include whether it should expand or discontinue services, such as its recent decision to Mac-enable its digital music service, Rhapsody®, and whether to accept business at special prices, such as special pricing on its Helix Media Delivery System®.

In this chapter, differential analysis, which reports the effects of decisions on total revenues and costs, is discussed. Practical approaches to setting product prices are also described and illustrated. Finally, how production bottlenecks influence product mix and pricing decisions is discussed.

Source: Alan L. Otten, "Economic Perspective Produces Steady Yields," from People Patterns, The Wall Street Journal, March 31, 1992, p. B1.

Obj 1 Prepare differential
analysis reports for a
variety of managerial
decisions.

Differential Analysis

Managerial decision making involves choosing between alternative courses of action. Although the managerial decision-making process varies by the type of decision, it normally involves the following steps:

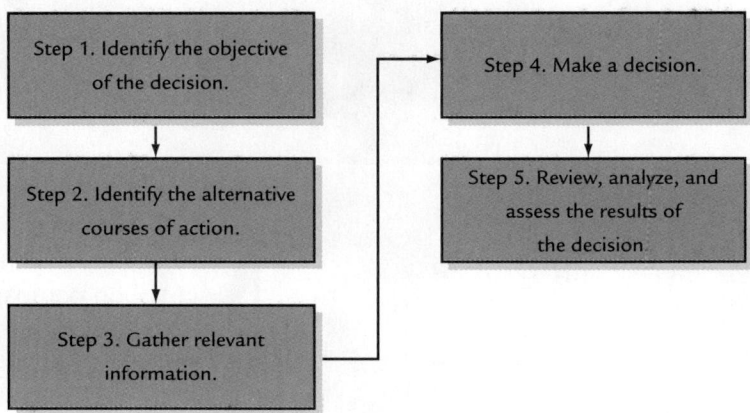

The objective (Step 1) for most decisions is to maximize the company's profits. The alternative courses of action (Step 2) could include actions such as discontinuing an unprofitable segment, replacing equipment, or offering a product at a special price to an exporter. The relevant information (Step 3) varies by decision, but oftentimes includes estimates and data that are not available in the accounting records. Making decisions (Step 4) is the most important function of managers. Once the decision is made, the results of the decision (Step 5) should be reviewed, analyzed, and assessed in terms of the initial objective of the decision.

Accounting facilitates the preceding process by:

1. Gathering relevant information for managerial decisions

2. Reporting this information to management

3. Providing management feedback on the results of the decisions

For managerial decisions, estimated future revenues and costs are relevant. Costs that have been incurred in the past are not relevant to the decision. These costs are called **sunk costs**.

Differential revenue is the amount of increase or decrease in revenue that is expected from a course of action as compared to an alternative. To illustrate, assume that equipment can be used to manufacture digital clocks or calculators. The differential revenue from making and selling digital clocks is $25,000, determined as follows:

Product	Estimated Revenue
Digital clocks	$175,000
Calculators	150,000
Differential revenue	$ 25,000

Differential cost is the amount of increase or decrease in cost that is expected from a course of action as compared to an alternative. For example,

The management of **Delta Air Lines** decided to discontinue its low-fare **Song Airline** subsidiary after assessing its profitability.

Have you ever walked out on a bad movie? The cost of the ticket is a sunk cost and, thus, irrelevant to the decision to walk out early.

if increasing advertising expenses from \$100,000 to \$150,000 is being considered, the differential cost is \$50,000.

Differential income (or loss) is the difference between the differential revenue and the differential costs. Differential income indicates that a decision is expected to be profitable, while a differential loss indicates the opposite.

Differential analysis, sometimes called *incremental analysis,* focuses on the effect of alternative courses of action on revenues and costs. An example of a reporting format for differential analysis is shown in Exhibit 1.

EXHIBIT 1 **Differential Analysis**

Differential revenue from alternatives:		
Revenue from alternative A	\$XXX	
Revenue from alternative B	XXX	
Differential revenue		\$ XXX
Differential cost of alternatives:		
Cost of alternative A	\$XXX	
Cost of alternative B	XXX	
Differential cost		XXX
Net differential income or loss from alternatives		**\$XXX**

In this chapter, differential analysis is illustrated for the following decisions:

1. Leasing or selling equipment
2. Discontinuing an unprofitable segment
3. Manufacturing or purchasing a needed part
4. Replacing fixed assets
5. Processing further or selling a product
6. Accepting additional business at a special price

Lease or Sell

Management may lease or sell a piece of equipment that is no longer needed. This may occur when a company changes its manufacturing process and can no longer use the equipment in the manufacturing process. In making a decision, differential analysis can be used.

To illustrate, assume that Marcus Company is considering leasing or disposing of the following equipment:

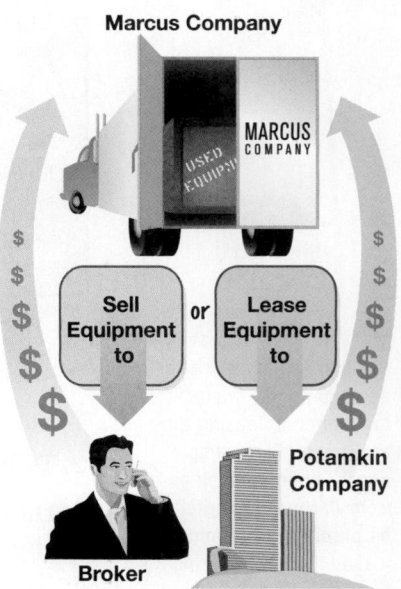

Cost of equipment	\$200,000
Less accumulated depreciation	120,000
Book value	\$ 80,000
Lease Option:	
Total revenue for five-year lease	\$160,000
Total estimated repair, insurance, and	
property tax expenses during life of lease	35,000
Residual value at end of fifth year of lease	0
Sell Option:	
Sales price	\$100,000
Commission on sales	6%

Exhibit 2 shows the differential analysis of whether to lease or sell the equipment.

EXHIBIT 2   Differential Analysis Report—Lease or Sell

Proposal to Lease or Sell Equipment June 22, 2010		
Differential revenue from alternatives:		
Revenue from lease	$160,000	
Revenue from sale	100,000	
Differential revenue from lease		$60,000
Differential cost of alternatives:		
Repair/insurance, and property: tax expenses from lease	$ 35,000	
Commission expense on sale ($100,000 × 6%)	6,000	
Differential cost of lease		29,000
Net differential income from the lease alternative		**$31,000**

Exhibit 2 includes only the differential revenues and differential costs associated with the lease or sell decision. The $80,000 book value ($200,000 – $120,000) of the equipment is a *sunk* cost and is not considered in the differential analysis shown in Exhibit 2. In other words, the $80,000 does not affect the decision to lease or sell the equipment.

The differential analysis shown in Exhibit 2 is verified by the more traditional analysis shown in Exhibit 3.

EXHIBIT 3   Traditional Analysis

Lease or Sell			
Lease alternative:			
Revenue from lease		$160,000	
Depreciation expense for remaining five years	$80,000		
Repair, insurance, and property tax expenses	35,000	115,000	
Net gain			$45,000
Sell alternative:			
Sales price		$100,000	
Book, value of equipment	$80,000		
Commission expense	6,000	86,000	
Net gain			14,000
Net differential income from the lease alternative			**$31,000**

Many companies that manufacture expensive equipment give customers the choice of leasing the equipment. For example, construction equipment from **Caterpillar** can either be purchased outright or leased through Caterpillar's financial services subsidiary.

To simplify, the following factors were not considered in Exhibits 2 and 3:

1. Differential revenue from investing funds

2. Differential income tax

Differential revenue (interest) could arise from investing the cash created by the two alternatives. Differential income tax could arise from differences in the timing of the income from the two alternatives and differences in the amount that is taxed. These factors are discussed in Chapter 15.

Discontinue a Segment or Product

A product, department, branch, territory, or other segment of a business may be generating losses. As a result, management may consider discontinuing (eliminating) the product or segment. In such cases, it may be erroneously assumed that the total company income will increase by eliminating the operating loss.

Discontinuing the product or segment usually eliminates all of the product's or segment's variable costs. Such costs include direct materials, direct labor, variable factory overhead, and sales commissions. However, fixed costs such as depreciation, insurance, and property taxes may not be eliminated. Thus, it is possible for total company income to decrease rather than increase if the unprofitable product or segment is discontinued.

To illustrate, the income statement for Battle Creek Cereal Co. is shown in Exhibit 4. As shown in Exhibit 4, Bran Flakes incurred an operating loss of $11,000. Because Bran Flakes has incurred annual losses for several years, management is considering discontinuing it.

EXHIBIT 4 Income (Loss) by Product

BATTLE CREEK CEREAL CO.
Condensed Income Statement
For the Year Ended August 31, 2010

	Corn Flakes	Toasted Oats	Bran Flakes	Total Company
Sales	$500,000	$400,000	$100,000	$1,000,000
Cost of goods sold:				
Variable costs	$220,000	$200,000	$ 60,000	$ 480,000
Fixed costs	120,000	80,000	20,000	220,000
Total cost of goods sold	$340,000	$280,000	$ 80,000	$ 700,000
Gross profit	$160,000	$120,000	$ 20,000	$ 300,000
Operating expenses:				
Variable expenses	$ 95,000	$ 60,000	$ 25,000	$ 180,000
Fixed expenses	25,000	20,000	6,000	51,000
Total operating expenses	$120,000	$ 80,000	$ 31,000	$ 231,000
Income (loss) from operations	$ 40,000	$ 40,000	$(11,000)	$ 69,000

If Bran Flakes is discontinued, what would be the total annual operating income of Battle Creek Cereal? The first impression is that total annual operating income would be $80,000, as shown below.

	Corn Flakes	Toasted Oats	Total Company
Income from operations	$40,000	$40,000	$80,000

However, the differential analysis report in Exhibit 5 indicates that discontinuing Bran Flakes actually decreases operating income by $15,000. This is because discontinuing Bran Flakes has no effect on fixed costs and expenses.

EXHIBIT | 5 | **Differential Analysis Report—Discontinue an Unprofitable Segment**

Proposal to Discontinue Bran Flakes September 29, 2010		
Differential revenue from annual sales of Bran Flakes:		
Revenue from sales		$100,000
Differential cost of annual sales of Bran Flakes:		
Variable cost of good sold	$60,000	
Variable operating expenses	25,000	85,000
Annual differential income from sales of Bran Flakes		**$ 15,000**

The differential analysis in Exhibit 5 is supported by the traditional analysis in Exhibit 6, which indicates that income from operations would decrease from $69,000 to $54,000.

EXHIBIT | 6 | **Traditional Analysis**

Proposal to Discontinue Bran Flakes September 29, 2010			
	Bran Flakes, Toasted Oats, and Corn Flakes	Discontinue Bran Flakes*	Toasted Oats and Corn Flakes
Sales	$1,000,000	$ 100,000	$900,000
Cost of goods sold:			
Variable costs	$ 480,000	$ 60,000	$420,000
Fixed costs	220,000	—	220,000
Total cost of goods sold	$ 700,000	$ 60,000	$640,000
Gross profit	$ 300,000	$ 40,000	$260,000
Operating expenses:			
Variable expenses	$ 180,000	$ 25,000	$155,000
Fixed expenses	51,000	—	51,000
Total operating expenses	$ 231,000	$ 25,000	$206,000
Income (loss) from operations	**$ 69,000**	**$ 15,000**	**$ 54,000**

*Fixed costs are assumed to remain unchanged with the discontinuance of Bran Flakes.

Exhibits 5 and 6 consider only the short-term (one-year) effects of discontinuing Bran Flakes. When discontinuing a product or segment, long-term effects should also be considered. For example, discontinuing Bran Flakes could decrease sales of other products. This might be the case if customers upset with the discontinuance of Bran Flakes quit buying other products from the company. Finally, employee morale and productivity might suffer if employees have to be laid off or relocated.

Ford Motor Co. purchases spark plugs, GPS units, nuts, and bolts from suppliers.

Make or Buy

Companies often manufacture products made up of components that are assembled into a final product. For example, an automobile manufacturer assembles tires, radios, motors, interior seats, transmissions, and other parts

into a finished automobile. In such cases, the manufacturer must decide whether to make a part or purchase it from a supplier.

Differential analysis can be used to decide whether to make or buy a part. The analysis is similar whether management is considering making a part that is currently being purchased or purchasing a part that is currently being made.

To illustrate, assume that an automobile manufacturer has been purchasing instrument panels for $240 a unit. The factory is currently operating at 80% of capacity, and no major increase in production is expected in the near future. The cost per unit of manufacturing an instrument panel internally is estimated as follows:

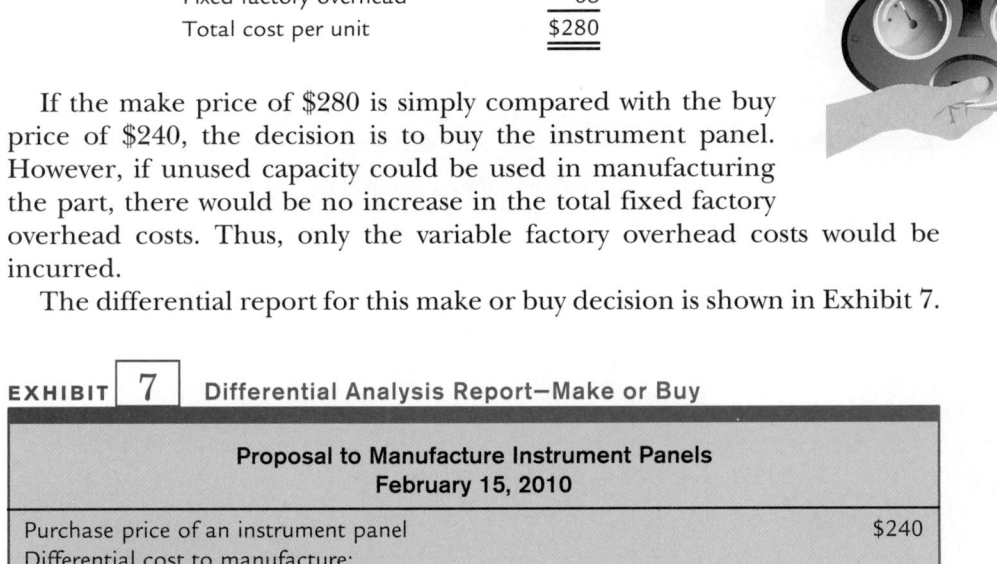

Direct materials	$ 80
Direct labor	80
Variable factory overhead	52
Fixed factory overhead	68
Total cost per unit	$280

If the make price of $280 is simply compared with the buy price of $240, the decision is to buy the instrument panel. However, if unused capacity could be used in manufacturing the part, there would be no increase in the total fixed factory overhead costs. Thus, only the variable factory overhead costs would be incurred.

The differential report for this make or buy decision is shown in Exhibit 7.

EXHIBIT | 7 | **Differential Analysis Report—Make or Buy**

Proposal to Manufacture Instrument Panels February 15, 2010		
Purchase price of an instrument panel		$240
Differential cost to manufacture:		
Direct materials	$80	
Direct labor	80	
Variable factory overhead	52	212
Cost savings from manufacturing an instrument panel		**$ 28**

As shown in Exhibit 7, there is a cost savings from manufacturing the instrument panel of $28 per panel. However, other factors should also be considered. For example, productive capacity used to make the instrument panel would not be available for other production. The decision may also affect the future business relationship with the instrument panel supplier. For example, if the supplier provides other parts, the company's decision to make instrument panels might jeopardize the timely delivery of other parts.

Replace Equipment

The usefulness of a fixed asset may decrease before it is worn out. For example, old equipment may no longer be as efficient as new equipment.

Estimated annual reduction
of costs of $75,000

Differential analysis can be used for decisions to replace fixed assets such as equipment and machinery. The analysis normally focuses on the costs of continuing to use the old equipment versus replacing the equipment. The book value of the old equipment is a sunk cost and, thus, is irrelevant.

To illustrate, assume that a business is considering replacing the following machine:

Old Machine	
Book value	$100,000
Estimated annual variable manufacturing costs	225,000
Estimated selling price	25,000
Estimated remaining useful life	5 years
New Machine	
Cost of new machine	$250,000
Estimated annual variable manufacturing costs	150,000
Estimated residual value	0
Estimated useful life	5 years

The differential report for the decision to replace the old machine is shown in Exhibit 8.

EXHIBIT 8   Differential Analysis Report—Replace Machine

Proposal to Replace Machine November 28, 2010		
Annual variable costs—present machine	$225,000	
Annual variable costs—new machine	150,000	
Annual differential decrease in cost	$ 75,000	
Number of years applicable	× 5	
Total differential decrease in cost	$375,000	
Proceeds from sale of present machine	25,000	$400,000
Cost of new machine		250,000
Net differential decrease in cost, five-year total		$150,000
Annual net differential decrease in cost—new machine		**$ 30,000**

As shown in Exhibit 8, there is an annual decrease in cost of $30,000 ($150,000 ÷ 5 years) from replacing the old machine. Thus, the decision should be to purchase the new machine and sell the old machine.

Other factors are often important in equipment replacement decisions. For example, differences between the remaining useful life of the old equipment and the estimated life of the new equipment could exist. In addition, the new equipment might improve the overall quality of the product and, thus, increase sales.

The time value of money and other uses for the cash needed to purchase the new equipment could also affect the decision to replace equipment.[1] The revenue that is forgone from an alternative use of an asset, such as cash, is called an **opportunity cost**. Although the opportunity cost is not recorded in the accounting records, it is useful in analyzing alternative courses of action.

To illustrate, assume that in the preceding illustration the cash outlay of $250,000 for the new machine, less the $25,000 proceeds from the sale of the

---

[1] The time value of money in purchasing equipment (capital assets) is discussed in Chapter 15.

old machine, could be invested to yield a 15% return. Thus, the annual opportunity cost related to the purchase of the new machine is $33,750 (15% × $225,000). Since the opportunity cost of $33,750 exceeds the annual cost savings of $30,000, the old machine should not be replaced.

Process or Sell

During manufacturing, a product normally progresses through various stages or processes. In some cases, a product can be sold at an intermediate stage of production, or it can be processed further and then sold.

Differential analysis can be used to decide whether to sell a product at an intermediate stage or to process it further. In doing so, the differential revenues and costs from further processing are compared. The costs of producing the intermediate product do not change, regardless of whether the intermediate product is sold or processed further. These costs are sunk costs and are irrelevant to the decision.

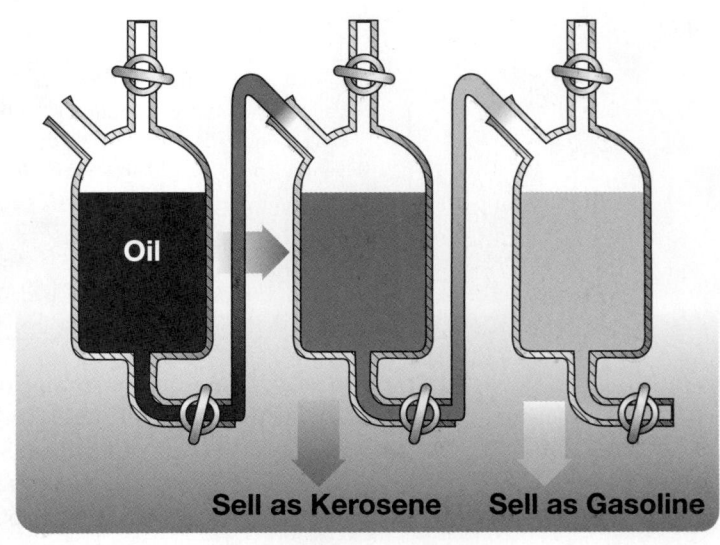

To illustrate, assume that a business produces kerosene as follows:

Kerosene:

Batch size	4,000 gallons
Cost of producing kerosene	$2,400 per batch
Selling price	$2.50 per gallon

The kerosene can be processed further to yield gasoline as follows:

Gasoline:

Input batch size	4,000 gallons
Less evaporation (20%)	800 (4,000 × 20%)
Output batch size	3,200 gallons
Additional processing costs	$650 per batch
Selling price	$3.50 per gallon

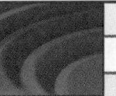

INTEGRITY, OBJECTIVITY, AND ETHICS IN BUSINESS

Related-Party Deals

The make-or-buy decision can be complicated if the purchase (buy) is being made by a related party. A related party is one in which there is direct or indirect control of one party over another or the presence of a family member in a transaction. Such dependence or familiarity may interfere with the appropriateness of the business transaction. One investor has said, "Related parties are akin to steroids used by athletes. If you're an athlete and you can cut the mustard, you don't need steroids to make yourself stronger or faster. By the same token, if you're a good company, you don't need related parties or deals that don't make sense." While related-party transactions are legal, GAAP (FASB Statement No. 56) and the Sarbanes-Oxley Act require that they must be disclosed under the presumption that such transactions are less than arm's length.

Source: Herb Greenberg, "Poor Relations: The Problem with Related-Party Transactions," Fortune Advisor *(February 5, 2001), p. 198.*

The differential report for the decision to process the kerosene further is shown in Exhibit 9.

EXHIBIT 9   Differential Analysis Report—Process or Sell

Proposal to Process Kerosene Further October 1, 2010		
Differential revenue from further processing per batch:		
Revenue from sale of gasoline [(4,000 gallons – 800 gallons evaporation) × $3.50]	$11,200	
Revenue from sale of kerosene (4,000 gallons × $2.50)	10,000	
Differential revenue		$1,200
Differential cost per batch:		
Additional cost of producing gasoline		650
Differential income from further processing gasoline per batch		**$ 550**

The initial cost of producing the kerosene of $2,400 is not considered in deciding whether to process kerosene further. This initial cost will be incurred, regardless of whether gasoline is produced and, thus, is a sunk cost.

As shown in Exhibit 9, there is additional income from further processing the kerosene into gasoline of $550 per batch. Therefore, the decision should be to process the kerosene further.

Accept Business at a Special Price

A company may be offered the opportunity to sell its products at prices other than normal prices. For example, an exporter may offer to sell a company's products overseas at special discount prices.

The Internet is forcing many companies to respond to "dynamic" pricing. For example, in *Priceline.com Inc.*'s "name your price" format, customers tell the company what they are willing to pay and then the company must decide if it is willing to sell at that price.

Differential analysis can be used to decide whether to accept additional business at a special price. The differential revenue from accepting the additional business is compared to the differential costs of producing and delivering the product to the customer.

The differential costs of accepting additional business depend on whether the company is operating at full capacity.

1. If the company is *operating at full capacity,* any additional production increases fixed and variable manufacturing costs. Selling and administrative expenses may also increase because of the additional business.

2. If the company is *operating below full capacity,* any additional production does not increase fixed manufacturing costs. In this case, the differential costs of the additional production are the variable manufacturing costs. Selling and administrative expenses may also increase because of the additional business.

To illustrate, assume that B-Ball Inc. manufactures basketballs as follows:

Order for 5,000 basketballs at $18 each

Monthly productive capacity	12,500 basketballs
Current monthly sales	10,000 basketballs
Normal (domestic) selling price	$30.00 per basketball
Manufacturing costs:	
Variable costs	$12.50 per basketball
Fixed costs	7.50
Total	$20.00 per basketball

B-Ball Inc. has received an offer from an exporter for 5,000 basketballs at $18 each. Production can be spread over three months without interfering with normal production or incurring overtime costs. Pricing policies in the domestic market will not be affected.

Comparing the special offer sales price of $18 with the manufacturing cost of $20 per basketball indicates that the offer should be rejected. However, as shown in Exhibit 10, differential analysis indicates that the offer should be accepted.

EXHIBIT 10   **Differential Analysis Report—Sell at Special Price**

Proposal to Sell Basketballs to Exporter March 10, 2010	
Differential revenue from accepting offer:	
Revenue from sale of 5,000 additional units at $18	$90,000
Differential cost of accepting offer:	
Variable costs of 5,000 additional units at $12.50	62,500
Differential income from accepting offer	**$27,500**

Proposals to sell products at special prices often require additional considerations. For example, special prices in one geographic area may result in price reductions in other areas with the result that total company sales decrease. Manufacturers must also conform to the Robinson-Patman Act, which prohibits price discrimination within the United States unless price differences can be justified by different costs.

Setting Normal Product Selling Prices

The *normal* selling price is the target selling price to be achieved in the long term. The normal selling price must be set high enough to cover all costs and expenses (fixed and variable) and provide a reasonable profit. Otherwise, the business will not survive.

In contrast, in deciding whether to accept additional business at a special price, only differential costs are considered. Any price above the differential costs will increase profits in the short term. However, in the long term, products are sold at normal prices rather than special prices.

Managers can use one of two market methods to determine selling price:

1. Demand-based concept
2. Competition-based concept

The demand-based concept sets the price according to the demand for the product. If there is high demand for the product, then the price is set high. Likewise, if there is a low demand for the product, then the price is set low.

The competition-based concept sets the price according to the price offered by competitors. For example, if a competitor reduces the price, then management adjusts the price to meet the competition. The market-based pricing approaches are discussed in greater detail in marketing courses.

Obj 2 Determine the selling price of a product, using the total cost, product cost, and variable cost concepts.

Hotels and motels use the demand-based concept in setting room rates. Room rates are set low during off-season travel periods (low demand) and high for peak-season travel periods (high demand) such as holidays.

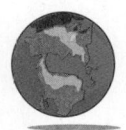

Managers can also use one of three cost-plus methods to determine the selling price:

1. Total cost concept
2. Product cost concept
3. Variable cost concept

Cost-plus methods determine the normal selling price by estimating a cost amount per unit and adding a markup, as shown below.

$$\text{Normal Selling Price} = \text{Cost Amount per Unit} + \text{Markup}$$

The cost amount per unit depends on the cost concept used. Management determines the **markup** based on the desired profit for the product. The markup should be sufficient to earn the desired profit plus cover any costs and expenses that are not included in the cost amount.

Total Cost Concept

Under the **total cost concept**, manufacturing cost plus the selling and administrative expenses are included in the total cost per unit. The markup per unit is then computed and added to total cost per unit to determine the normal selling price.

The total cost concept is applied using the following steps:

Step 1. Estimate the total manufacturing cost as shown below.

Manufacturing costs:	
Direct materials	$XXX
Direct labor	XXX
Factory overhead	XXX
Total manufacturing cost	$XXX

Step 2. Estimate the total selling and administrative expenses.
Step 3. Estimate the total cost as shown below.

Total manufacturing costs	$XXX
Selling and administrative expenses	XXX
Total cost	$XXX

Step 4. Divide the total cost by the number of units expected to be produced and sold to determine the total cost per unit, as shown below.

$$\text{Total Cost per Unit} = \frac{\text{Total Cost}}{\text{Estimated Units Produced and Sold}}$$

Step 5. Compute the markup percentage as follows:

$$\text{Markup Percentage} = \frac{\text{Desired Profit}}{\text{Total Cost}}$$

The desired profit is normally computed based on a rate of return on assets as follows:

$$\text{Desired Profit} = \text{Desired Rate of Return} \times \text{Total Assets}$$

Step 6. Determine the markup per unit by multiplying the mark-up percentage times the total cost per unit as follows:

Markup per Unit = Markup Percentage × Total Cost per Unit

Step 7. Determine the normal selling price by adding the markup per unit to the total cost per unit as follows:

Total cost per unit	$XXX
Markup per unit	XXX
Normal selling price per unit	$XXX

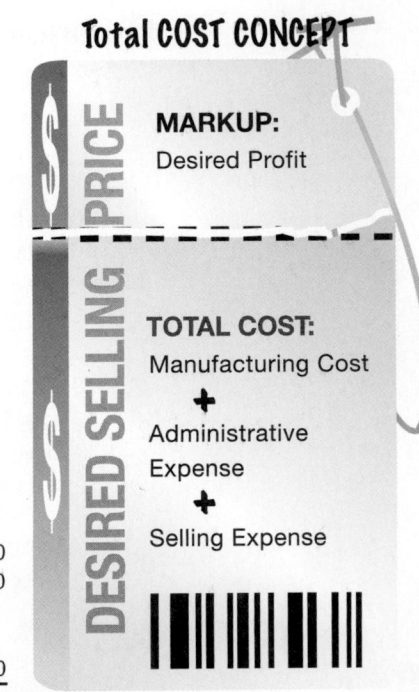

Total COST CONCEPT

DESIRED SELLING PRICE

MARKUP:
Desired Profit

TOTAL COST:
Manufacturing Cost
+
Administrative Expense
+
Selling Expense

To illustrate, assume the following data for 100,000 calculators that Digital Solutions Inc. expects to produce and sell during the current year:

Manufacturing costs:		
Direct materials ($3.00 × 100,000)		$ 300,000
Direct labor ($10.00 × 100,000)		1,000,000
Factory overhead:		
Variable costs ($1.50 × 100,000)	$150,000	
Fixed costs	50,000	200,000
Total manufacturing cost		$1,500,000
Selling and administrative expenses:		
Variable expenses ($1.50 × 100,000)	$150,000	
Fixed costs	20,000	
Total selling and administrative expenses		170,000
Total cost		$1,670,000
Desired rate of return		20%
Total assets		$800,000

Using the total cost concept, the normal selling price of $18.30 is determined as follows:

Step 1. Total manufacturing cost: $1,500,000
Step 2. Total selling and administrative expenses: $170,000
Step 3. Total cost: $1,670,000
Step 4. Total cost per unit: $16.70

$$\text{Total Cost per Unit} = \frac{\text{Total Cost}}{\text{Estimated Units Produced and Sold}}$$
$$= \frac{\$1,670,000}{100,000 \text{ units}} = \$16.70 \text{ per unit}$$

Step 5. Markup percentage: 9.6% (rounded)

$$\text{Desired Profit} = \text{Desired Rate of Return} \times \text{Total Assets}$$
$$= 20\% \times \$800,000 = \$160,000$$

$$\text{Markup Percentage} = \frac{\text{Desired Profit}}{\text{Total Cost}} = \frac{\$160,000}{\$1,670,000} = 9.6\% (\text{rounded})$$

Step 6. Markup per unit: $1.60

Markup per Unit = Markup Percentage × Total Cost per Unit

Markup per Unit = 9.6% × $16.70 = $1.60 per unit

Step 7. Normal selling price: $18.30

Total cost per unit	$16.70
Markup per unit	1.60
Normal selling price per unit	$18.30

The ability of the selling price of $18.30 to generate the desired profit of $160,000 is illustrated by the income statement shown below.

Digital Solutions Inc.
Income Statement
For the Year Ended December 31, 2010

Sales (100,000 units × $18.30)		$1,830,000
Expenses:		
Variable (100,000 units × $16.00)	$1,600,000	
Fixed ($50,000 + $20,000)	70,000	1,670,000
Income from operations		$ 160,000

Product COST CONCEPT

DESIRED SELLING PRICE

MARKUP:

Administrative Expense

+

Selling Expense

+

Desired Profit

PRODUCT COST:

Manufacturing Cost

The total cost concept is often used by contractors who sell products to government agencies. This is because in many cases government contractors are required by law to be reimbursed for their products on a total-cost-plus-profit basis.

Product Cost Concept

Under the **product cost concept**, only the costs of manufacturing the product, termed the *product costs,* are included in the cost amount per unit to which the markup is added. Estimated selling expenses, administrative expenses, and desired profit are included in the markup. The markup per unit is then computed and added to the product cost per unit to determine the normal selling price.

The product cost concept is applied using the following steps:

Step 1. Estimate the total product costs as follows:

Product costs:	
Direct materials	$XXX
Direct labor	XXX
Factory overhead	XXX
Total product cost	$XXX

Step 2. Estimate the total selling and administrative expenses.

INTEGRITY, OBJECTIVITY, AND ETHICS IN BUSINESS

Price Fixing

Federal law prevents companies competing in similar markets from sharing cost and price information, or what is commonly termed "price fixing." For example, the Federal Trade Commission brought a suit against the major record labels and music retailers for conspiring to set CD prices at a minimum level, or MAP (minimum advertised price), In settling the suit, the major labels ceased their MAP policies and provided $143 million in cash and CDs for consumers.

Step 3. Divide the total product cost by the number of units expected to be produced and sold to determine the total product cost per unit, as shown below.

$$\text{Product Cost per Unit} = \frac{\text{Total Product Cost}}{\text{Estimated Units Produced and Sold}}$$

Step 4. Compute the markup percentage as follows:

$$\text{Markup Percentage} = \frac{\text{Desired Profit} + \begin{array}{l}\text{Total Selling and}\\\text{Administrative Expenses}\end{array}}{\text{Total Product Cost}}$$

The numerator of the markup percentage is the desired profit plus the total selling and administrative expenses. These expenses must be included in the markup percentage, since they are not included in the cost amount to which the markup is added.

As illustrated for the total cost concept, the desired profit is normally computed based on a rate of return on assets as follows:

$$\text{Desired Profit} = \text{Desired Rate of Return} \times \text{Total Assets}$$

Step 5. Determine the markup per unit by multiplying the markup percentage times the product cost per unit as follows:

$$\text{Markup per Unit} = \text{Markup Percentage} \times \text{Product Cost per Unit}$$

Step 6. Determine the normal selling price by adding the markup per unit to the product cost per unit as follows:

Product cost per unit	$XXX
Markup per unit	XXX
Normal selling price per unit	$XXX

To illustrate, assume the same data for the production and sale of 100,000 calculators by Digital Solutions Inc. as in the preceding example. The normal selling price of $18.30 is determined under the product cost concept as follows:

Step 1. Total product cost: $1,500,000
Step 2. Total selling and administrative expenses: $170,000
Step 3. Total product cost per unit: $15.00

$$\text{Total Cost per Unit} = \frac{\text{Total Product Cost}}{\text{Estimated Units Produced and Sold}}$$

$$\text{Total Cost per Unit} = \frac{\$1,500,000}{100,000 \text{ units}} = \$15.00 \text{ per unit}$$

Step 4. Markup percentage: 22%

$$\text{Desired Profit} = \text{Desired Rate of Return} \times \text{Total Assets}$$

$$\text{Desired Profit} = 20\% \times \$800,000 = \$160,000$$

$$\text{Markup Percentage} = \frac{\text{Desired Profit} + \begin{array}{l}\text{Total Selling and}\\\text{Administrative Expenses}\end{array}}{\text{Total Product Cost}}$$

$$\text{Markup Percentage} = \frac{\$160,000 + \$170,000}{\$1,500,000} = \frac{\$330,000}{\$1,500,000} = 22\%$$

Step 5. Markup per unit: $3.30

$$\text{Markup per Unit} = \text{Markup Percentage} \times \text{Product Cost per Unit}$$

$$\text{Markup per Unit} = 22\% \times \$15.00 = \$3.30 \text{ per unit}$$

Step 6. Normal selling price: $18.30

Total product cost per unit	$15.00
Markup per unit	3.30
Normal selling price per unit	$18.30

Variable Cost Concept

Under the **variable cost concept**, only variable costs are included in the cost amount per unit to which the markup is added. All variable manufacturing costs, as well as variable selling and administrative expenses, are included in the cost amount. Fixed manufacturing costs, fixed selling and administrative expenses, and desired profit are included in the markup. The markup per unit is then added to the variable cost per unit to determine the normal selling price.

The variable cost concept is applied using the following steps:

Step 1. Estimate the total variable product cost as follows:

Variable product costs:	
Direct materials	$XXX
Direct labor	XXX
Variable factory overhead	XXX
Total variable product cost	$XXX

Step 2. Estimate the total variable selling and administrative expenses.
Step 3. Determine the total variable cost as follows:

Total variable product cost	$XXX
Total variable selling and administrative expenses	XXX
Total variable cost	$XXX

Step 4. Compute the variable cost per unit as follows:

$$\text{Variable Cost per Unit} = \frac{\text{Total Variable Cost}}{\text{Estimated Units Produced and Sold}}$$

Step 5. Compute the markup percentage as follows:

$$\text{Markup Percentage} = \frac{\text{Desired Profit} + \text{Total Fixed Costs and Expenses}}{\text{Total Variable Cost}}$$

The numerator of the markup percentage is the desired profit plus the total fixed costs (fixed factory overhead) and expenses (selling and administrative). These fixed costs and expenses must be included in the markup percentage, since they are not included in the cost amount to which the markup is added.

As illustrated for the total and product cost concepts, the desired profit is normally computed based on a rate of return on assets as follows:

$$\text{Desired Profit} = \text{Desired Rate of Return} \times \text{Total Assets}$$

Step 6. Determine the markup per unit by multiplying the markup percentage times the variable cost per unit as follows:

Markup per Unit = Markup Percentage × Variable Cost per Unit

Step 7. Determine the normal selling price by adding the markup per unit to the variable cost per unit as follows:

Variable cost per unit	$XXX
Markup per unit	XXX
Normal selling price per unit	$XXX

To illustrate, assume the same data for the production and sale of 100,000 calculators by Digital Solutions Inc. as in the preceding example. The normal selling price of $18.30 is determined under the variable cost concept as follows:

Step 1. Total variable product cost: $1,450,000

Variable product costs:	
Direct materials ($3 × 100,000)	$ 300,000
Direct labor ($10 × 100,000)	1,000,000
Variable factory overhead ($1.50 × 100,000)	150,000
Total variable product cost	$1,450,000

Step 2. Total variable selling and administrative expenses: $150,000 ($1.50 × 100,000)

Step 3. Total variable cost: $1,600,000 ($1,450,000 + $150,000)

Step 4. Variable cost per unit: $16.00

$$\text{Variable Cost per Unit} = \frac{\text{Total Variable Cost}}{\text{Estimated Units Produced and Sold}}$$

$$\text{Variable Cost per Unit} = \frac{\$1,600,000}{100,000 \text{ units}} = \$16 \text{ per unit}$$

Step 5. Markup percentage: 14.4% (rounded)

Desired Profit = Desired Rate of Return × Total Assets

Desired Profit = 20% × $800,000 = $160,000

$$\text{Markup Percentage} = \frac{\text{Desired Profit} + \text{Total Fixed Costs and Expenses}}{\text{Total Variable Cost}}$$

$$\text{Markup Percentage} = \frac{\$160,000 + \$50,000 + \$20,000}{\$1,600,000} = \frac{\$230,000}{\$1,600,000}$$

Markup Percentage = 14.4%(rounded)

Step 6. Markup per unit: $2.30

Markup per Unit = Markup Percentage × Variable Cost per Unit

Markup per Unit = 14.4% × $16.00 = $2.30 per unit

Variable COST CONCEPT

DESIRED SELLING PRICE

MARKUP:
Total Fixed Costs
+
Desired Profit

VARIABLE COST:
Variable Manufacturing Cost
+
Variable Administrative and Selling Expenses

Step 7. Normal selling price: $18.30

Total variable cost per unit	$16.00
Markup per unit	2.30
Normal selling price per unit	$18.30

Choosing a Cost-Plus Approach Cost Concept

All three cost-plus concepts produced the same selling price ($18.30) for Digital Solutions Inc. The three cost-plus concepts are summarized in Exhibit 11.

EXHIBIT 11   Cost-Plus Approach to Setting Normal Selling Prices

Normal Selling Price = Cost Amount per Unit + Markup

$$\text{Cost Amount per Unit} = \frac{\text{Cost Amount}}{\text{Estimated Units Produced and Sold}}$$

Markup = Cost Amount per Unit × Markup Percentage

Cost-Plus Concept	Cost Amount	Markup Percentages
Total cost	Manufacturing (product) costs: 　Direct materials 　Direct labor 　Factory overhead Selling and administrative expenses	$\dfrac{\text{Desired Profit}}{\text{Total Cost}}$
Product cost	Manufacturing (product) costs: 　Direct materials 　Direct labor 　Factory overhead	$\dfrac{\text{Desired Profit} + \text{Total Selling and Administrative Expenses}}{\text{Total Product Cost}}$
Variable cost	Variable manufacturing (product) costs: 　Direct materials 　Direct labor 　Variable factory overhead Variable selling and administrative expenses	$\dfrac{\text{Desired Profit} + \text{Total Fixed Costs and Expenses}}{\text{Total Variable Cost}}$

Estimated, rather than actual, costs and expenses may be used with any of the three cost-plus concepts. Management should be careful, however, when using estimated or standard costs in applying the cost-plus approach. Specifically, estimates should be based on normal (attainable) operating levels and not theoretical (ideal) levels of performance. In product pricing, the use of estimates based on ideal- or maximum-capacity operating levels could lead to setting product prices too low. In such cases, the costs of such factors as normal spoilage or normal periods of idle time might not be considered.

The decision-making needs of management are also an important factor in selecting a cost concept for product pricing. For example, managers who often make special pricing decisions are more likely to use the variable cost concept. In contrast, a government defense contractor would be more likely to use the total cost concept.

Activity-Based Costing

As illustrated, costs are important in setting product prices and decision making. Inaccurate costs may lead to incorrect decisions and prices. To more accurately measure the costs and expenses, some companies use

activity-based costing. **Activity-based costing (ABC)** identifies and traces costs and expenses to activities and then to specific products.

Activity-based costing is particularly useful when manufacturing operations involve large amounts of factory overhead. In such cases, traditional overhead allocation bases such as units produced, direct labor hours, direct labor costs, or machine hours may yield inaccurate cost allocations. This, in turn, may result in distorted product costs and product prices.[2]

Target Costing

Target costing is a method of setting prices that combines market-based pricing with a cost-reduction emphasis. Under target costing, a future selling price is anticipated, using the demand-based or the competition-based concepts. The target cost is then determined by subtracting a desired profit from the expected selling price, as shown below.

Target Cost = Expected Selling Price − Desired Profit

Target costing tries to reduce costs as shown in Exhibit 12. The bar at the left in Exhibit 12 shows the actual cost and profit that can be earned during the current period. The bar at the right shows that the market price is expected to decline in the future. The target cost is estimated as the difference between the expected market price and the desired profit.

EXHIBIT 12 Target Cost Concept

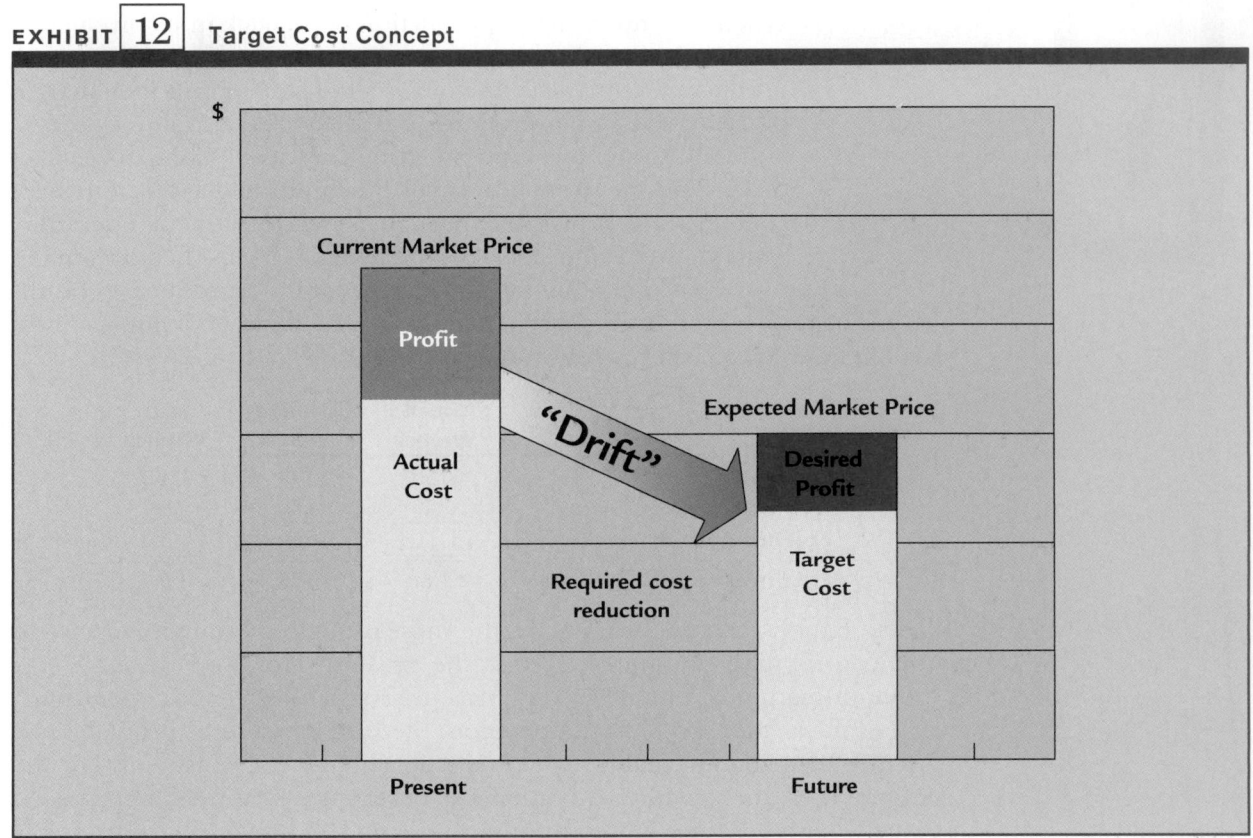

The target cost is normally less than the current cost. Thus, managers must try to reduce costs from the design and manufacture of the product.

[2] Activity-based costing for a service business is discussed and illustrated in Chapter 10.

The planned cost reduction is sometimes referred to as the cost "drift." Costs can be reduced in a variety of ways such as the following:

1. Simplifying the design
2. Reducing the cost of direct materials
3. Reducing the direct labor costs
4. Eliminating waste

Target costing is especially useful in highly competitive markets such as the market for personal computers. Such markets require continual product cost reductions to remain competitive.

Obj 3 Compute the relative profitability of products in bottleneck production processes.

Production Bottlenecks, Pricing, and Profits

A production **bottleneck** (or *constraint*) is a point in the manufacturing process where the demand for the company's product exceeds the ability to produce the product. The **theory of constraints (TOC)** is a manufacturing strategy that focuses on reducing the influence of bottlenecks on production processes.

The sand in the hourglass can pass only as fast as the narrowest point in the hourglass will allow.

Bottleneck

Production Bottlenecks and Profits

When a company has a production bottleneck in its production process, it should attempt to maximize its profits, subject to the production bottleneck. In doing so, the unit contribution margin of each product per production bottleneck constraint is used.

To illustrate, assume that PrideCraft Tool Company makes three types of wrenches: small, medium, and large. All three products are processed through a heat treatment operation, which hardens the steel tools. PrideCraft Tool's heat treatment process is operating at full capacity and is a production bottleneck. The product unit contribution margin and the number of hours of heat treatment used by each type of wrench are as follows:

	Small Wrench	Medium Wrench	Large Wrench
Unit selling price	$130	$140	$160
Unit variable cost	40	40	40
Unit contribution margin	$ 90	$100	$120
Heat treatment hours per unit	1 hr.	4 hrs.	8 hrs.

The large wrench appears to be the most profitable product because its unit contribution margin of $120 is the greatest. However, the unit contribution margin can be misleading in a production bottleneck operation.

In a production bottleneck operation, the best measure of profitability is the unit contribution margin per production bottleneck constraint. For PrideCraft Tool, the production bottleneck constraint is heat treatment process hours. Therefore, the unit contribution margin per bottleneck constraint is expressed as follows:

$$\text{Unit Contribution Margin per Production Bottleneck Hour} = \frac{\text{Unit Contribution Margin}}{\text{Heat Treatment Hours per Unit}}$$

The unit contribution per production bottleneck hour for each of the wrenches produced by PrideCraft Tool is computed below.

Small Wrenches

$$\text{Unit Contribution Margin per Production Bottleneck Hour} = \frac{\$90}{1 \text{ hr.}} = \$90 \text{ per hr.}$$

Medium Wrenches

$$\text{Unit Contribution Margin per Production Bottleneck Hour} = \frac{\$100}{4 \text{ hrs.}} = \$25 \text{ per hr.}$$

Large Wrenches

$$\text{Unit Contribution Margin per Production Bottleneck Hour} = \frac{\$120}{8 \text{ hrs.}} = \$15 \text{ per hr.}$$

The small wrench produces the highest unit contribution margin per production bottleneck hour (heat treatment) of $90 per hour. In. contrast, the large wrench has the largest contribution margin per unit of $120, but has the smallest unit contribution margin per production bottleneck hour of $15 per hour. Thus, the small wrench is the most profitable product per production bottleneck hour.

Production Bottlenecks and Pricing

When a company has a production bottleneck, the unit contribution margin per bottleneck hour is a measure of each product's profitability. This measure can be used to adjust product prices to reflect the product's use of the bottleneck.

To illustrate, the large wrench produced by PrideCraft Tool Company uses eight bottleneck hours, but produces a contribution margin per unit of only $120. As a result, the large wrench is the least profitable of the wrenches per bottleneck hour ($15 per hour).

PrideCraft Tool Company can improve the profitability of producing large wrenches by any combination of the following:

1. Increase the selling price of the large wrenches.

2. Decrease the variable cost per unit of the large wrenches.

3. Decrease the heat treatment hours required for the large wrenches.

Assume that the variable cost per unit and the heat treatment hours for the large wrench cannot be decreased. In this case, PrideCraft Tool might be able to increase the selling price of the large wrenches.

The price of the large wrench that would make it as profitable as the small wrench is determined as follows:[3]

$$\text{Unit Contribution Margin per Bottleneck Hour for Small Wrench} = \frac{\text{Revised Price of Large Wrench} - \text{Unit Variable Cost for Large Wrench}}{\text{Bottleneck Hours per Unit for Large Wrench}}$$

---

[3] Assuming that the selling price of the large wrench cannot be increased, the same approach (equation) could be used to determine the decrease in variable cost per unit or decrease in bottleneck hours that is required to make the large wrench as profitable as the small wrench.

$$\$90 = \frac{\text{Revised Price of Large Wrench} - \$40}{8}$$

$$\$720 = \text{Revised Price of Large Wrench} - \$40$$

$$\$760 = \text{Revised Price of Large Wrench}$$

If the large wrench's price is increased to $760, it would provide the same unit contribution margin per bottleneck hour as the small wrench, as shown below.

$$\frac{\text{Unit Contribution Margin per}}{\text{Bottleneck Hour}} = \frac{\text{Unit Contribution Margin}}{\text{Heat Treatment Hours per Unit}}$$

$$\frac{\text{Unit Contribution Margin per}}{\text{Bottleneck Hour}} = \frac{\$760 - \$40}{8 \text{ hrs.}} = \$90 \text{ per hr.}$$

At a price of $760, Pride Craft Tool Company would be indifferent between producing and selling the small wrench or the large wrench. This assumes that there is unlimited demand for the products. If the market were unwilling to purchase the large wrench at a price of $760, then the company should produce and sell the small wrenches.

How Businesses Make Money

What Is a Product?

A product is often thought of in terms beyond just its physical attributes. For example, why a customer buys a product usually impacts how a business markets the product. Other considerations, such as warranty needs, servicing needs, and perceived quality, also affect business strategies.

Consider the four different types of products listed below. For these products, the frequency of purchase, the profit per unit, and the number of retailers differ. As a result, the sales and marketing approach for each product differs.

Product	Type of Product	Frequency of Purchase	Profit per Unit	Number of Retailers	Sales/Marketing Approach
Snickers®	Convenience	Often	Low	Many	Mass advertising
Sony® TV	Shopping	Occasional	Moderate	Many	Mass advertising; personal selling
Diamond ring	Specialty	Seldom	High	Few	Personal selling
Prearranged funeral	Unsought	Rare	High	Few	Aggressive selling

Key Points

1. Prepare differential analysis reports for a variety of managerial decisions.

   Differential analysis reports for leasing or selling, discontinuing a segment or product, making or buying, replacing equipment, processing or selling, and accepting business at a special price are illustrated in the text. Each analysis focuses on the differential revenues and/or costs of the alternative courses of action.

2. Determine the selling price of a product, using the total cost, product cost, and variable cost concepts.

   The three cost concepts commonly used in applying the cost-plus approach to product pricing are summarized in Exhibit 11.

   Activity-based costing can be used to provide more accurate cost information in applying cost-plus concepts when indirect costs are

insignificant. Target costing combines market-based methods with a cost-reduction emphasis.

3. Compute the relative profitability of products in bottleneck production processes.

The profitability of a product in a bottleneck production environment may not be accurately shown in the contribution margin product report. Instead, the best measure of profitability is determined by dividing the contribution margin per unit by the bottleneck hours per unit. The resulting measure indicates the product's profitability per hour of bottleneck use. This information can be used to support product pricing decisions.

Key Terms

Activity-based costing (ABC) An accounting framework based on determining the cost of activities and allocating these costs to products using activity rates.

Bottleneck A condition that occurs when product demand exceeds product capacity.

Differential analysis The area of accounting concerned with the effect of alternative courses of action on revenues and costs.

Differential cost The amount of increase or decrease in cost expected from a particular course of action compared with an alternative.

Differential income (or loss) The difference between differential revenue and differential cost.

Differential revenue The amount of increase or decrease in revenue expected from a particular course of action as compared with an alternative.

Markup An amount that is added to a "cost" amount to determine product price.

Opportunity cost The amount of income forgone from an alternative to a proposed use of cash or its equivalent.

Product cost concept A concept used in applying the cost-plus approach to product pricing in which only the costs of manufacturing the product, termed the *product costs,* are included in the cost amount to which the markup is added.

Sunk cost A cost that is not affected by subsequent decisions.

Target costing A concept used to design and manufacture a product at a cost that will deliver a target profit for a given market-determined price.

Theory of constraints (TOC) A manufacturing strategy that attempts to remove the influence of bottlenecks (constraints) on a process.

Total cost concept A concept used in applying the cost-plus approach to product pricing in which all the costs of manufacturing the product plus the selling and administrative expenses are included in the cost amount to which the markup is added.

Variable cost concept Often referred to as *variable costing,* a method of reporting variable and fixed costs that includes only the variable manufacturing costs in the cost of the product.

Illustrative Problem

Inez Company recently began production of a new product, M, which required the investment of $1,600,000 in assets. The costs of producing and selling 80,000 units of Product M are estimated as follows:

Variable costs:	
Direct materials	$ 10.00 per unit
Direct labor	6.00
Factory overhead	4.00
Selling and administrative expenses	5.00
Total	$ 25.00 per unit
Fixed costs:	
Factory overhead	$800,000
Selling and administrative expenses	400,000

Inez Company is currently considering establishing a selling price for Product M. The president of Inez Company has decided to use the cost-plus approach to product pricing and has indicated that Product M must earn a 10% rate of return on invested assets.

Instructions

1. Determine the amount of desired profit from the production and sale of Product M.

2. Assuming that the total cost concept is used, determine (a) the cost amount per unit, (b) the markup percentage, and (c) the selling price of Product M.

3. Assuming that the product cost concept is used, determine (a) the cost amount per unit, (b) the markup percentage, and (c) the selling price of Product M.

4. Assuming that the variable cost concept is used, determine (a) the cost amount per unit, (b) the markup percentage, and (c) the selling price of Product M.

5. Assume that for the current year, the selling price of Product M was $42 per unit. To date, 60,000 units have been produced and sold, and analysis of the domestic market indicates that 15,000 additional units are expected to be sold during the remainder of the year. Recently, Inez Company received an offer from Wong Inc. for 4,000 units of Product M at $28 each. Wong Inc. will market the units in Korea under its own brand name, and no additional selling and administrative expenses associated with the sale will be incurred by Inez Company. The additional business is not expected to affect the domestic sales of Product M, and the additional units could be produced during the current year, using existing capacity. (a) Prepare a differential analysis report of the proposed sale to Wong Inc. (b) Based on the differential analysis report in (a), should the proposal be accepted?

Solution

1. $160,000 ($1,600,000 × 10%)

2. a. Total costs:

Variable ($25 × 80,000 units)	$2,000,000
Fixed ($800,000 + $400,000)	1,200,000
Total	$3,200,000

Cost amount per unit: $3,200,000 ÷ 80,000 units = $40.00

b. $$\text{Markup Percentage} = \frac{\text{Desired Profit}}{\text{Total Costs}}$$

$$\text{Markup Percentage} = \frac{\$160,000}{\$3,200,000} = 5\%$$

c.
Cost amount per unit	$40.00
Markup ($40 × 5%)	2.00
Selling price	$42.00

3. a. Total manufacturing costs:

Variable ($20 × 80,000 units)	$1,600,000
Fixed factory overhead	800,000
Total	$2,400,000

Cost amount per unit: $2,400,000 ÷ 80,000 units = $30.00

b. Markup Percentage $= \dfrac{\text{Desired Profit} + \text{Total Selling and Administrative Expenses}}{\text{Total Manufacturing Costs}}$

Markup Percentage $= \dfrac{\$160{,}000 + \$400{,}000 + (\$5 \times 80{,}000 \text{ units})}{\$2{,}400{,}000}$

Markup Percentage $= \dfrac{\$160{,}000 + \$400{,}000 + \$400{,}000}{\$2{,}400{,}000}$

Markup Percentage $= \dfrac{\$960{,}000}{\$2{,}400{,}000} = 40\%$

c.
Cost amount per unit	$30.00
Markup ($30 × 40%)	12.00
Selling price	$42.00

4. a. Variable cost amount per unit: $25

Total variable costs: $25 × 80,000 units = $2,000,000

b. Markup Percentage $= \dfrac{\text{Desired Profit} + \text{Total Fixed Costs}}{\text{Total Variable Costs}}$

Markup Percentage $= \dfrac{\$160{,}000 + \$800{,}000 + \$400{,}000}{\$2{,}000{,}000}$

Markup Percentage $= \dfrac{\$1{,}360{,}000}{\$2{,}000{,}000} = 68\%$

c.
Cost amount per unit	$25.00
Markup ($25 × 68%)	17.00
Selling price	$42.00

5. a. **Proposal to Sell to Wong Inc.**

Differential revenue from accepting offer:	
Revenue from sale of 4,000 additional units at $28	$112,000
Differential cost from accepting offer:	
Variable production costs of 4,000 additional units at $20	80,000
Differential income from accepting offer	$ 32,000

b. The proposal should be accepted.

Self-Examination Questions (Answers appear at the end of chapter)

1. Marlo Company is considering discontinuing a product. The costs of the product consist of $20,000 fixed costs and $15,000 variable costs. The variable operating expenses related to the product total $4,000. What is the differential cost?

   A. $19,000
   B. $15,000
   C. $35,000
   D. $39,000

2. Victor Company is considering disposing of equipment that was originally purchased for $200,000 and has $150,000 of accumulated depreciation to date. The same equipment would cost $310,000 to replace. What is the sunk cost?

   A. $50,000
   B. $150,000
   C. $200,000
   D. $310,000

3. Henry Company is considering spending $100,000 for a new grinding machine. This amount could be invested to yield a 12% return. What is the opportunity cost?

   A. $112,000

   B. $88,000

   C. $12,000

   D. $100,000

4. For which cost concept used in applying the cost-plus approach to product pricing are fixed manufacturing costs, fixed selling and administrative expenses, and desired profit allowed for in determining the markup?

   A. Total cost

   B. Product cost

   C. Variable cost

   D. Standard cost

5. Mendosa Company produces three products. All the products use a furnace operation, which is a production bottleneck. The following information is available:

	Product 1	Product 2	Product 3
Unit volume—March	1,000	1,500	1,000
Per-unit information:			
Sales price	$35	$33	$29
Variable cost	15	15	15
Unit contribution margin	$20	$18	$14
Furnace hours	4	3	2

   From a profitability perspective, which product should be emphasized in April's advertising campaign?

   A. Product 1

   B. Product 2

   C. Product 3

   D. All three

Class Discussion Questions

1. Explain the meaning of (a) differential revenue, (b) differential cost, and (c) differential income.

2. It was reported that **Exabyte Corporation,** a fast growing Colorado marketer of backup tape drives, has decided to purchase key components of its product from others. For example, **Sony Corporation of America** provides Exabyte with mechanical decks, and **Solectron Corporation** provides circuit boards. A former chief executive officer of Exabyte stated, "If we'd tried to build our own plants, we could never have grown that fast or maybe survived." The decision to purchase key product components is an example of what type of decision illustrated in this chapter?

3. A company could sell a building for $250,000 or lease it for $2,500 per month. What would need to be considered in determining if the lease option would be preferred?

4. A chemical company has a commodity-grade and premium-grade product. Why might the company elect to process the commodity-grade product further to the premium-grade product?

5. A company accepts incremental business at a special price that exceeds the variable cost. What other issues must the company consider in deciding whether to accept the business?

6. A company fabricates a component at a cost of $6.00. A supplier offers to supply the same component for $5.50. Under what circumstances is it reasonable to purchase from the supplier?

7. Many fast-food restaurant chains, such as **McDonald's,** will occasionally discontinue restaurants in their system. What are some financial considerations in deciding to eliminate a store?

8. In the long run, the normal selling price must be set high enough to cover what factors?

9. Why might the use of ideal standards in applying the cost-plus approach to product pricing lead to setting product prices that are too low?

10. Although the cost-plus approach to product pricing may be used by management as a general guideline, what are some examples of other factors that managers should also consider in setting product prices?

11. What method of determining product cost may be appropriate in settings where the manufacturing process is complex?

12. How does the target cost concept differ from cost-plus approaches?

13. Under what circumstances is it appropriate to use the target cost concept?

14. What is a production bottleneck?

15. What is the appropriate measure of a product's value when a firm is operating under production bottlenecks?

Exercises

E12-1

Lease or sell decision

Obj 1

SPREADSHEET

✓ a. Differential revenue from lease, $20,000

Inman Construction Company is considering selling excess machinery with a book value of $280,000 (original cost of $400,000 less accumulated depreciation of $120,000) for $292,000, less a 5% brokerage commission. Alternatively, the machinery can be leased for a total of $312,000 for five years, after which it is expected to have no residual value. During the period of the lease, Inman Construction Company's costs of repairs, insurance, and property tax expenses are expected to be $36,000.

a. Prepare a differential analysis report, dated January 3, 2010, for the lease or sell decision.

b. On the basis of the data presented, would it be advisable to lease or sell the machinery? Explain.

E12-2

Differential analysis report for a discontinued product

Obj 1

✓ a. Differential variable costs, $227,280

A condensed income statement by product line for British Beverage Inc. indicated the following for Royal Cola for the past year:

Sales	$254,000
Cost of goods sold	122,000
Gross profit	$132,000
Operating expenses	156,000
Loss from operations	$ (24,000)

It is estimated that 16% of the cost of goods sold represents fixed factory overhead costs and that 20% of the operating expenses are fixed. Since Royal Cola is only one of many products, the fixed costs will not be materially affected if the product is discontinued.

a. Prepare a differential analysis report, dated March 3, 2010, for the proposed discontinuance of Royal Cola.

b. Should Royal Cola be retained? Explain.

E12-3

Differential analysis report for a discontinued product

Obj 1

SPREADSHEET

✓ a. Differential income: bowls, $17,980

The condensed product-line income statement for Suffolk China Ware Company for the month of December is as follows:

Suffolk China Ware Company
Product-Line Income Statement
For the Month Ended December 31, 2010

	Bowls	Plates	Cups
Sales	$54,000	$68,500	$24,500
Cost of goods sold	22,400	31,700	11,900
Gross profit	$31,600	$36,800	$12,600
Selling and administrative expenses	28,300	25,300	20,400
Income from operations	$ 3,300	$11,500	$ (7,800)

Fixed costs are 15% of the cost of goods sold and 40% of the selling and administrative expenses. Suffolk China Ware assumes that fixed costs would not be materially affected if the Cups line were discontinued.

a. Prepare a differential analysis report for all three products for December, 2010.
b. Should the Cups line be retained? Explain.

E12-4

Segment analysis, Charles Schwab Corporation

Obj 1

The **Charles Schwab Corporation** is one of the more innovative brokerage and financial service companies in the United States. The company provided information about its major business segments as follows (in millions) for 2007:

	Individual Investor	Institutional Investor	Corporate and Retirement Services
Revenues	$3,352	$1,121	$506
Income from operations	1,237	482	139
Depreciation	98	25	15

a. How do you believe Schwab defines the difference between the "Individual Investor" and "Institutional Investor" segments?
b. Provide a specific example of a variable and fixed cost in the "Individual Investor" segment.
c. Estimate the contribution margin for each segment.
d. If Schwab decided to sell its "Institutional Investor" accounts to another company, estimate how much operating income would decline.

E12-5

Decision to discontinue a product

Obj 1

On the basis of the following data, the general manager of Sole Mates Inc. decided to discontinue Children's Shoes because it reduced income from operations by $28,000. What is the flaw in this decision?

Sole Mates Inc.
Product-Line Income Statement
For the Year Ended August 31,2010

	Children's Shoes	Men's Shoes	Women's Shoes	Total
Sales	$170,000	$300,000	$500,000	$970,000
Costs of goods sold:				
Variable costs	$100,000	$150,000	$220,000	$470,000
Fixed costs	50,000	60,000	120,000	230,000
Total cost of goods sold	$150,000	$210,000	$340,000	$700,000
Gross profit	$ 20,000	$ 90,000	$160,000	$270,000
Selling and administrative expenses:				
Variable selling and admin. expenses	$ 30,000	$ 45,000	$ 95,000	$170,000
Fixed selling and admin. expenses	18,000	20,000	25,000	63,000
Total selling and admin. expenses	$ 48,000	$ 65,000	$120,000	$233,000
Income (loss) from operations	$(28,000)	$ 25,000	$ 40,000	$ 37,000

E12-6

Make-or-buy decision

Obj 1

SPREADSHEET

✓ a. Cost savings from making, $6.20 per case

Companion Computer Company has been purchasing carrying cases for its portable computers at a delivered cost of $68 per unit. The company, which is currently operating below full capacity, charges factory overhead to

production at the rate of 40% of direct labor cost. The fully absorbed unit costs to produce comparable carrying cases are expected to be as follows:

Direct materials	$25.00
Direct labor	32.00
Factory overhead (40% of direct labor)	12.80
Total cost per unit	$69.80

If Companion Computer Company manufactures the carrying cases, fixed factory overhead costs will not increase and variable factory overhead costs associated with the cases are expected to be 15% of the direct labor costs.

a. Prepare a differential analysis report, dated October 11, 2010, for the make-or-buy decision.

b. On the basis of the data presented, would it be advisable to make the carrying cases or to continue buying them? Explain.

E12-7

Make-or-buy decision

Obj 1

SPREADSHEET

The Theater Arts Guild of Chicago (TAG-C) employs five people in its Publication Department. These people lay out pages for pamphlets, brochures, and other publications for the TAG-C productions. The pages are delivered to an outside company for printing. The company is considering an outside publication service for the layout work. The outside service is quoting a price of $15 per layout page. The budget for the Publication Department for 2010 is as follows:

Salaries	$220,000
Benefits	35,000
Supplies	30,000
Office expenses	25,000
Office depreciation	30,000
Computer depreciation	22,000
Total	$362,000

The department expects to lay out 20,000 pages for 2010. The computers used by the department have an estimated residual value of $7,000. The Publication Department office space would be used for future administrative needs, if the department's function were purchased from the outside.

a. Prepare a differential analysis report, dated December 15, 2009, for the make-or-buy decision, considering the 2010 differential revenues and costs.

b. On the basis of your analysis in part (a), should the page layout work be purchased from an outside company?

c. What additional considerations might factor into the decision making?

E12-8

Machine replacement decision

Obj 1

A company is considering replacing an old piece of machinery, which cost $600,000 and has $350,000 of accumulated depreciation to date, with a new machine that costs $450,000. The old equipment could be sold for $72,000. The annual variable production costs associated with the old machine are estimated to be $165,000 for eight years. The annual variable production costs for the new machine are estimated to be $112,750 for eight years.

a. Determine the total and annualized differential income or loss anticipated from replacing the old machine.

b. What is the sunk cost in this situation?

E12-9

Differential analysis report for
machine replacement

Obj 1

SPREADSHEET

✓ a. Annual differential
increase in costs,
$7,200

Singapore Digital Components Company assembles circuit boards by using a manually operated machine to insert electronic components. The original cost of the machine is $60,000, the accumulated depreciation is $24,000, its remaining useful life is five years, and its residual value is negligible. On February 20, 2010, a proposal was made to replace the present manufacturing procedure with a fully automatic machine that will cost $111,000. The automatic machine has an estimated useful life of five years and no significant residual value. For use in evaluating the proposal, the accountant accumulated the following annual data on present and proposed operations:

	Present Operations	Proposed Operations
Sales	$290,000	$290,000
Direct materials	$ 86,000	$ 86,000
Direct labor	40,000	—
Power and maintenance	8,000	30,000
Taxes, insurance, etc.	4,000	7,000
Selling and administrative expenses	65,000	65,000
Total expenses	$203,000	$188,000

a. Prepare a differential analysis report for the proposal to replace the machine. Include in the analysis both the net differential change in costs anticipated over the five years and the net annual differential change in costs anticipated.
b. Based only on the data presented, should the proposal be accepted?
c. What are some of the other factors that should be considered before a final decision is made?

E12-10

Sell or process further

Obj 1

✓ a. $205

Bunyon Lumber Company incurs a cost of $490 per hundred board feet in processing certain "rough-cut" lumber, which it sells for $635 per hundred board feet. An alternative is to produce a "finished cut" at a total processing cost of $565 per hundred board feet, which can be sold for $840 per hundred board feet. What is the amount of (a) the differential revenue, (b) differential cost, and (c) differential income for processing rough-cut lumber into finished cut?

E12-11

Sell or process further

Obj 1

SPREADSHEET

Seattle Roast Coffee Company produces Columbian coffee in batches of 8,000 pounds. The standard quantity of materials required in the process is 8,000 pounds, which cost $5.00 per pound. Columbian coffee can be sold without further processing for $10.80 per pound. Columbian coffee can also be processed further to yield Decaf Columbian, which can be sold for $12.50 per pound. The processing into Decaf Columbian requires additional processing costs of $10,500 per batch. The additional processing will also cause a 5% loss of product due to evaporation.

a. Prepare a differential analysis report for the decision to sell or process further.
b. Should Seattle Roast sell Columbian coffee or process further and sell Decaf Columbian?
c. Determine the price of Decaf Columbian that would cause neither an advantage nor disadvantage for processing further and selling Decaf Columbian.

E12-12

Decision on accepting additional business

Obj 1

✓ a. Differential income, $126,000

Down Home Jeans Co. has an annual plant capacity of 65,000 units, and current production is 45,000 units. Monthly fixed costs are $40,000, and variable costs are $22 per unit. The present selling price is $35 per unit. On March 18, 2010, the company received an offer from Fields Company for 18,000 units of the product at $29 each. Fields Company will market the units in a foreign country under its own brand name. The additional business is not expected to affect the domestic selling price or quantity of sales of Down Home Jeans Co.

a. Prepare a differential analysis report for the proposed sale to Fields Company.
b. Briefly explain the reason why accepting this additional business will increase operating income.
c. What is the minimum price per unit that would produce a contribution margin?

E12-13

Accepting business at a special price

Obj 1

Power Serve Company expects to operate at 85% of productive capacity during April. The total manufacturing costs for April for the production of 30,000 batteries are budgeted as follows:

Direct materials	$285,000
Direct labor	104,000
Variable factory overhead	31,000
Fixed factory overhead	58,000
Total manufacturing costs	$478,000

The company has an opportunity to submit a bid for 2,000 batteries to be delivered by April 30 to a government agency. If the contract is obtained, it is anticipated that the additional activity will not interfere with normal production during April or increase the selling or administrative expenses. What is the unit cost below which Power Serve Company should not go in bidding on the government contract?

E12-14

Decision on accepting additional business

Obj 1

SPREADSHEET

✓ a. Differential revenue, $1,875,000

Roadworthy Tire and Rubber Company has capacity to produce 170,000 tires. Roadworthy presently produces and sells 130,000 tires for the North American market at a price of $90 per tire. Roadworthy is evaluating a special order from a European automobile company, Euro Motors. Euro is offering to buy 25,000 tires for $75 per tire. Roadworthy's accounting system indicates that the total cost per tire is as follows:

Direct materials	$32
Direct labor	8
Factory overhead (60% variable)	25
Selling and administrative expenses (35% variable)	20
Total	$85

Roadworthy pays a selling commission equal to 5% of the selling price on North American orders, which is included in the variable portion of the selling and administrative expenses. However, this special order would not have a sales commission. If the order was accepted, the tires would be shipped overseas for an additional shipping cost of $6.00 per tire. In addition, Euro has made the order conditional on receiving European safety certification. Roadworthy estimates that this certification would cost $125,000.

a. Prepare a differential analysis report dated May 4, 2010, for the proposed sale to Euro Motors.

b. What is the minimum price per unit that would be financially acceptable to Roadworthy?

E12-15

Total cost concept of product costing

Obj 2

✓ d. $318

MyPhone Inc. uses the total cost concept of applying the cost-plus approach to product pricing. The costs of producing and selling 5,000 units of cellular phones are as follows:

Variable costs:		Fixed costs:	
Direct materials	$125 per unit	Factory overhead	$215,000
Direct labor	45	Selling and adm. exp.	75,000
Factory overhead	40		
Selling and adm. exp.	30		
Total	$240 per unit		

MyPhone desires a profit equal to a 25% rate of return on invested assets of $400,000.

a. Determine the amount of desired profit from the production and sale of cellular phones.

b. Determine the total costs and the cost amount per unit for the production and sale of 5,000 units of cellular phones.

c. Determine the total cost markup percentage (rounded to two decimal places) for cellular phones.

d. Determine the selling price of cellular phones. Round to the nearest dollar.

E12-16

Product cost concept of product pricing

Obj 2

✓ b. 25.69%

Based on the data presented in Exercise 12-15, assume that MyPhone Inc. uses the product cost concept of applying the cost-plus approach to product pricing.

a. Determine the total manufacturing costs and the cost amount per unit for the production and sale of 5,000 units of cellular phones.

b. Determine the product cost markup percentage (rounded to two decimal places) for cellular phones.

c. Determine the selling price of cellular phones. Round to the nearest dollar.

E12-17

Variable cost concept of product pricing

Obj 2

✓ b. 32.5%

Based on the data presented in Exercise 12-15, assume that MyPhone Inc. uses the variable cost concept of applying the cost-plus approach to product pricing.

a. Determine the variable costs and the cost amount per unit for the production and sale of 5,000 units of cellular phones.

b. Determine the variable cost markup percentage (rounded to two decimal places) for cellular phones.

c. Determine the selling price of cellular phones. Round to the nearest dollar.

E12-18

Target costing

Obj 2

Toyota Motor Corporation uses target costing. Assume that Toyota marketing personnel estimate that the competitive selling price for the Camry in the upcoming model year will need to be $22,000. Assume further that the Camry's total unit cost for the upcoming model year is estimated to be $18,100 and that Toyota requires a 20% profit margin on selling price (which is equivalent to a 25% markup on total cost).

a. What price will Toyota establish for the Camry for the upcoming model year?

b. What impact will target costing have on Toyota, given the assumed information?

E12-19

Target costing

Obj 2

✓ b. $16

Laser Cast, Inc., manufactures color laser printers. Model A200 presently sells for $400 and has a total product cost of $320, as follows:

Direct materials	$230
Direct labor	60
Factory overhead	30
Total	$320

It is estimated that the competitive selling price for color laser printers of this type will drop to $380 next year. Laser Cast has established a target cost to maintain its historical markup percentage on product cost. Engineers have provided the following cost reduction ideas:

1. Purchase a plastic printer cover with snap-on assembly. This will reduce the amount of direct labor by nine minutes per unit.
2. Add an inspection step that will add six minutes per unit of direct labor but reduce the materials cost by $8 per unit.
3. Decrease the cycle time of the injection molding machine from four minutes to three minutes per part. Thirty percent of the direct labor and 42% of the factory overhead is related to running injection molding machines.

The direct labor rate is $25 per hour.

a. Determine the target cost for Model A200 assuming that the historical markup on product cost is maintained.
b. Determine the required cost reduction.
c. Evaluate the three engineering improvements to determine if the required cost reduction (drift) can be achieved.

E12-20

Product decisions under bottlenecked operations

Obj 3

Armstrong Alloys Inc. has three grades of metal product, Type 5, Type 10, and Type 20 Financial data for the three grades are as follows:

	Type 5	Type 10	Type 20
Revenues	$36,000	$40,000	$22,000
Variable cost	$22,500	$20,000	$15,000
Fixed cost	6,000	6,000	6,000
Total cost	$28,500	$26,000	$21,000
Income from operations	$ 7,500	$14,000	$ 1,000
Number of units	÷ 5,000	÷ 5,000	÷ 5,000
Income from operations per unit	$ 1.50	$ 2.80	$ 0.20

Armstrong's operations require all three grades to be melted in a furnace before being formed. The furnace runs 24 hours a day, 7 days a week, and is a production bottleneck. The furnace hours required per unit of each product are as follows:

Type 5:	5 hours
Type 10:	10 hours
Type 20:	5 hours

The Marketing Department is considering a new marketing and sales campaign. Which product should be emphasized in the marketing and sales campaign in order to maximize profitability?

E12-21

Product decisions under bottlenecked operations

Obj 3

✓ a. Total income from operations, $88,000

Ohio Glass Company manufactures three types of safety plate glass: large, medium, and small. All three products have high demand. Thus, Ohio Glass is able to sell all the safety glass that it can make. The production process includes an autoclave operation, which is a pressurized heat treatment. The autoclave is a production bottleneck. Total fixed costs are $74,000. In addition, the following information is available about the three products:

	Large	Medium	Small
Unit selling price	$120	$100	$90
Unit variable cost	96	85	75
Unit contribution margin	$ 24	$ 15	$15
Autoclave hours per unit	4	2	1
Total process hours per unit	8	6	3
Budgeted units of production	3,000	3,000	3,000

a. Determine the contribution margin by glass type and the total company income from operations for the budgeted units of production.
b. Prepare an analysis showing which product is the most profitable per bottleneck hour.

E12-22

Product pricing under bottlenecked operations

Obj 3

✓ Medium, $115

Based on the data presented in Exercise 12-21, assume that Ohio Glass wanted to price all products so that they produced the same profit potential as the highest profit product. Thus, determine the prices for each of the products so that they would produce a profit equal to the highest profit product.

Problems

P12-1

Differential analysis report involving opportunity costs

Obj 1

SPREADSHEET

On March 1, Midway Distribution Company is considering leasing a building and buying the necessary equipment to operate a public warehouse. Alternatively, the company could use the funds to invest in $750,000 of 7% U.S. Treasury bonds that mature in 14 years. The bonds could be purchased at face value. The following data have been assembled:

Cost of equipment	$750,000
Life of equipment	14 years
Estimated residual value of equipment	$76,000
Yearly costs to operate the warehouse, excluding depreciation of equipment	$195,000
Yearly expected revenues—years 1–7	$330,000
Yearly expected revenues—years 8–14	$280,000

Instructions

1. Prepare a report as of March 1, 2010, presenting a differential analysis of the proposed operation of the warehouse for the 14 years as compared with present conditions.
2. Based on the results disclosed by the differential analysis, should the proposal be accepted?
3. If the proposal is accepted, what is the total estimated income from operations of the warehouse for the 14 years?

P12-2

Differential analysis report for machine replacement proposal

Obj 1

SPREADSHEET

Flint Tooling Company is considering replacing a machine that has been used in its factory for two years. Relevant data associated with the operations of the old machine and the new machine, neither of which has any estimated residual value, are as follows:

Old Machine

Cost of machine, eight-year life	$48,000
Annual depreciation (straight-line)	6,000
Annual manufacturing costs, excluding depreciation	14,500
Annual nonmanufacturing operating expenses	2,900
Annual revenue	29,600
Current estimated selling price of the machine	18,000

New Machine

Cost of machine, six-year life	$58,500
Annual depreciation (straight-line)	9,750
Estimated annual manufacturing costs, exclusive of depreciation	5,200

Annual nonmanufacturing operating expenses and revenue are not expected to be affected by purchase of the new machine.

Instructions

1. Prepare a differential analysis report as of May 22, 2010, comparing operations utilizing the new machine with operations using the present equipment. The analysis should indicate the differential income that would result over the six-year period if the new machine is acquired.
2. List other factors that should be considered before a final decision is reached.

P12-3

Differential analysis report for sales promotion proposal

Obj 1

SPREADSHEET

✓ Differential income, tennis shoe, $225,000

Glide Shoe Company is planning a one-month campaign for May to promote sales of one of its two shoe products. A total of $125,000 has been budgeted for advertising, contests, redeemable coupons, and other promotional activities. The following data have been assembled for their possible usefulness in deciding which of the products to select for the campaign.

	Tennis Shoe	Walking Shoe
Unit selling price	$110	$100
Unit production costs:		
Direct materials	$ 20	$ 22
Direct labor	8	9
Variable factory overhead	5	6
Fixed factory overhead	12	10
Total unit production costs	$ 45	$ 47
Unit variable selling expenses	7	5
Unit fixed selling expenses	16	12
Total unit costs	$ 68	$ 64
Operating income per unit	$ 42	$ 36

No increase in facilities would be necessary to produce and sell the increased output. It is anticipated that 5,000 additional units of tennis shoes or 6,000 additional units of walking shoes could be sold without changing the unit selling price of either product.

Instructions

1. Prepare a differential analysis report as of May 13, 2010, presenting the additional revenue and additional costs anticipated from the promotion of tennis shoes and walking shoes.
2. The sales manager had tentatively decided to promote walking shoes, estimating that operating income would be increased by $91,000 ($36 operating income per unit for 6,000 units, less promotion expenses of $125,000). The manager also believed that the selection of tennis shoes would increase operating income by $85,000 ($42 operating income per unit for 5,000 units, less promotion expenses of $125,000). State briefly your reasons for supporting or opposing the tentative decision.

P12-4

Differential analysis report for further processing

Obj 1

✓ 1. Differential revenue, $25,300

The management of Allegheny Valley Aluminum Co. is considering whether to process aluminum ingot further into rolled aluminum. Rolled aluminum can be sold for $1,600 per ton, and ingot can be sold without further processing for $950 per ton. Ingot is produced in batches of 66 tons by smelting 400 tons of bauxite, which costs $450 per ton. Rolled aluminum will require additional processing costs of $425 per ton of ingot, and 1.2 tons of ingot will produce 1 ton of rolled aluminum (due to trim losses).

Instructions

1. Prepare a report as of December 20, 2010, presenting a differential analysis associated with the further processing of aluminum ingot to produce rolled aluminum.
2. Briefly report your recommendations.

P12-5

Product pricing using the cost-plus approach concepts; differential analysis report for accepting additional business

Objs 1, 2

✓ 3. b. Markup percentage, 28%

Night Watch Company recently began production of a new product, the halogen light, which required the investment of $500,000 in assets. The costs of producing and selling 12,000 halogen lights are estimated as follows:

Variable costs per unit:		Fixed costs:	
Direct materials	$22	Factory overhead	$120,000
Direct labor	12	Selling and administrative	
Factory overhead	6	expenses	60,000
Selling and administrative expenses	4		
Total	$44		

Night Watch Company is currently considering establishing a selling price for the halogen light. The president of Night Watch Company has decided to use the cost-plus approach to product pricing and has indicated that the halogen light must earn a 12% rate of return on invested assets.

Instructions

1. Determine the amount of desired profit from the production and sale of the halogen light.
2. Assuming that the total cost concept is used, determine (a) the cost amount per unit, (b) the markup percentage (rounded to two decimal places), and (c) the selling price of the halogen light (rounded to nearest whole dollar).
3. Assuming that the product cost concept is used, determine (a) the cost amount per unit, (b) the markup percentage, and (c) the selling price of the halogen light.
4. Assuming that the variable cost concept is used, determine (a) the cost amount per unit, (b) the markup percentage (rounded to two decimal places), and (c) the selling price of the halogen light (rounded to nearest whole dollar).
5. Comment on any additional considerations that could influence establishing the selling price for the halogen light.
6. Assume that as of September 1, 2010, 7,000 units of halogen light have been produced and sold during the current year. Analysis of the domestic market indicates that 3,000 additional units of the halogen light are expected to be sold during the remainder of the year at the normal product price determined under the total cost concept. On September 5, Night Watch Company received an offer from Forever Glow Inc. for 2,000 units of the halogen light at $45 each. Forever Glow Inc. will market the units in Japan under its own brand name, and no selling and administrative expenses associated with the sale will be incurred by Night Watch Company. The additional business is not expected to affect the domestic sales of the halogen light, and the additional units could be produced using existing capacity.
   a. Prepare a differential analysis report of the proposed sale to Forever Glow Inc.
   b. Based on the differential analysis report in part (a), should the proposal be accepted?

P12-6

Product pricing and profit analysis with bottleneck operations

Objs 1, 3

SPREADSHEET

✓ 1. Ethylene, $34

Delaware Bay Chemical Company produces three products: ethylene, butane, and ester. Each of these products has high demand in the market, and Delaware Bay Chemical is able to sell as much as it can produce of all three. The reaction operation is a bottleneck in the process and is running at 100% of capacity. Delaware Bay wants to improve chemical operation profitability. The variable conversion cost is $7 per process hour. The fixed cost is $550,000. In addition, the cost analyst was able to determine the following information about the three products:

	Ethylene	Butane	Ester
Budgeted units produced	9,000	9,000	9,000
Total process hours per unit	3	3	2
Reactor hours per unit	1.0	0.8	0.5
Unit selling price	$165	$128	$115
Direct materials cost per unit	$110	$75	$85

The reaction operation is part of the total process for each of these three products. Thus, for example, 1.0 of the 3 hours required to process ethylene are associated with the reactor.

Instructions

1. Determine the unit contribution margin for each product.
2. Provide an analysis to determine the relative product profitabilities, assuming that the reactor is a bottleneck.
3. Assume that management wishes to improve profitability by increasing prices on selected products. At what price would ethylene and ester need to be offered in order to produce the same relative profitability as butane?

Activities

A12-1

Product pricing

ETHICS

Lucinda Lopez is a cost accountant for Northern Apparel Inc. Marcus Murry, vice president of marketing, has asked Lucinda to meet with representatives of Northern Apparel's major competitor to discuss product cost data. Marcus indicates that the sharing of these data will enable Northern to determine a fair and equitable price for its products.

Would it be ethical for Lucinda to attend the meeting and share the relevant cost data?

A12-2

Decision on accepting additional business

A manager of Fairways and Greens Sporting Goods Company is considering accepting an order from an overseas customer. This customer has requested an order for 20,000 dozen golf balls at a price of $24 per dozen. The variable cost to manufacture a dozen golf balls is $18 per dozen. The full cost is $26 per dozen. Fairways and Greens has a normal selling price of $34 per dozen. Fairways and Greens' plant has just enough excess capacity on the second shift to make the overseas order.

What are some considerations in accepting or rejecting this order?

A12-3

Accept business at a special price

If you are not familiar with *Priceline.com Inc.*, go to its Web site. Assume that an individual "names a price" of $70 on Priceline.com for a room in Dallas, Texas, on August 24. Assume that August 24 is a Saturday, with low expected room demand in Dallas at a *Marriott International, Inc.*, hotel, so there is excess room capacity. The fully allocated cost per room per day is assumed from hotel records as follows:

Housekeeping labor cost*	$ 34
Hotel depreciation expense	42
Cost of room supplies (soap, paper, etc.)	6
Laundry labor and material cost*	10
Cost of desk staff	5
Utility cost (mostly air conditioning)	4
Total cost per room per day	$101

*Both housekeeping and laundry staff include many part-time workers, so that the workload is variable to demand.

Should Marriott accept the customer bid for a night in Dallas on August 24 at a price of $70?

A12-4

Cost-plus and target costing concepts

The following conversation took place between Cam Hudson, vice president of marketing, and Alan Attawry, controller of Digi-Comp Computer Company:

Cam: I am really excited about our new computer coming out. I think it will be a real market success.

Alan: I'm really glad you think so. I know that our success will be determined by our price. If our price is too high, our competitors will be the ones with the market success.

Cam: Don't worry about it. We'll just mark our product cost up by 25% and it will all work out. I know we'll make money at those markups. By the way, what does the estimated product cost look like?

Alan: Well, there's the rub. The product cost looks as if it's going to come in at around $1,200. With a 25% markup, that will give us a selling price of $1,500.

Cam: I see your concern. That's a little high. Our research indicates that computer prices are dropping and that this type of computer should be selling for around $1,250 when we release it to the market.

Alan: I'm not sure what to do.

Cam: Let me see if I can help. How much of the $1,200 is fixed cost?

Alan: About $200.

Cam: There you go. The fixed cost is sunk. We don't need to consider it in our pricing decision. If we reduce the product cost by $200, the new price with a 25% markup would be right at $1,250. Boy, I was really worried for a minute there. I knew something wasn't right.

a. If you were Alan, how would you respond to Cam's solution to the pricing problem?
b. How might target costing be used to help solve this pricing dilemma?

A12-5

Pricing decisions and markup on variable costs

Many businesses are offering their products and services over the Internet. Some of these companies and their Internet addresses are listed below.

Company Name	Internet Address (URL)	Product
Delta Air Lines	http://www.delta.com	Airline tickets
Amazon.com	http://www.amazon.com	Books
Dell Inc.	http://www.dell.com	Personal computers

a. In groups of three, assign each person in your group to one of the Internet sites listed above. For each site, determine the following:

1. A product (or service) description.

2. A product price.

3. A list of costs that are required to produce and sell the product selected in part (1) as listed in the annual report on SEC Form 10-K.

4. Whether the costs identified in part (3) are fixed costs or variable costs.

b. Which of the three products do you believe has the largest markup on variable cost?

Answers to Self-Examination Questions

1. **A** Differential cost is the amount of increase or decrease in cost that is expected from a particular course of action compared with an alternative. For Marlo Company, the differential cost is $19,000 (answer A). This is the total of the variable product costs ($15,000) and the variable operating expenses ($4,000), which would not be incurred if the product is discontinued.

2. **A** A sunk cost is not affected by later decisions. For Victor Company, the sunk cost is the $50,000 (answer A) book value of the equipment, which is equal to the original cost of $200,000 (answer C) less the accumulated depreciation of $150,000 (answer B).

3. **C** The amount of income that could have been earned from the best available alternative to a proposed use of cash is the opportunity cost. For Henry Company, the opportunity cost is 12% of $100,000, or $12,000 (answer C).

4. **C** Under the variable cost concept of product pricing (answer C), fixed manufacturing costs, fixed administrative and selling expenses, and desired profit are allowed for in determining the markup. Only desired profit is allowed for in the markup under the total cost concept (answer A). Under the product cost concept (answer B), total selling and administrative expenses and desired profit are allowed for in determining the markup. Standard cost (answer D) can be used under any of the cost-plus approaches to product pricing.

5. **C** Product 3 has the highest unit contribution margin per bottleneck hour ($14/2 = $7). Product 1 (answer A) has the largest unit contribution margin, but the lowest unit contribution per bottleneck hour ($20/4 = $5), so it is the least profitable product in the constrained environment. Product 2 (answer B) has the highest total profitability in March (1,500 units × $18), but this does not suggest that it has the highest profit potential. Product 2's unit contribution per bottleneck hour ($18/3 = $6) is between Products 1 and 3. Answer D is not true, since the products all have different profit potential in terms of unit contribution margin per bottleneck hour.

Budgeting and Standard Cost Systems

13

You may have financial goals for your life. To achieve these goals, it is necessary to plan for future expenses. For example, you may consider taking a part-time job to save money for school expenses for the coming school year. How much money would you need to earn and save in order to pay these expenses? One way to find an answer to this question would be to prepare a budget. A budget would show an estimate of your expenses associated with school, such as tuition, fees, and books. In addition, you would have expenses for day-to-day living, such as rent, food, and clothing. You might also have expenses for travel and entertainment. Once the school year begins, you can use the budget as a tool for guiding your spending priorities during the year.

The budget is used in businesses in much the same way as it can be used in personal life. For example, **The North Face** sponsors mountain climbing expeditions throughout the year for professional and amateur climbers. These events require budgeting to plan trip expenses, much like you might use a budget to plan a vacation.

Budgeting is also used by The North Face to plan the manufacturing costs associated with its outdoor clothing and equipment production. For example, budgets would be used to determine the number of coats to be produced, number of people to be employed, and amount of material to be purchased. The budget provides the company with a "game plan" for the year. In this chapter, you will see how budgets can be used for financial planning and control. This chapter concludes by describing and illustrating standard cost accounting systems.

Nature and Objectives of Budgeting

Budgets play an important role for organizations of all sizes and forms. For example, budgets are used in managing the operations of government agencies, churches, hospitals, and other nonprofit organizations. Individuals and families also use budgeting in managing their financial affairs. This chapter describes and illustrates budgeting for a manufacturing company.

Objectives of Budgeting

Budgeting involves (1) establishing specific goals, (2) executing plans to achieve the goals, and (3) periodically comparing actual results with the goals. In doing so, budgeting affects the following managerial functions:

1. Planning
2. Directing
3. Controlling

The relationships of these activities are illustrated in Exhibit 1.

EXHIBIT 1 | Planning, Directing, and Controlling

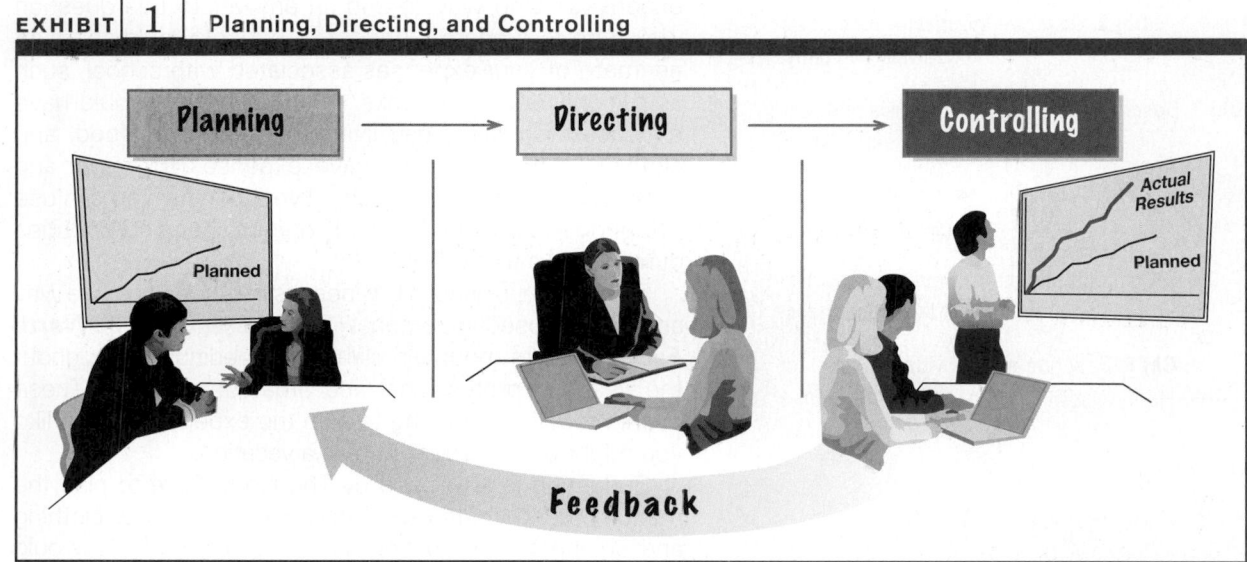

Planning involves setting goals as a guide for making decisions. Budgeting supports the planning process by requiring all departments and other organizational units to establish their goals for the future. These goals help motivate employees. In addition, the budgeting process often identifies areas where operations can be improved or inefficiencies eliminated.

Directing involves decisions and actions to achieve budgeted goals. Budgeting aids in coordinating management's decisions and actions to achieve the company's budgeted goals. A budgetary unit of a company is called a **responsibility center**. Each responsibility center is led by a manager who has the authority and responsibility for achieving the center's budgeted goals.

Controlling involves comparing actual performance against the budgeted goals. Such comparisons provide feedback to managers and employees about their performance. If necessary, responsibility centers can use such feedback to adjust their activities in the future.

A budget is like a road map. It charts a future course for a company in financial terms and thus aids the company in navigating through the year to reach its destination.

Human Behavior and Budgeting

Human behavior problems can arise in the budgeting process in the following situations:

1. Budgeted goals are set too tight, which are very hard or impossible to achieve.

2. Budgeted goals are set too loose, which are very easy to achieve.

3. Budgeted goals conflict with the objectives of the company and employees.

These behavior problems are illustrated in Exhibit 2.

EXHIBIT **2** **Human Behavior Problems in Budgeting**

Budget Goals Too Tight   Budget Goals Too Loose   Conflicting Budget Goals

Setting Budget Goals Too Tightly

Employees and managers may become discouraged if budgeted goals are set too high. That is, if budgeted goals are viewed as unrealistic or unachievable, the budget may have a negative effect on the ability of the company to achieve its goals.

Reasonable, attainable goals are more likely to motivate employees and managers. For this reason, it is important that employees and managers be involved in the budgeting process. Involving employees in the budgeting process provides employees with a sense of control and thus more of a commitment in meeting budgeted goals. Finally, involving employees and managers also encourages cooperation across departments and responsibility centers. Such cooperation increases awareness of each department's importance to the overall goals of the company.

Setting Budget Goals Too Loosely

Although it is desirable to establish attainable goals, it is undesirable to plan lower goals than may be possible. Such budget "padding" is termed **budgetary slack**. Managers may plan slack in the budget in order to provide a

"cushion" for unexpected events or improve the appearance of operations. Budgetary slack can be reduced by properly training employees and managers in the importance of realistic, attainable budgets.

Slack budgets may cause a "spend it or lose it" mentality. This often occurs at the end of the budget period when actual spending is less than the budget. Employees and managers may spend the remaining budget on unnecessary purchases in order to avoid having their budget reduced for the next period.

Setting Conflicting Budget Goals

Goal conflict occurs when the employees' or managers' self-interest differs from the company's objectives or goals. Goal conflict may also occur among responsibility centers such as departments.

To illustrate, assume that the sales department manager is given an increased sales goal and as a result accepts customers who are poor credit risks. This, in turn, causes bad debt expense to increase and profitability to decline. Likewise, a manufacturing department manager may be told to reduce costs. As a result, the manufacturing department manager might use lower-cost direct materials, which are also of lower quality. As a result, customer complaints and returns might increase significantly, which would adversely affect the company's profitability.

INTEGRITY, OBJECTIVITY, AND ETHICS IN BUSINESS

Budget Games

The budgeting system is designed to plan and control a business. However, it is common for the budget to be "gamed" by its participants. For example, managers may pad their budgets with excess resources. In this way, the managers have additional resources for unexpected events during the period. If the budget is being used to establish the incentive plan, then sales managers have incentives to understate the sales potential of a territory in order to ensure hitting their quotas. Other times, managers engage in "land grabbing," which occurs when they overstate the sales potential of a territory in order to guarantee access to resources. If managers believe that unspent resources will not roll over to future periods, then they may be encouraged to "spend it or lose it," causing wasteful expenditures. These types of problems can be partially overcome by separating the budget into planning and incentive components. This is why many organizations have two budget processes, one for resource planning and another, more challenging budget, for motivating managers.

Western Digital Corporation, a computer hard drive manufacturer, introduced a new Web-based B&P (budget and planning) system to perform a continuous rolling budget. According to the financial executives at the company, "We're never [again] comparing results to old operating plans that were set months ago."

Budgeting Systems

Budgeting systems vary among companies and industries. For example, the budget system used by **Ford Motor Company** differs from that used by **Delta Air Lines.** However, the basic budgeting concepts discussed in this section apply to all types of businesses and organizations.

The budgetary period for operating activities normally includes the fiscal year of a company. A year is short enough that future operations can be estimated fairly accurately, yet long enough that the future can be viewed in a broad context. However, for control purposes, annual budgets are usually subdivided into shorter time periods, such as quarters of the year, months, or weeks.

A variation of fiscal-year budgeting, called **continuous budgeting**, maintains a 12-month projection into the future. The 12-month budget is

continually revised by replacing the data for the month just ended with the budget data for the same month in the next year. A continuous budget is illustrated in Exhibit 3.

EXHIBIT 3 | **Continuous Budgeting**

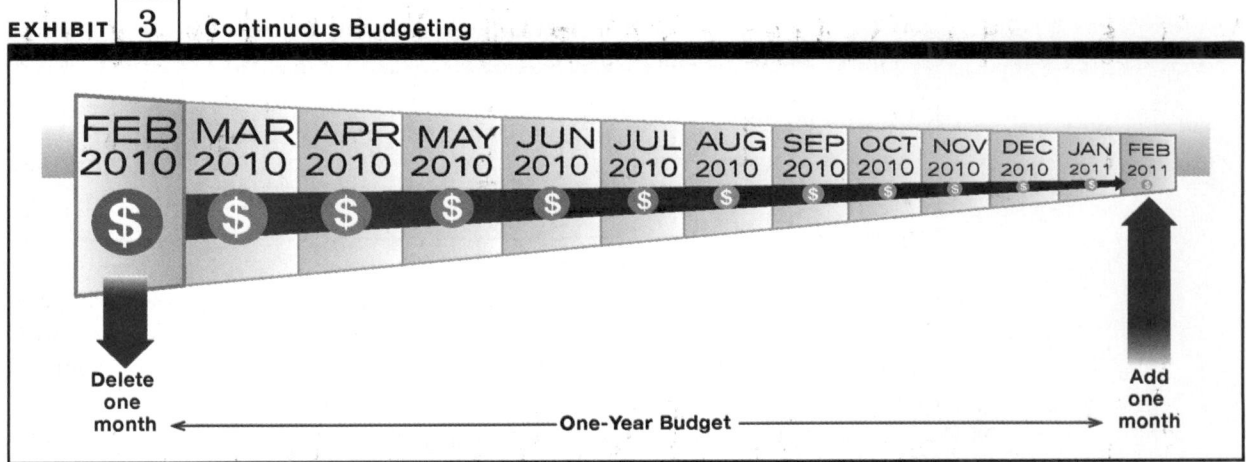

Developing an annual budget usually begins several months prior to the end of the current year. This responsibility is normally assigned to a budget committee. Such a committee often consists of the budget director, the controller, the treasurer, the production manager, and the sales manager. The budget process is monitored and summarized by the Accounting Department, which reports to the committee.

There are several methods of developing budget estimates. One method, termed **zero-based budgeting**, requires managers to estimate sales, production, and other operating data as though operations are being started for the first time. This approach has the benefit of taking a fresh view of operations each year. A more common approach is to start with last year's budget and revise it for actual results and expected changes for the coming year. Two major budgets using this approach are the static budget and the flexible budget.

Static Budget

A **static budget** shows the expected results of a responsibility center for only one activity level. Once the budget has been determined, it is not changed, even if the activity changes. Static budgeting is used by many service companies and for some functions of manufacturing companies, such as purchasing, engineering, and accounting.

To illustrate, the static budget for the Assembly Department of Colter Manufacturing Company is shown in Exhibit 4. A disadvantage of static budgets is that they do not adjust for changes in activity levels. For example, assume that the Assembly Department of Colter Manufacturing spent $70,800 for the year ended July 31, 2010. Thus, the Assembly Department spent $10,800 ($70,800 − $60,000), or 18% ($10,800/$60,000) more than budgeted. Is this good news or bad news?

The first reaction is that this is bad news and the Assembly Department was inefficient in spending more than budgeted. However, assume that the Assembly Department's budget was based on plans to assemble 8,000 units

EXHIBIT 4   **Static Budget**

	A	B
1	**Colter Manufacturing Company**	
2	**Assembly Department Budget**	
3	**For the Year Ending July 31, 2010**	
4	Direct labor	$40,000
5	Electric power	5,000
6	Supervisor salaries	15,000
7	Total department costs	$60,000
8		

during the year. If 10,000 units were actually assembled, the additional $10,800 spent in excess of budget might be good news. That is, the Assembly Department assembled 25% (2,000 units/8,000 units) more than planned for only 18% more cost.

Flexible Budget

Unlike static budgets, **flexible budgets** show the expected results of a responsibility center for several activity levels. A flexible budget is, in effect, a series of static budgets for different levels of activity.

To illustrate, a flexible budget for the Assembly Department of Colter Manufacturing Company is shown in Exhibit 5.

EXHIBIT 5   **Flexible Budget**

	A	B	C	D	
1	**Colter Manufacturing Company**				
2	**Assembly Department Budget**				
3	**For the Year Ending July 31, 2010**				
4		**Level 1**	**Level 2**	**Level 3**	
5	Units of production	8,000	9,000	10,000	← Step 1
6	Variable cost:				
7	Direct labor ($5 per unit)	$40,000	$45,000	$50,000	
8	Electric power ($0.50 per unit)	4,000	4,500	5,000	
9	Total variable cost	$44,000	$49,500	$55,000	
10	Fixed cost:				
11	Electric power	$ 1,000	$ 1,000	$ 1,000	
12	Supervisor salaries	15,000	15,000	15,000	
13	Total fixed cost	$16,000	$16,000	$16,000	
14	Total department costs	$60,000	$65,500	$71,000	

Step 2 brackets rows 6–12. Step 3 brackets columns B–D. Step 1 points to row 5.

A flexible budget is constructed as follows:

Step 1. Identify the relevant activity levels. The relevant levels of activity could be expressed in units, machine hours, direct labor hours, or some other activity base. In Exhibit 5, the levels of activity are 8,000, 9,000, and 10,000 units of production.

Step 2. Identify the fixed and variable cost components of the costs being budgeted. In Exhibit 5, the electric power cost is separated into its fixed cost ($1,000 per year) and variable cost ($0.50 per unit). The direct labor is a variable cost, and the supervisor salaries are all fixed costs.

Step 3. Prepare the budget for each activity level by multiplying the variable cost per unit by the activity level and then adding the monthly fixed cost.

Many hospitals use flexible budgeting to plan the number of nurses for patient floors. These budgets use a measure termed "relative value units," which is a measure of nursing effort. The more patients and the more severe their illnesses, the higher the total relative value units, and thus the higher the staffing budget.

With a flexible budget, actual costs can be compared to the budgeted costs for actual activity. To illustrate, assume that the Assembly Department spent $70,800 to produce 10,000 units. Exhibit 5 indicates that the Assembly Department was *under* budget by $200 ($71,000 – $70,800).

Under the static budget in Exhibit 4, the Assembly Department was $10,800 *over* budget. This comparison is illustrated in Exhibit 6.

EXHIBIT | 6 | **Static and Flexible Budgets**

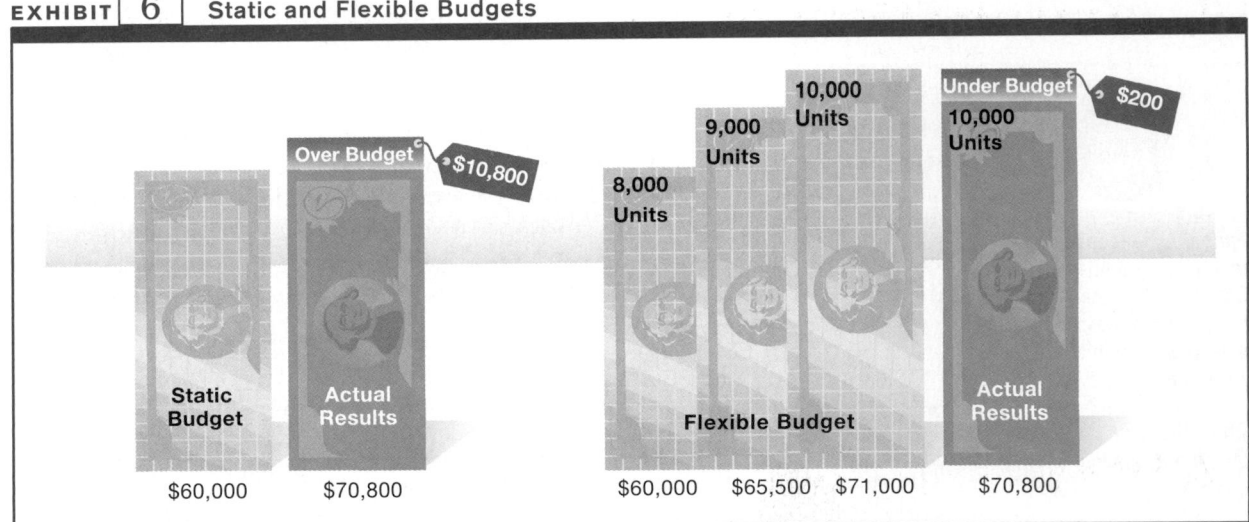

The flexible budget for the Assembly Department is much more accurate and useful than the static budget. This is because the flexible budget adjusts for changes in the level of activity.

Computerized Budgeting Systems

In developing budgets, companies use a variety of computerized approaches. Two of the most popular computerized approaches use:

1. Spreadsheet software such as *Microsoft* Excel
2. Integrated budget and planning (B&P) software systems

Integrated computerized budget and planning systems speed up and reduce the cost of preparing the budget. This is especially true when large quantities of data need to be processed.

B&P software systems are also useful in continuous budgeting. For example, the latest B&P systems use the Web (Intranet) to link thousands of employees together during the budget process. Employees can input budget data onto Web pages that are integrated and summarized throughout the company. In this way, a company can quickly and consistently integrate top-level strategies and goals to lower-level operational goals. These latest B&P

One survey reported that 67% of the companies relied on spreadsheets for budgeting and planning.
Source: Tim Reason, "Budgeting in the Real World," *CFO Magazine*, July 1, 2005.

How Businesses Make Money

Build versus Harvest

Budgeting systems are not "one size fits all" solutions but must adapt to the underlying business conditions. For example, a business can adopt either a build strategy or a harvest strategy. A *build* strategy is one where the business is designing, launching, and growing new products and markets. Build strategies often require short-term profit sacrifice in order to grow market share. **Apple Inc's.** iPhone® is an example of a product managed under a build strategy. A *harvest* strategy is often employed for business units with mature products enjoying high market share in low-growth industries. **H.J. Heinz Company**'s Ketchup® and **P&G**'s *Ivory* soap are examples of such products. A build strategy often has greater uncertainty, unpredictability, and change than a harvest strategy. The difference between these strategies implies different budgeting approaches.

The build strategy should employ a budget approach that is flexible to the uncertainty of the business. Thus, budgets should adapt to changing conditions by allowing periodic revisions and flexible targets. The budget serves as a short-term planning tool to guide management in executing an uncertain and evolving product market strategy.

In a harvest strategy, the business is often much more stable and is managed to maximize profitability and cash flow. Because cost control is much more important in this strategy, the budget is used to restrict the actions of managers.

Fujitsu, a Japanese technology company, used B&P to reduce its budgeting process from 6–8 weeks down to 10–15 days.

Obj 2 Describe the master budget for a manufacturing company.

software systems are moving companies closer to the real-time budget, wherein the budget is being "rolled" every day.[1]

Companies may also use computer simulation models to analyze the impact of various assumptions and operating alternatives on the budget. For example, the budget can be revised to show the impact of a proposed change in indirect labor wage rates. Likewise, the budgetary effect of a proposed product line can be determined.

Master Budget

The **master budget** is an integrated set of operating, investing, and financing budgets for a period of time. Most companies prepare the master budget on a yearly basis.

For a manufacturing company, the master budget consists of the following integrated budgets:

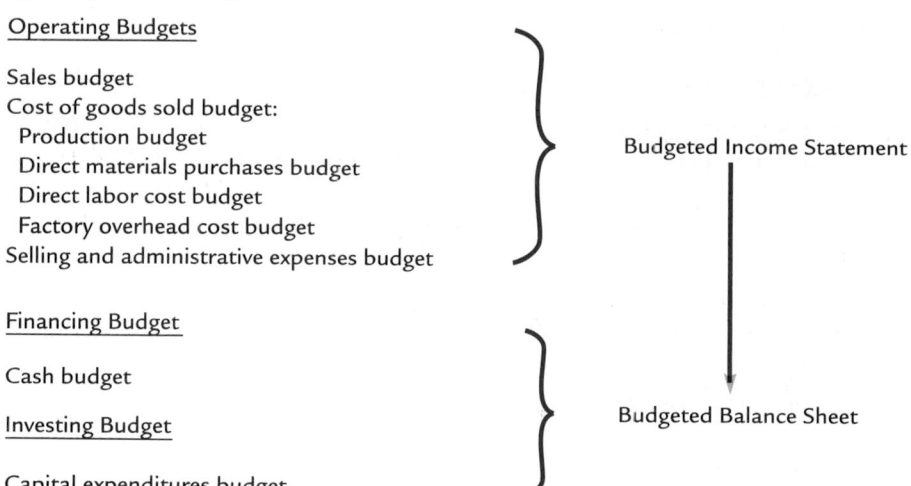

Operating Budgets

Sales budget
Cost of goods sold budget:
  Production budget
  Direct materials purchases budget
  Direct labor cost budget
  Factory overhead cost budget
Selling and administrative expenses budget

} Budgeted Income Statement

Financing Budget

Cash budget

Investing Budget

Capital expenditures budget

} Budgeted Balance Sheet

---

[1] Janet Kersnar, "Rolling Along," *CFO Europe*, September 14, 2004.

As shown on the previous page, the master budget is an integrated set of budgets that tie together a company's operating, financing, and investing activities into an integrated plan for the coming year.

The master budget begins with preparing the operating budgets, which form the budgeted income statement. The income statement budgets are normally prepared in the following order beginning with the sales budget:

1. Sales budget
2. Production budget
3. Direct materials purchases budget
4. Direct labor cost budget
5. Factory overhead cost budget
6. Cost of goods sold budget
7. Selling and administrative expenses budget
8. Budgeted income statement

After the budgeted income statement is prepared, the budgeted balance sheet is prepared. Two major budgets comprising the budgeted balance sheet are the cash budget and the capital expenditures budget.

Exhibit 7 shows the relationships among the income statement budgets.

EXHIBIT | **7** | **Income Statement Budgets**

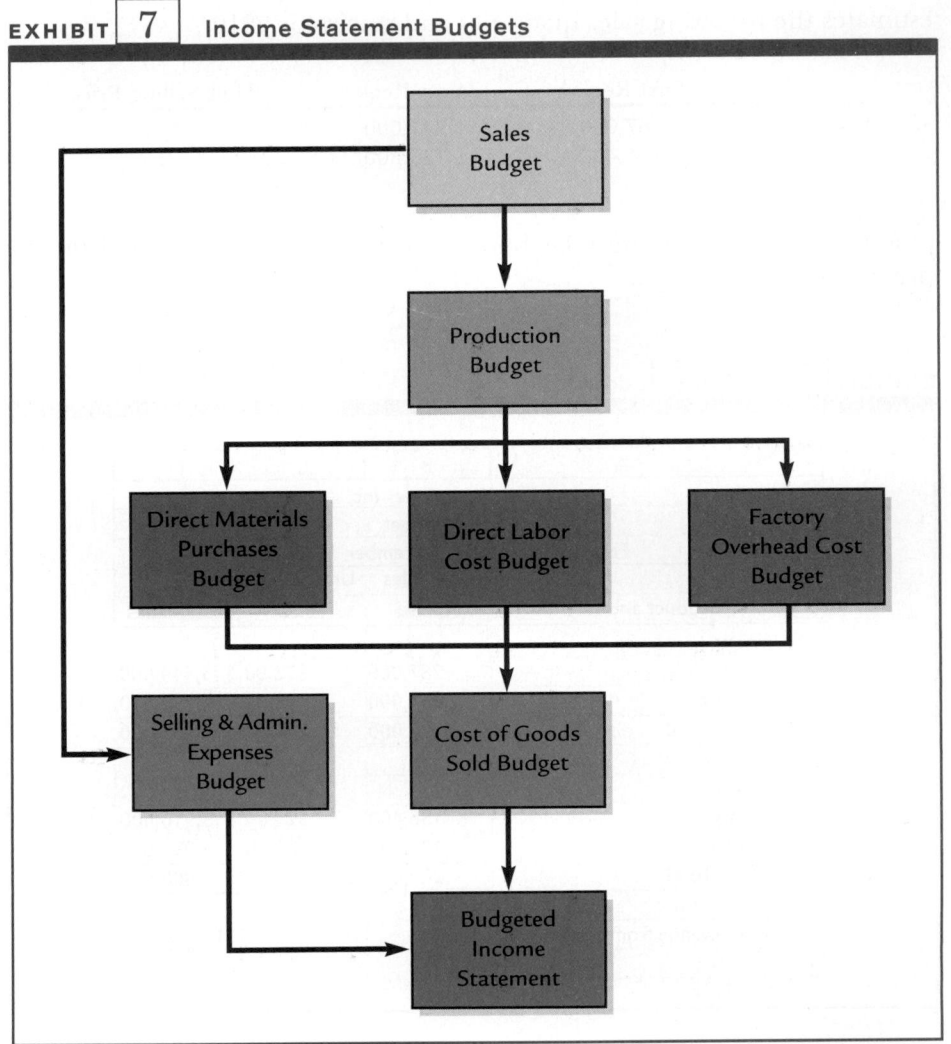

Income Statement Budgets

The integrated budgets that support the income statement budget are described and illustrated in this section. Elite Accessories Inc., a small manufacturing company, is used as a basis for illustration.

Sales Budget

The **sales budget** begins by estimating the quantity of sales. As a starting point, the prior year's sales quantities are often used. These sales quantities are then revised for such factors as the following:

1. Backlog of unfilled sales orders from the prior period
2. Planned advertising and promotion
3. Productive capacity
4. Projected pricing changes
5. Findings of market research studies
6. Expected industry and general economic conditions

Once sales quantities are estimated, the expected sales revenue can be determined by multiplying the volume by the expected unit sales price.

To illustrate, Elite Accessories Inc. manufactures wallets and handbags that are sold in two regions, the East and West Regions. Elite Accessories estimates the following sales quantities and prices for 2010:

	East Region	West Region	Unit Selling Price
Wallets	287,000	241,000	$12
Handbags	156,400	123,600	25

Exhibit 8 illustrates the sales budget for Elite Accessories based on the preceding data.

EXHIBIT 8   **Sales Budget**

	A	B	C	D
1	Elite Accessories Inc.			
2	Sales Budget			
3	For the Year Ending December 31, 2010			
4		Unit Sales	Unit Selling	
5	Product and Region	Volume	Price	Total Sales
6	Wallet:			
7	East	287,000	$12.00	$ 3,444,000
8	West	241,000	12.00	2,892,000
9	Total	528,000		$ 6,336,000
10				
11	Handbag:			
12	East	156,400	$25.00	$ 3,910,000
13	West	123,600	25.00	3,090,000
14	Total	280,000		$ 7,000,000
15				
16	Total revenue from sales			$13,336,000

Production Budget

The production budget should be integrated with the sales budget to ensure that production and sales are kept in balance during the year. The **production budget** estimates the number of units to be manufactured to meet budgeted sales and desired inventory levels.

The budgeted units to be produced are determined as follows:

Expected units to be sold	XXX units
Plus desired units in ending inventory	+ XXX
Less estimated units in beginning inventory	− XXX
Total units to be produced	XXX units

Elite Accessories Inc. expects the following inventories of wallets and handbags:

	Estimated Inventory January 1, 2010	Desired Inventory December 31, 2010
Wallets	88,000	80,000
Handbags	48,000	60,000

Exhibit 9 illustrates the production budget for Elite Accessories Inc.

EXHIBIT 9 Production Budget

	A	B	C
1	Elite Accessories Inc.		
2	Production Budget		
3	For the Year Ending December 31, 2010		
4		Units	
5		Wallet	Handbag
6	Expected units to be sold (from Exhibit 8)	528,000	280,000
7	Plus desired ending inventory, December 31, 2010	80,000	60,000
8	Total	608,000	340,000
9	Less estimated beginning inventory, January 1, 2010	88,000	48,000
10	Total units to be produced	520,000	292,000

Direct Materials Purchases Budget

The direct materials purchases budget should be integrated with the production budget to ensure that production is not interrupted during the year. The **direct materials purchases budget** estimates the quantities of direct materials to be purchased to support budgeted production and desired inventory levels.

The direct materials to be purchased are determined as follows:

Materials required for production	XXX
Plus desired ending materials inventory	+ XXX
Less estimated beginning materials inventory	− XXX
Direct materials to be purchased	XXX

Elite Accessories Inc. uses leather and lining in producing wallets and handbags. The quantity of direct materials expected to be used for each unit of product is as follows:

Wallet	Handbag
Leather: 0.30 sq. yd. per unit	Leather: 1.25 sq. yds. per unit
Lining: 0.10 sq. yd. per unit	Lining: 0.50 sq. yd. per unit

Elite Accessories Inc. expects the following direct materials inventories of leather and lining:

	Estimated Direct Materials Inventory January 1, 2010	Desired Direct Materials Inventory December 31, 2010
Leather	18,000 sq. yds.	20,000 sq. yds.
Lining	15,000 sq. yds.	12,000 sq. yds.

The estimated price per square yard of leather and lining during 2010 is shown below.

	Price per Square Yard
Leather	$4.50
Lining	1.20

Exhibit 10 illustrates the direct materials purchases budget for Elite Accessories Inc.

EXHIBIT 10   **Direct Materials Purchases Budget**

	A	B	C	D	E
1		Elite Accessories Inc.			
2		Direct Materials Purchases Budget			
3		For the Year Ending December 31, 2010			
4			Direct Materials		
5			Leather	Lining	Total
6	Square yards required for production:				
7	Wallet (Note A)		156,000	52,000	
8	Handbag (Note B)		365,000	146,000	
9	Plus desired inventory, December 31, 2010		20,000	12,000	
10	Total		541,000	210,000	
11	Less estimated inventory, January 1, 2010		18,000	15,000	
12	Total square yards to be purchased		523,000	195,000	
13	Unit price (per square yard)		× $4.50	× $1.20	
14	Total direct materials to be purchased		$2,353,500	$234,000	$2,587,500
15					
16	Note A:	Leather: 520,000 units × 0.30 sq. yd. per unit = 156,000 sq. yds.			
17		Lining: 520,000 units × 0.10 sq. yd. per unit = 52,000 sq. yds.			
18					
19	Note B:	Leather: 292,000 units × 1.25 sq. yds. per unit = 365,000 sq. yds.			
20		Lining: 292,000 units × 0.50 sq. yd. per unit = 146,000 sq. yds.			

The timing of the direct materials purchases should be coordinated between the Purchasing and Production Departments so that production is not interrupted.

Direct Labor Cost Budget

The **direct labor cost budget** estimates the direct labor hours and related cost needed to support budgeted production.

Elite Accessories Inc. estimates that the following direct labor hours are needed to produce a wallet and handbag:

Wallet	Handbag
Cutting Department: 0.10 hr. per unit	Cutting Department: 0.15 hr. per unit
Sewing Department: 0.25 hr. per unit	Sewing Department: 0.40 hr. per unit

The estimated direct labor hourly rates for the Cutting and Sewing departments during 2010 are shown below.

	Hourly Rate
Cutting Department	$12
Sewing Department	15

Exhibit 11 illustrates the direct labor cost budget for Elite Accessories Inc.

EXHIBIT 11   **Direct Labor Cost Budget**

	A	B	C	D	E
1		Elite Accessories Inc.			
2		Direct Labor Cost Budget			
3		For the Year Ending December 31, 2010			
4			Cutting	Sewing	Total
5	Hours required for production:				
6		Wallet (Note A)	52,000	130,000	
7		Handbag (Note B)	43,800	116,800	
8		Total	95,800	246,800	
9	Hourly rate		× $12.00	× $15.00	
10	Total direct labor cost		$1,149,600	$3,702,000	$4,851,600
11					
12	Note A:	Cutting Department: 520,000 units × 0.10 hr. per unit = 52,000 hrs.			
13		Sewing Department: 520,000 units × 0.25 hr. per unit = 130,000 hrs.			
14					
15	Note B:	Cutting Department: 292,000 units × 0.15 hr. per unit = 43,800 hrs.			
16		Sewing Department: 292,000 units × 0.40 hr. per unit = 116,800 hrs.			

As shown in Exhibit 11, for Elite Accessories Inc. to produce 520,000 wallets, 52,000 hours (520,000 units × 0.10 hr. per unit) of labor are required in the Cutting Department. Likewise, to produce 292,000 handbags, 43,800 hours (292,000 units × 0.15 hour per unit) of labor are required in the Cutting Department. Thus, the estimated total direct labor cost for the Cutting Department is $1,149,600 [(52,000 hrs. + 43,800 hrs.) × $12 per hr.)]. In a similar manner, the direct labor hours and cost for the Sewing Department are determined.

The direct labor needs should be coordinated between the Production and Personnel Departments so that there will be enough labor available for production.

Factory Overhead Cost Budget

The **factory overhead cost budget** estimates the cost for each item of factory overhead needed to support budgeted production. Exhibit 12 illustrates the factory overhead cost budget for Elite Accessories Inc.

EXHIBIT 12   Factory Overhead Cost Budget

	A	B
1	Elite Accessories Inc.	
2	Factory Overhead Cost Budget	
3	For the Year Ending December 31, 2010	
4	Indirect factory wages	$ 732,800
5	Supervisor salaries	360,000
6	Power and light	306,000
7	Depreciation of plant and equipment	288,000
8	Indirect materials	182,800
9	Maintenance	140,280
10	Insurance and property taxes	79,200
11	Total factory overhead cost	$2,089,080

The factory overhead cost budget shown in Exhibit 12 may be supported by departmental schedules. Such schedules normally separate factory overhead costs into fixed and variable costs to better enable department managers to monitor and evaluate costs during the year.

The factory overhead cost budget should be integrated with the production budget to ensure that production is not interrupted during the year.

Cost of Goods Sold Budget

The **cost of goods sold budget** is prepared by integrating the following budgets:

1. Direct materials purchases budget (Exhibit 10)
2. Direct labor cost budget (Exhibit 11)
3. Factory overhead cost budget (Exhibit 12)

In addition, the estimated and desired inventories for direct materials, work in process, and finished goods must be integrated into the cost of goods sold budget.

Elite Accessories Inc. expects the following direct materials, work in process, and finished goods inventories:

	Estimated Inventory Jan. 1, 2010	Desired Inventory Dec. 31, 2010
Direct materials:		
Leather	$ 81,000 (18,000 sq. yds. × $4.50)	$ 90,000 (20,000 sq. yds. × $4.50)
Lining	18,000 (15,000 sq. yds. × $1.20)	14,400 (12,000 sq. yds. × $1.20)
Total direct materials	$ 99,000	$ 104,400
Work in process:	$ 214,400	$ 220,000
Finished goods:	$1,095,600	$1,565,000

Exhibit 13 illustrates the cost of goods sold budget for Elite Accessories Inc. It indicates that total manufacturing costs of $9,522,780 are budgeted to be incurred in 2010. Of this total, $2,582,100 is budgeted for direct materials, $4,851,600 is budgeted for direct labor, and $2,089,080 is budgeted for factory overhead. After considering work in process inventories, the total budgeted cost of goods manufactured and transferred to finished goods during 2010 is $9,517,180. Based on expected sales, the budgeted cost of goods sold is $9,047,780.

EXHIBIT 13   **Cost of Goods Sold Budget**

	A	B	C	D	E	F	
1		Elite Accessories Inc.					
2		Cost of Goods Sold Budget					
3		For the Year Ending December 31, 2010					
4	Finished goods inventory, January 1, 2010					$ 1,095,600	
5	Work in process inventory, January 1, 2010				$ 214,400		
6	Direct materials:						
7	Direct materials inventory,						
8	January 1, 2010			$ 99,000			
9	Direct materials purchases (from Exhibit 10)			2,587,500	←		Direct materials
10	Cost of direct materials available for use			$2,686,500			purchases
11	Less direct materials inventory,						budget
12	December 31, 2010			104,400			
13	Cost of direct materials placed in production			$2,582,100			Direct labor
14	Direct labor (from Exhibit 11)			4,851,600	←		cost budget
15	Factory overhead (from Exhibit 12)			2,089,080	←		Factory overhead
16	Total manufacturing costs				9,522,780		cost budget
17	Total work in process during period				$9,737,180		
18	Less work in process inventory,						
19	December 31, 2010				220,000		
20	Cost of goods manufactured					9,517,180	
21	Cost of finished goods available for sale					$10,612,780	
22	Less finished goods inventory,						
23	December 31, 2010					1,565,000	
24	Cost of goods sold					$ 9,047,780	
25							

Selling and Administrative Expenses Budget

The sales budget is often used as the starting point for the selling and administrative expenses budget. For example, a budgeted increase in sales may require more advertising expenses.

Exhibit 14 illustrates the selling and administrative expenses budget for Elite Accessories Inc. The selling and administrative expenses budget shown in Exhibit 14 is normally supported by departmental schedules. For example, an advertising expense schedule for the Marketing Department could include the advertising media to be used (newspaper, direct mail, television), quantities (column inches, number of pieces, minutes), the cost per unit, and related costs per unit.

EXHIBIT 14 **Selling and Administrative Expenses Budget**

	A	B	C
1	Elite Accessories Inc.		
2	Selling and Administrative Expenses Budget		
3	For the Year Ending December 31, 2010		
4	Selling expenses:		
5	Sales salaries expense	$715,000	
6	Advertising expense	360,000	
7	Travel expense	115,000	
8	Total selling expenses		$1,190,000
9	Administrative expenses:		
10	Officers' salaries expense	$360,000	
11	Office salaries expense	258,000	
12	Office rent expense	34,500	
13	Office supplies expense	17,500	
14	Miscellaneous administrative expenses	25,000	
15	Total administrative expenses		695,000
16	Total selling and administrative expenses		$1,885,000

Budgeted Income Statement

The budgeted income statement is prepared by integrating the following budgets:

1. Sales budget (Exhibit 8)

2. Cost of goods sold budget (Exhibit 13)

3. Selling and administrative expenses budget (Exhibit 14)

In addition, estimates of other income, other expense, and income tax are also integrated into the budgeted income statement.

Exhibit 15 illustrates the budgeted income statement for Elite Accessories Inc. This budget summarizes the budgeted operating activities of the company. In doing so, the budgeted income statement allows management to assess the effects of estimated sales, costs, and expenses on profits for the year.

Balance Sheet Budgets

While the income statement budgets reflect the operating activities of the company, the balance sheet budgets reflect the financing and investing activities. In this section, the following balance sheet budgets are described and illustrated:

1. Cash budget (financing activity)

2. Capital expenditures budget (investing activity)

Cash Budget

The **cash budget** estimates the expected receipts (inflows) and payments (outflows) of cash for a period of time. The cash budget is integrated with the various operating budgets. In addition, the capital expenditures budget, dividends, and equity or long-term debt financing plans of the company affect the cash budget.

EXHIBIT 15   Budgeted Income Statement

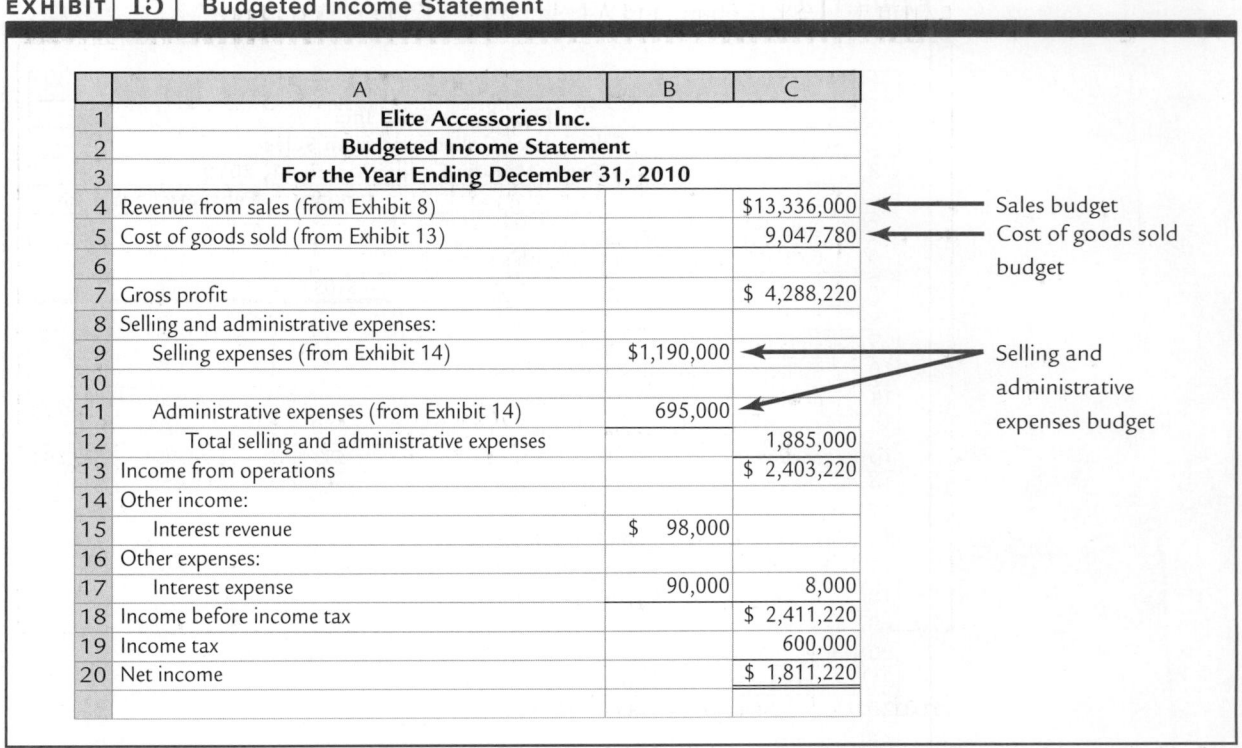

	A	B	C
1	**Elite Accessories Inc.**		
2	**Budgeted Income Statement**		
3	**For the Year Ending December 31, 2010**		
4	Revenue from sales (from Exhibit 8)		$13,336,000
5	Cost of goods sold (from Exhibit 13)		9,047,780
6			
7	Gross profit		$ 4,288,220
8	Selling and administrative expenses:		
9	Selling expenses (from Exhibit 14)	$1,190,000	
10			
11	Administrative expenses (from Exhibit 14)	695,000	
12	Total selling and administrative expenses		1,885,000
13	Income from operations		$ 2,403,220
14	Other income:		
15	Interest revenue	$ 98,000	
16	Other expenses:		
17	Interest expense	90,000	8,000
18	Income before income tax		$ 2,411,220
19	Income tax		600,000
20	Net income		$ 1,811,220

Sales budget

Cost of goods sold budget

Selling and administrative expenses budget

To illustrate, a monthly cash budget for January, February, and March 2010 for Elite Accessories Inc. is prepared. The preparation of the cash budget begins by estimating cash receipts.

Estimated Cash Receipts The primary source of estimated cash receipts is from cash sales and collections on account. In addition, cash receipts may be obtained from plans to issue equity or debt financing as well as other sources such as interest revenue.

To estimate cash receipts from cash sales and collections on account, a *schedule of collections from sales* is prepared. To illustrate, the following data for Elite Accessories Inc. are used:

	January	February	March
Sales:			
Budgeted sales	$1,080,000	$1,240,000	$970,000
Percent of cash sales	10%	10%	10%
Accounts receivable, January 1, 2010	$ 370,000		
Receipts from sales on account:			
From prior month's sales on account	40%		
From current month's sales on account	60		
	100%		

Using the preceding data, the schedule of collections from sales is prepared, as shown in Exhibit 16. Cash sales are determined by multiplying the percent of cash sales by the monthly budgeted sales. The cash receipts from sales on account are determined by adding the cash received from the prior month's sales on account (40%) and the cash received from the current

EXHIBIT 16 Schedule of Collections from Sales

	A	B	C	D	E
1		Elite Accessories Inc.			
2		Schedule of Collections from Sales			
3		For the Three Months Ending March 31, 2010			
4			January	February	March
5	Receipts from cash sales:				
6		Cash sales (10% × current month's sales—			
7		Note A)	$108,000	$ 124,000	$ 97,000
8					
9	Receipts from sales on account:				
10		Collections from prior month's sales (40% of			
11		previous month's credit sales—Note B)	$370,000	$ 388,800	$446,400
12		Collections from current month's sales (60%			
13		of current month's credit sales—Note C)	583,200	669,600	523,800
14	Total receipts from sales on account		$953,200	$1,058,400	$970,200
15					
16	Note A:	$108,000 = $1,080,000 × 10%			
17		$124,000 = $1,240,000 × 10%			
18		$ 97,000 = $ 970,000 × 10%			
19					
20	Note B:	$370,000, given as January 1, 2010, Accounts Receivable balance			
21		$388,800 = $1,080,000 × 90% × 40%			
22		$446,400 = $1,240,000 × 90% × 40%			
23					
24	Note C:	$583,200 = $1,080,000 × 90% × 60%			
25		$669,600 = $1,240,000 × 90% × 60%			
26		$523,800 = $ 970,000 × 90% × 60%			

month's sales on account (60%). To simplify, it is assumed that all accounts receivable are collected.

Estimated Cash Payments Estimated cash payments must be budgeted for operating costs and expenses such as manufacturing costs, selling expenses, and administrative expenses. In addition, estimated cash payments may be planned for capital expenditures, dividends, interest payments, or long-term debt payments.

To estimate cash payments for manufacturing costs, a *schedule of payments for manufacturing costs* is prepared. To illustrate, the following data for Elite Accessories Inc. are used:

	January	February	March
Manufacturing Costs:			
Budgeted manufacturing costs	$840,000	$780,000	$812,000
Depreciation on machines included			
in manufacturing costs	24,000	24,000	24,000
Accounts Payable:			
Accounts payable, January 1, 1010	$190,000		
Payments of manufacturing costs on account:			
From prior month's manufacturing costs	25%		
From current month's manufacturing costs	75		
	100%		

Using the preceding data, the schedule of payments for manufacturing costs is prepared, as shown in Exhibit 17. The cash payments are determined by adding the cash paid on costs incurred from the prior month (25%) to the cash paid on costs incurred in the current month (75%). The $24,000 of depreciation is excluded from all computations, since depreciation does not require a cash payment.

EXHIBIT 17 Schedule of Payments for Manufacturing Costs

	A	B	C	D	E
1		Elite Accessories Inc.			
2		Schedule of Payments for Manufacturing Costs			
3		For the Three Months Ending March 31, 2010			
4			January	February	March
5	Payments of prior month's manufacturing costs				
6	{[25% × previous month's manufacturing costs				
7	(less depreciation)]—Note A}		$190,000	$204,000	$189,000
8	Payments of current month's manufacturing costs				
9	{[75% × current month's manufacturing costs				
10	(less depreciation)]—Note B}		612,000	567,000	591,000
11	Total payments		$802,000	$771,000	$780,000
12					
13	Note A:	$190,000, given as January 1, 2010, Accounts Payable balance			
14		$204,000 = ($840,000 − $24,000) × 25%			
15		$189,000 = ($780,000 − $24,000) × 25%			
16					
17	Note B:	$612,000 = ($840,000 − $24,000) × 75%			
18		$567,000 = ($780,000 − $24,000) × 75%			
19		$591,000 = ($812,000 − $24,000) × 75%			

Completing the Cash Budget Assume the additional data for Elite Accessories Inc. shown below.

Cash balance on January 1, 2010	$280,000
Quarterly taxes paid on March 31, 2010	150,000
Quarterly interest expense paid on January 10, 2010	22,500
Quarterly interest revenue received on March 21, 2010	24,500
Sewing equipment purchased in February 2010	274,000

Selling and administrative expenses (paid in month incurred):

January	February	March
$160,000	$165,000	$145,000

Using the preceding data, the *cash budget* is prepared, as shown in Exhibit 18. Elite Accessories Inc. has estimated that a *minimum cash balance* of $340,000 is required at the end of each month to support its operations. This minimum cash balance is compared to the estimated ending cash balance for each month. In this way, any expected cash excess or deficiency is determined.

Exhibit 18 indicates that Elite Accessories expects a cash excess at the end of January of $16,700. This excess could be invested in temporary income-producing securities such as U.S. Treasury bills or notes. In contrast,

EXHIBIT 18   Cash Budget

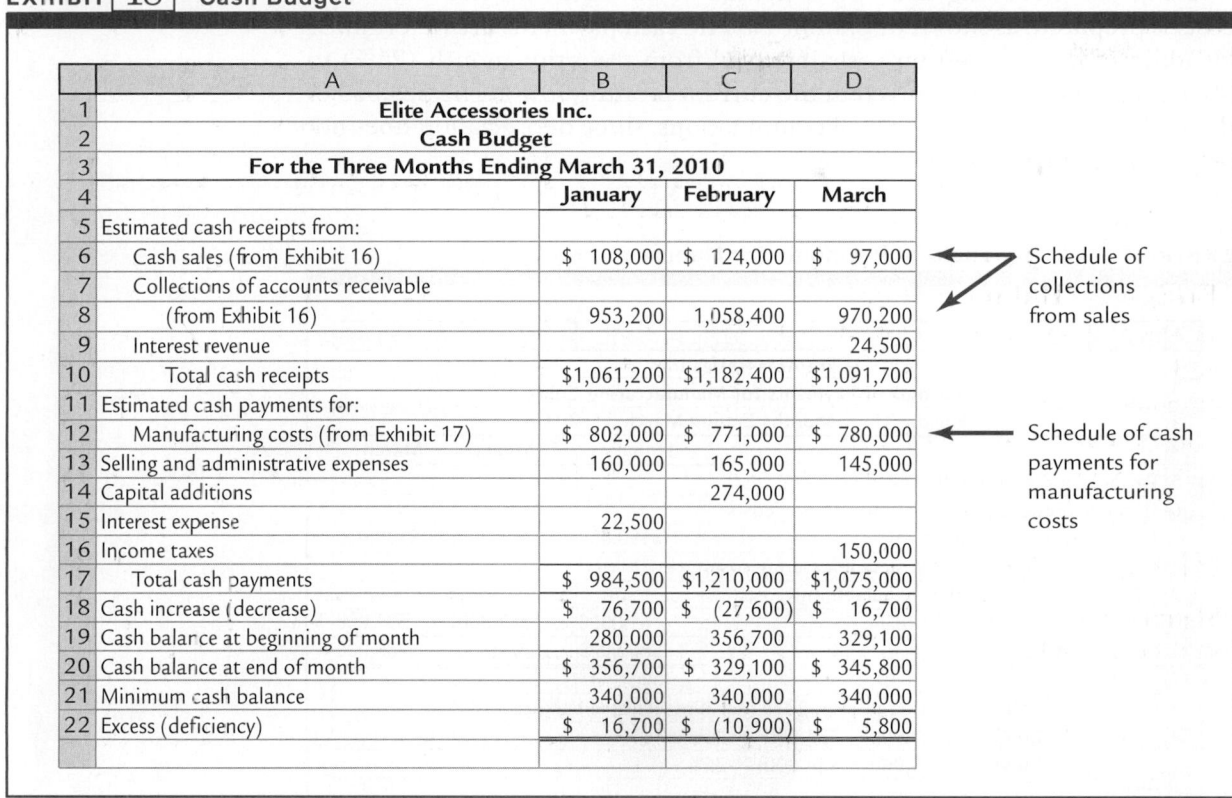

	A	B	C	D
1	Elite Accessories Inc.			
2	Cash Budget			
3	For the Three Months Ending March 31, 2010			
4		January	February	March
5	Estimated cash receipts from:			
6	Cash sales (from Exhibit 16)	$ 108,000	$ 124,000	$ 97,000
7	Collections of accounts receivable			
8	(from Exhibit 16)	953,200	1,058,400	970,200
9	Interest revenue			24,500
10	Total cash receipts	$1,061,200	$1,182,400	$1,091,700
11	Estimated cash payments for:			
12	Manufacturing costs (from Exhibit 17)	$ 802,000	$ 771,000	$ 780,000
13	Selling and administrative expenses	160,000	165,000	145,000
14	Capital additions		274,000	
15	Interest expense	22,500		
16	Income taxes			150,000
17	Total cash payments	$ 984,500	$1,210,000	$1,075,000
18	Cash increase (decrease)	$ 76,700	$ (27,600)	$ 16,700
19	Cash balance at beginning of month	280,000	356,700	329,100
20	Cash balance at end of month	$ 356,700	$ 329,100	$ 345,800
21	Minimum cash balance	340,000	340,000	340,000
22	Excess (deficiency)	$ 16,700	$ (10,900)	$ 5,800

Schedule of collections from sales

Schedule of cash payments for manufacturing costs

the estimated cash deficiency at the end of February of $10,900 might require Elite Accessories to borrow cash from its bank.

Capital Expenditures Budget

The **capital expenditures budget** summarizes plans for acquiring fixed assets. Such expenditures are necessary as machinery and other fixed assets wear out or become obsolete. In addition, purchasing additional fixed assets may be necessary to meet increasing demand for the company's product.

To illustrate, a five-year capital expenditures budget for Elite Accessories Inc. is shown in Exhibit 19.

EXHIBIT 19   Capital Expenditures Budget

	A	B	C	D	E	F
1	Elite Accessories Inc.					
2	Capital Expenditures Budget					
3	For the Five Years Ending December 31, 2014					
4	Item	2010	2011	2012	2013	2014
5	Machinery—Cutting Department	$400,000			$280,000	$360,000
6	Machinery—Sewing Department	274,000	$260,000	$560,000	200,000	
7	Office equipment		90,000			60,000
8	Total	$674,000	$350,000	$560,000	$480,000	$420,000

As shown in Exhibit 19, capital expenditures budgets are often prepared for five to ten years into the future. This is necessary since fixed assets often must be ordered years in advance. Likewise, it could take years to construct new buildings or other production facilities.

The capital expenditures budget should be integrated with the operating and financing budgets. For example, depreciation of new manufacturing equipment affects the factory overhead cost budget. The plans for financing the capital expenditures also affect the cash budget.

Budgeted Balance Sheet

The budgeted balance sheet is prepared based on the operating, financing, and investing budgets of the master budget. The budgeted balance sheet is dated as of the end of the budget period and is similar to a normal balance sheet except that estimated amounts are used. For this reason, a budgeted balance sheet for Elite Accessories Inc. is not illustrated.

Standards

Obj 3 Describe the types of standards and how they are established.

Standards are performance goals. Manufacturing companies normally use **standard cost** for each of the three following product costs:

1. Direct materials
2. Direct labor
3. Factory overhead

Accounting systems that use standards for product costs are called **standard cost systems**. Standard cost systems enable management to determine the following:

1. How much a product *should* cost (standard cost)
2. How much it does cost (actual cost)

When actual costs are compared with standard costs, the exceptions or cost variances are reported. This reporting by the *principle of exceptions* allows management to focus on correcting the cost variances.

Drivers for **United Parcel Service (UPS)** are expected to drive a standard distance per day. Salespersons for **The Limited** are expected to meet sales standards.

Setting Standards

The standard-setting process normally requires the joint efforts of accountants, engineers, and other management personnel. The accountant converts the results of judgments and process studies into dollars and cents. Engineers with the aid of operation managers identify the materials, labor, and machine requirements needed to produce the product. For example, engineers estimate direct materials by studying the product specifications and estimating normal spoilage. Time and motion studies may be used to determine the direct labor required for each manufacturing operation. Engineering studies may also be used to determine standards for factory overhead, such as the amount of power needed to operate machinery.

Setting standards often begins with analyzing past operations. However, caution must be used when relying on past cost data. For example, inefficiencies may be contained within past costs. In addition, changes in technology, machinery, or production methods may make past costs irrelevant for future operations.

Standards may be integrated into computerized manufacturing operations so that variances are automatically detected and reported and operations are adjusted during manufacturing.

Kaizen costing uses ideal standards to motivate changes and improvement. *Kaizen* is a Japanese term meaning "continuous improvement."

Types of Standards

Standards imply an acceptable level of production efficiency. One of the major objectives in setting standards is to motivate employees to achieve efficient operations.

Tight, unrealistic standards may have a negative impact on performance. This is because employees may become frustrated with an inability to meet the standards and may give up trying to do their best. Standards that can be achieved only under perfect operating conditions, such as no idle time, no machine breakdowns, and no materials spoilage, are called **ideal standards** or **theoretical standards**.

Standards that are too loose might not motivate employees to perform at their best. This is because the standard level of performance can be reached too easily. As a result, operating performance may be lower than what could be achieved.

Currently attainable standards, sometimes called *normal standards,* are standards that can be attained with reasonable effort. Such standards, which are used by most companies, allow for normal production difficulties and mistakes. For example, currently attainable standards allow for normal materials spoilage and machine breakdowns. When reasonable standards are used, employees focus more on cost and are more likely to put forth their best efforts.

An example from the game of golf illustrates the distinction between ideal and normal standards. In golf, "par" is an ideal standard for most players. Each player's USGA (United States Golf Association) handicap is the player's normal standard. The motivation of average players is to beat their handicaps because beating par is unrealistic for most players.

The difference between currently attainable and ideal standards is illustrated below.

Currently attainable
(person best)

Ideal
(world record)

Reviewing and Revising Standards

Standard costs should be periodically reviewed to ensure that they reflect current operating conditions. Standards should not be revised, however, just because they differ from actual costs. For example, the direct labor standard would not be revised just because employees are unable to meet properly set standards. On the other hand, standards should be revised when prices, product designs, labor rates, or manufacturing methods change.

Criticisms of Standard Costs

Some criticisms of using standard costs for performance evaluation include the following:

1. Standards limit operating improvements by discouraging improvement beyond the standard.

2. Standards are too difficult to maintain in a dynamic manufacturing environment, resulting in "stale standards."

3. Standards can cause employees to lose sight of the larger objectives of the organization by focusing only on efficiency improvement.

4. Standards can cause employees to unduly focus on their own operations to the possible harm of other operations that rely on them.

Regardless of these criticisms, standards are widely used. In addition, standard costs are only one part of the performance evaluation system used by most companies. As discussed in this chapter, other nonfinancial performance measures are often used to supplement standard costs, with the result that many of the preceding criticisms are overcome.

Aluminum beverage cans were redesigned to taper slightly at the top of the can, which reduces the amount of aluminum required per can. As a result, beverage can manufacturers reduced the standard amount of aluminum per can.

INTEGRITY, OBJECTIVITY, AND ETHICS IN BUSINESS

Company Reputation: The Best of the Best

Harris Interactive annually ranks American corporations in terms of reputation. The ranking is based on how respondents rate corporations on 20 attributes in six major areas. The six areas are emotional appeal, products and services, financial performance, workplace environment, social responsibility, and vision and leadership. What are the five highest-ranked companies in its 2008 survey? The five highest (best) ranked companies were *Johnson & Johnson, Google, Sony Corporation, The Coca-Cola Company,* and *Kraft Foods Inc.*

Source: Harris Interactive, 2009.

Budgetary Performance Evaluation

Obj 4 Describe and illustrate how standards are used in budgeting.

As discussed earlier in this chapter, the master budget assists a company in planning, directing, and controlling performance. The control function, or budgetary performance evaluation, compares the actual performance against the budget.

To illustrate, Western Rider Inc., a manufacturer of blue jeans, uses standard costs in its budgets. The standards for direct materials, direct labor, and factory overhead are separated into the following two components.

1. Standard price

2. Standard quantity

The standard cost per unit for direct materials, direct labor, and factory overhead is computed as follows:

$$\text{Standard Cost per Unit} = \text{Standard Price} \times \text{Standard Quantity}$$

Western Rider's standard costs per unit for its XL jeans are shown in Exhibit 20.

EXHIBIT 20 | Standards Cost for XL Jeans

Manufacturing Costs	Standard Price	×	Standard Quantity per Pair	=	Standard Cost per Pair of XL Jeans
Direct materials	$5.00 per sq. yd.		1.5 sq. yds.		$ 7.50
Direct labor	$9.00 per hr.		0.80 hr. per pair		7.20
Factory overhead	$6.00 per hr.		0.80 hr. per pair		4.80
Total standard cost per pair					$19.50

As shown in Exhibit 20, the standard cost per pair of XL jeans is $19.50, which consists of $7.50 for direct materials, $7.20 for direct labor, and $4.80 for factory overhead.

The standard price and standard quantity are separated for each product cost. For example, Exhibit 20 indicates that for each pair of XL jeans, the standard price for direct materials is $5.00 per square yard and the standard quantity is 1.5 square yards. The standard price and quantity are separated because the department responsible for their control is normally different. For example, the direct materials price per square yard is controlled by the Purchasing Department, and the direct materials quantity per pair is controlled by the Production Department.

As illustrated earlier in this chapter, the master budget is prepared based on planned sales and production. The budgeted costs for materials purchases, direct labor, and factory overhead are determined by multiplying their standard costs per unit by the planned level of production. Budgeted (standard) costs are then compared to actual costs during the year for control purposes.

Budget Performance Report

The report that summarizes actual costs, standard costs, and the differences for the units produced is called a **budget performance report**. To illustrate, assume that Western Rider produced the following pairs of jeans during June:

XL jeans produced and sold	5,000 pairs
Actual costs incurred in June:	
Direct materials	$ 40,150
Direct labor	38,500
Factory overhead	22,400
Total costs incurred	$101,050

Exhibit 21 illustrates the budget performance report for June for Western Rider Inc. The report summarizes the actual costs, standard costs, and the differences for each product cost. The differences between actual and standard costs are called **cost variances**. A **favorable cost variance** occurs when the actual cost is less than the standard cost. An **unfavorable cost variance** occurs when the actual cost exceeds the standard cost.

The budget performance report shown in Exhibit 21 is based on the actual units produced in June of 5,000 XL jeans. Even though 6,000 XL jeans might have been *planned* for production, the budget performance report is based on *actual* production.

EXHIBIT 21 **Budget Performance Report**

WESTERN RIDER INC.
Budget Performance Report
For the Month Ended June 30,2010

Manufacturing Costs	Actual Costs	Standard Cost at Actual Volume (5,000 pairs of XL Jeans)*	Cost Variance— (Favorable) Unfavorable
Direct materials	$ 40,150	$37,500	$ 2,650
Direct labor	38,500	36,000	2,500
Factory overhead	22,400	24,000	(1,600)
Total manufacturing costs	$101,050	$97,500	$ 3,550

* 5,000 pairs × $7.50 per pair = $37,500
  5,000 pairs × $7.20 per pair = $36,000
  5,000 pairs × $4.80 per pair = $24,000

Manufacturing Cost Variances

The **total manufacturing cost variance** is the difference between total standard costs and total actual cost for the units produced. As shown in Exhibit 21, the total manufacturing cost unfavorable variance and the variance for each product cost are as follows:

	Cost Variance (Favorable) Unfavorable
Direct materials	$ 2,650
Direct labor	2,500
Factory overhead	(1,600)
Total manufacturing variance	$ 3,550

For control purposes, each product cost variance is separated into two additional variances as shown in Exhibit 22. The total direct materials variance is separated into a *price* and *quantity* variance. This is because standard and actual direct materials costs are computed as follows:

$$
\begin{array}{lll}
\text{Actual Direct Materials Cost} & = & \text{Actual Price} \quad \times \quad \text{Actual Quantity} \\
-\,\underline{\text{Standard Direct Materials Cost}} & = & -\,\underline{\text{Standard Price}} \quad \times \quad -\,\underline{\text{Standard Quantity}} \\
\text{Direct Materials Cost Variance} & = & \text{Price Difference} \times \quad \text{Quantity Difference}
\end{array}
$$

Thus, the actual and standard direct materials costs may differ because of either a price difference (variance) or a quantity difference (variance).

Likewise, the total direct labor variance is separated into a *rate* and a *time* variance. This is because standard and actual direct labor costs are computed as follows:

$$
\begin{array}{lll}
\text{Actual Direct Labor Cost} & = & \text{Actual Rate} \quad \times \quad \text{Actual Time} \\
-\,\underline{\text{Standard Direct Labor Cost}} & = & -\,\underline{\text{Standard Rate}} \quad \times \quad -\,\underline{\text{Standard Time}} \\
\text{Direct Labor Cost Variance} & = & \text{Rate Difference} \times \quad \text{Time Difference}
\end{array}
$$

EXHIBIT 22 **Manufacturing Cost Variances**

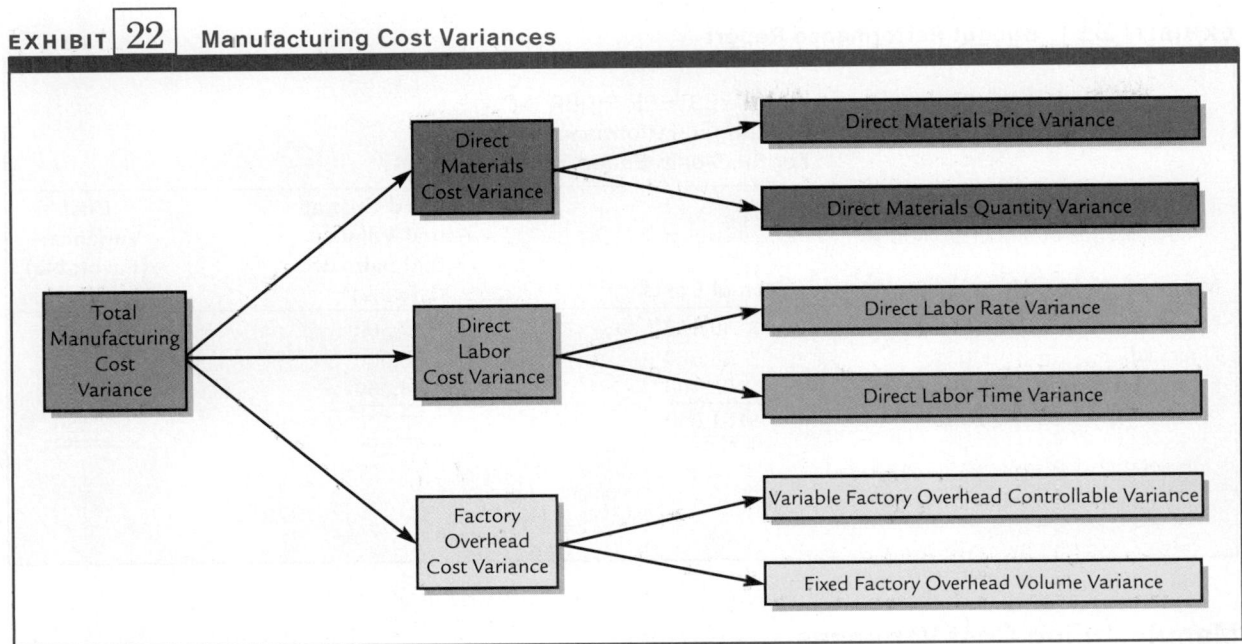

Therefore, the actual and standard direct labor costs may differ because of either a rate difference (variance) or a time difference (variance).

The total factory overhead variance is separated into a *controllable* and *volume* variance. Because factory overhead has fixed and variable cost elements, it is more complex to analyze than direct materials and direct labor, which are variable costs. The controllable variance is similar to a price or rate variance, and the volume variance is similar to the quantity or time variance.

In the next section, the price and quantity variances for direct materials and the rate and time variances for direct labor are described and illustrated. The controllable and volume variances for factory overhead are described and illustrated in the appendix to this chapter.

Obj 5 Compute and interpret direct materials and direct labor variances.

Direct Materials and Direct Labor Variances

As indicated in the prior section, the total direct materials and direct labor variances are separated into the following variances for analysis and control purposes:

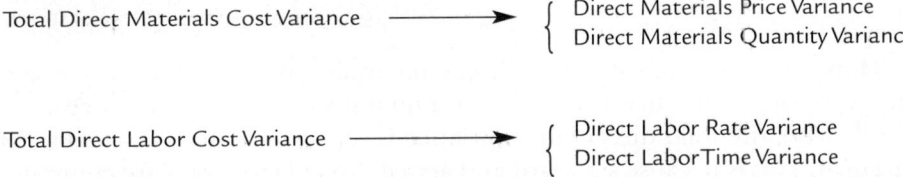

As a basis for illustration, the variances for Western Rider Inc.'s June operations shown in Exhibit 21 are used.

Direct Materials Variances

During June, Western Rider reported an unfavorable total direct materials cost variance of $2,650 for the production of 5,000 XL style jeans, as shown

in Exhibit 21. This variance was based on the following actual and standard costs:

Actual costs	$40,150
Standard costs	37,500
Total direct materials cost variance	$ 2,650

The actual costs incurred of $40,150 consist of the following:

Actual Direct Materials Cost = Actual Price × Actual Quantity
Actual Direct Materials Cost = ($5.50 per sq. yd.) × (7,300 sq. yds.)
Actual Direct Materials Cost = $40,150

The standard costs of $37,500 consist of the following:

Standard Direct Materials Cost = Standard Price × Standard Quantity
Standard Direct Materials Cost = ($5.00 per sq. yd.) × (7,500 sq. yds.)
Standard Direct Materials Cost = $37,500

The standard price of $5.00 per square yard is taken from Exhibit 20. In addition, Exhibit 20 indicates that 1.5 square yards is the standard for producing one pair of XL jeans. Thus, 7,500 (5,000 × 1.5) square yards is the standard for producing 5,000 pairs of XL jeans.

Comparing the actual and standard cost computations shown above indicates that the total direct materials unfavorable cost variance of $2,650 is caused by the following:

1. A price per square yard of $0.50 ($5.50 − $5.00) more than standard
2. A quantity usage of 200 square yards (7,300 sq. yds. − 7,500 sq. yds.) less than standard

The impact of these differences from standard is reported and analyzed as a direct materials *price* variance and direct materials *quantity* variance.

Direct Materials Price Variance

The **direct materials price variance** is computed as follows:

Direct Materials Price Variance = (Actual Price − Standard Price)
× Actual Quantity

If the actual price per unit exceeds the standard price per unit, the variance is unfavorable. This positive amount (unfavorable variance) can be thought of as increasing costs. If the actual price per unit is less than the standard price per unit, the variance is favorable. This negative amount (favorable variance) can be thought of as decreasing costs.

To illustrate, the direct materials price variance for Western Rider Inc. is computed as follows:[2]

Direct Materials Price Variance = (Actual Price − Standard Price)
× Actual Quantity
Direct Materials Price Variance = ($5.50 − $5.00) × 7,300 sq. yds.
Direct Materials Price Variance = $3,650 Unfavorable Variance

Most restaurants use standards to control the amount of food served to customers. For example, **Darden Restaurants, Inc.**, the operator of the **Red Lobster** chain, establishes standards for the number of shrimp, scallops, or clams on a seafood plate.

[2] To simplify, it is assumed that there is no change in the beginning and ending materials inventories. Thus, the amount of materials budgeted for production equals the amount purchased.

As shown on the previous page, Western Rider has an unfavorable direct materials price variance of $3,650 for June.

Direct Materials Quantity Variance

The **direct materials quantity variance** is computed as follows:

Direct Materials Quantity Variance = (Actual Quantity − Standard Quantity)
× Standard Price

If the actual quantity for the units produced exceeds the standard quantity, the variance is unfavorable. This positive amount (unfavorable variance) can be thought of as increasing costs. If the actual quantity for the units produced is less than the standard quantity, the variance is favorable. This negative amount (favorable variance) can be thought of as decreasing costs.

To illustrate, the direct materials quantity variance for Western Rider Inc. is computed as follows:

Direct Materials Quantity Variance = (Actual Quantity − Standard Quantity)
× Standard Price

Direct Materials Quantity Variance = (7,300 sq. yds. − 7,500 sq. yds.) × $5.00

Direct Materials Quantity Variance = $1,000 Favorable Variance

As shown above, Western Rider has a favorable direct materials quantity variance of $1,000 for June.

Direct Materials Variance Relationships

The relationship among the *total* direct materials cost variance, the direct materials *price* variance, and the direct materials *quantity* variance is shown in Exhibit 23.

EXHIBIT 23 | Direct Materials Variance Relationships

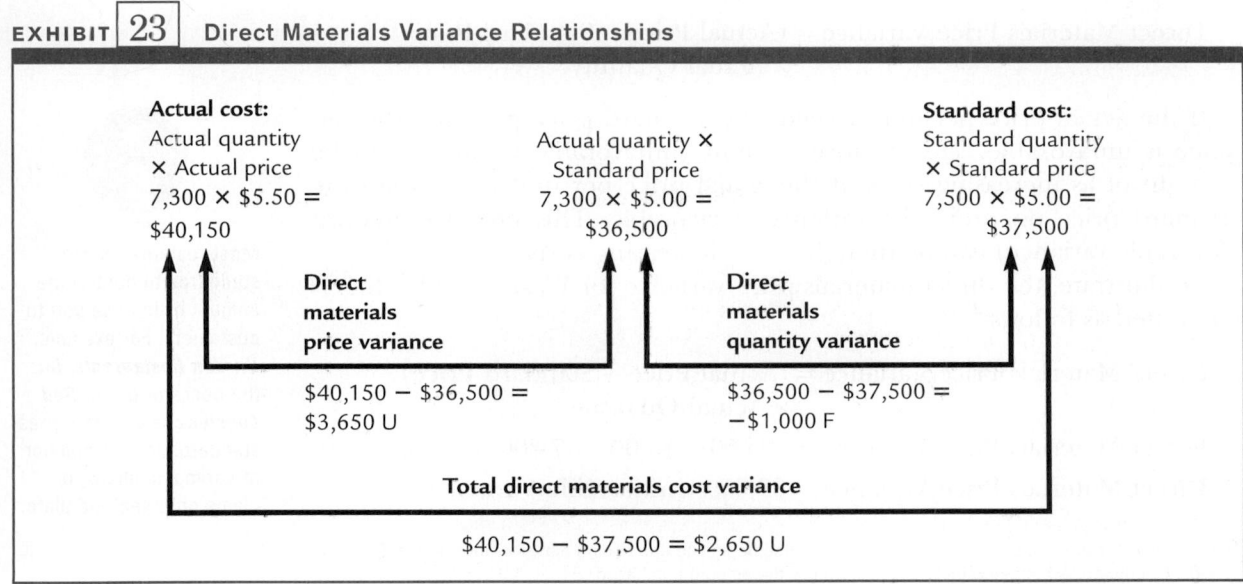

Reporting Direct Materials Variances

The direct materials quantity variances should be reported to the manager responsible for the variance. For example, an unfavorable quantity variance might be caused by either of the following:

1. Equipment that has not been properly maintained

2. Low-quality (inferior) direct materials

In the first case, the operating department responsible for maintaining the equipment should be held responsible for the variance. In the second case, the Purchasing Department should be held responsible.

Not all variances are controllable. For example, an unfavorable materials price variance might be due to market-wide price increases. In this case, there is nothing the Purchasing Department might have done to avoid the unfavorable variance. On the other hand, if materials of the same quality could have been purchased from another supplier at the standard price, the variance was controllable.

The price of a pound of copper has doubled since 2005.

Direct Labor Variances

During June, Western Rider reported an unfavorable total direct labor cost variance of $2,500 for the production of 5,000 XL style jeans, as shown in Exhibit 21. This variance was based on the following actual and standard costs:

The *Internal Revenue Service* publishes a time standard for completing a tax return. The average 1040EZ return is expected to require 8.3 hours to prepare.

Actual costs	$38,500
Standard costs	36,000
Total direct labor cost variance	$ 2,500

The actual costs incurred of $38,500 consist of the following:

Actual Direct Labor Cost = Actual Rate per Hour × Actual Time

Actual Direct Labor Cost = ($10.00 per hr.) × (3,850 hrs.)

Actual Direct Labor Cost = $38,500

The standard costs of $36,000 consist of the following:

Standard Direct Labor Cost = Standard Rate per Hour × Standard Time

Standard Direct Labor Cost = ($9.00 per hr.) × (4,000 hrs.)

Standard Direct Labor Cost = $36,000

The standard rate of $9.00 per direct labor hour is taken from Exhibit 20. In addition, Exhibit 20 indicates that 0.80 hour is the standard time required for producing one pair of XL jeans. Thus, 4,000 (5,000 × 0.80) direct labor hours is the standard for producing 5,000 pairs of XL jeans.

Comparing the actual and standard cost computations shown above indicates that the total direct labor unfavorable cost variance of $2,500 is caused by the following:

1. A rate of $1.00 per hour ($10.00 – $9.00) more than standard

2. A quantity of 150 hours (4,000 hrs. – 3,850 hrs.) less than standard

The impact of these differences from standard is reported and analyzed as a direct labor *rate* variance and a direct labor *time* variance.

Direct Labor Rate Variance

The **direct labor rate variance** is computed as follows:

$$\text{Direct Labor Rate Variance} = (\text{Actual Rate per Hour} - \text{Standard Rate per Hour}) \times \text{Actual Hours}$$

If the actual rate per hour exeeds the standard rate per hour, the variance is unfavorable. This positive amount (unfavorable variance) can be thought of as increasing costs. If the actual rate per hour is less than the standard rate per hour, the variance is favorable. This negative amount (favorable variance) can be thought of as decreasing costs.

To illustrate, the direct labor rate variance for Western Rider Inc. is computed as follows:

$$\text{Direct Labor Rate Variance} = (\text{Actual Rate per Hour} - \text{Standard Rate per Hour}) \times \text{Actual Hours}$$

$$\text{Direct Labor Rate Variance} = (\$10.00 - \$9.00) \times 3,850 \text{ hours}$$

$$\text{Direct Labor Rate Variance} = \$3,850 \text{ Unfavorable Variance}$$

As shown above, Western Rider has an unfavorable direct labor rate variance of $3,850 for June.

Direct Labor Time Variance

The **direct labor time variance** is computed as follows:

$$\text{Direct Labor Time Variance} = (\text{Actual Direct Labor Hours} - \text{Standard Direct Labor Hours}) \times \text{Standard Rate per Hour}$$

If the actual direct labor hours for the units produced exceeds the standard direct labor hours, the variance is unfavorable. This positive amount (unfavorable variance) can be thought of as increasing costs. If the actual direct labor hours for the units produced is less than the standard direct labor hours, the variance is favorable. This negative amount (favorable variance) can be thought of as decreasing costs.

To illustrate, the direct labor time variance for Western Rider Inc. is computed as follows:

$$\text{Direct Labor Time Variance} = (\text{Actual Direct Labor Hours} - \text{Standard Direct Labor Hours}) \times \text{Standard Rate per Hour}$$

$$\text{Direct Labor Time Variance} = (3,850 \text{ hours} - 4,000 \text{ direct labor hours}) \times \$9.00$$

$$\text{Direct Labor Time Variance} = -\$1,350 \text{ Favorable Variance}$$

As shown above, Western Rider has a favorable direct labor time variance of $1,350 for June.

Direct Labor Variance Relationships

The relationship among the *total* direct labor cost variance, the direct labor *rate* variance, and the direct labor *time* variance is shown in Exhibit 24.

EXHIBIT 24 | Direct Labor Variance Relationships

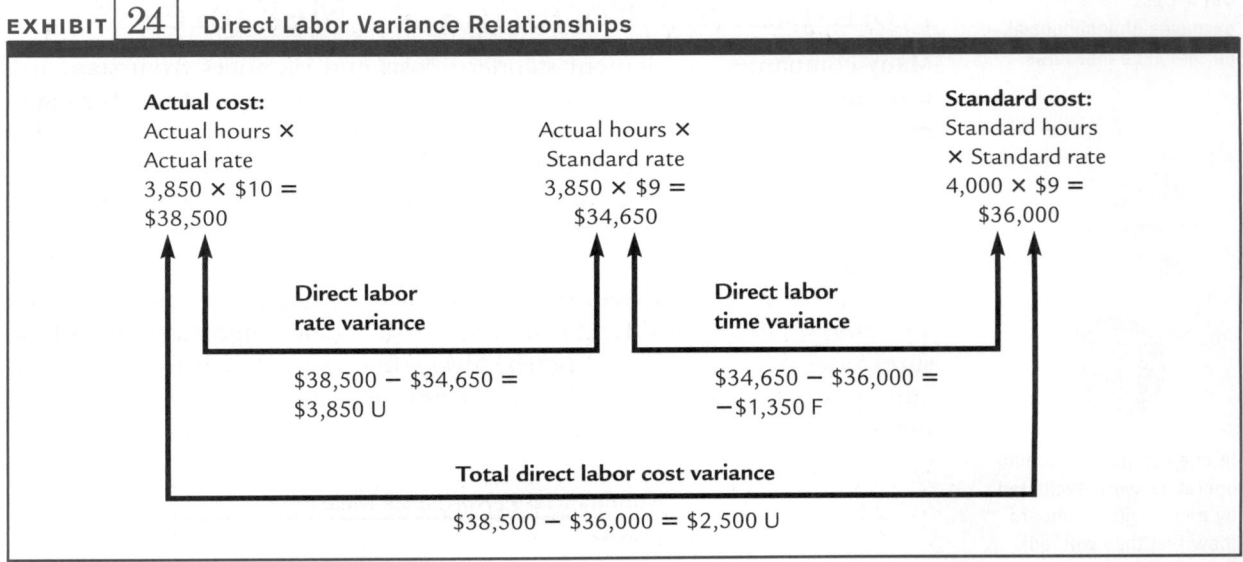

Actual cost:
Actual hours ×
Actual rate
3,850 × $10 =
$38,500

Actual hours ×
Standard rate
3,850 × $9 =
$34,650

Standard cost:
Standard hours
× Standard rate
4,000 × $9 =
$36,000

Direct labor rate variance

$38,500 − $34,650 =
$3,850 U

Direct labor time variance

$34,650 − $36,000 =
−$1,350 F

Total direct labor cost variance

$38,500 − $36,000 = $2,500 U

Reporting Direct Labor Variances

Production supervisors are normally responsible for controlling direct labor cost. For example, an investigation could reveal the following causes for unfavorable rate and time variances:

1. An unfavorable rate variance may be caused by the improper scheduling and use of employees. In such cases, skilled, highly paid employees may be used in jobs that are normally performed by unskilled, lower-paid employees. In this case, the unfavorable rate variance should be reported to the managers who schedule work assignments.

2. An unfavorable time variance may be caused by a shortage of skilled employees. In such cases, there may be an abnormally high turnover rate among skilled employees. In this case, production supervisors with high turnover rates should be questioned as to why their employees are quitting.

Direct Labor Standards for Nonmanufacturing Activities

Direct labor time standards can also be developed for use in administrative, selling, and service activities. This is most appropriate when the activity involves a repetitive task that produces a common output. In these cases, the use of standards is similar to that for a manufactured product.

To illustrate, standards could be developed for customer service personnel who process sales orders. A standard time for processing a sales order (the output) could be developed. The variance between the actual and the standard time could then be used to control sales order processing costs. Similar standards could be developed for computer help desk operators, nurses, and insurance application processors.

When labor-related activities are not repetitive, direct labor time standards are less commonly used. This often occurs when the time spent to perform the activity is not directly related to a unit of output. For example, the time spent by a senior executive or the work of a research and development scientist is not easily related to a measurable output. In these cases, the costs and expenses are normally controlled using static budgets.

Hospitals use time standards, termed *standard treatment protocols*, to evaluate the efficiency of performing hospital procedures.

Obj 6 Describe and provide examples of nonfinancial performance measures.

In one company, machine operators were evaluated by a labor time standard (how fast they worked). This resulted in poor-quality products, which led the company to supplement its labor time standard with a product quality standard.

Nonfinancial Performance Measures

Many companies supplement standard costs and variances from standards with nonfinancial performance measures. A **nonfinancial performance measure** expresses performance in a measure other than dollars. For example, airlines use on-time performance, percent of bags lost, and number of customer complaints as nonfinancial performance measures. Such measures are often used to evaluate the time, quality, or quantity of a business activity.

Using financial and nonfinancial performance measures aids managers and employees in considering multiple performance objectives. Such measures often bring additional perspectives, such as quality of work, to evaluating performance. Some examples of nonfinancial performance measures include the following:

Nonfinancial Performance Measures

Inventory turnover
Percent on-time delivery
Elapsed time between a customer order and product delivery
Customer preference rankings compared to competitors
Response time to a service call
Time to develop new products
Employee satisfaction
Number of customer complaints

Nonfinancial measures are often linked to either the inputs or outputs of an activity or process. A **process** is a sequence of activities for performing a task. The relationship between an activity or a process and its inputs and outputs is shown below.

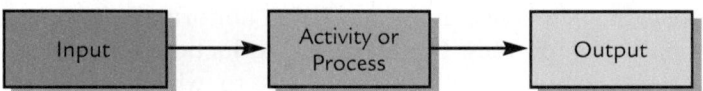

To illustrate, the counter service activity of a fast-food restaurant is used. The following input/outputs could be identified for providing customer service:

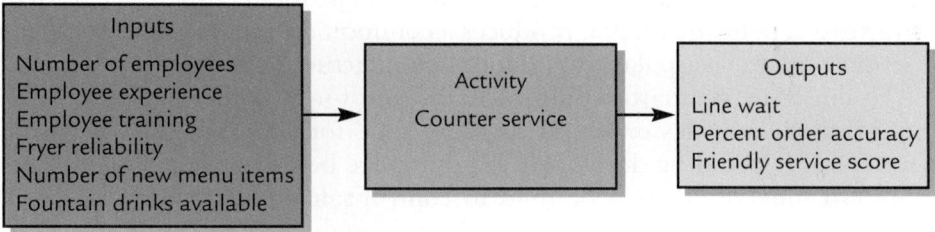

The customer service outputs of the counter service activity include the following:

1. Line wait for the customer

2. Percent order accuracy in serving the customer

3. Friendly service experience for the customer

Some of the inputs that impact the customer service outputs include the following:

1. Number of employees
2. Employee experience
3. Employee training
4. Fryer (and other cooking equipment) reliability
5. Number of new menu items
6. Fountain drink availability

A fast-food restaurant can develop a set of linked nonfinancial performance measures across inputs and outputs. The output measures tell management how the activity is performing, such as keeping the line wait to a minimum. The input measures are used to improve the output measures. For example, if the customer line wait is too long, then improving employee training or hiring more employees could improve the output (decrease customer line wait).

Appendix

Factory Overhead Variances

Factory overhead costs are analyzed differently from direct labor and direct materials costs. This is because factory overhead costs have fixed and variable cost elements. For example, indirect materials and factory supplies normally behave as a variable cost as units produced changes. In contrast, straight-line plant depreciation on factory machinery is a fixed cost.

Factory overhead costs are budgeted and controlled by separating factory overhead into fixed and variable costs. Doing so allows the preparation of flexible budgets and analysis of factory overhead controllable and volume variances.

The Factory Overhead Flexible Budget

The preparation of a flexible budget was described and illustrated earlier in this chapter. Exhibit 25 illustrates a flexible factory overhead budget for Western Rider Inc. for June 2010.

Exhibit 25 indicates that the budgeted factory overhead rate for Western Rider is $6.00, as computed below.

$$\text{Factory Overhead Rate} = \frac{\text{Budgeted Factory Overhead at Normal Capacity}}{\text{Normal Productive Capacity}}$$

$$\text{Factory Overhead Rate} = \frac{\$30,000}{5,000 \text{ direct labor hrs.}} = \$6.00 \text{ per direct labor hr.}$$

The normal productive capacity is expressed in terms of an activity base such as direct labor hours, direct labor cost, or machine hours. For Western Rider, 100% of normal capacity is 5,000 direct labor hours. The budgeted factory overhead cost at 100% of normal capacity is $30,000, which consists of variable overhead of $18,000 and fixed overhead of $12,000.

EXHIBIT 25 Factory Overhead Cost Budget Indicating Standard Factory Overhead Rate

	A	B	C	D	E
1	Western Rider Inc.				
2	Factory Overhead Cost Budget				
3	For the Month Ending June 30, 2010				
4	Percent of normal capacity	80%	90%	100%	110%
5	Units produced	5,000	5,625	6,250	6,875
6	Direct labor hours (0.80 hr. per unit)	4,000	4,500	5,000	5,500
7	Budgeted factory overhead:				
8	Variable costs:				
9	Indirect factory wages	$ 8,000	$ 9,000	$10,000	$11,000
10	Power and light	4,000	4,500	5,000	5,500
11	Indirect materials	2,400	2,700	3,000	3,300
12	Total variable cost	$14,400	$16,200	$18,000	$19,800
13	Fixed costs:				
14	Supervisory salaries	$ 5,500	$ 5,500	$ 5,500	$ 5,500
15	Depreciation of plant				
16	and equipment	4,500	4,500	4,500	4,500
17	Insurance and property taxes	2,000	2,000	2,000	2,000
18	Total fixed cost	$12,000	$12,000	$12,000	$12,000
19	Total factory overhead cost	$26,400	$28,200	$30,000	$31,800
20					
21	Factory overhead rate per direct labor hour, $30,000/5,000 hours = $6.00				
22					

For analysis purposes, the budgeted factory overhead rate is subdivided into a variable factory overhead rate and a fixed factory overhead rate. For Western Rider, the variable overhead rate is $3.60 per direct labor hour, and the fixed overhead rate is $2.40 per direct labor hour, as computed below.

$$\frac{\text{Variable Factory}}{\text{Overhead}} = \frac{\text{Budgeted Fixed Overhead at Normal Capacity}}{\text{Normal Productive Capacity}}$$

$$\frac{\text{Variable Factory}}{\text{Overhead Rate}} = \frac{\$18,000}{5,000 \text{ direct labor hrs.}} = \$3.60 \text{ per direct labor hr.}$$

$$\frac{\text{Fixed Factory}}{\text{Overhead Rate}} = \frac{\text{Budgeted Variable Overhead at Normal Capacity}}{\text{Normal Productive Capacity}}$$

$$\frac{\text{Fixed Factory}}{\text{Overhead Rate}} = \frac{\$12,000}{5,000 \text{ direct labor hrs.}} = \$2.40 \text{ per direct labor hr.}$$

To summarize, the budgeted factory overhead rates for Western Rider Inc. are as follows:

Variable factory overhead rate	$3.60
Fixed factory overhead rate	2.40
Total factory overhead rate	$6.00

As mentioned earlier, factory overhead variances can be separated into a controllable variance and a volume variance as discussed in the next sections.

Variable Factory Overhead Controllable Variance

The variable factory overhead **controllable variance** is the difference between the actual variable overhead costs and the budgeted variable overhead for actual production. It is computed as shown below.

$$\begin{array}{c} \text{Variable Factory Overhead} \\ \text{Controllable Variance} \end{array} = \begin{array}{c} \text{Actual Variable} \\ \text{Factory Overhead} \end{array} - \begin{array}{c} \text{Budgeted Variable} \\ \text{Factory Overhead} \end{array}$$

If the actual variable overhead is less than the budgeted variable overhead, the variance is favorable. If the actual variable overhead exceeds the budgeted variable overhead, the variance is unfavorable.

The **budgeted variable factory overhead** is the standard variable overhead for the *actual* units produced. It is computed as follows:

$$\begin{array}{c} \text{Budgeted Variable} \\ \text{Factory Overhead} \end{array} = \begin{array}{c} \text{Standard Hours for} \\ \text{Actual Units Produced} \end{array} \times \begin{array}{c} \text{Variable Factory} \\ \text{Overhead Rate} \end{array}$$

To illustrate, the budgeted variable overhead for Western Rider for June is $14,400, as computed below.

$$\begin{array}{c} \text{Budgeted Variable} \\ \text{Factory Overhead} \end{array} = \begin{array}{c} \text{Standard Hours for} \\ \text{Actual Units Produced} \end{array} \times \begin{array}{c} \text{Variable Factory} \\ \text{Overhead Rate} \end{array}$$

$$\begin{array}{c} \text{Budgeted Variable} \\ \text{Factory Overhead} \end{array} = 4,000 \text{ direct labor hrs.} \times \$3.60$$

$$\begin{array}{c} \text{Budgeted Variable} \\ \text{Factory Overhead} \end{array} = \$14,400$$

The preceding computation is based on the fact that Western Rider produced 5,000 XL jeans, which requires a standard of 4,000 (5,000 × 0.8 hr.) direct labor hours. The variable factory overhead rate of $3.60 was computed earlier. Thus, the budgeted variable factory overhead is $14,400 (4,000 direct labor hrs. × $3.60).

During June, assume that Western Rider incurred the following actual factory overhead costs:

	Actual Costs in June
Variable factory overhead	$10,400
Fixed factory overhead	12,000
Total actual factory overhead	$22,400

Based on the actual variable factory overhead incurred in June, the variable factory overhead controllable variance is a $4,000 favorable variance, as computed below.

$$\begin{array}{c} \text{Variable Factory Overhead} \\ \text{Controllable Variance} \end{array} = \begin{array}{c} \text{Actual Variable} \\ \text{Factory Overhead} \end{array} - \begin{array}{c} \text{Budgeted Variable} \\ \text{Factory Overhead} \end{array}$$

$$\text{Variable Factory Overhead} \atop \text{Controllable Variance} = \$10,400 - \$14,400$$

$$\text{Variable Factory Overhead} \atop \text{Controllable Variance} = -\$4,000 \text{ Favorable Variance}$$

The variable factory overhead controllable variance indicates the ability to keep the factory overhead costs within the budget limits. Since variable factory overhead costs are normally controllable at the department level, responsibility for controlling this variance usually rests with department supervisors.

Fixed Factory Overhead Volume Variance

Western Rider's budgeted factory overhead is based on a 100% normal capacity of 5,000 direct labor hours, as shown in Exhibit 25. This is the expected capacity that management believes will be used under normal business conditions. Exhibit 25 indicates that the 5,000 direct labor hours is less than the total available capacity of 110%, which is 5,500 direct labor hours.

The fixed factory overhead **volume variance** is the difference between the budgeted fixed overhead at 100% of normal capacity and the standard fixed overhead for the actual units produced. It is computed as follows:

$$\text{Fixed Factory} \atop \text{Overhead} \atop \text{Volume Variance} = \left(\begin{array}{c} \text{Standard Hours} \\ \text{for 100\% of} \\ \text{Normal Capacity} \end{array} - \begin{array}{c} \text{Standard Hours for} \\ \text{Actual Units} \\ \text{Produced} \end{array} \right) \times \begin{array}{c} \text{Fixed Factory} \\ \text{Overhead Rate} \end{array}$$

The volume variance measures the use of fixed overhead resources (plant and equipment). The interpretation of an unfavorable and a favorable fixed factory overhead volume variance is as follows:

1. *Unfavorable* fixed factory overhead variance. The actual units produced is *less than* 100% of normal capacity; thus, the company used its fixed overhead resources (plant and equipment) less than would be expected under normal operating conditions.

2. *Favorable* fixed factory overhead variance. The actual units produced is *more than* 100% of normal capacity; thus, the company used its fixed overhead resources (plant and equipment) more than would be expected under normal operating conditions.

To illustrate, the volume variance for Western Rider is a $2,400 unfavorable variance, as computed below.

$$\text{Fixed Factory} \atop \text{Overhead} \atop \text{Volume Variance} = \left(\begin{array}{c} \text{Standard Hours} \\ \text{for 100\% of} \\ \text{Normal Capacity} \end{array} - \begin{array}{c} \text{Standard Hours for} \\ \text{Actual Units} \\ \text{Produced} \end{array} \right) \times \begin{array}{c} \text{Fixed Factory} \\ \text{Overhead Rate} \end{array}$$

$$\text{Fixed Factory} \atop \text{Overhead} \atop \text{Volume Variance} = \left(\begin{array}{c} 5,000 \text{ direct} \\ \text{labor hrs.} \end{array} - \begin{array}{c} 4,000 \text{ direct} \\ \text{labor hrs.} \end{array} \right) \times \$2.40$$

$$\text{Fixed Factory} \atop \text{Overhead} \atop \text{Volume Variance} = \$2,400 \text{ Unfavorable Variance}$$

Since Western Rider produced 5,000 XL jeans during June, the standard for the actual units produced is 4,000 (5,000 × 0.80) direct labor hours. This is 1,000 hours less than the 5,000 standard hours of normal capacity. The fixed overhead rate of $2.40 was computed earlier. Thus, the unfavorable fixed factory overhead volume variance is $2,400 (1,000 direct labor hrs. × $2.40).

Exhibit 26 illustrates graphically the fixed factory overhead volume variance for Western Rider Inc. The budgeted fixed overhead does not change and is $12,000 at all levels of production. At 100% of normal capacity (5,000 direct labor hours), the standard fixed overhead line intersects the budgeted fixed costs line. For production levels *more than* 100% of normal capacity (5,000 direct labor hours), the volume variance is *favorable*. For production levels *less than* 100% of normal capacity (5,000 direct labor hours), the volume variance is *unfavorable*.

EXHIBIT 26 Graph of Fixed Overhead Volume Variance

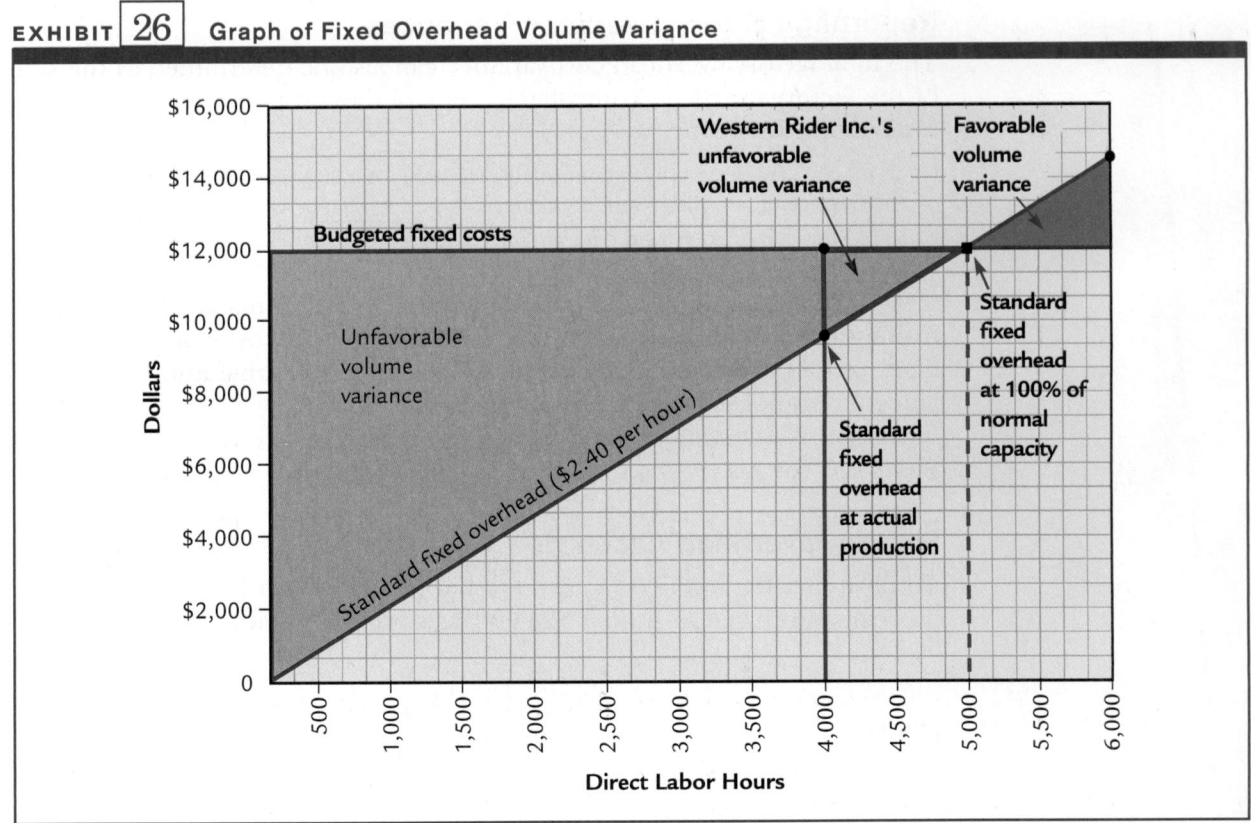

Exhibit 26 indicates that Western Rider's volume variance is unfavorable in June because the actual production is 4,000 direct labor hours, or 80% of normal volume. The unfavorable volume variance of $2,400 can be viewed as the cost of the unused capacity (1,000 direct labor hours).

An unfavorable volume variance may be due to factors such as the following:

1. Failure to maintain an even flow of work

2. Machine breakdowns

3. Work stoppages caused by lack of materials or skilled labor

4. Lack of enough sales orders to keep the factory operating at normal capacity

Management should determine the causes of the unfavorable variance and consider taking corrective action. For example, a volume variance caused by an uneven flow of work could be remedied by changing operating procedures. Lack of sales orders may be corrected through increased advertising.

Favorable volume variances may not always be desirable. For example, in an attempt to create a favorable volume variance, manufacturing managers might run the factory above the normal capacity. This is favorable when the additional production can be sold. However, if the additional production cannot be sold, it must be stored as inventory, which would incur storage costs. In this case, a favorable volume variance may actually reduce company profits.

Reporting Factory Overhead Variances

The total factory overhead cost variance can also be determined as the sum of the factory overhead controllable and volume variances, as shown below for Western Rider Inc.

Variable factory overhead controllable variance	–$4,000	Favorable Variance
Fixed factory overhead volume variance	2,400	Unfavorable Variance
Total factory overhead cost variance	–$1,600	Favorable Variance

A **factory overhead cost variance report** is useful to management in controlling factory overhead costs. Budgeted and actual costs for variable and fixed factory overhead along with the related controllable and volume variances are reported by each cost element.

Exhibit 27 illustrates a factory overhead cost variance report for Western Rider Inc. for June.

Factory Overhead Account

To illustrate, the applied factory overhead for Western Rider for the 5,000 XL jeans produced in June is $24,000, as computed below.

$$\text{Actual Factory Overhead} = \frac{\text{Standard Hours for}}{\text{Actual Units Produced}} \times \frac{\text{Total Factory}}{\text{Overhead Rate}}$$

$$\text{Actual Factory Overhead} = \left(5{,}000 \ \frac{\text{jeans}}{} \times \frac{0.80 \ \text{direct labor hr.}}{\text{per pair of jeans}}\right) \times \$6.00$$

$$\text{Actual Factory Overhead} = 4{,}000 \ \text{direct labor hrs.} \times \$6.00 = \$24{,}000$$

The total actual factory overhead for Western Rider, as shown in Exhibit 27, was $22,400. Thus, the total factory overhead cost variance for Western Rider for June is a $1,600 favorable variance, as computed below.

$$\frac{\text{Total Factory Overhead}}{\text{Cost Variance}} = \frac{\text{Actual Factory}}{\text{Overhead}} - \frac{\text{Applied Factory}}{\text{Overhead}}$$

$$\frac{\text{Total Factory Overhead}}{\text{Cost Variance}} = \$22{,}400 - \$24{,}000 = -\$1{,}600 \ \text{Favorable Variance}$$

EXHIBIT 27   Factory Overhead Cost Variance Report

	A	B	C	D	E
1		Western Rider Inc.			
2		Factory Overhead Cost Variance Report			
3		For the Month Ending June 30, 2010			
4	Productive capacity for the month (100% of normal)	5,000 hours			
5	Actual production for the month	4,000 hours			
6					
7		**Budget**			
8		**(at Actual**		**Variances**	
9		**Production)**	**Actual**	**Favorable**	**Unfavorable**
10	Variable factory overhead costs:				
11	Indirect factory wages	$ 8,000	$ 5,100	$2,900	
12	Power and light	4,000	4,200		$ 200
13	Indirect materials	2,400	1,100	1,300	
14	Total variable factory				
15	overhead cost	$14,400	$10,400		
16	Fixed factory overhead costs:				
17	Supervisory salaries	$ 5,500	$ 5,500		
18	Depreciation of plant and				
19	equipment	4,500	4,500		
20	Insurance and property taxes	2,000	2,000		
21	Total fixed factory				
22	overhead cost	$12,000	$12,000		
23	Total factory overhead cost	$26,400	$22,400		
24	Total controllable variances			$4,200	$ 200
25					
26					
27	Net controllable variance—favorable				$4,000
28	Volume variance—unfavorable:				
29	Capacity not used at the standard rate for fixed				
30	factory overhead—1,000 × $2.40				2,400
31	Total factory overhead cost variance—favorable				$1,600
32					

At the end of the period, the factory overhead account normally has a balance. A positive balance in Factory Overhead represents underapplied overhead. Underapplied overhead occurs when actual factory overhead costs exceed the applied factory overhead. A negative balance in Factory Overhead represents overapplied overhead. Overapplied overhead occurs when actual factory overhead costs are less than the applied factory overhead.

The difference between the actual factory overhead and the applied factory overhead is the total factory overhead cost variance. Thus, underapplied and overapplied factory overhead account balances represent the following total factory overhead cost variances:

1. *Underapplied* Factory Overhead = *Unfavorable* Total Factory Overhead Cost Variance

2. *Overapplied* Factory Overhead = *Favorable* Total Factory Overhead Cost Variance

The factory overhead account for Western Rider Inc. for the month ending June 30, 2010, is shown below.

Factory Overhead Account

Actual factory overhead ($10,400 + $12,000)	$22,400
Less applied factory overhead (4,000 hours × 6.00 per hour)	24,000
Balance, overapplied factory overhead, June 30	−$ 1,600

The $1,600 overapplied factory overhead account balance shown above and the total factory cost variance shown in Exhibit 27 are the same.

The variable factory overhead controllable variance and the volume variance can be computed by comparing the factory overhead account with the budgeted total overhead for the actual level produced, as shown below.

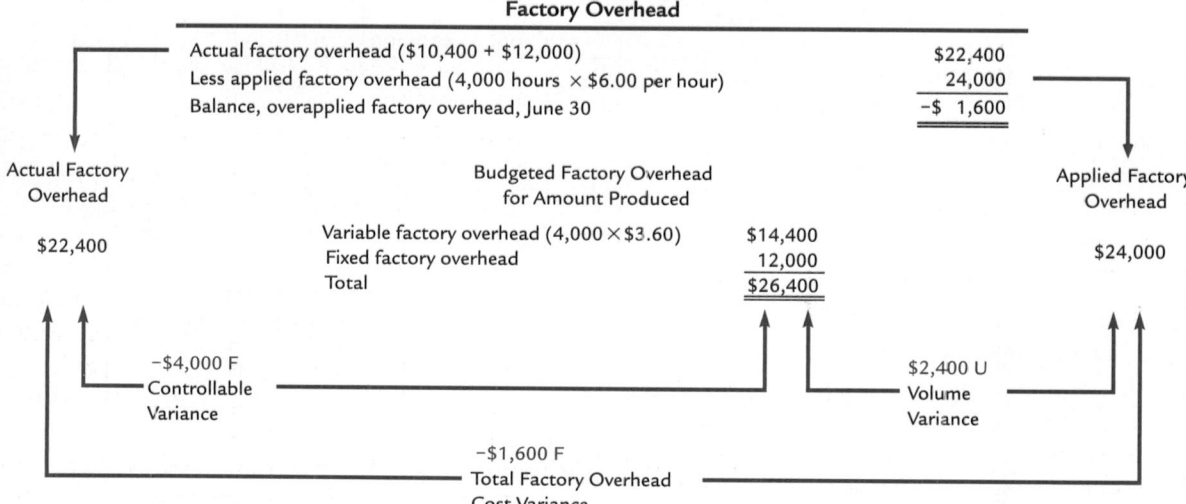

The controllable and volume variances are determined as follows:

1. The difference between the actual overhead incurred and the budgeted overhead is the *controllable* variance.

2. The difference between the applied overhead and the budgeted overhead is the *volume* variance.

If the actual factory overhead exceeds (is less than) the budgeted factory overhead, the controllable variance is unfavorable (favorable). In contrast, if the applied factory overhead is less than (exceeds) the budgeted factory overhead, the volume variance is unfavorable (favorable).

For many of the individual factory overhead costs, quantity and price variances can be computed similar to that for direct materials and direct labor. For example, the indirect factory labor cost variance may include both time and rate variances. Likewise, the indirect materials cost variance may include both a quantity variance and a price variance. Such variances are illustrated in advanced textbooks.

Key Points

1. **Describe budgeting, its objectives, its impact on human behavior, and types of budget systems.**

Budgeting involves (1) establishing specific goals, (2) executing plans to achieve the goals, and (3) periodically comparing actual results with these goals. In addition, budget goals should be established to avoid problems in human behavior. Thus, budgets should not be set too tightly, too loosely, or to cause goal conflict. Budgeting systems can use fiscal-year budgeting, continuous budgeting, or zero-based budgeting. Two major types of budgets are the static budget and the flexible budget. The static budget does not adjust with changes in activity while the flexible budget does adjust with changes in activity. Computers can be useful in speeding the budgetary process and in preparing timely budget performance reports. In addition, simulation models can be used to determine the impact of operating alternatives on various budgets.

2. **Describe the master budget for a manufacturing company.**

The master budget consists of the budgeted income statement and budgeted balance sheet. These two budgets are developed from detailed supporting budgets. The income statement supporting budgets are the sales budget, production budget, direct materials purchases budget, direct labor cost budget, factory overhead cost budget, cost of goods sold budget, and selling and administrative expenses budget. Both the cash budget and the capital expenditures budget support the budgeted balance sheet. The cash budget consists of budgeted cash receipts and budgeted cash payments. The capital expenditures budget is an important tool for planning expenditures for fixed assets.

3. **Describe the types of standards and how they are established.**

Standards represent performance benchmarks that can be compared to actual results in evaluating performance. Standards are developed, reviewed, and revised by accountants and engineers based on studies of operations. Standards are established so that they are neither too high nor too low but are attainable.

4. **Describe and illustrate how standards are used in budgeting.**

Budgets are prepared by multiplying the standard cost per unit by the planned production. To measure performance, the standard cost per unit is multiplied by the actual number of units produced, and the actual results are compared with the standard cost at actual volumes (cost variance).

5. **Compute and interpret direct materials and direct labor variances.**

The direct materials cost variance can be separated into a direct materials price and a quantity variance. The direct materials price variance is calculated by multiplying the actual quantity by the difference between the actual and standard price. The direct materials quantity variance is calculated by multiplying the standard price by the difference between the actual materials used and the standard materials at actual volumes.

The direct labor cost variance can be separated into a direct labor rate and time variance. The direct labor rate variance is calculated by multiplying the actual hours worked by the difference between the actual labor rate and the standard labor rate. The direct labor time variance is calculated by multiplying the standard labor rate by the difference between the actual labor hours worked and the standard labor hours at actual volumes.

6. **Describe and provide examples of nonfinancial performance measures.**

Many companies use a combination of financial and nonfinancial measures in order for multiple perspectives to be incorporated in evaluating performance. Combining financial and nonfinancial measures helps employees balance cost efficiency with quality and customer service performance. Nonfinancial measures are often used in conjunction with the inputs or outputs of a process or activity.

Key Terms

Budget An accounting device used to plan and control resources of operational departments and divisions.

Budget performance report A report comparing actual results with budget figures.

Budgetary slack Excess resources set within a budget to provide for uncertain events.

Budgeted variable factory overhead The standard variable overhead for the actual units produced.

Capital expenditures budget The budget summarizing future plans for acquiring plant facilities and equipment.

Cash budget A budget of estimated cash receipts and payments.

Continuous budgeting A method of budgeting that provides for maintaining a 12-month projection into the future.

Controllable variance The difference between the actual amount of variable factory overhead cost incurred and the amount of variable factory overhead budgeted for the standard product.

Cost of goods sold budget A budget of the estimated direct materials, direct labor, and factory overhead consumed by sold products.

Cost variance The difference between the actual cost and the standard cost at actual volumes.

Currently attainable standards Standards that represent levels of operation that can be obtained with reasonable effort.

Direct labor cost budget A budget that estimates the direct labor hours and related costs needed to support budgeted production.

Direct labor rate variance The cost associated with the difference between the standard rate and the actual rate paid for direct labor used in producing a commodity.

Direct labor time variance The cost associated with the difference between the standard hours and the actual hours of direct labor spent producing a commodity.

Direct materials price budget The cost associated with the difference between the standard price and the actual price of direct materials used in producing a commodity.

Direct materials price variance The difference between the actual price and standard price times the actual quantity.

Direct materials purchases budget A budget that uses the production budget as a starting point.

Direct materials quantity variance The cost associated with the difference between the standard quantity and the actual quantity of direct materials used in producing a commodity.

Favorable cost variance Actual cost is less than standard cost.

Factory overhead cost budget A budget that estimates the cost for each item of factory overhead needed to support budgeted production.

Factory overhead cost variance report Reports budgeted and actual costs for variable and fixed factory overhead for each cost element along with the related controllable and volume variance.

Flexible budget A budget that adjusts for varying rates of activity.

Goal conflict Situation when individual self-interest differs from business objectives.

Ideal standards Standards that can be achieved only under perfect operating conditions, such as no idle time, no machine breakdowns, and no materials spoilage; also called *theoretical standards.*

Master budget The comprehensive budget plan linking the individual budgets related to sales, cost of goods sold, operating expenses, project, capital expenditures, and cash.

Nonfinancial performance measure A performance measure expressed in other than dollars.

Process A sequence of activities linked together for performing a particular task.

Production budget A budget of estimated unit production.

Responsibility center A budgetary unit within a company for which a manager is assigned responsibility over costs, revenues, or assets.

Sales budget A budget that indicates for each product (1) the quantity of estimated sales, and (2) the expected unit selling price.

Standard cost A detailed estimate of what a product should cost.

Standard cost systems Accounting systems that use standards for each manufacturing cost entering into the finished product.

Standards Performance goals.

Static budget A budget that does not adjust to changes in activity levels.

Theoretical standards Standards that can be achieved only under perfect operating conditions, such as no idle time, no machine breakdowns, and no materials spoilage; also called *ideal standards*.

Total manufacturing cost variance The difference between the total actual cost and the total standard cost for the units produced.

Unfavorable cost variance Actual cost exceeds standard cost.

Volume variance The difference between the budgeted fixed overhead at 100% of normal capacity and the standard fixed overhead for the actual units produced.

Zero-based budgeting A concept of budgeting that requires all levels of management to start from zero and estimate budget data as if there had been no previous activities in their units.

Illustrative Problem

Hawley Inc. manufactures woven baskets for national distribution. The standard costs for the manufacture of Folk Art style baskets were as follows:

	Standard Costs	Actual Costs
Direct materials	1,500 lbs. at $35	1,600 lbs. at $32
Direct labor	4,800 hrs. at $11	4,500 hrs. at $11.80
Factory overhead	Rates per labor hour, based on 100% of normal capacity of 5,500 labor hrs.:	
	Variable cost, $2.40	$12,300 variable cost
	Fixed cost, $3.50	$19,250 fixed cost

Instructions

1. Determine the quantity variance, price variance, and total direct materials cost variance for the Folk Art style baskets.

2. Determine the time variance, rate variance, and total direct labor cost variance for the Folk Art style baskets.

3. Appendix: Determine the controllable variance, volume variance, and total factory overhead cost variance for the Folk Art style baskets.

Solution

1.   **Direct Materials Cost Variance**

Quantity variance:
 Direct Materials Quantity Variance = (Actual Quantity − Standard Quantity) × Standard Price
 Direct Materials Quantity Variance = (1,600 lbs. − 1,500 lbs.) × $35 per lb.
 Direct Materials Quantity Variance = $3,500 Unfavorable Variance

Price variance:
 Direct Materials Price Variance = (Actual Price − Standard Price) × Actual Quantity
 Direct Materials Price Variance = ($32 per lb. − $35 per lb.) × 1,600 lbs.
 Direct Materials Price Variance = −$4,800 Favorable Variance

Total direct materials cost variance:
 Direct Materials Cost Variance = Direct Materials Quantity Variance + Direct Materials Price Variance
 Direct Materials Cost Variance = $3,500 + $(4,800)
 Direct Materials Cost Variance = −$1,300 Favorable Variance

2.	**Direct Labor Cost Variance**

Time variance:

Direct Labor Time Variance = (Actual Direct Labor Hours − Standard Direct Labor Hours) × Standard Rate per Hour

Direct Labor Time Variance = (4,500 hrs. − 4,800 hrs.) × $11 per hour

Direct Labor Time Variance = −$3,300 Favorable Variance

Rate variance:

Direct Labor Rate Variance = (Actual Rate per Hour − Standard Rate per Hour) × Actual Hours

Direct Labor Rate Variance = ($11.80 − $11.00) × 4,500 hrs.

Direct Labor Rate Variance = $3,600 Unfavorable Variance

Total direct labor cost variance:

Direct Labor Cost Variance = Direct Labor Time Variance + Direct Labor Rate Variance

Direct Labor Cost Variance = ($3,300) + $3,600

Direct Labor Cost Variance = $300 Unfavorable Variance

3. Appendix	**Factory Overhead Cost Variance**

Variable factory overhead—controllable variance:

$$\frac{\text{Variable Factory Overhead}}{\text{Controllable Variance}} = \frac{\text{Actual Variable}}{\text{Factory Overhead}} - \frac{\text{Budgeted Variable}}{\text{Factory Overhead}}$$

$$\frac{\text{Variable Factory Overhead}}{\text{Controllable Variance}} = \$12,300 - \$11,520^{*}$$

$$\frac{\text{Variable Factory Overhead}}{\text{Controllable Variance}} = \$780 \text{ Unfavorable Variance}$$

* 4,800 hrs. $2.40 per hour

Fixed factory overhead volume variance:

$$\frac{\text{Fixed Factory}}{\text{Overhead Volume}}_{\text{Variance}} = \left(\frac{\text{Standard Hours for100\%}}{\text{of Normal Capacity}} - \frac{\text{Standard Hours for}}{\text{Actual Units Produced}} \right) \times \frac{\text{Fixed Factory}}{\text{Overhead Rate}}$$

$$\frac{\text{Fixed Factory}}{\text{Overhead Volume}}_{\text{Variance}} = (5,500 \text{ hrs.} - 4,800 \text{ hrs.}) \times \$3.50 \text{ per hr.}$$

$$\frac{\text{Fixed Factory}}{\text{Overhead Volume}}_{\text{Variance}} = 2,450 \text{ Unfavorable Variance}$$

Total factory overhead cost variance:

$$\frac{\text{Factory Overhead}}{\text{Cost Variance}} = \frac{\text{Variable Factory Overhead}}{\text{Controllable Variance}} + \frac{\text{Fixed Factory Overhead}}{\text{Volume Variance}}$$

$$\frac{\text{Factory Overhead}}{\text{Cost Variance}} = \$780 + \$2,450$$

$$\frac{\text{Factory Overhead}}{\text{Cost Variance}} = \$3,230 \text{ Unfavorable Variance}$$

Self-Examination Questions (Answers appear at the end of chapter)

1. Static budgets are often used by:

   A. production departments

   B. administrative departments

   C. responsibility centers

   D. capital projects

2. The total estimated sales for the coming year is 250,000 units. The estimated inventory at the beginning of the year is 22,500 units, and the desired inventory at the end of the year is 30,000 units. The total production indicated in the production budget is:

   A. 242,500 units

   B. 257,500 units

   C. 280,000 units

   D. 302,500 units

3. Dixon Company expects $650,000 of credit sales in March and $800,000 of credit sales in April. Dixon historically collects 70% of its

sales in the month of sale and 30% in the following month. How much cash does Dixon expect to collect in April?

A. $800,000

B. $560,000

C. $755,000

D. $1,015,000

4. The actual and standard direct materials costs for producing a specified quantity of product are as follows:

Actual:	51,000 pounds at $5.05	$257,550
Standard:	50,000 pounds at $5.00	$250,000

The direct materials price variance is:

A. $50 unfavorable

B. $2,500 unfavorable

C. $2,550 unfavorable

D. $7,550 unfavorable

5. Bower Company produced 4,000 units of product. Each unit requires 0.5 standard hour. The standard labor rate is $12 per hour. Actual direct labor for the period was $22,000 (2,200 hours × $10 per hour). The direct labor time variance is:

A. 200 hours unfavorable

B. $2,000 unfavorable

C. $4,000 favorable

D. $2,400 unfavorable

Class Discussion Questions

1. What are the three major objectives of budgeting?

2. What is the manager's role in a responsibility center?

3. Briefly describe the type of human behavior problems that might arise if budget goals are set too tightly.

4. Give an example of budgetary slack.

5. What behavioral problems are associated with setting a budget too loosely?

6. What behavioral problems are associated with establishing conflicting goals within the budget?

7. When would a company use zero-based budgeting?

8. Under what circumstances would a static budget be appropriate?

9. How do computerized budgeting systems aid firms in the budgeting process?

10. What is the first step in preparing a master budget?

11. Why should the production requirements set forth in the production budget be carefully coordinated with the sales budget?

12. Why should the timing of direct materials purchases be closely coordinated with the production budget?

13. In preparing the budget for the cost of goods sold, what are the three budgets from which data on relevant estimates of quantities and costs are combined with data on estimated inventories?

14. a. Discuss the purpose of the cash budget.

   b. If the cash for the first quarter of the fiscal year indicates excess cash at the end of each of the first two months, how might the excess cash be used?

15. How does a schedule of collections from sales assist in preparing the cash budget?

16. Give an example of how the capital expenditures budget affects other operating budgets.

17. What are the basic objectives in the use of standard costs?

18. How can standards be used by management to help control costs?

19. What is meant by reporting by the "principle of exceptions," as the term is used in reference to cost control?

20. How often should standards be revised?

21. How are standards used in budgetary performance evaluation?

22. a. What are the two variances between the actual cost and the standard cost for direct materials?

    b. Discuss some possible causes of these variances.

23. The materials cost variance report for Nickols Inc. indicates a large favorable materials price variance and a significant unfavorable materials quantity variance. What might have caused these offsetting variances?

24. a. What are the two variances between the actual cost and the standard cost for direct labor?

    b. Who generally has control over the direct labor cost?

25. A new assistant controller recently was heard to remark: "All the assembly workers in this plant are covered by union contracts, so there should be no labor variances." Was the controller's remark correct? Discuss.

26. Would the use of standards be appropriate in a nonmanufacturing setting, such as a fast-food restaurant?

27. Briefly explain why firms might use non-financial performance measures.

Exercises

E13-1

Flexible budget for selling and administrative expenses

Obj 1

SPREADSHEET

✓ Total selling and administrative expenses at $125,000 sales, $66,350

Agent Blaze uses flexible budgets that are based on the following data:

Sales commissions	8% of sales
Advertising expense	21% of sales
Miscellaneous selling expense	$2,250 plus 3% of sales
Office salaries expense	$15,000 per month
Office supplies expense	4% of sales
Miscellaneous administrative expense	$1,600 per month plus 2% of sales

Prepare a flexible selling and administrative expenses budget for January 2010 for sales volumes of $100,000, $125,000, and $150,000. (Use Exhibit 5 as a model.)

E13-2

Static budget vs. flexible budget

Obj 1

SPREADSHEET

✓ b. Excess of actual over budget for March, $53,000

The production supervisor of the Machining Department for Nell Company agreed to the following monthly static budget for the upcoming year:

Nell Company
Machining Department
Monthly Production Budget

Wages	$540,000
Utilities	36,000
Depreciation	60,000
Total	$636,000

The actual amount spent and the actual units produced in the first three months of 2010 in the Machining Department were as follows:

	Amount Spent	Units Produced
January	$600,000	110,000
February	570,000	100,000
March	545,000	90,000

The Machining Department supervisor has been very pleased with this performance, since actual expenditures have been less than the monthly budget. However, the plant manager believes that the budget should not remain fixed

for every month but should "flex" or adjust to the volume of work that is produced in the Machining Department. Additional budget information for the Machining Department is as follows:

Wages per hour	$18.00
Utility cost per direct labor hour	$1.20
Direct labor hours per unit	0.25
Planned unit production	120,000

a. Prepare a flexible budget for the actual units produced for January, February, and March in the Machining Department. Assume depreciation is a fixed cost.
b. Compare the flexible budget with the actual expenditures for the first three months. What does this comparison suggest?

E13-3

Flexible budget for Fabrication Department

Obj 1

SPREADSHEET

✓ Total department cost at 12,000 units, $1,029,000

Steelcase Inc. is one of the largest manufacturers of office furniture in the United States. In Grand Rapids, Michigan, it produces filing cabinets in two departments: Fabrication and Trim Assembly. Assume the following information for the Fabrication Department:

Steel per filing cabinet	45 pounds
Direct labor per filing cabinet	20 minutes
Supervisor salaries	$140,000 per month
Depreciation	$22,000 per month
Direct labor rate	$21 per hour
Steel cost	$1.45 per pound

Prepare a flexible budget for 12,000, 15,000, and 18,000 filing cabinets for the month of October 2010, similar to Exhibit 5, assuming that inventories are not significant.

E13-4

Sales and production budgets

Obj 2

SPREADSHEET

✓ b. Model DL total production, 7,985 units

Harmony Audio Company manufactures two models of speakers, DL and XL. Based on the following production and sales data for September 2009, prepare (a) a sales budget and (b) a production budget.

	DL	XL
Estimated inventory (units), September 1	240	60
Desired inventory (units), September 30	275	52
Expected sales volume (units):		
East Region	3,700	3,250
West Region	4,250	3,700
Unit sales price	$125	$195

E13-5

Professional fees earned budget

Obj 2

SPREADSHEET

✓ Total professional fees earned, $10,153,500

Roberts and Chou, CPAs, offer three types of services to clients: auditing, tax, and small business accounting. Based on experience and projected growth, the following billable hours have been estimated for the year ending December 31, 2010:

	Billable Hours
Audit Department:	
Staff	32,400
Partners	4,800
Tax Department:	
Staff	24,800
Partners	3,100
Small Business Accounting Department:	
Staff	4,500
Partners	630

The average billing rate for staff is $130 per hour, and the average billing rate for partners is $250 per hour. Prepare a professional fees earned budget for Roberts and Chou, CPAs, for the year ending December 31, 2010, using the following column headings and showing the estimated professional fees by type of service rendered:

Billable Hours	Hourly Rate	Total Revenue

E13-6

Professional labor cost budget

Obj 2

SPREADSHEET

✓ Staff total labor cost, $1,851,000

Based on the data in Exercise 13-5 and assuming that the average compensation per hour for staff is $30 and for partners is $125, prepare a professional labor cost budget for Roberts and Chou, CPAs, for the year ending December 31, 2010. Use the following column headings:

Staff	Partners

E13-7

Direct materials purchases budget

Obj 2

SPREADSHEET

✓ Total cheese purchases, $123,163

Marino's Frozen Pizza Inc. has determined from its production budget the following estimated production volumes for 12" and 16" frozen pizzas for April 2010:

	Units	
	12" Pizza	16" Pizza
Budgeted production volume	15,100	22,700

There are three direct materials used in producing the two types of pizza. The quantities of direct materials expected to be used for each pizza are as follows:

	12" Pizza	16" Pizza
Direct materials:		
Dough	0.90 lb. per unit	1.50 lbs. per unit
Tomato	0.60	1.00
Cheese	0.75	1.25

In addition, Marino's has determined the following information about each material:

	Dough	Tomato	Cheese
Estimated inventory, April 1, 2010	580 lbs.	205 lbs.	325 lbs.
Desired inventory, April 30, 2010	610 lbs.	200 lbs.	355 lbs.
Price per pound	$1.20	$2.60	$3.10

Prepare April's direct materials purchases budget for Marino's Frozen Pizza Inc.

E13-8

Direct materials purchases budget

Obj 2

SPREADSHEET

✓ Concentrate budgeted purchases, $107,600

Coca-Cola Enterprises is the largest bottler of Coca-Cola® in North America. The company purchases Coke® and Sprite® concentrate from *The Coca-Cola Company,* dilutes and mixes the concentrate with carbonated water, and then fills the blended beverage into cans or plastic two-liter bottles. Assume that the estimated

production for Coke and Sprite two-liter bottles at the Dallas, Texas, bottling plant are as follows for the month of March:

Coke	214,000 two-liter bottles
Sprite	163,000 two-liter bottles

In addition, assume that the concentrate costs $80 per pound for both Coke and Sprite and is used at a rate of 0.2 pound per 100 liters of carbonated water in blending Coke and 0.15 pound per 100 liters of carbonated water in blending Sprite. Assume that two-liter bottles cost $0.08 per bottle and carbonated water costs $0.06 per liter.

Prepare a direct materials purchases budget for March 2010, assuming no changes between beginning and ending inventories for all three materials.

E13-9

Direct labor cost budget

Obj 2

SPREADSHEET

✓ Total direct labor cost, Assembly, $208,860

Hammer Racket Company manufactures two types of tennis rackets, the Junior and Pro Striker models. The production budget for October for the two rackets is as follows:

	Junior	Pro Striker
Production budget	7,600 units	22,100 units

Both rackets are produced in two departments, Forming and Assembly. The direct labor hours required for each racket are estimated as follows:

	Forming Department	Assembly Department
Junior	0.25 hour per unit	0.40 hour per unit
Pro Striker	0.35 hour per unit	0.65 hour per unit

The direct labor rate for each department is as follows:

Forming Department	$16.00 per hour
Assembly Department	$12.00 per hour

Prepare the direct labor cost budget for October 2010.

E13-10

Production and direct labor cost budgets

Obj 2

SPREADSHEET

✓ a. Total production of 501 Jeans, 54,000

Levi Strauss & Co. manufactures slacks and jeans under a variety of brand names, such as Dockers® and 501 Jeans®. Slacks and jeans are assembled by a variety of different sewing operations. Assume that the sales budget for Dockers and 501 Jeans shows estimated sales of 24,700 and 53,600 pairs, respectively, for January 2010. The finished goods inventory is assumed as follows:

	Dockers	501 Jeans
January 1 estimated inventory	1,110	1,490
January 31 desired inventory	410	1,890

Assume the following direct labor data per 10 pairs of Dockers and 501 Jeans for four different sewing operations:

	Direct Labor per 10 Pairs	
	Dockers	501 Jeans
Inseam	18 minutes	12 minutes
Outerseam	22	15
Pockets	7	9
Zipper	10	6
Total	57 minutes	42 minutes

a. Prepare a production budget for January. Prepare the budget in two columns: Dockers™ and 501 Jeans™.

b. Prepare the January direct labor cost budget for the four sewing operations, assuming a $12.50 wage per hour for the inseam and outerseam sewing operations and a $16 wage per hour for the pocket and zipper sewing operations. Prepare the direct labor cost budget in four columns: inseam, outerseam, pockets, and zipper.

E13-11

Factory overhead cost budget

Obj 2

SPREADSHEET

✓ Total variable factory overhead costs, $264,000

Venus Candy Company budgeted the following costs for anticipated production for September 2010:

Advertising expenses	$275,000	Production supervisor wages	$132,000
Manufacturing supplies	15,000	Production control salaries	35,000
Power and light	44,000	Executive officer salaries	280,000
Sales commissions	300,000	Materials management salaries	38,000
Factory insurance	26,000	Factory depreciation	21,000

Prepare a factory overhead cost budget, separating variable and fixed costs. Assume that factory insurance and depreciation are the only factory fixed costs.

E13-12

Cost of goods sold budget

Obj 2

SPREADSHEET

✓ Cost of goods sold, $425,420

The controller of Swiss Ceramics Inc. wishes to prepare a cost of goods sold budget for June. The controller assembled the following information for constructing the cost of goods sold budget:

Direct materials:	Enamel	Paint	Porcelain	Total
Total direct materials purchases budgeted for June	$33,840	$5,340	$118,980	$158,160
Estimated inventory, June 1, 2010	1,150	2,800	4,330	8,280
Desired inventory, June 30, 2010	2,400	2,050	6,000	10,450

Direct labor cost:	Kiln Department	Decorating Department	Total
Total direct labor cost budgeted for June	$41,600	$142,400	$184,000

Finished goods inventories:		Dish	Bowl	Figurine	Total
Estimated inventory, June 1, 2010		$4,060	$2,970	$2,470	$ 9,500
Desired inventory, June 30, 2010		3,350	4,150	3,590	11,090
Work in process inventories:					
Estimated inventory, June 1, 2010	$ 2,800				
Desired inventory, June 30, 2010	1,880				
Budgeted factory overhead costs for June:					
Indirect factory wages	$64,900				
Depreciation of plant and equipment	12,600				
Power and light	4,900				
Indirect materials	3,700				
Total	$86,100				

Use the preceding information to prepare a cost of goods sold budget for June 2010.

E13-13

Schedule of cash collections
of accounts receivable

Obj 2

SPREADSHEET

✓ **Total cash collected
in July, $520,350**

Pet Joy Wholesale Inc., a pet wholesale supplier, was organized on May 1, 2010. Projected sales for each of the first three months of operations are as follows:

May	$360,000
June	450,000
July	600,000

The company expects to sell 10% of its merchandise for cash. Of sales on account, 50% are expected to be collected in the month of the sale, 35% in the month following the sale, and the remainder in the second month following the sale.

Prepare a schedule indicating cash collections from sales for May, June, and July.

E13-14

Schedule of cash collections
of accounts receivable

Obj 2

SPREADSHEET

✓ **Total cash collected
in August, $300,000**

Office Mate Supplies Inc. has "cash and carry" customers and credit customers. Office Mate estimates that 25% of monthly sales are to cash customers, while the remaining sales are to credit customers. Of the credit customers, 20% pay their accounts in the month of sale, while the remaining 80% pay their accounts in the month following the month of sale. Projected sales for the first three months of 2010 are as follows:

August	$250,000
September	290,000
October	270,000

The Accounts Receivable balance on July 31, 2010, was $200,000.

Prepare a schedule of cash collections from sales for August, September, and October.

E13-15

Schedule of cash payments

Obj 2

SPREADSHEET

✓ **Total cash payments
in August, $79,440**

Excel Learning Systems Inc. was organized on May 31, 2010. Projected selling and administrative expenses for each of the first three months of operations are as follows:

June	$117,400
July	110,500
August	100,400

Depreciation, insurance, and property taxes represent $25,000 of the estimated monthly expenses. The annual insurance premium was paid on May 31, and property taxes for the year will be paid in December. Sixty percent of the remainder of the expenses are expected to be paid in the month in which they are incurred, with the balance to be paid in the following month.

Prepare a schedule indicating cash payments for selling and administrative expenses for June, July, and August.

E13-16

Schedule of cash payments

Obj 2

SPREADSHEET

✓ **Total cash payments
in September,
$123,300**

Rejuvenation Physical Therapy Inc. is planning its cash payments for operations for the third quarter (July–September), 2011. The Accrued Expenses Payable balance on July 1 is $24,000. The budgeted expenses for the next three months are as follows:

	July	August	September
Salaries	$ 58,200	$ 63,500	$ 74,500
Utilities	5,300	5,600	7,100
Other operating expenses	48,500	52,700	58,200
Total	$112,000	$121,800	$139,800

Other operating expenses include $10,500 of monthly depreciation expense and $600 of monthly insurance expense that was prepaid for the year on March 1 of the current year. Of the remaining expenses, 70% are paid in the month in which they are incurred, with the remainder paid in the following month. The Accrued Expenses Payable balance on July 1 relates to the expenses incurred in June.

Prepare a schedule of cash payments for operations for July, August, and September.

E13-17

Capital expenditures budget

Obj 2

SPREADSHEET

✓ Total capital expenditures in 2010, $7,000,000

On January 1, 2010, the controller of Gardeneer Tools Inc. is planning capital expenditures for the years 2010–2013. The controller interviewed several Gardeneer executives to collect the necessary information for the capital expenditures budget. Excerpts of the interviews are shown below.

Director of Facilities: A construction contract was signed in late 2009 for the construction of a new factory building at a contract cost of $13,000,000. The construction is scheduled to begin in 2010 and be completed in 2011.

Vice President of Manufacturing: Once the new factory building is finished, we plan to purchase $1.7 million in equipment in late 2011. I expect that an additional $200,000 will be needed early in the following year (2012) to test and install the equipment before we can begin production. If sales continue to grow, I expect we'll need to invest another million in equipment in 2013.

Vice President of Marketing: We have really been growing lately. I wouldn't be surprised if we need to expand the size of our new factory building in 2013 by at least 40%. Fortunately, we expect inflation to have minimal impact on construction costs over the next four years. Additionally, I would expect the cost of the expansion to be proportional to the size of the expansion.

Director of Information Systems: We need to upgrade our information systems to wireless network technology. It doesn't make sense to do this until after the new factory building is completed and producing product. During 2012, once the factory is up and running, we should equip the whole facility with wireless technology. I think it would cost us $1,600,000 today to install the technology. However, prices have been dropping by 25% per year, so it should be less expensive at a later date.

President: I am excited about our long-term prospects. My only short-term concern is financing the $7,000,000 of construction costs on the portion of the new factory building scheduled to be completed in 2010.

Use the interview information above to prepare a capital expenditures budget for Gardeneer Tools Inc. for the years 2010–2013.

E13-18

Standard product cost

Obj 3

Hickory Furniture Company manufactures unfinished oak furniture. Hickory uses a standard cost system. The direct labor, direct materials, and factory overhead standards for an unfinished dining room table are as follows:

Direct labor:	standard rate	$18.00 per hr.
	standard time per unit	2.5 hrs.
Direct materials (oak):	standard price	$9.50 per bd. ft.
	standard quantity	18 bd. ft.
Variable factory overhead:	standard rate	$2.80 per direct labor hr.
Fixed factory overhead:	standard rate	$1.20 per direct labor hr.

Determine the standard cost per dining room table.

E13-19

Budget performance report

Obj 4

SPREADSHEET

✓ b. Direct labor cost variance, $160 U

Warwick Bottle Company (WBC) manufactures plastic two-liter bottles for the beverage industry. The cost standards per 100 two-liter bottles are as follows:

Cost Category	Standard Cost per 100 Two-Liter Bottles
Direct labor	$1.32
Direct materials	5.34
Factory overhead	0.34
Total	$7.00

At the beginning of July, WBC management planned to produce 650,000 bottles. The actual number of bottles produced for July was 700,000 bottles. The actual costs for July of the current year were as follows:

Cost Category	Actual Cost for the Month Ended July 31, 2010
Direct labor	$ 9,400
Direct materials	36,500
Factory overhead	2,400
Total	$48,300

a. Prepare the July manufacturing standard cost budget (direct labor, direct materials, and factory overhead) for WBC, assuming planned production.
b. Prepare a budget performance report for manufacturing costs, showing the total cost variances for direct materials, direct labor, and factory overhead for July.
c. Interpret the budget performance report.

E13-20

Direct materials variances

Obj 5

✓ a. Price variance, $2,730 F

The following data relate to the direct materials cost for the production of 2,000 automobile tires:

Actual:	54,600 lbs. at $1.80	$98,280
Standard:	53,400 lbs. at $1.85	$98,790

a. Determine the price variance, quantity variance, and total direct materials cost variance.
b. To whom should the variances be reported for analysis and control?

E13-21

Standard direct materials cost per unit from variance data

Obj 5

The following data relating to direct materials cost for March of the current year are taken from the records of Play Tyme Inc., a manufacturer of plastic toys:

Quantity of direct materials used	5,000 lbs.
Actual unit price of direct materials	$2.40 per lb.
Units of finished product manufactured	1,200 units
Standard direct materials per unit of finished product	4 lbs.
Direct materials quantity variance—unfavorable	$500
Direct materials price variance—favorable	$500

Determine the standard direct materials cost per unit of finished product, assuming that there was no inventory of work in process at either the beginning or the end of the month.

E13-22

Standard product cost, direct materials variance

Obj 5

H.J. Heinz Company uses standards to control its materials costs. Assume that a batch of ketchup (1,500 pounds) has the following standards:

	Standard Quantity	Standard Price
Whole tomatoes	2,500 lbs.	$ 0.45 per lb.
Vinegar	140 gal.	2.75 per gal.
Corn syrup	12 gal.	10.00 per gal.
Salt	56 lbs.	2.50 per lb.

The actual materials in a batch may vary from the standard due to tomato characteristics. Assume that the actual quantities of materials for batch K103 were as follows:

2,600 lbs. of tomatoes
135 gal. of vinegar
13 gal. of corn syrup
55 lbs. of salt

a. Determine the standard unit materials cost per pound for a standard batch.
b. Determine the direct materials quantity variance for batch K103.

E13-23

Direct labor variances

Obj 5

✓ a. Rate variance, $730 U

The following data relate to labor cost for production of 5,500 cellular telephones:

Actual:	3,650 hrs. at $15.20	$55,480
Standard:	3,710 hrs. at $15.00	$55,650

a. Determine the rate variance, time variance, and total direct labor cost variance.
b. Discuss what might have caused these variances.

E13-24

Direct labor variances

Obj 5

✓ a. Time variance, $510 U

Alpine Bicycle Company manufactures mountain bikes. The following data for May of the current year are available:

Quantity of direct labor used	600 hrs.
Actual rate for direct labor	$12.50 per hr.
Bicycles completed in May	280
Standard direct labor per bicycle	2 hrs.
Standard rate for direct labor	$12.75 per hr.
Planned bicycles for May	310

Determine the direct labor rate and time variances.

E13-25

Direct materials and direct labor variances

Obj 5

✓ Direct materials quantity variance, $600 U

At the beginning of October, Cornerstone Printers Company budgeted 16,000 books to be printed in October at standard direct materials and direct labor costs as follows:

Direct materials	$24,000
Direct labor	8,000
Total	$32,000

The standard materials price is $0.60 per pound. The standard direct labor rate is $10 per hour. At the end of October, the actual direct materials and direct labor costs were as follows:

Actual direct materials	$21,600
Actual direct labor	7,200
Total	$28,800

There were no direct materials price or direct labor rate variances for October. In addition, assume no changes in the direct materials inventory balances in October. Cornerstone Printers Company actually produced 14,000 units during October.

Determine the direct materials quantity and direct labor time variances.

E13-26

Direct labor standards for nonmanufacturing expenses

Obj 5

✓ a. $1,440

St. Luke Hospital began using standards to evaluate its Admissions Department. The standards were broken into two types of admissions as follows:

Type of Admission	Standard Time to Complete Admission Record
Unscheduled admission	40 min.
Scheduled admission	10 min.

The unscheduled admission took longer, since name, address, and insurance information needed to be determined at the time of admission. Information was collected on scheduled admissions prior to the admissions, which was less time consuming.

The Admissions Department employs two full-time people (40 productive hours per week, with no overtime) at $18 per hour. For the most recent week, the department handled 66 unscheduled and 240 scheduled admissions.

a. How much was actually spent on labor for the week?

b. What are the standard hours for the actual volume for the week?

c. Calculate a time variance, and report how well the department performed for the week.

E13-27

Nonfinancial performance measures

Obj 6

Tri-County College wishes to monitor the efficiency and quality of its course registration process.

a. Identify three input and three output measures for this process.

b. Why would Tri-County College use nonfinancial measures for monitoring this process?

E13-28

Nonfinancial performance measures

Obj 6

Under Par, Inc., is an Internet retailer of golf equipment. Customers order golf equipment from the company, using an online catalog. The company processes these orders and delivers the requested product from its warehouse. The company wants to provide customers with an excellent purchase experience in order to expand the business through favorable word-of-mouth advertising and to drive repeat business. To help monitor performance, the company developed a set of performance measures for its order placement and delivery process.

Average computer response time to customer "clicks"

Dollar amount of returned goods

Elapsed time between customer order and product delivery

Maintenance dollars divided by hardware investment

Number of customer complaints divided by the number of orders

Number of misfilled orders divided by the number of orders

Number of orders per warehouse employee

Number of page faults or errors due to software programming errors

Number of software fixes per week

Server (computer) downtime

Training dollars per programmer

a. For each performance measure, identify it as either an input or output measure related to the "order placement and delivery" process.

b. Provide an explanation for each performance measure.

E13-29

Factory overhead cost variances

Appendix

SPREADSHEET

✓ Volume variance, $12,750 U

The following data relate to factory overhead cost for the production of 5,000 computers:

Actual:	Variable factory overhead	$125,000
	Fixed factory overhead	34,000
Standard:	5,000 hrs. at $30	150,000

If productive capacity of 100% was 8,000 hours and the factory overhead cost budgeted at the level of 5,000 standard hours was $162,750, determine the variable factory overhead controllable variance, fixed factory overhead volume variance, and total factory overhead cost variance. The fixed factory overhead rate was $4.25 per hour.

E13-30

Factory overhead cost
variances

Appendix

✓ a. $1,000 F

Perma Weave Textiles Corporation began January with a budget for 30,000 hours of production in the Weaving Department. The department has a full capacity of 40,000 hours under normal business conditions. The budgeted overhead at the planned volumes at the beginning of January was as follows:

Variable overhead	$ 75,000
Fixed overhead	52,000
Total	$127,000

The actual factory overhead was $128,500 for January. The actual fixed factory overhead was as budgeted. During January, the Weaving Department had standard hours at actual production volume of 31,000 hours.

a. Determine the variable factory overhead controllable variance.
b. Determine the fixed factory overhead volume variance.

E13-31

Factory overhead variance
corrections

Appendix

The data related to Acclaim Sporting Goods Company's factory overhead cost for the production of 50,000 units of product are as follows:

Actual:	Variable factory overhead	$269,000
	Fixed factory overhead	180,000
Standard:	76,000 hrs. at $6.00	456,000
	($3.60 for variable factory overhead)	

Productive capacity at 100% of normal was 75,000 hours, and the factory overhead cost budgeted at the level of 76,000 standard hours was $456,000. Based on these data, the chief cost accountant prepared the following variance analysis:

Variable factory overhead controllable variance:		
Actual variable factory overhead cost incurred	$269,000	
Budgeted variable factory overhead for 76,000 hours	273,600	
Variance—favorable		-$4,600
Fixed factory overhead volume variance:		
Normal productive capacity at 100%	75,000 hrs.	
Standard for amount produced	76,000	
Productive capacity not used	1,000 h...	
Standard variable factory overhead rate	× $6.00	
Variance—unfavorable		6,000
Total factory overhead cost variance—unfavorable		$1,400

Identify the errors in the factory overhead cost variance analysis.

E13-32

Factory overhead cost
variance report

Appendix

✓ Net controllable
variance, $500 U

Scientific Molded Products Inc. prepared the following factory overhead cost budget for the Trim Department for August 2010, during which it expected to use 10,000 hours for production:

Variable overhead cost:		
Indirect factory labor	$24,000	
Power and light	4,000	
Indirect materials	12,000	
Total variable cost		$ 40,000
Fixed overhead cost:		
Supervisory salaries	$30,000	
Depreciation of plant and equipment	23,400	
Insurance and property taxes	21,600	
Total fixed cost		75,000
Total factory overhead cost		$115,000

Scientific Molded Products has available 15,000 hours of monthly productive capacity in the Trim Department under normal business conditions. During August, the Trim Department actually used 11,000 hours for production. The actual fixed costs were as budgeted. The actual variable overhead for August was as follows:

Actual variable factory overhead cost:	
Indirect factory labor	$27,000
Power and light	4,000
Indirect materials	13,500
Total variable cost	$44,500

Construct a factory overhead cost variance report for the Trim Department for August.

Problems

P13-1

Sales, production, direct materials purchases, and direct labor cost

Obj 2

SPREADSHEET

✓ 3. Total direct materials purchases, $7,721,394

The budget director of Regal Furniture Company requests estimates of sales, production, and other operating data from the various administrative units every month. Selected information concerning sales and production for August 2010 is summarized as follows:

a. Estimated sales of King and Prince chairs for August by sales territory:

Northern Domestic:
King .... 5,500 units at $750 per unit
Prince .... 6,900 units at $520 per unit
Southern Domestic:
King .... 3,200 units at $690 per unit
Prince .... 4,000 units at $580 per unit
International:
King .... 1,450 units at $780 per unit
Prince .... 900 units at $600 per unit

b. Estimated inventories at August 1:

Direct materials:
Fabric .... 4,500 sq. yds.
Wood .... 6,000 lineal ft.
Filler .... 2,800 cu. ft.
Springs .... 6,700 units

Finished products:
King .... 950 units
Prince .... 280 units

c. Desired inventories at August 31:

Direct materials:
    Fabric . . . . . . .4,300 sq. yds.
    Wood . . . . . . .6,200 lineal ft.
    Filler . . . . .3,100 cu. ft.
    Springs . . . . . .7,500 units

Finished products:
    King . . . . 800 units
    Prince . . . . 400 units

d. Direct materials used in production:

In manufacture of King:
    Fabric . . . . 5.0 sq. yds. per unit of product
    Wood . . . . 35 lineal ft. per unit of product
    Filler . . . . 3.8 cu. ft. per unit of product
    Springs . . . . 14 units per unit of product
In manufacture of Prince:
    Fabric . . . . 3.5 sq. yds. per unit of product
    Wood . . . . 25 lineal ft. per unit of product
    Filler . . . . 3.2 cu. ft. per unit of product
    Springs . . . . 10 units per unit of product

e. Anticipated purchase price for direct materials:

Fabric . . . . $12.00 per sq. yd.
Wood . . . . 8.00 per lineal ft.

Filler . . . . . $3.50 per cu. ft.
Springs . . . 4.50 per unit

f. Direct labor requirements:

King:
    Framing Department . . . . 2.5 hrs. at $12 per hr.
    Cutting Department . . . . / . . . 1.5 hrs. at $11 per hr.
    Upholstery Department . . . . . . 2.4 hrs. at $14 per hr.
Prince:
    Framing Department . . . . 1.8 hrs. at $12 per hr.
    Cutting Department . . . . 0.5 hrs. at $11 per hr.
    Upholstery Department . . . . . . 2.0 hrs. at $14 per hr.

Instructions

1. Prepare a sales budget for August.
2. Prepare a production budget for August.
3. Prepare a direct materials purchases budget for August.
4. Prepare a direct labor cost budget for August.

P13-2

Budgeted income statement
and supporting budgets

Obj 2

SPREADSHEET

✓ 4. **Total direct labor
cost in Assembly
Dept., $85,605**

The budget director of Heads Up Athletic Co., with the assistance of the controller, treasurer, production manager, and sales manager, has gathered the following data for use in developing the budgeted income statement for January 2010:

a. Estimated sales for January:

Batting helmet . . . . 3,700 units at $70 per unit
Football helmet . . . . . . 7,200 units at $142 per unit

b. Estimated inventories at January 1:

Direct materials:
Plastic . . . . 800 lbs.
Foam lining . . . . . 520 lbs.

Finished products:
Batting helmet . . . . . 310 units at $33 per unit
Football helmet . . . . 420 units at $57 per unit

c. Desired inventories at January 31:

Direct materials:
Plastic . . . . 1,240 lbs.
Foam lining . . . . .   450 lbs.

Finished products:
Batting helmet . . . . . 290 units at $34 per unit
Football helmet . . . . 520 units at $58 per unit

d. Direct materials used in production:

In manufacture of batting helmet:
Plastic . . . . 1.20 lbs. per unit of product
Foam lining . . . . 0.50 lb. per unit of product
In manufacture of football helmet:
Plastic . . . . 2.80 lbs. per unit of product
Foam lining . . . . 1.40 lbs. per unit of product

e. Anticipated cost of purchases and beginning and ending inventory of direct materials:

Plastic . . . . $7.50 per lb.
Foam lining . . . . $5.00 per lb.

f. Direct labor requirements:

Batting helmet:
Molding Department. . . . . 0.20 hr. at $15 per hr.
Assembly Department . . . . 0.50 hr. at $13 per hr.
Football helmet:
Molding Department. . . . . 0.30 hr. at $15 per hr.
Assembly Department . . . . 0.65 hr. at $13 per hr.

g. Estimated factory overhead costs for January:

Indirect factory wages . . . . $115,000   Power and light $18,000
Depreciation of plant and equipment . . .   32,000   Insurance and property tax . . .   8,700

h. Estimated operating expenses for January:

Sales salaries expense $275,300
Advertising expense.   139,500
Office salaries expense   83,100
Depreciation expense—office equipment   5,800
Telephone expense—selling   3,200
Telephone expense—administrative.   900
Travel expense—selling.   46,200
Office supplies expense   4,900
Miscellaneous administrative expense   5,200

i. Estimated other income and expense for January:

Interest revenue $14,500
Interest expense   17,400

j. Estimated tax rate: 30%

Instructions

1. Prepare a sales budget for January.
2. Prepare a production budget for January.
3. Prepare a direct materials purchases budget for January.
4. Prepare a direct labor cost budget for January.
5. Prepare a factory overhead cost budget for January.
6. Prepare a cost of goods sold budget for January. Work in process at the beginning of January is estimated to be $12,500, and work in process at the end of January is desired to be $13,500.
7. Prepare a selling and administrative expenses budget for January.
8. Prepare a budgeted income statement for January.

P13-3

Cash budget

Obj 2

SPREADSHEET

✓ 1. August deficiency, $21,100

The controller of Dash Shoes Inc. instructs you to prepare a monthly cash budget for the next three months. You are presented with the following budget information:

	June	July	August
Sales	$120,000	$150,000	$200,000
Manufacturing costs	50,000	65,000	72,000
Selling and administrative expenses	35,000	40,000	45,000
Capital expenditures	—	—	48,000

The company expects to sell about 10% of its merchandise for cash. Of sales on account, 60% are expected to be collected in full in the month following the sale and the remainder the following month. Depreciation, insurance, and property tax expense represent $8,000 of the estimated monthly manufacturing costs. The annual insurance premium is paid in February, and the annual property taxes are paid in November. Of the remainder of the manufacturing costs, 80% are expected to be paid in the month in which they are incurred and the balance in the following month.

Current assets as of June 1 include cash of $45,000, marketable securities of $65,000, and accounts receivable of $143,400 ($105,000 from May sales and $38,400 from April sales). Sales on account in April and May were $96,000 and $105,000, respectively. Current liabilities as of June 1 include a $60,000, 12%, 90-day note payable due August 20 and $8,000 of accounts payable incurred in May for manufacturing costs. All selling and administrative expenses are paid in cash in the period they are incurred. It is expected that $3,500 in dividends will be received in June. An estimated income tax payment of $18,000 will be made in July. Dash Shoes' regular quarterly dividend of $8,000 is expected to be declared in July and paid in August. Management desires to maintain a minimum cash balance of $35,000.

Instructions

1. Prepare a monthly cash budget and supporting schedules for June, July, and August 2010.
2. On the basis of the cash budget prepared in part (1), what recommendation should be made to the controller?

P13-4

Direct materials and direct labor variance analysis

Obj 5

✓ c. Direct labor time variance, $1,095 F

Best Bathware Company manufactures faucets in a small manufacturing facility. The faucets are made from zinc. Manufacturing has 50 employees. Each employee presently provides 36 hours of labor per week. Information about a production week is as follows:

Standard wage per hr.	$14.60
Standard labor time per faucet	15 min.
Standard number of lbs. of zinc	1.6 lbs.
Standard price per lb. of zinc	$11.50
Actual price per lb. of zinc	$11.75
Actual lbs. of zinc used during the week	12,400 lbs.
Number of faucets produced during the week	7,500
Actual wage per hr.	$15.00
Actual hrs. per week	1,800 hrs.

Instructions

Determine (a) the standard cost per unit for direct materials and direct labor; (b) the price variance, quantity variance, and total direct materials cost variance; and (c) the rate variance, time variance, and total direct labor cost variance.

P13-5

Direct materials and direct labor, variance analysis; Appendix: Factory overhead cost variance analysis.

Obj 5

SPREADSHEET

✓ a. Direct materials price variance, $7,060 F

Road Ready Tire Co. manufactures automobile tires. Standard costs and actual costs for direct materials, direct labor, and factory overhead incurred for the manufacture of 5,200 tires were as follows:

	Standard Costs	Actual Costs
Direct materials	71,000 lbs. at $5.10	70,600 lbs. at $5.00
Direct labor	1,300 hrs. at $17.50	1,330 hrs. at $17.80
Factory overhead	Rates per direct labor hr., based on 100% of normal capacity of 1,350 direct labor hrs.:	
	Variable cost, $3.10	$4,000 variable cost
	Fixed cost, $4.90	$6,615 fixed cost

Each tire requires 0.25 hour of direct labor.

Instructions

Determine (a) the price variance, quantity variance, and total direct materials cost variance; (b) the rate variance, time variance, and total direct labor cost variance; and (c) Appendix: variable factory overhead controllable variance, the fixed factory overhead volume variance, and total factory overhead cost variance.

P13-6

Standards for nonmanufacturing expenses

Obj 6

✓ 2. $256 F

The Radiology Department provides imaging services for Parkside Medical Center. One important activity in the Radiology Department is transcribing digitally recorded analyses of images into a written report. The manager of the Radiology Department determined that the average transcriptionist could type 750 lines of a report in an hour. The plan for the first week in May called for 60,000 typed lines to be written. The Radiology Department has two transcriptionists. Each transcriptionist is hired from an employment firm that requires temporary employees to be hired for a minimum of a 40-hour week. Transcriptionists are paid $16.00 per hour. The manager offered a bonus if the department could type more than 65,000 lines for the week, without overtime. Due to high service demands, the transcriptionists typed more lines in the first week of May than planned. The actual amount of lines typed in the first week of May was 72,000 lines, without overtime. As a result, the bonus caused the average transcriptionist hourly rate to increase to $19.00 per hour during the first week in May.

Instructions

1. If the department typed 60,000 lines according to the original plan, what would have been the labor time variance?
2. What was the labor time variance as a result of typing 72,000 lines?
3. What was the labor rate variance as a result of the bonus?
4. The manager is trying to determine if a better decision would have been to hire a temporary transcriptionist to meet the higher typing demands in the first week of May, rather than paying out the bonus. If another employee was hired from the employment firm, what would have been the labor time variance in the first week?
5. Which decision is better, paying the bonus or hiring another transcriptionist?
6. Are there any performance-related issues that the labor time and rate variances fail to consider? Explain.

P13-7

Appendix: Standard factory overhead variance report

Obj 4

SPREADSHEET

✓ **Controllable variance, $640 F**

Bio-Care, Inc., a manufacturer of disposable medical supplies, prepared the following factory overhead cost budget for the Assembly Department for March 2010. The company expected to operate the department at 100% of normal capacity of 18,000 hours.

Variable costs:		
Indirect factory wages	$135,000	
Power and light	93,600	
Indirect materials	25,200	
Total variable cost		$253,800
Fixed costs:		
Supervisory salaries	$ 72,000	
Depreciation of plant and equipment	51,500	
Insurance and property taxes	24,100	
Total fixed cost		147,600
Total factory overhead cost		$401,400

During March, the department operated at 16,900 hours, and the factory overhead costs incurred were indirect factory wages, $126,320; power and light,

$88,110; indirect materials, $23,220; supervisory salaries, $72,000; depreciation of plant and equipment, $51,500; and insurance and property taxes, $24,100.

Instructions

Prepare a factory overhead cost variance report for March. To be useful for cost control, the budgeted amounts should be based on 16,900 hours.

Activities

A13-1
Ethics and professional conduct in business

ETHICS

The director of marketing for Eclipse Computer Co., Lori Keller, had the following discussion with the company controller, Deon Johnson, on July 26 of the current year:

Lori: Deon, it looks like I'm going to spend much less than indicated on my July budget.

Deon: I'm glad to hear it.

Lori: Well, I'm not so sure it's good news. I'm concerned that the president will see that I'm under budget and reduce my budget in the future. The only reason that I look good is that we've delayed an advertising campaign. Once the campaign hits in September, I'm sure my actual expenditures will go up. You see, we are also having our sales convention in September. Having the advertising campaign and the convention at the same time is going to kill my September numbers.

Deon: I don't think that's anything to worry about. We all expect some variation in actual spending month to month. What's really important is staying within the budgeted targets for the year. Does that look as if it's going to be a problem?

Lori: I don't think so, but just the same, I'd like to be on the safe side.

Deon: What do you mean?

Lori: Well, this is what I'd like to do. I want to pay the convention-related costs in advance this month. I'll pay the hotel for room and convention space and purchase the airline tickets in advance. In this way, I can charge all these expenditures to July's budget. This would cause my actual expenses to come close to budget for July. Moreover, when the big advertising campaign hits in September, I won't have to worry about expenditures for the convention on my September budget as well. The convention costs will already be paid. Thus, my September expenses should be pretty close to budget.

Deon: I can't tell you when to make your convention purchases, but I'm not too sure that it should be expensed on July's budget.

Lori: What's the problem? It looks like "no harm, no foul" to me. I can't see that there's anything wrong with this—it's just smart management.

How should Deon Johnson respond to Lori Keller's request to expense the advanced payments for convention-related costs against July's budget?

A13-2
Evaluating budgeting systems

Children's Hospital of the King's Daughters Health System in Norfolk, Virginia, introduced a new budgeting method that allowed the hospital's annual plan to be updated for changes in operating plans. For example, if the budget was based on

400 patient-days (number of patients × number of days in the hospital) and the actual count rose to 450 patient-days, the variable costs of staffing, lab work, and medication costs could be adjusted to reflect this change. The budget manager stated, "I work with hospital directors to turn data into meaningful information and effect change before the month ends."

a. What budgeting methods are being used under the new approach?
b. Why are these methods superior to the former approaches?

A13-3

Service company static decision making

A bank manager of First Union Bank Inc. uses the managerial accounting system to track the costs of operating the various departments within the bank. The departments include Cash Management, Trust, Commercial Loans, Mortgage Loans, Operations, Credit Card, and Branch Services. The budget and actual results for the Operations Department are as follows:

Resources	Budget	Actual
Salaries	$200,000	$200,000
Benefits	30,000	30,000
Supplies	45,000	42,000
Travel	20,000	30,000
Training	25,000	35,000
Overtime	25,000	20,000
Total	$345,000	$357,000
Excess of actual over budget	$ 12,000	

a. What information is provided by the budget? Specifically, what questions can the bank manager ask of the Operations Department manager?
b. What information does the budget fail to provide? Specifically, could the budget information be presented differently to provide even more insight for the bank manager?

A13-4

Objectives of the master budget

Domino's Pizza L.L.C. operates pizza delivery and carryout restaurants. The annual report describes its business as follows:

We offer a focused menu of high-quality, value-priced pizza with three types of crust (Hand-Tossed, Thin Crust, and Deep Dish), along with buffalo wings, bread sticks, cheesy bread, CinnaStix®, and Coca-Cola® products. Our hand-tossed pizza is made from fresh dough produced in our regional distribution centers. We prepare every pizza using real cheese, pizza sauce made from fresh tomatoes, and a choice of high-quality meat and vegetable toppings in generous portions. Our focused menu and use of premium ingredients enable us to consistently and efficiently produce the highest-quality pizza.

Over the 41 years since our founding, we have developed a simple, cost-efficient model. We offer a limited menu, our stores are designed for delivery and carry-out, and we do not generally offer dine-in service. As a result, our stores require relatively small, lower-rent locations and limited capital expenditures.

How would a master budget support planning, directing, and control for Domino's?

A13-5

Integrity and evaluating budgeting systems

The city of Western Heights has an annual budget cycle that begins on July 1 and ends on June 30. At the beginning of each budget year, an annual budget is established for each department. The annual budget is divided by 12 months to provide a constant monthly static budget. On June 30, all unspent budgeted monies for the budget year from the various city departments must be "returned" to the General Fund. Thus, if department heads fail to use their budget by year-end, they will lose it. A budget analyst prepared a chart of the difference between the monthly actual and budgeted amounts for the recent fiscal year. The chart was as follows:

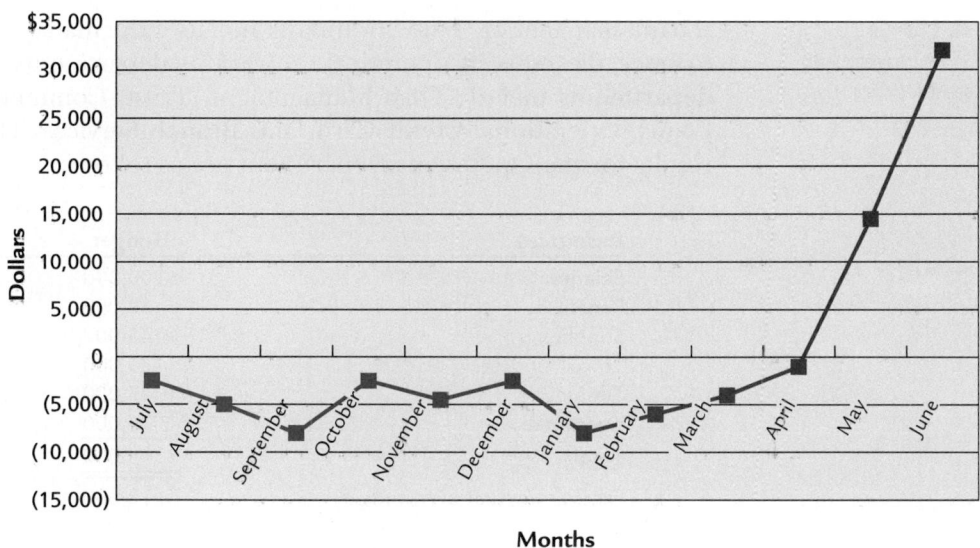

a. Interpret the chart.
b. Suggest an improvement in the budget system.

A13-6

Ethics and professional conduct in business using nonmanufacturing standards

ETHICS

Michael McIntyre is a cost analyst with Mid-States Insurance Company. Mid-States is applying standards to its claims payment operation. Claims payment is a repetitive operation that could be evaluated with standards. Michael used time and motion studies to identify an ideal standard of 36 claims processed per hour. The Claims Processing Department manager, Kimberly Mann, has rejected this standard and has argued that the standard should be 30 claims processed per hour. Kimberly and Michael were unable to agree, so they decided to discuss this matter openly at a joint meeting with the vice president of operations, who would arbitrate a final decision. Prior to the meeting, Michael wrote the following memo to the VP.

> To: T. J. Logan, Vice President of Operations
> From: Michael McIntyre
> Re: Standards in the Claims Processing Department
>
> As you know, Kimberly and I are scheduled to meet with you to discuss our disagreement with respect to the appropriate standards for the Claims Processing Department. I have conducted time and motion studies and have determined that the ideal standard is 36 claims processed per hour. Kimberly argues that 30 claims processed per hour would be more appropriate. I believe she is trying to "pad" the budget with some slack. I'm not sure what she is trying to get away with, but I believe

a tight standard will drive efficiency up in her area. I hope you will agree when we meet with you next week.

Discuss the ethical and professional issues in this situation.

A13-7

Nonfinancial performance measures

The senior management of Calvin Company has proposed the following three performance measures for the company:

1. Net income as a percent of stockholders' equity
2. Revenue growth
3. Employee satisfaction

Management believes these three measures combine both financial and nonfinancial measures and are thus superior to using just financial measures.

What advice would you give Calvin Company for improving its performance measurement system?

A13-8

Nonfinancial performance measures

The controller of a manufacturing company used a number of measures to provide managers information about the performance of its manufacturing operation. Three measures used by the company are:

• Scrap Index: The sales dollar value of scrap for the period.
• Orders Past Due: Sales dollar value of orders that were scheduled for shipment, but were not shipped during the period.
• Buyer's Misery Index: Number of different customers that have orders that are late (scheduled for shipment, but not shipped).

1. Why do you think the scrap index is measured at sales dollar value, rather than at cost?
2. How is the "orders past due" measure different from the "buyer's misery index," or are the two measures just measuring the same thing?

A13-9

Variance interpretation

Sound Sensation Inc. is a small manufacturer of electronic musical instruments. The plant manager received the following variable factory overhead report for the period:

	Actual	Budgeted Variable Factory Overhead at Actual Production	Controllable Variance
Supplies	$28,000	$26,520	$1,480 U
Power and light	35,000	33,990	1,010 U
Indirect factory wages	26,112	20,400	5,712 U
Total	$89,112	$80,910	$8,202 U

Actual units produced: 10,200 (85% of practical capacity)

The plant manager is not pleased with the $8,202 unfavorable variable factory overhead controllable variance and has come to discuss the matter with the controller. The following discussion occurred:

Plant Manager: I just received this factory report for the latest month of operation. I'm not very pleased with these figures. Before these numbers go to headquarters, you and I will need to reach an understanding.

Controller: Go ahead, what's the problem?

Plant Manager: What's the problem? Well, everything. Look at the variance. It's too large. If I understand the accounting approach being used here, you are assuming that my costs are variable to the units produced. Thus, as the production volume declines, so should these costs. Well, I don't believe that these costs are variable at all. I think they are fixed costs. As a result, when we operate below capacity, the costs really don't go down at all. I'm being penalized for costs I have no control over at all. I need this report to be redone to reflect this fact. If anything, the difference between actual and budget is essentially a volume variance. Listen, I know that you're a team player. You really need to reconsider your assumptions on this one.

If you were in the controller's position, how would you respond to the plant manager?

Answers to Self-Examination Questions

1. **B** Administrative departments (answer B), such as Purchasing or Human Resources, will often use static budgeting. Production departments (answer A) frequently use flexible budgets. Responsibility centers (answer C) can use either static or flexible budgeting. Capital expenditure budgets are used to plan capital projects (answer D).

2. **B** The total production indicated in the production budget is 257,500 units (answer B), which is computed as follows:

Sales	250,000 units
Plus desired ending inventory	30,000 units
Total	280,000 units
Less estimated beginning inventory	22,500 units
Total production	257,500 units

3. **C** Dixon expects to collect 70% of April sales ($560,000) plus 30% of the March sales ($195,000) in April, for a total of $755,000

(answer C). Answer A is 100% of April sales. Answer B is 70% of April sales. Answer D adds 70% of both March and April sales.

4. **C** The unfavorable direct materials price variance of $2,550 is determined as follows:

Actual price	$5.05 per pound
Standard price	5.00
Price variance—unfavorable	$0.05 per pound

Direct materials price variance: $2,550 = ($0.05 × 5,100 actual pounds

5. **D** The unfavorable direct labor time variance of $2,400 is determined as follows:

Actual direct labor time	2,200 hours
Standard direct labor time	2,000
Direct labor time variance	200 hours

Direct labor time variance: Unfavorable $2,400 = (200 x $12 standard rate)

Performance Evaluation for Decentralized Operations

14

Have you ever wondered why large retail stores like **Wal-Mart, The Home Depot,** and **Sports Authority** are divided into departments? Dividing into departments allows retailers to provide products and expertise in specialized areas, while offering a broad line of products. Departments also allow companies to assign responsibility for financial performance. This information can be used to make product decisions, evaluate operations, and guide company strategy. Strong performance in a department might be attributed to a good department manager, who might be rewarded with a promotion. Poor departmental performance might lead to a change in the mix of products that the department sells.

Like retailers, most businesses organize into operational units, such as divisions and departments. For example, **K2 Sports,** a leading maker of athletic and outdoor equipment, manages its business across four primary business segments: Marine and Outdoor, Action Sports, Team Sports, and Footwear and Apparel. These segments are further divided into product lines, such as K2 skis, Rawlings athletic equipment, Marmot outdoor products, and WGP Paintball.

Managers are responsible for running the operations of their segment of the business. Each segment is evaluated based on operating profit, and this information is used to plan and control K2's operations.

In this chapter, the role of accounting in assisting managers in planning and controlling organizational units, such as departments, divisions, and stores, is described and illustrated.

Obj 1 Describe the advantages and disadvantages of decentralized operations.

Procter & Gamble is organized around products such as Tide (laundry soap), Braun (home appliance), Charmin (bath tissue), CoverGirl (cosmetics), and Crest (tooth paste).

Wachovia Corporation, a national bank, decentralized decisions about how the bank does business over the Internet. Each business unit independently decides how it will conduct business over the Internet. For example, the Mortgage Loan Division allows customers to check current mortgage rates and apply for mortgages online.

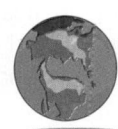

When the *Pizza Hut* chain added chicken to its menu, *Kentucky Fried Chicken (KFC)* retaliated with an advertising campaign against Pizza Hut. However, Pizza Hut and KFC are owned by the same company, *Yum! Brands, Inc.*

Centralized and Decentralized Operations

In a *centralized* company, all major planning and operating decisions are made by top management. For example, a one-person, owner-manager-operated company is centralized because all plans and decisions are made by one person. In a small owner-manager-operated business, centralization may be desirable. This is because the owner-manager's close supervision ensures that the business will be operated in the way the owner-manager wishes.

In a *decentralized* company, managers of separate divisions or units are delegated operating responsibility. The division (unit) managers are responsible for planning and controlling the operations of their divisions. Divisions are often structured around products, customers, or regions.

The proper amount of decentralization for a company depends on the company's unique circumstances. For example, in some companies, division managers have authority over all operations, including fixed asset purchases. In other companies, division managers have authority over profits but not fixed asset purchases.

Advantages of Decentralization

For large companies, it is difficult for top management to do the following:

1. Maintain daily contact with all operations
2. Maintain operating expertise in all product lines and services

In such cases, delegating authority to managers closest to the operations usually results in better decisions. These managers often anticipate and react to operating data more quickly than could top management. These managers also can focus their attention on becoming "experts" in their area of operation.

Decentralized operations provide excellent training for managers. Delegating responsibility allows managers to develop managerial experience early in their careers. This helps a company retain managers, some of whom may be later promoted to top management positions.

Managers of decentralized operations often work closely with customers. As a result, they tend to identify with customers and thus are often more creative in suggesting operating and product improvements. This helps create good customer relations.

Disadvantages of Decentralization

A primary disadvantage of decentralized operations is that decisions made by one manager may negatively affect the profits of the company. For example, managers of divisions whose products compete with each other might start a price war that decreases the profits of both divisions and thus the overall company.

Another disadvantage of decentralized operations is that they may result in duplicate assets and expenses. For example, each manager of a product line might have a separate sales force and office support staff.

The advantages and disadvantages of decentralization are summarized in Exhibit 1.

EXHIBIT 1 **Advantages and Disadvantages of Decentralized Operations**

Advantages of Decentralization
Allows managers closest to the operations to make decisions
Provides excellent training for managers
Allows managers to become experts in their area of operation
Helps retain managers
Improves creativity and customer relations

Disadvantages of Decentralization
Decisions made by managers may negatively affect the profits of the company
Duplicates assets and expenses

Responsibility Accounting

In a decentralized business, accounting assists managers in evaluating and controlling their areas of responsibility, called *responsibility centers*. **Responsibility accounting** is the process of measuring and reporting operating data by responsibility center.

Three types of responsibility centers are:

1. Cost centers, which have responsibility over costs

2. Profit centers, which have responsibility over revenues and costs

3. Investment centers, which have responsibility over revenue, costs, and investment in assets

Responsibility Accounting for Cost Centers

Obj 2 Prepare a responsibility accounting report for a cost center.

A **cost center** manager has responsibility for controlling costs. For example, the supervisor of the Power Department has responsibility for the costs of providing power. A cost center manager does not make decisions concerning sales or the amount of fixed assets invested in the center.

Cost centers may vary in size from a small department to an entire manufacturing plant. In addition, cost centers may exist within other cost centers. For example, an entire university or college could be viewed as a cost center, and each college and department within the university could also be a cost center, as shown in Exhibit 2.

Responsibility accounting for cost centers focuses on controlling and reporting of costs. Budget performance reports that report budgeted and actual costs are normally prepared for each cost center.

Exhibit 3 on page 575 illustrates budget performance reports for the following cost centers:

1. Vice President, Production

2. Manager, Plant A

3. Supervisor, Department 1—Plant A

Exhibit 3 shows how cost centers are often linked together within a company. For example, the budget performance report for Department 1—Plant A supports the report for Plant A, which supports the report for the vice president of production.

EXHIBIT 2   Cost Centers in a University

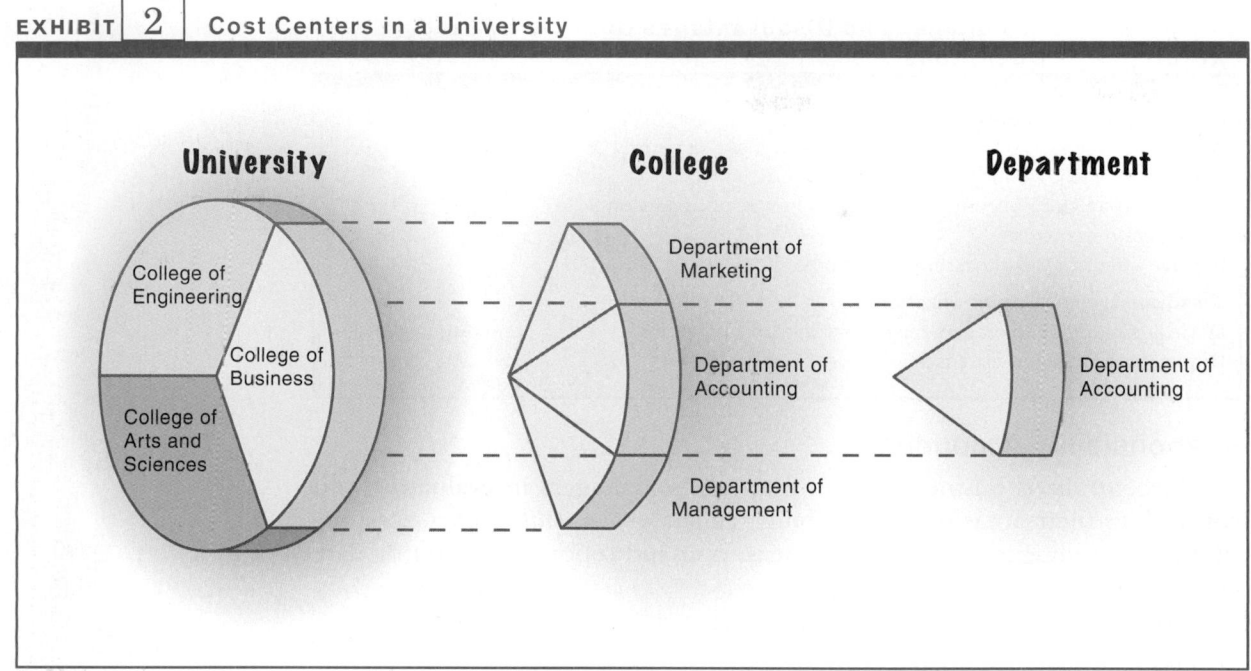

The reports in Exhibit 3 show the budgeted costs and actual costs along with the differences. Each difference is classified as either *over* budget or *under* budget. Such reports allow cost center managers to focus on areas of significant differences.

For example, the supervisor for Department 1 of Plant A can focus on why the materials cost was over budget. The supervisor might discover that excess materials were scrapped. This could be due to such factors as machine malfunctions, improperly trained employees, or low quality materials.

As shown in Exhibit 3, responsibility accounting reports are usually more summarized for higher levels of management. For example, the budget performance report for the manager of Plant A shows only administration and departmental data. This report enables the plant manager to identify the departments responsible for major differences. Likewise, the report for the vice president of production summarizes the cost data for each plant.

Obj 3 Prepare a responsibility accounting report for a profit center.

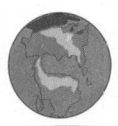

Lester B. Korn of ***Korn/Ferry International*** offered the following strategy for young executives en route to top management positions: "Get profit-center responsibility."

Responsibility Accounting for Profit Centers

A **profit center** manager has the responsibility and authority for making decisions that affect revenues and costs and, thus, profits. Profit centers may be divisions, departments, or products.

The manager of a profit center does not make decisions concerning the fixed assets invested in the center. However, profit centers are an excellent training assignment for new managers.

Responsibility accounting for profit centers focuses on reporting revenues, expenses, and income from operations. Thus, responsibility accounting reports for profit centers take the form of income statements.

The profit center income statement should include only revenues and expenses that are controlled by the manager. **Controllable revenues** are

EXHIBIT 3 | Responsibility Accounting Reports for Cost Centers

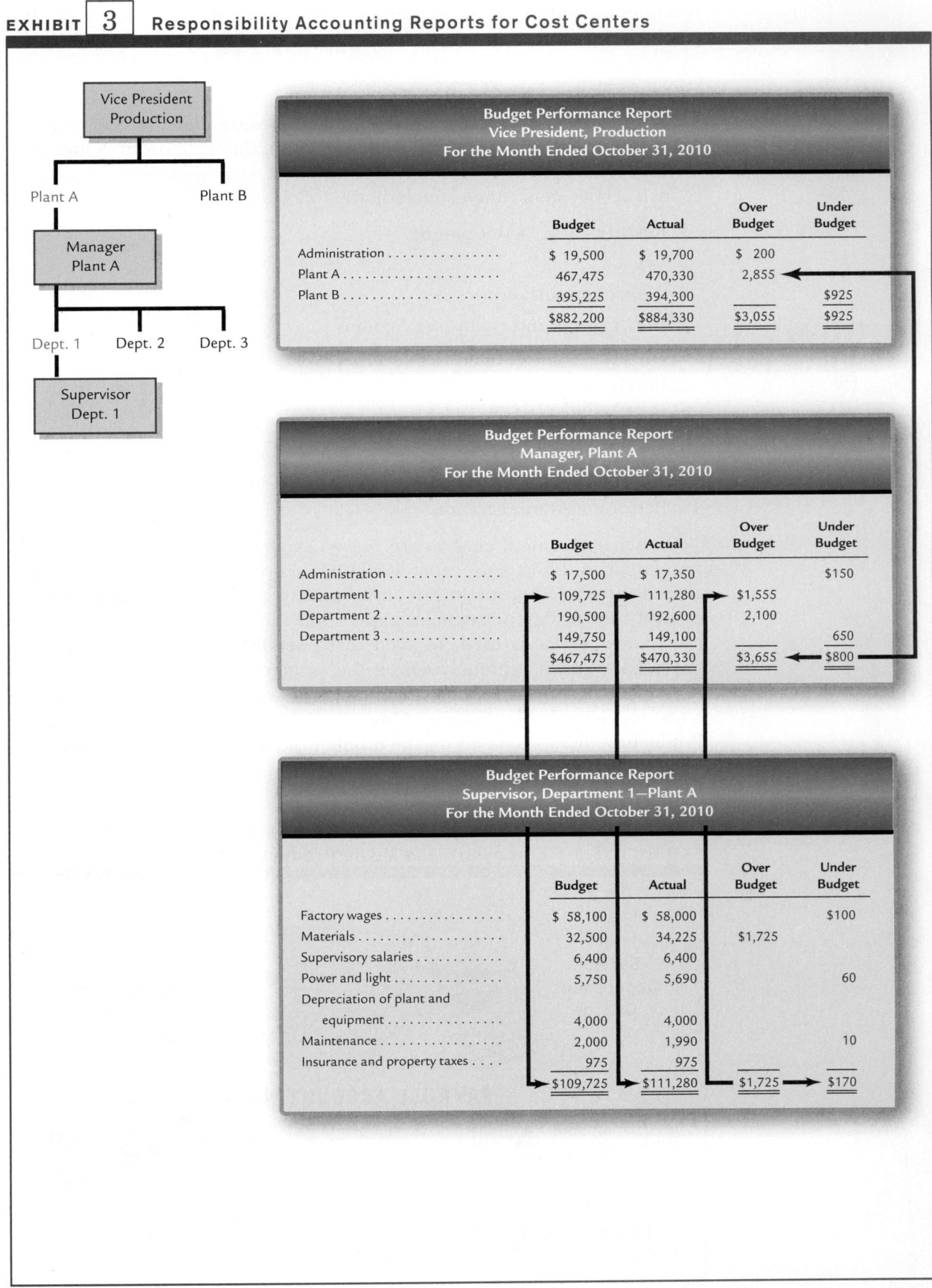

Vice President Production

Plant A   Plant B

Manager Plant A

Dept. 1   Dept. 2   Dept. 3

Supervisor Dept. 1

Budget Performance Report
Vice President, Production
For the Month Ended October 31, 2010

	Budget	Actual	Over Budget	Under Budget
Administration	$ 19,500	$ 19,700	$ 200	
Plant A	467,475	470,330	2,855	
Plant B	395,225	394,300		$925
	$882,200	$884,330	$3,055	$925

Budget Performance Report
Manager, Plant A
For the Month Ended October 31, 2010

	Budget	Actual	Over Budget	Under Budget
Administration	$ 17,500	$ 17,350		$150
Department 1	109,725	111,280	$1,555	
Department 2	190,500	192,600	2,100	
Department 3	149,750	149,100		650
	$467,475	$470,330	$3,655	$800

Budget Performance Report
Supervisor, Department 1—Plant A
For the Month Ended October 31, 2010

	Budget	Actual	Over Budget	Under Budget
Factory wages	$ 58,100	$ 58,000		$100
Materials	32,500	34,225	$1,725	
Supervisory salaries	6,400	6,400		
Power and light	5,750	5,690		60
Depreciation of plant and equipment	4,000	4,000		
Maintenance	2,000	1,990		10
Insurance and property taxes	975	975		
	$109,725	$111,280	$1,725	$170

revenues earned by the profit center. **Controllable expenses** are costs that can be influenced (controlled) by the decisions of profit center managers.

Service Department Charges

The controllable expenses of profit centers include *direct operating expenses* such as sales salaries and utility expenses. In addition, a profit center may incur expenses provided by internal centralized *service departments*. Examples of such service departments include the following:

1. Research and Development
2. Legal
3. Telecommunications
4. Information and Computer Systems
5. Facilities Management
6. Purchasing
7. Publications and Graphics
8. Payroll Accounting
9. Transportation
10. Personnel Administration

Service department charges are *indirect* expenses to a profit center. They are similar to the expenses that would be incurred if the profit center purchased the services from outside the company. A profit center manager has control over service department expenses if the manager is free to choose how much service is used. In such cases, **service department charges** are allocated to profit centers based on the usage of the service by each profit center. For example, Exhibit 4 shows the allocation of payroll accounting costs to Nova Entertainment Group's (NEG) Theme Park and Movie Production divisions based on the number of payroll checks processed.

EXHIBIT | **4**   Payroll Accounting Department Charges to NEG's Theme Park and Movie Production Divisions

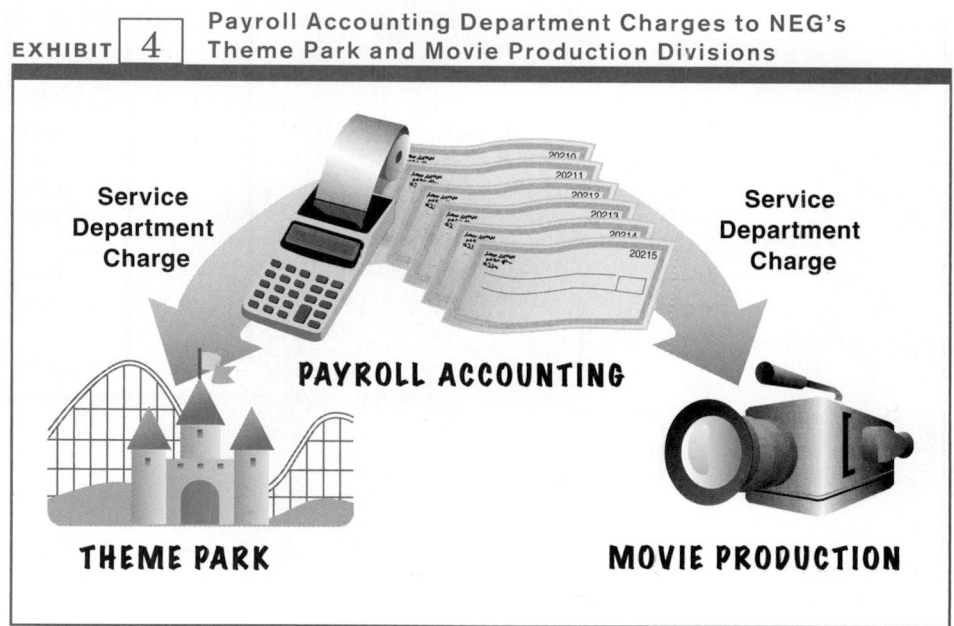

To illustrate, Nova Entertainment Group (NEG), a diversified entertainment company, is used. NEG has the following two operating divisions organized as profit centers:

1. Theme Park Division
2. Movie Production Division

The revenues and direct operating expenses for the two divisions are shown below. The operating expenses consist of direct expenses, such as the wages and salaries of a division's employees.

	Theme Park Division	Movie Production Division
Revenues	$6,000,000	$2,500,000
Operating expenses	2,495,000	405,000

NEG's service departments and the expenses they incurred for the year ended December 31, 2010, are as follows:

Purchasing	$400,000
Payroll Accounting	255,000
Legal	250,000
Total	$905,000

Employees of **IBM** speak of "green money" and "blue money." Green money comes from customers. Blue money comes from providing services to other IBM departments via service department charges. IBM employees note that blue money is easier to earn than green money; yet from the stockholders' perspective, green money is the only money that counts.

An activity base for each service department is used to charge service department expenses to the Theme Park and Movie Production divisions. The activity base for each service department is a measure of the services performed. For NEG, the service department activity bases are as follows:

Department	Activity Base
Purchasing	Number of purchase requisitions
Payroll Accounting	Number of payroll checks
Legal	Number of billed hours

The use of services by the Theme Park and Movie Production divisions is as follows:

Division	Service Usage		
	Purchasing	Payroll Accounting	Legal
Theme Park	25,000 purchase requisitions	12,000 payroll checks	100 billed hrs.
Movie Production	15,000	3,000	900
Total	40,000 purchase requisitions	15,000 payroll checks	1,000 billed hrs.

The rates at which services are charged to each division are called *service department charge rates*. These rates are computed as follows:

$$\text{Service Department Charge Rate} = \frac{\text{Service Department Expense}}{\text{Total Service Department Usage}}$$

NEG's service department charge rates are computed as follows:

$$\frac{\text{Purchasing}}{\text{Charge Rate}} = \frac{\$400,000}{40,000 \text{ purchase requisitions}} = \$10 \text{ per purchase requisition}$$

$$\text{Payroll Charge Rate} = \frac{\$255,000}{15,000 \text{ payroll checks}} = \$17 \text{ per payroll check}$$

$$\text{Legal Charge Rate} = \frac{\$250,000}{1,000 \text{ billed hrs.}} = \$250 \text{ per hr.}$$

The services used by each division are multiplied by the service department charge rates to determine the service charges for each division, as shown below.

$$\text{Service Department Charge} = \text{Service Usage} \times \text{Service Department Charge Rate}$$

Exhibit 5 illustrates the service department charges and related computations for NEG's Theme Park and Movie Production divisions.

EXHIBIT | **5** | Service Department Charges to NEG Divisions

NOVA ENTERTAINMENT GROUP Service Department Charges to NEG Divisions For the Year Ended December 31, 2010		
Service Department	**Theme Park Division**	**Movie Production Division**
Purchasing (Note A)	$250,000	$150,000
Payroll Accounting (Note B)	204,000	51,000
Legal (Note C)	25,000	225,000
Total service department charges	$479,000	$426,000

Note A:
25,000 purchase requisitions × $10 per purchase requisition = $250,000
15,000 purchase requisitions × $10 per purchase requisition = $150,000
Note B:
12,000 payroll checks × $17 per check = $204,000
 3,000 payroll checks × $17 per check = $51,000
Note C:
100 hours × $250 per hour = $25,000
900 hours × $250 per hour = $225,000

The differences in the service department charges between the two divisions can be explained by the nature of their operations and, thus, usage of services. For example, the Theme Park Division employs many part-time employees who are paid weekly. As a result, the Theme Park Division requires 12,000 payroll checks and incurs a $204,000 payroll service department charge (12,000 × $17). In contrast, the Movie Production Division has more permanent employees who are paid monthly. Thus, the Movie Production Division requires only 3,000 payroll checks and incurs a payroll service department charge of $51,000 (3,000 × $17).

Profit Center Reporting

The divisional income statements for NEG are shown in Exhibit 6. In evaluating the profit center manager, the income from operations should be compared over time to a budget. However, it should not be compared across

profit centers, since the profit centers are usually different in terms of size, products, and customers.

EXHIBIT 6 | Divisional Income Statements—NEG

NOVA ENTERTAINMENT GROUP Divisional Income Statements For the Year Ended December 31, 2010		
	Theme Park Division	Movie Production Division
Revenues*	$6,000,000	$2,500,000
Operating expenses	2,495,000	405,000
Income from operations before service department charges	$3,505,000	$2,095,000
Less service department charges:		
Purchasing	$ 250,000	$ 150,000
Payroll Accounting	204,000	51,000
Legal	25,000	225,000
Total service department charges	$ 479,000	$ 426,000
Income from operations	$3,026,000	$1,669,000

* For a profit center that sells products, the income statement would show: Net sales − Cost of goods sold = Gross profit. The operating expenses would be deducted from the gross profit to get the income from operations before service department charges.

Responsibility Accounting for Investment Centers

Obj 4 Compute and interpret the rate of return on investment, the residual income, and the balanced scorecard for an investment center.

An **investment center** manager has the responsibility and the authority to make decisions that affect not only costs and revenues but also the assets invested in the center. Investment centers are often used in diversified companies organized by divisions. In such cases, the divisional manager has authority similar to that of a chief operating officer or president of a company.

Since investment center managers have responsibility for revenues and expenses, *income from operations* is part of investment center reporting. In addition, because the manager has responsibility for the assets invested in the center, the following two additional measures of performance are used:

1. Rate of return on investment
2. Residual income

To illustrate, DataLink Inc., a cellular phone company with three regional divisions, is used. Condensed divisional income statements for the Northern, Central, and Southern divisions of DataLink are shown in Exhibit 7.

Using only income from operations, the Central Division is the most profitable division. However, income from operations does not reflect the amount of assets invested in each center. For example, the Central Division could have twice as many assets as the Northern Division. For this reason, performance measures that consider the amount of invested assets, such as the rate of return on investment and residual income, are used.

EXHIBIT 7 | Divisional Income Statements—DataLink Inc.

DATALINK INC. Divisional Income Statements For the Year Ended December 31, 2010	Northern Division	Central Division	Southern Division
Revenues	$560,000	$672,000	$750,000
Operating expenses	336,000	470,400	562,500
Income from operations before service department charges	$224,000	$201,600	$187,500
Service department charges	154,000	117,600	112,500
Income from operations	$ 70,000	$ 84,000	$ 75,000

Rate of Return on Investment

The interest you earn on a savings account is *your* "rate of return on investment."

Since investment center managers control the amount of assets invested in their centers, they should be evaluated based on the use of these assets. One measure that considers the amount of assets invested is the **rate of return on investment (ROI)** or *rate of return on assets*. It is computed as follows:

$$\text{Rate of Return on Investment (ROI)} = \frac{\text{Income from Operations}}{\text{Invested Assets}}$$

The rate of return on investment is useful because the three factors subject to control by divisional managers (revenues, expenses, and invested assets) are considered. The higher the rate of return on investment, the better the division is using its assets to generate income. In effect, the rate of return on investment measures the income (return) on each dollar invested. As a result, the rate of return on investment can be used as a common basis for comparing divisions with each other.

To illustrate, the invested assets of DataLink's three divisions are as follows:

	Invested Assets
Northern Division	$350,000
Central Division	700,000
Southern Division	500,000

Using the income from operations for each division shown in Exhibit 7, the rate of return on investment for each division is computed below.

Northern Division:

$$\text{Rate of Return on Investment} = \frac{\text{Income from Operations}}{\text{Invested Assets}} = \frac{\$70,000}{\$350,000} = 20\%$$

Central Division:

$$\text{Rate of Return on Investment} = \frac{\text{Income from Operations}}{\text{Invested Assets}} = \frac{\$84,000}{\$700,000} = 12\%$$

Southern Division:

$$\text{Rate of Return on Investment} = \frac{\text{Income from Operations}}{\text{Invested Assets}} = \frac{\$75,000}{\$500,000} = 15\%$$

Although the Central Division generated the largest income from operations, its rate of return on investment (12%) is the lowest. Hence, relative to the assets invested, the Central Division is the least profitable division. In comparison, the rate of return on investment of the Northern Division is 20%, and the Southern Division is 15%.

To analyze differences in the rate of return on investment across divisions, the **DuPont formula** for the rate of return on investment is often used.[1] The DuPont formula views the rate of return on investment as the product of the following two factors:

1. **Profit margin**, which is the ratio of income from operations to sales
2. **Investment turnover**, which is the ratio of sales to invested assets

Using the DuPont formula, the rate of return on investment is expressed as follows:

Rate of Return on Investment = Profit Margin × Investment Turnover

$$\text{Rate of Return on Investment} = \frac{\text{Income from Operations}}{\text{Sales}} \times \frac{\text{Sales}}{\text{Invested Assets}}$$

The DuPont formula is useful in evaluating divisions. This is because the profit margin and the investment turnover reflect the following underlying operating relationships of each division:

1. Profit margin indicates *operating profitability* by computing the rate of profit earned on each sales dollar.
2. Investment turnover indicates *operating efficiency* by computing the number of sales dollars generated by each dollar of invested assets.

If a division's profit margin increases, and all other factors remain the same, the division's rate of return on investment will increase. For example, a division might add more profitable products to its sales mix and thus increase its operating profit, profit margin, and rate of return on investment.

If a division's investment turnover increases, and all other factors remain the same, the division's rate of return on investment will increase. For example, a division might attempt to increase sales through special sales promotions and thus increase operating efficiency, investment turnover, and rate of return on investment.

The graphic at the right illustrates the relationship of the rate of return on investment, the profit margin, and investment turnover. Specifically, more income can be earned by either increasing the investment turnover (turning the crank faster), by increasing the profit margin (increasing the size of the opening), or both.

Using the DuPont formula yields the same rate of return on investment for each of DataLink's divisions, as shown below.

$$\text{Rate of Return on Investment} = \frac{\text{Income from Operations}}{\text{Sales}} \times \frac{\text{Sales}}{\text{Invested Assets}}$$

---

[1] The DuPont formula was created by a financial executive of *E. I. du Pont Nemours and Company* in 1919.

Northern Division:

$$\text{Rate of Return on Investment} = \frac{\$70,000}{\$560,000} \times \frac{\$560,000}{\$350,000} = 12.5\% \times 1.6 = 20\%$$

Central Division:

$$\text{Rate of Return on Investment} = \frac{\$84,000}{\$672,000} \times \frac{\$672,000}{\$700,000} = 12.5\% \times 0.96 = 12\%$$

Southern Division:

$$\text{Rate of Return on Investment} = \frac{\$75,000}{\$750,000} \times \frac{\$750,000}{\$500,000} = 10\% \times 1.5 = 15\%$$

The Northern and Central divisions have the same profit margins of 12.5%. However, the Northern Division's investment turnover of 1.6 is larger than that of the Central Division's turnover of 0.96. By using its invested assets more efficiently, the Northern Division's rate of return on investment of 20% is 8 percentage points higher than the Central Division's rate of return of 12%.

The Southern Division's profit margin of 10% and investment turnover of 1.5 are lower than those of the Northern Division. The product of these factors results in a return on investment of 15% for the Southern Division, compared to 20% for the Northern Division.

Even though the Southern Division's profit margin is lower than the Central Division's, its higher turnover of 15 results in a rate of return of 15%, which is greater than the Central Division's rate of return of 12%.

To increase the rate of return on investment, the profit margin and investment turnover for a division may be analyzed. For example, assume that the Northern Division is in a highly competitive industry in which the profit margin cannot be easily increased. As a result, the division manager might focus on increasing the investment turnover.

To illustrate, assume that the revenues of the Northern Division could be increased by $56,000 through increasing operating expenses, such as advertising, to $385,000. The Northern Division's income from operations will increase from $70,000 to $77,000, as shown below.

Revenues ($560,000 + $56,000)	$616,000
Operating expenses	385,000
Income from operations before service department charges	$231,000
Service department charges	154,000
Income from operations	$ 77,000

The rate of return on investment for the Northern Division, using the DuPont formula, is recomputed as follows:

$$\text{Rate of Return on Investment} = \frac{\text{Income from Operations}}{\text{Sales}} \times \frac{\text{Sales}}{\text{Invested Assets}}$$

$$\text{Rate of Return on Investment} = \frac{\$77,000}{\$616,000} \times \frac{\$616,000}{\$350,000} = 12.5\% \times 1.76 = 22\%$$

Although the Northern Division's profit margin remains the same (12.5%), the investment turnover has increased from 1.6 to 1.76, an increase of 10% (0.16 ÷ 1.6). The 10% increase in investment turnover increases the rate of return on investment by 10% (from 20% to 22%).

The rate of return on investment is also useful in deciding where to invest additional assets or expand operations. For example, DataLink should give priority to expanding operations in the Northern Division because it earns the highest rate of return on investment. In other words, an investment in the Northern Division will return 20 cents (20%) on each dollar invested. In contrast, investments in the Central and Southern divisions will earn only 12 cents and 15 cents per dollar invested.

A disadvantage of the rate of return on investment as a performance measure is that it may lead divisional managers to reject new investments that could be profitable for the company as a whole. To illustrate, assume the following rates of return for the Northern Division of DataLink:

Current rate of return on investment	20%
Minimum acceptable rate of return on investment set by top management	10%
Expected rate of return on investment for new project	14%

The CFO of **Millennium Chemicals** stated: "We had too many divisional executives who failed to spend money on capital projects with more than satisfactory returns because those projects would have lowered the average return on assets of their particular business."

How Businesses Make Money

Return on Investment

The annual reports of public companies must provide segment disclosure information identifying revenues, income from operations, and total assets. This information can be used to compute the return on investment for the segments of a company. For example, **The E.W. Scripps Company,** a media company, operates three major segments:

1. Newspapers: Owns and operates daily and community newspapers in 14 markets in the United States.
2. Scripps Networks: Owns and operates five national television networks: Home and Garden Television, Food Network, DIY Network, Fine Living, and Great American Country.
3. Broadcast Television: Owns and operates several local televisions in various markets.

The DuPont formulas for these segments, as derived from a recent annual report, are as follows:

	Segment Profit Margin	×	Investment Turnover	=	Return on Investment
Newspapers	34.9%		0.55		19.2%
Scripps Networks	42.0%		0.67		28.1%
Broadcast Television	31.6%		0.69		21.8%

As can be seen from the data, E.W. Scripps' three business segments (Newspapers, Scripps Networks, and Broadcast Television) have relatively low investment turnover, with all three being slightly above 0.50. Each of these segments also had very strong profit margins, ranging from 31.6% to 42.0%. Multiplying the profit margin by the investment turnover yields the ROI. The ROI is strong for the three primary business segments.

If the manager of the Northern Division invests in the new project, the Northern Division's overall rate of return will decrease from 20% due to

averaging. Thus, the division manager might decide to reject the project, even though the new project's expected rate of return of 14% exceeds DataLink's minimum acceptable rate of return of 10%.

Residual Income

Residual income is useful in overcoming some of the disadvantages of the rate of return on investment. **Residual income** is the excess of income from operations over a minimum acceptable income from operations, as shown below.[2]

Income from operations	$XXX
Less minimum acceptable income from operations as a percent of invested assets	XXX
Residual income	$XXX

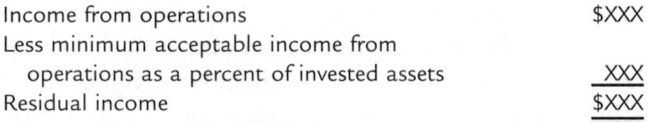

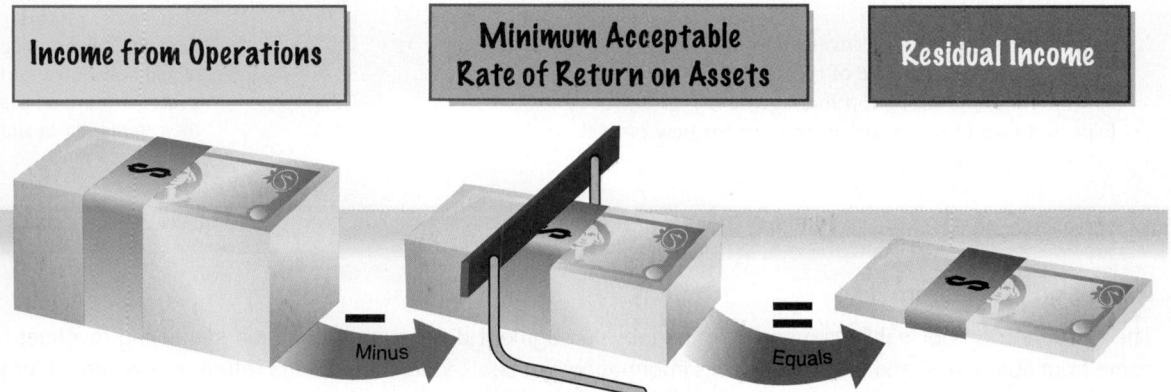

The minimum acceptable income from operations is computed by multiplying the company minimum rate of return by the invested assets. The minimum rate is set by top management, based on such factors as the cost of financing.

To illustrate, assume that DataLink Inc. has established 10% as the minimum acceptable rate of return on divisional assets. The residual incomes for the three divisions are as follows:

	Northern Division	Central Division	Southern Division
Income from operations	$70,000	$84,000	$75,000
Less minimum acceptable income from operations as a percent of invested assets:			
$350,000 × 10%	35,000		
$700,000 × 10%		70,000	
$500,000 × 10%			50,000
Residual income	$35,000	$14,000	$25,000

[2] Another popular term for residual income is economic value added (EVA), which has been trademarked by the consulting firm **Stern Stewart & Co.**

The Northern Division has more residual income ($35,000) than the other divisions, even though it has the least amount of income from operations ($70,000). This is because the invested assets are less for the Northern Division than for the other divisions.

The major advantage of residual income as a performance measure is that it considers both the minimum acceptable rate of return, invested assets, and the income from operations for each division. In doing so, residual income encourages division managers to maximize income from operations in excess of the minimum. This provides an incentive to accept any project that is expected to have a rate of return in excess of the minimum.

To illustrate, assume the following rates of return for the Northern Division of DataLink:

Current rate of return on investment	20%
Minimum acceptable rate of return on investment set by top management	10%
Expected rate of return on investment for new project	14%

If the manager of Northern Division is evaluated using only return on investment, the division manager might decide to reject the new project. This is because investing in the new project will decrease Northern's current rate of return of 20%. Thus, the manager might reject the new project, even though its expected rate of return of 14% exceeds DataLink's minimum acceptable rate of return of 10%.

In contrast, if the manager of the Northern Division is evaluated using residual income, the new project would probably be accepted because it will increase the Northern Division's residual income. In this way, residual income supports both divisional and overall company objectives.

The Balanced Scorecard[3]

The **balanced scorecard** is a set of multiple performance measures for a company. In addition to financial performance, a balanced scorecard normally includes performance measures for customer service, innovation and learning, and internal processes, as shown in Exhibit 8.

Performance measures for learning and innovation often revolve around a company's research and development efforts. For example, the number of new products developed during a year and the time it takes to bring new products to the market are performance measures for innovation. Performance measures for learning could include the number of employee training sessions and the number of employees who are cross-trained in several skills.

Performance measures for customer service include the number of customer complaints and the number of repeat customers. Customer surveys can also be used to gather measures of customer satisfaction with the company as compared to competitors.

Performance measures for internal processes include the length of time it takes to manufacture a product. The amount of scrap and waste is a measure of the efficiency of a company's manufacturing processes. The number of customer returns is a performance measure of both the manufacturing and sales ordering processes.

Merck & Co., Inc. measures the number of drugs in its FDA (Food and Drug Administration) approval pipeline and the length of time it takes to turn ideas into marketable products.

[3] The balanced scorecard was developed by R. S. Kaplan and D. P. Norton and explained in *The Balanced Scorecard: Translating Strategy into Action* (Cambridge: Harvard Business School Press, 1996).

EXHIBIT **8**   The Balanced Scorecard

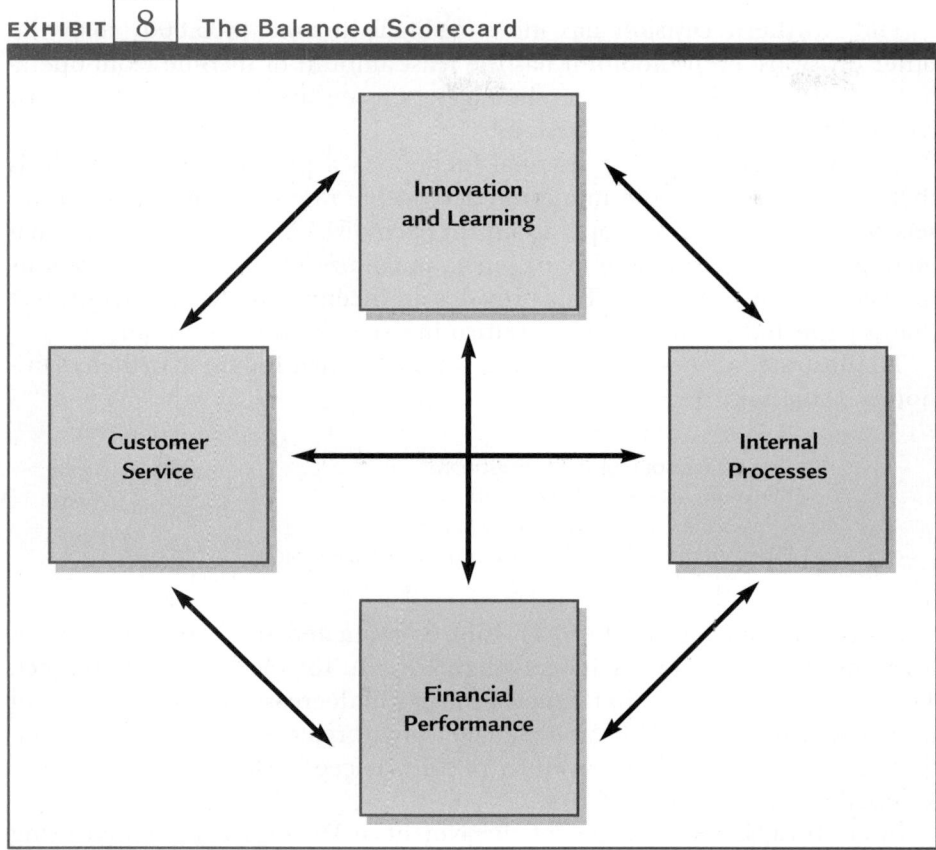

All companies will use financial performance measures. Some financial performance measures have been discussed earlier in this chapter and include income from operations, rate of return on investment, and residual income.

The balanced scorecard attempts to identify the underlying nonfinancial drivers, or causes, of financial performance related to innovation and learning, customer service, and internal processes. In this way, the financial performance may be improved. For example, customer satisfaction is often measured by the number of repeat customers. By increasing the number of repeat customers, sales and income from operations can be increased.

Some common performance measures used in the balanced scorecard approach are shown below.

A survey by **Bain & Co.**, a consulting firm, indicated that 57% of large companies use the balanced scorecard.

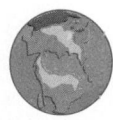

Hilton Hotels Corporation uses a balanced scorecard to measure employee satisfaction, customer loyalty, and financial performance.

Innovation and Learning	**Internal Processes**
Number of new products	Waste and scrap
Number of new patents	Time to manufacture products
Number of cross-trained employees	Number of defects
Number of training hours	Number of rejected sales orders
Number of ethics violations	Number of stockouts
Employee turnover	Labor utilization

Customer Service	**Financial**
Number of repeat customers	Sales
Customer brand recognition	Income from operations
Delivery time to customer	Return on investment
Customer satisfaction	Profit margin and investment turnover
Number of sales returns	Residual income
Customer complaints	Actual versus budgeted (standard) costs

Transfer Pricing

Obj 5 Describe and illustrate how the market price, negotiated price, and cost price approaches to transfer pricing may be used by decentralized segments of a business.

When divisions transfer products or render services to each other, a **transfer price** is used to charge for the products or services.[4] Since transfer prices will affect a division's financial performance, setting a transfer price is a sensitive matter for the managers of both the selling and buying divisions.

Three common approaches to setting transfer prices are as follows:

1. Market price approach
2. Negotiated price approach
3. Cost approach

Transfer prices may be used for cost, profit, or investment centers. The objective of setting a transfer price is to motivate managers to behave in a manner that will increase the overall company income. As will be illustrated, however, transfer prices may be misused in such a way that overall company income suffers.

Transfer prices can be set as low as the variable cost per unit or as high as the market price. Often, transfer prices are negotiated at some point between variable cost per unit and market price. Exhibit 9 shows the possible range of transfer prices.

EXHIBIT 9   **Commonly Used Transfer Prices**

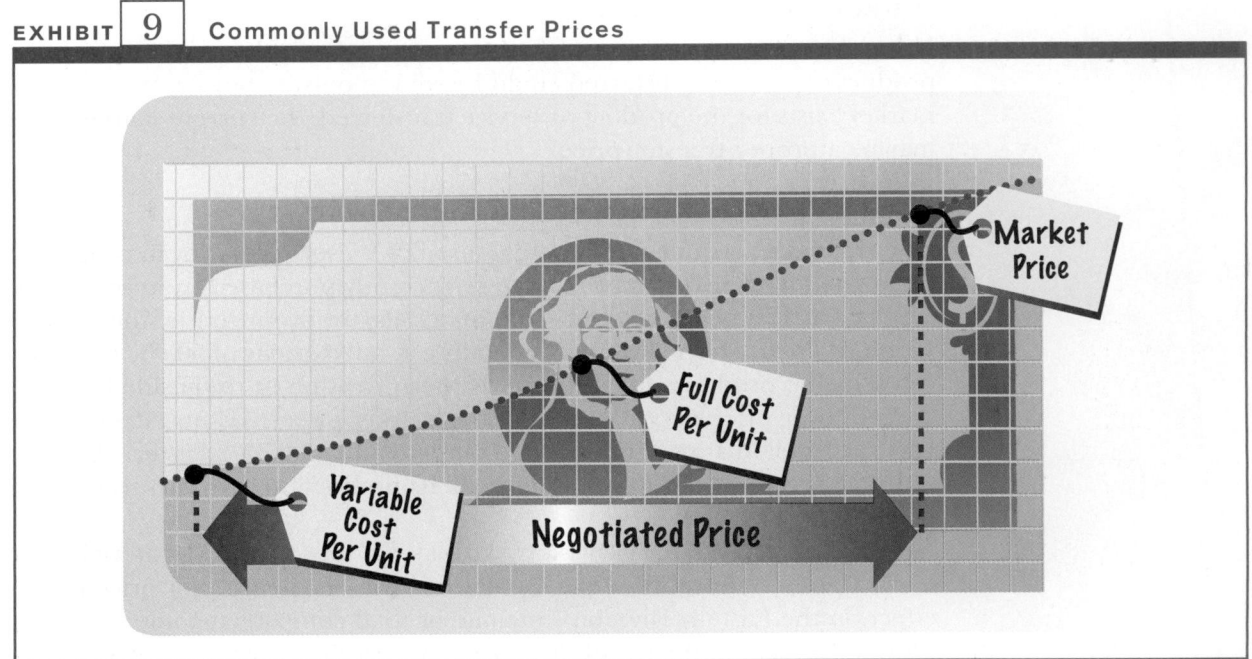

To illustrate, Wilson Company, a packaged snack food company with no service departments, is used. Wilson Company has two operating divisions (Eastern and Western) that are organized as investment centers. Condensed income statements for Wilson Company, assuming no transfers between divisions, are shown in Exhibit 10.

---

[4] The discussion in this chapter highlights the essential concepts of transfer pricing. In-depth discussion of transfer pricing can be found in advanced texts.

EXHIBIT 10 Income Statements—No Transfers Between Divisions

	Eastern Division	Western Division	Total Company
WILSON COMPANY			
Income Statements			
For the Year Ended December 31, 2010			
Sales:			
50,000 units × $20 per unit	$1,000,000		$1,000,000
20,000 units × $40 per unit		$800,000	800,000
			$1,800,000
Expenses:			
Variable:			
50,000 units × $10 per unit	$ 500,000		$ 500,000
20,000 units × $30* per unit		$600,000	600,000
Fixed	300,000	100,000	400,000
Total expenses	$ 800,000	$700,000	$1,500,000
Income from operations	$ 200,000	$100,000	$ 300,000

* $20 of the $30 per unit represents materials costs, and the remaining $10 per unit represents other variable conversion expenses incurred within the Western Division.

Market Price Approach

Using the **market price approach**, the transfer price is the price at which the product or service transferred could be sold to outside buyers. If an outside market exists for the product or service transferred, the current market price may be a proper transfer price.

$$\text{Transfer Price} = \text{Market Price}$$

To illustrate, assume that materials used by Wilson Company in producing snack food in the Western Division are currently purchased from an outside supplier at $20 per unit. The same materials are produced by the Eastern Division. The Eastern Division is operating at full capacity of 50,000 units and can sell all it produces to either the Western Division or to outside buyers.

A transfer price of $20 per unit (the market price) has no effect on the Eastern Division's income or total company income. The Eastern Division will earn revenues of $20 per unit on all its production and sales, regardless of who buys its product.

Likewise, the Western Division will pay $20 per unit for materials (the market price). Thus, the use of the market price as the transfer price has no effect on the Eastern Division's income or total company income.

In this situation, the use of the market price as the transfer price is proper. The condensed divisional income statements for Wilson Company would be the same as shown in Exhibit 10.

Negotiated Price Approach

If unused or excess capacity exists in the supplying division (the Eastern Division), and the transfer price is equal to the market price, total company profit may not be maximized. This is because the manager of the Western Division will be indifferent toward purchasing materials from the Eastern Division or from outside suppliers. That is, in both cases the Western Division manager pays $20 per unit (the market price). As a result, the Western Division may purchase the materials from outside suppliers.

If, however, the Western Division purchases the materials from the Eastern Division, the difference between the market price of $20 and the variable costs of the Eastern Division of $10 per unit (from Exhibit 10) can cover fixed costs and contribute to overall company profits. Thus, the Western Division manager should be encouraged to purchase the materials from the Eastern Division.

The **negotiated price approach** allows the managers to agree (negotiate) among themselves on a transfer price. The only constraint is that the transfer price be less than the market price, but greater than the supplying division's variable costs per unit, as shown below.

Variable Costs per Unit < Transfer Price < Market Price

To illustrate, assume that instead of a capacity of 50,000 units, the Eastern Division's capacity is 70,000 units. In addition, assume that the Eastern Division can continue to sell only 50,000 units to outside buyers.

A transfer price less than $20 would encourage the manager of the Western Division to purchase from the Eastern Division. This is because the Western Division is currently purchasing its materials from outside suppliers at a cost of $20 per unit. Thus, its materials cost would decrease, and its income from operations would increase.

At the same time, a transfer price above the Eastern Division's variable costs per unit of $10 (from Exhibit 10) would encourage the manager of the Eastern Division to supply materials to the Western Division. In doing so, the Eastern Division's income from operations would also increase.

Exhibit 11 illustrates the divisional and company income statements, assuming that the Eastern and Western division managers agree to a transfer price of $15.

EXHIBIT 11 Income Statements—Negotiated Transfer Price

WILSON COMPANY Income Statements For the Year Ended December 31, 2010			
	Eastern Division	Western Division	Total Company
Sales:			
50,000 units × $20 per unit	$1,000,000		$1,000,000
20,000 units × $15 per unit	300,000		300,000
20,000 units × $40 per unit		$800,000	800,000
	$1,300,000	$800,000	$2,100,000
Expenses:			
Variable:			
70,000 units × $10 per unit	$ 700,000		$ 700,000
20,000 units × $25* per unit		$500,000	500,000
Fixed	300,000	100,000	400,000
Total expenses	$1,000,000	$600,000	$1,600,000
Income from operations	$ 300,000	$200,000	$ 500,000

* $10 of the $25 represents variable conversion expenses incurred solely within the Western Division, and $15 per unit represents the transfer price per unit from the Eastern Division.

The Eastern Division increases its sales by $300,000 (20,000 units × $15 per unit) to $1,300,000. As a result, the Eastern Division's income from

operations increases by $100,000 ($300,000 sales – $200,000 variable costs) to $300,000, as shown in Exhibit 11.

The increase of $100,000 in the Eastern Division's income can also be computed as follows:

$$\begin{matrix}\text{Increase in Eastern} \\ \text{(Supplying) Division's} \\ \text{Income from Operations}\end{matrix} = \left(\begin{matrix}\text{Transfer} \\ \text{Price}\end{matrix} - \begin{matrix}\text{Variable Cost} \\ \text{per Unit}\end{matrix}\right) \times \begin{matrix}\text{Units} \\ \text{Transferred}\end{matrix}$$

$$\begin{matrix}\text{Increase in Eastern} \\ \text{(Supplying) Division's} \\ \text{Income from Operations}\end{matrix} = (\$15 - \$10) \times 20,000 \text{ units} = \$100,000$$

Western Division's materials cost decreases by $5 per unit ($20 – $15) for a total of $100,000 (20,000 units × $5 per unit). Thus, Western Division's income from operations increases by $100,000 to $200,000, as shown in Exhibit 11.

The increase of $100,000 in the Western Division's income can also be computed as follows:

$$\begin{matrix}\text{Increase in Western} \\ \text{(Purchasing) Division's} \\ \text{Income from Operations}\end{matrix} = (\text{Market Price} - \text{Transfer Price}) \times \begin{matrix}\text{Units} \\ \text{Transferred}\end{matrix}$$

$$\begin{matrix}\text{Increase in Western} \\ \text{(Purchasing) Division's} \\ \text{Income from Operations}\end{matrix} = (\$20 - \$15) \times 20,000 \text{ units} = \$100,000$$

Comparing Exhibits 10 and 11 shows that Wilson Company's income from operations increased by $200,000, as shown below.

	Income from Operations		
	No Units Transferred (Exhibit 10)	**20,000 Units Transferred at $15 per Unit (Exhibit 11)**	**Increase (Decrease)**
Eastern Division	$200,000	$300,000	$100,000
Western Division	100,000	200,000	100,000
Wilson Company	$300,000	$500,000	$200,000

In the preceding illustration, any negotiated transfer price between $10 and $20 is acceptable, as shown below.

$$\text{Variable Cost per Unit} < \text{Transfer Price} < \text{Market Price}$$

$$\$10 < \text{Transfer Price} < \$20$$

Any transfer price within this range will increase the overall income from operations for Wilson Company by $200,000. However, the increases in the Eastern and Western divisions' income from operations will vary depending on the transfer price.

To illustrate, a transfer price of $16 would increase the Eastern Division's income from operations by $120,000, as shown below.

$$\begin{matrix} \text{Increase in Eastern} \\ \text{(Supplying) Division's} \\ \text{Income from Operations} \end{matrix} = \left(\begin{matrix} \text{Transfer} \\ \text{Price} \end{matrix} - \begin{matrix} \text{Variable Cost} \\ \text{per Unit} \end{matrix} \right) \times \begin{matrix} \text{Units} \\ \text{Transferred} \end{matrix}$$

$$\begin{matrix} \text{Increase in Eastern} \\ \text{(Supplying) Division's} \\ \text{Income from Operations} \end{matrix} = (\$16 - \$10) \times 20,000 \text{ units} = \$120,000$$

A transfer price of $16 would increase the Western Division's income from operations by $80,000, as shown below.

$$\begin{matrix} \text{Increase in Western} \\ \text{(Purchasing) Division's} \\ \text{Income from Operations} \end{matrix} = (\text{Market Price} - \text{Transfer Price}) \times \begin{matrix} \text{Units} \\ \text{Transferred} \end{matrix}$$

$$\begin{matrix} \text{Increase in Western} \\ \text{(Purchasing) Division's} \\ \text{Income from Operations} \end{matrix} = (\$20 - \$16) \times 20,000 \text{ units} = \$80,000$$

With a transfer price of $16, Wilson Company's income from operations still increases by $200,000, which consists of the Eastern Division's increase of $120,000 plus the Western Division's increase of $80,000.

As shown above, negotiated price provides each division manager with an incentive to negotiate the transfer of materials. At the same time, the overall company's income from operations will also increase. However, the negotiated approach only applies when the supplying division has excess capacity. In other words, the supplying division cannot sell all its production to outside buyers at the market price.

Cost Price Approach

Under the **cost price approach**, cost is used to set transfer prices. A variety of costs may be used in this approach, including the following:

1. Total product cost per unit
2. Variable product per unit

If total product cost per unit is used, direct materials, direct labor, and factory overhead are included in the transfer price. If variable product cost per unit is used, the fixed factory overhead cost is excluded from the transfer price.

Actual costs or standard (budgeted) costs may be used in applying the cost price approach. If actual costs are used, inefficiencies of the producing (supplying) division are transferred to the purchasing division. Thus, there is little incentive for the producing (supplying) division to control costs. For this reason, most companies use standard costs in the cost price approach. In this way, differences between actual and standard costs remain with the producing (supplying) division for cost control purposes.

The cost price approach is most often used when the responsibility centers are organized as cost centers. When the responsibility centers are organized as profit or investment centers, the cost price approach is normally not used.

For example, using the cost price approach when the supplying division is organized as a profit center ignores the supplying division manager's responsibility for earning profits. In this case, using the cost price approach prevents the supplying division from reporting any profit (revenues – costs)

on the units transferred. As a result, the division manager has little incentive to transfer units to another division, even though it may be in the best interests of the company.

INTEGRITY, OBJECTIVITY, AND ETHICS IN BUSINESS

Shifting Income Through Transfer Prices

Transfer prices allow companies to minimize taxes by shifting taxable income from countries with high tax rates to countries with low taxes. For example, **Glaxo-SmithKline**, a British company, and the second biggest drug maker in the world, had been in a dispute with the U.S. Internal Revenue Service (IRS) over international transfer prices since the early 1990s. The company pays U.S. taxes on income from its U.S. Division and British taxes on income from the British Division. The IRS, however, claimed that the transfer prices on sales from the British Division to the U.S. Division were too high, which reduced profits and taxes in the U.S. Division. The company received a new tax bill from the IRS in 2005 for almost $1.9 billion related to the transfer pricing issue, raising the total bill to almost $5 billion. In January 2006, the company agreed to settle this dispute with the IRS for $3.4 billion, the largest tax settlement in history.

Source: J. Whalen, "Glaxo Gets New IRS Bill Seeking Another $1.9 Billion in BackTax," *The Wall Street Journal*, January 27, 2005.

Key Points

1. **Describe the advantages and disadvantages of decentralized operations.**

   The advantages of decentralization may include better decisions by the managers closest to the operations, more time for top management to focus on strategic planning, training for managers, improved ability to serve customers and respond to their needs, and improved manager morale. The disadvantages of decentralization may include failure of the company to maximize profits because decisions made by one manager may affect other managers in such a way that the profitability of the entire company may suffer.

2. **Prepare a responsibility accounting report for a cost center.**

   Since managers of cost centers have responsibility and authority to make decisions regarding costs, responsibility accounting for cost centers focuses on costs. The primary accounting tools for planning and controlling costs for a cost center are budgets and budget performance reports. An example of a budget performance report is shown in Exhibit 1.

3. **Prepare a responsibility accounting report for a profit center.**

   In preparing a profitability report for a profit center, operating expenses are subtracted from revenues in order to determine the income from operations before service department charges. Service department charges are then subtracted in order to determine the income from operations of the profit center. An example of a divisional income statement is shown in Exhibit 5.

4. **Compute and interpret the rate of return on investment, the residual income, and the balanced scorecard for an investment center.**

   The rate of return on investment for an investment center is the income from operations divided by invested assets. The rate of return on investment may also be computed as the product of (1) the profit margin and (2) the investment turnover. Residual income for an investment center is the excess of income from operations over a minimum amount of desired income from operations. The balanced scorecard combines nonfinancial measures in order

to help managers consider the underlying causes of financial performance and trade-offs between short-term and long-term performance.

5. Describe and illustrate how the market price, negotiated price, and cost price approaches to transfer pricing may be used by decentralized segments of a business.

Under the market price approach, the transfer price is the price at which the product or service transferred could be sold to outside buyers. Market price should be used when the supplier division is able to sell to outsiders and is operating at capacity.

Under the negotiated price approach, the managers of decentralized units agree (negotiate) among themselves as to the transfer price. Negotiated prices should be used when the supplier division is operating below capacity.

Under the cost price approach, cost is used as the basis for setting transfer prices. A variety of cost concepts may be used, such as total product cost per unit or variable product cost per unit. In addition, actual costs or standard (budgeted) costs may be used. The cost price approach should be used for supplier divisions that are organized as cost centers.

Key Terms

Balanced scorecard A performance evaluation approach that incorporates multiple performance dimensions by combining financial and nonfinancial measures.

Controllable expenses Costs that can be influenced by the decisions of a manager of a cost, profit, or investment center.

Controllable revenues Revenues that can be influenced by the decisions of a manager of a profit or investment center.

Cost center A decentralized unit in which the department or division manager has responsibility for the control of costs incurred and the authority to make decisions that affect these costs.

Cost price approach An approach to transfer pricing that uses cost as the basis for setting the transfer price.

DuPont formula An expanded expression of return on investment determined by multiplying the profit margin by the investment turnover.

Investment center A decentralized unit in which the manager has the responsibility and authority to make decisions that affect not only costs and revenues but also the fixed assets available to the center.

Investment turnover A component of the rate of return on investment computed as the ratio of sales to invested assets.

Market price approach An approach to transfer pricing that uses the price at which the product

or service transferred could be sold to outside buyers as the transfer price.

Negotiated price approach An approach to transfer pricing that allows managers of decentralized units to agree (negotiate) among themselves as to the transfer price.

Profit center A decentralized unit in which the manager has the responsibility and the authority to make decisions that affect both costs and revenues (and thus profits).

Profit margin A component of the rate of return on investment computed as the ratio of income from operations to sales.

Rate of return on investment (ROI) A measure of managerial efficiency in the use of investments in assets computed as income from operations divided by invested assets.

Residual income The excess of divisional income from operations over a "minimum" acceptable income from operations.

Responsibility accounting The process of measuring and reporting operating data by areas of responsibility.

Service department charges The costs of services provided by an internal service department and transferred to a responsibility center.

Transfer price The price charged one decentralized unit by another for the goods or services provided.

Illustrative Problem

Quinn Company has two divisions, Domestic and International. Invested assets and condensed income statement data for each division for the past year ended December 31, 2011, are as follows:

	Domestic Division	International Division
Revenues	$675,000	$480,000
Operating expenses	450,000	372,400
Service department charges	90,000	50,000
Invested assets	600,000	384,000

Instructions

1. Prepare condensed income statements for the past year for each division.

2. Using the DuPont formula, determine the profit margin, investment turnover, and rate of return on investment for each division.

3. If management's minimum acceptable rate of return is 10%, determine the residual income for each division.

Solution

1.

Quinn Company
Divisional Income Statements
For the Year Ended December 31, 2011

	Domestic Division	International Division
Revenues	$675,000	$480,000
Operating expenses	450,000	372,400
Income from operations before service department charges	$225,000	$107,600
Service department charges	90,000	50,000
Income from operations	$135,000	$ 57,600

2. Rate of return on investment (ROI) = Profit margin × Investment turnover

$$\text{Rate of return on investment: (ROI)} = \frac{\text{Income from Operations}}{\text{Sales}} \times \frac{\text{Sales}}{\text{Invested Assets}}$$

$$\text{Domestic Division: ROI} = \frac{\$135,000}{\$675,000} \times \frac{\$675,000}{\$600,000}$$

$$\text{ROI} = 20\% \times 1.125$$

$$\text{ROI} = 22.5\%$$

$$\text{International Division: ROI} = \frac{\$57,600}{\$480,000} \times \frac{\$480,000}{\$384,000}$$

$$\text{ROI} = 12\% \times 1.25$$

$$\text{ROI} = 15\%$$

3. Domestic Division: $75,000 [$135,000 − (10% × $600,000)]
   International Division: $19,200 [$57,600 − (10% × $384,000)]

Self-Examination Questions (Answers appear at the end of chapter)

1. When the manager has the responsibility and authority to make decisions that affect costs and revenues but no responsibility for or authority over assets invested in the department, the department is called:

   A. a cost center

   B. a profit center

   C. an investment center

   D. a service department

2. The Accounts Payable Department has expenses of $600,000 and makes 150,000 payments to the various vendors who provide products and services to the divisions. Division A has income from operations of $900,000, before service department charges, and requires 60,000 payments to vendors. If the Accounts Payable Department is treated as a service department, what is Division A's income from operations?

   A. $300,000

   B. $900,000

   C. $660,000

   D. $540,000

3. Division A of Kern Co. has sales of $350,000, cost of goods sold of $200,000, operating expenses of $30,000, and invested assets of $600,000. What is the rate of return on investment for Division A?

   A. 20%

   B. 25%

   C. 33%

   D. 40%

4. Division L of Liddy Co. has a rate of return on investment of 24% and an investment turnover of 1.6. What is the profit margin?

   A. 6%

   B. 15%

   C. 24%

   D. 38%

5. Which approach to transfer pricing uses the price at which the product or service transferred could be sold to outside buyers?

   A. Cost price approach

   B. Negotiated price approach

   C. Market price approach

   D. Standard cost approach

Class Discussion Questions

1. Differentiate between a cost center and a profit center.

2. Differentiate between a profit center and an investment center.

3. In what major respect would budget performance reports prepared for the use of plant managers of a manufacturing business with cost centers differ from those prepared for the use of the various department supervisors who report to the plant managers?

4. For what decisions is the manager of a cost center *not* responsible?

5. *Weyerhaeuser* developed a system that assigns service department expenses to user divisions on the basis of actual services consumed by the division. Here are a number of Weyerhaeuser's activities in its central Financial Services Department:

   • Payroll

   • Accounts payable

   • Accounts receivable

   • Database administration—report preparation

   For each activity, identify an activity base that could be used to charge user divisions for service.

6. What is the major shortcoming of using income from operations as a performance measure for investment centers?

7. Why should the factors under the control of the investment center manager (revenues, expenses, and invested assets) be considered in computing the rate of return on investment?

8. In a decentralized company in which the divisions are organized as investment centers, how could a division be considered the least

profitable, even though it earned the largest amount of income from operations?

9. How does using the rate of return on investment facilitate comparability between divisions of decentralized companies?

10. The rates of return on investment for Fosina Co.'s three divisions, East, Central, and West, are 26%, 20%, and 15%, respectively. In expanding operations, which of Fosina Co.'s divisions should be given priority? Explain.

11. Why would a firm use a balanced scorecard in evaluating divisional performance?

12. What is the objective of transfer pricing?

13. When is the negotiated price approach preferred over the market price approach in setting transfer prices?

14. Why would standard cost be a more appropriate transfer cost between cost centers than actual cost?

15. When using the negotiated price approach to transfer pricing, within what range should the transfer price be established?

Exercises

E14-1

Budget performance reports for cost centers

Obj 2

✓ a. (c) $2,640

Partially completed budget performance reports for Iliad Company, a manufacturer of air conditioners, are provided below.

Iliad Company
Budget Performance Report–Vice President, Production
For the Month Ended April 30, 2010

Plant	Budget	Actual	Over Budget	Under Budget
Mid-Atlantic Region	$ 416,000	$416,000		$ 0
West Region	297,600	296,000		1,600
South Region	(g)	(h)	(i)	
	$ (j)	$ (k)	$ (l)	$1,600

Iliad Company
Budget Peformance Report–Manager, South Region Plant
For the Month Ended April 30, 2010

Department	Budget	Actual	Over Budget	Under Budget
Chip Fabrication	$ (a)	$ (b)	$ (c)	
Electronic Assembly	85,120	86,240	1,120	
Final Assembly	137,120	136,640		$480
	$ (d)	$ (e)	$ (f)	$480

Iliad Company
Budget Performance Report–Supervisor, Chip Fabrication
For the Month Ended April 30, 2010

Department	Budget	Actual	Over Budget	Under Budget
Factory wages	$ 24,640	$ 26,400	$ 1,760	
Materials	69,600	69,120		$480
Power and light	3,840	4,560	720	
Maintenance	6,720	7,360	640	
	$104,800	$107,440	$ 3,120	$480

a. Complete the budget performance reports by determining the correct amounts for the lettered spaces.

b. Compose a memo to Dana Johnson, vice president of production for Iliad Company, explaining the performance of the Production Division for April.

E14-2

Divisional income statements

Obj 3

✓ **Residential Division income from operations, $78,900**

The following data were summarized from the accounting records for DeSalvo Construction Company for the year ended June 30, 2010:

Cost of goods sold:		Service department charges:	
Residential Division	$415,200	Residential Division	$ 56,400
Industrial Division	206,350	Industrial Division	35,480
Administrative expenses:		Net sales:	
Residential Division	$ 74,500	Residential Division	$625,000
Industrial Division	72,400	Industrial Division	367,500

Prepare divisional income statements for DeSalvo Construction Company.

E14-3

Service department charges and activity bases

Obj 3

For each of the following service departments, identify an activity base that could be used for charging the expense to the profit center.

a. Central Purchasing
b. Legal
c. Accounts Receivable
d. Duplication Services
e. Electronic Data Processing
f. Telecommunications

E14-4

Activity bases for service department charges

Obj 3

For each of the following service departments, select the activity base listed that is most appropriate for charging service expenses to responsible units.

Service Department	Activity Base
a. Central Purchasing	1. Number of travel claims
b. Training	2. Number of payroll checks
c. Conferences	3. Number of sales invoices
d. Telecommunications	4. Number of purchase requisitions
e. Accounts Receivable	5. Number of telephone lines
f. Employee Travel	6. Number of employees trained
g. Payroll Accounting	7. Number of computers
h. Computer Support	8. Number of conference attendees

E14-5

Service department charges

Obj 3

✓ **b. Commercial payroll, $12,468**

In divisional income statements prepared for Mills Construction Company, the Payroll Department costs are charged back to user divisions on the basis of the number of payroll checks, and the Purchasing Department costs are charged back on the basis of the number of purchase requisitions. The Payroll Department had expenses of $45,900, and the Purchasing Department had expenses of $22,000 for the year. The following annual data for Residential, Commercial, and Government Contract Divisions were obtained from corporate records:

	Residential	Commercial	Government Contract
Sales	$460,000	$610,000	$1,400,000
Number of employees:			
Weekly payroll (52 weeks per year)	125	70	75
Monthly payroll	32	43	30
Number of purchase requisitions per year	2,100	1,500	1,400

a. Determine the total amount of payroll checks and purchase requisitions processed per year by each division.
b. Using the activity base information in (a), determine the annual amount of payroll and purchasing costs charged back to the Residential, Commercial, and Government Contract divisions from payroll and purchasing services.

c. Why does the Residential Division have a larger service department charge than the other two divisions, even though its sales are lower?

E14-6

Service department charges and activity bases

Obj 3

✓ b. Help desk, $30,600

Harris Corporation, a manufacturer of electronics and communications systems, uses a service department charge system to charge profit centers with Computing and Communications Services (CCS) service department costs. The following table identifies an abbreviated list of service categories and activity bases used by the CCS department. The table also includes some assumed cost and activity base quantity information for each service for April.

CCS Service Category	Activity Base	Assumed Cost	Assumed Activity Base Quantity
Help desk	Number of calls	$ 88,400	2,600
Network center	Number of devices monitored	609,375	9,750
Electronic mail	Number of user accounts	67,080	6,450
Local voice support	Number of phone extensions	152,720	9,200

One of the profit centers for Harris Corporation is the Communication Systems (COMM) sector. Assume the following information for the COMM sector:

- The sector has 3,000 employees, of whom 40% are office employees.
- All the office employees have a phone, and 75% of them have a computer on the network.
- Ninety-five percent of the employees with a computer also have an e-mail account.
- The average number of help desk calls for April was 1.0 call per individual with a computer.
- There are 250 additional printers, servers, and peripherals on the network beyond the personal computers.

a. Determine the service charge rate for the four CCS service categories for April.

b. Determine the charges to the COMM sector for the four CCS service categories for April.

E14-7

Divisional income statements with service department charges

Obj 3

SPREADSHEET

✓ **Retail income from operations, $1,386,134**

Encounter Sporting Goods Company has two divisions, Wholesale and Retail, and two corporate service departments, Tech Support and Accounts Payable. The corporate expenses for the year ended December 31, 2010, are as follows:

Tech Support Department	$ 705,000
Accounts Payable Department	278,000
Other corporate administrative expenses	415,000
Total corporate expense	$1,398,000

The other corporate administrative expenses include officers' salaries and other expenses required by the corporation. The Tech Support Department charges the divisions for services rendered, based on the number of computers in the department, and the Accounts Payable Department charges divisions for

services, based on the number of checks issued. The usage of service by the two divisions is as follows:

	Tech Support	Accounts Payable
Wholesale Division	300 computers	7,060 checks
Retail Division	200	12,940
Total	500 computers	20,000 checks

The service department charges of the Tech Support Department and the Accounts Payable Department are considered controllable by the divisions. Corporate administrative expenses are not considered controllable by the divisions. The revenues, cost of goods sold, and operating expenses for the two divisions are as follows:

	Wholesale	Retail
Revenues	$6,720,000	$5,712,000
Cost of goods sold	3,528,000	2,688,000
Operating expenses	1,260,000	1,176,000

Prepare the divisional income statements for the two divisions.

E14-8

Corrections to service department charges

Obj 3

SPREADSHEET

✓ b. Income from operations, Cargo Division, $80,500

Trans-Continental Airlines, Inc., has two divisions organized as profit centers, the Passenger Division and the Cargo Division. The following divisional income statements were prepared:

Trans-Continental Airlines, Inc.
Divisional Income Statements
For the Year Ended June 30, 2010

	Passenger Division		Cargo Division	
Revenues		$1,400,000		$1,400,000
Operating expenses		950,000		1,200,000
Income from operations before		$ 450,000		$ 200,000
service department charges				
Less service department charges:				
Training	$ 80,000		$ 80,000	
Flight scheduling	75,000		75,000	
Reservations	105,000	260,000	105,000	260,000
Income from operations		$ 190,000		$ (60,000)

The service department charge rate for the service department costs was based on revenues. Since the revenues of the two divisions were the same, the service department charges to each division were also the same.

The following additional information is available:

	Passenger Division	Cargo Division	Total
Number of personnel trained	200	50	250
Number of flights	250	350	600
Number of reservations requested	14,000	0	14,000

a. Does the income from operations for the two divisions accurately measure performance?

b. Correct the divisional income statements, using the activity bases provided on the preceding page in revising the service department charges.

E14-9

Profit center responsibility reporting

Objs 3, 5

SPREADSHEET

✓ Income from operations, Action Sports Division, $571,400

X-Out Sporting Goods Co. operates two divisions—the Action Sports Division and the Team Sports Division. The following income and expense accounts were provided as of June 30, 2010, the end of the current fiscal year, after all adjustments, including those for inventories, were recorded:

Sales—Action Sports (AS) Division	$14,500,000
Sales—Team Sports (TS) Division	17,600,000
Cost of Goods Sold—Action Sports (AS) Division	8,700,000
Cost of Goods Sold—Team Sports (TS) Division	10,208,000
Sales Expense—Action Sports (AS) Division	2,320,000
Sales Expense—Team Sports (TS) Division	2,464,000
Administrative Expense—Action Sports (AS) Division	1,450,000
Administrative Expense—Team Sports (TS) Division	1,566,400
Advertising Expense	642,000
Transportation Expense	314,960
Accounts Receivable Collection Expense	201,750
Warehouse Expense	1,600,000

The bases to be used in allocating expenses, together with other essential information, are as follows:

a. Advertising expense—incurred at headquarters, charged back to divisions on the basis of usage: Action Sports Division, $256,800; Team Sports Division, $385,200.

b. Transportation expense—charged back to divisions at a charge rate of $12.40 per bill of lading: Action Sports Division, 12,000 bills of lading; Team Sports Division, 13,400 bills of lading.

c. Accounts receivable collection expense—incurred at headquarters, charged back to divisions at a charge rate of $7.50 per invoice: Action Sports Division, 12,400 sales invoices; Team Sports Division, 14,500 sales invoices.

d. Warehouse expense—charged back to divisions on the basis of floor space used in storing division products: Action Sports Division, 120,000 square feet; Team Sports Division, 80,000 square feet.

Prepare a divisional income statement with two column headings: Action Sports Division and Team Sports Division. Provide supporting schedules for determining service department charges.

E14-10

Rate of return on investment

Obj 4

✓ a. Health Care Division, 16%

The income from operations and the amount of invested assets in each division of Devon Industries are as follows:

	Income from Operations	Invested Assets
Sporting Goods Division	$80,000	$400,000
Health Care Division	41,600	260,000
Commercial Division	70,400	320,000

a. Compute the rate of return on investment for each division.

b. Which division is the most profitable per dollar invested?

E14-11

Residual income

Obj **4**

✓ **a. Sporting Goods Division, $40,000**

Based on the data in Exercise 14-10, assume that management has established a 10% minimum acceptable rate of return for invested assets.

a. Determine the residual income for each division.
b. Which division has the most residual income?

E14-12

Determining missing items in rate of return computation

Obj **4**

✓ **d. 0.70**

One item is omitted from each of the following computations of the rate of return on investment:

Rate of Return on Investment	=	Profit Margin	×	Investment Turnover
22%	=	10%	×	(a)
(b)	=	16%	×	0.75
18%	=	(c)	×	1.50
14%	=	20%	×	(d)
(e)	=	15%	×	1.60

Determine the missing items, identifying each by the appropriate letter.

E14-13

Profit margin, investment turnover, and rate of return on investment

Obj **4**

✓ **a. ROI, 15%**

The condensed income statement for the International Division of King Industries Inc. is as follows (assuming no service department charges):

Sales	$1,200,000
Cost of goods sold	600,000
Gross profit	$ 600,000
Administrative expenses	300,000
Income from operations	$ 300,000

The manager of the International Division is considering ways to increase the rate of return on investment.

a. Using the DuPont formula for rate of return on investment, determine the profit margin, investment turnover, and rate of return on investment of the International Division, assuming that $2,000,000 of assets have been invested in the International Division.
b. If expenses could be reduced by $60,000 without decreasing sales, what would be the impact on the profit margin, investment turnover, and rate of return on investment for the International Division?

E14-14

Rate of return on investment

Obj **4**

✓ **a. Media Networks ROI, 15.4%**

The Walt Disney Company has four major sectors, described as follows:

• **Media Networks:** The ABC television and radio network, Disney channel, ESPN, A&E, E!, and Disney.com.
• **Parks and Resorts:** Walt Disney World Resort, Disneyland, Disney Cruise Line, and other resort properties.
• **Studio Entertainment:** Walt Disney Pictures, Touchstone Pictures, Hollywood Pictures, Miramax Films, and Buena Vista Theatrical Productions.
• **Consumer Products:** Character merchandising, Disney stores, books, and magazines.

Disney recently reported sector income from operations, revenue, and invested assets (in millions) as follows:

	Income from Operations	Revenue	Invested Assets
Media Networks	$4,285	$15,046	$27,692
Parks and Resorts	1,710	10,626	16,311
Studio Entertainment	1,201	7,491	10,812
Consumer Products	631	2,347	1,553

a. Use the DuPont formula to determine the rate of return on investment for the four Disney sectors. Round whole percents to one decimal place and investment turnover to two decimal places.

b. How do the four sectors differ in their profit margin, investment turnover, and return on investment?

E14-15

Determining missing items in rate of return and residual income computations

Obj 4

✓ c. $92,400

Data for Schmidt Company is presented in the following table of rates of return on investment and residual incomes:

Invested Assets	Income from Operations	Rate of Return of Investment	Minimum Rate of Return	Minimum Acceptable Income from Operations	Residual Income
$840,000	$210,000	(a)	14%	(b)	(c)
$500,000	(d)	(e)	(f)	$64,000	$27,500
$320,000	(g)	16%	(h)	$40,000	(i)
$240,000	$48,000	(j)	12%	(k)	(l)

Determine the missing items, identifying each item by the appropriate letter.

E14-16

Determining missing items from computations

Obj 4

✓ a. (e) $520,000

Data for the North, South, East, and West divisions of McGonigel Company are as follows:

	Sales	Income from Operations	Invested Assets	Rate of Return of Investment	Profit Margin	Investment Turnover
North	$525,000	(a)	(b)	18%	12%	(c)
South	(d)	$65,000	(e)	(f)	10%	1.25
East	$700,000	(g)	$350,000	15%	(h)	(i)
West	$800,000	$140,000	$1,000,000	(j)	(k)	(l)

a. Determine the missing items, identifying each by the letters (a) through (l). Round whole percents to one decimal place and investment turnover to two decimal places.

b. Determine the residual income for each division, assuming that the minimum acceptable rate of return established by management is 10%.

c. Which division is the most profitable in terms of (1) return on investment and (2) residual income?

E14-17

Rate of return on investment, residual income

Obj 4

Hilton Hotels Corporation provides lodging services around the world. The company is separated into three major divisions.

- **Hotel Ownership:** Hotels owned and operated by Hilton.
- **Managing and Franchising:** Hotels franchised to others or managed for others.
- **Timeshare:** Resort properties managed for timeshare vacation owners.

Financial information for each division, from a recent annual report, is as follows (in millions):

	Hotel Ownership	Managing and Franchising	Timeshare
Revenues	$4,985	$2,527	$ 650
Income from operations	904	600	152
Total assets	9,681	5,191	1,078

a. Use the DuPont formula to determine the return on investment for each of the Hilton business divisions. Round whole percents to one decimal place and investment turnover to one decimal place.

b. Determine the residual income for each division, assuming a minimum acceptable income of 10% of total assets. Round minimal acceptable return to the nearest million dollars.

c. Interpret your results.

E14-18

Balanced scorecard

Obj 4

American Express Company is a major financial services company, noted for its American Express® card. Below are some of the performance measures used by the company in its balanced scorecard.

Average cardmember spending	Number of merchant signings
Cards in force	Number of card choices
Earnings growth	Number of new card launches
Hours of credit consultant training	Return on equity
Investment in information technology	Revenue growth
Number of Internet features	

For each measure, identify whether the measure best fits the innovation, customer, internal process, or financial dimension of the balanced scorecard.

E14-19

Balanced scorecard

Obj 4

Several years ago, *United Parcel Service (UPS)* believed that the Internet was going to change the parcel delivery market and would require UPS to become a more nimble and customer-focused organization. As a result, UPS replaced its old measurement system, which was 90% oriented toward financial performance, with a balanced scorecard. The scorecard emphasized four "point of arrival" measures, which were:

1. Customer satisfaction index—a measure of customer satisfaction.
2. Employee relations index—a measure of employee sentiment and morale.
3. Competitive position—delivery performance relative to competition.
4. Time in transit—the time from order entry to delivery.

a. Why did UPS introduce a balanced scorecard and nonfinancial measures in its new performance measurement system?

b. Why do you think UPS included a factor measuring employee sentiment?

E14-20

Decision on transfer pricing

Obj 5

✓ a. $1,225,000

Electronic components used by the Engine Division of Armstrong Manufacturing are currently purchased from outside suppliers at a cost of $200 per unit. However, the same materials are available from the Components Division. The Components Division has unused capacity and can produce the materials needed by the Engine Division at a variable cost of $165 per unit.

a. If a transfer price of $180 per unit is established and 35,000 units of materials are transferred, with no reduction in the Components Division's current sales, how much would Armstrong Manufacturing's total income from operations increase?

b. How much would the Engine Division's income from operations increase?

c. How much would the Components Division's income from operations increase?

E14-21

Decision on transfer pricing

Obj 5

✓ b. $350,000

Based on Armstrong Manufacturing's data in Exercise 14-20, assume that a transfer price of $190 has been established and that 35,000 units of materials are transferred, with no reduction in the Components Division's current sales.

a. How much would Armstrong Manufacturing's total income from operations increase?

b. How much would the Engine Division's income from operations increase?

c. How much would the Components Division's income from operations increase?

d. If the negotiated price approach is used, what would be the range of acceptable transfer prices and why?

Problems

P14-1

Budget performance report for a cost center

Obj 2

SPREADSHEET

Amoruso Parts Company sells vehicle parts to automotive companies. The Truck Division is organized as a cost center. The budget for the Truck Division for the month ended October 31, 2010, is as follows (in thousands):

Customer service salaries	$ 260,450
Insurance and property taxes	54,600
Distribution salaries	415,400
Marketing salaries	489,700
Engineer salaries	398,500
Warehouse wages	279,100
Equipment depreciation	87,500
Total	$1,985,250

During October, the costs incurred in the Truck Division were as follows:

Customer service salaries	$ 333,370
Insurance and property taxes	52,960
Distribution salaries	411,250
Marketing salaries	548,460
Engineer salaries	390,530
Warehouse wages	267,930
Equipment depreciation	87,500
Total	$2,092,000

Instructions

1. Prepare a budget performance report for the director of the Truck Division for the month of October.
2. For which costs might the director be expected to request supplemental reports?

P14-2

Profit center responsibility reporting

Obj 3

SPREADSHEET

✓ 1. Income from operations, Metro Division, $274,400

Browning Transportation Co. has three regional divisions organized as profit centers. The chief executive officer (CEO) evaluates divisional performance, using income from operations as a percent of revenues. The following quarterly income and expense accounts were provided from the trial balance as of December 31, 2010:

Revenues—East Division	$600,000
Revenues—West Division	710,000
Revenues—Metro Division	980,000
Operating Expenses—East Division	362,400
Operating Expenses—West Division	393,540
Operating Expenses—Metro Division	527,760
Corporate Expenses—Shareholder Relations	87,500
Corporate Expenses—Customer Support	300,000
Corporate Expenses—Legal	122,400
General Corporate Officers' Salaries	204,000

The company operates three service departments: Shareholder Relations, Customer Support, and Legal. The Shareholder Relations Department conducts a variety of services for shareholders of the company. The Customer Support Department is the company's point of contact for new service, complaints, and requests for repair. The department believes that the number of customer contacts is an activity base for this work. The Legal Department provides legal services for division management. The department believes that the number of hours billed is an activity base for this work. The following additional information has been gathered:

	East	West	Metro
Number of customer contacts	3,750	4,500	6,750
Number of hours billed	850	1,360	1,190

Instructions

1. Prepare quarterly income statements showing income from operations for the three divisions. Use three column headings: East, West, and Metro.
2. Identify the most successful division according to the profit margin. Round to two decimal places.
3. Provide a recommendation to the CEO for a better method for evaluating the performance of the divisions. In your recommendation, identify the major weakness of the present method.

P14-3

Divisional income statements and rate of return on investment analysis

Obj 4

SPREADSHEET

✓ 2. Bread Division, ROI, 13.5%

Sunshine Baking Company is a diversified food products company with three operating divisions organized as investment centers. Condensed data taken from the records of the three divisions for the year ended June 30, 2010, are as follows:

	Bread Division	Snack Cake Division	Retail Bakeries Division
Sales	$ 8,100,000	$ 8,700,000	$7,800,000
Cost of goods sold	4,980,000	5,400,000	4,600,000
Operating expenses	1,662,000	1,995,000	1,484,000
Invested assets	10,800,000	10,875,000	6,000,000

The management of Sunshine Baking Company is evaluating each division as a basis for planning a future expansion of operations.

Instructions

1. Prepare condensed divisional income statements for the three divisions, assuming that there were no service department charges.
2. Using the DuPont formula for rate of return on investment, compute the profit margin, investment turnover, and rate of return on investment for each division.
3. If available funds permit the expansion of operations of only one division, which of the divisions would you recommend for expansion, based on parts (1) and (2)? Explain.

P14-4

Effect of proposals on divisional performance

Obj 4

SPREADSHEET

✓ 1. ROI, 14.4%

A condensed income statement for the Snowboard Division of New Wave Rides Inc. for the year ended December 31, 2010, is as follows:

Sales	$1,200,000
Cost of goods sold	826,000
Gross profit	$ 374,000
Operating expenses	230,000
Income from operations	$ 144,000
Invested assets	$1,000,000

Assume that the Snowboard Division received no charges from service departments. The president of New Wave Rides has indicated that the division's rate of return on a $1,000,000 investment must be increased to at least 18% by the end of the next year if operations are to continue. The division manager is considering the following three proposals:

Proposal 1: Transfer equipment with a book value of $40,000 to other divisions at no gain or loss and lease similar equipment. The annual lease payments would exceed the amount of depreciation expense on the old equipment by $24,000. This increase in expense would be included as part of the cost of goods sold. Sales would remain unchanged.

Proposal 2: Purchase new and more efficient machining equipment and thereby reduce the cost of goods sold by $120,000. Sales would remain unchanged, and the old equipment, which has no remaining book value, would be scrapped at no gain or loss. The new equipment would increase invested assets by an additional $600,000 for the year.

* publication 17
  make sure for 2011

— 4012

Patrick
(418) 951-7111

vgy tech 2000

503 680
0785

Jamie
Flicker

11:30-3:30 -13
20th - After 11

4 + 3 rows
← columns

Universal
changer

(408) 270-4240

21

Freeman Ins Fin Services Inc
John Freeman CLU® ChFC® CASL®, Agent

5927 SE 86th Avenue
Portland, OR 97266-4711
Bus 503 228 1311
john.freeman.gzo3@statefarm.com

April 1   (503) 241-5660

~~Oct~~ 19 Nov

11:00 am

503-777-
2893

1
2
3
4
5
6
7
8
9
10   820
11
12
13
14
15
16
17
18
19
20
21

Proposal 3: Reduce invested assets by discontinuing an engine line. This action would eliminate sales of $330,000, cost of goods sold of $286,300, and operating expenses of $65,000. Assets of $420,000 would be transferred to other divisions at no gain or loss.

Instructions

1. Using the DuPont formula for rate of return on investment, determine the profit margin, investment turnover, and rate of return on investment for the Snowboard Division for the past year.
2. Prepare condensed estimated income statements and compute the invested assets for each proposal.
3. Using the DuPont formula for rate of return on investment, determine the profit margin, investment turnover, and rate of return on investment for each proposal.
4. Which of the three proposals would meet the required 18% rate of return on investment?
5. If the Snowboard Division were in an industry where the profit margin could not be increased, how much would the investment turnover have to increase to meet the president's required 18% rate of return on investment?

P14-5

Divisional performance
analysis and evaluation

Obj 4

SPREADSHEET

✓ 2. Touring Bike
Division ROI, 24.5%

The vice president of operations of Rucker-Putnam Bike Company is evaluating the performance of two divisions organized as investment centers. Invested assets and condensed income statement data for the past year for each division are as follows:

	Touring Bike Division	Off-Road Bike Division
Sales	$2,800,000	$2,950,000
Cost of goods sold	1,240,000	1,375,000
Operating expenses	1,168,000	1,073,500
Invested assets	1,600,000	2,950,000

Instructions

1. Prepare condensed divisional income statements for the year ended December 31, 2010, assuming that there were no service department charges.
2. Using the DuPont formula for rate of return on investment, determine the profit margin, investment turnover, and rate of return on investment for each division.
3. If management desires a minimum acceptable rate of return of 18%, determine the residual income for each division.
4. Discuss the evaluation of the two divisions, using the performance measures determined in parts (1), (2), and (3).

P14-6

Transfer pricing

Obj 5

SPREADSHEET

✓ 3. Total income from
operations, $308,000

Bay Area Scientific, Inc. manufactures electronic products, with two operating divisions, the Performance Materials and Communication Technologies divisions. Condensed divisional income statements, which involve no intracompany transfers and which include a breakdown of expenses into variable and fixed components, are as follows:

Bay Area Scientific, Inc.
Divisional Income Statements
For the Year Ended December 31, 2010

	Performance Materials Division	Communication Technologies Division	Total
Sales:			
8,000 units @ $ 78 per unit	$624,000		$ 624,000
12,000 units @ $152 per unit		$1,824,000	1,824,000
	$624,000	$1,824,000	$2,448,000
Expenses:			
Variable:			
8,000 units @ $ 58 per unit	$464,000		$ 464,000
12,000 units @ $108* per unit		$1,296,000	1,296,000
Fixed	124,000	288,000	412,000
Total expenses	$588,000	$1,584,000	$2,172,000
Income from operations	$ 36,000	$ 240,000	$ 276,000

*$78 of the $108 per unit represents materials costs, and the remaining $30 per unit represents other variable conversion expenses incurred within the Communication Technologies Division.

The Performance Materials Division is presently producing 8,000 units out of a total capacity of 9,600 units. Materials used in producing the Communication Technologies Division's product are currently purchased from outside suppliers at a price of $78 per unit. The Performance Materials Division is able to produce the materials used by the Communication Technologies Division. Except for the possible transfer of materials between divisions, no changes are expected in sales and expenses.

Instructions

1. Would the market price of $78 per unit be an appropriate transfer price for Bay Area Scientific, Inc.? Explain.

2. If the Communication Technologies Division purchases 1,600 units from the Performance Materials Division, rather than externally, at a negotiated transfer price of $64 per unit, how much would the income from operations of each division and the total company income from operations increase?

3. Prepare condensed divisional income statements for Bay Area Scientific, Inc., based on the data in part (2).

4. If a transfer price of $70 per unit is negotiated, how much would the income from operations of each division and the total company income from operations increase?

5. a. What is the range of possible negotiated transfer prices that would be acceptable for Bay Area Scientific, Inc.?

   b. Assuming that the managers of the two divisions cannot agree on a transfer price, what price would you suggest as the transfer price?

Activities

A14-1
Ethics and professional
conduct in business

ETHICS

Evigi Company has two divisions, the Semiconductor Division and the PC Division. The PC Division may purchase semiconductors from the Semiconductor Division or from outside suppliers. The Semiconductor Division sells

semiconductor products both internally and externally. The market price for semiconductors is $150 per 100 semiconductors. Dan Robbin is the controller of the PC Division, and Jamie Palders is the controller of the Semiconductor Division. The following conversation took place between Dan and Jamie:

Dan: I hear you are having problems selling semiconductors out of your division. Maybe I can help.

Jamie: You've got that right. We're producing and selling at about 80% of our capacity to outsiders. Last year we were selling 100% of capacity. Would it be possible for your division to pick up some of our excess capacity? After all, we are part of the same company.

Dan: What kind of price could you give me?

Jamie: Well, you know as well as I that we are under strict profit responsibility in our divisions, so I would expect to get market price, $150 for 100 semiconductors.

Dan: I'm not so sure we can swing that. I was expecting a price break from a "sister" division.

Jamie: Hey, I can only take this "sister" stuff so far. If I give you a price break, our profits will fall from last year's levels. I don't think I could explain that. I'm sorry, but I must remain firm—market price. After all, it's only fair—that's what you would have to pay from an external supplier.

Dan: Fair or not, I think we'll pass. Sorry we couldn't have helped.

Was Dan behaving ethically by trying to force the Semiconductor Division into a price break? Comment on Jamie's reactions.

A14-2

Service department charges

The Customer Service Department of Schweitzer Industries asked the Publications Department to prepare a brochure for its training program. The Publications Department delivered the brochures and charged the Customer Service Department a rate that was 25% higher than could be obtained from an outside printing company. The policy of the company required the Customer Service Department to use the internal publications group for brochures. The Publications Department claimed that it had a drop in demand for its services during the fiscal year, so it had to charge higher prices in order to recover its payroll and fixed costs.

Should the cost of the brochure be transferred to the Customer Service Department in order to hold the department head accountable for the cost of the brochure? What changes in policy would you recommend?

A14-3

Evaluating divisional performance

The three divisions of Monstore Foods are Snack Goods, Cereal, and Frozen Foods. The divisions are structured as investment centers. The following responsibility reports were prepared for the three divisions for the prior year:

	Snack Goods	Cereal	Frozen Foods
Revenues	$1,500,000	$ 2,400,000	$1,350,000
Operating expenses	684,600	1,179,000	483,000
Income from operations before service department charges	$ 815,400	$ 1,221,000	$ 867,000
Service department charges:			
Promotion	$ 210,000	$ 415,000	$ 325,000
Legal	95,400	86,000	164,000
	$ 305,400	$ 501,000	$ 489,000
Income from operations	$ 510,000	$ 720,000	$ 378,000
Invested assets	$2,500,000	$ 4,800,000	$1,800,000

1. Which division is making the best use of invested assets and thus should be given priority for future capital investments?
2. Assuming that the minimum acceptable rate of return on new projects is 12%, would all investments that produce a return in excess of 12% be accepted by the divisions?
3. Can you identify opportunities for improving the company's financial performance?

A14-4

Evaluating division performance over time

The Truck Division of Estatoe Motors Inc. has been experiencing revenue and profit growth during the years 2008–2010. The divisional income statements are provided below.

Estatoe Motors Inc.
Divisional Income Statements, Truck Division
For the Years Ended December 31, 2008–2010

	2008	2009	2010
Sales	$840,000	$1,200,000	$1,400,000
Cost of goods sold	605,000	856,000	987,000
Gross profit	$235,000	$ 344,000	$ 413,000
Operating expenses	109,000	128,000	133,000
Income from operations	$126,000	$ 216,000	$ 280,000

Assume that there are no charges from service departments. The vice president of the division, Eddie Wadsley, is proud of his division's performance over the last three years. The president of Estatoe Motors Inc., Kurt Hartisan, is discussing the division's performance with Eddie, as follows:

Eddie: As you can see, we've had a successful three years in the Truck Division.

Kurt: I'm not too sure.

Eddie: What do you mean? Look at our results. Our income from operations has more than doubled, while our profit margins are improving.

Kurt: I am looking at your results. However, your income statements fail to include one very important piece of information; namely, the invested assets. You have been investing a great deal of assets into the division. You had $420,000 in invested assets in 2008, $800,000 in 2009, and $1,750,000 in 2010.

Eddie: You are right. I've needed the assets in order to upgrade our technologies and expand our operations. The additional assets are one reason we have been able to grow and improve our profit margins. I don't see that this is a problem.

Kurt: The problem is that we must maintain a 20% rate of return on invested assets.

1. Determine the profit margins for the Truck Division for 2008–2010.
2. Compute the investment turnover for the Truck Division for 2008–2010.
3. Compute the rate of return on investment for the Truck Division for 2008–2010.
4. Evaluate the division's performance over the 2008–2010 time period. Why was Kurt concerned about the performance?

A14-5

Evaluating division
performance

Casual Living Inc. is a privately held diversified company with five separate divisions organized as investment centers. A condensed income statement for the Apparel Division for the past year, assuming no service department charges, is as follows:

Casual Living Inc.—Apparel Division
Income Statement
For the Year Ended December 31, 2009

Sales	$22,500,000
Cost of goods sold	16,870,000
Gross profit	$ 5,630,000
Operating expenses	1,130,000
Income from operations	$ 4,500,000
Invested assets	$30,000,000

The manager of the Apparel Division was recently presented with the opportunity to add an additional product line, which would require invested assets of $15,000,000. A projected income statement for the new product line is as follows:

New Product Line
Projected Income Statement
For the Year Ended December 31, 2010

Sales	$ 9,000,000
Cost of goods sold	5,200,000
Gross profit	$ 3,800,000
Operating expenses	2,450,000
Income from operations	$ 1,350,000

The Apparel Division currently has $30,000,000 in invested assets, and Casual Living Inc.'s overall rate of return on investment, including all divisions, is 8%. Each division manager is evaluated on the basis of divisional rate of return on investment, and a bonus equal to $9,000 for each percentage point by which the division's rate of return on investment exceeds the company average is awarded each year.

The president is concerned that the manager of the Apparel Division rejected the addition of the new product line, when all estimates indicated that the product line would be profitable and would increase overall company income. You have been asked to analyze the possible reasons why the Apparel Division manager rejected the new product line.

1. Determine the rate of return on investment for the Apparel Division for the past year.
2. Determine the Apparel Division manager's bonus for the past year.
3. Determine the estimated rate of return on investment for the new product line. Round whole percents to one decimal place.
4. Why might the manager of the Apparel Division decide to reject the new product line? Support your answer by determining the projected rate of return on investment for 2010, assuming that the new product line was launched in the Apparel Division, and 2010 actual operating results were similar to those of 2009.
5. Can you suggest an alternative performance measure for motivating division managers to accept new investment opportunities that would increase the overall company income and rate of return on investment?

A14-6

The balanced scorecard and EVA

GROUP

Divide responsibilities between two groups, with one group going to the home page of *The Palladium Group* at **http://www.thepalladiumgroup.com**, and the second group going to the home page of *Stern Stewart & Co.* at **http://www.eva.com**. The Palladium Group is a consulting firm that helped develop the balanced scorecard concept. Stern Stewart & Co. is a consulting firm that developed the concept of economic value added (EVA), another method of measuring corporate and divisional performance, similar to residual income.

After reading about the balanced scorecard at the palladiumgroup.com site, prepare a brief report describing the balanced scorecard and its claimed advantages. In the Stern group, use links in the home page of Stern Stewart & Co. to learn about EVA. After reading about EVA, prepare a brief report describing EVA and its claimed advantages. After preparing these reports, both groups should discuss their research and prepare a brief analysis comparing and contrasting these two approaches to corporate and divisional performance measurement.

Answers to Self-Examination Questions

1. **B** The manager of a profit center (answer B) has responsibility for and authority over costs and revenues. If the manager has responsibility for only costs, the department is called a cost center (answer A). If the responsibility and authority extend to the investment in assets as well as costs and revenues, it is called an investment center (answer C). A service department (answer D) provides services to other departments. A service department could be a cost center, a profit center, or an investment center.

2. **C** $600,000/150,000 = $4 per payment. Division A anticipates 60,000 payments or $240,000 (60,000 × $4) in service department charges from the Accounts Payable Department. Income from operations is thus $900,000 − $240,000, or $660,000. Answer A assumes that all of the service department overhead is assigned to Division A, which would be incorrect, since Division A does not use all of the accounts payable service. Answer B incorrectly assumes that there are no service department charges from Accounts Payable. Answer D incorrectly determines the accounts payable transfer rate from Division A's income from operations.

3. **A** The rate of return on investment for Division A is 20% (answer A), computed as follows:

$$\text{Rate of Return on Investment (ROI)} = \frac{\text{Income from Operations}}{\text{Invested Assets}}$$

$$\text{ROI} = \frac{\$350,000 - \$200,000 - \$30,000}{\$600,000} = 20\%$$

4. **B** The profit margin for Division L of Liddy Co. is 15% (answer B), computed as follows:

$$\text{Rate of Return on Investment (ROI)} = \text{Profit Margin} \times \text{Investment Turnover}$$

$$24\% = \text{Profit Margin} \times 1.6$$

$$15\% = \text{Profit Margin}$$

5. **C** The market price approach (answer C) to transfer pricing uses the price at which the product or service transferred could be sold to outside buyers. The cost price approach (answer A) uses cost as the basis for setting transfer prices. The negotiated price approach (answer B) allows managers of decentralized units to agree (negotiate) among themselves as to the proper transfer price. The standard cost approach (answer D) is a version of the cost price approach that uses standard costs in setting transfer prices.

Capital Investment Analysis

Learning Objectives

After studying this chapter, you should be able to:

Obj 1 Explain the nature and importance of capital investment analysis.

Obj 2 Evaluate capital investment proposals using the average rate of return and cash payback methods.

Obj 3 Evaluate capital investment proposals using the net present value and internal rate of return methods.

Obj 4 List and describe factors that complicate capital investment analysis.

Obj 5 Diagram the capital rationing process.

W hy are you paying tuition, studying this text, and spending time and money on a higher education? Most people believe that the money and time spent now will return them more earnings in the future. In other words, the cost of higher education is an investment in your future earning ability. How would you know if this investment is worth it?

One method would be for you to compare the cost of a higher education against the estimated increase in your future earning power. The bigger the difference between your expected future earnings and the cost of your education, the better the investment. The same is true for the investments businesses make in fixed assets. Business organizations use a variety of methods to compare the cost of an investment to its future earnings and cash flows.

For example, **Carnival Corporation** is the largest vacation cruise company in the world, with over 85 cruise ships that sail to locations around the world. Carnival's fleet required an investment of nearly $29 billion, with each new ship costing approximately $600 million. Carnival used capital investment analysis to compare this investment with the future earnings ability of the ships over their 30-year expected lives. Carnival must be satisfied with its investments, because it has signed agreements with shipyards to add an additional 22 cruise ships to its fleet from 2008 through 2012.

In this chapter, the methods used to make investment decisions, which may involve thousands, millions, or even billions of dollars, are described and illustrated. The similarities and differences among the most commonly used methods of evaluating investment proposals, as well as the benefits of each method, are emphasized. Qualitative considerations affecting investment analyses, considerations complicating investment analyses, and the process of allocating available investment funds among competing proposals are also discussed.

Obj 1 Explain the nature and importance of capital investment analysis.

A CFO survey of capital investment analysis methods used by large U.S. companies reported the following:

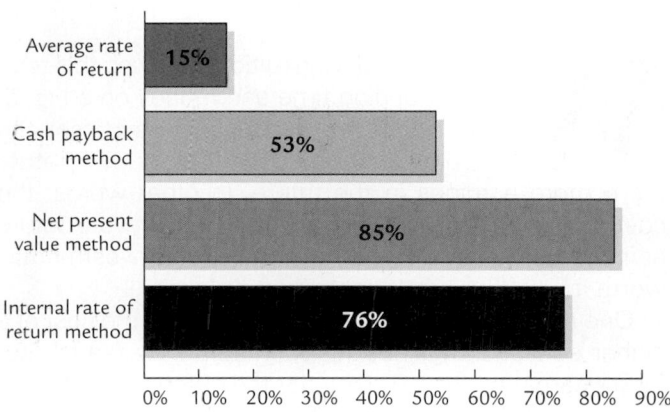

Percentage of Respondents Reporting the Use of the Methods as "Always" or "Often"

Average rate of return — 15%
Cash payback method — 53%
Net present value method — 85%
Internal rate of return method — 76%

Source: Patricia A. Ryan and Glenn P. Ryan, "Capital Budgeting Practice of the Fortune 1000: How Have Things Changed?" *Journal of Business and Management* (Winter 2002).

Nature of Capital Investment Analysis

Companies use capital investment analysis to evaluate long-term investments. **Capital investment analysis** (or *capital budgeting*) is the process by which management plans, evaluates, and controls investments in fixed assets. Capital investments use funds and affect operations for many years and must earn a reasonable rate of return. Thus, capital investment decisions are some of the most important decisions that management makes.

Capital investment evaluation methods can be grouped into the following categories:

Methods That Do Not Use Present Values

1. Average rate of return method
2. Cash payback method

Methods That Use Present Values

1. Net present value method
2. Internal rate of return method

The two methods that use present values consider the time value of money. The **time value of money concept** recognizes that an amount of cash invested today will earn income and thus has value over time.

Obj 2 Evaluate capital investment proposals using the average rate of return and cash payback methods.

During 2007, **Delta Air Lines** invested $1.0 billion in capital expenditures, which focused primarily on customer service initiatives, such as new flight equipment and improvements at Delta's Atlanta and New York–JFK hubs.

Methods Not Using Present Values

The methods not using present values are often useful in evaluating capital investment proposals that have relatively short useful lives. In such cases, the timing of the cash flows (the time value of money) is less important.

Since the methods not using present values are easy to use, they are often used to screen proposals. Minimum standards for accepting proposals are set, and proposals not meeting these standards are dropped. If a proposal meets the minimum standards, it may be subject to further analysis using the present value methods.

Average Rate of Return Method

The **average rate of return**, sometimes called the *accounting rate of return*, measures the average income as a percent of the average investment. The average rate of return is computed as follows:

$$\text{Average Rate of Return} = \frac{\text{Estimated Average Annual Income}}{\text{Average Investment}}$$

In the preceding equation, the numerator is the average of the annual income expected to be earned from the investment over its life, after deducting depreciation. The denominator is the average investment (book value) over the life of the investment. Assuming straight-line depreciation, the average investment is computed as follows:

$$\text{Average Investment} = \frac{\text{Initial Cost} + \text{Residual Value}}{2}$$

To illustrate, assume that management is evaluating the purchase of a new machine as follows:

Cost of new machine	$500,000
Residual value	0
Estimated total income from machine	200,000
Expected useful life	4 years

The average estimated annual income from the machine is $50,000 ($200,000/4 years). The average investment is $250,000, as computed below.

$$\text{Average Investment} = \frac{\text{Initial Cost} + \text{Residual Value}}{2}$$
$$= \frac{\$500,000 + \$0}{2} = \$250,000$$

The average rate of return on the average investment is 20%, as computed below.

$$\text{Average Rate of Return} = \frac{\text{Estimated Average Annual Income}}{\text{Average Investment}}$$
$$= \frac{\$50,000}{\$250,000} = 20\%$$

The average rate of return of 20% should be compared to the minimum rate of return required by management. If the average rate of return equals or exceeds the minimum rate, the machine should be purchased or considered for further analysis.

Several capital investment proposals can be ranked by their average rates of return. The higher the average rate of return, the more desirable the proposal. For example, assume that management is considering two capital investment proposals with the following average rates of return:

	Proposal A	Proposal B
Average Rate of Return	20%	25%

If only the average rate of return is considered, Proposal B, with an average rate of return of 25%, is preferred over Proposal A.

The average rate of return has the following three advantages:

1. It is easy to compute.
2. It includes the entire amount of income earned over the life of the proposal.
3. It emphasizes accounting income, which is often used by investors and creditors in evaluating management performance.

The average rate of return has the following two disadvantages:

1. It does not directly consider the expected cash flows from the proposal.
2. It does not directly consider the timing of the expected cash flows.

Cash Payback Method

A capital investment uses cash and must return cash in the future to be successful. The expected period of time between the date of an investment and the recovery in cash of the amount invested is the **cash payback period**.

When annual net cash inflows are equal, the cash payback period is computed as follows:

$$\text{Cash Payback Period} = \frac{\text{Initial Cost}}{\text{Annual Net Cash Inflow}}$$

To illustrate, assume that management is evaluating the purchase of the following new machine:

Cost of new machine	$200,000
Cash revenues from machine per year	50,000
Expenses of machine per year	30,000
Depreciation per year	20,000

To simplify, the revenues and expenses other than depreciation are assumed to be in cash. Hence, the net cash inflow per year from use of the machine is as follows:

Net cash inflow per year:		
Cash revenues from machine		$50,000
Less cash expenses of machine:		
Expenses of machine	$30,000	
Less depreciation	20,000	10,000
Net cash inflow per year		$40,000

The time required for the net cash flow to equal the cost of the new machine is the payback period. Thus, the estimated cash payback period for the investment is five years, as computed below.

$$\text{Cash Payback Period} = \frac{\text{Initial Cost}}{\text{Annual Net Cash Inflow}} = \frac{\$200,000}{\$40,000} = 5 \text{ years}$$

In the preceding illustration, the annual net cash inflows are equal ($40,000 per year). When the annual net cash inflows are not equal, the cash payback period is determined by adding the annual net cash inflows until the cumulative total equals the initial cost of the proposed investment.

To illustrate, assume that a proposed investment has an initial cost of $400,000. The annual and cumulative net cash inflows over the proposal's six-year life are as follows:

Year	Net Cash Flow	Cumulative Net Cash Flow
1	$ 60,000	$ 60,000
2	80,000	140,000
3	105,000	245,000
4	155,000	400,000
5	100,000	500,000
6	90,000	590,000

The cumulative net cash flow at the end of Year 4 equals the initial cost of the investment, $400,000. Thus, the payback period is four years, as shown in the graph on the following page.

If the initial cost of the proposed investment had been $450,000, the cash payback period would occur during Year 5. Since $100,000 of net cash flow is

expected during Year 5, the additional $50,000 to increase the cumulative total to $450,000 occurs halfway through the year ($50,000/$100,000). Thus, the cash payback period would be 4½ years.[1]

A short cash payback period is desirable. This is because the sooner cash is recovered, the sooner it can be reinvested in other projects. In addition, there is less chance of losses from changing economic conditions or other risks such as a decreasing customer demand when the payback period is short.

A short cash payback period is also desirable for repaying debt used to purchase the investment. The sooner the cash is recovered, the sooner the debt can be paid.

A disadvantage of the cash payback method is that it ignores cash flows occurring after the payback period. In addition, the cash payback method does not use present value concepts in valuing cash flows occurring in different periods.

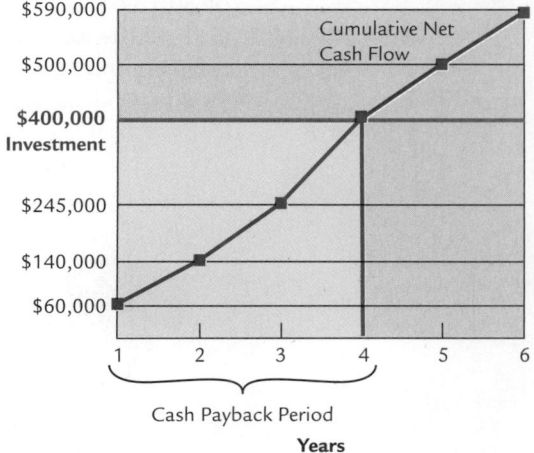

Methods Using Present Values

Obj 3 Evaluate capital investment proposals using the net present value and internal rate of return methods.

An investment in fixed assets may be viewed as purchasing a series of net cash flows over a period of time. The timing of when the net cash flows will be received is important in determining the value of a proposed investment.

Present value methods use the amount and timing of the net cash flows in evaluating an investment. The two methods of evaluating capital investments using present values are as follows:

1. Net present value method
2. Internal rate of return method

Present Value Concepts

Both the net present value and the internal rate of return methods use the following two **present value concepts**:

1. Present value of an amount
2. Present value of an annuity

Present value concepts can also be used to evaluate personal finances. For example, you can determine house or car payments under various interest rate and term assumptions using present value concepts.

Present Value of an Amount

If you were given the choice, would you prefer to receive $1 now or $1 three years from now? You should prefer to receive $1 now, because you could invest the $1 and earn interest for three years. As a result, the amount you would have after three years would be greater than $1.

To illustrate, assume that you have $1 to invest as follows:

Amount to be invested	$1
Period to be invested	3 years
Interest rate	12%

After one year, the $1 earns interest of $0.12 ($1 × 12%) and thus will grow to $1.12 ($1 × 1.12). In the second year, the $1.12 earns 12% interest

[1] Unless otherwise stated, net cash inflows are received uniformly throughout the year.

of $0.134 ($1.12 × 12%) and thus will grow to $1.254 ($1.12 × 1.12) by the end of the second year. This process of interest earning interest is called *compounding*. By the end of the third year, your $1 investment will grow to $1.404 as shown below.

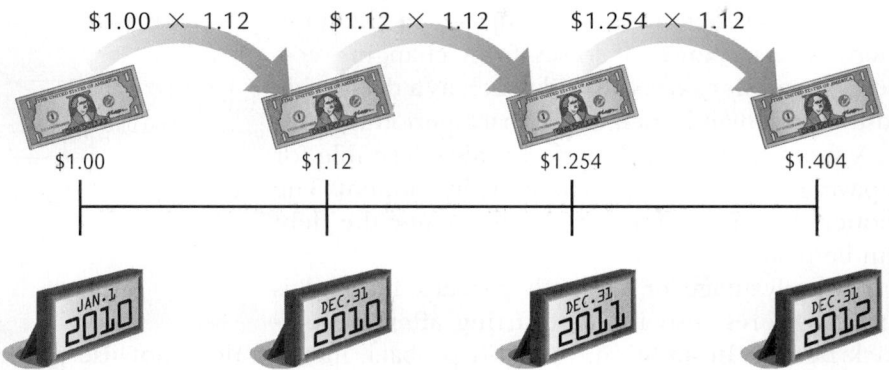

On January 1, 2010, what is the present value of $1.404 to be received on December 31, 2012? This is a present value question. The answer can be determined with the aid of a present value of $1 table. For example, the partial table in Exhibit 1 indicates that the present value of $1 to be received in three years with earnings compounded at the rate of 12% a year is 0.712. Multiplying 0.712 by $1.404 yields $1 as follows:

Present Value		Amount to Be Received in 3 Years		Present Value of $1 to Be Received in 3 Years (from Exhibit 1)
$1	=	$1.404	×	0.712

EXHIBIT 1   Partial Present Value of $1 Table

Present Value of $1 at Compound Interest					
Year	6%	10%	12%	15%	20%
1	0.943	0.909	0.893	0.870	0.833
2	0.890	0.826	0.797	0.756	0.694
3	0.840	0.751	0.712	0.658	0.579
4	0.792	0.683	0.636	0.572	0.482
5	0.747	0.621	0.567	0.497	0.402
6	0.705	0.564	0.507	0.432	0.335
7	0.665	0.513	0.452	0.376	0.279
8	0.627	0.467	0.404	0.327	0.233
9	0.592	0.424	0.361	0.284	0.194
10	0.558	0.386	0.322	0.247	0.162

In other words, the present value of $1.404 to be received in three years using a compound interest rate of 12% is $1, as shown on the next page.

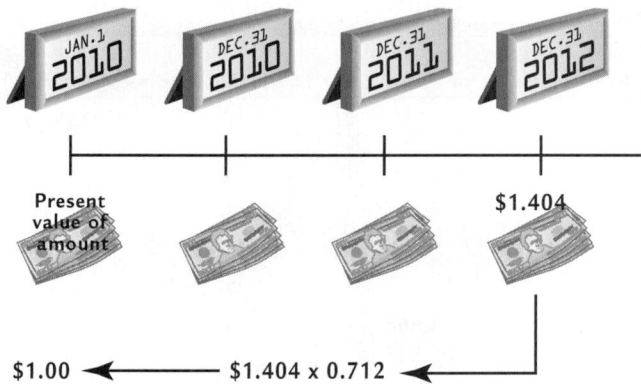

Present Value of an Annuity

An **annuity** is a series of equal net cash flows at fixed time intervals. Cash payments for monthly rent, salaries, and bond interest are all examples of annuities.

The present value of an annuity is the sum of the present values of each cash flow. That is, the **present value of an annuity** is the amount of cash needed today to yield a series of equal net cash flows at fixed time intervals in the future.

To illustrate, the present value of a $100 annuity for five periods at 12% could be determined by using the present value factors in Exhibit 1. Each $100 net cash flow could be multiplied by the present value of $1 at a 12% factor for the appropriate period and summed to determine a present value of $360.50, as shown below.

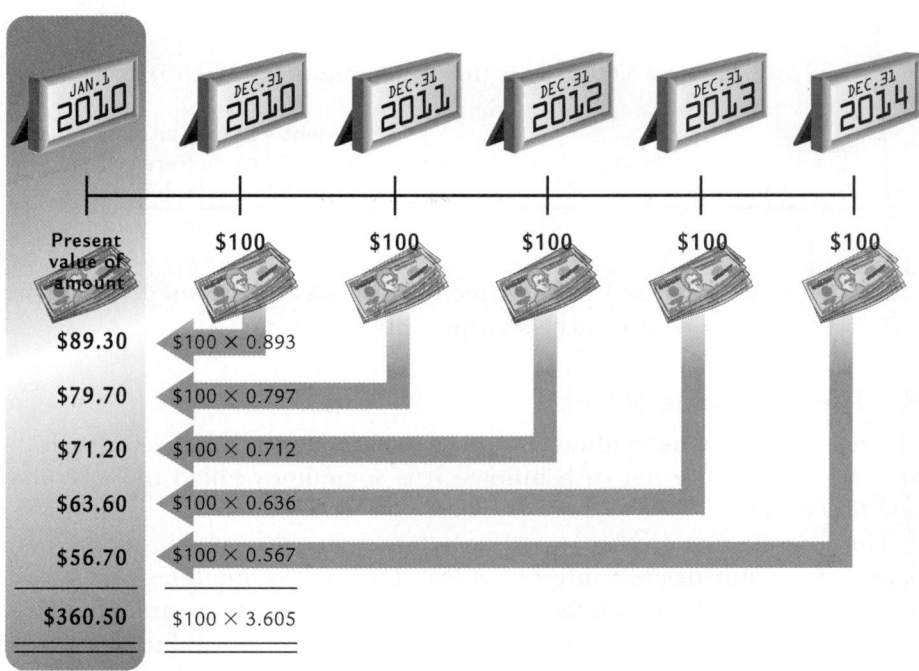

Using a present value of an annuity table is a simpler approach. Exhibit 2 is a partial table of present value of annuity factors.

EXHIBIT	2	Partial Present Value of an Annuity Table

			Present Value of an Annuity of $1 at Compound Interest		
Year	6%	10%	12%	15%	20%
1	0.943	0.909	0.893	0.870	0.833
2	1.833	1.736	1.690	1.626	1.528
3	2.673	2.487	2.402	2.283	2.106
4	3.465	3.170	3.037	2.855	2.589
5	4.212	3.791	3.605	3.353	2.991
6	4.917	4.355	4.111	3.785	3.326
7	5.582	4.868	4.564	4.160	3.605
8	6.210	5.335	4.968	4.487	3.837
9	6.802	5.759	5.328	4.772	4.031
10	7.360	6.145	5.650	5.019	4.192

The present value factors in the table shown in Exhibit 2 are the sum of the present value of $1 factors in Exhibit 1 for the number of annuity periods. Thus, 3.605 in the annuity table (Exhibit 2) is the sum of the five present value of $1 factors at 12%, as shown below.

	Present Value of $1 (Exhibit 1)
Present value of $1 for 1 year @12%	0.893
Present value of $1 for 2 years @12%	0.797
Present value of $1 for 3 years @12%	0.712
Present value of $1 for 4 years @12%	0.636
Present value of $1 for 5 years @12%	0.567
Present value of an annuity of $1 for 5 years (from Exhibit 2)	3.605

Multiplying $100 by 3.605 yields the same amount ($360.50) as follows:

Present Value		Amount to Be Received Annually for 5 Years		Present Value of an Annuity of $1 to Be Received for 5 Years (Exhibit 2)
$360.50	=	$100	×	3.605

This amount ($360.50) is the same as what was determined in the preceding illustration by five successive multiplications.

Net Present Value Method

The **net present value method** compares the amount to be invested with the present value of the net cash inflows. It is sometimes called the *discounted cash flow method*.

The interest rate (return) used in net present value analysis is the company's minimum desired rate of return. This rate, sometimes termed the *hurdle rate,* is based on such factors as the purpose of the investment and the cost of obtaining funds for the investment. If the present value of the cash inflows equals or exceeds the amount to be invested, the proposal is desirable.

A 55-year-old janitor won a $5 million lottery jackpot, payable in 21 annual installments of $240,245. Unfortunately, the janitor died after collecting only one payment. What happens to the remaining unclaimed payments? In this case, the lottery winnings were auctioned off for the benefit of the janitor's estate. The winning bid approximated the present value of the remaining cash flows, or about $2.1 million.

To illustrate, assume the following data for a proposed investment in new equipment:

Cost of new equipment	$ 200,000
Expected useful life	5 years
Minimum desired rate of return	10%
Expected cash flows to be received each year:	
Year 1	$ 70,000
Year 2	60,000
Year 3	50,000
Year 4	40,000
Year 5	40,000
Total expected cash flows	$ 260,000

The present value of the net cash flow for each year is computed by multiplying the net cash flow for the year by the present value factor of $1 for that year as shown below.

Year	Present Value of $1 at 10%	Net Cash Flow	Present Value of Net Cash Flow
1	0.909	$ 70,000	$ 63,630
2	0.826	60,000	49,560
3	0.751	50,000	37,550
4	0.683	40,000	27,320
5	0.621	40,000	24,840
Total		$260,000	$202,900
Amount to be invested			200,000
Net present value			$ 2,900

The preceding computations are also graphically illustrated as shown below.

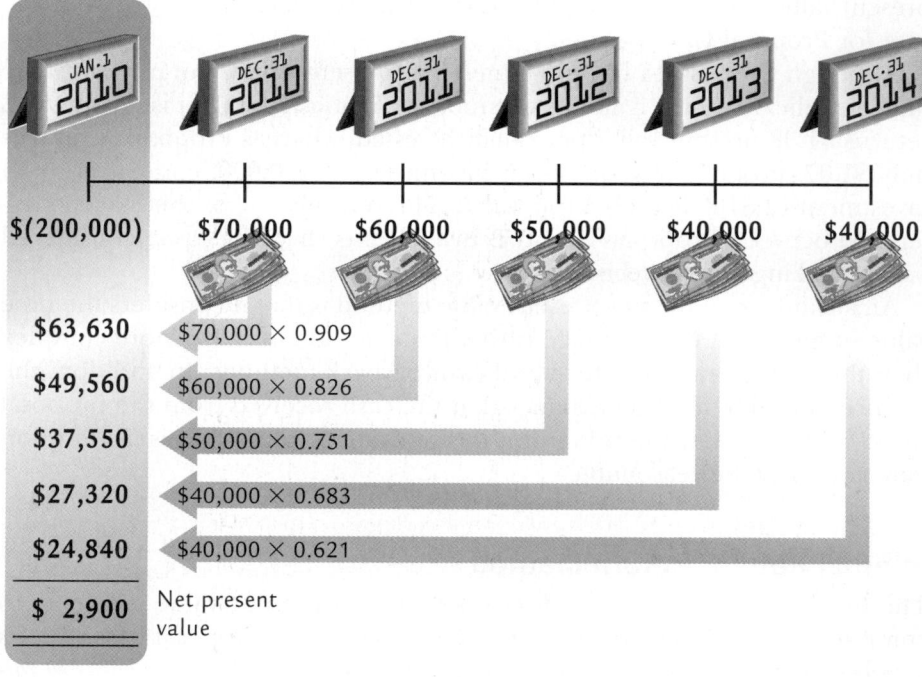

The net present value of $2,900 indicates that the purchase of the new equipment is expected to recover the investment and provide more than the minimum rate of return of 10%. Thus, the purchase of the new equipment is desirable.

When capital investment funds are limited and the proposals involve different investments, a ranking of the proposals can be prepared by using a present value index. The **present value index** is computed as follows:

$$\text{Present Value Index} = \frac{\text{Total Present Value of Net Cash Flow}}{\text{Amount to Be Invested}}$$

The present value index for the investment in the preceding illustration is 1.0145, as computed below.

$$\text{Present Value Index} = \frac{\text{Total Present Value of Net Cash Flow}}{\text{Amount to Be Invested}}$$

$$\text{Present Value Index} = \frac{\$202,900}{\$200,000} = 1.0145$$

To illustrate, assume that a company is considering three proposals. The net present value and the present value index for each proposal are as follows:

	Proposal A	Proposal B	Proposal C
Total present value of net cash flow	$107,000	$86,400	$86,400
Amount to be invested	100,000	80,000	90,000
Net present value	$ 7,000	$ 6,400	$ (3,600)
Present value index:			
Proposal A ($107,000/$100,000)	1.07		
Proposal B ($86,400/$80,000)		1.08	
Proposal C ($86,400/$90,000)			0.96

A project will have a present value index greater than 1 when the net present value is positive. This is the case for Proposals A and B. When the net present value is negative, the present value index will be less than 1, as is the case for Proposal C.

Although Proposal A has the largest net present value, the present value indices indicate that it is not as desirable as Proposal B. That is, Proposal B returns $1.08 present value per dollar invested, whereas Proposal A returns only $1.07. Proposal B requires an investment of $80,000, compared to an investment of $100,000 for Proposal A. The possible use of the $20,000 difference between Proposals A and B investments should also be considered before making a final decision.

An advantage of the net present value method is that it considers the time value of money. A disadvantage is that the computations are more complex than the average rate of return and cash payback methods. In addition, the net present value method assumes that the cash received from the proposal can be reinvested at the minimum desired rate of return. This assumption may not always be reasonable.

The use of spreadsheet software such as *Microsoft* Excel can simplify present value computations.

Internal Rate of Return Method

The **internal rate of return (IRR) method** uses present value concepts to compute the rate of return from a capital investment proposal based on its expected net cash flows. This method, sometimes called the *time-adjusted rate*

of return method, starts with the proposal's net cash flows and works backward to estimate the proposal's expected rate of return.

To illustrate, assume that management is evaluating the following proposal to purchase new equipment:

Cost of new equipment	$33,530
Yearly expected cash flows to be received	10,000
Expected life	5 years
Minimum desired rate of return	12%

The present value of the net cash flows, using the present value of an annuity table in Exhibit 2, is $2,520, as shown in Exhibit 3.

EXHIBIT **3**   **Net Present Value Analysis at 12%**

Annual net cash flow (at the end of each of five years)	$ 10,000
Present value of an annuity of $1 at 12% for five years (Exhibit 2)	× 3,605
Present value of annual net cash flows	$ 36,050
Less amount to be invested	33,530
Net present value	$ 2,520

In Exhibit 3, the $36,050 present value of the cash inflows, based on a 12% rate of return, is greater than the $33,530 to be invested. Thus, the internal rate of return must be greater than 12%. Through trial and error, the rate of return equating the $33,530 cost of the investment with the present value of the net cash flows can be determined to be 15%, as shown below.

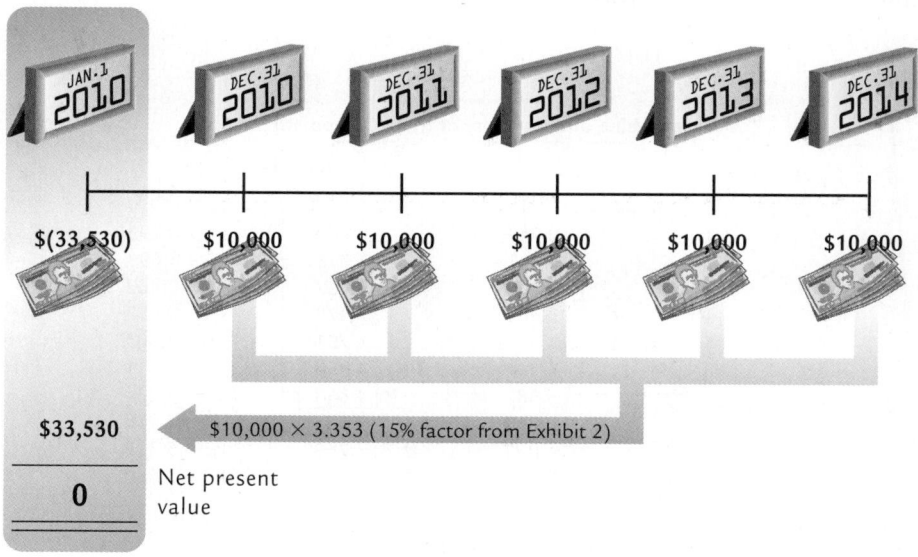

When equal annual net cash flows are expected from a proposal, as in the above example, the internal rate of return can be determined as follows:[2]

---

[2] To simplify, equal annual net cash flows are assumed. If the net cash flows are not equal, spreadsheet software can be used to determine the rate of return.

Step 1. Determine a present value factor for an annuity of $1 as follows:

$$\text{Present Value Factor for an Annuity of } \$1 = \frac{\text{Amount to Be Invested}}{\text{Equal Annual Net Cash Flows}}$$

Step 2. Locate the present value factor determined in Step 1 in the present value of an annuity of $1 table (Exhibit 2) as follows:

    a. Locate the number of years of expected useful life of the investment in the Year column.

    b. Proceed horizontally across the table until you find the present value factor computed in Step 1.

Step 3. Identify the internal rate of return by the heading of the column in which the present value factor in Step 2 is located.

To illustrate, assume that management is evaluating the following proposal to purchase new equipment:

Cost of new equipment	$97,360
Yearly expected cash flows to be received	20,000
Expected useful life	7 years

The present value factor for an annuity of $1 is 4.868, as shown below.

$$\text{Present Value Factor for an Annuity of } \$1 = \frac{\text{Amount to Be Invested}}{\text{Equal Annual Net Cash Flows}}$$

$$\text{Present Value Factor for an Annuity } \$1 = \frac{\$97,360}{\$20,000} = 4.868$$

Using the following partial present value of an annuity of $1 table and a period of seven years, the factor 4.868 is related to 10%. Thus, the internal rate of return for this proposal is 10%.

Present Value of an Annuity of $1 at Compound Interest				
			Step 3	
Year	6%		10%	12%
1	0.943		0.909	0.893
2	1.833		1.736	1.690
3	2.673		2.487	2.402
4	3.465		3.170	3.037
5	4.212		3.791	3.605
6	4.917	Step 2(b)	4.355	4.111
Step 2(a)　7	5.582		4.868	4.564
8	6.210		5.335	4.968
9	6.802		5.759	5.328
10	7.360		6.145	5.650

Step 1: Determine present value factor for an annuity of $1 $= \dfrac{\$97,360}{\$20,000} = 4.863$

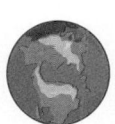

The minimum acceptable rate of return for **Owens Corning** is 18%; for **General Electric Company**, it is 20%. The CFO of Owens Corning states, "I'm here to challenge anyone—even the CEO—who gets emotionally attached to a project that doesn't reach our benchmark."

If the minimum acceptable rate of return is 10%, then the proposal is considered acceptable. Several proposals can be ranked by their internal rates of return. The proposal with the highest rate is the most desirable.

A primary advantage of the internal rate of return method is that the present values of the net cash flows over the entire useful life of the proposal are considered. In addition, all proposals can be compared based on their internal rates of return.

The primary disadvantage of the internal rate of return method is that the computations are more complex. Also, like the net present value method, it assumes that the cash received from a proposal can be reinvested at the internal rate of return. This assumption may not always be reasonable.

Factors that Complicate Capital Investment Analysis

Obj 4 List and describe factors that complicate capital investment analysis.

Four widely used methods of evaluating capital investment proposals have been described and illustrated in this chapter. In practice, additional factors such as the following may impact capital investment decisions:

1. Income tax
2. Proposals with unequal lives
3. Leasing versus purchasing
4. Uncertainty
5. Changes in price levels
6. Qualitative factors

How Businesses Make Money

Panera Bread Store Rate of Return

Panera Bread owns, operates, and franchises bakery-cafes throughout the United States. A recent annual report to the Securities and Exchange Commission (SEC Form 10-K) disclosed the following information about an average company-owned store:

Operating profit	$ 302,000
Depreciation	98,000
Investment	1,000,000

Assume that the operating profit and depreciation will remain unchanged for the next 10 years. Assume operating profit plus depreciation approximates annual net cash flows, and that the investment residual value will be zero. The average rate of return and internal rate of return can then be estimated. The average rate of return on a company-owned store is:

$$\frac{\$302,000}{\$1,000,000/2} = 60.4\%$$

The internal rate of return is calculated by first determining the present value of an annuity of $1:

$$\text{Present value of an annuity of } \$1 = \frac{\$1,000,000}{\$302,000 + \$98,000} = 2.50$$

For a period of three years, this factor implies an internal rate of return near 10% (from Exhibit 2). However, if we more realistically assumed these cash flows for 10 years, Panera's company-owned stores generate an estimated internal rate of return of approximately 38% (from a spreadsheet calculation). Clearly, both investment evaluation methods indicate a highly successful business.

Income Tax

The impact of income taxes on capital investment decisions can be material. For example, in determining depreciation for federal income tax purposes, useful lives that are much shorter than the actual useful lives are often used. Also, depreciation for tax purposes often differs from depreciation for financial statement purposes. As a result, the timing of the cash flows for income taxes can have a significant impact on capital investment analysis.[3]

Unequal Proposal Lives

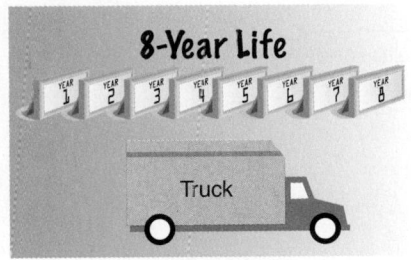

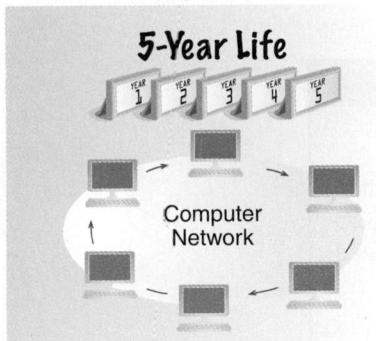

The prior capital investment illustrations assumed that the alternative proposals had the same useful lives. In practice, however, proposals often have different lives.

To illustrate, assume that a company is considering purchasing a new truck or a new computer network. The data for each proposal are shown below.

	Truck	Computer Network
Cost	$100,000	$100,000
Minimum desired rate of return	10%	10%
Expected useful life	8 years	5 years
Yearly expected cash flows to be received:		
Year 1	$ 30,000	$ 30,000
Year 2	30,000	30,000
Year 3	25,000	30,000
Year 4	20,000	30,000
Year 5	15,000	35,000
Year 6	15,000	0
Year 7	10,000	0
Year 8	10,000	0
Total	$155,000	$155,000

The expected cash flows and net present value for each proposal are shown in Exhibit 4. Because of the unequal useful lives, however, the net present values in Exhibit 4 are not comparable.

To make the proposals comparable, the useful lives are adjusted to end at the same time. In this illustration, this is done by assuming that the truck will be sold at the end of five years. The selling price (residual value) of the truck at the end of five years is estimated and included in the cash inflows. Both proposals will then cover five years; thus, the net present value analyses will be comparable.

To illustrate, assume that the truck's estimated selling price (residual value) at the end of Year 5 is $40,000. Exhibit 5 shows the truck's revised present value analysis assuming a five-year life.

As shown in Exhibit 5, the net present value for the truck exceeds the net present value for the computer network by $1,835 ($18,640 – $16,805). Thus, the truck is the more attractive of the two proposals.

---

[3] The impact of taxes on capital investment analysis is covered in advanced accounting textbooks.

EXHIBIT 4 Net Present Value Analysis—Unequal Lives of Proposals

	A	B	C	D
1		Truck		
2	Year	Present	Net	Present
3		Value of	Cash	Value of
4		$1 at 10%	Flow	Net Cash Flow
5	1	0.909	$ 30,000	$ 27,270
6	2	0.826	30,000	24,780
7	3	0.751	25,000	18,775
8	4	0.683	20,000	13,660
9	5	0.621	15,000	9,315
10	6	0.564	15,000	8,460
11	7	0.513	10,000	5,130
12	8	0.467	10,000	4,670
13	Total		$155,000	$112,060
14				
15	Amount to be invested			100,000
16	Net present value			$ 12,060

	A	B	C	D
1		Computer Network		
2	Year	Present	Net	Present
3		Value of	Cash	Value of
4		$1 at 10%	Flow	Net Cash Flow
5	1	0.909	$ 30,000	$ 27,270
6	2	0.826	30,000	24,780
7	3	0.751	30,000	22,530
8	4	0.683	30,000	20,490
9	5	0.621	35,000	21,735
10	Total		$155,000	$116,805
11				
12	Amount to be invested			100,000
13	Net present value			$ 16,805

EXHIBIT 5 Net Present Value Analysis—Equalized Lives of Proposals

	A	B	C	D
1		Truck—Revised to 5-Year Life		
2	Year	Present	Net	Present
3		Value of	Cash	Value of
4		$1 at 10%	Flow	Net Cash Flow
5	1	0.909	$ 30,000	$ 27,270
6	2	0.826	30,000	24,780
7	3	0.751	25,000	18,775
8	4	0.683	20,000	13,660
9	5	0.621	15,000	9,315
10	5 (Residual			
11	value)	0.621	40,000	24,840
12	Total		$160,000	$118,640
13				
14	Amount to be invested			100,000
15	Net present value			$ 18,640

Truck Net Present Value Greater than Computer Network Net Present Value by $1,835

Lease Versus Capital Investment

Leasing fixed assets is common in many industries. For example, hospitals often lease medical equipment. Some advantages of leasing a fixed asset include the following:

1. The company has use of the fixed asset without spending large amounts of cash to purchase the asset.

2. The company eliminates the risk of owning an obsolete asset.

3. The company may deduct the annual lease payments for income tax purposes.

A disadvantage of leasing a fixed asset is that it is normally more costly than purchasing the asset. This is because the lessor (owner of the asset) includes in the rental price not only the costs of owning the asset, but also a profit.

The methods of evaluating capital investment proposals illustrated in this chapter can also be used to decide whether to lease or purchase a fixed asset.

Uncertainty

All capital investment analyses rely on factors that are uncertain. For example, estimates of revenues, expenses, and cash flows are uncertain. This is especially true for long-term capital investments. Errors in one or more of the estimates could lead to incorrect decisions. Methods that consider the impact of uncertainty on capital investment analysis are discussed in advanced accounting and finance textbooks.

Changes in Price Levels

Price levels normally change as the economy improves or deteriorates. General price levels often increase in a rapidly growing economy, which is called **inflation**. During such periods, the rate of return on an investment should exceed the rising price level. If this is not the case, the cash returned on the investment will be less than expected.

Price levels may also change for foreign investments. This occurs as currency exchange rates change. **Currency exchange rates** are the rates at which currency in another country can be exchanged for U.S. dollars.

If the amount of local dollars that can be exchanged for one U.S. dollar increases, then the local currency is said to be weakening to the dollar. When a company has an investment in another country where the local currency is weakening, the return on the investment, as expressed in U.S. dollars, is adversely impacted. This is because the expected amount of local currency returned on the investment would purchase fewer U.S. dollars.[4]

Qualitative Considerations

Some benefits of capital investments are qualitative in nature and cannot be estimated in dollar terms. However, if a company does not consider qualitative considerations, an acceptable investment proposal could be rejected.

Some examples of qualitative considerations that may influence capital investment analysis include the impact of the investment proposal on the following:

1. Product quality

2. Manufacturing flexibility

3. Employee morale

4. Manufacturing productivity

5. Market (strategic) opportunities

IBM decided to develop molecular and atomic-level nanotechnology based more on its strategic market potential than on an economic analysis of cash flows.

---

[4] Further discussion on accounting for foreign currency transactions is available on the companion Web site at academic.cengage.com/accounting/warren.

Many qualitative factors, such as those listed above, may be as important as, if not more important than, quantitative factors.

Capital Rationing

Obj 5 Diagram the capital rationing process.

Capital rationing is the process by which management allocates funds among competing capital investment proposals. In this process, management often uses a combination of the methods described in this chapter, as shown in Exhibit 6.

EXHIBIT 6 | **Capital Rationing Decision Process**

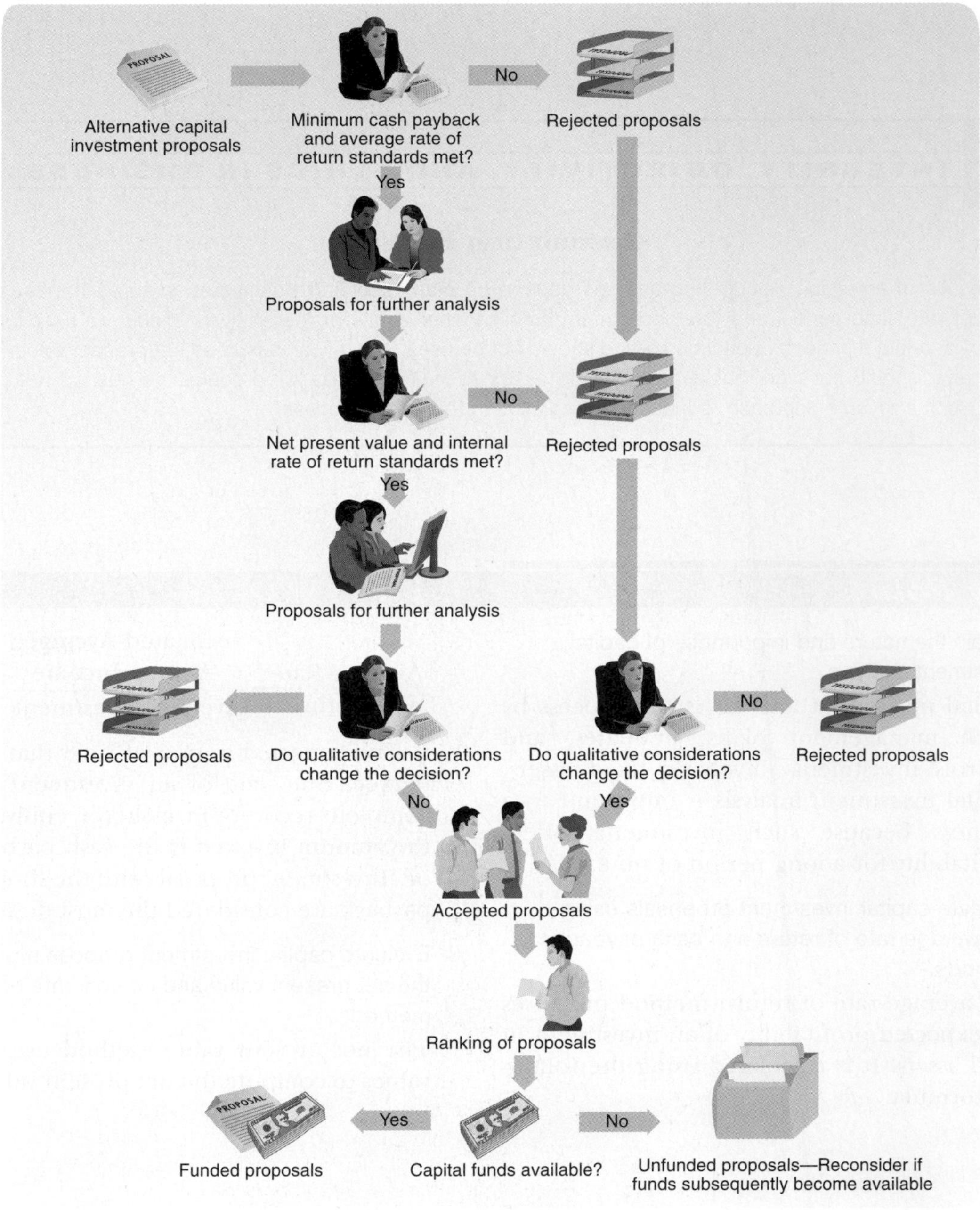

Alternative capital investment proposals

Minimum cash payback and average rate of return standards met? — No → Rejected proposals

Yes

Proposals for further analysis

Net present value and internal rate of return standards met? — No → Rejected proposals

Yes

Proposals for further analysis

Rejected proposals ← Do qualitative considerations change the decision? No

Do qualitative considerations change the decision? — No → Rejected proposals

Yes

Accepted proposals

Ranking of proposals

Funded proposals ← Yes — Capital funds available? — No → Unfunded proposals—Reconsider if funds subsequently become available

Exhibit 6 illustrates the capital rationing decision process. Alternative proposals are initially screened by establishing minimum standards using the cash payback and the average rate of return methods. The proposals that survive this screening are further analyzed, using the net present value and internal rate of return methods.

Qualitative factors related to each proposal should also be considered throughout the capital rationing process. For example, new equipment might improve the quality of the product and thus increase consumer satisfaction and sales.

At the end of the capital rationing process, accepted proposals are ranked and compared with the funds available. Proposals that are selected for funding are included in the capital expenditures budget. Unfunded proposals may be reconsidered if funds later become available.

INTEGRITY, OBJECTIVITY, AND ETHICS IN BUSINESS

Assumption Fudging

The results of any capital budgeting analysis depend on many subjective estimates, such as the cash flows, discount rate, time period, and total investment amount. The results of the analysis should be used to either support or reject a project. Capital budgeting should not be used to justify an assumed net present value. That is, the analyst should not work backward, filling in assumed numbers that will produce the desired net present value. Such a reverse approach reduces the credibility of the entire process.

Key Points

1. Explain the nature and importance of capital investment analysis.

   Capital investment analysis is the process by which management plans, evaluates, and controls investments involving fixed assets. Capital investment analysis is important to a business because such investments affect profitability for a long period of time.

2. Evaluate capital investment proposals using the average rate of return and cash payback methods.

   The average rate of return method measures the expected profitability of an investment in fixed assets. It is calculated using the following formula:

   $$\frac{\text{Average Rate}}{\text{of Return}} = \frac{\text{Estimated Average Annual Income}}{\text{Average Investment}}$$

   The expected period of time that will pass between the date of an investment and the complete recovery in cash (or equivalent) of the amount invested is the cash payback period. Investment proposals with the shortest cash payback are considered the most desirable.

3. Evaluate capital investment proposals using the net present value and internal rate of return methods.

   The net present value method uses present values to compute the net present value of the

cash flows expected from a proposal. The net present values of the cash flows are then compared across proposals. The present value of a cash flow is computed by looking up the present value of $1 from a table of present values and multiplying it by the amount of the future cash flow, as shown in the text.

The internal rate of return method uses present values to compute the rate of return from the net cash flows expected from capital investment proposals. When equal annual net cash flows are expected from a proposal, the computations are simplified by using a table of the present value of an annuity, as shown in the text.

4. List and describe factors that complicate capital investment analysis.

Factors that may complicate capital investment analysis include the impact of the federal income tax, unequal lives of alternative proposals, leasing, uncertainty, changes in price levels, and qualitative considerations. A brief description of the effect of each of these factors appears in the text.

5. Diagram the capital rationing process.

Capital rationing refers to the process by which management allocates available investment funds among competing capital investment proposals. A diagram of the capital rationing process appears in Exhibit 6.

Key Terms

Annuity A series of equal cash flows at fixed intervals.

Average rate of return A method of evaluating capital investment proposals that focuses on the expected profitability of the investment.

Capital investment analysis The process by which management plans, evaluates, and controls long-term capital investments involving fixed assets.

Capital rationing The process by which management allocates available investment funds among competing capital investment proposals.

Cash payback period The expected period of time that will elapse between the date of a capital expenditure and the complete recovery in cash (or equivalent) of the amount invested.

Currency exchange rate The rate at which currency in another country can be exchanged for local currency.

Inflation A period when prices in general are rising and the purchasing power of money is declining.

Internal rate of return method A method of analyzing proposed capital investments that focuses on using present value concepts to compute the rate of return from the net cash flows expected from the investment.

Net present value method A method of analyzing proposed capital investments that focuses on the present value of the cash flows expected from the investments.

Present value concept Cash today is not the equivalent of the same amount of money to be received in the future.

Present value index An index computed by dividing the total present value of the net cash flow to be received from a proposed capital investment by the amount to be invested.

Present value of an annuity The sum of the present values of a series of equal cash flows to be received at fixed intervals.

Time value of money concept The concept that an amount of money invested today will earn interest.

Illustrative Problem

The capital investment committee of Hopewell Company is currently considering two projects. The estimated income from operations and net cash flows expected from each project are shown on the next page.

Year	Project A Income from Operations	Project A Net Cash Flow	Project B Income from Operations	Project B Net Cash Flow
1	$ 6,000	$ 22,000	$13,000	$ 29,000
2	9,000	25,000	10,000	26,000
3	10,000	26,000	8,000	24,000
4	8,000	24,000	8,000	24,000
5	11,000	27,000	3,000	19,000
	$44,000	$124,000	$42,000	$122,000

Each project requires an investment of $80,000. Straight-line depreciation will be used, and no residual value is expected. The committee has selected a rate of 15% for purposes of the net present value analysis.

Instructions

1. Compute the following:

   a. The average rate of return for each project.

   b. The net present value for each project. Use the present value of $1 table appearing in this chapter.

2. Why is the net present value of Project B greater than Project A, even though its average rate of return is less?

3. Prepare a summary for the capital investment committee, advising it on the relative merits of the two projects.

Solution

1. a. Average rate of return for Project A:

$$\frac{\$44,000 \div 5}{(\$80,000 + \$0) \div 2} = 22\%$$

Average rate of return for Project B:

$$\frac{\$42,000 \div 5}{(\$80,000 + \$0) \div 2} = 21\%$$

b. Net present value analysis:

Year	Present Value of $1 at 15%	Net Cash Flow Project A	Net Cash Flow Project B	Present Value of Net Cash Flow Project A	Present Value of Net Cash Flow Project B
1	0.870	$ 22,000	$ 29,000	$19,140	$25,230
2	0.756	25,000	26,000	18,900	19,656
3	0.658	26,000	24,000	17,108	15,792
4	0.572	24,000	24,000	13,728	13,728
5	0.497	27,000	19,000	13,419	9,443
Total		$124,000	$122,000	$82,295	$83,849
Amount to be invested				80,000	80,000
Net present value				$ 2,295	$ 3,849

2. Project B has a lower average rate of return than Project A because Project B's total income from operations for the 5 years is $42,000, which is $2,000 less than Project A's. Even so, the net present value of Project B is greater than that of Project A, because Project B has higher cash flows in the early years.

3. Both projects exceed the selected rate established for the net present value analysis. Project A has a higher average rate of return, but Project B offers a larger net present value. Thus, if only one of the two projects can be accepted, Project B would be the more attractive.

Self-Examination Questions (Answers appear at the end of chapter)

1. Methods of evaluating capital investment proposals that ignore present value include:

    A. average rate of return

    B. cash payback

    C. both A and B

    D. neither A nor B

2. Management is considering a $100,000 investment in a project with a 5-year life and no residual value. If the total income from the project is expected to be $60,000 and recognition is given to the effect of straight-line depreciation on the investment, the average rate of return is:

    A. 12%

    B. 24%

    C. 60%

    D. 75%

3. The expected period of time that will elapse between the date of a capital investment and the complete recovery of the amount of cash invested is called:

    A. the average rate of return period

    B. the cash payback period

    C. the net present value period

    D. the internal rate of return period

4. A project that will cost $120,000 is estimated to generate cash flows of $25,000 per year for 8 years. What is the net present value of the project, assuming a 10% required rate of return? (Use the present value tables in this chapter.)

    A. $11,675

    B. $13,375

    C. $75,000

    D. $95,000

5. A project is estimated to generate cash flows of $40,000 per year for 10 years. The cost of the project is $226,000. What is the internal rate of return for this project?

    A. 8%

    B. 10%

    C. 12%

    D. 15%

Class Discussion Questions

1. What are the principal objections to the use of the average rate of return method in evaluating capital investment proposals?

2. Discuss the principal limitations of the cash payback method for evaluating capital investment proposals.

3. Why would the average rate of return differ from the internal rate of return on the same project?

4. What information does the cash payback period ignore that is included by the net present value method?

5. Your boss has suggested that a one-year payback period is the same as a 100% average rate of return. Do you agree?

6. Why would the cash payback method understate the attractiveness of a project with a large residual value?

7. Why would the use of the cash payback period for analyzing the financial performance of theatrical releases from a motion picture production studio be supported over the net present value method?

8. A net present value analysis used to evaluate a proposed equipment acquisition indicated a $7,900 net present value. What is the meaning of the $7,900 as it relates to the desirability of the proposal?

9. Two projects have an identical net present value of $9,000. Are both projects equal in desirability?

10. What are the major disadvantages of the use of the net present value method of analyzing capital investment proposals?

11. What are the major disadvantages of the use of the internal rate of return method of analyzing capital investment proposals?

12. What provision of the Internal Revenue Code is especially important to consider in analyzing capital investment proposals?

13. What method can be used to place two capital investment proposals with unequal useful lives on a comparable basis?

14. What are the major advantages of leasing a fixed asset rather than purchasing it?

15. Give an example of a qualitative factor that should be considered in a capital investment analysis related to acquiring automated factory equipment.

16. *Monsanto Company,* a large chemical and fibers company, invested $37 million in state-of-the-art systems to improve process control, laboratory automation, and local area network (LAN) communications. The investment was not justified merely on cost savings but was also justified on the basis of qualitative considerations. Monsanto management viewed the investment as a critical element toward achieving its vision of the future. What qualitative and quantitative considerations do you believe Monsanto would have considered in its strategic evaluation of these investments?

Exercises

E15-1

Average rate of return

Obj 2

✓ Testing equipment, 5.5%

The following data are accumulated by Eco-Labs, Inc. in evaluating two competing capital investment proposals:

	Testing Equipment	Vehicle
Amount of investment	$80,000	$28,000
Useful life	6 years	8 years
Estimated residual value	0	0
Estimated total income over the useful life	$13,200	$14,000

Determine the expected average rate of return for each proposal. Round to one decimal place.

E15-2

Average rate of return—cost savings

Obj 2

Master Fab Inc. is considering an investment in equipment that will replace direct labor. The equipment has a cost of $115,000 with a $10,000 residual value and a 10-year life. The equipment will replace one employee who has an average wage of $26,000 per year. In addition, the equipment will have operating and energy costs of $5,500 per year.

Determine the average rate of return on the equipment, giving effect to straight-line depreciation on the investment.

E15-3

Average rate of return—new product

Obj 2

✓ **Average annual income, $138,000**

Pocket Pilot Inc. is considering an investment in new equipment that will be used to manufacture a mobile communications device. The device is expected to generate additional annual sales of 6,000 units at $280 per unit. The equipment has a cost of $640,000, residual value of $50,000, and an 8-year life. The equipment can only be used to manufacture the device. The cost to manufacture the device is shown below.

Cost per unit:	
Direct labor	$ 45.00
Direct materials	180.00
Factory overhead (including depreciation)	32.00
Total cost per unit	$257.00

Determine the average rate of return on the equipment.

E15-4

Calculate cash flows

Obj 2

✓ **Year 1: ($102,900)**

Out of Eden, Inc. is planning to invest in new manufacturing equipment to make a new garden tool. The new garden tool is expected to generate additional annual sales of 9,000 units at $42 each. The new manufacturing equipment will cost $156,000 and is expected to have a 10-year life and $12,000 residual value. Selling expenses related to the new product are expected to be 5% of sales revenue. The cost to manufacture the product includes the following on a per-unit basis:

Direct labor	$ 7.00
Direct materials	23.40
Fixed factory overhead—depreciation	1.60
Variable factory overhead	3.60
Total	$35.60

Determine the net cash flows for the first year of the project, Years 2–9, and for the last year of the project.

E15-5

Cash payback period

Obj 2

✓ **Location 1: 6 years**

Primera Banco is evaluating two capital investment proposals for a drive-up ATM kiosk, each requiring an investment of $360,000 and each with an 8-year life and expected total net cash flows of $480,000. Location 1 is expected to provide equal annual net cash flows of $60,000, and Location 2 is expected to have the following unequal annual net cash flows:

Year 1	$120,000
Year 2	90,000
Year 3	75,000
Year 4	75,000
Year 5	30,000
Year 6	30,000
Year 7	30,000
Year 8	30,000

Determine the cash payback period for both location proposals.

E15-6

Cash payback method

Obj 2

SPREADSHEET

✓ **a. Liquid Soap: 3 years**

Gentle Care Products Company is considering an investment in one of two new product lines. The investment required for either product line is $500,000. The net cash flows associated with each product are shown on the next page:

Year	Liquid Soap	Body Lotion
1	$190,000	$100,000
2	180,000	100,000
3	130,000	100,000
4	110,000	100,000
5	80,000	100,000
6	50,000	100,000
7	30,000	100,000
8	30,000	100,000
Total	$800,000	$800,000

a. Recommend a product offering to Gentle Care Products Company, based on the cash payback period for each product line.

b. Why is one product line preferred over the other, even though they both have the same total net cash flows through eight periods?

E15-7

Net present value method

Obj 3

✓ a. NPV $27,370

The following data are accumulated by Reynolds Company in evaluating the purchase of $104,000 of equipment, having a four-year useful life:

	Net Income	Net Cash Flow
Year 1	$38,000	$64,000
Year 2	23,000	49,000
Year 3	11,000	37,000
Year 4	(1,000)	25,000

a. Assuming that the desired rate of return is 15%, determine the net present value for the proposal. Use the table of the present value of $1 appearing in Exhibit 1 of this chapter.

b. Would management be likely to look with favor on the proposal? Explain.

E15-8

Net present value method

Obj 3

✓ a. 2011, $11,000

Rapid Delivery, Inc. is considering the purchase of an additional delivery vehicle for $38,000 on January 1, 2010. The truck is expected to have a five-year life with an expected residual value of $5,000 at the end of five years. The expected additional revenues from the added delivery capacity are anticipated to be $60,000 per year for each of the next five years. A driver will cost $43,000 in 2010, with an expected annual salary increase of $2,000 for each year thereafter. The insurance for the truck is estimated to cost $4,000 per year.

a. Determine the expected annual net cash flows from the delivery truck investment for 2010–2014.

b. Calculate the net present value of the investment, assuming that the minimum desired rate of return is 12%. Use the present value of $1 table appearing in Exhibit 1 of this chapter.

c. Is the additional truck a good investment based on your analysis?

E15-9

Net present value method—annuity

Obj 3

✓ a. $24 million

Hideaway Hotels is considering the construction of a new hotel for $150 million. The expected life of the hotel is 30 years with no residual value. The hotel is expected to earn revenues of $44 million per year. Total expenses, including depreciation, are expected to be $25 million per year. Hideaway management has set a minimum acceptable rate of return of 14%.

a. Determine the equal annual net cash flows from operating the hotel.

b. Calculate the net present value of the new hotel using the present value factor of an annuity of $1 at 14% for 30 periods of 7.0027. Round to the nearest million dollars.

c. Does your analysis support construction of the new hotel?

E15-10

Net present value method—annuity

Obj 3

✓ a. $69,000

E & T Excavation Company is planning an investment of $245,000 for a bulldozer. The bulldozer is expected to operate for 1,500 hours per year for five years. Customers will be charged $130 per hour for bulldozer work. The bulldozer operator costs $32 per hour in wages and benefits. The bulldozer is expected to require annual maintenance costing $15,000. The bulldozer uses fuel that is expected to cost $42 per hour of bulldozer operation.

a. Determine the equal annual net cash flows from operating the bulldozer.
b. Determine the net present value of the investment, assuming that the desired rate of return is 10%. Use the table of present values of an annuity of $1 in the chapter. Round to the nearest dollar.
c. Should E & T invest in the bulldozer, based on this analysis?

E15-11

Net present value method

Obj 3

✓ a. $288,800,000

Carnival Corporation has recently placed into service some of the largest cruise ships in the world. One of these ships, the *Carnival Dream,* can hold up to 3,600 passengers and cost $750 million to build. Assume the following additional information:

• There will be 300 cruise days per year operated at a full capacity of 3,600 passengers.
• The variable expenses per passenger are estimated to be $90 per cruise day.
• The revenue per passenger is expected to be $450 per cruise day.
• The fixed expenses for running the ship, other than depreciation, are estimated to be $100,000,000 per year.
• The ship has a service life of 10 years, with a residual value of $120,000,000 at the end of 10 years.

a. Determine the annual net cash flow from operating the cruise ship.
b. Determine the net present value of this investment, assuming a 12% minimum rate of return. Use the present value tables provided in the chapter in determining your answer.

E15-12

Present value index

Obj 3

✓ Location A, 1.07

Hot on the Spot Doughnuts has computed the net present value for capital expenditure locations A and B, using the net present value method. Relevant data related to the computation are as follows:

	Location A	Location B
Total present value of net cash flow	$ 371,290	$ 396,096
Amount to be invested	347,000	412,600
Net present value	$ (24,290)	$ (16,504)

Determine the present value index for each proposal.

E15-13

Net present value method and present value index

Obj 3

✓ b. Packing Machine, 1.18

MVP Sports Equipment Company is considering an investment in one of two machines. The sewing machine will increase productivity from sewing 150 baseballs per hour to sewing 270 per hour. The contribution margin is $0.48 per baseball. Assume that any increased production of baseballs can be sold. The second machine is an automatic packing machine for the golf ball line. The packing machine will reduce packing labor cost. The labor cost saved is equivalent to $26 per hour. The sewing machine will cost $384,600, have an eight-year life, and will operate for 1,700 hours per year. The packing machine will cost $157,900, have an eight-year life, and will operate for 1,600 hours per year. MVP seeks a minimum rate of return of 15% on its investments.

a. Determine the net present value for the two machines. Use the table of present values of an annuity of $1 in the chapter. Round to the nearest dollar.

b. Determine the present value index for the two machines. Round to two decimal places.

c. If MVP has sufficient funds for only one of the machines and qualitative factors are equal between the two machines, in which machine should it invest?

E15-14

Average rate of return, cash payback period, net present value method

Objs 2, 3

✓ b. 4 years

Great Plains Transportation Inc. is considering acquiring equipment at a cost of $246,000. The equipment has an estimated life of 10 years and no residual value. It is expected to provide yearly net cash flows of $61,500. The company's minimum desired rate of return for net present value analysis is 10%.

Compute the following:

a. The average rate of return, giving effect to straight-line depreciation on the investment.

b. The cash payback period.

c. The net present value. Use the table of the present value of an annuity of $1 appearing in this chapter. Round to the nearest dollar.

E15-15

Payback period, net present value analysis, and qualitative considerations

Objs 2, 3, 4

✓ a. 4 years

The plant manager of Shannon Electronics Company is considering the purchase of new automated assembly equipment. The new equipment will cost $2,400,000. The manager believes that the new investment will result in direct labor savings of $600,000 per year for 10 years.

a. What is the payback period on this project?

b. What is the net present value, assuming a 10% rate of return? Use the present value tables appearing in this chapter.

c. What else should the manager consider in the analysis?

E15-16

Internal rate of return method

Obj 3

✓ a. 3.326

The internal rate of return method is used by Carlisle Construction Co. in analyzing a capital expenditure proposal that involves an investment of $49,890 and annual net cash flows of $15,000 for each of the six years of its useful life.

a. Determine a present value factor for an annuity of $1 which can be used in determining the internal rate of return.

b. Using the factor determined in part (a) and the present value of an annuity of $1 table appearing in this chapter, determine the internal rate of return for the proposal.

E15-17

Internal rate of return method

Obj 3

The Canyons Resort, a Utah ski resort, recently announced a $400 million expansion of lodging properties, lifts, and terrain. Assume that this investment is estimated to produce $95.42 million in equal annual cash flows for each of the first 10 years of the project life.

Determine the expected internal rate of return of this project for 10 years, using the present value of an annuity of $1 table found in Exhibit 2.

E15-18

Internal rate of return method—two projects

Obj 3

✓ a. Delivery truck, 15%

Cousin's Salted Snack Company is considering two possible investments: a delivery truck or a bagging machine. The delivery truck would cost $39,287 and could be used to deliver an additional 48,200 bags of taquitos chips per year. Each bag of chips can be sold for a contribution margin of $0.42. The delivery truck operating expenses, excluding depreciation, are $0.60 per mile for 18,000 miles per year. The bagging machine would replace an old bagging machine,

and its net investment cost would be $65,718. The new machine would require three fewer hours of direct labor per day. Direct labor is $18 per hour. There are 250 operating days in the year. Both the truck and the bagging machine are estimated to have seven-year lives. The minimum rate of return is 13%. However, Cousin's has funds to invest in only one of the projects.

a. Compute the internal rate of return for each investment. Use the table of present values of an annuity of $1 in the chapter.
b. Provide a memo to management with a recommendation.

E15-19

Net present value method and internal rate of return method

Obj 3

✓ a. ($10,582)

Buckeye Healthcare Corp. is proposing to spend $109,296 on an eight-year project that has estimated net cash flows of $22,000 for each of the eight years.

a. Compute the net present value, using a rate of return of 15%. Use the table of present values of an annuity of $1 in the chapter.
b. Based on the analysis prepared in part (a), is the rate of return (1) more than 15%, (2) 15%, or (3) less than 15%? Explain.
c. Determine the internal rate of return by computing a present value factor for an annuity of $1 and using the table of the present value of an annuity of $1 presented in the text.

E15-20

Identify error in capital investment analysis calculations

Obj 3

Horizon Solutions Inc. is considering the purchase of automated machinery that is expected to have a useful life of five years and no residual value. The average rate of return on the average investment has been computed to be 20%, and the cash payback period was computed to be 5.5 years.

Do you see any reason to question the validity of the data presented? Explain.

E15-21

Net present value—unequal lives

Objs 3, 4

SPREADSHEET

✓ Net present value, Apartment Complex, $24,530

Lordsland Development Company has two competing projects: an apartment complex and an office building. Both projects have an initial investment of $720,000. The net cash flows estimated for the two projects are as follows:

| | Net Cash Flow | |
Year	Apartment Complex	Office Building
1	$225,000	$290,000
2	200,000	290,000
3	200,000	230,000
4	140,000	220,000
5	140,000	
6	105,000	
7	80,000	
8	50,000	

The estimated residual value of the apartment complex at the end of Year 4 is $325,000.

Determine which project should be favored, comparing the net present values of the two projects and assuming a minimum rate of return of 15%. Use the table of present values in the chapter.

E15-22

Net present value–unequal lives

Objs 3, 4

A La Mode, Inc. is considering one of two investment options. Option 1 is a $40,000 investment in new blending equipment that is expected to produce equal annual cash flows of $12,000 for each of seven years. Option 2 is a $45,000 investment in a new computer system that is expected to produce equal annual cash flows of $15,500 for each of five years. The residual value of the blending equipment at the end of the fifth year is estimated to be $8,000. The computer system has no expected residual value at the end of the fifth year.

    Assume there is sufficient capital to fund only one of the projects. Determine which project should be selected, comparing the (a) net present values and (b) present value indices of the two projects, assuming a minimum rate of return of 10%. Round the present value index to two decimal places. Use the table of present values in the chapter.

Problems

P15-1

Average rate of return method, net present value method, and analysis

Objs 2, 3

SPREADSHEET

✓ 1.a. 17.5%

The capital investment committee of Cross Continent Trucking Inc. is considering two investment projects. The estimated income from operations and net cash flows from each investment are as follows:

	Warehouse		Tracking Technology	
Year	Income from Operations	Net Cash Flow	Income from Operations	Net Cash Flow
1	$ 42,000	$138,000	$ 89,000	$185,000
2	42,000	138,000	69,000	165,000
3	42,000	138,000	34,000	130,000
4	42,000	138,000	14,000	110,000
5	42,000	138,000	4,000	100,000
Total	$210,000	$690,000	$210,000	$690,000

    Each project requires an investment of $480,000. Straight-line depreciation will be used, and no residual value is expected. The committee has selected a rate of 15% for purposes of the net present value analysis.

Instructions

1. Compute the following:
   a. The average rate of return for each investment. Round to one decimal place.
   b. The net present value for each investment. Use the present value of $1 table appearing in this chapter.
2. Prepare a brief report for the capital investment committee, advising it on the relative merits of the two projects.

P15-2

Cash payback period, net present value method, and analysis

Objs 2, 3

SPREADSHEET

✓ 1. b. *Home & Garden,* $127,158

At Home Publications Inc. is considering two new magazine products. The estimated net cash flows from each product are as follows:

Year	Home & Garden	Music Beat
1	$150,000	$125,000
2	120,000	145,000
3	105,000	100,000
4	84,000	70,000
5	41,000	60,000
Total	$500,000	$500,000

Each product requires an investment of $270,000. A rate of 10% has been selected for the net present value analysis.

Instructions

1. Compute the following for each product:
   a. Cash payback period.
   b. The net present value. Use the present value of $1 table appearing in this chapter.
2. Prepare a brief report advising management on the relative merits of each of the two products.

P15-3

Net present value method, present value index, and analysis

Obj 3

SPREADSHEET

✓ 2. Branch office expansion, 1.07

United Bankshores, Inc. wishes to evaluate three capital investment projects by using the net present value method. Relevant data related to the projects are summarized as follows:

	Branch Office Expansion	Computer System Upgrade	Install Internet Bill-Pay
Amount to be invested.	$700,000	$475,000	$280,000
Annual net cash flows:			
Year 1	350,000	250,000	160,000
Year 2	325,000	225,000	110,000
Year 3	300,000	200,000	80,000

Instructions

1. Assuming that the desired rate of return is 15%, prepare a net present value analysis for each project. Use the present value of $1 table appearing in this chapter.
2. Determine a present value index for each project. Round to two decimal places.
3. Which project offers the largest amount of present value per dollar of investment? Explain.

P15-4

Net present value method, internal rate of return method, and analysis

Obj 3

✓ 1. a. Radio station, $110,250

The management of Quest Media Inc. is considering two capital investment projects. The estimated net cash flows from each project are as follows:

Year	Radio Station	TV Station
1	$350,000	$700,000
2	350,000	700,000
3	350,000	700,000
4	350,000	700,000

The radio station requires an investment of $999,250, while the TV station requires an investment of $2,125,900. No residual value is expected from either project.

Instructions

1. Compute the following for each project:
   a. The net present value. Use a rate of 10% and the present value of an annuity of $1 table appearing in this chapter.
   b. A present value index. Round to two decimal places.

2. Determine the internal rate of return for each project by (a) computing a present value factor for an annuity of $1 and (b) using the present value of an annuity of $1 table appearing in this chapter.
3. What advantage does the internal rate of return method have over the net present value method in comparing projects?

P15-5

Evaluate alternative capital investment decisions

Objs 3, 4

SPREADSHEET

✓ 1. Site B, $159,920

The investment committee of Grid Iron Restaurants Inc. is evaluating two restaurant sites. The sites have different useful lives, but each requires an investment of $565,000. The estimated net cash flows from each site are as follows:

	Net Cash Flows	
Year	Site A	Site B
1	$225,000	$280,000
2	225,000	280.000
3	225,000	280,000
4	225,000	280,000
5	225,000	
6	225,000	

The committee has selected a rate of 20% for purposes of net present value analysis. It also estimates that the residual value at the end of each restaurant's useful life is $0, but at the end of the fourth year, Site A's residual value would be $290,000.

Instructions

1. For each site, compute the net present value. Use the present value of an annuity of $1 table appearing in this chapter. (Ignore the unequal lives of the projects.)
2. For each site, compute the net present value, assuming that Site A is adjusted to a four-year life for purposes of analysis. Use the present value of $1 table appearing in this chapter.
3. Prepare a report to the investment committee, providing your advice on the relative merits of the two sites.

P15-6

Capital rationing decision involving four proposals

Objs 2, 3, 5

SPREADSHEET

✓ 5. Proposal B, 1.26

Grant Communications Inc. is considering allocating a limited amount of capital investment funds among four proposals. The amount of proposed investment, estimated income from operations, and net cash flow for each proposal are as follows:

	Investment	Year	Income from Operations	Net Cash Flow
Proposal A:	$425,000	1	$ 40,000	$ 125,000
		2	40,000	125,000
		3	40,000	125,000
		4	15,000	100,000
		5	(35,000)	50,000
			$100,000	$ 525,000
Proposal B:	$610,000	1	$158,000	$ 280,000
		2	158,000	280,000
		3	78,000	200,000
		4	28,000	150,000
		5	(22,000)	100,000
			$400,000	$1,010,000

(Continued)

	Investment	Year	Income from Operations	Net Cash Flow
Proposal C:	$275,000	1	$ 45,000	$ 100,000
		2	45,000	100,000
		3	45,000	100,000
		4	45,000	100,000
		5	35,000	90,000
			$215,000	$ 490,000
Proposal D:	$190,000	1	$ 22,000	$ 60,000
		2	22,000	60,000
		3	22,000	60,000
		4	2,000	40,000
		5	2,000	40,000
			$ 70,000	$ 260,000

The company's capital rationing policy requires a maximum cash payback period of three years. In addition, a minimum average rate of return of 12% is required on all projects. If the preceding standards are met, the net present value method and present value indexes are used to rank the remaining proposals.

Instructions

1. Compute the cash payback period for each of the four proposals.

2. Giving effect to straight-line depreciation on the investments and assuming no estimated residual value, compute the average rate of return for each of the four proposals. Round to one decimal place.

3. Using the following format, summarize the results of your computations in parts (1) and (2). By placing the calculated amounts in the first two columns on the left and by placing a check mark in the appropriate column to the right, indicate which proposals should be accepted for further analysis and which should be rejected.

Proposal	Cash Payback Period	Average Rate of Return	Accept for Further Analysis	Reject
A				
B				
C				
D				

4. For the proposals accepted for further analysis in part (3), compute the net present value. Use a rate of 12% and the present value of $1 table appearing in this chapter. Round to the nearest dollar.

5. Compute the present value index for each of the proposals in part (4). Round to two decimal places.

6. Rank the proposals from most attractive to least attractive, based on the present values of net cash flows computed in part (4).

7. Rank the proposals from most attractive to least attractive, based on the present value indexes computed in part (5). Round to two decimal places.

8. Based on the analyses, comment on the relative attractiveness of the proposals ranked in parts (6) and (7).

Activities

A15-1

Ethics and professional conduct in businessiconicon

ETHICS

Dawn Jeffries was recently hired as a cost analyst by Carenet Medical Supplies Inc. One of Dawn's first assignments was to perform a net present value analysis for a new warehouse. Dawn performed the analysis and calculated a present value index of 0.75. The plant manager, I. M. Madd, is very intent on purchasing the warehouse because he believes that more storage space is needed. I. M. Madd asks Dawn into his office and the following conversation takes place:

I. M.: Dawn, you're new here, aren't you?

Dawn: Yes, sir.

I. M.: Well, Dawn, let me tell you something. I'm not at all pleased with the capital investment analysis that you performed on this new warehouse. I need that warehouse for my production. If I don't get it, where am I going to place our output?

Dawn: Hopefully with the customer, sir.

I. M.: Now don't get smart with me.

Dawn: No, really, I was being serious. My analysis does not support constructing a new warehouse. The numbers don't lie, the warehouse does not meet our investment return targets. In fact, it seems to me that purchasing a warehouse does not add much value to the business. We need to be producing product to satisfy customer orders, not to fill a warehouse.

I. M.: Listen, you need to understand something. The headquarters people will not allow me to build the warehouse if the numbers don't add up. You know as well as I that many assumptions go into your net present value analysis. Why don't you relax some of your assumptions so that the financial savings will offset the cost?

Dawn: I'm willing to discuss my assumptions with you. Maybe I overlooked something.

I. M.: Good. Here's what I want you to do. I see in your analysis that you don't project greater sales as a result of the warehouse. It seems to me, if we can store more goods, then we will have more to sell. Thus, logically, a larger warehouse translates into more sales. If you incorporate this into your analysis, I think you'll see that the numbers will work out. Why don't you work it through and come back with a new analysis? I'm really counting on you on this one. Let's get off to a good start together and see if we can get this project accepted.

What is your advice to Dawn?

A15-2

Personal investment analysis

A Masters of Accountancy degree at Mid-State University would cost $10,000 for an additional fifth year of education beyond the bachelor's degree. Assume that all tuition is paid at the beginning of the year. A student considering this investment must evaluate the present value of cash flows from possessing a graduate degree versus holding only the undergraduate degree. Assume that the average student with an undergraduate degree is expected to earn an annual salary of $46,000 per year (assumed to be paid at the end of the year) for 10 years. Assume that the average student with a graduate Masters of Accountancy degree is expected to earn an annual salary of $57,000 per year (assumed to be

paid at the end of the year) for nine years after graduation. Assume a minimum rate of return of 10%.

1. Determine the net present value of cash flows from an undergraduate degree. Use the present value tables provided in this chapter.
2. Determine the net present value of cash flows from a Masters of Accountancy degree, assuming no salary is earned during the graduate year of schooling.
3. What is the net advantage or disadvantage of pursuing a graduate degree under these assumptions?

A15-3

Changing prices

International Electronics Inc. invested $1,000,000 to build a plant in a foreign country. The labor and materials used in production are purchased locally. The plant expansion was estimated to produce an internal rate of return of 20% in U.S. dollar terms. Due to a currency crisis, the currency exchange rate between the local currency and the U.S. dollar doubled from two local units per U.S. dollar to four local units per U.S. dollar.

a. Assume that the plant produced and sold product in the local economy. Explain what impact this change in the currency exchange rate would have on the project's internal rate of return.
b. Assume that the plant produced product in the local economy but exported the product back to the United States for sale. Explain what impact the change in the currency exchange rate would have on the project's internal rate of return under this assumption.

A15-4

Qualitative issues in investment analysis

The following are some selected quotes from senior executives:

*CEO, **Worthington Industries** (a high technology steel company): "We try to find the best technology, stay ahead of the competition, and serve the customer. . . . We'll make any investment that will pay back quickly . . . but if it is something that we really see as a must down the road, payback is not going to be that important."*

*Chairman of **Amgen Inc.** (a biotech company): "You cannot really run the numbers, do net present value calculations, because the uncertainties are really gigantic. . . . You decide on a project you want to run, and then you run the numbers [as a reality check on your assumptions]. Success in a business like this is much more dependent on tracking rather than on predicting, much more dependent on seeing results over time, tracking and adjusting and readjusting, much more dynamic, much more flexible."*

*Chief Financial Officer of **Merck & Co., Inc.** (a pharmaceutical company): " . . . at the individual product level—the development of a successful new product requires on the order of $230 million in R&D, spread over more than a decade—discounted cash flow style analysis does not become a factor until development is near the point of manufacturing scale-up effort. Prior to that point, given the uncertainties associated with new product development, it would be lunacy in our business to decide that we know exactly what's going to happen to a product once it gets out."*

Explain the role of capital investment analysis for these companies.

A15-5

Net present value method

SPREADSHEET

Metro-Goldwyn-Mayer Studios Inc. (MGM) is a major producer and distributor of theatrical and television filmed entertainment. Regarding theatrical films, MGM states, "Our feature films are exploited through a series of sequential domestic and international distribution channels, typically beginning with theatrical

exhibition. Thereafter, feature films are first made available for home video generally six months after theatrical release; for pay television, one year after theatrical release; and for syndication, approximately three to five years after theatrical release."

Assume that MGM produces a film during early 2011 at a cost of $195 million, and releases it halfway through the year. During the last half of 2011, the film earns revenues of $235 million at the box office. The film requires $50 million of advertising during the release. One year later, by the end of 2012, the film is expected to earn MGM net cash flows from home video sales of $36 million. By the end of 2013, the film is expected to earn MGM $43 million from pay TV; and by the end of 2014, the film is expected to earn $12 million from syndication.

a. Determine the net present value of the film as of the beginning of 2011 if the desired rate of return is 20%. To simplify present value calculations, assume all annual net cash flows occur at the end of each year. Use the table of the present value of $1 appearing in Exhibit 1 of this chapter. Round to the nearest whole million dollars.

b. Under the assumptions provided here, is the film expected to be financially successful?

A15-6

Capital investment analysis

GROUP PROJECT

In one group, find a local business, such as a copy shop, that rents time on desktop computers for an hourly rate. Determine the hourly rate. In the other group, determine the price of a mid-range desktop computer at http://www.dell.com. Combine this information from the two groups and perform a capital budgeting analysis. Assume that one student will use the computer for 40 hours per semester for the next three years. Also assume that the minimum rate of return is 10%. In performing your analysis, use the present value factor for 5% compounded for six semiannual periods of 5.08

Does your analysis support the student purchasing the computer?

Answers to Self-Examination Questions

1. **C** Methods of evaluating capital investment proposals that ignore the time value of money are categorized as methods that ignore present value. This category includes the average rate of return method (answer A) and the cash payback method (answer B).

2. **B** The average rate of return is 24% (answer B), determined by dividing the expected average annual earnings by the average investment, as follows:

$$\frac{\$60,000 \div 5}{(\$100,000 + \$0) \div 2} = 24\%$$

3. **B** Of the four methods of analyzing proposals for capital investments, the cash payback period (answer B) refers to the expected period of time required to recover the amount of cash to be invested. The average rate of return (answer A) is a measure of the anticipated profitability of a proposal. The net present value method (answer C) reduces the expected future net cash flows originating from a proposal to their present values. The internal rate of return method (answer D) uses present value concepts to compute the rate of return from the net cash flows expected from the investment.

4. **B** The net present value is determined as follows:

Present value of $25,000 for 8 years at 10% ($25,000 × 5.335)	$133,375
Less: Project cost	120,000
Net present value	$ 13,375

5. **C** The internal rate of return for this project is determined by solving for the present value of an annuity factor that when multiplied by $40,000 will equal $226,000. By division, the factor is:

$$\frac{\$226,000}{\$40,000} = 5.65$$

In Exhibit 2, scan along the $n = 10$ years row until finding the 5.65 factor. The column for this factor is 12%.

Double-Entry Accounting Systems

Throughout this text, transactions are recorded and summarized by using the accounting equation and the integrated financial statement framework. Transactions were recorded as pluses or minuses for each item affected by a transaction. At the same time, the effects of the transaction on the financial statements were shown. The equality of the accounting equation aided in preventing and detecting errors. That is, total assets must always equal total liabilities plus stockholders' equity.

Double-entry accounting also uses the accounting equation. However, double-entry accounting uses debit and credit rules as an additional control on the accuracy of recording transactions. This appendix describes and illustrates the basic elements of double-entry accounting.

In a double-entry accounting system, transactions are recorded in accounts. An *account*, in its simplest form, has three parts.

1. A title, which identifies the accounting equation element recorded in the account.
2. A space for recording increases in the amount of the element.
3. A space for recording decreases in the amount of the element.

The account form presented below is called a **T account** because it resembles the letter T. The left side of the account is called the debit side, and the right side is called the credit side.[1]

Title	
Left side	Right side
debit	*credit*

Amounts entered on the left side of an account, regardless of the account title, are called debits to the account. When debits are entered in an account, the account is said to be *debited*. Amounts entered on the right side of an account are called credits, and the account is said to be *credited*. Debits and credits are sometimes abbreviated as *Dr.* and *Cr.*

To illustrate, a T account for Cash is shown below.

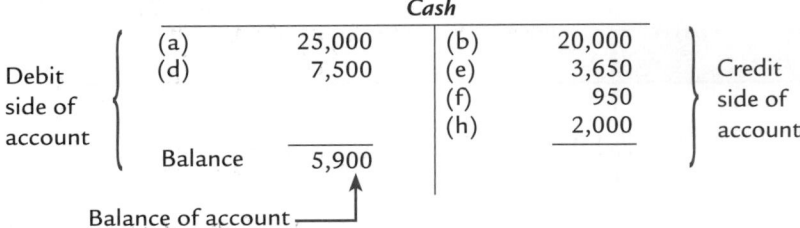

Recording transactions in accounts using double-entry accounting follows certain rules. For example, increases in assets are recorded on the

[1] The terms *debit* and *credit* are derived from the Latin *debere* and *credere*.

debit (left side) of the account. Likewise, decreases in assets are recorded on the credit (right side) of the account. With an asset account, the excess of debits over its credits is the balance of the account.

To illustrate, the preceding cash account is used. The receipt of cash (increase in Cash) of $25,000 in transaction (a) is entered on the debit (left) side of the cash account. A reference notation (letter or date of the transaction) is also entered into the account. The reference notation provides a means of backtracking to the underlying transaction data, should any questions arise.

The payment of cash (decrease in Cash) of $20,000 in transaction (b) is entered on the credit (right) side of the account. The balance of the cash account of $5,900 is the excess of debits over credits, as shown below.

Debits ($25,000 + $7,500)	$32,500
Less credits ($20,000 + $3,650 + $950 + $2,000)	26,600
Balance of Cash as of November 30, 2011	$ 5,900

The balance of the cash account is inserted in the account, in the Debit column. In this way, the balance is identified as a debit balance.

Rules of Debit and Credit

A standard method of recording debits and credits in accounts is essential to ensure that businesses record transactions in a similar manner. The rules of debit and credit are shown in Exhibit 1.

EXHIBIT 1   Rules of Debit and Credit; Normal Balances of Accounts

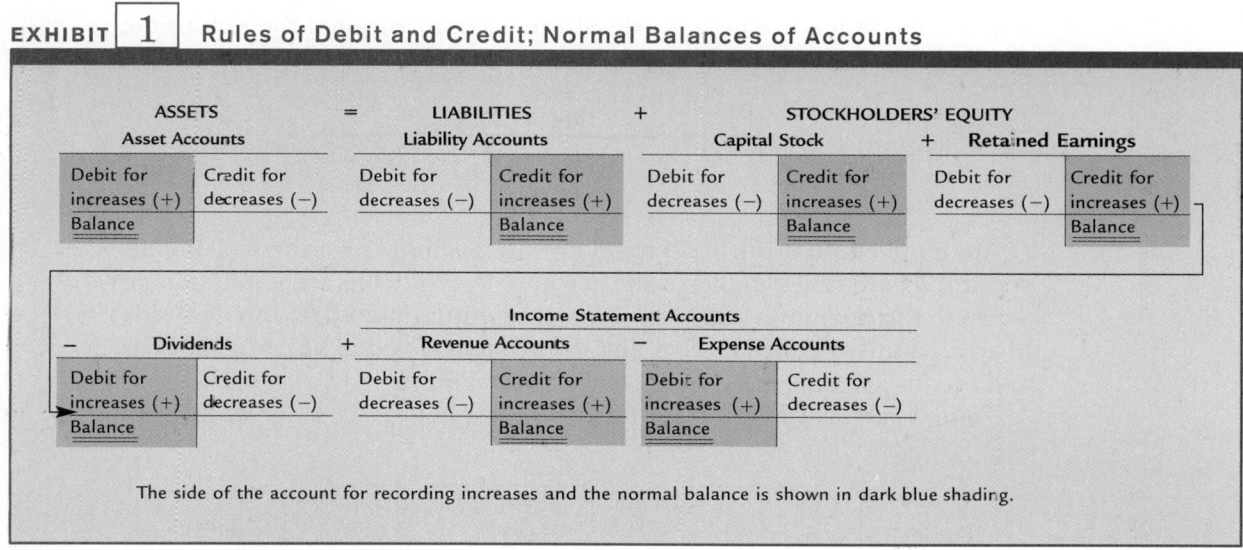

Exhibit 1 illustrates the following characteristics of the rules of debit and credit.

1. The normal balance of an account is the side of the account used to record increases. Thus, the normal balance of an asset account is a debit balance, while the normal balance of a liability account is a credit balance. This characteristic is often useful in detecting errors in the recording process. That is, when an account normally having a debit balance

actually has a credit balance, or vice versa, an error has occurred or an unusual situation exists.

2. Asset accounts (on the left side of the accounting equation) are increased by debits and have a normal debit balance. The only exception is that some asset accounts, called *contra asset accounts,* are increased by credits and have normal credit balances. As the words *contra asset* imply, these accounts offset the normal debit balances of asset accounts. For example, accumulated depreciation, an offset to plant assets, is increased by credits and has a normal credit balance. Thus, accumulated depreciation is a contra asset account.

3. Liability and stockholders' equity accounts (on the right side of the accounting equation) are increased by credits and have normal credit balances.

4. Dividend accounts appear on the right side of the accounting equation and decrease stockholders' equity (retained earnings). Thus, dividends accounts are increased by debits and have a normal debit balance. In this sense, the dividend accounts can be thought of as a type of contra account to retained earnings.

5. Revenue accounts appear on the right side of the accounting equation and increase stockholders' equity (retained earnings). Thus, revenue accounts are increased by credits and have normal credit balances.

6. Expense accounts appear on the right side of the accounting equation and decrease stockholders' equity (retained earnings). Thus, expense accounts are increased by debits and have a normal debit balance. Expense accounts can be thought of as a type of contra account. In this case, expense accounts can be thought of as contra accounts to revenues.

The rules of debit and credit require that for each transaction, the total debits equal the total credits. That is, each transaction must be recorded so that the total debits for the transaction equal the total credits.

To illustrate, assume that a company pays cash of $500 for supplies. The asset account Supplies is debited (increased) by $500 and Cash is credited (decreased) by $500. Likewise, if the company provides services and receives $2,000 from customers, Cash is debited (increased) and Fees Earned is credited (increased) by $2,000. This equality of debits and credits for each transaction provides a control over the recording of transactions.

To summarize, under double-entry accounting each transaction is recorded using the rules shown in Exhibit 1. In doing so, the total debits equal the total credits for each transaction.

The Journal

Under double-entry accounting, each transaction is initially entered in chronological order in a record called a *journal.* In this way, the journal documents the history of the company. The process of recording transactions in the journal is called *journalizing.* The specific transaction record entered in the journal is called a *journal entry.*

In practice, companies use a variety of formats for recording journal entries. A small company may use one all-purpose journal, sometimes called a **general journal.** Alternatively, another company may use **special journals** for recording different types of transactions. To simplify, a basic two-column general journal is used in this appendix.

Illustration of Double-Entry Accounting

Assume that on November 1, 2010, Lee Dunbar organizes a corporation that will be known as Web Solutions. The first phase of Lee's business plan is to operate Web Solutions as a service business providing assistance to individuals and small businesses by developing Web pages and configuring and installing application software. Lee expects this initial phase of the business to last one to two years. During this period, Web Solutions will gather information on the software and hardware needs of customers. During the second phase of the business plan, Web Solutions will expand into an Internet-based retailer of software and hardware to individuals and small business markets.

To start the business, Lee deposits $25,000 in a bank account in the name of Web Solutions in return for shares of stock in the corporation. This first transaction increases Cash and Capital Stock by $25,000. This transaction is recorded in the journal using the following steps:

Step 1. The date of the transaction is entered in the Date column.
Step 2. The title of the account to be debited is recorded at the left-hand margin under the Description column, and the amount to be debited is entered in the Debit column.
Step 3. The title of the account to be credited is listed below and to the right of the debited account title, and the amount to be credited is entered in the Credit column.

Using the preceding steps, transaction (a) is recorded in the journal as follows:

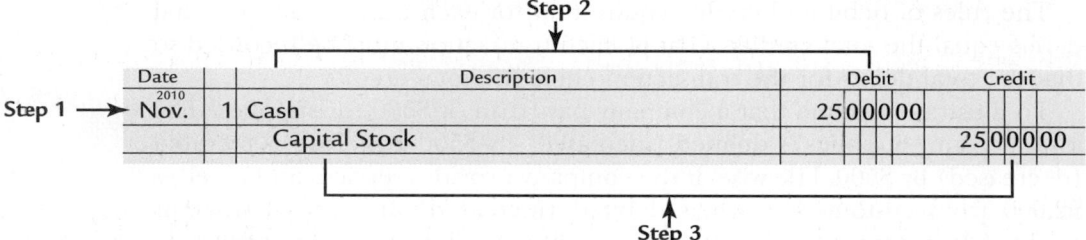

The increase in the asset is debited to the cash account. The increase in stockholders' equity (capital stock) is credited to the capital stock account. As other assets are acquired, the increases are also recorded as debits to asset accounts. Likewise, other increases in stockholders' equity will be recorded as credits to stockholders' equity accounts.

Web Solutions entered into the following additional transactions during the remainder of November:

Nov. 5 Purchased land for $20,000, paying cash. The land is located in a new business park with convenient access to transportation facilities. Web Solutions plans to rent office space and equipment during the first phase of its business plan. During the second phase, the company plans to build an office and warehouse on the land.

10 Purchased supplies on account for $1,350.

18 Received $7,500 for services provided to customers for cash.

30 Paid expenses as follows: wages, $2,125; rent, $800; utilities, $450; and miscellaneous, $275.

30 Paid creditors on account, $950.

30 Paid stockholder (Lee Dunbar) dividends of $2,000.

The journal entries to record these transactions follow.

Nov.	5	Land	20 0 0 0 00	
		Cash		20 0 0 0 00
	10	Supplies	1 3 5 0 00	
		Accounts Payable		1 3 5 0 00
	18	Cash	7 5 0 0 00	
		Fees Earned		7 5 0 0 00
	30	Wages Expense	2 1 2 5 00	
		Rent Expense	8 0 0 00	
		Utilities Expense	4 5 0 00	
		Miscellaneous Expense	2 7 5 00	
		Cash		3 6 5 0 00
	30	Accounts Payable	9 5 0 00	
		Cash		9 5 0 00
	30	Dividends	2 0 0 0 00	
		Cash		2 0 0 0 00

Posting to the Ledger

The journal lists the chronological history of businesses' transactions. Periodically, the journal entries must be transferred to the accounts. The group of accounts for a business is called its *general ledger*. The list of accounts in the general ledger is called the *chart of accounts*. The accounts are normally listed in the order in which they appear in the financial statements, beginning with the balance sheet and concluding with the income statement.

The chart of accounts for Web Solutions is shown in Exhibit 2.

EXHIBIT 2 Chart of Accounts for Web Solutions

Balance Sheet Accounts	Income Statement Accounts
Assets	**Revenue**
Cash	Fees Earned
Accounts Receivable	Rent Revenue
Supplies	**Expenses**
Prepaid Insurance	Wages Expense
Office Equipment	Rent Expense
Accumulated Depreciation	Depreciation Expense
Land	Utilities Expense
Liabilities	Supplies Expense
Accounts Payable	Insurance Expense
Wages Payable	Miscellaneous Expense
Unearned Rent	
Stockholders' Equity	
Capital Stock	
Retained Earnings	
Dividends	

The process of transferring the journal entry debits and credits to the accounts in the ledger is called *posting.* To illustrate the posting process, Web Solutions' November 1 transaction, along with its posting to the cash and capital stock accounts, is shown in Exhibit 3.

EXHIBIT 3 Posting a Journal Entry

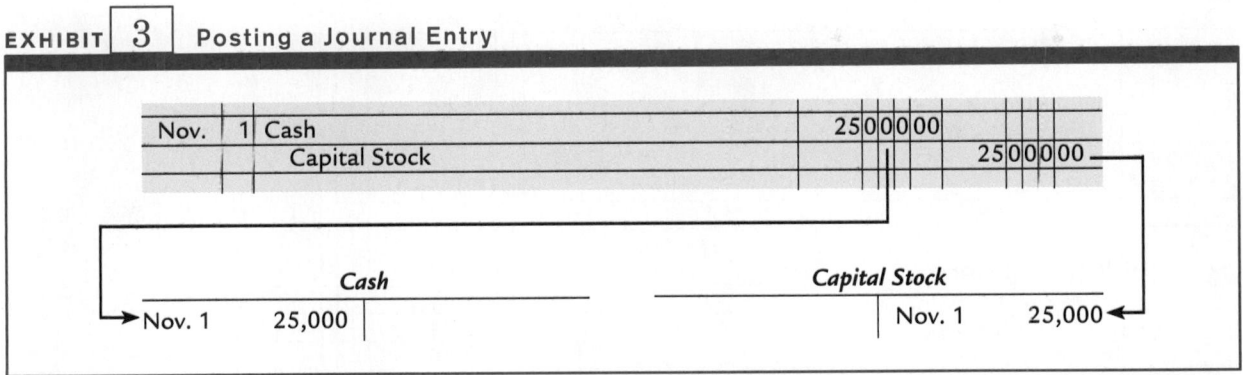

The debits and credits for each journal entry are posted to the accounts in the order in which they occur in the journal. In posting to the accounts, the date is entered followed by the amount of the entry. After the journal entries have been posted, the ledger becomes a chronological history of transactions by account. The posting of Web Solutions' remaining journal entries is shown in Exhibit 7 on page 658.

Trial Balance and Financial Statements

Errors may occur in posting debits and credits from the journal to the ledger. One way to detect such errors is by preparing a *trial balance.* Double-entry accounting requires that debits must always equal credits. The trial balance verifies this equality. The steps in preparing a trial balance are as follows:

Step 1. List the name of the company, the title of the trial balance, and the date the trial balance is prepared.
Step 2. List the accounts from the ledger and enter their debit or credit balance in the Debit or Credit column of the trial balance.
Step 3. Total the Debit and Credit columns of the trial balance.
Step 4. Verify that the total of the Debit column equals the total of the Credit column.

The trial balance for Web Solutions as of December 31, 2010, is shown in Exhibit 4. The account balances in Exhibit 4 are taken from the November 30 balances in the ledger shown in Exhibit 7.

The trial balance does not provide complete proof of the accuracy of the ledger. It indicates only that the debits and the credits are equal. However, this proof is still of value as errors often affect the equality of debits and credits.

If the two totals of a trial balance are not equal, an error has occurred. In such a case, the error must be located and corrected before financial statements are prepared. This ability to detect errors in recording when the trial

EXHIBIT 4 | Trial Balance

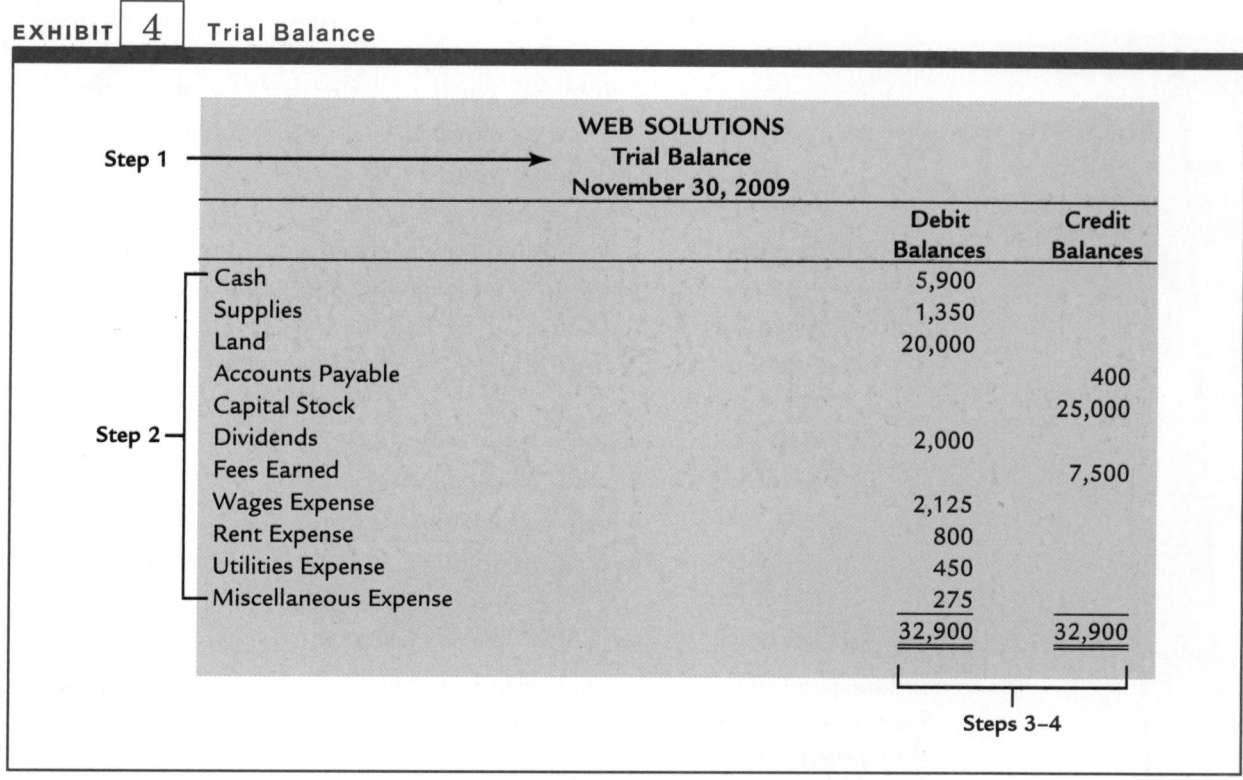

balance totals are not equal is a primary control feature of the double-entry accounting system.

The trial balance can be used as the source of data for preparing financial statements. The financial statements prepared in a double-entry accounting system are similar to those described and illustrated in the text. For this reason, the financial statements are not illustrated in this appendix.

Review of Double-Entry Accounting

As a review of the double-entry accounting financial reporting system, Web Solutions' transactions for December are used. The journal entries for the following December transactions are shown in Exhibit 5.

Dec. 1 Paid a premium of $2,400 for a comprehensive insurance policy covering liability, theft, and fire. The policy covers a 2-year period.

    1 Paid rent for December, $800. The company from which Web Solutions is renting its store space now requires the payment of rent on the first day of each month rather than at the end of the month.

    1 Received an offer from a local retailer to rent the land purchased on November 5. The retailer plans to use the land as a parking lot for its employees and customers. Web Solutions agreed to rent the land to the retailer for three months with the rent payable in advance. Web Solutions received $360 for three months' rent beginning December 1.

    4 Purchased office equipment on account from Executive Supply Co. for $1,800.

    6 Paid $180 for a newspaper advertisement.

   11 Paid creditors $400.

Dec. 13 Paid a receptionist and a part-time assistant $950 for two weeks' wages.

16 Received $3,100 from fees earned for the first half of December.

16 Earned fees on account totaling $1,750 for the first half of December.

20 Paid $1,800 to Executive Supply Co. on the debt owed from the December 4 transaction.

21 Received $650 from customers in payment of their accounts.

23 Purchased $1,450 of supplies by paying $550 cash and charging the remainder on account.

27 Paid the receptionist and the part-time assistant $1,200 for two weeks' wages.

31 Paid $310 telephone bill for the month.

31 Paid $225 electric bill for the month.

31 Received $2,870 from fees earned for the second half of December.

31 Earned fees on account totaling $1,120 for the second half of December.

31 Paid dividends of $2,000 to stockholders.

The posting of the journal entries to the ledger accounts is shown in Exhibit 7 on page 658. The trial balance shown in Exhibit 6 indicates that after posting December transactions to the general ledger, the total of the debit balances of accounts equals the total of the credit balances.

EXHIBIT 5   Journal Entries: December Transactions for Web Solutions

Date		Description	Debit	Credit
Dec.	1	Prepaid Insurance	2 40 0 00	
		Cash		2 40 0 00
	1	Rent Expense	80 0 00	
		Cash		80 0 00
	1	Cash	36 0 00	
		Unearned Rent		36 0 00
	4	Office Equipment	1 80 0 00	
		Accounts Payable		1 80 0 00
	6	Miscellaneous Expense	18 0 00	
		Cash		18 0 00
	11	Accounts Payable	40 0 00	
		Cash		40 0 00
	13	Wages Expense	95 0 00	
		Cash		95 0 00
	16	Cash	3 10 0 00	
		Fees Earned		3 10 0 00
	16	Accounts Receivable	1 75 0 00	
		Fees Earned		1 75 0 00

EXHIBIT 5 Continued

			Debit	Credit
20	Accounts Payable		1 80 0 00	
	Cash			1 80 0 00
21	Cash		6 50 00	
	Accounts Receivable			6 50 00
23	Supplies		1 45 0 00	
	Cash			5 50 00
	Accounts Payable			9 00 00
27	Wages Expense		1 20 0 00	
	Cash			1 20 0 00
31	Utilities Expense		3 10 00	
	Cash			3 10 00
31	Utilities Expense		2 25 00	
	Cash			2 25 00
31	Cash		2 87 0 00	
	Fees Earned			2 87 0 00
31	Accounts Receivable		1 12 0 00	
	Fees Earned			1 12 0 00
31	Dividends		2 00 0 00	
	Cash			2 00 0 00

EXHIBIT 6 Trial Balance for Web Solutions

WEB SOLUTIONS
Trial Balance
December 31, 2010

	Debit Balances	Credit Balances
Cash	2,065	
Accounts Receivable	2,220	
Supplies	2,800	
Prepaid Insurance	2,400	
Office Equipment	1,800	
Land	20,000	
Accounts Payable		900
Unearned Rent		360
Capital Stock		25,000
Dividends	4,000	
Fees Earned		16,340
Wages Expense	4,275	
Rent Expense	1,600	
Utilities Expense	985	
Miscellaneous Expense	455	
	42,600	42,600

EXHIBIT 7 Ledger for Web Solutions

Cash

Nov.	1	25,000	Nov.	5	20,000
	18	7,500		30	3,650
				30	950
				30	2,000
		32,500			26,600
Nov. 30	Bal.	5,900	Dec.	1	2,400
Dec.	1	360		1	800
	16	3,100		6	180
	21	650		11	400
	31	2,870		13	950
				20	1,800
				23	550
				27	1,200
				31	310
				31	225
				31	2,000
		12,880			10,815
Dec. 31	Bal.	2,065			

Accounts Receivable

Dec.	16	1,750	Dec.	21	650
	31	1,120			
Dec. 31	Bal.	2,220			

Supplies

Nov.	10	1,350	
Dec.	23	1,450	
Dec. 31	Bal.	2,800	

Prepaid Insurance

Dec.	1	2,400	

Office Equipment

Dec.	4	1,800	

Land

Nov.	5	20,000	

Accounts Payable

Nov.	30	950	Nov.	10	1,350
			Nov. 30	Bal.	400
Dec.	11	400	Dec.	4	1,800
	20	1,800		23	900
		2,200			3,100
			Dec. 31	Bal.	900

Unearned Rent

			Dec.	1	360

Capital Stock

			Nov.	1	25,000

Dividends

Nov.	30	2,000	
Dec.	31	2,000	
Dec. 31	Bal.	4,000	

Fees Earned

			Nov.	18	7,500
			Dec.	16	3,100
				16	1,750
				31	2,870
				31	1,120
			Dec. 31	Bal.	16,340

Wages Expense

Nov.	30	2,125	
Dec.	13	950	
	27	1,200	
Dec. 31	Bal.	4,275	

Rent Expense

Nov.	30	800	
Dec.	1	800	
Dec. 31	Bal.	1,600	

Utilities Expense

Nov.	30	450	
Dec.	31	310	
	31	225	
Dec. 31	Bal.	985	

Miscellaneous Expense

Nov.	30	275	
Dec.	6	180	
Dec. 31	Bal.	455	

Exercises

E-1

Rules of debit and credit

The following table summarizes the rules of debit and credit. For each of the items (a) through (l), indicate whether the proper answer is a debit or a credit.

	Increase	Decrease	Normal Balance
Balance sheet accounts:			
Asset	Debit	(a)	(b)
Liability	Credit	(c)	(d)
Stockholders' equity:			
Capital stock	(e)	Debit	(f)
Retained earnings	(g)	Debit	Credit
Dividends	Debit	(h)	Debit
Income statement accounts:			
Revenue	(i)	(j)	(k)
Expense	(l)	Credit	Debit

E-2

Identifying transactions

Cycle Tours Co. is a travel agency. The nine transactions recorded by Cycle Tours during February 2010, its first month of operations, are indicated in the following T accounts:

Cash			
(1)	25,000	(2)	1,750
(7)	10,000	(3)	3,600
		(4)	2,700
		(6)	7,500
		(9)	2,500

Equipment	
(3)	18,000

Dividends	
(9)	2,500

Accounts Receivable			
(5)	13,500	(7)	10,000

Accounts Payable			
(6)	7,500	(3)	14,400

Service Revenue			
		(5)	13,500

Supplies			
(2)	1,750	(8)	1,050

Capital Stock			
		(1)	25,000

Operating Expenses	
(4)	2,700
(8)	1,050

Indicate for each debit and each credit: (a) whether an asset, liability, capital stock, dividend, revenue, or expense account was affected and (b) whether the account was increased (+) or decreased (–). Present your answers in the following form, with transaction (1) given as an example:

Transaction	Account Debited		Account Credited	
	Type	Effect	Type	Effect
(1)	asset	+	capital stock	+

E-3

Journal entries

Based upon the T accounts in Exercise 2, prepare the nine journal entries from which the postings were made.

E-4

Trial balance

SPREADSHEET

✓ Total Debit column:
$45,400

Based upon the data presented in Exercise 2, prepare an unadjusted trial balance, listing the accounts in their proper order.

E-5

Normal entries for accounts

During the month, Genesis Labs Co. has a substantial number of transactions affecting each of the following accounts. State for each account whether it is likely to have (a) debit entries only, (b) credit entries only, or (c) both debit and credit entries.

1. Accounts Payable
2. Accounts Receivable
3. Cash
4. Fees Earned

5. Insurance Expense
6. Dividends
7. Supplies Expense

E-6

Normal balances of accounts

Identify each of the following accounts of Sesame Services Co. as asset, liability, stockholders' equity, revenue, or expense, and state in each case whether the normal balance is a debit or a credit.

a. Accounts Payable
b. Accounts Receivable
c. Capital Stock
d. Cash
e. Dividends

f. Fees Earned
g. Office Equipment
h. Rent Expense
i. Supplies
j. Wages Expense

E-7

Cash account balance

During the month, Racoon Co. received $319,750 in cash and paid out $269,900 in cash.

a. Do the data indicate that Racoon Co. earned $49,850 during the month? Explain.
b. If the balance of the cash account is $72,350 at the end of the month, what was the cash balance at the beginning of the month?

E-8

Account balances

✓ c. $284,175

a. During July, $90,300 was paid to creditors on account, and purchases on account were $115,150. Assuming the July 31 balance of Accounts Payable was $39,000, determine the account balance on July 1.
b. On May 1, the accounts receivable account balance was $36,200. During May, $315,000 was collected from customers on account. Assuming the May 31 balance was $41,600, determine the fees billed to customers on account during May.
c. On April 1, the cash account balance was $18,275. During April, cash receipts totaled $279,100 and the April 30 balance was $13,200. Determine the cash payments made during April.

E-9

Transactions

Derby Co. has the following accounts in its ledger: Cash; Accounts Receivable; Supplies; Office Equipment; Accounts Payable; Capital Stock; Retained Earnings; Dividends; Fees Earned; Rent Expense; Advertising Expense; Utilities Expense; Miscellaneous Expense.

Journalize the following selected transactions for March 2009 in a two-column journal.

Mar. 1 Paid rent for the month, $3,000.

2 Paid advertising expense, $1,800.

5 Paid cash for supplies, $900.

6 Purchased office equipment on account, $12,300.

10 Received cash from customers on account, $4,100.

15 Paid creditor on account, $1,200.

27 Paid cash for repairs to office equipment, $500.

30 Paid telephone bill for the month, $180.

31 Fees earned and billed to customers for the month, $26,800.

31 Paid electricity bill for the month, $315.

31 Paid dividends, $2,000.

E-10

Journalizing and posting

On August 7, 2010, Mainsail Co. purchased $2,190 of supplies on account.

a. Journalize the August 7, 2010 transaction.

b. Prepare a T account for Supplies. Enter a debit balance of $1,050 as of August 1, 2010.

c. Prepare a T account for Accounts Payable. Enter a credit balance of $15,600 as of August 1, 2010.

d. Post the August 7, 2010 transaction to the accounts.

E-11

Transactions and T accounts

The following selected transactions were completed during February of the current year:

1. Billed customers for fees earned, $41,730.
2. Purchased supplies on account, $1,800.
3. Received cash from customers on account, $39,150.
4. Paid creditors on account, $1,100.

a. Journalize the above transactions in a two-column journal, using the appropriate number to identify the transactions. Journal entry explanations may be omitted.

b. Post the entries prepared in (a) to the following T accounts: Cash, Supplies, Accounts Receivable, Accounts Payable, Fees Earned. To the left of each amount posted in the accounts, place the appropriate number to identify the transactions.

E-12

Trial balance

SPREADSHEET

✓ Total of Credit column: $696,350.

The accounts in the ledger of Aznar Co. as of October 31, 2010, are listed in alphabetical order as follows. All accounts have normal balances. The balance of the cash account has been intentionally omitted.

Accounts Payable	$ 28,000	Notes Payable	$ 60,000
Accounts Receivable	56,250	Prepaid Insurance	4,500
Capital Stock	50,000	Rent Expense	90,000
Cash	?	Retained Earnings	79,850
Dividends	30,000	Supplies	3,150
Fees Earned	465,000	Supplies Expense	11,850
Insurance Expense	9,000	Unearned Rent	13,500
Land	127,500	Utilities Expense	62,250
Miscellaneous Expense	13,350	Wages Expense	262,500

Prepare an unadjusted trial balance, listing the accounts in their proper order and inserting the missing figure for cash.

Problems

P-1

Journal entries and trial balance

SPREADSHEET

On October 1, 2010, Cody Doerr established Banyan Realty, which completed the following transactions during the month:

a. Cody Doerr transferred cash from a personal bank account to an account to be used for the business in exchange for capital stock, $17,500.
b. Purchased supplies on account, $1,000.
c. Earned sales commissions, receiving cash, $12,250.
d. Paid rent on office and equipment for the month, $3,800.
e. Paid creditor on account, $600.
f. Paid dividends, $3,000.
g. Paid automobile expenses (including rental charge) for month, $1,500, and miscellaneous expenses, $400.
h. Paid office salaries, $3,100.
i. Determined that the cost of supplies used was $725.

Instructions

1. Journalize entries for transactions (a) through (i), using the following account titles: Cash; Supplies; Accounts Payable; Capital Stock; Dividends; Sales Commissions; Rent Expense; Office Salaries Expense; Automobile Expense; Supplies Expense; Miscellaneous Expense. Journal entry explanations may be omitted.
2. Prepare T accounts, using the account titles in (1). Post the journal entries to these accounts, placing the appropriate letter to the left of each amount to identify the transaction. Determine the account balances, after all posting is complete. Accounts containing only a single entry do not need a balance.
3. Prepare an unadjusted trial balance as of October 31, 2010.

P-2

Journal entries and trial balance

SPREADSHEET

✓ 4. Total of Debit column: $560,750

Dodge City Realty acts as an agent in buying, selling, renting, and managing real estate. The unadjusted trial balance on July 31, 2010, is shown below.

Dodge City Realty
Unadjusted Trial Balance
July 31, 2010

	Debit Balances	Credit Balances
Cash	33,920	
Accounts Receivable	57,200	
Prepaid Insurance	7,200	
Office Supplies	1,600	
Land	—	
Accounts Payable		9,920
Unearned Rent		—
Notes Payable		—
Capital Stock		10,000
Retained Earnings		40,480
Dividends	25,600	
Fees Earned		352,000
Salary and Commission Expense	224,000	
Rent Expense	28,000	
Advertising Expense	22,880	
Automobile Expense	10,240	
Miscellaneous Expense	1,760	
	412,400	412,400

The following business transactions were completed by Dodge City Realty during August 2010:

Aug. 1 Purchased office supplies on account, $2,100.

　　　2 Paid rent on office for month, $4,000.

　　　3 Received cash from clients on account, $44,600.

　　　5 Paid annual insurance premiums, $5,700.

　　　9 Returned a portion of the office supplies purchased on August 1, receiving full credit for their cost, $400.

　　17 Paid advertising expense, $5,500.

　　23 Paid creditors on account, $4,950.

　　29 Paid miscellaneous expenses, $500.

　　30 Paid automobile expense (including rental charges for an automobile), $1,500.

　　31 Discovered an error in computing a commission; received cash from the salesperson for the overpayment, $1,000.

　　31 Paid salaries and commissions for the month, $27,800.

　　31 Recorded revenue earned and billed to clients during the month, $83,000.

　　31 Purchased land for a future building site for $75,000, paying $10,000 in cash and giving a note payable for the remainder.

　　31 Paid dividends, $5,000.

　　31 Rented land purchased on August 31 to a local university for use as a parking lot during football season (September, October, and November); received advance payment of $3,600.

Instructions

1. Record the August 1, 2010 balance of each account in the appropriate balance column of a T account, and write Balance to identify the opening amounts.

2. Journalize the transactions for August in a two-column journal.

3. Post the journal entries to the T accounts, placing the date to the left of each amount to identify the transaction. Determine the balances for all accounts with more than one posting.

4. Prepare a trial balance of the ledger as of August 31, 2010.

Process Cost Systems

A **process manufacturer** produces products that are indistinguishable from each other, using a continuous production process. For example, an oil refinery processes crude oil through a series of steps to produce a barrel of gasoline. One barrel of gasoline, the product, cannot be distinguished from another barrel. Other examples of process manufacturers include paper producers, chemical processors, aluminum smelters, and food processors.

The cost accounting system used by process manufacturers is called the **process cost system.** A process cost system records product costs for each manufacturing department or process.

In contrast, a job order manufacturer produces custom products for customers or batches of similar products. For example, a custom printer produces wedding invitations, graduation announcements, or other special print items that are tailored to the specifications of each customer. Each item manufactured is unique to itself. Other examples of job order manufacturers include furniture manufacturers, shipbuilders, and home builders.

As described and illustrated in Chapter 10, the cost accounting system used by job order manufacturers is called the *job order cost system.* A job order cost system records product costs for each job using job cost sheets.

Some examples of process and job order manufacturers are shown below.

Process Manufacturers		Job Order Manufacturers	
Company	Product	Company	Product
Pepsi	soft drinks	*Walt Disney*	movies
Alcoa	aluminum	*Nike, Inc.*	athletic shoes
Intel	computer chips	*Tiger Woods Design*	golf courses
Apple	iPhone	*Heritage Log Homes*	log homes
Hershey Foods	chocolate bars	*DDB Advertising Agency*	advertising

Comparing Job Order and Process Cost Systems

Process and job order cost systems are similar in that each system:

1. Records and summarizes product costs.
2. Classifies product costs as direct materials, direct labor, and factory overhead.
3. Allocates factory overhead costs to products.
4. Uses a perpetual inventory system for materials, work in process, and finished goods.
5. Provides useful product cost information for decision making.

Process and job costing systems are different in several ways. As a basis for illustrating these differences, the cost systems for Frozen Delight and Legend Guitars are used.

Exhibit 1 illustrates the process cost system for Frozen Delight, an ice cream manufacturer. As a basis for comparison, Exhibit 1 also illustrates the job order cost system for Legend Guitars, a custom guitar manufacturer. Legend Guitars was described and illustrated in Chapter 10.

EXHIBIT 1 | **Process Cost and Job Order Cost Systems**

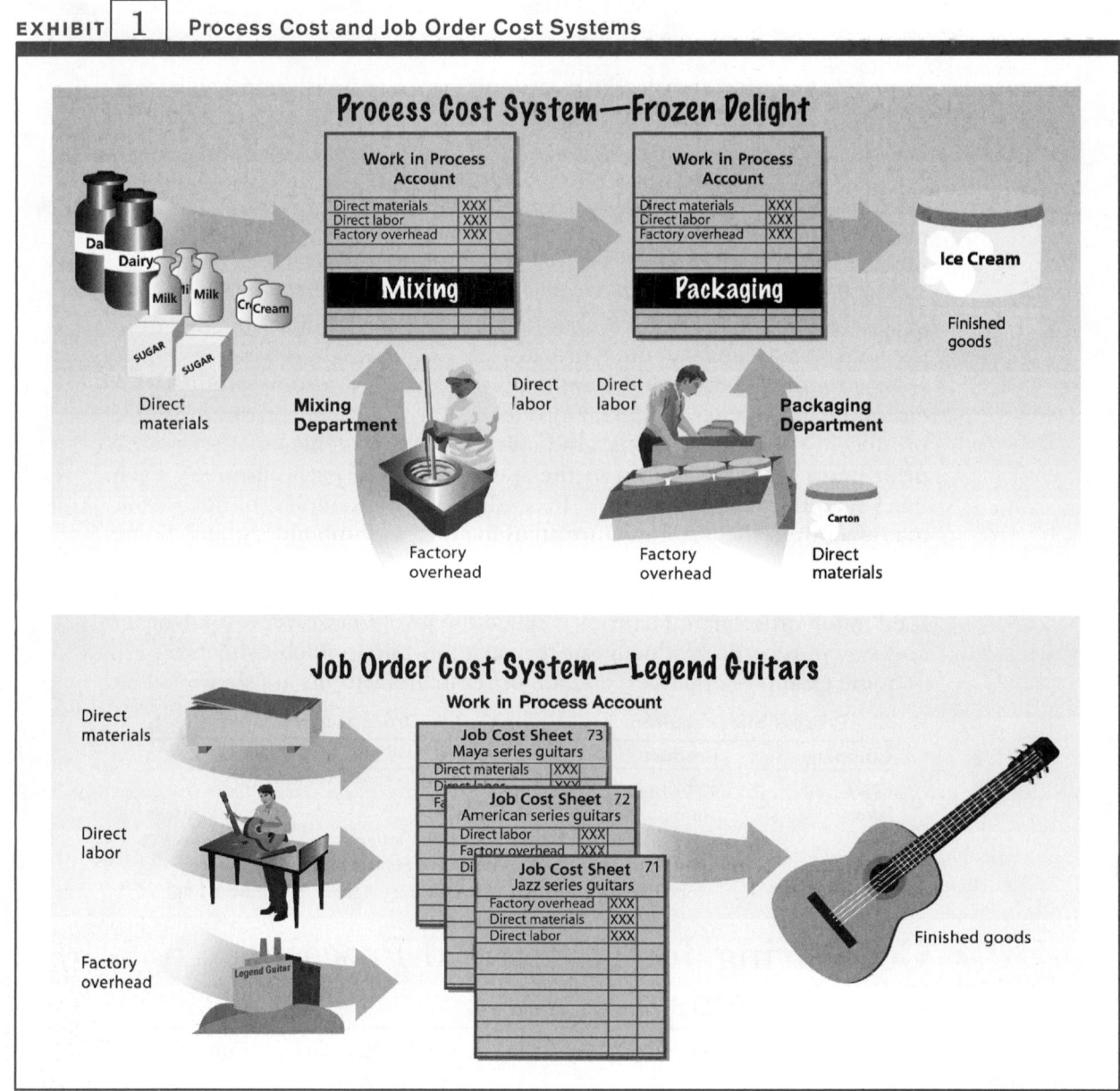

Exhibit 1 indicates that Frozen Delight manufactures ice cream using two departments:

1. Mixing Department mixes the ingredients using large vats.
2. Packaging Department puts the ice cream into cartons for shipping to customers.

Since each gallon of ice cream is similar, product costs are recorded in each department's work in process account. As shown in Exhibit 1, Frozen Delight accumulates (records) the cost of making ice cream in *work in process*

accounts for the Mixing and Packaging departments. The product costs of making a gallon of ice cream include:

1. *Direct materials cost,* which includes milk, cream, sugar, and packing cartons. All materials costs are added at the beginning of the process for both the Mixing Department and the Packaging Department.
2. *Direct labor cost,* which is incurred by employees in each department who run the equipment and load and unload product.
3. *Factory overhead costs,* which include the utility costs (power) and depreciation on the equipment.

When the Mixing Department completes the mixing process, its product costs are transferred to the Packaging Department. When the Packaging Department completes its process, the product costs are transferred to Finished Goods. In this way, the cost of the product (a gallon of ice cream) accumulates across the entire production process.

In contrast, Exhibit 1 shows that Legend Guitars accumulates (records) product costs by jobs using a job cost sheet for each type of guitar. Thus, Legend Guitars uses just one work in process account. As each job is completed, its product costs are transferred to Finished Goods.

In a job order cost system, the work in process at the end of the period is the sum of the job cost sheets for partially completed jobs. In a process cost system, the work in process at the end of the period is determined by allocating costs between completed and partially completed units within each department.

Materials costs can be as high as 70% of the total product costs for many process manufacturers.

Cost Flows for a Process Manufacturer

Exhibit 2 illustrates the *physical flow* of materials for Frozen Delight. Ice cream is made in a manufacturing plant in a similar way as you would at home, except on a larger scale.

EXHIBIT 2   **Physical Flows for a Process Manufacturer**

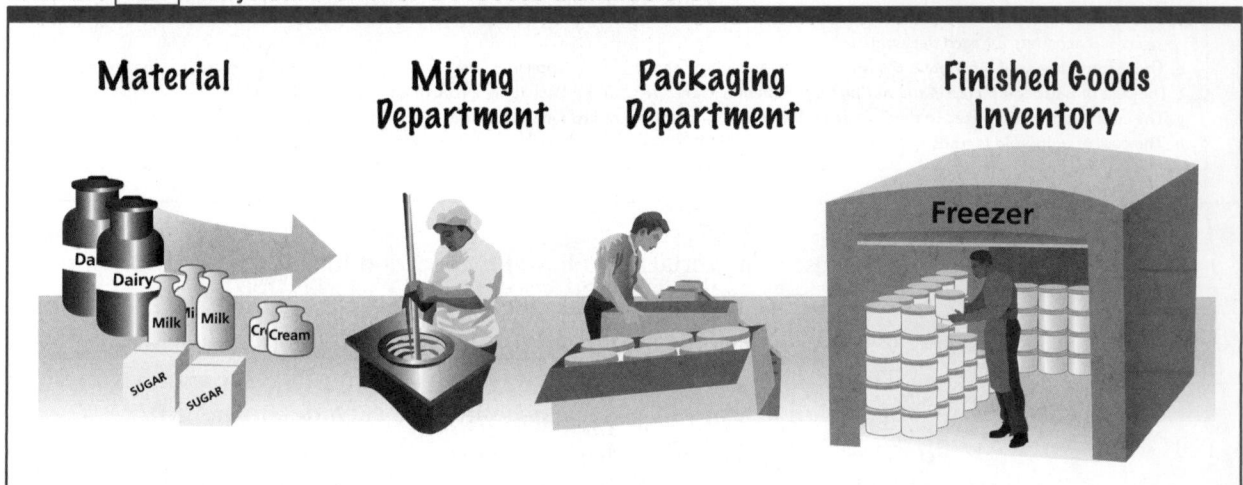

In the Mixing Department, direct materials in the form of milk, cream, and sugar are placed into a vat. An employee (direct labor) fills each vat, sets the cooling temperature, and sets the mix speed. The vat is cooled (refrigerated) as the direct materials are being mixed by agitators (paddles). Factory overhead is incurred in the form of power to run the vat (electricity) and vat (equipment) depreciation.

In the Packaging Department, the ice cream is received from the Mixing Department in a form ready for packaging. The Packaging Department uses direct labor and factory overhead (conversion costs) to package the ice cream into one-gallon containers (direct materials). The ice cream is then transferred to finished goods where it is frozen and stored in refrigerators prior to shipment to customers (stores).

The *cost flows* in a process cost accounting system are similar to the *physical flow* of materials described above. The cost flows for Frozen Delight are illustrated in Exhibit 3.

EXHIBIT 3 Cost Flows for a Process Manufacturer—Frozen Delight

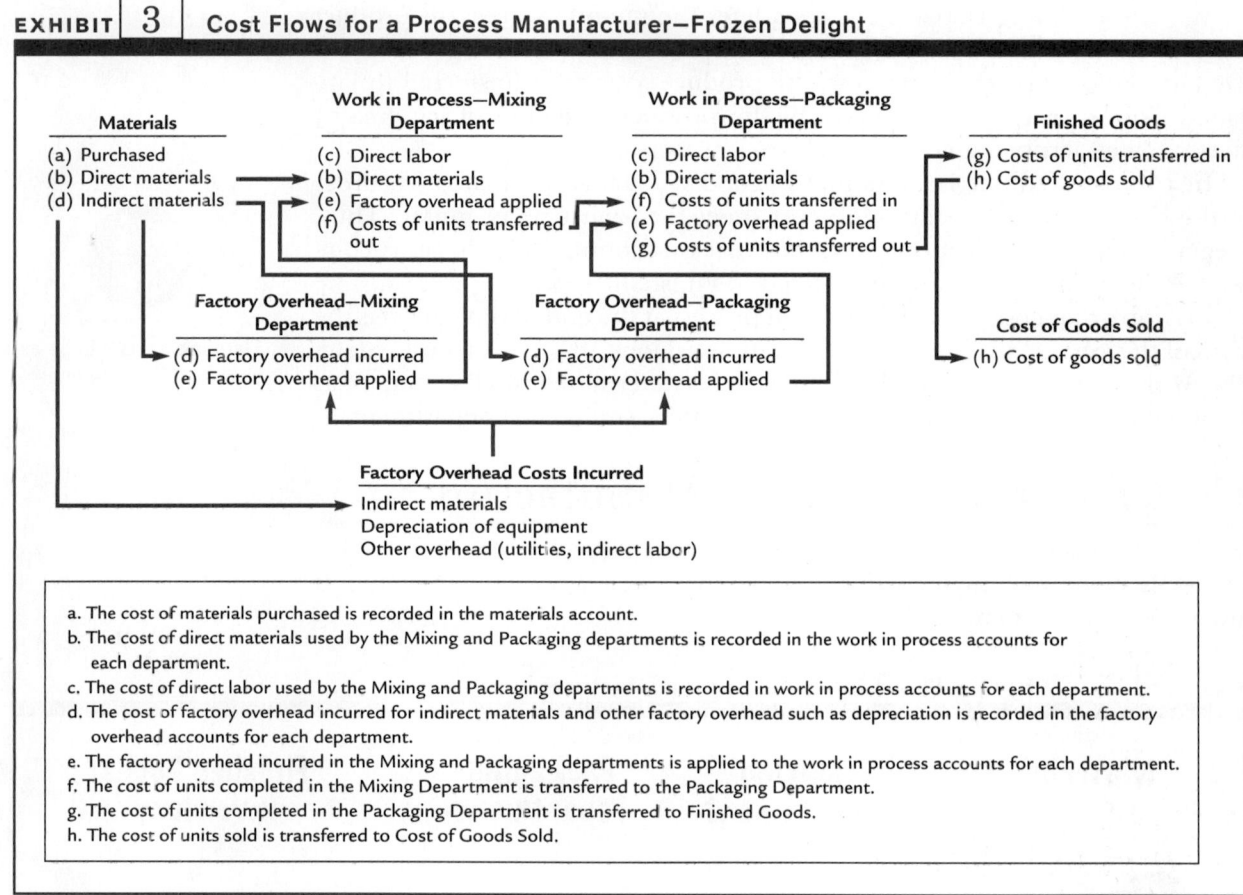

a. The cost of materials purchased is recorded in the materials account.

b. The cost of direct materials used by the Mixing and Packaging departments is recorded in the work in process accounts for each department.

c. The cost of direct labor used by the Mixing and Packaging departments is recorded in work in process accounts for each department.

d. The cost of factory overhead incurred for indirect materials and other factory overhead such as depreciation is recorded in the factory overhead accounts for each department.

e. The factory overhead incurred in the Mixing and Packaging departments is applied to the work in process accounts for each department.

f. The cost of units completed in the Mixing Department is transferred to the Packaging Department.

g. The cost of units completed in the Packaging Department is transferred to Finished Goods.

h. The cost of units sold is transferred to Cost of Goods Sold.

As shown in Exhibit 3, the Mixing and Packaging Departments have separate factory overhead accounts. The factory overhead costs incurred for indirect materials, depreciation, and other overhead are recorded as an increase to each department's factory overhead account. The overhead is applied to work in process by increasing each department's work in process account and decreasing the department's factory overhead account.

Exhibit 3 illustrates how the Mixing and Packaging departments have separate work in process accounts. Each work in process account is increased for the direct materials, direct labor, and applied factory overhead. In addition, the work in process account for the Packaging Department is increased for the cost of the units transferred in from the Mixing Department. Each work in process account is decreased for the cost of the units transferred to the next department.

Lastly, Exhibit 3 shows that the finished goods account is increased for the cost of the units transferred from the Packaging Department. The finished goods account is decreased for the cost of the units sold, which is recorded as an increase in to the cost of goods sold account.

Average Cost Method

A cost flow assumption must be used as product costs flow through manufacturing processes. In this appendix, the average cost flow method is illustrated for S&W Ice Cream Company (S&W).[1]

Determining Costs Using the Average Cost Method

S&W's operations are similar to those of Frozen Delight. Like Frozen Delight, S&W mixes direct materials (milk, cream, sugar) in refrigerated vessels and has two manufacturing departments, Mixing and Packaging.

The manufacturing data for the Mixing Department for July 2010 are as follows:

Work in process inventory, July 1, 5,000 gallons (70% completed)	$ 6,200
Direct materials cost incurred in July, 60,000 gallons	66,000
Direct labor cost incurred in July	10,500
Factory overhead applied in July	6,405
Total production costs to account for	$89,105
Cost of goods transferred to Packaging in July (includes units in process on July 1), 62,000 gallons	?
Cost of work in process inventory, July 31, 3,000 gallons, 25% completed as to conversion costs	?

Using the average cost method, the objective is to allocate the total costs of production of $89,105 to the following:

1. The 62,000 gallons completed and transferred to the Packaging Department

2. The 3,000 gallons in the July 31 (ending) work in process inventory

[1] The first-in, first-out and last-in, first-out cost flow assumptions are described and illustrated in advanced cost accounting textbooks and courses.

The preceding costs show two question marks. These amounts are determined by preparing a cost of production report using the following four steps:

Step 1. Determine the units to be assigned costs.

Step 2. Compute equivalent units of production.

Step 3. Determine the cost per equivalent unit.

Step 4. Allocate costs to transferred out and partially completed units.

Under the average cost method, all production costs (materials and conversion costs) are combined for determining equivalent units and cost per equivalent unit. To simplify, this approach is used in this appendix.

Step 1: Determine the Units to Be Assigned Costs

The first step is to determine the units to be assigned costs. A unit can be any measure of completed production, such as tons, gallons, pounds, barrels, or cases. For S&W, a unit is a gallon of ice cream.

S&W's Mixing Department had 65,000 gallons of direct materials to account for during July, as shown here.

Total gallons to account for:	
Work in process, July	5,000 gallons
Received from materials storeroom	60,000
Total units to account for by the Packaging Department	65,000 gallons

There are two groups of units to be assigned costs for the period.

Group 1	Units completed and transferred out
Group 2	Units in the July 31 (ending) work in process inventory

During July, the Mixing Department completed and transferred 62,000 gallons to the Packaging Department. Of the 60,000 gallons started in July, 57,000 (60,000 − 3,000) gallons were completed and transferred to the Packaging Department. Thus, the ending work in process inventory consists of 3,000 gallons.

The total units (gallons) to be assigned costs for S&W can be summarized as follows:

Group 1	Units transferred out to the Packaging Department in July	62,000 gallons
Group 2	Work in process inventory, July 31	3,000
	Total gallons to be assigned costs	65,000 gallons

The total units (gallons) to be assigned costs (65,000 gallons) equal the total units to account for (65,000 gallons).

Step 2: Compute Equivalent Units of Production

S&W has 3,000 gallons of whole units in the work in process inventory for the Mixing Department on July 31. Since these units are 25% complete, the number of equivalent units in process in the Mixing Department on July 31 is 750 gallons (3,000 gallons × 25%). Since the units transferred to the Packaging Department have been completed, the whole units (62,000 gallons) transferred are the same as the equivalent units transferred.

The total equivalent units of production for the Mixing Department are determined by adding the equivalent units in the ending work in process inventory to the units transferred and completed during the period as shown below.

Equivalent units completed and transferred to the Packaging Department during July	62,000 gallons
Equivalent units in ending work in process, July 31	750
Total equivalent units	62,750 gallons

Step 3: Determine the Cost per Equivalent Unit

Since materials and conversion costs are combined under the average cost method, the cost per equivalent unit is determined by dividing the total production costs by the total equivalent units of production as follows:

$$\text{Cost per Equivalent Unit} = \frac{\text{Total Production Costs}}{\text{Total Equivalent Units}}$$

$$\text{Cost per Equivalent Unit} = \frac{\text{Total Production Costs}}{\text{Total Equivalent Units}} = \frac{\$89,105}{62,750 \text{ gallons}} = \$1.42$$

The cost per equivalent unit shown above is used in Step 4 to allocate the production costs to the completed and partially completed units.

Step 4: Allocate Costs to Transferred Out and Partially Completed Units

The cost of transferred and partially completed units is determined by multiplying the cost per equivalent unit times the equivalent units of production. For the Mixing Department, these costs are determined as follows:

Group 1	Transferred out to the Packaging Department (62,000 gallons × $1.42)	$88,040
Group 2	Work in process inventory, July 31 (3,000 gallons × 25% × $1.42)	1,065
	Total production costs assigned	$89,105

The Cost of Production Report

The July cost of production report for S&W's Mixing Department is shown in Exhibit 4. This cost of production report summarizes the following:

1. The units for which the department is accountable and the disposition of those units

2. The production costs incurred by the department and the allocation of those costs between completed and partially completed units

Cost Flows for a Process Cost System

Exhibit 5 on page 673 shows the flow of costs for each transaction. Note that the highlighted amounts in Exhibit 5 were determined from assigning the costs charged to production in the Mixing Department. These amounts were computed and are shown at the bottom of the cost of production report for the department in Exhibit 4. Likewise, the amount transferred out of the Packaging Department to Finished Goods would have also been determined from a cost of production report for the Packaging Department.

EXHIBIT 4   Cost of Production Report for S&W's Mixing Department—Average Cost

	A	B	C
1	S&W Ice Cream Company		
2	Cost of Production Report—Mixing Department		
3	For the Month Ended July 31, 2010		
4	UNITS		
5		Whole Units	Equivalent Units
6			of Production
7	Units to account for during production:		
8	Work in process inventory, July 1	5,000	
9	Received from materials storeroom	60,000	
10	Total units accounted for by the Mixing Department	65,000	
11			
12	Units to be assigned costs:		
13	Transferred to Packaging Department in July	62,000	62,000
14	Inventory in process, July 31 (25% completed)	3,000	750
15	Total units to be assigned costs	65,000	62,750
16			
17	COSTS		
18			
19	Cost per equivalent unit:		
20	Total production costs for July in Mixing Department		$89,105
21	Total equivalent units (from Step 2 above)		÷62,750
22	Cost per equivalent unit		$ 1.42
23			
24	Costs assigned to production:		
25	Inventory in process, July 1		$ 6,200
26	Direct materials, direct labor, and factory overhead incurred in July		82,905
27	Total costs accounted for by the Mixing Department		$89,105
28			
29			
30	Costs allocated to completed and partially completed units:		
31	Transferred to Packaging Department in July (62,000 gallons × $1.42)		$88,040
32	Inventory in process, July 31 (3,000 gallons × 25% × $1.42)		1,065
33	Total costs assigned by the Mixing Department		$89,105
34			

Step 1 (rows 4–5), Step 2 (rows 4–6), Step 3 (rows 19–27), Step 4 (rows 30–33)

Using the Cost of Production Report for Decision Making

The cost of production report is often used by managers for decisions involving the control and improvement of operations. To illustrate, cost of production reports for Holland Beverage Company are used. Finally, the computation and use of yield is discussed.

Holland Beverage Company

A cost of production report may be prepared in greater detail than shown in Exhibit 4. This greater detail can help managers isolate problems and seek opportunities for improvement.

To illustrate, the Blending Department of Holland Beverage Company prepared cost of production reports for April and May. To simplify, assume that the Blending Department had no beginning or ending work in process inventory in either month. In other words, all units started were completed

EXHIBIT 5 S&W's Cost Flows

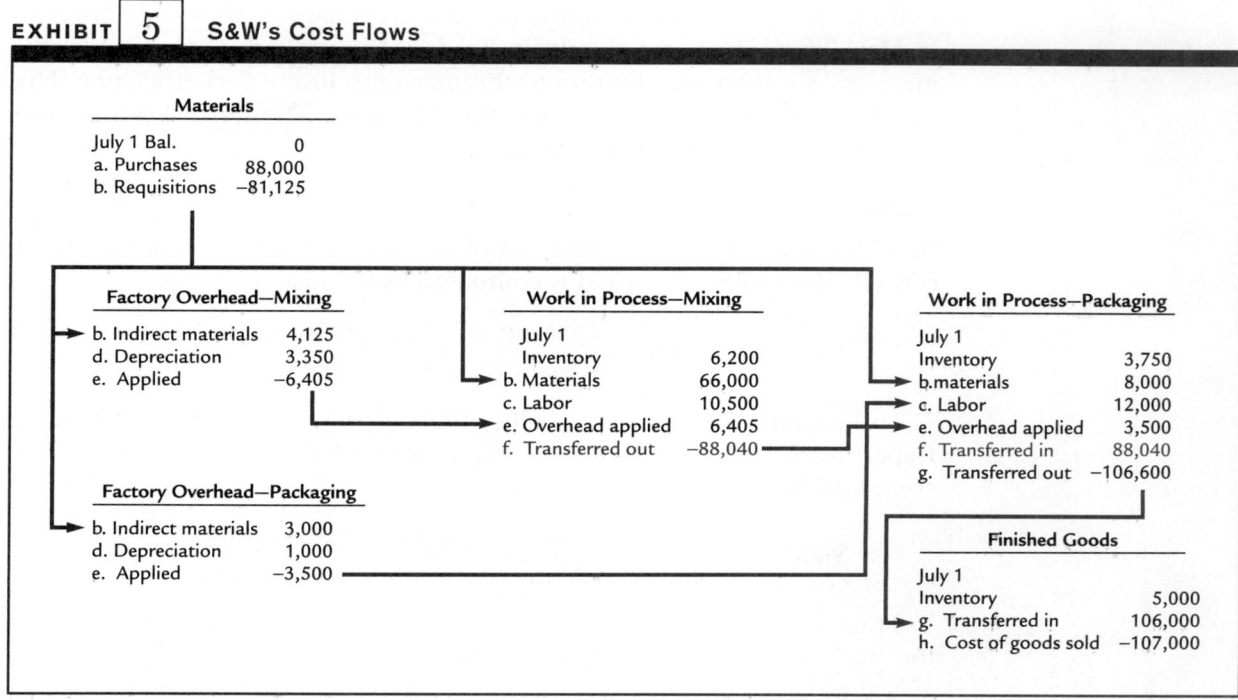

in each month. The cost of production reports for April and May in the Blending Department are as follows:

	A	B	C	D
1	**Cost of Production Reports**			
2	**Holland Beverage Company—Blending Department**			
3	**For the Months Ended April 30 and May 31, 2010**			
4		**April**	**May**	
5	Direct materials	$ 20,000	$ 40,600	
6	Direct labor	15,000	29,400	
7	Energy	8,000	20,000	
8	Repairs	4,000	8,000	
9	Tank cleaning	3,000	8,000	
10	Total	$ 50,000	$106,000	
11	Units completed	÷100,000	÷200,000	
12	Cost per unit	$ 0.50	$ 0.53	
13				

The May results indicate that total unit costs have increased from $0.50 to $0.53, or 6% from April. To determine the possible causes for this increase, the cost of production report is restated in per-unit terms by dividing the costs by the number of units completed, as shown below.

	A	B	C	D
1	**Blending Department**			
2	**Per-Unit Expense Comparisons**			
3		**April**	**May**	**% Change**
4	Direct materials	$0.200	$0.203	1.50%
5	Direct labor	0.150	0.147	−2.00%
6	Energy	0.080	0.100	25.00%
7	Repairs	0.040	0.040	0.00%
8	Tank cleaning	0.030	0.040	33.33%
9	Total	$0.500	$0.530	6.00%
10				

Both energy and tank cleaning per-unit costs have increased significantly in May. These increases should be further investigated. For example, the increase in energy may be due to the machines losing fuel efficiency. This could lead management to repair the machines. The tank cleaning costs could be investigated in a similar fashion.

Yield

In addition to unit costs, managers of process manufacturers are also concerned about yield. The yield is computed as follows:

$$\text{Yield} = \frac{\text{Quantity of Material Output}}{\text{Quantity of Material Input}}$$

To illustrate, assume that 1,000 pounds of sugar entered the Packaging Department, and 980 pounds of sugar were packed. The yield is 98% as computed below.

$$\text{Yield} = \frac{\text{Quantity of Material Output}}{\text{Quantity of Material Input}} = \frac{980 \text{ pounds}}{1,000 \text{ pounds}} = 98\%$$

Thus, 2% (100% – 98%) or 20 pounds of sugar was lost or spilled during the packing process. Managers can investigate significant changes in yield over time or significant differences in yield from industry standards.

Exercises

E1

Entries for materials cost flows in a process cost system

The Hershey Foods Company manufactures chocolate confectionery products. The three largest raw materials are cocoa beans, sugar, and dehydrated milk. These raw materials first go into the Blending Department. The blended product is then sent to the Molding Department, where the bars of candy are formed. The candy is then sent to the Packing Department, where the bars are wrapped and boxed. The boxed candy is then sent to the distribution center, where it is eventually sold to food brokers and retailers.

Show the accounts increased and decreased for each of the following business events:

a. Materials used by the Blending Department
b. Transfer of blended product to the Molding Department
c. Transfer of chocolate to the Packing Department
d. Transfer of boxed chocolate to the distribution center
e. Sale of boxed chocolate

E2

Flowchart of accounts related to service and processing departments

Alcoa Inc. is the world's largest producer of aluminum products. One product that Alcoa manufactures is aluminum sheet products for the aerospace industry. The entire output of the Smelting Department is transferred to the Rolling Department. Part of the fully processed goods from the Rolling Department are sold as rolled sheet, and the remainder of the goods are transferred to the Converting Department for further processing into sheared sheet.

Prepare a chart of the flow of costs from the processing department accounts into the finished goods accounts and then into the cost of goods sold account. The relevant accounts are as follows:

Cost of Goods Sold
Materials
Factory Overhead—Smelting Department
Factory Overhead—Rolling Department
Factory Overhead—Converting Department

Finished Goods—Rolled Sheet
Finished Goods—Sheared Sheet
Work in Process—Smelting Department
Work in Process—Rolling Department
Work in Process—Converting Department

E3

Equivalent units of production

✓ a. 26,300

The Converting Department of Osaka Napkin Company uses the average cost method and had 2,000 units in work in process that were 60% complete at the beginning of the period. During the period, 25,200 units were completed and transferred to the Packing Department. There were 1,100 units in process that were 30% complete at the end of the period.

a. Determine the number of whole units to be accounted for and to be assigned costs for the period.
b. Determine the number of equivalent units of production for the period.

E4

Equivalent units of production

✓ a. 92,500 units to be accounted for

Units of production data for the two departments of Atlantic Cable and Wire Company for August of the current fiscal year are as follows:

	Drawing Department	Winding Department
Work in process, August 1	2,100 units, 50% completed	2,000 units, 30% completed
Completed and transferred to next processing department during August	90,000 units	89,200 units
Work in process, August 31	2,500 units, 55% completed	2,800 units, 25% completed

Each department uses the average cost method.

a. Determine the number of whole units to be accounted for and to be assigned costs and the equivalent units of production for the Drawing Department.
b. Determine the number of whole units to be accounted for and to be assigned costs and the equivalent units of production for the Winding Department.

E5

Equivalent units of production

✓ a. 16,500

The following information concerns production in the Finishing Department for March. The Finishing Department uses the average cost method.

ACCOUNT Work in Process—Finishing Department

Date	Item	
Mar. 1	Bal., 15,000 units, 40% completed	24,600
31	Direct materials, 144,000 units	345,000
31	Direct labor	163,200
31	Factory overhead	86,700
31	Goods transferred, 142,500 units	−578,550
31	Bal., ? units, 60% completed	40,950

a. Determine the number of units in work in process inventory at the end of the month.

b. Determine the number of whole units to be accounted for and to be assigned costs and the equivalent units of production for March.

E6

Equivalent units of production and related costs

SPREADSHEET

✓ b. 86,870 units

The charges to Work in Process—Baking Department for a period as well as information concerning production are as follows. The Baking Department uses the average cost method, and all direct materials are placed in process during production.

Work in Process—Baking Department	
Bal., 8,000 units, 70% completed	12,900
Direct materials, 82,300 units	161,000
Direct labor	91,800
Factory overhead	81,780
To Finished Goods, 85,400 units	?
Bal., 4,900 units, 30% completed	?

Determine the following:

a. The number of whole units to be accounted for and to be assigned costs
b. The number of equivalent units of production
c. The cost per equivalent unit
d. The cost of the units transferred to Finished Goods
e. The cost of ending Work in Process

E7

Cost per equivalent unit

✓ a. $11.50

The following information concerns production in the Forging Department for June. The Forging Department uses the average cost method.

ACCOUNT Work in Process—Forging Department		
Date	Item	
June 1	Bal., 2,000 units, 40% completed	9,120
30	Direct materials, 46,200 units	324,800
30	Direct labor	137,045
30	Factory overhead	75,400
30	Goods transferred, 45,900 units	?
30	Bal., 2,300 units, 70% completed	?

a. Determine the cost per equivalent unit.
b. Determine the cost of the units transferred to Finished Goods.
c. Determine the cost of ending Work in Process.

E8

Cost of production report

SPREADSHEET

✓ Cost per equivalent unit, $6.00

The increases to Work in Process—Roasting Department for Boston Coffee Company for December 2010 as well as information concerning production are as follows:

Work in process, December 1, 1,500 pounds, 40% completed	$ 3,600
Coffee beans added during December, 92,500 pounds	391,420
Conversion costs during December	167,900
Work in process, December 31, 900 pounds, 80% completed	—
Goods finished during December, 93,100 pounds	—

Prepare a cost of production report, using the average cost method.

E9

Cost of production report

SPREADSHEET

✓ **Cost per equivalent unit, $11.00**

Prepare a cost of production report for the Cutting Department of Chota Carpet Company for October 2010. Use the average cost method with the following data:

Work in process, October 1, 9,000 units, 75% completed	$ 75,000
Materials added during October from Weaving Department, 105,000 units	807,750
Direct labor for October	175,200
Factory overhead for October	92,100
Goods finished during October (includes goods in process, October 1), 103,500 units	—
Work in process, October 31, 10,500 units, 10% completed	—

E10

Decision making

SPREADSHEET

Oasis Bottling Company bottles popular beverages in the Bottling Department. The beverages are produced by blending concentrate with water and sugar. The concentrate is purchased from a concentrate producer. The concentrate producer sets higher prices for the more popular concentrate flavors. Below is a simplified Bottling Department cost of production report separating the costs of bottling the four flavors.

	A	B	C	D	E
1		Orange	Cola	Lemon-Lime	Root Beer
2	Concentrate	$ 6,650	$135,000	$ 99,000	$ 3,600
3	Water	2,100	36,000	27,000	1,200
4	Sugar	3,500	60,000	45,000	2,000
5	Bottles	7,700	132,000	99,000	4,400
6	Flavor changeover	3,500	6,000	4,500	5,000
7	Conversion cost	2,625	24,000	18,000	1,500
8	Total cost transferred to finished goods	$26,075	$393,000	$292,500	$17,700
9	Number of cases	3,500	60,000	45,000	2,000
10					

Beginning and ending work in process inventories are negligible, so they are omitted from the cost of production report. The flavor changeover cost represents the cost of cleaning the bottling machines between production runs of different flavors.

Prepare a memo to the production manager analyzing this comparative cost information. In your memo, provide recommendations for further action, along with supporting schedules showing the total cost per case and the cost per case by cost element.

E11

Decision making

SPREADSHEET

Instant Memories Inc. produces photographic paper for printing digital images. One of the processes for this operation is a coating (solvent spreading) operation, where chemicals are coated onto paper stock. There has been some concern about the cost performance of this operation. As a result, you have begun an investigation. You first discover that all materials and conversion prices have been stable for the last six months. Thus, increases in prices for inputs are not an explanation for increasing costs. However, you have discovered three possible problems from some of the operating personnel whose quotes follow:

Operator 1: "I've been keeping an eye on my operating room instruments. I feel as though our energy consumption is becoming less efficient."

Operator 2: "Every time the coating machine goes down, we produce waste on shutdown and subsequent startup. It seems like during the last half year we have had more unscheduled machine shutdowns than in the past. Thus, I feel as though our yields must be dropping."

Operator 3: "My sense is that our coating costs are going up. It seems to me like we are spreading a thicker coating than we should. Perhaps the coating machine needs to be recalibrated."

The Coating Department had no beginning or ending inventories for any month during the study period. The following data from the cost of production report are made available:

	A	B	C	D	E	F	G
1		January	February	March	April	May	June
2	Paper stock	$72,960	$69,120	$ 76,800	$69,120	$65,280	$61,440
3	Coating	$16,416	$17,280	$ 21,120	$21,600	$21,216	$23,040
4	Conversion cost (incl. energy)	$36,480	$34,560	$ 38,400	$34,560	$32,640	$30,720
5	Pounds input to the process	95,000	90,000	100,000	90,000	85,000	80,000
6	Pounds transferred out	91,200	86,400	96,000	86,400	81,600	76,800
7							

a. Prepare a table showing the paper cost per output pound, coating cost per output pound, conversion cost per output pound, and yield for each month.
b. Interpret your table results.

Problems

P1

Equivalent units and related costs; cost of production report: average cost method

SPREADSHEET

✓ **Transferred to Packaging Dept., $74,000**

Olde Stone Mill Flour Company manufactures flour by a series of three processes, beginning in the Milling Department. From the Milling Department, the materials pass through the Sifting and Packaging departments, emerging as packaged refined flour.

The balance in the account Work in Process—Sifting Department was as follows on December 1, 2010:

Work in Process—Sifting Department (1,200 units, 75% completed) $4,500

The following costs were charged to Work in Process—Sifting Department during December:

Direct materials transferred from Milling Department: 14,500 units $51,400
Direct labor   14,350
Factory overhead   7,125

During December, 14,800 units of flour were completed. The balance of Work in Process—Sifting Department on December 31 was 900 units, 75% completed.

Instructions

Prepare a cost of production report for the Sifting Department for December, using the average cost method.

P2

Cost of production report: average cost method

SPREADSHEET

✓ Cost per equivalent unit, $4.90

Starburst Coffee Company roasts and packs coffee beans. The process begins in the Roasting Department. From the Roasting Department, the coffee beans are transferred to the Packaging Department.

On January 1, 2010, the balance of the account Work in Process - Roasting Department was as follows:

Work in Process – Roasting Department (9,400 units, 80% completed)	$37,600

The account Work in Process - Roasting Department was increased during January by the following costs:

Direct materials (65,200 units)	$135,600
Direct labor	109,152
Factory overhead	67,900

During January, 66,800 units were completed and transferred to the Packaging Department. As of January 31, 2010 there were 7,800 units, 60% complete in the Roasting Department.

Instructions

Prepare a cost of production report for the Roasting Department, using the average cost method.

A

Accelerated depreciation method A depreciation method that provides for a higher depreciation amount in the first year of the asset's use, followed by a gradually declining amount of depreciation.

Account A record in which increases and decreases in a financial statement element are recorded.

Account form The form of balance sheet presented with assets on the left-hand side and the liabilities and stockholders' equity on the right-hand side.

Accounting An information system that provides reports to stakeholders about the economic activities and condition of a business.

Accounting cycle The process that begins with the analysis of transactions and ends with the preparation of the accounting records for the next accounting period.

Accounting equation Assets = Liabilities + Stockholders' Equity

Accounting period concept An accounting concept in which accounting data are recorded and summarized by periods.

Accounts payable Liabilities for amounts incurred from purchases of products or services in the normal operations of a business.

Accounts receivable Receivables created by selling merchandise or services on credit.

Accounts receivable analysis Analysis of a company's ability to collect its accounts receivable.

Accounts receivable turnover The relationship between net sales and accounts receivable computed by dividing the net sales by the average net accounts receivable; measures how frequently during the year the accounts receivable are being converted to cash.

Accrual basis of accounting A system of accounting in which revenue is recorded as it is earned and expenses are recorded when they generate revenue.

Accruals Recognition of revenue when earned or expenses when incurred regardless of when cash is received or disbursed.

Accrued assets Revenues that have been earned at the end of an accounting period but have not been recorded in the accounts; sometimes called accrued revenues.

Accrued expenses Expenses that have been incurred at the end of an accounting period but have not been recorded in the accounts; sometimes called accrued liabilities.

Accrued liabilities Expenses that have been incurred at the end of an accounting period but have not been recorded in the accounts; sometimes called accrued expenses.

Accrued revenues Revenues that have been earned at the end of an accounting period but have not been recorded in the accounts; sometimes called accrued revenues.

Accumulated depreciation An offsetting or contra asset account used to record depreciation on a fixed asset.

Activity base (driver) A measure of activity that is related to changes in cost and is used in the denominator in calculating the predetermined factory overhead rate to assign factory overhead costs to cost objects.

Activity cost pools Cost accumulations that are associated with a given activity, such as machine usage, inspections, moving, and production setups.

Activity-based costing (ABC) An accounting framework based on determining the cost of activities and allocating these costs to products using activity rates.

Adequate disclosure concept An accounting concept that requires financial statements to include all relevant data a reader needs to understand the financial condition and performance of a business.

Adjustment process A process required by the accrual basis of accounting in which the accounts are updated prior to preparing financial statements.

Administrative expenses Expenses incurred in the administration or general operations of the business.

Aging the receivables The process of analyzing the accounts receivable and classifying them according to various age groupings, with the due date being the base point for determining age.

Allowance for doubtful accounts The contra asset account for accounts receivable.

Allowance method The method of accounting for uncollectible accounts that provides an expense for uncollectible receivables in advance of their write-off.

Amortization The periodic transfer of the cost of an intangible asset to expense.

Annuity A series of equal cash flows at fixed intervals.

Assets The resources owned by a business.

Average inventory cost flow method The method of inventory costing that is based upon the assumption that costs should be charged against revenue by using the weighted average unit cost of the items sold.

Average rate of return A method of evaluating capital investment proposals that focuses on the expected profitability of the investment.

B

Bad debt expense The operating expense incurred because of the failure to collect receivables.

Balance sheet A list of the assets, liabilities, and owner's equity as of a specific date, usually at the close of the last day of a month or a year.

Balanced scorecard A performance evaluation approach that incorporates multiple performance dimensions by combining financial and nonfinancial measures.

Bank reconciliation The analysis that details the items responsible for the

difference between the cash balance reported in the bank statement and the cash balance in the ledger.

Bank statement A summary of all transactions mailed to the depositor by the bank each month.

Bond A form of interest-bearing note used by corporations to borrow on a long-term basis.

Bond indenture The contract between a corporation issuing bonds and the bondholders.

Bonds payable A type of long-term debt financing with interest that is normally paid semiannually.

Book inventory The amount of inventory recorded in the accounting records.

Book value The cost of a fixed asset minus accumulated depreciation on the asset.

Bottleneck A condition that occurs when product demand exceeds product capacity.

Break-even point The level of business operations at which revenues and expired costs are equal.

Budget An accounting device used to plan and control resources of operational departments and divisions.

Budget performance report A report comparing actual results with budget figures.

Budgetary slack Excess resources set within a budget to provide for uncertain events.

Budgeted variable factory overhead The standard variable overhead for the actual units produced.

Business An organization in which basic resources (inputs), such as materials and labor, are assembled and processed to provide goods and services (outputs) to customers.

Business entity concept An accounting concept that limits the economic data in the accounting system of a specific business or entity to data related directly to the activities of that business or entity.

Business stakeholder A person or entity that has an interest in the economic performance of a business.

C

Capital expenditures The costs of acquiring fixed assets, adding a component, or replacing a component of fixed assets.

Capital expenditures budget The budget summarizing future plans for acquiring plant facilities and equipment.

Capital investment analysis The process by which management plans, evaluates, and controls long-term capital investments involving fixed assets.

Capital rationing The process by which management allocates available investment funds among competing capital investment proposals.

Capital stock The portion of a corporation's stockholders' equity contributed by investors (owners) in exchange for shares of stock.

Cash Coins, currency (paper money), checks, money orders, and money on deposit available for unrestricted withdrawal from banks and other financial institutions.

Cash basis of accounting A system of accounting in which only transactions involving increases or decreases of the entity's cash are recorded.

Cash budget A budget of estimated cash receipts and payments.

Cash dividend A cash distribution of earnings by a corporation to its shareholders.

Cash equivalents Highly liquid investments that are usually reported with cash on the balance sheet.

Cash payback period The expected period of time that will elapse between the date of a capital expenditure and the complete recovery in cash (or equivalent) of the amount invested.

Cash short and over The account used to record the difference between the amount of cash in a cash register and the amount of cash that should be on hand according to the records.

Classified balance sheet A balance sheet prepared with various sections, subsections, and captions that aid in its interpretation and analysis.

Common stock The basic type of stock issued to stockholders of a corporation when a corporation has issued only one class of stock.

Common-sized statement A financial statement in which all items are expressed only in relative terms.

Compensating balance A requirement by some banks requiring depositors to maintain minimum cash balances in their bank accounts.

Contingent liabilities Potential liabilities if certain events occur in the future.

Continuous budgeting A method of budgeting that provides for maintaining a 12-month projection into the future.

Contract rate The periodic interest to be paid on the bonds that is identified in the bond indenture; expressed as a percentage of the face amount of the bond.

Contribution margin Sales less variable cost of goods sold and variable selling and administrative expenses.

Contribution margin ratio The percentage of each sales dollar that is available to cover the fixed costs and provide income from operations.

Control environment The overall attitude of management and employees about the importance of controls.

Controllable expenses Costs that can be influenced by the decisions of a manager of a cost, profit, or investment center.

Controllable revenues Revenues that can be influenced by the decisions of a manager of a profit or investment center.

Controllable variance The difference between the actual amount of variable factory overhead cost incurred and the amount of variable factory overhead budgeted for the standard product.

Controlling account The account in the general ledger that summarizes the balances of the accounts in the subsidiary ledger.

Conversion costs The combination of direct labor and factory overhead costs.

Copyright An exclusive right to publish and sell a literary, artistic, or musical composition.

Corporation A business organized under state or federal statutes as a separate legal entity.

Cost A payment of cash (or a commitment to pay cash in the future) for the purpose of generating revenues.

Cost accounting system A system used to accumulate manufacturing costs for decision-making and financial reporting purposes.

Cost allocation The process of assigning indirect costs to a cost object, such as a job.

Cost behavior The manner in which a cost changes in relation to its activity base (driver).

Cost center A decentralized unit in which the department or division manager has responsibility for the control of costs incurred and the authority to make decisions that affect these costs.

Cost concept An accounting concept that determines the amount initially entered into the accounting records for purchases.

Cost of goods sold The cost of products sold; may also be referred to as cost of merchandise sold or cost of sales.

Cost of goods sold budget A budget of the estimated direct materials, direct labor, and factory overhead consumed by sold products.

Cost of merchandise purchased The cost of merchandise purchased during a period computed as purchases less purchases returns and allowances, less purchases discounts, plus freight in.

Cost of merchandise sold The cost of products sold; may also be referred to as cost of sales or cost of goods sold.

Cost of sales The cost of products sold; may also be referred to as cost of merchandise sold or cost of goods sold.

Cost price approach An approach to transfer pricing that uses cost as the basis for setting the transfer price.

Cost variance The difference between the actual cost and the standard cost at actual volumes.

Cost-volume-profit analysis The systematic examination of the relationships among costs, expenses, sales, and operating profit or loss.

Cost-volume-profit chart A chart used to assist management in understanding the relationships among costs, expenses, sales, and operating profit or loss.

Credit memorandum A form used by a seller to inform the buyer of the amount the seller proposes to decrease the account receivable due from the buyer.

Credit period The amount of time the buyer is allowed in which to pay the seller.

Credit terms Terms for payment on account by the buyer to the seller.

Currency exchange rate The rate at which currency in another country can be exchanged for local currency.

Current assets Cash and other assets that are expected to be converted to cash or sold or used up through the normal operations of the business within 1 year or less.

Current liabilities Liabilities that will be due within a short time (usually 1 year or less) and that are to be paid out of current assets.

Current position analysis Analysis of a company's ability to pay its current liabilities.

Current ratio A financial ratio that is computed by dividing current assets by current liabilities.

Currently attainable standards Standards that represent levels of operation that can be attained with reasonable effort.

D

Debit memorandum A form used by a buyer to inform the seller of the amount the buyer proposes to decrease the account payable due the seller.

Deferrals Delayed recordings of expenses or revenues.

Deferred expenses Items that are initially recorded as assets but are expected to become expenses over time or through the normal operations of the business; sometimes called prepaid expenses.

Deferred revenues Items that are initially recorded as liabilities but are expected to become revenues over time or through the normal operations of the business; sometimes called unearned revenues.

Depletion The process of transferring the cost of natural resources to an expense account.

Depreciation The systematic periodic transfer of the cost of a fixed asset to an expense account during its expected useful life.

Differential analysis The area of accounting concerned with the effect of alternative courses of action on revenues and costs.

Differential cost The amount of increase or decrease in cost expected from a particular course of action compared with an alternative.

Differential income (or loss) The difference between differential revenue and differential cost.

Differential revenue The amount of increase or decrease in revenue expected from a particular course of action as compared with an alternative.

Direct labor cost Wages of factory workers who are directly involved in converting materials into a finished product.

Direct labor cost budget A budget that estimates the direct labor hours and related costs needed to support budgeted production.

Direct labor rate variance The cost associated with the difference between the standard rate and the actual rate paid for direct labor used in producing a commodity.

Direct labor time variance The cost associated with the difference between the standard hours and the actual hours of direct labor spent producing a commodity.

Direct materials cost The cost of materials that are an integral part of the finished product.

Direct materials price budget The cost associated with the difference between the standard price and the actual price

of direct materials used in producing a commodity.

Direct materials price variance The difference between the actual price and standard price times the actual quantity.

Direct materials purchases budget A budget that uses the production budget as a starting point.

Direct materials quantity variance The cost associated with the difference between the standard quantity and the actual quantity of direct materials used in producing a commodity.

Direct write-off method The method of accounting for uncollectible accounts that recognizes the expense only when accounts are judged to be worthless.

Discount on bonds payable The excess of the face amount of bonds over their issue price.

Dividend yield A ratio, computed by dividing the annual dividends paid per share of common stock by the market price per share at a specific date, which indicates the rate of return to stockholders in terms of cash dividend distributions.

Dividends Distributions of the earnings of a corporation to its stockholders.

Dividends per share Measures the extent to which earnings are being distributed to common shareholders.

Double-declining balance method A method of depreciation that provides periodic depreciation expense based on the declining book value of a fixed asset over its estimated life.

DuPont formula An expanded expression of return on investment determined by multiplying the profit margin by the investment turnover.

E

Earnings per share (EPS) A measure of profitability computed by dividing net income, reduced by preferred dividends, by the number of shares outstanding.

Earnings per share (EPS) on common stock Net income per share of common stock outstanding during a period.

Electronic data interchange (EDI) An information technology that allows different business organizations to use computers to communicate orders, relay information, and make or receive payments.

Electronic funds transfer (EFT) A system in which computers rather than paper (money, checks, etc.) are used to effect cash transactions.

Elements of internal control The control environment, risk assessment, control activities, information and communication, and monitoring.

Employee fraud The intentional act of deceiving an employer for personal gain.

Employee involvement A philosophy that grants employees the responsibility and authority to make their own decisions about their operations.

Enterprise resource planning A system used to plan and control internal and supply chain operations.

Expenses Costs used to earn (generate) revenues.

Extraordinary item An event or transaction reported on the income statement that is (1) unusual in nature and (2) infrequent in occurrence.

F

Factory overhead cost All of the costs of operating the factory except for direct materials and direct labor.

Factory overhead cost budget A budget that estimates the cost for each item of factory overhead needed to support budgeted production.

Factory overhead cost variance report Reports budgeted and actual costs for variable and fixed factory overhead for each cost element along with the related controllable and volume variances.

Favorable cost variance Actual cost is less than standard cost.

Fees earned Revenues received from providing services.

Financial accounting The branch of accounting that is associated with preparing reports for users external to the business.

Financial Accounting Standards Board (FASB) The authoritative body that has the primary responsibility for developing accounting principles.

Financial accounting system A system that includes (1) a set of rules for determining what, when, and the amount that should be recorded for an economic event; (2) a framework for facilitating preparing financial statements; and, (3) one or more controls to determine whether errors could have arisen in the recording process.

Financial statements Financial reports that summarize the effects of events on a business.

Financing activities Business activities that involve obtaining funds to begin and operate a business.

Finished goods inventory The cost of finished products on hand that have not been sold.

Finished goods ledger The subsidiary ledger that contains the individual accounts for each kind of commodity or product produced.

First-in, first-out (FIFO) inventory method A method of inventory costing based on the assumption that the costs of merchandise sold should be charged against revenue in the order in which the costs were incurred.

Fixed assets Long-lived or relatively permanent tangible assets that are used in the normal business operations; sometimes called plant assets.

Fixed costs Costs that tend to remain the same in amount, regardless of variations in the level of activity.

Flexible budget A budget that adjusts for varying rates of activity.

FOB (free on board) destination Freight terms in which the seller pays the transportation costs from the shipping point to the final destination.

FOB (free on board) shipping point Freight terms in which the buyer pays the transportation costs from the shipping point to the final destination.

Freight in Freight costs incurred in obtaining merchandise.

Fringe benefits Benefits provided to employees in addition to wages and salaries.

G

General expenses Expenses incurred in the administration or general operations of the business; sometimes called administrative expenses.

Generally accepted accounting principles (GAAP) Rules for the way financial statements should be prepared.

Goal conflict Situation when individual self-interest differs from business objectives.

Going concern concept An accounting concept that assumes a business will continue operating for an indefinite period of time.

Goodwill An intangible asset of a business that is created from favorable factors such as location, product quality, reputation, and managerial skill, as verified from a merger transaction.

Gross pay The total earnings of an employee for a payroll period.

Gross profit Sales minus the cost of merchandise sold.

H

High-low method A technique that uses the highest and lowest total cost as a basis for estimating the variable cost per unit and the fixed cost component of a mixed cost.

Horizontal analysis Financial analysis that compares an item in a current statement with the same item in prior statements.

I

Ideal standards Standards that can be achieved only under perfect operating conditions, such as no idle time, no machine breakdowns, and no materials spoilage; also called theoretical standards.

Income from operations The excess of gross profit over total operating expenses. Sometimes called operating income.

Income statement A summary of the revenue and expenses for a specific period of time, such as a month or a year.

Indirect method A method of preparing the statement of cash flows that reconciles net income with net cash flows from operating activities.

Inflation A period when prices in general are rising and the purchasing power of money is declining.

Intangible assets Long-lived assets that are useful in the operations of a business, are not held for sale, and are without physical qualities.

Interest payable A liability to pay interest on a due date.

Internal control The policies and procedures used to safeguard assets, ensure accurate business information, and ensure compliance with laws and regulations.

Internal rate of return method A method of analyzing proposed capital investments that focuses on using present value concepts to compute the rate of return from the net cash flows expected from the investment.

International Accounting Standards Board An authoritative body that establishes accounting principles and practices for companies outside of the United States.

Inventory analysis A company's ability to manage its inventory effectively.

Inventory shortage The amount by which the merchandise for sale, as indicated by the balance of the merchandise inventory account, is larger than the total amount of merchandise counted during the physical inventory. Sometimes called inventory shrinkage.

Inventory shrinkage The amount by which the merchandise for sale, as indicated by the balance of the merchandise inventory account, is larger than the total amount of merchandise counted during the physical inventory. Sometimes called inventory shortage.

Inventory turnover The relationship between the volume of goods sold and inventory, computed by dividing the cost of goods sold by the average inventory.

Investing activities Business activities that involve obtaining the necessary resources to start and operate the business.

Investment center A decentralized unit in which the manager has the responsibility and authority to make decisions that affect not only costs and revenues but also the fixed assets available to the center.

Investment turnover A component of the rate of return on investment computed as the ratio of sales to invested assets.

Invoice The bill that the seller sends to the buyer.

J

Job cost sheet An account in the work-in-process subsidiary ledger in which the costs charged to a particular job order are recorded.

Job order cost system A type of cost accounting system that provides for a separate record of the cost of each particular quantity of product that passes through the factory.

Just-in-time (JIT) processing A business philosophy that focuses on eliminating time, cost, and poor quality within manufacturing processes.

L

Last-in, first-out (LIFO) inventory method A method of inventory costing based on the assumption that the most recent merchandise inventory costs should be charged against revenue.

Lead time The elapsed time between starting a unit of product into the beginning of a process and its completion.

Liabilities The rights of creditors that represent a legal obligation to repay an amount borrowed according to terms of the borrowing agreement.

LIFO conformity rule A financial reporting rule requiring a firm that elects to use LIFO inventory valuation for tax purposes to also use LIFO for external financial reporting.

LIFO reserve A required disclosure for LIFO firms, showing the difference between inventory valued under FIFO and inventory valued under LIFO.

Limited liability company (LLC) A form of corporation that combines attributes of a partnership and a corporation in that it is organized as a corporation; but it can elect to be taxed as a partnership.

Liquidity Refers to the ability to convert an asset to cash.

Long-term liabilities Liabilities due beyond one year or liabilities that will be paid out of noncurrent assets.

Low-cost strategy A strategy where a company designs and produces products or services at a lower cost than its competitors.

Lower-of-cost-or-market (LCM) method A method of valuing inventory that reports the inventory at the lower of its cost or current market value (replacement cost).

M

Management's Discussion and Analysis (MD&A) An annual report disclosure that provides management's analysis of the results of operations and financial condition.

Managerial accounting The branch of accounting that aids management in making financing, investing, and operating decisions for the company.

Manufacturing businesses A type of business that changes basic inputs into products that are sold to individual customers.

Margin of safety The difference between current sales revenue and the sales at the break-even point.

Market price approach An approach to transfer pricing that uses the price at which the product or service transferred could be sold to outside buyers as the transfer price.

Market rate of interest The effective rate of interest at the time the bonds were issued.

Markup An amount that is added to a "cost" amount to determine product price.

Master budget The comprehensive budget plan linking the individual budgets related to sales, cost of goods sold, operating expenses, project, capital expenditures, and cash.

Matching concept An accounting concept that requires expenses of a period to be matched with the revenue generated during that period.

Materials inventory The cost of materials that have not yet entered into the manufacturing process.

Materials ledger The subsidiary ledger containing the individual accounts for each type of material.

Materials requisition The form or electronic transmission used by a manufacturing department to authorize the issuance of materials from the storeroom.

Maturity value The amount that is due at the maturity or due date of a note.

Merchandise available for sale The cost of merchandise available for sale to customers.

Merchandise inventory Merchandise on hand (not sold) at the end of an accounting period.

Merchandising businesses Businesses that sell products they purchase from other businesses to customers.

Mixed costs Costs with both variable and fixed characteristics.

Multiple-step income statement A form of income statement that contains several sections, subsections, and subtotals.

N

Negotiated price approach An approach to transfer pricing that allows managers of decentralized units to agree (negotiate) among themselves as to the transfer price.

Net income The excess of revenues over expenses.

Net loss The excess of expenses over revenues.

Net pay Gross pay less payroll deductions; the amount the employer is obligated to pay the employee.

Net present value method A method of analyzing proposed capital investments that focuses on the present value of the cash flows expected from the investments.

Net realizable value For a receivable, the amount of cash expected to be realized in the future. For inventory, the estimated selling price of an item of inventory less any direct costs of disposal, such as sales commissions.

Net sales Gross sales less sales returns and allowances and sales discounts.

Nonfinancial performance measure A performance measure expressed in other than dollars.

Non-value-added lead time The time that units wait in inventories, move unnecessarily, and wait during machine breakdowns.

Note payable A type of short- or long-term financing that requires payment of the amount borrowed plus interest.

Notes receivable Written claim against debtors who promise to pay the amount of the note plus interest at an agreed upon rate.

Number of days' sales in inventory The relationship between the volume of sales and inventory, computed by dividing the inventory at the end of the year by the average daily cost of goods sold.

Number of days' sales in receivables The relationship between sales and accounts receivable, computed by dividing the average accounts receivable by the average daily sales.

Number of times interest charges are earned A ratio that measures creditor margin of safety for interest payments, calculated as income before interest and taxes divided by interest expense.

O

Objectivity concept An accounting concept that requires accounting records and data reported in financial statements be based on objective evidence.

Operating activities Business activities that involve using the business's resources to implement its business strategy.

Operating income The excess of gross profit over total operating expenses. Sometimes called income from operations.

Operating leverage A measure of the relative mix of a business's variable costs and fixed costs, computed as contribution margin divided by income from operations.

Opportunity cost The amount of income forgone from an alternative to a proposed use of cash or its equivalent.

Other expense Expenses that cannot be traced directly to operations.

Other income Revenue from sources other than the primary operating activities of a business.

Outstanding stock The stock in the hands of stockholders.

Overapplied factory overhead The amount of factory overhead applied in excess of the actual factory overhead costs incurred for production during a period.

Owner's equity The financial rights of the owner.

P

Par The monetary amount printed on a stock certificate.

Partnership A business owned by two or more individuals.

Patents Exclusive rights to produce and sell goods with one or more unique features.

Payroll The total amount paid to employees for a certain period.

Period costs Those costs that are used up in generating revenue during the current period and that are not involved in the manufacturing process.

Periodic inventory system The inventory method in which the inventory records do not show the amount available for sale or sold during the period.

Perpetual inventory system The inventory system in which each purchase and sale of merchandise is recorded in an inventory account.

Petty cash fund A special-purpose cash fund to pay relatively small amounts.

Physical inventory A detailed listing of the merchandise for sale at the end of an accounting period.

Predetermined factory overhead rate The rate used to apply factory overhead costs to the goods manufactured. The rate is determined from budgeted overhead cost and estimated activity usage data at the beginning of the fiscal period.

Preferred stock A class of stock with preferential rights over common stock.

Premium on bonds payable The excess of the issue price of bonds over their face amount.

Premium on stock The excess of the issue price of a stock over its par value.

Premium-price strategy A strategy where a company tries to design and produce products or services that serve unique market needs, allowing it to charge premium prices.

Prepaid expenses Assets resulting from the prepayment of future expenses such as insurance or rent that are expected to become expenses over time or through the normal operations of the business; often called *deferred expenses*.

Present value concept Cash today is not the equivalent of the same amount of money to be received in the future.

Present value index An index computed by dividing the total present value of the next cash flow to be received from a proposed capital investment by the amount to be invested.

Present value of an annuity The sum of the present values of a series of equal cash flows to be received at fixed intervals.

Price-earnings (P/E) ratio The ratio of the market price per share of common stock, at a specific date, to the annual earnings per share.

Prime costs The combination of direct materials and direct labor costs.

Process A sequence of activities linked together for performing a particular task.

Process cost system A type of cost accounting system in which costs are accumulated by department or process within a factory.

Process-oriented layout Organizing work in a plant or administrative function around processes (tasks).

Product cost concept A concept used in applying the cost-plus approach to product pricing in which only the costs of manufacturing the product, termed the product costs, are included in the cost amount to which the markup is added.

Product costs The three components of manufacturing costs: direct materials, direct labor, and factory overhead costs.

Production budget A budget of estimated unit production.

Product-oriented layout Organizing work in a plant or administrative function around products; sometimes referred to as product cells.

Profit center A decentralized unit in which the manager has the responsibility and the authority to make decisions that affect both costs and revenues (and thus profits).

Profit margin A component of the rate of return on investment computed as the ratio of income from operations to sales.

Profitability The ability of a firm to earn income.

Profit-volume chart A chart used to assist management in understanding the relationship between profit and volume.

Proprietorship A business owned by one individual.

Pull manufacturing A just-in-time method wherein customer orders trigger the release of finished goods, which triggers production, which triggers release of materials from suppliers.

Purchases discounts Discounts taken by the buyer for early payment of an invoice.

Purchases returns and allowances From the buyer's perspective, returned merchandise or an adjustment for defective merchandise.

Push manufacturing Materials are released into production and work in process is released into finished goods in anticipation of future sales.

Q

Quick assets Cash and other current assets that can be quickly converted to cash, such as marketable securities and receivables.

Quick ratio A financial ratio that measure the ability to pay current liabilities with quick assets (cash, marketable securities, accounts receivable).

R

Radio frequency identification devices Electronic tags (chips) placed on or embedded within products that can be read by radio waves and that allow instant monitoring of product location.

Rate earned on common stockholders' equity A measure of profitability computed by dividing net income less preferred dividends by average common stockholders' equity.

Rate earned on stockholders' equity A measure of profitability computed by dividing net income by average total stockholders' equity.

Rate earned on total assets A measure of the profitability of assets, without regard to the equity of creditors and stockholders in the assets.

Rate of return on investment (ROI) A measure of managerial efficiency in the use of investments in assets computed as income from operations divided by invested assets.

Ratio of fixed assets to long-term liabilities A leverage ratio that measures the margin of safety of long-term creditors, calculated as the net fixed assets divided by the long-term liabilities.

Ratio of liabilities to stockholders' equity A comprehensive leverage ratio that measures the relationship of the claims of creditors to stockholders' equity.

Ratio of net sales to assets Ratio that measures how effectively a company uses its assets, computed as net sales divided by average total assets.

Receivables All money claims against other entities, including people, business firms, and other organizations.

Receiving report The form or electronic transmission used by the receiving personnel to indicate that materials have been received and inspected.

Relevant range The range of activity over which changes in cost are of interest to management.

Report form The form of balance sheet in which assets, liabilities, and stockholders' equity are reported in a downward sequence.

Residual income The excess of divisional income from operations over a "minimum" acceptable income from operations.

Residual value The estimated value of a fixed asset at the end of its useful life.

Responsibility accounting The process of measuring and reporting operating data by areas of responsibility.

Responsibility center A budgetary unit within a company for which a manager is assigned responsibility over costs, revenues, or assets.

Retained earnings Net income retained in a corporation.

Retained earnings statement A summary of the changes in the retained earnings of a corporation for a specific period of time, such as a month or a year.

Revenue The increase in assets from selling products or services to customers.

Revenue expenditures Costs that benefit only the current period or costs incurred for normal maintenance and repairs of fixed assets.

S

Sales Revenues received from selling products.

Sales budget A budget that indicates for each product (1) the quantity of estimated sales, and (2) the expected unit selling price.

Sales discounts From the seller's perspective, discounts that a seller can offer the buyer for early payment.

Sales mix The relative distribution of sales among the various products available for sale.

Sales returns and allowances From the seller's perspective, returned merchandise or an adjustment for damaged or defective merchandise.

Sarbanes-Oxley Act of 2002 An act passed by Congress to restore public confidence and trust in the financial statements of companies.

Securities and Exchange Commission An agency of the U.S. government that has authority over the accounting and financial disclosures for corporations whose stock is traded and sold to the public

Selling expenses Costs directly related to the selling of a product or service such as sales salaries and advertising expenses.

Service businesses A type of business that provides services rather than products to customers.

Service department charges The costs of services provided by an internal service department and transferred to a responsibility center.

Setup The effort required to prepare an operation for a new production run.

Single-step income statement A form of income statement in which the total of all expenses is deducted from the total of all revenues.

Six Sigma A method of improving product quality and manufacturing processes developed by Motorola Corporation that consists of five steps: define, measure, analyze, improve, and control.

Solvency The ability of a firm to pay its debts as they come due.

Special–purpose fund A cash fund used for a special business need.

Specific identification inventory cost flow method An inventory cost flow method where the cost of each inventory unit is separately identified.

Standard cost A detailed estimate of what a product should cost.

Standard cost systems Accounting systems that use standards for each manufacturing cost entering into the finished product.

Standards Performance goals.

Stated value A value, similar to par value, approved by the board of directors of a corporation for no-par stock.

Statement of cash flows A summary of the cash receipts and cash payments for a specific period of time, such as a month or a year.

Statement of financial condition Reports the financial condition as of a point in time; often referred to as the balance sheet.

Static budget A budget that does not adjust to changes in activity levels.

Stock dividend A distribution of shares of stock to stockholders.

Stock split The reduction in the par or stated value of common stock and issuance of a proportionate number of additional shares.

Stockholders' equity The stockholders' rights to the assets of a business.

Stockholders Investors who purchase stock in a corporation.

Straight-line method A method of depreciation that provides for equal periodic depreciation expense over the estimated life of a fixed asset.

Subsidiary ledger A ledger containing individual accounts with a common characteristic.

Sunk cost A cost that is not affected by subsequent decisions.

Supply chain management The coordination and control of materials, services, information, and finances as they move in a process from the supplier, through the manufacturer, wholesaler, and retailer to the consumer.

T

Tangible assets Assets such as machinery, buildings, computers, office furnishings, trucks, and automobiles that have physical characteristics.

Target costing A concept used to design and manufacture a product at a cost that will deliver a target profit for a given market-determined price.

Taxable income The income of a corporation that is subject to taxes as determined according to the tax laws.

Temporary differences Differences between taxable income and income before income taxes that are created because items are recognized in one period for tax purposes and in another period for income statement purposes.

Theoretical standards Standards that can be achieved only under perfect operating conditions, such as no idle time, no machine breakdowns, and no materials spoilage; also called ideal standards.

Theory of constraints (TOC) A manufacturing strategy that attempts to remove the influence of bottlenecks (constraints) on a process.

Time tickets The form on which the amount of time spent by each employee and the labor costs incurred for each individual job, or for factory overhead, are recorded.

Time value of money concept The concept that an amount of money invested today will earn interest.

Total cost concept A concept used in applying the cost-plus approach to product pricing in which all the costs of manufacturing the product plus the selling and administrative expenses are included in the cost amount to which the markup is added.

Total manufacturing cost variance The difference between the total actual cost and the total standard cost for the units produced.

Trademark A name, term, or symbol used to identify a business and its products.

Transaction An economic event that under generally accepted accounting principles (GAAP) affects an element of the accounting equation and therefore must be recorded.

Transfer price The price charged one decentralized unit by another for the goods or services provided.

Treasury stock Stock that a corporation has once issued and then reacquires.

U

Underapplied factory overhead The actual factory overhead costs incurred in excess of the amount of factory overhead applied for production during a period.

Unearned revenues Items that are initially recorded as liabilities but are expected to become revenues over time or through the normal operations of the business.

Unfavorable cost variance Actual cost exceeds standard cost.

Unit contribution margin The dollars available from each unit of sales to cover fixed costs and provide income from operations.

Unit of measure concept An accounting concept requiring that economic data be recorded in dollars.

V

Value-added lead time The time required to manufacture a unit of product or other output.

Variable cost concept A concept used in applying the cost-plus approach to product pricing in which only variable costs are included in the cost amount to which the markup is added.

Variable costing A method of reporting variable and fixed costs that includes only the variable manufacturing costs in the cost of the product.

Variable costs Costs that vary in total dollar amount as the level of activity changes.

Vertical analysis An analysis that compares each item in a current statement with a total amount within the same statement.

Volume variance The difference between the budgeted fixed overhead at 100% of normal capacity and the standard fixed overhead for the actual units produced.

Voucher Any document that serves as proof of authority to pay cash.

Voucher system A set of procedures for authorizing and recording liabilities and cash payments.

W

Working capital The excess of the current assets of a business over its current liabilities.

Work–in–process (WIP) inventory The direct materials costs, the direct labor costs, and the factory overhead costs that have entered into the manufacturing process but are associated with products that have not been finished.

Z

Zero-based budgeting A concept of budgeting that requires all levels of management to start from zero and estimate budget data as if there had been no previous activities in their units.

A

ABC (activity-based costing) method, 387–390, 480–481
Accelerated depreciation method, 251
Account, defined, 83, 649
Account form, defined, 134
Account payable, defined, 7
Accounting
  accrual basis of, 99
  cash basis of, 100
  defined, 9
  nature of, 2–6
  role in business, 9–10
Accounting concepts, 16–22
  accounting period, 20
  adequate disclosure, 20
  business entity, 17–18
  cost, 18–19
  going concern, 19
  matching, 19, 81–82
  objectivity, 19
  responsible reporting, 20–22
  unit of measure, 20
Accounting cycle, defined, 103
Accounting equation, defined, 13
Accounting for
  cost centers, responsibility, 573–574
  depreciation, 248–253
  investment centers, 579–586
  merchandising businesses, 127–166
  profit centers, 574–579
Accounting frauds, 21
Accounting period concept, defined, 20
Accounting rate of return, 614
Accounting system
  controls for, 46–47
  double-entry, 649–663
  elements of, 45–47
  framework of, 45–46
  for manufacturing businesses, 360–418
  rules for, 45
Accounts, chart of, 83, 653
Accounts payable, defined, 85
Accounts receivable
  analysis of, defined, 321
  defined, 7, 86, 207
Accounts receivable turnover, defined, 321
Accrual accounting
  adjustment process, 88–94
  concepts, 80–126
  defined, 81
Accrual basis of accounting, 99–103
  accounting cycle for, 103
  concepts of, 81–82
  defined, 99
  importance of, 102–103
  using accrual basis of, 101
Accruals, 89–94

Accrued
  assets, 90
  expenses, defined, 90
  liabilities, defined, 90
  revenues, 90
Accumulated depreciation, defined, 92
ACH (automated clearing house), 181
Activity base (driver), defined, 371–372, 420
Activity cost pools, defined, 387
Activity-based costing (ABC) method, 387–390, 480–481
Adequate disclosure concept, defined, 20
Adjustment process
  accrual accounting, 88–94
  defined, 88
Administrative expenses, defined, 9, 133
Aging the receivables, defined, 214
Allocation base, 371
Allowance account, write-offs to, 212–213
Allowance for doubtful accounts, defined, 211
Allowance method
  defined, 210
  for uncollectible accounts, 211–217
Allowances
  purchase returns and, 131, 142–143
  sales returns and, 130–131, 139, 140–141
American Institute of Certified Public Accountants, 22
Amortization, defined, 256
Analysis of receivables method for uncollectibles, 214–215
Analytical measures
  other, 317–318
  summary of, 332–333
Analytical methods, 313–318
  common-sized statements, 317
  horizontal analysis, 313–315
  vertical analysis, 315–317
Anderson, Kerrii, 89
Annuity
  defined, 619
  present value of an, 619–620
Asset improvements, 247
Assets
  current, 97
  defined, 8
  fixed, 97
  intangible, 8, 98
  quick, 320
  rate earned on, 326–327
Association of Certified Fraud Examiners, 170
Automated clearing house (ACH), 181
Average cost method, 669–671

Average inventory cost flow method
  defined, 220
  use of, 223–224
Average rate of return method, 614–615

B

B&P (budget and planning) software, 509–510
Bad debt expense, defined, 209
Balance sheet (see also Statement of financial condition)
  budgeted, 523
  classified, 96
  comparative, 149
  defined, 11
  example of, 14, 56, 60, 97, 136
  financial statements and, 13, 56–57, 60–61, 96–98, 134–135
  objectives of, 10
Balance sheet budgets, 518–522
Balanced scorecard, 585–586
The Balanced Scorecard: Translating Strategy into Action (Kaplan & Norton), 585
Bank accounts, 179–182
Bank errors, 186
Bank reconciliation, 183–186
  defined, 183
  example of, 185
Bank statements, 179–182
  defined, 179
  example of, 181
  use of as control over cash, 182
Bankers' ratio, 319
Bar code scanning devices, 367
Blockbuster business strategy, 382
Bond, defined, 282
Bond indenture, defined, 282
Bonds, 8, 282–284
Bonds payable
  defined, 8
  discount on, 284
  premium on, 284
Book value, defined, 93, 251
Bottleneck, defined, 482
Bowerman, Bill, 312
Break-even chart, 434–435
Break-even point
  defined, 428–429
  effect of changes in, 432
Budget
  balance sheet, 518–523
  capital expenditures, 522–523
  cash, 518–522
  cost of goods sold, 516–517
  defined, 504
  direct labor cost, 515